Introductory Algebra

An Applied Approach

9th Edition

Richard N. Aufmann | Joanne S. Lockwood

Australia • Brazil • Japan • Korea • Mexico • Singapore • Spain • United Kingdom • United States

Introductory Algebra: An Applied Approach, 9th Edition

Sources:

Introductory Algebra: An Applied Approach, 9th Edition
Richard N. Aufmann | Joanne S. Lockwood

Beginning Algebra, 5th Edition
Alfonse Gobran

Senior Project Development Manager:
Linda deStefano

Market Development Manager:
Heather Kramer

Senior Production/Manufacturing Manager:
Donna M. Brown

Production Editorial Manager:
Kim Fry

Sr. Rights Acquisition Account Manager:
Todd Osborne

ISBN-13: 978-1-285-91098-7

ISBN-10: 1-285-91098-2

Cengage Learning
5191 Natorp Boulevard
Mason, Ohio 45040
USA

Cengage Learning is a leading provider of customized learning solutions with office locations around the globe, including Singapore, the United Kingdom, Australia, Mexico, Brazil, and Japan. Locate your local office at:
international.cengage.com/region.

Cengage Learning products are represented in Canada by Nelson Education, Ltd.
For your lifelong learning solutions, visit **www.cengage.com/custom.**
Visit our corporate website at **www.cengage.com.**

Printed in the United States of America

Ask the Authors!

We have taught math for many years. During that time, we have had students ask us a number of questions about mathematics and this course. Here you find some of the questions we have been asked most often, starting with the big one.

Dick Aufmann

Joanne Lockwood

Why do I have to take this course? You may have heard that *"Math is everywhere."* That is probably a slight exaggeration, but math does find its way into many disciplines. There are obvious places like engineering, science, and medicine. There are other disciplines such as business, social science, and political science where math may be less obvious but still essential. If you are going to be an artist, writer, or musician, the direct connection to math may be even less obvious. Even so, as art historians who have studied the Mona Lisa have shown, there is a connection to math. But, suppose you find these reasons not all that compelling. **There is still a reason to learn basic math skills: You will be a better consumer and be able to make better financial choices for you and your family.** For instance, is it better to buy a car or lease a car? Math can provide an answer.

I find math difficult. Why is that? It is true that some people, even very smart people, find math difficult. Some of this can be traced to previous math experiences. If your basic skills are lacking, it is more difficult to understand the math in a new math course. Some of the difficulty can be attributed to the ideas and concepts in math. They can be quite challenging to learn. Nonetheless, most of us can learn and understand the ideas in the math courses that are required for graduation. **If you want math to be less difficult, practice. When you have finished practicing, practice some more.** Ask an athlete, actor, singer, dancer, artist, doctor, skateboarder, or (name a profession) what it takes to become successful and the one common characteristic they all share is that they practiced—a lot.

Why is math important? As we mentioned earlier, math is found in many fields of study. There are, however, other reasons to take a math course. Primary among these reasons is to become a better problem solver. Math can help you learn critical thinking skills. It can help you develop a logical plan to solve a problem. Math can help you see relationships between ideas and to identify patterns. **When employers are asked what they look for in a new employee, being a problem solver is one of the highest ranked criteria.**

What do I need to do to pass this course? The most important thing you must do is to know and understand the requirements outlined by your instructor. These requirements are usually given to you in a syllabus. Once you know what is required, you can chart a course of action. Set time aside to study and do homework. If possible, choose your classes so that you have a free hour after your math class. Use this time to review your lecture notes, rework examples given by the instructor, and begin your homework. All of us eventually need help, so know where you can get assistance with this class. This means knowing your instructor's office hours, the hours of the math help center, and how to access available online resources. And finally, do not get behind. **Try to do some math EVERY day, even if it is for only 20 minutes.**

Brief Contents

Chapters 1 – 11 excerpted from:
Introductory Algebra: An Applied Approach
9th Edition
Richard N. Aufmann and Joanne S. Lockwood

Material reprinted from:
Beginning Algebra
5th Edition
Alfonse Gobran

Brief Contents

Contents

CHAPTER

AIM for Success

This important chapter outlines some study skills that are used by students who have been successful in this course. Topics include how to stay motivated, making a commitment to succeed, how to manage your time, and preparing for and taking tests. There is a complete guide to the textbook and how to use its features to become a successful student.

CHAPTER

Prealgebra Review

CHAPTER 4 Polynomials 187

CHAPTER 5 Factoring 231

CHAPTER  Rational Expressions 281

Preface

Among the many questions we ask when we begin the process of revising a textbook, the most important is, "How can we improve the learning experience for the student?" We find answers to this question in a variety of ways, but most commonly by talking to students and instructors and by evaluating the written feedback we receive from instructors. Bearing this feedback in mind, our ultimate goal as we set out to create the ninth edition of *Introductory Algebra: An Applied Approach* was to provide students with more materials to help them better understand the underlying concepts presented in this course. As a result, we have made the following changes to the new edition.

New to this edition is the **Focus on Success** vignette that appears at the beginning of each chapter. **Focus on Success** offers practical tips for improving study habits and performance on tests and exams.

We now include an **Apply the Concept** box in many objectives in which a new concept is introduced. This feature gives an immediate real-world example of how that concept is applied. For instance, after percent equations are introduced, there is an Apply the Concept example that uses a percent equation to find the concentration of jasmine in a perfume.

The definition and key concept boxes have been enhanced in this edition; they now include examples to show how the general case translates to specific cases.

In each exercise set, the first group of exercises is now titled **Concept Check.** The **Concept Check** exercises focus on the concepts that lie behind the skills developed in the section. We consider an understanding of these concepts essential to a student's success in mastering the skills required to complete the exercises that follow.

Every chapter contains **Check Your Progress** exercises. This feature appears approximately mid-chapter and tests students' understanding of the concepts presented to that point in the chapter.

Critical Thinking exercises are included at the end of every exercise set. They may involve further exploration or analysis of the topic at hand. They may also integrate concepts introduced earlier in the text.

We trust that the new and enhanced features of the ninth edition will help students more successfully engage with the content. By narrowing the gap between the concrete and the abstract, between the real world and the theoretical, students should more plainly see that mastering the skills and topics presented is well within their reach and well worth the effort.

New to This Edition

- **Apply the Concept** boxes show how a just introduced concept can be applied to real-world problems.
- **Concept Check** exercises appear at the beginning of each exercise set.
- Enhanced definition/key concept boxes now provide examples that illustrate how the general case applies to specific cases.
- The **Focus on Success** feature at the beginning of each chapter offers practical guidance to help students develop positive study habits.
- **Check Your Progress** exercises appear approximately mid-chapter and test students' understanding of the concepts presented thus far in the chapter.

- **In the News** articles within the exercise sets have been updated, as have application problems throughout the text.
- **Critical Thinking** exercises appear at the end of each exercise set.
- **Projects or Group Activities** are now included at the end of each exercise set.
- **Chapter A, AIM for Success,** now appears as the first chapter of the text. This chapter describes skills used by students who have been successful in this course. Topics include how to stay motivated, making a commitment to success, time management, and how to prepare for and take tests. A guide to the textbook is included to help students use its features effectively.
- More annotations have been added to the worked Examples, to more effectively explain the steps of the solutions.
- Many of the **Chapter Summaries** have been expanded to include more entries and more descriptive explanations.

Organizational Changes

We have made the following changes in order to improve the effectiveness of the textbook and enhance the student's learning experience.

- In Chapter 1, Section 1.5, we changed the format of the rules for finding factors of a number. Students will find this rule box easier to use when determining whether 2, 3, or 5 is a factor of a number.
- Section 3.1 in the eighth edition is now two sections in the ninth edition.

  Section 3.1 Introduction to Equations

  A To determine whether a given number is a solution of an equation

  B To solve an equation of the form $x + a = b$

  C To solve an equation of the form $ax = b$

  Section 3.2 The Basic Percent Equation and the Uniform Motion Equation

  A To solve application problems using the basic percent equation

  B To solve uniform motion problems

  Students will now have greater mastery of solving equations of the form $ax = b$ prior to the lessons on using the basic percent equation and the uniform motion equation, both of which are equations of the form $ax = b$.
- In Section 3.3, both the markup equation and the basic discount equation are now in definition boxes to highlight the equations that are used to solve markup and discount problems. Included in each definition box is an example of a markup or discount problem.
- In Chapter 4, Section 4.4 is titled Integer Exponents and Scientific Notation. This section has been reorganized and expanded in order to provide students with more assistance in learning the difficult topic of integer exponents. There are many more examples for students to learn from. The exercise set has been expanded from 4 pages to 6 pages in order to provide students with more practice in simplifying expressions with negative exponents and in writing numbers in scientific notation.

- Section 5.4 in the eighth edition has been split into two sections in the ninth edition. The new Section 5.4 develops factoring of the difference of two squares and perfect-square trinomials. The definition boxes are more explicit and include more examples. The new Section 5.5 is devoted to factoring polynomials completely. Now students can concentrate in Section 5.5 on applying all their factoring skills to factoring polynomials completely.
- Section 5.6 on solving equations by factoring now includes a boxed list of the steps used in solving a quadratic equation by factoring.
- The objectives in Section 6.6 have been reorganized. Now in Objective 6.6A, students learn how to solve proportions and are introduced to applications of solving proportions. There are now more examples for the student to study, and the exercise set is longer. The student has more opportunity to master problem solving involving proportions. The topic of Objective 6.6B is solving problems involving similar triangles.
- The exposition in Section 6.8 has been expanded to provide more examples which apply the basic concepts of work problems. There is a gradual development of solving these problems. There is also more assistance in setting up the uniform motion problems in this section. There are several more work problems and uniform motion problems for the student to solve, and there is a wide variety of each type of word problem.
- In the exercises for Section 7.2, Linear Equations in Two Variables, there are a greater variety of exercises and many more exercises that will help students learn the concepts. There is a group of exercises in which students are given equations in the form $Ax + By = C$ and asked to write them in the form $y = mx + b$. This provides them with the experience they need before graphing equations of the form $Ax + By = C$.
- In Section 7.3, the approach to graphing equations using the slope and y-intercept has changed. Now students are instructed to first move up or down from the y-intercept (change in y), and then move right or left (change in x) to plot a second point. The exercise set for Section 7.3 has been expanded to give students more practice using graphing concepts.
- The organization of Section 7.4 was changed to the following:

  A To find the equation of a line using the equation $y = mx + b$

  B To find the equation of a line using the point-slope formula

  C To find the equation of a line given two points

  Instructors can elect to cover only Objective A, only Objective B, or both Objectives A and B when presenting the topic of finding the equation of a line given a point and the slope of a line.
- The exercise set for Section 10.4 has been expanded to give students more practice with solving radical equations and applications of radical equations.
- The exercise set for Section 11.4 has been expanded. The Critical Thinking exercises and the Project or Group Activities will provide students with the opportunity to better understand the concepts related to graphs of quadratic equations. The last Project instructs students in using a graphing calculator to graph parabolas and find their x-intercepts.

Take AIM and Succeed!

An Objective-Based Approach

Introductory Algebra: An Applied Approach is organized around a carefully constructed hierarchy of **objectives.** This "objective-based" approach provides an integrated learning path that enables you to find resources such as assessment tools (both within the text and online), videos, tutorials, and additional exercises for each objective in the text.

1 Each Chapter Opener outlines the learning **OBJECTIVES** that appear in each section of the chapter. The list of objectives serves as a resource to guide you in your study and review of the topics.

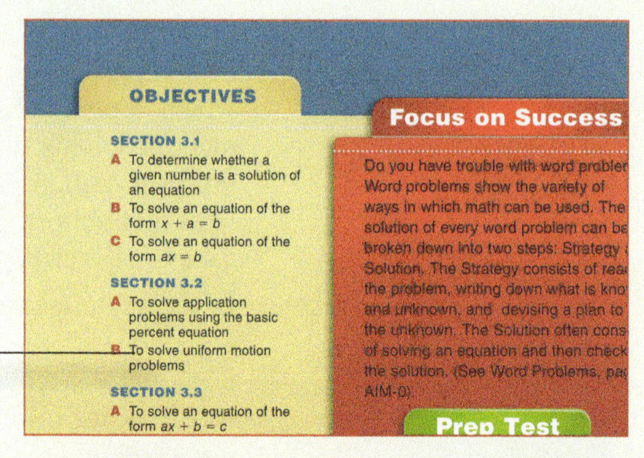

OBJECTIVES

SECTION 3.1

A To determine whether a given number is a solution of an equation

B To solve an equation of the form $x + a = b$

C To solve an equation of the form $ax = b$

SECTION 3.2

A To solve application problems using the basic percent equation

B To solve uniform motion problems

SECTION 3.3

A To solve an equation of the form $ax + b = c$

Focus on Success

Do you have trouble with word probler Word problems show the variety of ways in which math can be used. The solution of every word problem can be broken down into two steps: Strategy a Solution. The Strategy consists of reac the problem, writing down what is kno and unknown, and devising a plan to the unknown. The Solution often cons of solving an equation and then check the solution. (See Word Problems, pa AIM-0).

Prep Test

2 Taking the **PREP TEST** for each chapter will help you determine which topics you need to study more carefully and which topics you need only review. The **ANSWERS** to the **PREP TEST** provide references to the **OBJECTIVES** on which the exercises are based.

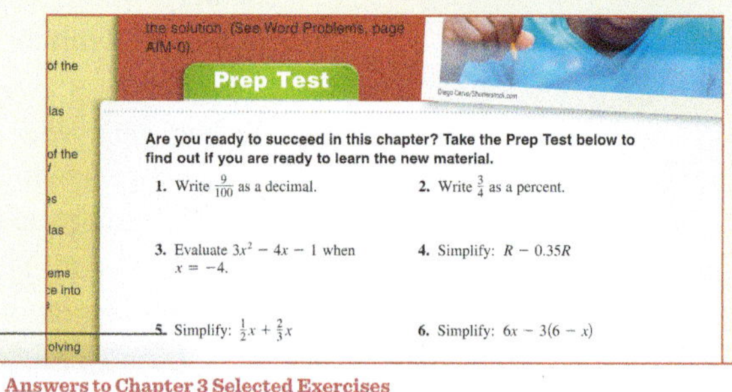

the solution. (See Word Problems, page AIM-0).

Prep Test

Diego Cervo/Shutterstock.com

Are you ready to succeed in this chapter? Take the Prep Test below to find out if you are ready to learn the new material.

1. Write $\frac{9}{100}$ as a decimal.
2. Write $\frac{3}{4}$ as a percent.
3. Evaluate $3x^2 - 4x - 1$ when $x = -4$.
4. Simplify: $R - 0.35R$
5. Simplify: $\frac{1}{2}x + \frac{2}{3}x$
6. Simplify: $6x - 3(6 - x)$

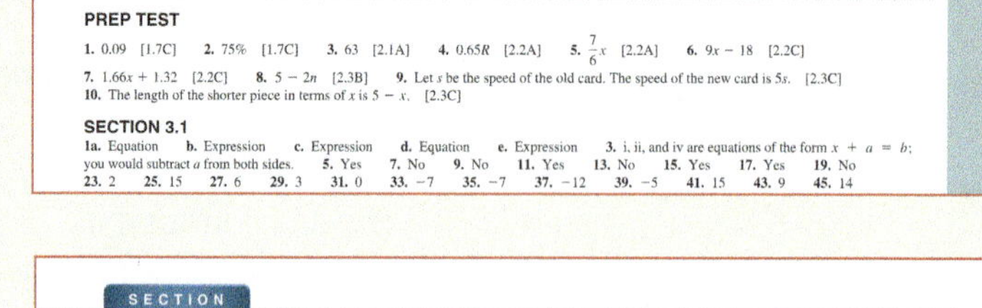

Answers to Chapter 3 Selected Exercises

PREP TEST

1. 0.09 [1.7C] **2.** 75% [1.7C] **3.** 63 [2.1A] **4.** $0.65R$ [2.2A] **5.** $\frac{7}{6}x$ [2.2A] **6.** $9x - 18$ [2.2C]
7. $1.66x + 1.32$ [2.2C] **8.** $5 - 2n$ [2.3B] **9.** Let s be the speed of the old card. The speed of the new card is $5s$. [2.3C]
10. The length of the shorter piece in terms of x is $5 - x$. [2.3C]

SECTION 3.1

1a. Equation **b.** Expression **c.** Expression **d.** Equation **e.** Expression **3.** i, ii, and iv are equations of the form $x + a = b$; you would subtract a from both sides. **5.** Yes **7.** No **9.** No **11.** Yes **13.** No **15.** Yes **17.** Yes **19.** No
23. 2 **25.** 15 **27.** 6 **29.** 3 **31.** 0 **33.** −7 **35.** −7 **37.** −12 **39.** −5 **41.** 15 **43.** 9 **45.** 14

3 In every section, an **OBJECTIVE STATEMENT** introduces each new topic of discussion. Videos are available for each objective.

SECTION **3.1** Introduction to Equations

OBJECTIVE A *To determine whether a given number is a solution of an equation*

An **equation** expresses the equality of two mathematical expressions. The expressions can be either numerical or variable expressions.

$9 + 3 = 12$
$3x - 2 = 10$
$y^2 + 4 = 2y - 1$
$z = 2$
Equations

The equation at the right is true if the variable is

$x + 8 = 13$

Point of Interest

One of the most famous equations ever stated is $E = mc^2$. This equation, stated by Albert Einstein,

4 Section exercises are keyed to **OBJECTIVE STATEMENTS.**

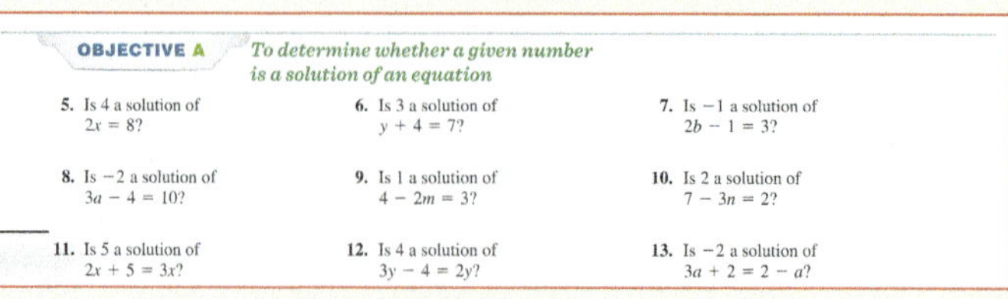

OBJECTIVE A *To determine whether a given number is a solution of an equation*

5. Is 4 a solution of $2x = 8$?
6. Is 3 a solution of $y + 4 = 7$?
7. Is −1 a solution of $2b - 1 = 3$?
8. Is −2 a solution of $3a - 4 = 10$?
9. Is 1 a solution of $4 - 2m = 3$?
10. Is 2 a solution of $7 - 3n = 2$?
11. Is 5 a solution of $2x + 5 = 3x$?
12. Is 4 a solution of $3y - 4 = 2y$?
13. Is −2 a solution of $3a + 2 = 2 - a$?

An Objective-Based Review

This "objective-based" approach continues through the end-of-chapter review and addresses a broad range of study styles by offering a **wide variety of review tools.**

CHECK YOUR PROGRESS exercises appear approximately mid-chapter and test your understanding of the concepts presented up to that point in the chapter.

CHECK YOUR PROGRESS: CHAPTER 3

1. Is 3 a solution of $2a(a - 1) = 3a + 3$?
2. Solve: $x + 7 = -4$
3. Solve: $-3y = -27$
4. What is 45% of 160?
5. Solve: $6 - 4a = -10$
6. Is $-\frac{1}{4}$ a solution of $8t + 1 = -1$?

At the end of each chapter, you will find a **CHAPTER SUMMARY** containing **KEY WORDS** and **ESSENTIAL RULES AND PROCEDURES** presented in the chapter. Each entry includes an objective reference and a page reference that show where in the chapter the concept was introduced. An example demonstrating the concept is also included.

CHAPTER 3 Summary

Key Words	Examples
An equation expresses the equality of two mathematical expressions. [3.1A, p. 110]	$3 + 2(4x - 5) = x + 4$ is an eq
A solution of an equation is a number that, when substituted for	-2 is a solution of $2 - 3x = 8$ b

By completing the **CHAPTER REVIEW EXERCISES,** you can practice working on problems in an order that is different from the order in which they were presented in the chapter. The **ANSWER** to each Chapter Review exercise includes a reference to the objective on which the exercise is based. This reference will help you quickly identify where to go if you need further practice with a particular concept.

CHAPTER 3 Review Exercises

1. Solve: $x + 3 = 24$
2. Solve: $x + 5(3x - 20) = 10(x - 4)$
3. Solve: $5x - 6 = 29$
4. Is 3 a solution of $5x - 2 = 4x + 5$?

Each **CHAPTER TEST** is designed to simulate a typical test of the concepts covered in the chapter. Each **ANSWER** includes an objective reference as well as a reference to a numbered Example, You Try It, or HOW TO in the text that is similar to the given test question.

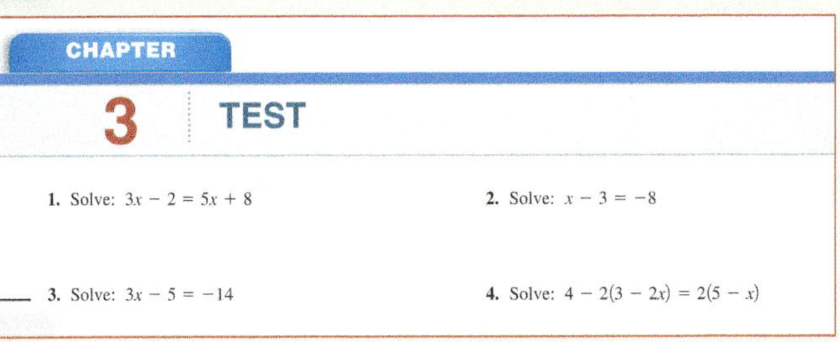

CHAPTER 3 TEST

1. Solve: $3x - 2 = 5x + 8$
2. Solve: $x - 3 = -8$
3. Solve: $3x - 5 = -14$
4. Solve: $4 - 2(3 - 2x) = 2(5 - x)$

CUMULATIVE REVIEW EXERCISES, which appear at the end of each chapter (beginning with Chapter 2), help you maintain previously learned skills. The **ANSWERS** include references to the section objectives on which the exercises are based.

Cumulative Review Exercises

1. Subtract: $-6 - (-20) - 8$
2. Multiply: $(-2)(-6)(-4)$
3. Subtract: $-\frac{5}{6} - \left(-\frac{7}{16}\right)$
4. Divide: $-\frac{7}{3} \div \frac{7}{6}$

A **FINAL EXAM** is provided following the last chapter of the text. The Final Exam is designed to simulate a comprehensive exam covering all the concepts presented in the text. The **ANSWERS** to the Final Exam questions are provided in the appendix at the back of the text and include references to the section objectives on which the questions are based.

FINAL EXAM

1. Evaluate $-|-3|$.
2. Subtract: $-15 - (-12) - 3$
3. Simplify: $-2^4 \cdot (-2)^4$
4. Simplify: $-7 - \frac{12 - 15}{2 - (-1)} \cdot (-4)$

Understanding the Concepts

Each of the following features is designed to give you a fuller understanding of the key concepts.

CONCEPT CHECK exercises promote conceptual understanding. Completing these exercises will deepen your understanding of the concepts you are learning and provide the foundation you need to successfully complete the remaining exercises in the exercise set.

3.2 EXERCISES

Concept Check

Identify the amount and the base.

1. 30 is 75% of 40.
2. 40% of 20 is 8.

Complete Exercises 3 and 4 by filling in the blanks with the correct number from the problem situation or with the word *unknown*.

3. **Problem Situation:** It rained on 24 of the 30 days of June. What percent of the days in June were rainy days?

   Using the formula $PB = A$, $P =$ ______, $B =$ ______, and $A =$ ______.

4. **Problem Situation:** You bought a used car and made a down payment of 25% of the purchase price of $16,000. How much was the down payment?

Definition/key concept boxes contain examples to illustrate how each definition or key concept is applied in practice.

Subtraction of Integers

To subtract one number from another, add the opposite of the second number to the first number.

EXAMPLES

1. Subtract: $-21 - (-40)$

   $-21 - (-40) = -21 + 40$ • Rewrite the subtraction as addition of the opposite.

   $= 19$ • Add.

2. Subtract: $15 - 51$

   $15 - 51 = 15 + (-51)$ • Rewrite the subtraction as addition of the opposite.

   $= -36$ • Add.

TAKE NOTE boxes alert you to concepts that require special attention.

Take Note

An equation has some properties that are similar to those of a balance scale. For instance, if a balance scale is in balance and equal weights are added to each side of the scale, then the balance scale remains in balance. If an equation is true, then adding the same number to each side of the equation produces another true equation.

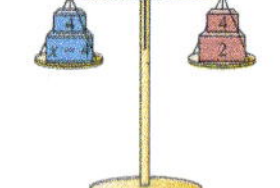

In solving an equation, the goal is to rewrite the given equation in the form *variable = constant*. The Addition Property of Equations is used to remove a *term* from one side of the equation by adding the opposite of that term to each side of the equation.

HOW TO 2 Solve: $x - 4 = 2$

$x - 4 = 2$ • The goal is to rewrite the equation in the form *variable = constant*.

$x - 4 + 4 = 2 + 4$ • Add 4 to each side of the equation.

$x + 0 = 6$ • Simplify.

$x = 6$ • The equation is in the form *variable = constant*.

Check: $x - 4 = 2$

$6 - 4 \mid 2$

$2 = 2$ A true equation

The solution is 6.

Because subtraction is defined in terms of addition, the Addition Property of Equations also makes it possible to subtract the same number from each side of an equation without changing the solution of the equation.

POINT OF INTEREST boxes, which relate to the topic under discussion, may be historical in nature or of general interest.

$I = 157.5$

The investment earned $157.50.

Point of Interest

In the jewelry industry, the amount of gold in a piece of jewelry is measured in *karats*. Pure gold is 24 karats. A necklace that is 18 karats is $\frac{18}{24} = 0.75 = 75\%$ gold.

The amount of a substance in a solution can be given as a percent of the total solution. For instance, if a certain fruit juice drink is advertised as containing 27% cranberry juice, then 27% of the contents of the bottle must be cranberry juice.

The method for solving problems involving mixtures is based on the **percent mixture equation** $Q = Ar$, where Q is the quantity of a substance in the solution, A is the amount of the solution, and r is the percent concentration of the substance.

APPLY THE CONCEPT

The formula for a perfume requires that the concentration of jasmine be 1.2% of the total amount of perfume. How many ounces of jasmine are in a 2-ounce bottle of this perfume?

To find the number of ounces of jasmine, solve $Q = Ar$ for Q.

Application of the Concepts

The section exercises offer many opportunities to put the concepts you are learning into practice.

APPLY THE CONCEPT boxes illustrate how an arithmetic operation is applied to a real-world situation so that you understand how the operation is used in everyday life.

The simple interest that an investment earns is given by the **simple interest equation** $I = Prt$, where I is the simple interest, P is the principal, or amount invested, r is the simple interest rate, and t is the time.

APPLY THE CONCEPT

A $1500 investment has an annual simple interest rate of 7%. Find the simple interest earned on the investment after 18 months.

To find the interest, solve $I = Prt$ for I.

The time is given in months but the interest rate is an annual rate. Therefore, we must convert 18 months to years. 18 months $= \frac{18}{12}$ years $= 1.5$ years

$$I = Prt$$
$$I = 1500(0.07)(1.5) \quad \bullet\ P = 1500, r = 0.07, t = 1.5$$
$$I = 157.5$$

The investment earned $157.50.

Point of Interest
In the jewelry industry, the amount of gold in a piece of

The amount of a substance in a solution can be given as a percent of the total solution. For instance, if a certain fruit juice drink is advertised as containing 27% cranberry juice, then 27% of the contents of the bottle must be cranberry juice.

THINK ABOUT IT exercises promote deeper conceptual understanding. Completing these exercises will expand your understanding of the concepts being addressed.

58. Joe and John live 2 mi apart. They leave their houses at the same time and walk toward each other until they meet. Joe walks faster than John does.
a. Is the distance walked by Joe less than, equal to, or greater than the distance walked by John?
b. Is the time spent walking by Joe less than, equal to, or greater than the time spent walking by John?
c. What is the total distance traveled by both Joe and John?

CRITICAL THINKING exercises may involve further exploration or analysis of the topic at hand. They may also integrate concepts introduced earlier in the text.

Critical Thinking

80. The sum of two negative integers is −9. Find the integers.

81. Given the list of numbers −4, −3, −10, 9, and 15, find the largest difference that can be obtained by subtracting one number in the list from another number in the list.

82. If a and b are integers, is the expression $|a + b| = |a| + |b|$ always true, sometimes true, or never true?

83. Is the difference between two integers always smaller than either one of the numbers in the subtraction? If not, give an example in which the difference between two integers is greater than either integer.

Working through the application exercises that contain **REAL DATA** will prepare you to answer questions and solve problems that you encounter outside of class, using facts and information that you gather on your own.

IN THE NEWS exercises help you understand the importance of mathematics in our everyday world. These application exercises are based on information taken from popular media sources such as newspapers, magazines, and the Internet.

96% silk?

48. At a cosmetics company, 40 L of pure aloe cream are mixed with 50 L of a moisturizer that is 64% aloe. What is the percent concentration of aloe in the resulting mixture?

49. **Ethanol Fuel** See the news clipping at the right. *Gasohol* is a type of fuel made by mixing ethanol with gasoline. E10 is a fuel mixture of 10% ethanol and 90% gasoline. E20 contains 20% ethanol and 80% gasoline. How many gallons of ethanol must be added to 100 gal of E10 to make E20?

50. A hair stylist combines 12 oz of shampoo that is 20% conditioner with an 8-ounce bottle of pure shampoo. What is the percent concentration of conditioner in the 20-ounce mixture?

51. How many ounces of pure chocolate must be added to 150 oz of chocolate topping that is 50% chocolate to make a topping that is 75% chocolate?

52. A recipe for a rice dish calls for 8 oz of pure wild rice and 12 oz of a rice mixture that is 20% wild rice. What is the percent concentration of wild rice in the 20-ounce

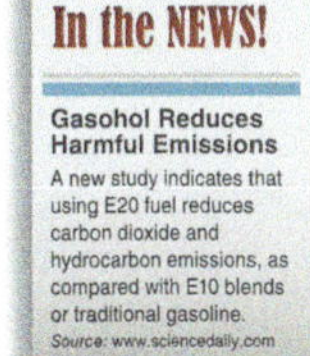

By completing the **WRITING** exercises, you will improve your communication skills while increasing your understanding of mathematical concepts.

81. Does the sentence "Solve $3x - 4(x - 1)$" make sense? Why or why not?

82. The equation $x = x + 1$ has no solution, whereas the solution of the equation $2x + 3 = 3$ is zero. Is there a difference between no solution and a solution of zero? Explain your answer.

83. I am thinking of a number. When I subtract 4 from the number and then take 300% of the result, my new result is equal to the original number. What is the original number?

Focus on Study Skills

An emphasis on setting a foundation of good study habits is woven into the text.

UPDATED!

CHAPTER A, AIM FOR SUCCESS, outlines study skills that are used by students who have been successful in this course. By making Chapter A the first chapter of the text, the stage is set for a successful beginning to the course.

New **FOCUS ON SUCCESS** appears at the start of each Chapter Opener. These tips are designed to help you make the most of the text and your time as you progress through the course and prepare for tests and exams.

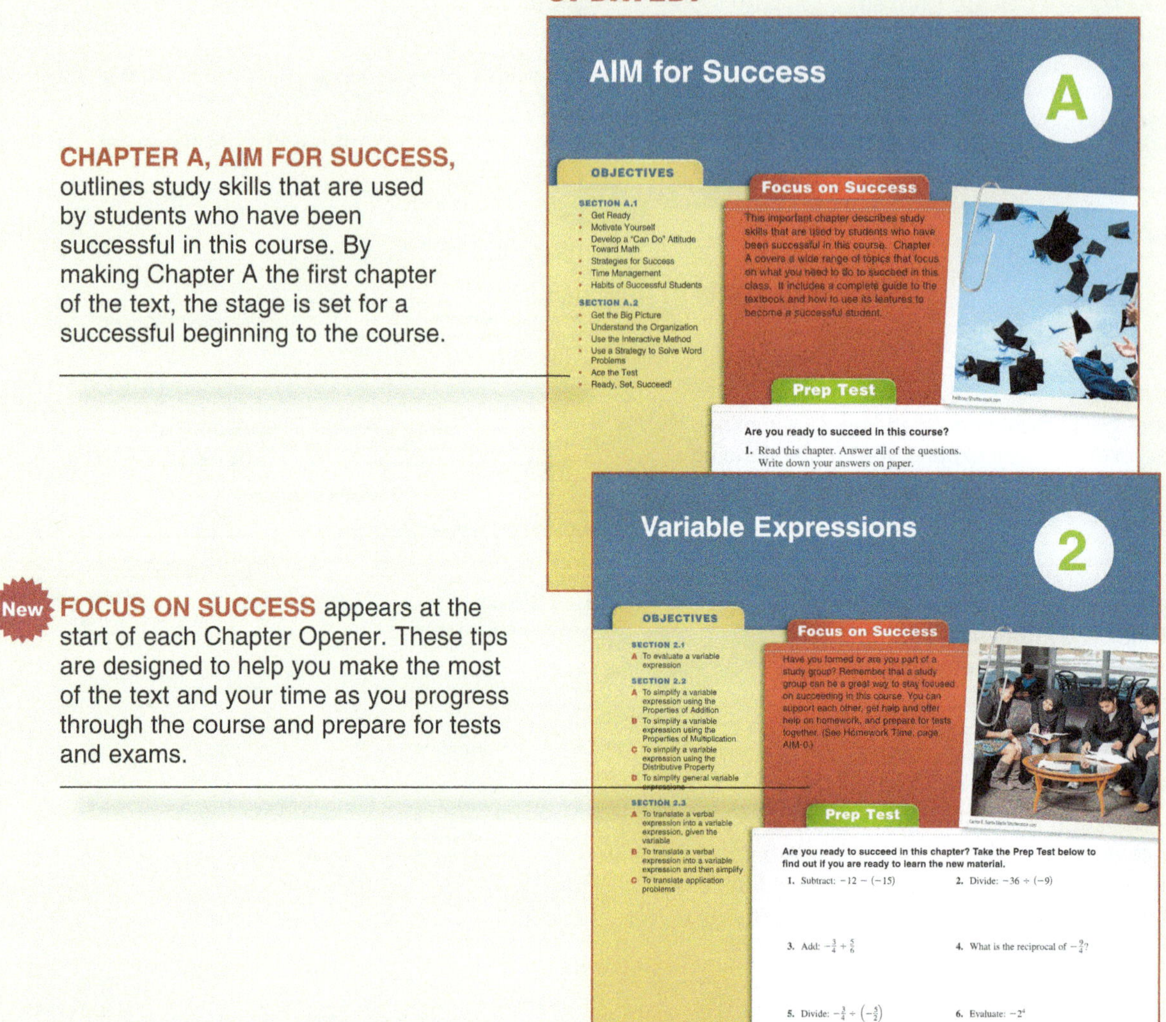

AIM for Success A

OBJECTIVES

SECTION A.1

- Get Ready
- Motivate Yourself
- Develop a "Can Do" Attitude Toward Math
- Strategies for Success
- Time Management
- Habits of Successful Students

SECTION A.2

- Get the Big Picture
- Understand the Organization
- Use the Interactive Method
- Use a Strategy to Solve Word Problems
- Ace the Test
- Ready, Set, Succeed!

Focus on Success

This important chapter describes study skills that are used by students who have been successful in this course. Chapter A covers a wide range of topics that focus on what you need to do to succeed in this class. It includes a complete guide to the textbook and how to use its features to become a successful student.

Prep Test

Are you ready to succeed in this course?

1. Read this chapter. Answer all of the questions. Write down your answers on paper.

Variable Expressions 2

OBJECTIVES

SECTION 2.1

A To evaluate a variable expression

SECTION 2.2

A To simplify a variable expression using the Properties of Addition

B To simplify a variable expression using the Properties of Multiplication

C To simplify a variable expression using the Distributive Property

D To simplify general variable expressions

SECTION 2.3

A To translate a verbal expression into a variable expression, given the variable

B To translate a verbal expression into a variable expression and then simplify

C To translate application problems

Focus on Success

Have you formed or are you part of a study group? Remember that a study group can be a great way to stay focused on succeeding in this course. You can support each other, get help and offer help on homework, and prepare for tests together. (See Homework Time, page AIM-0.)

Prep Test

Are you ready to succeed in this chapter? Take the Prep Test below to find out if you are ready to learn the new material.

1. Subtract: $-12 - (-15)$
2. Divide: $-36 \div (-9)$
3. Add: $-\frac{3}{4} + \frac{5}{6}$
4. What is the reciprocal of $-\frac{9}{4}$?
5. Divide: $-\frac{3}{4} \div \left(-\frac{5}{2}\right)$
6. Evaluate: -2^4

TIPS FOR SUCCESS boxes outline good study habits and function as reminders throughout the text.

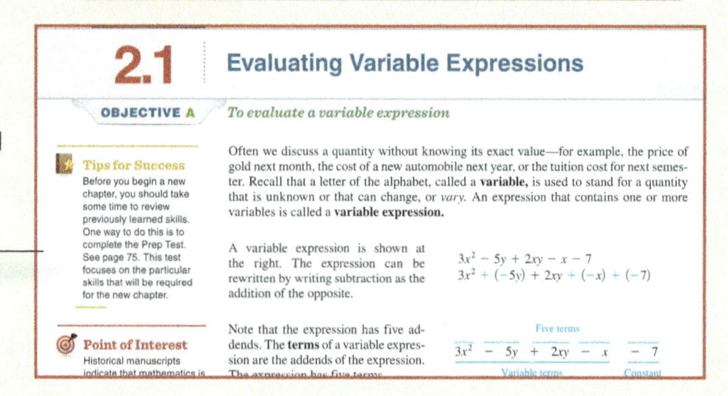

2.1 Evaluating Variable Expressions

OBJECTIVE A *To evaluate a variable expression*

Tips for Success
Before you begin a new chapter, you should take some time to review previously learned skills. One way to do this is to complete the Prep Test. See page 75. This test focuses on the particular skills that will be required for the new chapter.

Often we discuss a quantity without knowing its exact value—for example, the price of gold next month, the cost of a new automobile next year, or the tuition cost for next semester. Recall that a letter of the alphabet, called a **variable,** is used to stand for a quantity that is unknown or that can change, or *vary.* An expression that contains one or more variables is called a **variable expression.**

A variable expression is shown at the right. The expression can be rewritten by writing subtraction as the addition of the opposite.

$$3x^2 - 5y + 2xy - x - 7$$
$$3x^2 + (-5y) + 2xy + (-x) + (-7)$$

Note that the expression has five addends. The **terms** of a variable expression are the addends of the expression.

Point of Interest
Historical manuscripts

Focus on Skills and Problem Solving

The following features exemplify the emphasis on skills and the problem-solving process.

HOW TO examples provide solutions with detailed explanations for selected topics in each section.

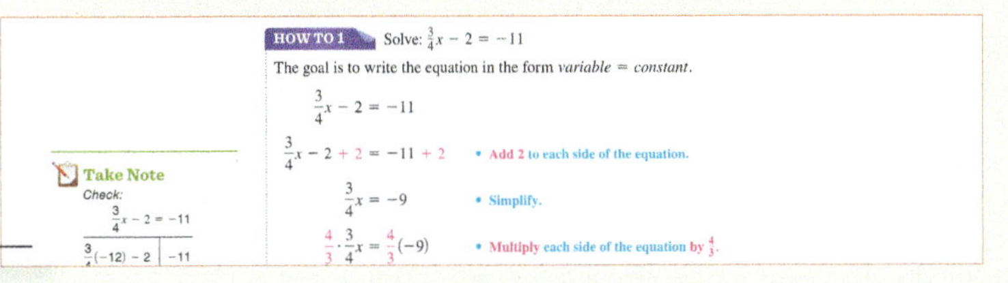
HOW TO 1 Solve: $\frac{3}{4}x - 2 = -11$

The goal is to write the equation in the form *variable* = *constant*.

$\frac{3}{4}x - 2 = -11$

$\frac{3}{4}x - 2 + 2 = -11 + 2$ • Add 2 to each side of the equation.

$\frac{3}{4}x = -9$ • Simplify.

$\frac{4}{3} \cdot \frac{3}{4}x = \frac{4}{3}(-9)$ • Multiply each side of the equation by $\frac{4}{3}$.

Take Note

Check: $\frac{3}{4}x - 2 = -11$

$\frac{3}{4}(-12) - 2 \mid -11$

INTEGRATING TECHNOLOGY margin notes offer optional instruction in the use of a scientific calculator.

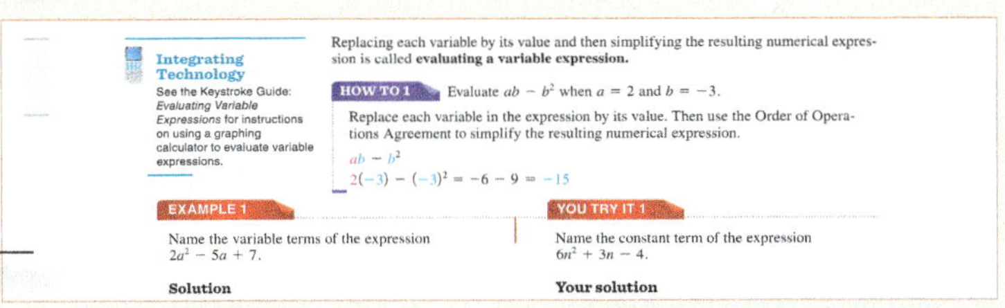
Integrating Technology

See the Keystroke Guide: *Evaluating Variable Expressions* for instructions on using a graphing calculator to evaluate variable expressions.

Replacing each variable by its value and then simplifying the resulting numerical expression is called **evaluating a variable expression.**

HOW TO 1 Evaluate $ab - b^2$ when $a = 2$ and $b = -3$.

Replace each variable in the expression by its value. Then use the Order of Operations Agreement to simplify the resulting numerical expression.

$ab - b^2$

$2(-3) - (-3)^2 = -6 - 9 = -15$

EXAMPLE 1 Name the variable terms of the expression $2a^2 - 5a + 7$.

Solution

YOU TRY IT 1 Name the constant term of the expression $6n^2 + 3n - 4$.

Your solution

The **EXAMPLE/YOU TRY IT** matched pairs are designed to actively involve you in the learning process. The You Try Its are based on the Examples. These problems are paired so that you can easily refer to the steps in the Example as you work through the accompanying You Try It.

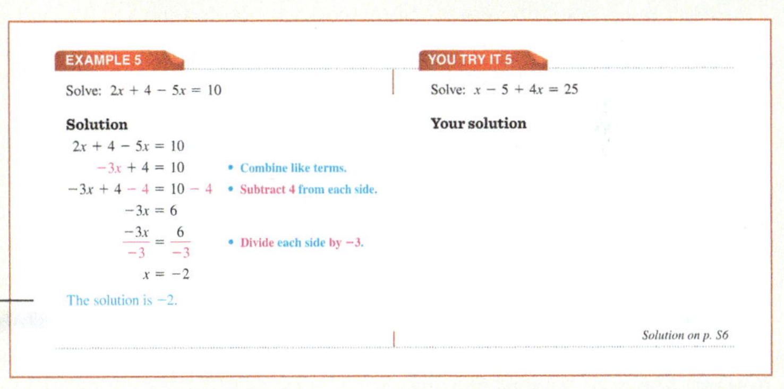
EXAMPLE 5 Solve: $2x + 4 - 5x = 10$

Solution

$2x + 4 - 5x = 10$

$-3x + 4 = 10$ • Combine like terms.

$-3x + 4 - 4 = 10 - 4$ • Subtract 4 from each side.

$-3x = 6$

$\frac{-3x}{-3} = \frac{6}{-3}$ • Divide each side by -3.

$x = -2$

The solution is -2.

YOU TRY IT 5 Solve: $x - 5 + 4x = 25$

Your solution

Solution on p. S6

Complete, **WORKED-OUT SOLUTIONS** to the You Try Its are included in an appendix at the back of the text. Compare your solution to the solution given in the appendix to obtain immediate feedback and reinforcement of the concept you are studying.

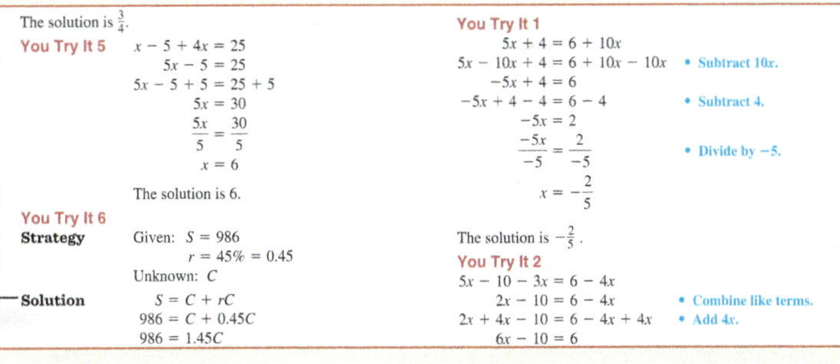
The solution is $\frac{3}{4}$.

You Try It 5

$x - 5 + 4x = 25$

$5x - 5 = 25$

$5x - 5 + 5 = 25 + 5$

$5x = 30$

$\frac{5x}{5} = \frac{30}{5}$

$x = 6$

The solution is 6.

You Try It 6

Strategy Given: $S = 986$

$r = 45\% = 0.45$

Unknown: C

Solution $S = C + rC$

$986 = C + 0.45C$

$986 = 1.45C$

You Try It 1

$5x + 4 = 6 + 10x$

$5x - 10x + 4 = 6 + 10x - 10x$ • Subtract $10x$.

$-5x + 4 = 6$

$-5x + 4 - 4 = 6 - 4$ • Subtract 4.

$-5x = 2$

$\frac{-5x}{-5} = \frac{2}{-5}$ • Divide by -5.

$x = -\frac{2}{5}$

The solution is $-\frac{2}{5}$.

You Try It 2

$5x - 10 - 3x = 6 - 4x$

$2x - 10 = 6 - 4x$ • Combine like terms.

$2x + 4x - 10 = 6 - 4x + 4x$ • Add $4x$.

$6x - 10 = 6$

The **PROBLEM-SOLVING APPROACH** used throughout the text emphasizes the importance of problem-solving strategies. Model strategies are presented as guides for you to follow as you attempt the You Try Its that accompany the numbered Examples.

EXAMPLE 3

A wallpaper hanger charges a fee of $25 plus $12 for each roll of wallpaper used in a room. If the total charge for hanging wallpaper is $97, how many rolls of wallpaper were used?

Strategy

To find the number of rolls of wallpaper used, write and solve an equation using n to represent the number of rolls of wallpaper used.

$25 plus $12 for each roll of wallpaper	is	$97

YOU TRY IT 3

The fee charged by a ticketing agency for a concert is $3.50 plus $17.50 for each ticket purchased. If your total charge for tickets is $161, how many tickets did you purchase?

Your strategy

PROJECTS OR GROUP ACTIVITIES appear at the end of each exercise set. Your instructor may assign these individually, or you may be asked to work through the activities in groups.

UPDATED!

Projects or Group Activities

70. Geometry Write an expression in factored form for the shaded portion in each of the following diagrams. Use the equation for the area of a rectangle ($A = LW$) and the equation for the area of a circle ($A = \pi r^2$).

a. b. c.

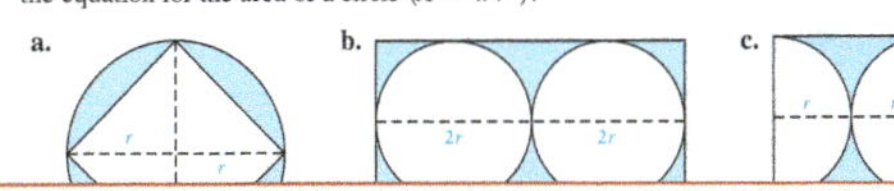

Additional Resources — Get More from Your Textbook!

Instructor Resources

Annotated Instructor's Edition (AIE)

(ISBN 978-1-133-36582-2)

The Annotated Instructor's Edition features answers to all of the problems in the text, as well as an appendix denoting those problems that can be found in Enhanced WebAssign.

PowerLecture with Diploma®

(ISBN 978-1-285-16165-5)

This DVD provides the instructor with dynamic media tools for teaching. Create, deliver, and customize tests (both print and online) in minutes with Diploma's Computerized Testing featuring algorithmic equations. Easily build solution sets for homework or exams using Solution Builder's online solutions manual. Quickly and easily update your syllabus with the Syllabus Creator, which was created by the authors and contains the new edition's table of contents.

Complete Solutions Manual (ISBN 978-1-285-42071-4)

Author: Pat Foard, South Plains College

The Complete Solutions Manual provides worked-out solutions to all of the problems in the text.

Instructor's Resource Binder with Appendix

(ISBN 978-1-285-42073-8)

Author: Maria H. Andersen, Muskegon Community College; Appendices by Richard N. Aufmann, Palomar College, and Joanne S. Lockwood, Nashua Community College

Each section of the main text is discussed in uniquely designed Teaching Guides that contain tips, examples, activities, worksheets, overheads, assessments, and solutions to all worksheets and activities.

Solution Builder

This online instructor database offers complete, worked-out solutions to all exercises in the text, allowing you to create customized, secure solutions printouts (in PDF format) matched exactly to the problems you assign in class. For more information, visit www.cengage.com/solutionbuilder.

Enhanced WebAssign®

Printed Access Card: 978-0-538-73810-1

Online Access Code: 978-1-285-18181-3

Exclusively from Cengage Learning, Enhanced WebAssign combines the exceptional mathematics content that you know and love with the most powerful online homework solution, WebAssign. Enhanced WebAssign engages students with immediate feedback, rich tutorial content, and interactive, fully customizable eBooks (YouBook), helping students to develop a deeper conceptual understanding of their subject matter. Online assignments can be built by selecting from thousands of text-specific problems or supplemented with problems from any Cengage Learning textbook.

Student Resources

Student Solutions Manual

(ISBN 978-1-285-41727-1)

Author: Pat Foard, South Plains College

Go beyond answers and improve your grade! This manual provides worked-out, step-by-step solutions to the odd-numbered problems in the text. The Student Solutions Manual gives you the information you need to truly understand how the problems are solved.

Student Workbook (ISBN 978-1-285-42072-1)

Author: Maria H. Andersen, Muskegon Community College

Get a head start. The Student Workbook contains assessments, activities, and worksheets for classroom discussions, in-class activities, and group work.

AIM for Success Student Practice Sheets

(ISBN 978-1-285-16163-1)

Author: Christine S. Verity

AIM for Success Student Practice Sheets provide additional problems to help you learn the material.

Enhanced WebAssign

Printed Access Card: 978-0-538-73810-1

Online Access Code: 978-1-285-18181-3

Enhanced WebAssign (assigned by the instructor) provides you with instant feedback on homework assignments. This online homework system is easy to use and includes helpful links to textbook sections, video examples, and problem-specific tutorials.

Acknowledgments

The authors would like to thank the people who have reviewed the ninth edition and provided many valuable suggestions.

Becky Bradshaw, *Lake Superior College*
Harvey Cartine, *Warren County Community College*
Jim Dawson, *College of Southern Idaho*
Cindy Dickson, *College of Southern Idaho*
Estella G. Elliott, *College of Southern Idaho*
Stephen Ester, *Saint Petersburg College*
Cassie Firth, *Northern Oklahoma College*
Lori L. Grady, *University of Wisconsin–Whitewater*
Nicholas Grener, *California State University, East Bay*
Ryan Grossman, *Ivy Tech Community College–Indiana*
Autumn Hoover, *Angelo State University*
Pat Horacek, *Pensacola State College*
Kelly Jackson, *Camden County College*
Thomas Judge, *California State University, East Bay*
Katy Koe, *Lincoln College*
William Lind, *Bryant and Stratton College*
Renee Lustig, *LeCordon Bleu College of Culinary Arts*
David Maina, *Columbia College, Chicago*
Connie Meade, *College of Southern Idaho*
Eugenia M. Moreno, *Butte Community College*
Dan Quynh Nguyen, *California State University, East Bay*
Rod Oberdick, *Delaware Technical Community College*
Scott Phelps, *University of La Verne*
David Poock, *Davenport University*
Nolan Thomas Rice, *College of Southern Idaho*
Daria Santerre, *Norwalk Community College*
Patricia Shepherd, *Ivy Tech Community College*
Darlyn Thomas, *Hennepin Technical College*
Sherri Urcavich, *University of Wisconsin–Green Bay*
Dr. Pamela D. Walker, *Northwestern College*
Donna M. Weglarz, *Westwood College–DuPage*
Lisa Williams, *College of the Abermarle*
Solomon Lee Willis, *Cleveland Community College*
Jerry Jacob Woods, *Westwood College*
Chen Zhixiong, *New Jersey City University*

Special thanks go to Jean Bermingham for copyediting the manuscript and proofreading pages, to Pat Foard for preparing the solutions manuals, and to Lauri Semarne for her work in ensuring the accuracy of the text. We would also like to thank the many people at Cengage Learning who worked to guide the manuscript for the ninth edition from development through production.

Index of Applications

AIM for Success

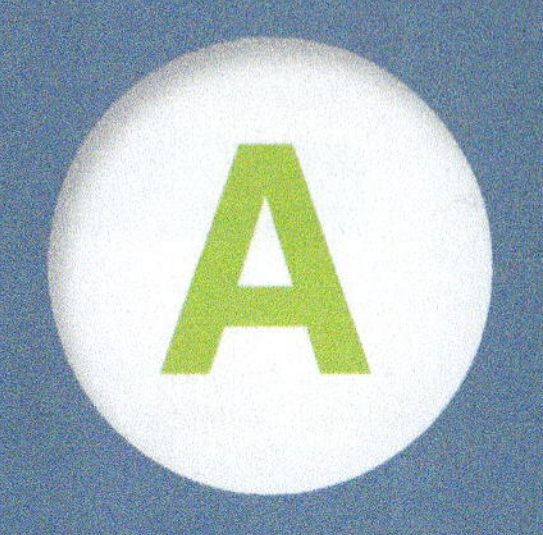

OBJECTIVES

SECTION A.1

- Get Ready
- Motivate Yourself
- Develop a "Can Do" Attitude Toward Math
- Strategies for Success
- Time Management
- Habits of Successful Students

SECTION A.2

- Get the Big Picture
- Understand the Organization
- Use the Interactive Method
- Use a Strategy to Solve Word Problems
- Ace the Test
- Ready, Set, Succeed!

Focus on Success

This important chapter describes study skills that are used by students who have been successful in this course. Chapter A covers a wide range of topics that focus on what you need to do to succeed in this class. It includes a complete guide to the textbook and how to use its features to become a successful student.

hxdbzxy/Shutterstock.com

Prep Test

Are you ready to succeed in this course?

1. Read this chapter. Answer all of the questions. Write down your answers on paper.
2. Write down your instructor's name.
3. Write down the classroom number.
4. Write down the days and times the class meets.
5. Bring your textbook, a notebook, and a pen or pencil to every class.
6. Be an active participant, not a passive observer.

SECTION

A.1 How to Succeed in This Course

Get Ready

We are committed to your success in learning mathematics and have developed many tools and resources to support you along the way.

DO YOU WANT TO EXCEL IN THIS COURSE?

Read on to learn about the skills you'll need and how best to use this book to get the results you want.

We have written this text in an *interactive* style. More about this later but, in short, this means that you are supposed to interact with the text. Do not just read the text! Work along with it. Ready? Let's begin!

WHY ARE YOU TAKING THIS COURSE?

Did you interact with the text, or did you just read the last question? Get some paper and a pencil or pen and answer the question. Really—you will have more success in math and other courses you take if you **actively participate.** Now, **interact.** Write down one reason you are taking this course.

Of course, we have no idea what you just wrote, but experience has shown us that many of you wrote something along the lines of "I have to take it to graduate" or "It is a prerequisite to another course I have to take" or "It is required for my major." Those reasons are perfectly fine. Every teacher has had to take courses that were not directly related to his or her major.

Intellistudies/Shutterstock.com

WHY DO YOU WANT TO SUCCEED IN THIS COURSE?

Think about why you want to succeed in this course. List the reasons here (not in your head . . . on the paper!):

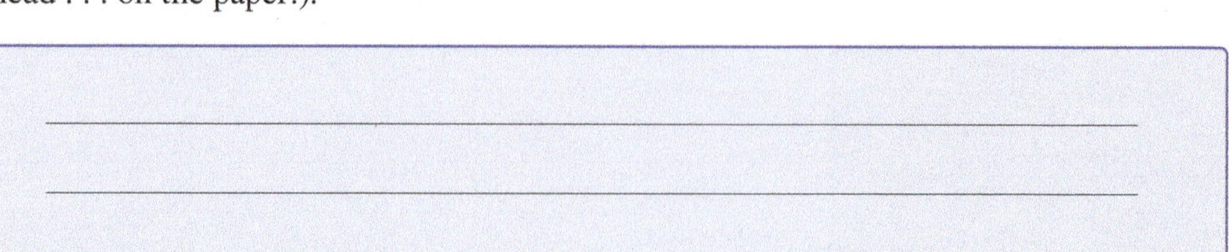

One reason you may have listed is that math skills are important in order to be successful in your chosen career. That is certainly an important reason. Here are some other reasons.

- Math is a skill that applies across careers, which is certainly a benefit in our world of changing job requirements. A good foundation in math may enable you to more easily make a career change.
- Math can help you learn critical thinking skills, an attribute all employers want.
- Math can help you see relationships between ideas and identify patterns.

Take Note
Motivation alone won't lead to success. For example, suppose a person who cannot swim is rowed out to the middle of a lake and thrown overboard. That person has a lot of motivation to swim, but most likely will drown without some help. You'll need motivation *and* learning in order to succeed.

Motivate Yourself

You'll find many real-life problems in this book, relating to sports, money, cars, music, and more. We hope that these topics will help you understand how mathematics is used in everyday life. To learn all of the necessary skills and to understand how you can apply them to your life outside of this course, **motivate** yourself to learn.

One of the reasons we asked you why you are taking this course was to provide motivation for you to succeed. When there is a reason to do something, that task is easier to accomplish. We understand that you may not want to be taking this course but, to achieve your career goal, this is a necessary step. Let your career goal be your motivation for success.

MAKE THE COMMITMENT TO SUCCEED!

With practice, you will improve your math skills. Skeptical? Think about when you first learned to drive a car, ride a skateboard, dance, paint, surf, or any other talent that you now have. You may have felt self-conscious or concerned that you might fail. But with time and practice, you learned the skill.

List a situation in which you accomplished your goal by spending time practicing and perfecting your skills (such as learning to play the piano or to play basketball):

You do not get "good" at something by doing it once a week. **Practice** is the backbone of any successful endeavor—including math!

Develop a "Can Do" Attitude Toward Math

You can do math! When you first learned the skills you just listed above, you may not have done them well. With practice, you got better. With practice, you will get better at math. Stay focused, motivated, and committed to success.

We cannot emphasize enough how important it is to overcome the "I Can't Do Math" syndrome. If you listen to interviews of very successful athletes after a particularly bad performance, you will note that they focus on the positive aspects of what they did, not the negative. Sports psychologists encourage athletes always to be positive—to have a "can do" attitude. Develop this attitude toward math and you will succeed.

Change your conversation about mathematics. Do not say "I can't do math," "I hate math," or "Math is too hard." These comments just give you an excuse to fail. You don't want to fail, and we don't want you to fail. Write it down now: **I can do math!**

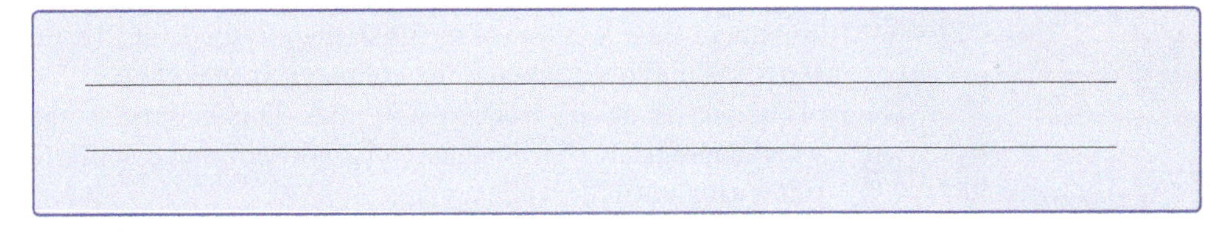

William Perugini/Shutterstock.com

Strategies for Success

PREPARE TO SUCCEED

There are a number of things that may be worrisome to you as you begin a new semester. List some of those things now.

Here are some of the concerns expressed by our students.

- **Tuition**
  Will I be able to afford school?
- **Job**
  I must work. Will my employer give me a schedule that will allow me to go to school?
- **Anxiety**
  Will I succeed?
- **Child care**
  What will I do with my kids while I'm in class or when I need to study?
- **Time**
  Will I be able to find the time to attend class and study?
- **Degree goals**
  How long will it take me to finish school and earn my degree?

These are all important and valid concerns. Whatever your concerns, acknowledge them. Choose an education path that allows you to accommodate your concerns. Make sure they don't prevent you from succeeding.

SELECT A COURSE

Many schools offer math assessment tests. These tests evaluate your present math skills. They don't evaluate how smart you are, so don't worry about your score on the test. If you are unsure about where you should start in the math curriculum, these tests can show you where to begin. You are better off starting at a level that is appropriate for you than starting with a more advanced class and then dropping it because you can't keep up. Dropping a class is a waste of time and money.

If you have difficulty with math, avoid short courses that compress the class into a few weeks. If you have struggled with math in the past, this environment does not give you the time to process math concepts. Similarly, avoid classes that meet once a week. The time delay between classes makes it difficult to make connections between concepts.

Some career goals require a number of math courses. If that is true of your major, try to take a math course every semester until you complete the requirements. Think about it this way. If you take, say, French I, and then wait two semesters before taking French II, you may forget a lot of material. Math is much the same. You must keep the concepts fresh in your mind.

wavebreakmedia ltd/Shutterstock.com

Time Management

One of the most important requirements in completing any task is to acknowledge the amount of time it will take to finish the job successfully. Before a construction company starts to build a skyscraper, the company spends months looking at how much time each of the phases of construction will take. This is done so that resources can be allocated when appropriate. For instance, it would not make sense to schedule the electricians to run wiring until the walls are up.

MANAGE YOUR TIME!

We know how busy you are outside of school. Do you have a full-time or a part-time job? Do you have children? Do you visit your family often? Do you play school sports or participate in the school orchestra or theater company? It can be stressful to balance all of the important activities and responsibilities in your life. Creating a time management plan will help you schedule enough time to do everything you need to do. Let's get started.

First, you need a calendar. You can use a daily planner, a calendar for a smartphone, or an online calendar, such as the ones offered by Google, MSN, or Yahoo. It is best to have a calendar on which you can fill in daily activities and be able to see a weekly or monthly view as well.

Start filling in your calendar now, even if it means stopping right here and finding a calendar. Some of the things you might include are:

- The hours each class meets
- Time for driving to and from work or school
- Leisure time, an important aspect of a healthy lifestyle
- Time for study. Plan at least one hour of study for each hour in class. This is a *minimum!*
- Time to eat
- Your work schedule
- Time for extracurricular activities such as sports, music lessons, or volunteer work
- Time for family and friends
- Time for sleep
- Time for exercise

Take Note

Be realistic about how much time you have. One gauge is that working 10 hours per week is approximately equivalent to taking one three-unit course. If your college considers 15 units a full load and you are working 10 hours per week, you should consider taking 12 units. The more you work, the fewer units you should take.

We really hope you did this. If not, please reconsider. One of the best pathways to success is understanding how much time it takes to succeed. When you finish your calendar, if it does not allow you enough time to stay physically and emotionally healthy, rethink some of your school or work activities. We don't want you to lose your job because you have to study math. On the other hand, we don't want you to fail in math because of your job.

If math is particularly difficult for you, consider taking fewer course units during the semesters you take math. This applies equally to any other subject that you may find difficult. There is no rule that you must finish college in four years. It is a myth—discard it now.

Now extend your calendar for the entire semester. Many of the entries will repeat, such as the time a class meets. In your extended calendar, include significant events that may disrupt your normal routine. These might include holidays, family outings, birthdays, anniversaries, or special events such as a concert or a football game. In addition to these events, be sure to include the dates of tests, the date of the final exam, and dates that projects or papers are due. These are all important semester events. Having them on your calendar will remind you that you need to make time for them.

CandyBox Images/Shutterstock.com

CLASS TIME

To be successful, **attend class.** You should consider your commitment to attend class as serious as your commitment to your job or to keeping an appointment with a dear friend. It is difficult to overstate the importance of attending class. If you miss work, you don't get paid. If you miss class, you are not getting the full benefit of your tuition dollar. You are losing money.

If, by some unavoidable situation, you cannot attend class, find out as soon as possible what was covered in class. You might:

- Ask a friend for notes and the assignment.
- Contact your instructor and get the assignment. Missing class is no excuse for not being prepared for the next class.
- Determine whether there are online resources that you can use to help you with the topics and concepts that were discussed in the class you missed.

Going to class is important. Once you are there, **participate in class.** Stay involved and active. When your instructor asks a question, try to at least mentally answer the question. If you have a question, ask. Your instructor expects questions and wants you to understand the concept being discussed.

HOMEWORK TIME

In addition to attending class, you must **do homework.** Homework is the best way to reinforce the ideas presented in class. You should plan on at least one to two hours of homework and study for each hour you are in class. We've had many students tell us that one to two hours seems like a lot of time. That may be true, but if you want to attain your goals, you must be willing to devote the time to being successful in this math course.

You should schedule study time just as if it were class time. To do this, write down where and when you study best. For instance, do you study best at home, in the library, at the math center, under a tree, or somewhere else? Some psychologists who research successful study strategies suggest that just by varying where you study, you can increase the effectiveness of a study session. While you are considering where you prefer to study, also think about the time of day during which your study period will be most productive. Write down your thoughts.

____

____

Look at what you have written, and be sure that you can consistently be in your favorite study environment at the time you have selected. Studying and homework are extremely important. Just as you should not miss class, **do not miss study time.**

Before we leave this important topic, we have a few suggestions. If at all possible, create a study hour right after class. The material will be fresh in your mind, and the immediate review, along with your homework, will help reinforce the concepts you are learning.

If you can't study right after class, make sure that you set aside some time *on the day of the class* to review notes and begin the homework. The longer you wait, the more difficult it will be to recall some of the important points covered during class. Study math in small chunks—one hour a day (perhaps not enough for most of us), every day, is better than seven hours in one sitting. If you are studying for an extended period of time, break up your study session by studying one subject for a while and then moving on to another subject. Try to alternate between similar or related courses. For instance, study math for a while, then science, and then back to math. Or study history for a while, then political science, and then back to history.

Meet some of the people in your class and try to **put together a study group.** The group could meet two or three times a week. During those meetings, you could quiz each other, prepare for a test, try to explain a concept to someone else in the group, or get help on a topic that is difficult for you.

After reading these suggestions, you may want to rethink where and when you study best. If so, do that now. Remember, however, that it is your individual style that is important. Choose what works for *you,* and stick to it.

Pattie Steib/Shutterstock.com

Habits of Successful Students

There are a number of habits that successful students use. Think about what these might be, and write them down.

____

____

What you have written is very important. The habits you have listed are probably the things you know you must do to succeed. Here is a list of some responses from successful students we have known.

- **Set priorities.** You will encounter many distractions during the semester. Do not allow them to prevent you from reaching your goal.

- **Take responsibility.** Your instructor, this textbook, tutors, math centers, and other resources are there to help you succeed. Ultimately, however, you must choose to learn. You must choose success.
- **Hang out with successful students.** Success breeds success. When you work and study with successful students, you are in an environment that will help you succeed. Seek out people who are committed to their goals.
- **Study regularly.** We have mentioned this before, but it is too important not to be repeated.
- **Self test.** Once every few days, select homework exercises from previous assignments and use them to test your understanding. Try to do these exercises without getting help from examples in the text. These self tests will help you gain confidence that you can do these types of problems on a test given in class.
- **Try different strategies.** If you read the text and are still having difficulty understanding a concept, consider going a step further. Contact the instructor or find a tutor. Many campuses have some free tutorial services. Go to the math or learning center. Consult another textbook. Be active and get the help you need.
- **Make flash cards.** This is one of the strategies that some math students do not think to try. Flash cards are a very important part of learning math. For instance, your instructor may use words or phrases such as *linear, quadratic, exponent, base, rational,* and many others. If you don't know the meanings of these words, you will not know what is being discussed.
- **Plod along.** Your education is not a race. The primary goal is to finish. Taking too many classes and then dropping some does not get you to the end any faster. Take only as many classes as you can successfully manage.

SECTION

A.2 How to Use This Text to Succeed in This Course

Helder Almeida/Shutterstock.com

Get the Big Picture

One of the major resources that you will have access to the entire semester is this textbook. We have written this text with you and your success in mind. The following is a guide to the features of this text that will help you succeed.

Actually, we want you to get the *really* big picture. Take a few minutes to read the table of contents. You may feel some anxiety about all the new concepts you will be learning. Try to think of this as an exciting opportunity to learn math. Now look through the entire book. Move quickly. Don't spend more than a few seconds on each page. Scan titles, look at pictures, and notice diagrams.

Getting this "big picture" view will help you see where this course is going. To reach your goal, it's important to get an idea of the steps you will need to take along the way.

As you look through the book, find topics that interest you. What's your preference? Racing? Sailing? TV? Amusement parks? Find the Index of Applications at the front of the book, and pull out three subjects that interest you. Write those topics here.

____

____

____

Understand the Organization

Look again at the Table of Contents. There are 11 chapters in this book. You'll see that every chapter is divided into sections, and each section contains a number of learning objectives. Each learning objective is labeled with a letter from A to E. Knowing how this book is organized will help you locate important topics and concepts as you're studying.

Before you start a new objective, take a few minutes to read the Objective Statement for that objective. Then, browse through the objective material. Especially note the words or phrases in bold type—these are important concepts that you'll need to know as you move along in the course. These words are good candidates for flash cards. If possible, include an example of the concept on the flash card, as shown at the left.

Flash Card

Rule for Multiplying Exponential Expressions

If m and n are integers, then $x^m \cdot x^n = x^{m+n}$.

Examples:

$x^4 \cdot x^7 = x^{4+7} = x^{11}$

$y \cdot y^5 = y^{1+5} = y^6$

$a^2 \cdot a^6 \cdot a = a^{2+6+1} = a^9$

You will also see important concepts and rules set off in boxes. Here is one about multiplication. These rules are also good candidates for flash cards.

Rule for Multiplying Exponential Expressions

If m and n are integers, then $x^m \cdot x^n = x^{m+n}$.

EXAMPLES

In each example below, we are multiplying two exponential expressions with the same base. Simplify the expression by adding the exponents.

1. $x^4 \cdot x^7 = x^{4+7} = x^{11}$
2. $y \cdot y^5 = y^{1+5} = y^6$
3. $a^2 \cdot a^6 \cdot a = a^{2+6+1} = a^9$

Leaf through Section 3.1 of Chapter 3. Write down words in bold and any concepts or rules that are displayed in boxes.

Use the Interactive Method

As we mentioned earlier, this textbook is based on an interactive approach. We want you to be actively involved in learning mathematics, and have given you many suggestions for getting "hands-on" with this book.

HOW TO Look on page 117. See HOW TO 2? A HOW TO introduces a concept (in this case, solving a percent equation) and includes a step-by-step solution of the type of exercise you will find in the homework.

HOW TO 2 70 is what percent of 80?

$P \cdot B = A$ • **Use the basic percent equation.**

$P(80) = 70$ • **$B = 80$, $A = 70$, and P is unknown.**

$\frac{P(80)}{80} = \frac{70}{80}$ • **Solve for P.**

$P = 0.875$ • **The question asked for a percent.**

$P = 87.5\%$ • **Convert the decimal to a percent.**

70 is 87.5% of 80.

Grab paper and a pencil and work along as you're reading through a HOW TO. When you're done, get a clean sheet of paper. Write down the problem and try to complete the solution without looking at your notes or at the book. When you're done, check your answer. If you got it right, you're ready to move on.

Look through the text and find three instances of a HOW TO. Write the concept illustrated in each HOW TO here.

Example/You Try It Pair You'll need hands-on practice to succeed in mathematics. When we show you an example, work it out yourself, right beside the solution. Use the Example/You Try It pairs to get the practice you need.

Take a look at page 112. Example 2 and You Try It 2 are shown here.

EXAMPLE 2

Solve: $x + 15 = 23$

Solution

$x + 15 = 23$

$x + 15 - 15 = 23 - 15$ • **Subtract 15 from each side.**

$x + 0 = 8$ • **Simplify each side.**

$x = 8$ • **Addition Property of Zero**

The solution is 8.

YOU TRY IT 2

Solve: $26 = y - 14$

Your solution

Solution on p. S4

You'll see that each Example is fully worked out. Study the Example by carefully working through each step. Then, try to complete the You Try It. Use the solution to the Example as a model for solving the You Try It. If you get stuck, the solutions to the You Try Its are provided in the back of the book. There is a page number directly following the You Try It that shows you where you can find the completely-worked-out solution. Use the solution to get a hint for the step on which you are stuck. Then, try again!

When you've arrived at your solution, check your work against the solution in the back of the book. Turn to page S4 to see the solution for You Try It 2.

Remember that sometimes there is more than one way to solve a problem. But your answer should always match the answer we've given in the back of the book. If you have any questions about whether your method will always work, check with your instructor.

Use a Strategy to Solve Word Problems

Learning to solve word problems is one of the reasons you are studying math. This is where you combine all of the critical thinking skills you have learned to solve practical problems.

Try not to be intimidated by word problems. Basically, what you need is a strategy that will help you come up with the equation you will need to solve the problem. When you are looking at a word problem, try the following:

- **Read the problem.** This may seem pretty obvious, but we mean really **read** it. Don't just scan it. Read the problem slowly and carefully.
- **Write down what is known and what is unknown.** Now that you have read the problem, go back and write down everything that is known. Next, write down what it is you are trying to find. *Write* this—don't just think it! Be as specific as you can. For instance, if you are asked to find a distance, don't just write "I need to find the distance." Be specific and write "I need to find the distance between Earth and the moon."
- **Think of a method to find the unknown.** For instance, is there a formula that relates the known and unknown quantities? This is certainly the most difficult step. Eventually, you must write an equation to be solved.
- **Solve the equation.** Be careful as you solve the equation. There is no sense in getting to this point and then making a careless mistake. The unknown in most word problems will include a unit such as feet, dollars, or miles per hour. When you write your answer, include the unit. An answer such as 20 doesn't mean much. Is it 20 feet, 20 dollars, 20 miles per hour, or something else?
- **Check your solution.** Now that you have an answer, go back to the problem and ask yourself whether it makes sense. This is an important step. For instance, if, according to your answer, the cost of a car is $2.51, you know that something went wrong.

In this text, the solution of every word problem is broken down into two steps, **Strategy** and **Solution.** The Strategy consists of the first three steps discussed above. The Solution is the last two steps. Here is an Example from page 120 of the text. Because you have not yet studied the concepts involved in the problem, you may not be able to solve it. However, note the detail in the Strategy. When you do the You Try It following an Example, be sure to include your own Strategy.

EXAMPLE 4

To make a certain color of blue, 4 oz of cyan must be contained in 1 gal of paint. What is the percent concentration of cyan in the paint?

Strategy

The cyan is given in ounces and the amount of paint is given in gallons. We must convert ounces to gallons or gallons to ounces. For this problem, we will convert gallons to ounces: 1 gal = 128 oz. Solve $Q = Ar$ for r, with $Q = 4$ and $A = 128$.

Solution

$Q = Ar$ • Use the percent mixture equation.

$4 = 128r$ • $Q = 4, A = 128$

$$\frac{4}{128} = \frac{128r}{128}$$

$0.03125 = r$

The percent concentration of cyan is 3.125%.

YOU TRY IT 4

The concentration of sugar in a certain breakfast cereal is 25%. If there are 2 oz of sugar contained in a bowl of cereal, how many ounces of cereal are in the bowl?

Your strategy

Your solution

Solutions on p. S5

When you have finished studying a section, **do the exercises your instructor has selected.** Math is not a spectator sport. You must practice every day. Do the homework and do not get behind.

Ace the Test

There are a number of features in this text that will help you prepare for a test. These features will help you even more if you do just one simple thing: When you are doing your homework, go back to each previous homework assignment for the current chapter and rework two exercises. That's right—just *two* exercises. You will be surprised at how much better prepared you will be for a test by doing this.

Here are some additional aids to help you **ace the test.**

Chapter Summary Once you've completed a chapter, look at the Chapter Summary. The Chapter Summary is divided into two sections: **Key Words** and **Essential Rules and Procedures.** Flip to page 470 to see the Chapter Summary for Chapter 9. The summary shows all of the important topics covered in the chapter. Do you see the reference following each topic? This reference shows you the objective and page in the text where you can find more information on the concept.

Write down one Key Word and one Essential Rule or Procedure. Explain the meaning of the reference "9.1A, page 446."

Chapter Review Exercises Turn to page 471 to see the Chapter Review Exercises for Chapter 9. When you do the review exercises, you're giving yourself an important opportunity to test your understanding of the chapter. The answer to each review exercise is given at the back of the book, along with the objective the question relates to. When you're done with the Chapter Review Exercises, check your answers. If you had trouble with any of the questions, you can restudy the objectives and retry some of the exercises in those objectives for extra help.

Go to the Answer Section at the back of the text. Find the answers for the Chapter Review Exercises for Chapter 9. Write down the answer to Exercise 25. Explain the meaning of the reference "9.2C."

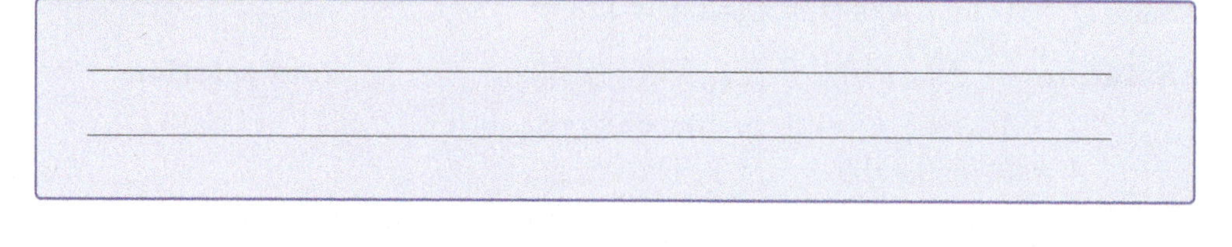

Chapter Test The Chapter Test for each chapter can be found after the Chapter Review Exercises and can be used to help you prepare for your exam. The answer to each question is given at the back of the book, along with both an objective reference and a reference to a HOW TO, Example, or You Try It that the question relates to. Think of these tests as "practice runs" for your in-class tests. Take the test in a quiet place, and try to work through it in the same amount of time that will be allowed for your actual exam.

The aids we have mentioned above will help you prepare for a test. You should begin your review *at least* two days before the test—three days is better. These aids will get you ready for the test.

Here are some suggestions to try while you are actually taking the test.

- **Try to relax.** We know that test situations make some students quite nervous or anxious. These feelings are normal. Try to stay calm and focused on what you know. If you have prepared as we have suggested, the answers will begin to come to you.
- **Scan the test.** Get a feeling for the big picture.
- **Read the directions carefully.** Make sure you answer each question fully.
- **Work the problems that are easiest for you first.** This will help you with your confidence and help reduce any nervous feelings you may have.

Ready, Set, Succeed!

It takes hard work and commitment to succeed, but we know you can do it! Doing well in mathematics is just one step you'll take on your path to success. Good luck. We wish you success.

Prealgebra Review

OBJECTIVES

SECTION 1.1
- **A** To use inequality symbols with integers
- **B** To use opposites and absolute value

SECTION 1.2
- **A** To add integers
- **B** To subtract integers
- **C** To solve application problems

SECTION 1.3
- **A** To multiply integers
- **B** To divide integers
- **C** To solve application problems

SECTION 1.4
- **A** To evaluate exponential expressions
- **B** To use the Order of Operations Agreement to simplify expressions

SECTION 1.5
- **A** To factor numbers
- **B** To find the prime factorization of a number
- **C** To find the least common multiple and greatest common factor

SECTION 1.6
- **A** To write a rational number in simplest form and as a decimal
- **B** To add rational numbers
- **C** To subtract rational numbers
- **D** To solve application problems

SECTION 1.7
- **A** To multiply rational numbers
- **B** To divide rational numbers
- **C** To convert among percents, fractions, and decimals
- **D** To solve application problems

SECTION 1.8
- **A** To find the measures of angles
- **B** To solve perimeter problems
- **C** To solve area problems

Focus on Success

Have you read Chapter A, AIM for Success? It describes study skills used by students who have been successful in their math courses. It gives you tips on how to stay motivated, how to manage your time, and how to prepare for exams. Chapter A also includes a complete guide to the textbook and how to use its features to be successful in this course. It starts on page AIM-1.

Katrina Brown/Shutterstock.com

Prep Test

Are you ready to succeed in this chapter? Take the Prep Test below to find out if you are ready to learn the new material.

1. What is 127.1649 rounded to the nearest hundredth?

2. Add: $3416 + 42{,}561 + 537$

3. Subtract: $5004 - 487$

4. Multiply: 407×28

5. Divide: $11{,}684 \div 23$

6. What is the smallest number that both 8 and 12 divide evenly?

7. What is the greatest number that divides both 16 and 20 evenly?

8. Without using 1, write 21 as a product of two whole numbers.

9. Represent the shaded portion of the figure as a fraction in simplest form.

10. Which of the following, if any, is not possible?
(i) $6 + 0$ **(ii)** $6 - 0$
(iii) 6×0 **(iv)** $6 \div 0$

SECTION

1.1 Introduction to Integers

OBJECTIVE A To use inequality symbols with integers

Valentyn Volkov/ Shutterstock.com

The desire to group similar items seems to be a human characteristic. For instance, biologists place similar animals in groups called *species*. Nutritionists classify foods according to *food groups;* for example, pasta, crackers, and rice are among the foods in the bread group.

Mathematicians place objects with similar properties in groups called *sets*. A **set** is a collection of objects. The objects in a set are called the **elements of the set.**

The **roster method** of writing a set encloses a list of the elements in braces. Thus the set of sections within an orchestra is written {brass, percussion, string, woodwind}. When the elements of a set are listed, each element is listed only once. For instance, if the list of numbers 1, 2, 3, 2, 3 were placed in a set, the set would be {1, 2, 3}.

The symbol $\in$ means "is an element of." $2 \in B$ is read "2 is an element of set B."

Given $C = \{3, 5, 9\}$, then $3 \in C$, $5 \in C$, and $9 \in C$. $7 \notin C$ is read "7 is not an element of set C."

The numbers that we use to count objects, such as the students in a classroom or the horses on a ranch, are the *natural numbers.*

Natural numbers $= \{1, 2, 3, 4, 5, 6, 7, 8, 9, 10, \ldots\}$

Point of Interest

The Alexandrian astronomer Ptolemy began using *omicron, O,* the first letter of the Greek word that means "nothing," as the symbol for zero in 150 A.D. It was not until the 13th century, however, that Fibonacci introduced 0 to the Western world as a placeholder so that we could distinguish, for example, 45 from 405.

The three dots mean that the list of natural numbers continues on and on, and that there is no largest natural number.

The natural numbers alone do not provide all the numbers that are useful in applications. For instance, a meteorologist also needs the number zero and numbers below zero.

Integers $= \{\ldots, -5, -4, -3, -2, -1, 0, 1, 2, 3, 4, 5, \ldots\}$

Each integer can be shown on a number line. The integers to the left of zero on the number line are called **negative integers.** The integers to the right of zero are called **positive integers,** or natural numbers. Zero is neither a positive nor a negative integer.

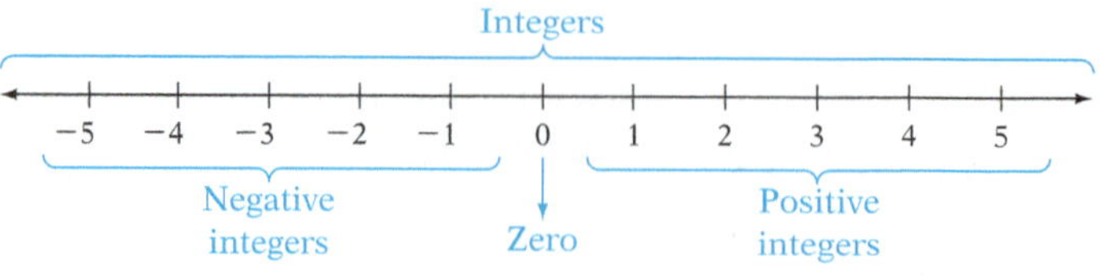

The **graph** of an integer is shown by placing a heavy dot on the number line directly above the number. The graphs of −3 and 4 are shown on the number line below.

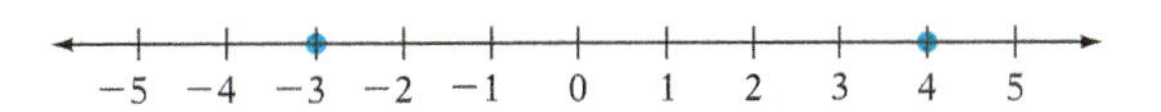

Consider the following sentences.

The quarterback threw the football and the receiver caught *it*.

A student purchased a computer and used *it* to write history papers.

In the first sentence, *it* is used to mean the football; in the second sentence, *it* means the computer. In language, the word *it* can stand for many different objects. Similarly, in mathematics, a letter of the alphabet can be used to stand for a number. Such a letter is called a **variable.** Variables are used in the following definition of inequality symbols.

Point of Interest

The symbols for "is less than" and "is greater than" were introduced by Thomas Harriot around 1630. Before that, ⊏ and ⊐ were used for > and <, respectively.

Inequality Symbols

If a and b are two numbers and a is to the left of b on the number line, then a **is less than** b. This is written $a < b$.

If a and b are two numbers and a is to the right of b on the number line, then a **is greater than** b. This is written $a > b$.

EXAMPLES

1. $-2 < 1$ — −2 is to the left of 1 on the number line. −2 is less than 1.
2. $3 > 0$ — 3 is to the right of 0 on the number line. 3 is greater than 0.

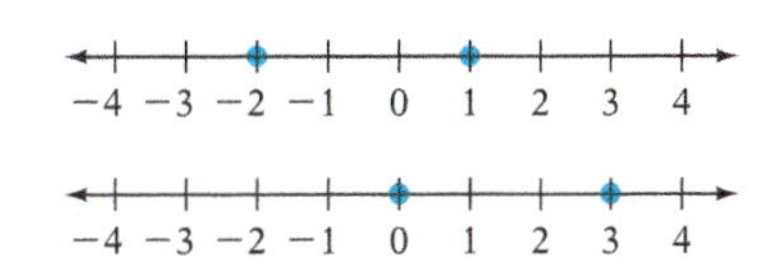

APPLY THE CONCEPT

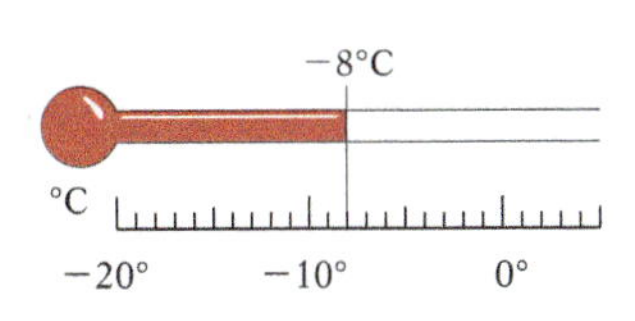

Which is the colder temperature, −8°C or −3°C?

The lesser number corresponds to the colder temperature.

$$-8 < -3$$

The colder temperature is −8°C.

There are also inequality symbols for **is less than or equal to (≤)** and **is greater than or equal to (≥).**

$7 \le 15$	7 is less than or equal to 15. This is true because $7 < 15$.	$6 \le 6$	6 is less than or equal to 6. This is true because $6 = 6$.

EXAMPLE 1

Use the roster method to write the set of negative integers greater than or equal to −4.

Solution

$A = \{-4, -3, -2, -1\}$ • **A set is designated by a capital letter.**

YOU TRY IT 1

Use the roster method to write the set of positive integers less than 7.

Your solution

Solution on p. S1

EXAMPLE 2

Given $A = \{-6, -2, 0\}$, which elements of set A are less than or equal to -2?

Solution

Find the order relation between each element of set A and -2.

$-6 < -2$

$-2 = -2$

$0 > -2$

The elements -6 and -2 are less than or equal to -2.

YOU TRY IT 2

Given $B = \{-5, -1, 5\}$, which elements of set B are greater than -1?

Your solution

Solution on p. S1

OBJECTIVE B

To use opposites and absolute value

Two numbers that are the same distance from zero on the number line but are on opposite sides of zero are **opposite numbers,** or **opposites.** The opposite of a number is also called its **additive inverse.**

The opposite of 5 is -5.

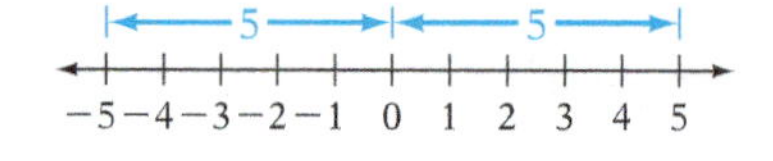

The opposite of -5 is 5.

Tips for Success

Some students think that they can "coast" at the beginning of this course because the topic of Chapter 1 is a review of prealgebra. However, this chapter lays the foundation for the entire course. Be sure you know and understand all the concepts presented. For example, study the properties of absolute value presented in this lesson.

The negative sign can be read "the opposite of."

$-(2) = -2$ The opposite of 2 is -2.

$-(-2) = 2$ The opposite of -2 is 2.

The **absolute value of a number** is its distance from zero on the number line. Therefore, the absolute value of a number is a positive number or zero. The symbol for absolute value is two vertical bars, $|\ |$.

The distance from 0 to 3 is 3. Therefore, the absolute value of 3 is 3.

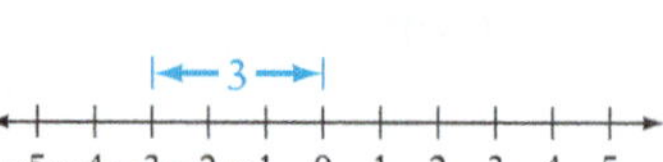

$|3| = 3$

The distance from 0 to -3 is 3. Therefore, the absolute value of -3 is 3.

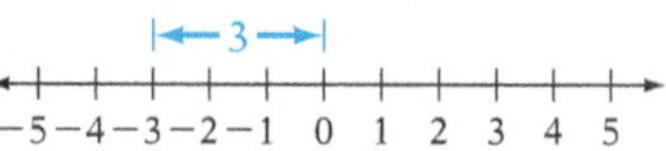

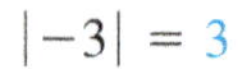

$|-3| = 3$

Point of Interest

The definition of *absolute value* given in the box is written in what is called rhetorical style. That is, it is written without the use of variables. This is how *all* mathematics was written prior to the Renaissance. During that period from the 14th to the 16th century, the idea of expressing a variable symbolically was developed. Using variables, the definition of absolute value is

$$|x| = \begin{cases} x, & x > 0 \\ 0, & x = 0 \\ -x, & x < 0 \end{cases}$$

Absolute Value

The absolute value of a positive number is the number itself.
The absolute value of a negative number is the opposite of the number.
The absolute value of zero is zero.

EXAMPLES

1. $|6| = 6$ **2.** $|-8| = 8$ **3.** $|0| = 0$

HOW TO 1 Evaluate: $-|-12|$

$-|-12| = -12$

- **The absolute value symbol does not affect the negative sign in front of the absolute value symbol.**

EXAMPLE 3

Evaluate $|-4|$ and $-|-10|$.

Solution

$|-4| = 4$

$-|-10| = -10$

YOU TRY IT 3

Evaluate $|-5|$ and $-|-23|$.

Your solution

EXAMPLE 4

Given $A = \{-12, 0, 4\}$, find the additive inverse of each element of set A.

Solution

$-(-12) = 12$

$-0 = 0$

$-(4) = -4$

- **Zero is neither positive nor negative.**

YOU TRY IT 4

Given $B = \{-11, 0, 8\}$, find the additive inverse of each element of set B.

Your solution

EXAMPLE 5

Given $C = \{-17, 0, 14\}$, find the absolute value of each element of set C.

Solution

$|-17| = 17$

$|0| = 0$

$|14| = 14$

YOU TRY IT 5

Given $D = \{-37, 0, 29\}$, find the absolute value of each element of set D.

Your solution

Solutions on p. S1

1.1 EXERCISES

Concept Check

1. Fill in the blank with *left* or *right*.

   a. On the number line, the number -7 is to the ____________ of the number -5.

   b. On the number line, the number -1 is to the ____________ of the number -8.

2. Fill in the blank with *positive* or *negative*.

   a. The opposite of a negative number is a ____________ number.

   b. The opposite of a positive number is a ____________ number.

3. The equation $|-10| = 10$ is read "the ____________ of negative ten is ten."

OBJECTIVE A *To use inequality symbols with integers*

For Exercises 4 to 13, place the correct symbol, < or >, between the two numbers.

4. $8 \quad -6$ **5.** $-14 \quad 16$ **6.** $-12 \quad 1$ **7.** $35 \quad 28$ **8.** $42 \quad 19$

9. $-42 \quad 27$ **10.** $0 \quad -31$ **11.** $-17 \quad 0$ **12.** $53 \quad -46$ **13.** $-27 \quad -38$

For Exercises 14 and 15, determine which of the following statements is true about n.
(i) n is positive. (ii) n is negative.
(iii) n is zero. (iv) n can be positive, negative, or zero.

14. The number n is to the right of the number 5 on the number line.

15. The number n is to the left of the number 5 on the number line.

For Exercises 16 to 19, use the roster method to write the set.

16. The positive integers less than or equal to 8

17. The positive integers less than 4

18. The negative integers greater than -7

19. The negative integers greater than or equal to -5

20. Given $D = \{-23, -18, -8, 0\}$, which elements of set D are less than -8?

21. Given $C = \{-33, -24, -10, 0\}$, which elements of set C are less than -10?

22. Given $E = \{-35, -13, 21, 37\}$, which elements of set E are greater than -10?

23. Given $F = \{-27, -14, 14, 27\}$, which elements of set F are greater than -15?

24. Given that set D is the negative integers greater than or equal to -10, which elements of set D are less than -4?

25. Given that set C is the negative integers greater than -8, which elements of set C are less than or equal to -3?

OBJECTIVE B *To use opposites and absolute value*

For Exercises 26 to 30, find the additive inverse.

26. 4 **27.** 8 **28.** -9 **29.** -28 **30.** -36

For Exercises 31 to 40, evaluate.

31. $-(-14)$ **32.** $-(-40)$ **33.** $-(77)$ **34.** $-(39)$ **35.** $-(-13)$

36. $|-74|$ **37.** $|-96|$ **38.** $-|-82|$ **39.** $-|-53|$ **40.** $-|81|$

For Exercises 41 to 48, place the correct symbol, $<$ or $>$, between the two expressions.

41. $|-83| \quad |58|$ **42.** $|22| \quad |-19|$ **43.** $|43| \quad |-52|$ **44.** $|-71| \quad |-92|$

45. $|-68| \quad |-42|$ **46.** $|12| \quad |-31|$ **47.** $|-45| \quad |-61|$ **48.** $|-28| \quad |43|$

49. Use the set $A = \{-8, -5, -2, 1, 3\}$.
a. Find the opposite of each element of set A.
b. Find the absolute value of each element of set A.

50. Use the set $B = \{-11, -7, -3, 1, 5\}$.
a. Find the opposite of each element of set B.
b. Find the absolute value of each element of set B.

51. True or false? The absolute value of a negative number n is greater than n.

Critical Thinking

52. If x represents a negative integer, then $-x$ represents a __________ integer.

53. If x is an integer, is the inequality $|x| < -3$ always true, sometimes true, or never true?

Projects or Group Activities

For Exercises 54 to 59, correct any statements that are false.

54. $-3 < -4$ **55.** $-5 \leq 5$ **56.** $-8 > -8$

57. $1 = \{1\}$ **58.** $3 \in \{1, 2\}$ **59.** $5 \notin \{1, 3, 5\}$

SECTION

1.2 Addition and Subtraction of Integers

OBJECTIVE A

To add integers

A number can be represented anywhere along the number line by an arrow. A positive number is represented by an arrow pointing to the right, and a negative number is represented by an arrow pointing to the left. The size of the number is represented by the length of the arrow.

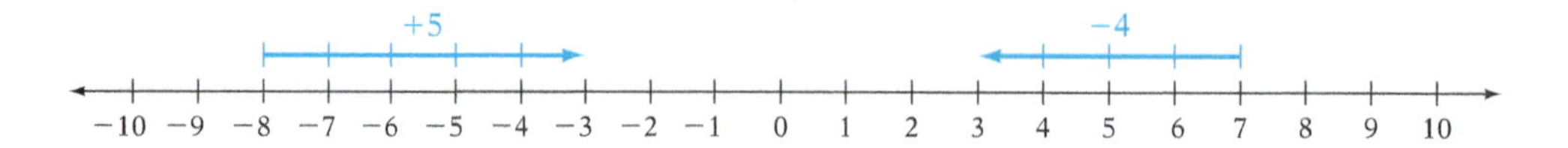

Addition is the process of finding the total of two numbers. The numbers being added are called **addends.** The total is called the **sum.** Addition of integers can be shown on the number line. To add integers, start at zero and draw, above the number line, an arrow representing the first number. At the tip of the first arrow, draw a second arrow representing the second number. The sum is below the tip of the second arrow.

$4 + 2 = 6$

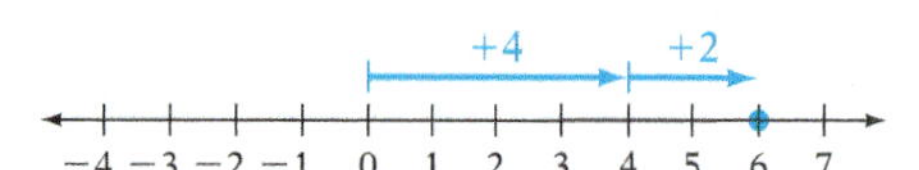

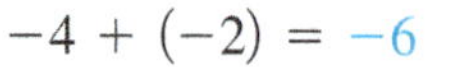

$-4 + (-2) = -6$

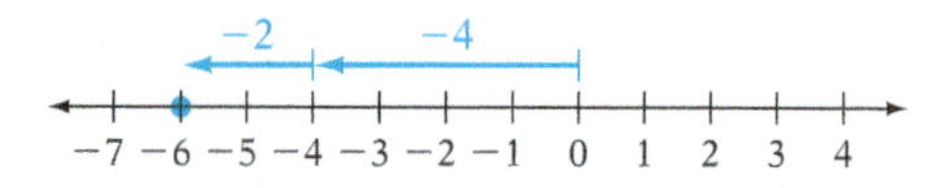

$-4 + 2 = -2$

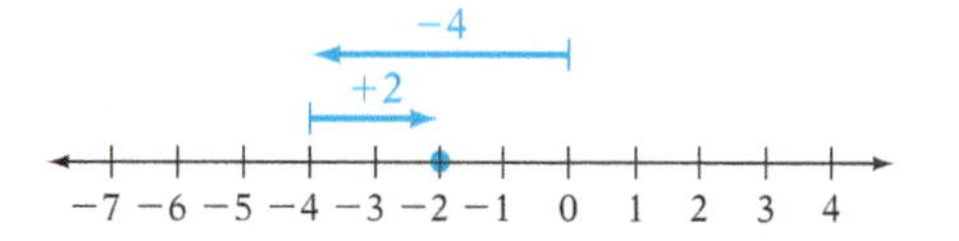

$4 + (-2) = 2$

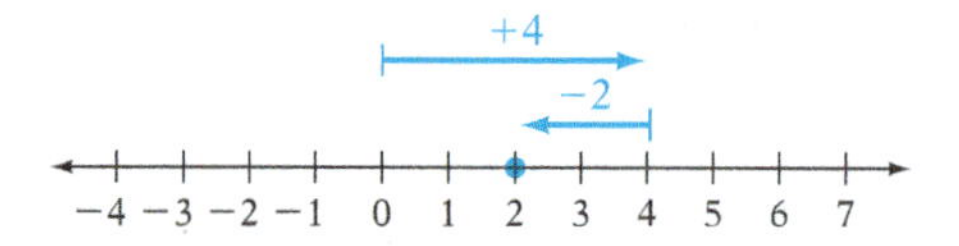

The pattern for addition shown on the number lines above is summarized in the following rules for adding integers.

Addition of Integers

To add two numbers with the same sign, add the absolute values of the numbers. Then attach the sign of the addends.

To add two numbers with different signs, find the absolute value of each number. Subtract the smaller of the absolute values from the larger. Then attach the sign of the number with the larger absolute value.

EXAMPLES

1. Add: $-12 + (-26)$
   $-12 + (-26) = -38$
   - The signs are the same.
   - Add the absolute values of the numbers $(12 + 26)$. Attach the sign of the addends.

2. Add: $-19 + 8$
   $|-19| = 19$; $|8| = 8$
   $19 - 8 = 11$
   $-19 + 8 = -11$
   - The signs are different.
   - Find the absolute value of each number.
   - Subtract the smaller absolute value from the larger.
   - Attach the sign of the number with the larger absolute value.

St. Paul, Minnesota

Tips for Success

One of the key instructional features of this text is the Example/You Try It pairs. Each example is completely worked. You are to solve the You Try It problems. When you are ready, check your solution against the one given in the Solutions section at the back of the book. The solution for You Try It 1 below is on page S1 (see the reference at the bottom right of the You Try It). See *AIM for Success* at the front of the book.

APPLY THE CONCEPT

Suppose you wake up in St. Paul, Minnesota, and the temperature is -12°F. By noon, the temperature has risen 7°F. What is the temperature at noon?

To find the temperature at noon, add 7° to -12°.

$$-12 + 7 = -5$$

The temperature at noon is -5°F.

HOW TO 1 Find the sum of -23, 47, -18, and -10.

Recall that a sum is the answer to an addition problem.

$$-23 + 47 + (-18) + (-10)$$
$$= 24 + (-18) + (-10)$$
$$= 6 + (-10) = -4$$

- **To add more than two numbers, add the first two numbers. Then add the sum to the third number. Continue until all the numbers are added.**

The phrase *the sum of* in HOW TO 1 above indicates the operation of addition. All of the phrases below indicate addition.

added to	-6 added to 9	$9 + (-6) = 3$
more than	3 more than -8	$-8 + 3 = -5$
the sum of	the sum of -2 and -8	$-2 + (-8) = -10$
increased by	-7 increased by 5	$-7 + 5 = -2$
the total of	the total of 4 and -9	$4 + (-9) = -5$
plus	6 plus -10	$6 + (-10) = -4$

EXAMPLE 1

Add: $-52 + (-39)$

Solution

$-52 + (-39) = -91$

YOU TRY IT 1

Add: $100 + (-43)$

Your solution

EXAMPLE 2

Add: $37 + (-52) + (-14)$

Solution

$37 + (-52) + (-14) = -15 + (-14)$
$= -29$

YOU TRY IT 2

Add: $-51 + 42 + 17 + (-102)$

Your solution

EXAMPLE 3

Find 11 more than -23.

Solution

$-23 + 11 = -12$

YOU TRY IT 3

Find -8 increased by 7.

Your solution

Solutions on p. S1

OBJECTIVE B *To subtract integers*

Look at the expressions below. Note that each expression equals the same number.

$8 - 3 = 5$ 8 minus 3 is 5.

$8 + (-3) = 5$ 8 plus the opposite of 3 is 5.

This example suggests the following.

Subtraction of Integers

To subtract one number from another, add the opposite of the second number to the first number.

EXAMPLES

1. Subtract: $-21 - (-40)$

$-21 - (-40) = -21 + 40$ • Rewrite the subtraction as addition of the opposite.

$= 19$ • Add.

2. Subtract: $15 - 51$

$15 - 51 = 15 + (-51)$ • Rewrite the subtraction as addition of the opposite.

$= -36$ • Add.

Chemical Element	*Boiling Point*	*Melting Point*
Mercury	357	−39
Radon	−62	−71
Xenon	−108	−112

APPLY THE CONCEPT

The table at the left shows the boiling point and the melting point, in degrees Celsius, of three chemical elements. Find the difference between the boiling point and the melting point of mercury.

To find the difference, subtract the melting point of mercury from the boiling point of mercury.

$$357 - (-39) = 357 + 39$$
$$= 396$$

The difference is 396°C.

HOW TO 2 Subtract: $-12 - (-21) - 15$

$-12 - (-21) - 15 = -12 + 21 + (-15)$

$= 9 + (-15) = -6$

• Rewrite each subtraction as addition of the opposite. Then add.

HOW TO 3 Find the difference between −8 and 7.

A *difference* is the answer to a subtraction problem.

$-8 - 7 = -8 + (-7)$

$= -15$

• Rewrite the subtraction as addition of the opposite. Then add.

Tips for Success

The HOW TO feature indicates an example with explanatory remarks. Using paper and pencil, you should work through the example. See *AIM for Success* at the front of the book.

The phrase *the difference between* in HOW TO 3 above indicates the operation of subtraction. All of the following phrases indicate subtraction.

Take Note

Note the order in which numbers are subtracted when the phrase *less than* is used. If you have \$10 and your friend has \$6 less than you do, then your friend has \$6 less than \$10, or \$10 − \$6 = \$4.

minus	−5 minus 11	$-5 - 11 = -16$
less	−3 less 5	$-3 - 5 = -8$
less than	−8 less than −2	$-2 - (-8) = 6$
the difference between	the difference between −5 and 4	$-5 - 4 = -9$
decreased by	−4 decreased by 9	$-4 - 9 = -13$
subtract . . . from	subtract 8 from −3	$-3 - 8 = -11$

EXAMPLE 4

Subtract: $-14 - 18 - (-21) - 4$

Solution

$$\begin{aligned} &-14 - 18 - (-21) - 4 \\ &\quad = -14 + (-18) + 21 + (-4) \\ &\quad = -32 + 21 + (-4) \\ &\quad = -11 + (-4) = -15 \end{aligned}$$

YOU TRY IT 4

Subtract: $-9 - (-12) - 17 - 4$

Your solution

EXAMPLE 5

Find 9 less than −4.

Solution

$-4 - 9 = -4 + (-9) = -13$

YOU TRY IT 5

Subtract −12 from −11.

Your solution

Solutions on p. S1

OBJECTIVE C *To solve application problems*

EXAMPLE 6

The average temperature on Mercury's sunlit side is 950°F. The average temperature on Mercury's dark side is −346°F. Find the difference between these two average temperatures.

Strategy

To find the difference, subtract the average temperature on the dark side (−346) from the average temperature on the sunlit side (950).

Solution

$$\begin{aligned} 950 - (-346) &= 950 + 346 \\ &= 1296 \end{aligned}$$

The difference between the average temperatures is 1296°F.

YOU TRY IT 6

The average daytime temperature on Mars is −17°F. The average nighttime temperature on Mars is −130°F. Find the difference between these two average temperatures.

Your strategy

Your solution

Solution on p. S1

1.2 EXERCISES

Concept Check

1. Explain how to add two integers with the same sign.
2. Explain how to add two integers with different signs.
3. What is the difference between the terms *minus* and *negative*?
4. Explain how to subtract two integers.

OBJECTIVE A *To add integers*

For Exercises 5 to 26, add.

5. $-3 + (-8)$
6. $-6 + (-9)$
7. $-8 + 3$
8. $-9 + 2$
9. $-3 + (-80)$
10. $-12 + (-1)$
11. $-23 + (-23)$
12. $-12 + (-12)$
13. $16 + (-16)$
14. $-17 + 17$
15. $48 + (-53)$
16. $19 + (-41)$
17. $-17 + (-3) + 29$
18. $13 + 62 + (-38)$
19. $-3 + (-8) + 12$
20. $-27 + (-42) + (-18)$
21. $13 + (-22) + 4 + (-5)$
22. $-14 + (-3) + 7 + (-21)$
23. $-22 + 20 + 2 + (-18)$
24. $-6 + (-8) + 14 + (-4)$
25. $-16 + (-17) + (-18) + 10$
26. $-25 + (-31) + 24 + 19$
27. Find the sum of -42 and -23.
28. What is 4 more than -8?
29. What is 16 more than -31?
30. Find -17 increased by 12.
31. Find the total of -17, -23, 43, and 19.
32. What is -8 added to -21?

For Exercises 33 and 34, without finding the sum, determine whether the sum is positive or negative.

33. $812 + (-537)$
34. The sum of -57 and -31

OBJECTIVE B *To subtract integers*

For Exercises 35 to 61, subtract.

35. $16 - 8$

36. $12 - 3$

37. $7 - 14$

38. $6 - 9$

39. $-7 - 2$

40. $-9 - 4$

41. $7 - (-2)$

42. $3 - (-4)$

43. $-6 - (-3)$

44. $-4 - (-2)$

45. $6 - (-12)$

46. $-12 - 16$

47. $-4 - 3 - 2$

48. $4 - 5 - 12$

49. $12 - (-7) - 8$

50. $-12 - (-3) - (-15)$

51. $-19 - (-19) - 18$

52. $-8 - (-8) - 14$

53. $-17 - (-8) - (-9)$

54. $7 - 8 - (-1)$

55. $-30 - (-65) - 29 - 4$

56. $-47 - (-67) - 13 - 15$

57. $-18 - 49 - (-84) - 27$

58. $-19 - 17 - (-36) - 12$

59. $48 - 19 - 29 - 51$

60. $21 - (-14) - 43 - 12$

61. $17 - (-17) - 14 - 21$

62. Find the difference between -21 and -36.

63. What is 9 less than -12?

64. What is 12 less than -27?

65. Find -21 decreased by 19.

66. What is -21 minus -37?

67. Subtract 41 from -22.

For Exercises 68 and 69, without finding the difference, determine whether the difference is positive or negative.

68. $-25 - 52$

69. The difference between 8 and -5

OBJECTIVE C *To solve application problems*

70. **Meteorology** Read the news clipping at the right. What is the difference between the record low temperature on February 10, 2011, and the previous record low temperature?

In the NEWS!

New Record Low Temperature in Oklahoma

February 11, 2011: Yesterday, Oklahoma set a new all-time record low temperature of −31°F. That's what the thermometer read in Nowata. This beat the previous record of −27°F. The new record was set the day after an all-time-record, 24-hour snowfall in Oklahoma of 27 in.

Source: www.srh.noaa.gov

Geography The elevation, or height, of places on Earth is measured in relation to sea level, or the average level of the ocean's surface. The table below shows height above sea level as a positive number and depth below sea level as a negative number. Use the table for Exercises 71 to 74.

Continent	*Highest Elevation (in meters)*		*Lowest Elevation (in meters)*	
Africa	Mt. Kilimanjaro	5895	Qattara Depression	−133
Asia	Mt. Everest	8850	Dead Sea	−400
Europe	Mt. Elbrus	5634	Caspian Sea	−28
America	Mt. Aconcagua	6960	Death Valley	−86

71. Find the difference in elevation between Mt. Aconcagua and Death Valley.

72. What is the difference in elevation between Mt. Kilimanjaro and the Qattara Depression?

73. For which continent shown is the difference between the highest and lowest elevations greatest?

74. For which continent shown is the difference between the highest and lowest elevations smallest?

Mt. Everest

Geography The graph at the right shows the depths of Earth's three deepest ocean trenches and the heights of its three tallest mountains. Use this graph for Exercises 75 to 77.

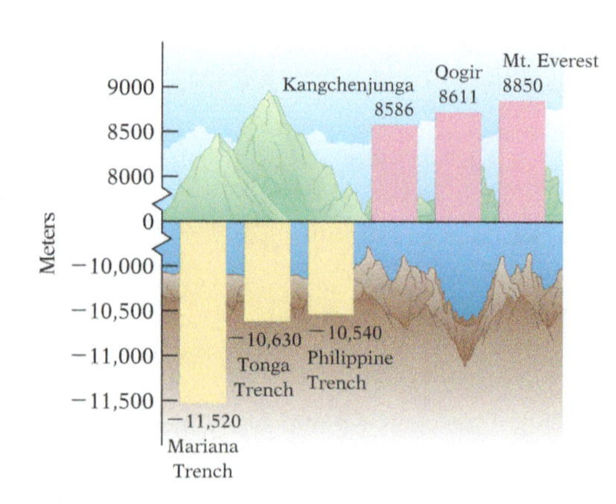

75. What is the difference between the depth of the Philippine Trench and the depth of the Mariana Trench?

76. What is the difference between the height of Mt. Everest and the depth of the Mariana Trench?

77. Could Mt. Everest fit in the Tonga Trench?

78. **Golf Scores** In golf, a player's score on a hole is 0 if the player completes the hole in *par.* **Par** is the number of strokes in which a golfer should complete a hole. In a golf match, scores are given both as a total number of strokes taken on all holes and as a value relative to par, such as -4 ("4 under par") or $+2$ ("2 over par").

a. See the news clipping at the right. Convert each of Ken Duke's scores for the first three days into a score relative to par.

b. In a golf tournament, a player's daily scores are added. Add Ken Duke's three daily scores to find his score, relative to par, for the first three days of the tournament.

c. Duke's score on the fourth day was 68. What was his final score, relative to par, for the four-day tournament?

In the NEWS!

Duke Leads 2011 Nationwide Tour Championship

With scores of 72, 68, and 70 on his first three days, Ken Duke leads going into the last day of this four-day tournament. Par for the 18-hole golf course at Daniel Island in Charleston, South Carolina, is 72.

Source: www.pgatour.com

79. **Ocean Research** The *Aurora Borealis* is a polar research ship currently under design. Plans call for the ship to be able to drill a hole 1000 m deep, even when it is sailing on seas as deep as 5000 m. (Source: European Science Foundation)

a. Suppose the *Aurora Borealis* is sailing at sea level, 4673 m above the ocean floor. It drills a hole in the ocean floor 852 m deep. Use a negative number to represent the depth of the hole below sea level.

b. Suppose the *Aurora Borealis* is sailing at sea level. It drills a hole 964 m deep in the ocean floor. The bottom of the hole is 4261 m below sea level. Use a negative number to represent the depth of the ocean floor below sea level.

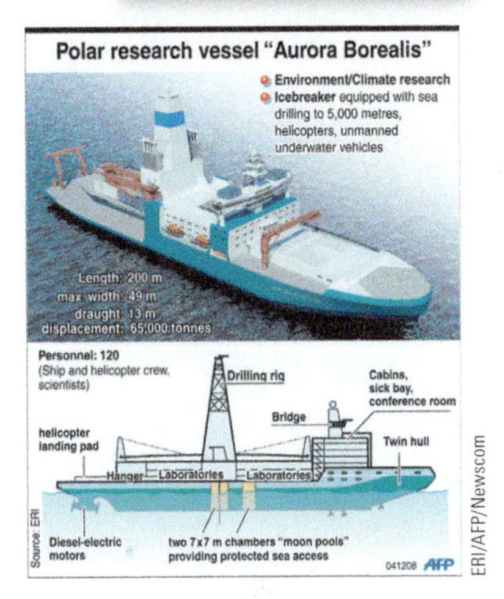

ERI/AFP/Newscom

Critical Thinking

80. The sum of two negative integers is -9. Find the integers.

81. Given the list of numbers -4, -3, -10, 9, and 15, find the largest difference that can be obtained by subtracting one number in the list from another number in the list.

82. If a and b are integers, is the expression $|a + b| = |a| + |b|$ always true, sometimes true, or never true?

83. Is the difference between two integers always smaller than either one of the numbers in the subtraction? If not, give an example in which the difference between two integers is greater than either integer.

Projects or Group Activities

84. Make up three addition problems such that each problem involves one positive and one negative addend, and each problem has a sum of -4. Then describe a strategy for writing these problems.

85. Make up three subtraction problems such that each problem involves a negative number subtracted from a negative number, and each problem has a difference of -6. Then describe a strategy for writing these problems.

SECTION

1.3 Multiplication and Division of Integers

OBJECTIVE A *To multiply integers*

Point of Interest

The cross × was first used as a symbol for multiplication in 1631 in a book titled *The Key to Mathematics.* Also in that year, another book, *Practice of the Analytical Art,* advocated the use of a dot to indicate multiplication.

Several different symbols are used to indicate multiplication. The numbers being multiplied are called **factors;** for instance, 3 and 2 are factors in each of the examples at the right. The result is called the **product.** Note that when parentheses are used and there is no operation symbol, the operation is multiplication.

$3 \times 2 = 6$

$3 \cdot 2 = 6$

$(3)(2) = 6$

$3(2) = 6$

$(3)2 = 6$

Multiplication is repeated addition of the same number. The product 3×5 is shown on the number line below.

5 5 5

0 1 2 3 4 5 6 7 8 9 10 11 12 13 14 15

5 is added 3 times.

$3 \times 5 = 5 + 5 + 5 = 15$

Now consider the product of a positive and a negative number.

−5 is added 3 times.

$$3(-5) = (-5) + (-5) + (-5) = -15$$

This example suggests that the product of a positive number and a negative number is negative. Here are a few more examples.

$4(-7) = -28$ $\quad -6 \cdot 7 = -42$ $\quad (-8)7 = -56$

To find the product of two negative numbers, look at the pattern at the right. As −5 multiplies a sequence of decreasing integers, the products increase by 5.

These numbers decrease by 1. These numbers increase by 5.

$-5 \times 3 = -15$

$-5 \times 2 = -10$

$-5 \times 1 = -5$

$-5 \times 0 = 0$

The pattern can be continued by requiring that the product of two negative numbers be positive.

$-5 \times (-1) = 5$

$-5 \times (-2) = 10$

$-5 \times (-3) = 15$

Multiplication of Integers

To multiply two numbers with the same sign, multiply the absolute values of the numbers. The product is positive.

To multiply two numbers with different signs, multiply the absolute values of the numbers. The product is negative.

EXAMPLES

1. $-4(-8) = 32$ • The signs are the same. The product is positive.
2. $5(-12) = -60$ • The signs are different. The product is negative.

Company	Net Income 1st Quarter of 2011
Expedia	51,000,000
Orbitz	−11,000,000
Priceline	105,000,000

APPLY THE CONCEPT

The table at the left shows the net income for the first quarter of 2011 for three online travel companies. (*Note:* Negative net income indicates a loss.) If net income for each company continued at the same level throughout 2011, what would be the 2011 annual net income for Orbitz?

To find the annual net income, multiply the net income for the first quarter by 4.

$$-11{,}000{,}000(4) = -44{,}000{,}000$$

If net income continued at the same level throughout 2011, the 2011 annual net income for Orbitz would be −$44,000,000.

HOW TO 1 Find the product of −8 and −16.

A *product* is the answer to a multiplication problem.

$-8(-16) = 128$ • **The signs are the same. The product is positive.**

The phrase *the product of* in HOW TO 1 above indicates the operation of multiplication. All of the phrases below indicate multiplication.

times	−7 times −9	$-7(-9) = 63$
the product of	the product of 12 and −8	$12(-8) = -96$
multiplied by	−15 multiplied by 11	$-15(11) = -165$
twice	twice −14	$2(-14) = -28$

HOW TO 2 Multiply: $-2(5)(-7)(-4)$

$$\begin{aligned} -2(5)(-7)(-4) &= -10(-7)(-4) \\ &= 70(-4) \\ &= -280 \end{aligned}$$

• **To multiply more than two numbers, multiply the first two numbers. Then multiply the product by the third number. Continue until all the numbers are multiplied.**

Consider the products shown at the right. Note that when there is an even number of negative factors, the product is positive. When there is an odd number of negative factors, the product is negative.

$$\begin{aligned} (-3)(-5) &= 15 \\ (-2)(-5)(-6) &= -60 \\ (-4)(-3)(-5)(-7) &= 420 \\ (-3)(-3)(-5)(-4)(-5) &= -900 \\ (-6)(-3)(-4)(-2)(-10)(-5) &= 7200 \end{aligned}$$

This idea can be summarized by the following useful rule: The product of an even number of negative factors is positive; the product of an odd number of negative factors is negative.

EXAMPLE 1

Multiply: $(-3)4(-5)$

Solution

$(-3)4(-5) = (-12)(-5) = 60$

YOU TRY IT 1

Multiply: $8(-9)10$

Your solution

Solution on p. S1

EXAMPLE 2

Multiply: $12(-4)(-3)(-5)$

Solution

$$\begin{aligned} 12(-4)(-3)(-5) &= (-48)(-3)(-5) \\ &= 144(-5) \\ &= -720 \end{aligned}$$

YOU TRY IT 2

Multiply: $(-2)3(-8)7$

Your solution

EXAMPLE 3

Find the product of -13 and -9.

Solution

$-13(-9) = 117$

YOU TRY IT 3

What is -9 times 34?

Your solution

Solutions on p. S1

OBJECTIVE B *To divide integers*

Take Note

Think of the fraction bar as meaning "divided by." Thus $\frac{8}{2}$ means 8 divided by 2. The number 2 is the **divisor.** The number 8 is the **dividend.** The result of the division, 4, is called the **quotient.**

For every division problem there is a related multiplication problem.

$$\frac{8}{2} = 4 \quad \text{because} \quad 4 \cdot 2 = 8.$$

Division — Related multiplication

This fact and the rules for multiplying integers can be used to illustrate the rules for dividing integers.

Note in the following examples that the quotient of two numbers with the same sign is positive.

$$\frac{12}{3} = 4 \text{ because } 4 \cdot 3 = 12. \qquad \frac{-12}{-3} = 4 \text{ because } 4(-3) = -12.$$

The next two examples illustrate that the quotient of two numbers with different signs is negative.

$$\frac{12}{-3} = -4 \text{ because } (-4)(-3) = 12. \qquad \frac{-12}{3} = -4 \text{ because } (-4)3 = -12.$$

Point of Interest

There was quite a controversy over the date on which the new millennium started because of the number zero. When our current calendar was created, numbering began with the year 1 because 0 had not yet been invented. Thus at the beginning of year 2, one year had elapsed; at the beginning of year 3, two years had elapsed; and so on. This meant that at the beginning of year 2000, 1999 years had elapsed. It was not until the beginning of year 2001 that 2000 years had elapsed and a new millennium began.

Division of Integers

To divide two numbers with the same sign, divide the absolute values of the numbers. The quotient is positive.

To divide two numbers with different signs, divide the absolute values of the numbers. The quotient is negative.

EXAMPLES

1. $(-18) \div (-2) = 9$ — • The signs are the same. The quotient is positive.
2. $-36 \div 9 = -4$ — • The signs are different. The quotient is negative.

Take Note

We can denote division using, for example, $-63 \div (-7)$, $-7\overline{)-63}$, or $\frac{-63}{-7}$.

HOW TO 3 Find the quotient of −63 and −7.

A *quotient* is the answer to a division problem.

$\frac{-63}{-7} = 9$ • The signs are the same. The quotient is positive.

The phrase *the quotient of* in HOW TO 3 above indicates the operation of division. All of the phrases below indicate division.

divided by	15 divided by −3	$15 \div (-3) = -5$
the quotient of	the quotient of −56 and −8	$(-56) \div (-8) = 7$
the ratio of	the ratio of 45 and −5	$45 \div (-5) = -9$
divide . . . by . . .	divide −100 by −20	$-100 \div (-20) = 5$

HOW TO 4 Simplify: $-\frac{-56}{7}$

$$-\frac{-56}{7} = -\left(\frac{-56}{7}\right) = -(-8) = 8$$

The properties of division are stated below. In these statements, the symbol ≠ is read "is not equal to."

Properties of Zero and One in Division

If $a \neq 0$, $\frac{0}{a} = 0$. Zero divided by any number other than zero is zero.

If $a \neq 0$, $\frac{a}{a} = 1$. Any number other than zero divided by itself is 1.

$\frac{a}{1} = a$ A number divided by 1 is the number.

$\frac{a}{0}$ is undefined. Division by zero is not defined.

EXAMPLES

1. $\frac{0}{-5} = 0$ **2.** $\frac{-4}{-4} = 1$ **3.** $\frac{-7}{1} = -7$ **4.** $\frac{-12}{0}$ is undefined.

The fact that $\frac{-12}{3} = -4$, $\frac{12}{-3} = -4$, and $-\frac{12}{3} = -4$ suggests the following rule.

If *a* and *b* are integers, and $b \neq 0$, then $\frac{-a}{b} = \frac{a}{-b} = -\frac{a}{b}$.

EXAMPLE 4

Divide: $(-120) \div (-8)$

Solution

$(-120) \div (-8) = 15$

- **The signs are the same. The quotient is positive.**

YOU TRY IT 4

Divide: $(-135) \div (-9)$

Your solution

EXAMPLE 5

Divide: $\frac{95}{-5}$

Solution

$\frac{95}{-5} = -19$

- **The signs are different. The quotient is negative.**

YOU TRY IT 5

Divide: $\frac{-72}{4}$

Your solution

EXAMPLE 6

Simplify: $-\frac{-81}{3}$

Solution

$-\frac{-81}{3} = -(-27) = 27$

YOU TRY IT 6

Simplify: $-\frac{36}{-12}$

Your solution

EXAMPLE 7

Find the quotient of 98 and −14.

Solution

$98 \div (-14) = -7$

YOU TRY IT 7

What is the ratio of −72 and −8?

Your solution

Solutions on p. S1

OBJECTIVE C *To solve application problems*

EXAMPLE 8

The daily high temperatures (in degrees Celsius) for six days in Anchorage, Alaska, were $-14°$, $3°$, $0°$, $-8°$, $2°$, and $-1°$. Find the average daily high temperature.

Strategy

To find the average daily high temperature:
- Add the six temperature readings.
- Divide the sum by 6.

Solution

$-14 + 3 + 0 + (-8) + 2 + (-1) = -18$

$-18 \div 6 = -3$

The average daily high temperature was $-3°$C.

YOU TRY IT 8

The daily low temperatures (in degrees Celsius) during one week were recorded as $-6°$, $-7°$, $0°$, $-5°$, $-8°$, $-1°$, and $-1°$. Find the average daily low temperature.

Your strategy

Your solution

Solution on p. S1

1.3 EXERCISES

Concept Check

For Exercises 1 and 2, fill in the blank with *positive* or *negative*.

1. a. The product of two numbers with the same sign is ______.

b. The product of two numbers with different signs is ______.

2. a. The quotient of two numbers with the same sign is ______.

b. The quotient of two numbers with different signs is ______.

OBJECTIVE A *To multiply integers*

For Exercises 3 to 18, multiply.

3. $(-12)(-5)$

4. $(-13)(-9)$

5. $-11(23)$

6. $-8(21)$

7. $6(-19)$

8. $17(-13)$

9. $7(5)(-3)$

10. $(-3)(-2)8$

11. $-3(-8)(-9)$

12. $-7(-6)(-5)$

13. $(-3)7(-2)8$

14. $-9(-4)(-8)(-10)$

15. $7(9)(-11)4$

16. $-12(-4)7(-2)$

17. $(-14)9(-11)0$

18. $(-13)(15)(-19)0$

19. What is -14 multiplied by -25?

20. What is 4 times -8?

21. Find the product of 4, -8, and 11.

22. Find the product of -2, -3, -4, and -5.

23. You multiply four positive integers and three negative integers. Is the product positive or negative?

OBJECTIVE B *To divide integers*

For Exercises 24 to 45, divide.

24. $12 \div (-6)$

25. $18 \div (-3)$

26. $(-72) \div (-9)$

27. $(-64) \div (-8)$

28. $-42 \div 6$

29. $(-56) \div 8$

30. $(-144) \div 12$

31. $(-93) \div (-3)$

32. $48 \div (-8)$

33. $57 \div (-3)$

34. $\frac{-44}{-4}$

35. $\frac{-36}{-9}$

36. $\frac{98}{-7}$

37. $\frac{85}{-5}$

38. $-\frac{-120}{8}$

39. $-\frac{-72}{4}$

40. $0 \div (-9)$

41. $0 \div (-14)$

42. $\frac{-261}{9}$

43. $\frac{-128}{4}$

44. $9 \div 0$

45. $(-21) \div 0$

46. Find the quotient of -132 and 11.

47. What is 15 divided by -15?

48. Divide -196 by -7.

49. Find the quotient of 342 and -9.

OBJECTIVE C *To solve application problems*

50. **Meteorology** The daily high temperatures for a six-day period in Barrow, Alaska, were −23°F, −29°F, −21°F, −28°F, −28°F, and −27°F. Calculate the average daily high temperature.

Barrow, Alaska

Doug Allan/Getty Images

51. **Meteorology** The daily low temperatures for a 10-day period in a midwestern city were −4°F, −9°F, −5°F, −2°F, −4°F, −1°F, −2°F, −1°F, 0°F, and −2°F. Calculate the average daily low temperature for this city.

52. **Meteorology** The average low temperature for five consecutive days was −12°C. If the average low temperature after the sixth day was −13°C, was the low temperature on the sixth day higher or lower than −12°C?

53. **Testing** To discourage random guessing on a multiple-choice exam, a professor assigns 5 points for a correct answer, -2 points for an incorrect answer, and 0 points for leaving the question blank. What is the score for a student who had 20 correct answers, had 13 incorrect answers, and left 7 questions blank?

54. **Testing** To discourage random guessing on a multiple-choice exam, a professor assigns 7 points for a correct answer, -3 points for an incorrect answer, and -1 point for leaving the question blank. What is the score for a student who had 17 correct answers, had 8 incorrect answers, and left 2 questions blank?

In the NEWS!

Decline in Circulation of Newspapers Continues

The rate of decline in the circulation of newspapers in the United States has accelerated. Of the top 25 newspapers in this country, all posted decreased circulation except for the *Wall Street Journal.* The decrease reflects the increasing popularity of online news sources.

Source: www.nytimes.com

55. **Newspapers** See the news clipping at the right. The table below shows the declining number of evening newspapers published in the United States. (*Source:* Newspaper Association of America) Find the average annual change in the number of evening newspapers published.

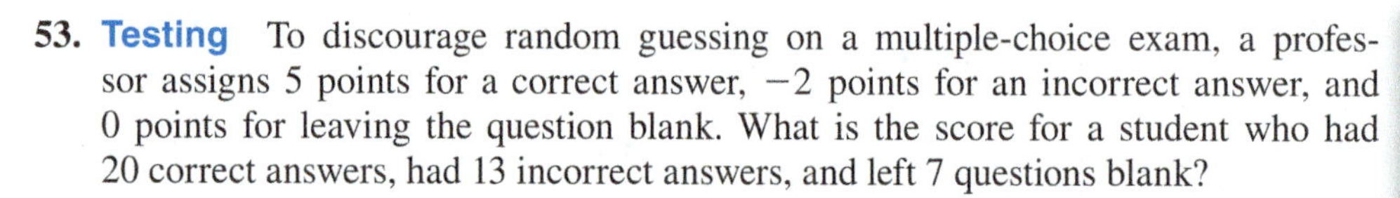

Year	*2005*	*2006*	*2007*	*2008*	*2009*
Change in number of evening newspapers	−8	−31	−49	−19	−18

Critical Thinking

56. If $x \in \{-6, -2, 7\}$, for which value of x does the expression $-3x$ have the greatest value?

57. If $-4x$ equals a positive integer, is x a positive or a negative integer? Explain your answer.

Projects or Group Activities

For Exercises 58 to 60, find the pattern in the list of numbers. Then find the next three numbers in the pattern.

58. 5, −15, 45, −135, . . .

59. −2, 4, −8, 16, . . .

60. −3, −12, −48, −192, . . .

SECTION

1.4 Exponents and the Order of Operations Agreement

OBJECTIVE A *To evaluate exponential expressions*

Point of Interest

René Descartes (1596–1650) was the first mathematician to use exponential notation extensively as it is used today. However, for some unknown reason, he always used *xx* for x^2.

Repeated multiplication of the same factor can be written using an exponent.

$$2 \cdot 2 \cdot 2 \cdot 2 \cdot 2 = 2^5 \leftarrow \text{Exponent} \qquad a \cdot a \cdot a \cdot a = a^4 \leftarrow \text{Exponent}$$

(2 and a are each labeled Base.)

The **exponent** indicates how many times the factor, which is called the **base,** occurs in the multiplication. The multiplication $2 \cdot 2 \cdot 2 \cdot 2 \cdot 2$ is in **factored form.** The expression 2^5 is in **exponential form.**

2^1 is read "2 to the first power" or just "2." Usually the exponent 1 is not written.

2^2 is read "2 to the second power" or "2 squared."

2^3 is read "2 to the third power" or "2 cubed."

2^4 is read "2 to the fourth power."

a^4 is read "a to the fourth power."

The first three natural-number powers can be interpreted geometrically as length, area, and volume, respectively.

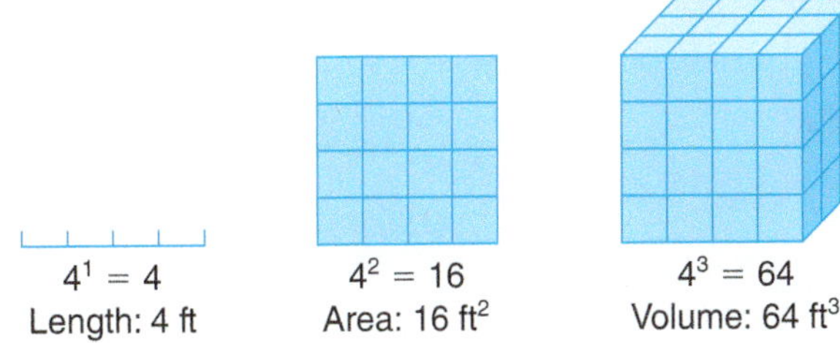

To evaluate an exponential expression, write each factor as many times as indicated by the exponent. Then multiply.

HOW TO 1 Evaluate $(-2)^4$.

$(-2)^4 = (-2)(-2)(-2)(-2)$ • Write −2 as a factor 4 times.

$= 16$ • Multiply.

Take Note

Note the difference between $(-2)^4$ and -2^4. $(-2)^4$ is the fourth power of −2:

$(-2)^4 = 16$

-2^4 is the opposite of the fourth power of 2:

$-2^4 = -16$.

HOW TO 2 Evaluate -2^4.

$-2^4 = -(2 \cdot 2 \cdot 2 \cdot 2)$ • Write 2 as a factor 4 times.

$= -16$ • Multiply.

EXAMPLE 1

Evaluate -5^3.

Solution

$-5^3 = -(5 \cdot 5 \cdot 5) = -125$

YOU TRY IT 1

Evaluate -6^3.

Your solution

EXAMPLE 2

Evaluate $(-4)^4$.

Solution

$(-4)^4 = (-4)(-4)(-4)(-4)$
$= 256$

YOU TRY IT 2

Evaluate $(-3)^4$.

Your solution

EXAMPLE 3

Evaluate $(-3)^2 \cdot 2^3$.

Solution

$(-3)^2 \cdot 2^3 = (-3)(-3) \cdot (2)(2)(2)$
$= 9 \cdot 8 = 72$

YOU TRY IT 3

Evaluate $(3^3)(-2)^3$.

Your solution

EXAMPLE 4

Evaluate $(-1)^6$.

Solution

The product of an even number of negative factors is positive. Therefore, $(-1)^6 = 1$.

YOU TRY IT 4

Evaluate $(-1)^7$.

Your solution

EXAMPLE 5

Evaluate $-2 \cdot (-3)^2 \cdot (-1)^9$.

Solution

$-2 \cdot (-3)^2 \cdot (-1)^9$
$= -2 \cdot 9 \cdot (-1)$ • $(-3)^2 = 9; (-1)^9 = -1$
$= 18$

YOU TRY IT 5

Evaluate $-2^2 \cdot (-1)^{12} \cdot (-3)^2$.

Your solution

Solutions on p. S1

OBJECTIVE B *To use the Order of Operations Agreement to simplify expressions*

Let's evaluate $2 + 3 \cdot 5$.

There are two arithmetic operations, addition and multiplication, in this expression. The operations could be performed in different orders. We could multiply first and then add, or we could add first and then multiply. To prevent there being more than one answer when simplifying a numerical expression, an Order of Operations Agreement has been established.

The Order of Operations Agreement

Step 1. Perform operations inside grouping symbols. Grouping symbols include parentheses ( ), brackets [ ], braces { }, the absolute value symbol | |, and the fraction bar.

Step 2. Simplify exponential expressions.

Step 3. Do multiplication and division as they occur from left to right.

Step 4. Do addition and subtraction as they occur from left to right.

EXAMPLE

Simplify: $(-4)^2 - 2(3 - 8)$

$(-4)^2 - 2(3 - 8)$

$= (-4)^2 - 2(-5)$ • Perform operations inside parentheses.

$= 16 - 2(-5)$ • Simplify exponential expressions.

$= 16 + 10$ • Do multiplication and division from left to right.

$= 26$ • Do addition and subtraction from left to right.

Integrating Technology

See the Keystroke Guide: *Basic Operations* for instruction on using a calculator to evaluate a numerical expression.

One or more of the steps listed above may not be needed to evaluate an expression. In that case, proceed to the next step in the Order of Operations Agreement.

HOW TO 3 Evaluate $\frac{4 + 8}{2 + 1} - (3 - 1) + 2$.

$\frac{4 + 8}{2 + 1} - (3 - 1) + 2 = \frac{12}{3} - 2 + 2$ • Perform operations above and below the fraction bar and inside parentheses.

$= 4 - 2 + 2$ • Do multiplication and division as they occur from left to right.

$= 2 + 2$ • Do addition and subtraction as they occur from left to right.

$= 4$

EXAMPLE 6

Evaluate $6 \div [4 - (6 - 8)] - 2^3$.

Solution

$6 \div [4 - (6 - 8)] - 2^3$

$= 6 \div [4 - (-2)] - 2^3$ • Perform operations inside grouping symbols.

$= 6 \div 6 - 2^3$

$= 6 \div 6 - 8$ • Simplify exponential expressions.

$= 1 - 8$ • Do multiplication and division from left to right.

$= -7$ • Do addition and subtraction from left to right.

YOU TRY IT 6

Evaluate $7 - 2[2 \cdot 3 - 7 \cdot 2]^2$.

Your solution

Solution on p. S2

EXAMPLE 7

Evaluate $4 - 3[4 - 2(6 - 3)] \div 2$.

Solution

$4 - 3[4 - 2(6 - 3)] \div 2$

$= 4 - 3[4 - 2 \cdot 3] \div 2$

$= 4 - 3[4 - 6] \div 2$

$= 4 - 3[-2] \div 2$

$= 4 + 6 \div 2$

$= 4 + 3$

$= 7$

- Perform operations inside grouping symbols.
- Do multiplication and division from left to right.
- Do addition and subtraction from left to right.

YOU TRY IT 7

Evaluate $18 - 5[8 - 2(2 - 5)] \div 10$.

Your solution

EXAMPLE 8

Evaluate $27 \div (5 - 2)^2 + (-3)^2 \cdot 4$.

Solution

$27 \div (5 - 2)^2 + (-3)^2 \cdot 4$

$= 27 \div 3^2 + (-3)^2 \cdot 4$

$= 27 \div 9 + 9 \cdot 4$

$= 3 + 9 \cdot 4$

$= 3 + 36$

$= 39$

- Perform operations inside grouping symbols.
- Simplify exponential expressions.
- Do multiplication and division from left to right.
- Do addition and subtraction from left to right.

YOU TRY IT 8

Evaluate $36 \div (8 - 5)^2 - (-3)^2 \cdot 2$.

Your solution

Solutions on p. S2

Concept Check

For Exercises 1 to 3, write the expression as an exponential expression.

1. Nine to the fifth power

2. y to the fourth power

3. Seven to the nth power

4. True or false? To evaluate the expression $6 + 7 \cdot 10$ means to determine the one number it is equal to.

OBJECTIVE A *To evaluate exponential expressions*

For Exercises 5 to 27, evaluate.

5. 6^2

6. 7^4

7. -7^2

8. -4^3

9. $(-3)^2$

10. $(-2)^3$

11. $(-3)^4$

12. $(-5)^3$

13. -4^4

14. $(-4)^4$

15. $2 \cdot (-3)^2$

16. $-2 \cdot (-4)^2$

17. $(-1)^9 \cdot 3^3$

18. $(-1)^8(-8)^2$

19. $(3)^3 \cdot 2^3$

20. $(5)^2 \cdot 3^3$

21. $(-3) \cdot 2^2$

22. $(-5) \cdot 3^4$

23. $2^3 \cdot 3^3 \cdot (-4)$

24. $(-3)^3 \cdot 5^2 \cdot 10$

25. $(-7) \cdot 4^2 \cdot 3^2$

26. $(-2) \cdot 2^3 \cdot (-3)^2$

27. $(-2)^3(-3)^2(-1)^7$

For Exercises 28 to 31, without finding the product, determine whether the product is positive or negative.

28. The fifth power of -18

29. The opposite of $(-7)^8$

30. $-(9^2)(-6^3)$

31. $(-9)^2(-6)^3$

OBJECTIVE B *To use the Order of Operations Agreement to simplify expressions*

For Exercises 32 to 58, evaluate by using the Order of Operations Agreement.

32. $4 - 8 \div 2$

33. $2^2 \cdot 3 - 3$

34. $2(3 - 4) - (-3)^2$

35. $16 - 32 \div 2^3$

36. $24 - 18 \div 3 + 2$

37. $8 - (-3)^2 - (-2)$

38. $8 - 2(3)^2$

39. $16 - 16 \cdot 2 \div 4$

40. $12 + 16 \div 4 \cdot 2$

41. $16 - 2 \cdot 4^2$

42. $27 - 18 \div (-3^2)$

43. $4 + 12 \div 3 \cdot 2$

44. $16 + 15 \div (-5) - 2$

45. $14 - 2^2 - (4 - 7)$

46. $3 - 2[8 - (3 - 2)]$

47. $-2^2 + 4[16 \div (3 - 5)]$

48. $6 + \dfrac{16 - 4}{2^2 + 2} - 2$

49. $24 \div \dfrac{3^2}{8 - 5} - (-5)$

50. $96 \div 2[12 + (6 - 2)] - 3^2$

51. $4[16 - (7 - 1)] \div 10$

52. $18 \div 2 - 4^2 - (-3)^2$

53. $18 \div (9 - 2^3) + (-3)$

54. $16 - 3(8 - 3)^2 \div 5$

55. $4(-8) \div [2(7 - 3)^2]$

56. $\dfrac{(-19) + (-2)}{6^2 - 29} \div (2 - 5)$

57. $16 - 4 \cdot \dfrac{3^3 - 7}{2^3 + 2} - (-2)^2$

58. $7 - 3[1 - (2 - (-3))^2]$

59. Which expression is equivalent to $15 + 15 \div 3 - 4^2$?

(i) $30 \div 3 - 16$ (ii) $15 + 5 - 16$ (iii) $15 + 5 + 16$ (iv) $15 + 15 \div (-1)^2$

Critical Thinking

60. The following was offered as the simplification of $6 + 2(4 - 9)$.

$$\begin{aligned} 6 + 2(4 - 9) &= 6 + 2(-5) \\ &= 8(-5) \\ &= -40 \end{aligned}$$

If this is a correct simplification, write *yes* for the answer. If it is incorrect, write *no* and explain the incorrect step.

Projects or Group Activities

61. In which column is the number 1 million, column A, B, or C?

A	B	C
1	8	27
64	125	216
.	.	.
.	.	.
.	.	.

CHECK YOUR PROGRESS: CHAPTER 1

1. Use the roster method to write the set of positive integers less than 9.

2. Given $A = \{-7, 0, 2, 5\}$, which elements of A are less than 1?

3. Find the additive inverse of -13.

4. Evaluate $|-44|$ and $-|-18|$.

5. Place the correct symbol, < or >, between the two expressions.
   $|31| \quad |-13|$

6. Add: $-47 + 23$

7. Subtract: $-11 - (-27)$

8. Add: $-32 + 40 + (-9)$

9. Subtract: $42 - (-82) - 65 - 7$

10. Multiply: $16(-2)$

11. Multiply: $-9(7)(-5)$

12. Divide: $250 \div (-25)$

13. Divide: $-\dfrac{-80}{-5}$

14. Divide: $\dfrac{-58}{0}$

15. Evaluate: $-3^2 \cdot (-2)^4$

16. Evaluate: $5 - 4[3 - 2(7 - 1)] \div 9$

17. Evaluate: $-4 \cdot 2^3 - \dfrac{1 - 13}{2^2 \cdot 3}$

18. Evaluate: $(8 - 3^2)^6 + (2 \cdot 3 - 7)^9$

19. **Temperature** Find the temperature after a rise of 8°C from -3°C.

20. **Temperature** The daily low temperatures (in degrees Celsius) during one week were recorded as $-8°$, $-12°$, $0°$, $-4°$, $5°$, $-7°$, and $-9°$. Find the average daily low temperature for the week.

SECTION

1.5 Factoring Numbers and Prime Factorization

OBJECTIVE A *To factor numbers*

A **factor of a number** is a natural number that divides the number with a remainder of 0.

The factors of 12 are 1, 2, 3, 4, 6, and 12 because each of these numbers divides 12 with a remainder of 0. Note that both the divisor and the quotient are factors of the dividend.

$12 \div 1 = 12$ $12 \div 4 = 3$
$12 \div 2 = 6$ $12 \div 6 = 2$
$12 \div 3 = 4$ $12 \div 12 = 1$

To find the factors of a number, try dividing the number by 1, 2, 3, 4, 5, ... Those numbers that divide the number evenly are its factors. Continue this process until the factors start to repeat.

HOW TO 1 Find all the factors of 40.

$40 \div 1 = 40$ 1 and 40 are factors.
$40 \div 2 = 20$ 2 and 20 are factors.
$40 \div 3$ Remainder is not 0.
$40 \div 4 = 10$ 4 and 10 are factors.
$40 \div 5 = 8$ 5 and 8 are factors.
$40 \div 6$ Remainder is not 0.
$40 \div 7$ Remainder is not 0.
$40 \div 8 = 5$ 8 and 5 are factors.

Factors are repeating. All the factors of 40 have been found.

1, 2, 4, 5, 8, 10, 20, and 40 are the factors of 40.

The following rules are helpful in finding the factors of a number.

Factoring Rules

2 is a factor of a number if the last digit of the number is 0, 2, 4, 6, or 8.
EXAMPLE: 528 ends in 8; therefore, 2 is a factor of 528. $(528 \div 2 = 264)$

3 is a factor of a number if the sum of the digits of the number is divisible by 3.
EXAMPLE: The sum of the digits of 378 is $3 + 7 + 8 = 18$. 18 is divisible by 3; therefore, 3 is a factor of 378. $(378 \div 3 = 126)$

5 is a factor of a number if the last digit of the number is 0 or 5.
EXAMPLE: 495 ends in 5; therefore, 5 is a factor of 495. $(495 \div 5 = 99)$

EXAMPLE 1

Find all the factors of 18.

Solution

$18 \div 1 = 18$ $18 \div 4$ Remainder is not 0.
$18 \div 2 = 9$ $18 \div 5$ Remainder is not 0.
$18 \div 3 = 6$ $18 \div 6 = 3$ The factors are repeating.

1, 2, 3, 6, 9, and 18 are the factors of 18.

YOU TRY IT 1

Find all the factors of 24.

Your solution

Solution on p. S2

OBJECTIVE B *To find the prime factorization of a number*

A natural number greater than 1 is a **prime number** if its only factors are 1 and the number. For instance, 11 is a prime number because the only factors of 11 are 1 and 11. A natural number greater than 1 that is not a prime number is a **composite number.** An example of a composite number is 6. It has factors of 1, 2, 3, and 6. The number 1 is neither a prime nor a composite number.

Prime numbers less than 50 = 2, 3, 5, 7, 11, 13, 17, 19, 23, 29, 31, 37, 41, 43, 47

The **prime factorization** of a number is the expression of the number as a product of its prime factors. We use a "T-diagram" to find the prime factors of a number. Begin with the smallest prime number as a trial divisor, and continue to use prime numbers as trial divisors until the final quotient is 1.

Take Note

A prime number that is a factor of a number is called a **prime factor** of the number. For instance, 3 is a prime factor of 18. However, 6 is not a prime factor of 18, although it is a factor of 18.

HOW TO 2 Find the prime factorization of 84.

	84	
2	42	$84 \div 2 = 42$
2	21	$42 \div 2 = 21$
3	7	$21 \div 3 = 7$
7	1	$7 \div 7 = 1$

The prime factorization of 84 is $2^2 \cdot 3 \cdot 7$.

Finding the prime factorization of larger numbers can be difficult. Try each prime number as a trial divisor until the square of the trial divisor exceeds the number.

Point of Interest

Prime numbers are an important part of cryptology, the study of secret codes. Codes based on prime numbers with hundreds of digits are used to send sensitive information over the Internet.

HOW TO 3 Find the prime factorization of 177.

	177
3	59
59	1

• **For 59, try prime numbers up to 11 only, because $11^2 = 121 > 59$.**

The prime factorization of 177 is $3 \cdot 59$.

EXAMPLE 2

Find the prime factorization of 132.

Solution

	132
2	66
2	33
3	11
11	1

$132 = 2^2 \cdot 3 \cdot 11$

YOU TRY IT 2

Find the prime factorization of 315.

Your solution

EXAMPLE 3

Find the prime factorization of 141.

Solution

	141
3	47
47	1

• **For 47, try prime numbers up to 7 only, because $7^2 > 47$.**

$141 = 3 \cdot 47$

YOU TRY IT 3

Find the prime factorization of 326.

Your solution

Solutions on p. S2

OBJECTIVE C *To find the least common multiple and greatest common factor*

The **least common multiple (LCM)** of two or more numbers is the smallest number that is a multiple of all the numbers. For instance, 24 is the LCM of 6 and 8 because it is the smallest number that is divisible by both 6 and 8. The LCM can be found by first writing each number as a product of prime factors. The LCM must contain all the prime factors of each number.

HOW TO 4 Find the LCM of 10 and 12.

Determine the prime factorization of each number.

$10 = 2 \cdot 5$

$12 = 2 \cdot 2 \cdot 3$

$\text{LCM} = \overbrace{2 \cdot \underbrace{2 \cdot 3}_{} \cdot 5}^{\text{Factors of 10}} = 60$ (Factors of 10: $2 \cdot 5$; Factors of 12: $2 \cdot 2 \cdot 3$)

Factors of 12

The LCM of 10 and 12 is 60.

HOW TO 5 Find the LCM of 8, 14, and 18.

Determine the prime factorization of each number.

$8 = 2 \cdot 2 \cdot 2 \qquad 14 = 2 \cdot 7 \qquad 18 = 2 \cdot 3 \cdot 3$

The LCM must contain the prime factors of 8, 14, and 18.

$\text{LCM} = 2 \cdot 2 \cdot 2 \cdot 3 \cdot 3 \cdot 7 = 504$

The **greatest common factor (GCF)** of two or more numbers is the greatest number that divides evenly into all the numbers. For instance, the GCF of 12 and 18 is 6, the largest number that divides evenly into 12 and 18. The GCF can be found by first writing each number as a product of prime factors. The GCF contains the prime factors common to both numbers.

HOW TO 6 Find the GCF of 36 and 90.

Determine the prime factorization of each number.

$36 = 2 \cdot 2 \cdot 3 \cdot 3$

$90 = 2 \cdot 3 \cdot 3 \cdot 5$

• **The common factors are shown in red.**

The GCF of 36 and 90 is $2 \cdot 3 \cdot 3 = 18$.

EXAMPLE 4

Find the LCM of 15, 20, and 30.

Solution

$15 = 3 \cdot 5 \quad 20 = 2 \cdot 2 \cdot 5 \quad 30 = 2 \cdot 3 \cdot 5$

$\text{LCM} = 2 \cdot 2 \cdot 3 \cdot 5 = 60$

YOU TRY IT 4

Find the LCM of 20 and 21.

Your solution

EXAMPLE 5

Find the GCF of 30, 45, and 60.

Solution

$30 = 2 \cdot 3 \cdot 5 \quad 45 = 3 \cdot 3 \cdot 5 \quad 60 = 2 \cdot 2 \cdot 3 \cdot 5$

$\text{GCF} = 3 \cdot 5 = 15$

YOU TRY IT 5

Find the GCF of 42 and 63.

Your solution

Solutions on p. S2

1.5 EXERCISES

Concept Check

1. Circle the numbers that divide evenly into 18.

1 2 3 4 5 6 7 8 9 10 11 12 13 14 15 16 17 18

These numbers are called the __________ of 18.

2. Circle the numbers that are multiples of both 2 and 3.

1 2 3 4 5 6 7 8 9 10 11 12 13 14 15 16 17 18

The least common multiple of 2 and 3 is __________.

OBJECTIVE A *To factor numbers*

For Exercises 3 to 26, find all the factors of the number.

3. 13 **4.** 30 **5.** 56 **6.** 28 **7.** 45 **8.** 33

9. 29 **10.** 22 **11.** 52 **12.** 37 **13.** 82 **14.** 69

15. 57 **16.** 64 **17.** 48 **18.** 46 **19.** 50 **20.** 54

21. 77 **22.** 66 **23.** 100 **24.** 80 **25.** 85 **26.** 96

27. True or false? If 6 is a factor of a number n, then 12 must also be a factor of n.

28. True or false? If 18 is a factor of a number n, then 6 must also be a factor of n.

OBJECTIVE B *To find the prime factorization of a number*

For Exercises 29 to 52, find the prime factorization of a number.

29. 14 **30.** 6 **31.** 72 **32.** 17 **33.** 24 **34.** 27

35. 36 **36.** 115 **37.** 26 **38.** 18 **39.** 49 **40.** 42

41. 31 **42.** 81 **43.** 62 **44.** 39 **45.** 89 **46.** 101

47. 144 **48.** 120 **49.** 175 **50.** 160 **51.** 400 **52.** 625

53. True or false? The prime factorization of 44 is $4 \cdot 11$.

54. True or false? A composite number must have at least two different prime factors.

OBJECTIVE C *To find the least common multiple and greatest common factor*

For Exercises 55 to 79, find the LCM.

55. 3, 8
56. 5, 11
57. 4, 6
58. 6, 8
59. 9, 12
60. 8, 14
61. 14, 20
62. 7, 21
63. 12, 36
64. 6, 10
65. 5, 12
66. 24, 45
67. 8, 20
68. 32, 80
69. 20, 28
70. 3, 8, 12
71. 6, 12, 18
72. 3, 5, 10
73. 6, 12, 24
74. 3, 8, 9
75. 4, 10, 14
76. 10, 15, 25
77. 8, 12, 18
78. 18, 27, 36
79. 14, 28, 35

For Exercises 80 to 104, find the GCF.

80. 4, 10
81. 9, 15
82. 5, 11
83. 11, 19
84. 6, 8
85. 7, 28
86. 6, 12
87. 14, 42
88. 8, 28
89. 24, 36
90. 60, 70
91. 72, 108
92. 40, 56
93. 48, 60
94. 35, 42
95. 6, 12, 20
96. 12, 18, 24
97. 6, 12, 18
98. 30, 45, 75
99. 24, 36, 60
100. 10, 30, 45
101. 26, 52, 78
102. 100, 150, 200
103. 36, 54, 360
104. 18, 27, 36

Critical Thinking

105. Find the largest factor of 333,333,333,333 that is less than 333,333,333,333.

106. Explain why 2 is the only even prime number.

Projects or Group Activities

107. Choose some prime numbers and find the square of each number. Now determine the number of factors in the square of each prime number. Make a conjecture as to the number of factors in the square of any prime number.

SECTION

1.6 Addition and Subtraction of Rational Numbers

OBJECTIVE A *To write a rational number in simplest form and as a decimal*

Take Note

The numbers $-\frac{4}{9}$, $\frac{-4}{9}$, and $\frac{4}{-9}$ all represent the same rational number.

Point of Interest

As early as 630 A.D., the Hindu mathematician Brahmagupta wrote a fraction as one number over another, separated by a space. The Arab mathematician al Hassar (around 1050 A.D.) was the first to show a fraction with a horizontal bar separating the numerator and denominator.

A **rational number** is the quotient of two integers. A rational number written in this way is commonly called a fraction. Some examples of rational numbers are shown at the right.

$$\frac{3}{4}, \quad \frac{-4}{9}, \quad \frac{15}{-4}, \quad \frac{8}{1}, \quad -\frac{5}{6}$$

Rational Numbers

A **rational number** is a number that can be written in the form $\frac{a}{b}$, where a and b are integers and $b \neq 0$.

EXAMPLES OF RATIONAL NUMBERS

1. $\frac{4}{5}$ **2.** $\frac{-2}{13}$ **3.** $\frac{9}{-5}$

Because an integer can be written as the quotient of the integer and 1, every integer is a rational number.

$$6 = \frac{6}{1} \qquad -8 = \frac{-8}{1}$$

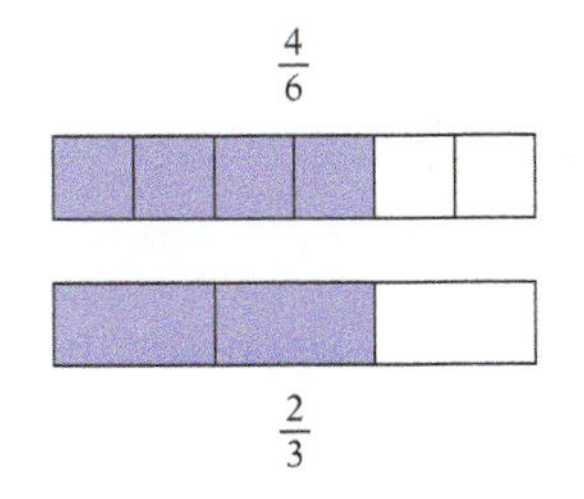

A fraction is in **simplest form** when there are no common factors in the numerator and the denominator. The fractions $\frac{4}{6}$ and $\frac{2}{3}$ are equivalent fractions because they represent the same part of a whole. However, the fraction $\frac{2}{3}$ is in simplest form because there are no common factors (other than 1) in the numerator and denominator.

To write a fraction in simplest form, eliminate the common factors from the numerator and denominator by using the fact that $1 \cdot \frac{a}{b} = \frac{a}{b}$.

$$\frac{4}{6} = \frac{2 \cdot 2}{2 \cdot 3} = \frac{2}{2} \cdot \frac{2}{3} = 1 \cdot \frac{2}{3} = \frac{2}{3}$$

The process of eliminating common factors is usually written as shown at the right.

$$\frac{4}{6} = \frac{\overset{1}{\cancel{2}} \cdot 2}{\underset{1}{\cancel{2}} \cdot 3} = \frac{2}{3}$$

HOW TO 1 Write $\frac{18}{30}$ in simplest form.

$$\frac{18}{30} = \frac{\overset{1}{\cancel{2}} \cdot \overset{1}{\cancel{3}} \cdot 3}{\underset{1}{\cancel{2}} \cdot \underset{1}{\cancel{3}} \cdot 5} = \frac{3}{5}$$

- **To eliminate the common factors, write the numerator and denominator in terms of prime factors. Then divide by the common factors.**

A rational number can also be written in **decimal notation.**

three tenths $0.3 = \frac{3}{10}$ forty-three thousandths $0.043 = \frac{43}{1000}$

A rational number written as a fraction can be written in decimal notation by dividing the numerator of the fraction by the denominator. Think of the fraction bar as meaning "divided by."

HOW TO 2

Write $\frac{5}{8}$ as a decimal.

$$\begin{array}{r} 0.625 \\ 8\overline{)\,5.000} \\ \underline{-4\,8} \\ 20 \\ \underline{-16} \\ 40 \\ \underline{-40} \\ 0 \end{array}$$

- Divide the numerator, 5, by the denominator, 8.

When the remainder is zero, the decimal is called a **terminating decimal.** The decimal 0.625 is a terminating decimal.

$$\frac{5}{8} = 0.625$$

HOW TO 3

Write $\frac{4}{11}$ as a decimal.

$$\begin{array}{r} 0.3636 \\ 11\overline{)\,4.0000} \\ \underline{-3\,3} \\ 70 \\ \underline{-66} \\ 40 \\ \underline{-33} \\ 70 \\ \underline{-66} \\ 4 \end{array}$$

- Divide the numerator, 4, by the denominator, 11.

No matter how long we continue to divide, the remainder is never zero. The decimal $0.\overline{36}$ is a **repeating decimal.** The bar over the 36 indicates that these digits repeat.

$$\frac{4}{11} = 0.\overline{36}$$

Every rational number can be written as a terminating or a repeating decimal. Some numbers—for example, $\sqrt{7}$ and π—have decimal representations that never terminate or repeat. These numbers are called **irrational numbers.**

$$\sqrt{7} \approx 2.6457513\ldots \qquad \pi \approx 3.1415926\ldots$$

The rational numbers and the irrational numbers taken together are called the **real numbers.**

Take Note

Rational numbers are fractions, such as $-\frac{6}{7}$ or $\frac{10}{3}$, in which the numerator and denominator are integers. Rational numbers are also represented by repeating decimals such as 0.25767676... or terminating decimals such as 1.73. An irrational number is neither a terminating decimal nor a repeating decimal. For instance, 2.454454445444445... is an irrational number.

The diagram below shows the relationships among some of the sets of numbers we have discussed. The arrows indicate that one set is contained completely within the other set.

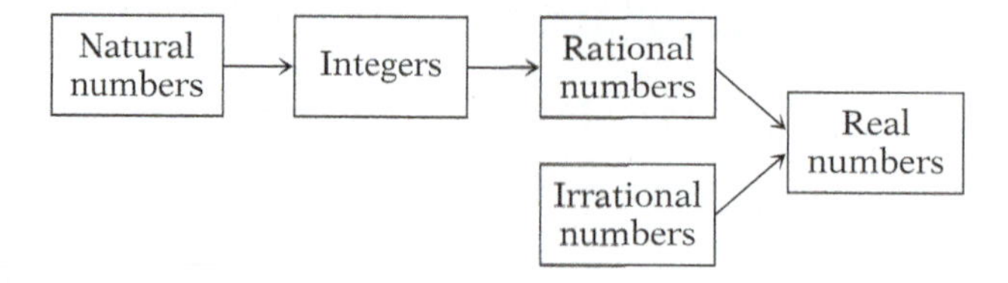

Note that there is no arrow between the rational numbers and the irrational numbers. Any given real number is either a rational number or an irrational number. It cannot be both. However, a natural number such as 7 can also be called an integer, a rational number, or a real number.

EXAMPLE 1

Write $\frac{90}{168}$ in simplest form.

Solution

$$\frac{90}{168} = \frac{\overset{1}{\cancel{2}} \cdot \overset{1}{\cancel{3}} \cdot 3 \cdot 5}{\underset{1}{\cancel{2}} \cdot 2 \cdot 2 \cdot \underset{1}{\cancel{3}} \cdot 7} = \frac{15}{28}$$

YOU TRY IT 1

Write $\frac{60}{140}$ in simplest form.

Your solution

EXAMPLE 2

Write $\frac{3}{20}$ as a decimal.

Solution

$$\frac{3}{20} = 3 \div 20 = 0.15$$

YOU TRY IT 2

Write $\frac{4}{9}$ as a decimal. Place a bar over the repeating digits.

Your solution

Solutions on p. S2

OBJECTIVE B *To add rational numbers*

Point of Interest

One of the earliest written mathematical documents is the Rhind Papyrus. It was discovered in Egypt in 1858 but is estimated to date from 1650 B.C. The Papyrus shows that the early Egyptian method of calculating with fractions was very different from the methods used today. The early Egyptians used unit fractions, which are fractions with a numerator of 1. With the exception of $\frac{2}{3}$, fractions with numerators other than 1 were written as the sum of two unit fractions. For instance, $\frac{2}{11}$ was written as $\frac{1}{6} + \frac{1}{66}$.

Two of the 7 squares in the rectangle have dark shading. This is $\frac{2}{7}$ of the entire rectangle. Three of the 7 squares in the rectangle have light shading. This is $\frac{3}{7}$ of the entire rectangle. A total of 5 squares are shaded. This is $\frac{5}{7}$ of the entire rectangle.

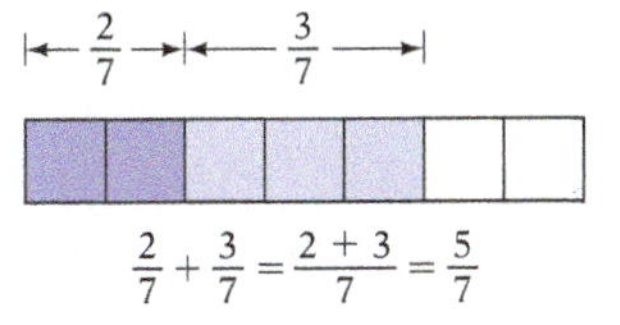

$\frac{2}{7} + \frac{3}{7} = \frac{2+3}{7} = \frac{5}{7}$

Addition of Fractions

To add two fractions with the same denominator, add the numerators and place the sum over the common denominator.

EXAMPLE

Add: $\frac{3}{16} + \frac{5}{16}$

$\frac{3}{16} + \frac{5}{16} = \frac{3+5}{16}$ • The denominators are the same. Add the numerators and place the sum over the common denominator.

$= \frac{8}{16} = \frac{1}{2}$ • Write the answer in simplest form.

To add fractions with different denominators, first rewrite the fractions as equivalent fractions with a common denominator. Then add the fractions. One common denominator is the least common multiple (LCM) of the denominators. The least common multiple of the denominators is frequently called the **least common denominator.**

HOW TO 4 Add: $\frac{7}{10} + \frac{11}{12}$

The LCM of 10 and 12 is 60.

$\frac{7}{10} + \frac{11}{12} = \frac{42}{60} + \frac{55}{60}$ • Rewrite each fraction as an equivalent fraction with a denominator of 60.

$= \frac{42 + 55}{60} = \frac{97}{60}$ • Add the fractions.

Take Note

In this text, we will normally leave answers as improper fractions and not change them to mixed numbers.

If one of the addends is a negative rational number, use the same rules used for addition of integers.

HOW TO 5 Add: $-\frac{5}{6} + \frac{3}{10}$

The LCM of 6 and 10 is 30.

$-\frac{5}{6} + \frac{3}{10} = -\frac{25}{30} + \frac{9}{30}$ • Rewrite each fraction as an equivalent fraction with a denominator of 30.

$= \frac{-25 + 9}{30}$ • Add the fractions.

$= \frac{-16}{30} = -\frac{8}{15}$

Take Note

Although we could write the answer as $\frac{-8}{15}$, in this text we write $-\frac{8}{15}$. That is, we place the negative sign in front of the fraction.

To add decimals, write the numbers so that the decimal points are in a vertical line. Then proceed as in the addition of integers. Write the decimal point in the answer directly below the decimal points in the problem.

HOW TO 6 Add: $-114.03 + 89.254$

$$\begin{array}{r} 114.030 \\ -\ 89.254 \\ \hline 24.776 \end{array}$$

• The signs are different. Find the difference between the absolute values of the numbers. $|-114.03| = 114.03$; $|89.254| = 89.254$

$-114.03 + 89.254$
$= -24.776$

• Attach the sign of the number with the larger absolute value. Because $|-114.03| > |89.254|$, use the sign of -114.03.

EXAMPLE 3

Add: $\frac{5}{16} + \left(-\frac{7}{40}\right)$

Solution

The LCM of 16 and 40 is 80.

$\frac{5}{16} + \left(-\frac{7}{40}\right) = \frac{25}{80} + \left(-\frac{14}{80}\right) = \frac{25 + (-14)}{80} = \frac{11}{80}$

YOU TRY IT 3

Add: $\frac{5}{9} + \left(-\frac{11}{12}\right)$

Your solution

Solution on p. S2

EXAMPLE 4

Find the total of $\frac{3}{4}$, $\frac{1}{6}$, and $\frac{5}{8}$.

Solution

The LCM of 4, 6, and 8 is 24.

$$\frac{3}{4} + \frac{1}{6} + \frac{5}{8} = \frac{18}{24} + \frac{4}{24} + \frac{15}{24}$$
$$= \frac{18 + 4 + 15}{24} = \frac{37}{24}$$

YOU TRY IT 4

Find $\frac{7}{8}$ more than $-\frac{5}{6}$.

Your solution

EXAMPLE 5

Add: $-4 + 2.37$

Solution

$-4 + 2.37 = -1.63$

YOU TRY IT 5

Add: $-6.12 + (-12.881)$

Your solution

Solutions on p. S2

OBJECTIVE C *To subtract rational numbers*

Subtracting fractions is similar to adding fractions in that the denominators must be the same.

Subtraction of Fractions

To subtract two fractions with the same denominator, subtract the numerators and place the difference over the common denominator.

EXAMPLE

Subtract: $\frac{7}{8} - \frac{5}{8}$

$\frac{7}{8} - \frac{5}{8} = \frac{7-5}{8}$

- **The denominators are the same. Subtract the numerators and place the difference over the common denominator.**

$= \frac{2}{8} = \frac{1}{4}$

- **Write the answer in simplest form.**

APPLY THE CONCEPT

You have $\frac{1}{2}$ c of sugar. You are making a dessert that requires $\frac{3}{4}$ c of sugar. How much sugar do you need to borrow from a neighbor?

To find the amount of sugar, subtract $\frac{1}{2}$ from $\frac{3}{4}$.

$$\frac{3}{4} - \frac{1}{2} = \frac{3}{4} - \frac{2}{4} = \frac{1}{4}$$

You need to borrow $\frac{1}{4}$ c of sugar from a neighbor.

HOW TO 7 Subtract: $-\frac{7}{8}-\left(-\frac{5}{12}\right)$

$$-\frac{7}{8}-\left(-\frac{5}{12}\right)=-\frac{21}{24}-\left(-\frac{10}{24}\right)$$

- The LCM of 8 and 12 is 24.

$$=\frac{-21-(-10)}{24}=\frac{-21+10}{24}$$

- Subtract the fractions.

$$=\frac{-11}{24}=-\frac{11}{24}$$

HOW TO 8 Subtract: $-2.984-(-1.45)$

$$-2.984-(-1.45)=-2.984+1.45=-1.534$$

EXAMPLE 6

Subtract: $-\frac{1}{2}-\frac{5}{6}-\left(-\frac{3}{4}\right)$

Solution • The LCM of 2, 6, and 4 is 12.

$$-\frac{1}{2}-\frac{5}{6}-\left(-\frac{3}{4}\right)=-\frac{6}{12}-\frac{10}{12}-\left(-\frac{9}{12}\right)$$

$$=\frac{-6-10-(-9)}{12}=\frac{-6-10+9}{12}=-\frac{7}{12}$$

YOU TRY IT 6

Subtract: $\frac{7}{8}-\left(-\frac{5}{12}\right)-\frac{1}{9}$

Your solution

EXAMPLE 7

Subtract: $45.2-56.89$

Solution

$45.2-56.89=-11.69$

YOU TRY IT 7

Subtract: $-12.03-19.117$

Your solution

Solutions on p. S2

OBJECTIVE D *To solve application problems*

EXAMPLE 8

A cabinet maker is joining two pieces of wood. What must be the measure of the cut made from the left side of the board so that the pieces fit as shown?

Strategy

To find the measure of the cut, subtract $\frac{5}{16}$ in. from $\frac{7}{8}$ in.

? in.

$\frac{5}{16}$ in.

$\frac{7}{8}$ in.

Solution

$$\frac{7}{8}-\frac{5}{16}=\frac{14}{16}-\frac{5}{16}=\frac{9}{16}$$

The cut must be made $\frac{9}{16}$ in. from the left side of the board.

YOU TRY IT 8

Barbara Walsh spent $\frac{1}{6}$ of her day studying, $\frac{1}{8}$ of her day in class, and $\frac{1}{4}$ of her day working. What fraction of her day did she spend on these three activities?

Your strategy

Your solution

Solution on p. S2

1.6 EXERCISES

Concept Check

1. To write $\frac{3}{4}$ as a decimal, divide ____________ by ____________. The quotient is 0.75, which is a ____________ decimal.
2. To add two fractions with the same denominator, add the ____________ and place the sum over the ____________.
3. To subtract two fractions with different denominators, first rewrite the fractions as ____________ fractions with a ____________.
4. Give an example of a number that is both an integer and a rational number.

OBJECTIVE A *To write a rational number in simplest form and as a decimal*

For Exercises 5 to 22, write the fraction in simplest form.

5. $\frac{7}{21}$ **6.** $\frac{10}{15}$ **7.** $-\frac{8}{22}$ **8.** $-\frac{8}{60}$ **9.** $-\frac{50}{75}$ **10.** $-\frac{20}{44}$

11. $\frac{12}{8}$ **12.** $\frac{36}{4}$ **13.** $\frac{0}{36}$ **14.** $\frac{12}{18}$ **15.** $-\frac{60}{100}$ **16.** $-\frac{14}{45}$

17. $-\frac{28}{20}$ **18.** $-\frac{20}{5}$ **19.** $-\frac{45}{3}$ **20.** $\frac{44}{60}$ **21.** $\frac{23}{46}$ **22.** $\frac{31}{93}$

For Exercises 23 to 34, write the fraction as a decimal. Place a bar over repeating digits.

23. $\frac{4}{5}$ **24.** $\frac{1}{8}$ **25.** $\frac{1}{6}$ **26.** $\frac{5}{6}$ **27.** $-\frac{1}{3}$ **28.** $-\frac{1}{20}$

29. $-\frac{2}{9}$ **30.** $-\frac{5}{11}$ **31.** $-\frac{7}{12}$ **32.** $\frac{7}{8}$ **33.** $\frac{11}{12}$ **34.** $\frac{4}{11}$

35. The denominator of a fraction that is in simplest form is a multiple of 3. You write the fraction as a decimal. Is the result a terminating or a repeating decimal?

OBJECTIVE B *To add rational numbers*

For Exercises 36 to 67, add.

36. $-\frac{1}{5}+\left(-\frac{4}{5}\right)$

37. $-\frac{2}{9}+\left(-\frac{4}{9}\right)$

38. $\frac{1}{6}+\left(-\frac{5}{6}\right)$

39. $-\frac{5}{8}+\frac{1}{8}$

40. $\frac{2}{3}+\frac{5}{12}$

41. $\frac{1}{2}+\frac{3}{8}$

42. $\frac{5}{8}+\frac{5}{6}$

43 $\frac{1}{18}+\frac{5}{27}$

44. $\frac{5}{12}+\left(-\frac{3}{8}\right)$

45. $-\frac{5}{6}+\frac{5}{9}$

46. $-\frac{6}{13}+\left(-\frac{17}{26}\right)$

47. $\frac{3}{5}+\left(-\frac{11}{12}\right)$

48. $-\frac{3}{4}+\left(-\frac{5}{6}\right)$

49. $-\frac{5}{8}+\frac{11}{12}$

50. $\frac{1}{3}+\frac{5}{6}+\frac{2}{9}$

51. $\frac{1}{2}+\frac{2}{3}+\frac{1}{6}$

52. $-\frac{3}{8}+\frac{5}{12}+\left(-\frac{3}{16}\right)$

53. $\frac{5}{16}+\left(-\frac{3}{4}\right)+\left(-\frac{7}{8}\right)$

54. $-\frac{1}{8}+\left(-\frac{11}{12}\right)+\frac{1}{3}$

55. $\frac{3}{8}+\left(-\frac{7}{12}\right)+\left(-\frac{5}{9}\right)$

56. $7.56 + 0.462$

57. $1.09 + 6.2$

58. $-32.1 + 6.7$

59. $5.138 + (-8.41)$

60. $-16.92 + 6.956$

61. $48 + (-34.12)$

62. $-19.84 + 17$

63. $-3.739 + (-2.03)$

64. $2.34 + (-3.7) + (-5.601)$

65. $-5.507 + (-4.91) + 15.2$

66. $-7.89 + 12.041 + (-4.151)$

67. $-3.04 + (-2.191) + (-0.06)$

68. What is $\frac{3}{4}$ more than $-\frac{5}{6}$?

69. Find the total of $\frac{5}{8}$ and $-\frac{5}{16}$.

70. Find $-\frac{5}{9}$ increased by $\frac{1}{6}$.

71. What is $-\frac{3}{8}$ added to $-\frac{5}{12}$?

72. Find 1.45 more than -7.

73. What is the sum of -4.23 and 3.06?

For Exercises 74 to 77, estimate each sum to the nearest integer. Do not find the exact sum.

74. $\frac{7}{8} + \frac{4}{5}$

75. $\frac{1}{3} + \left(-\frac{1}{2}\right)$

76. $-0.125 + 1.25$

77. $-1.3 + 0.2$

OBJECTIVE C *To subtract rational numbers*

For Exercises 78 to 107, subtract.

78. $\frac{3}{8} - \frac{5}{8}$

79. $\frac{5}{9} - \frac{8}{9}$

80. $-\frac{1}{6} - \frac{5}{6}$

81. $-\frac{3}{4} - \left(-\frac{1}{4}\right)$

82. $\frac{1}{9} - \frac{5}{27}$

83. $\frac{5}{8} - \frac{5}{6}$

84. $\frac{1}{2} - \frac{5}{8}$

85. $\frac{2}{3} - \frac{1}{12}$

86. $-\frac{11}{12} - \frac{5}{8}$

87. $-\frac{7}{13} - \left(-\frac{11}{26}\right)$

88. $-\frac{5}{6} - \frac{4}{9}$

89. $-\frac{3}{4} - \left(-\frac{5}{6}\right)$

90. $\frac{4}{5} - \left(-\frac{5}{12}\right)$

91. $\frac{3}{8} - \left(-\frac{3}{4}\right)$

92. $\frac{7}{16} - \left(-\frac{3}{4}\right) - \left(-\frac{5}{8}\right)$

93. $-\frac{1}{8} - \frac{5}{12} - \left(-\frac{5}{16}\right)$

94. $\frac{1}{2} - \frac{5}{6} - \frac{2}{3}$

95. $-\frac{19}{18} - \left(-\frac{5}{6}\right) - \left(-\frac{2}{9}\right)$

96. $\frac{5}{8} - \left(-\frac{7}{12}\right) + \frac{7}{9}$

97. $-\frac{1}{8} - \left(-\frac{11}{12}\right) - \frac{1}{3}$

98. $6.322 - 9.123$

99. $-43.1 - 19.37$

100. $-3.04 - (-5.128)$

101. $-25 - (-34.12)$

102. $-20.04 - (-41.2)$

103. $0.354 - 16$

104. $-1.023 - (-1.023)$

105. $-5.0614 - 2.31$

106. $4.32 - (-6.1) - (-4.032)$

107. $-1.204 - (-5.027) - 12.3$

108. What number is $\frac{5}{6}$ less than $-\frac{3}{8}$?

109. Find the difference between $\frac{1}{2}$ and $-\frac{5}{16}$.

110. What is $\frac{2}{3}$ less $\frac{3}{4}$?

111. What number is $\frac{4}{5}$ less than $-\frac{2}{15}$?

112. Find the difference between $-\frac{5}{9}$ and $-\frac{1}{6}$.

113. Find $\frac{5}{16}$ less $\frac{7}{12}$.

For Exercises 114 to 117, without finding the difference, determine whether the difference is positive or negative.

114. $\frac{1}{5} - \frac{1}{2}$

115. $0.0837 - 0.24$

116. $-21.765 - (-15.1)$

117. $-\frac{3}{4} - \left(-\frac{9}{10}\right)$

OBJECTIVE D *To solve application problems*

118. Food Science A recipe calls for $\frac{3}{4}$ c of vegetable broth. If a chef has $\frac{2}{3}$ c of vegetable broth, how much additional broth is needed for the recipe?

119. Carpentry A piece of lath $\frac{1}{16}$ in. thick is glued to the edges of a wood strip that is $\frac{3}{4}$ in. wide. What is the width of the wood and lath?

Oil Consumption The graph at the right shows the numbers of barrels of oil per day, in millions, that are consumed by various countries and the numbers of barrels of oil per day, in millions, those countries import. Use this graph for Exercises 120 to 123.

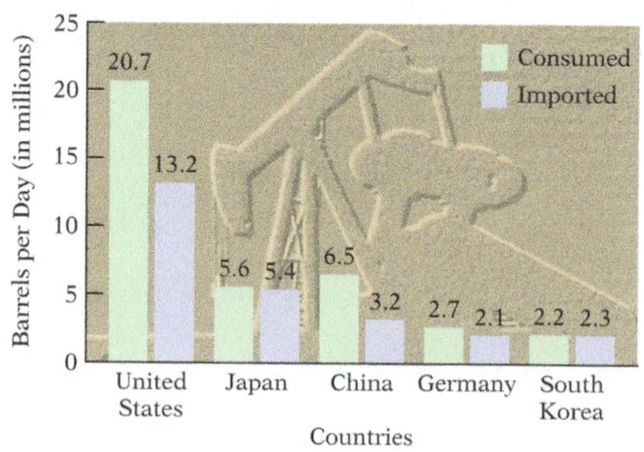

Oil Consumption by Country
Source: IEA

120. How many barrels of oil per day are consumed by these five countries?

121. How many barrels of oil per day are imported by these five countries?

122. For these five countries, what is the difference between the number of barrels of oil consumed per day and the number imported per day?

123. What is the largest difference among the numbers of barrels of oil consumed by these five countries?

Caffeine Content For Exercises 124 to 127, use the information in the news clipping at the right.

124. How much more caffeine does a 12-ounce serving of Diet Dr. Pepper contain than a 12-ounce serving of Dr. Pepper?

125. If you drink one 12-ounce serving of Diet Pepsi and one 12-ounce serving of Mountain Dew, how much caffeine have you consumed?

126. Find the difference in the caffeine content of a 12-ounce serving of Diet Coke and a 12-ounce serving of Diet Mountain Dew.

127. A 12-ounce cup of coffee may contain anywhere from 156 mg to 288 mg of caffeine. Find a combination of four different 12-ounce sodas that together contain less caffeine than one 12-ounce cup of coffee.

In the NEWS!

How Much Caffeine Do You Drink?

Food researchers at Auburn University conducted a study of the caffeine content of sodas, analyzing the amount of caffeine present in a 12-ounce serving.

Soda	Caffeine
Coca-Cola®	33.9 mg
Diet Coke®	46.3 mg
Dr. Pepper®	42.6 mg
Diet Dr. Pepper®	44.1 mg
Mountain Dew®	54.8 mg
Diet Mountain Dew®	55.2 mg
Pepsi®	38.9 mg
Diet Pepsi®	36.7 mg

Source: www.washingtonpost.com

Optometry A *diopter* is a measure of the strength of a lens. When lenses are combined, their strengths are added to find the total strength of the final lens. An optometrist can use this property of lenses to design an eyeglass lens that corrects more than one aspect of a person's vision. A negative diopter lens corrects nearsightedness and a positive diopter lens corrects farsightedness.

128. Find the total strength of a lens made by combining a –1.75 diopter lens with a −0.5 diopter lens.

129. Find the total strength of a lens made by combining a 1.50 diopter lens with a −3.75 diopter lens.

130. Will a −0.75 diopter lens combined with a lens that has a diopter measure greater than 1 create a lens with a positive diopter value or a negative diopter value?

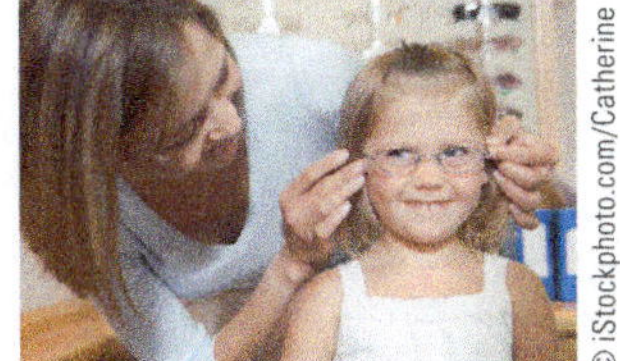

© iStockphoto.com/Catherine Yeulet

Critical Thinking

131. The numerator of a fraction is 1. If the denominator is replaced by −2, −3, −4, −5, . . . , are the resulting fractions getting smaller or larger?

132. The numerator of a fraction is −1. If the denominator is replaced by 2, 3, 4, 5, . . . , are the resulting fractions getting smaller or larger?

Projects or Group Activities

133. Use a calculator to determine the decimal representations of $\frac{17}{99}$, $\frac{45}{99}$, and $\frac{73}{99}$. Make a conjecture as to the decimal representation of $\frac{83}{99}$. Does your conjecture work for $\frac{33}{99}$? What about $\frac{1}{99}$?

134. A magic square is one in which the numbers in every row, column, and diagonal sum to the same number. Complete the magic square at the right.

$\frac{2}{3}$		
	$\frac{1}{6}$	$\frac{5}{6}$
		$-\frac{1}{3}$

135. Find three natural numbers a, b, and c such that $\frac{1}{a} + \frac{1}{b} + \frac{1}{c}$ is a natural number.

SECTION

1.7 Multiplication and Division of Rational Numbers

OBJECTIVE A To multiply rational numbers

The product $\frac{2}{3} \times \frac{4}{5}$ can be read "$\frac{2}{3}$ times $\frac{4}{5}$" or "$\frac{2}{3}$ of $\frac{4}{5}$." Reading the times sign as "of" can help with understanding the procedure for multiplying fractions.

$\frac{4}{5}$ of the bar is shaded. Shade $\frac{2}{3}$ of the $\frac{4}{5}$ already shaded.

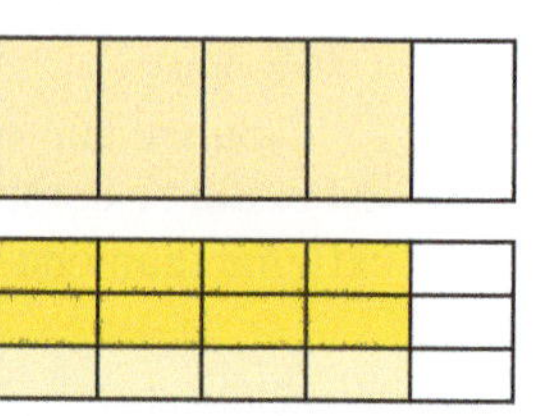

$\frac{8}{15}$ of the bar is then shaded dark yellow.

$\frac{2}{3}$ of $\frac{4}{5} = \frac{2}{3} \times \frac{4}{5} = \frac{2 \times 4}{3 \times 5} = \frac{8}{15}$

Take Note

Note that fractions do not need to have the same denominator in order to be multiplied.

Multiplication of Fractions

The product of two fractions is the product of the numerators over the product of the denominators.

EXAMPLES

1. $\frac{1}{5} \cdot \frac{2}{3} = \frac{1 \cdot 2}{5 \cdot 3} = \frac{2}{15}$

2. $\frac{3}{4} \cdot \frac{5}{8} = \frac{3 \cdot 5}{4 \cdot 8} = \frac{15}{32}$

APPLY THE CONCEPT

A seamstress is making 16 costumes for a dance recital. Each costume requires $\frac{3}{4}$ yd of fabric. How much fabric should the seamstress buy to make the 16 costumes?

To find the amount of fabric the seamstress should buy, multiply the amount of fabric needed for each costume $\left(\frac{3}{4}\right)$ by the number of costumes (16).

$$16 \cdot \frac{3}{4} = \frac{16}{1} \cdot \frac{3}{4} = \frac{16 \cdot 3}{1 \cdot 4} = \frac{48}{4} = 12$$

The seamstress should buy 12 yd of fabric.

Take Note

After multiplying two fractions, write the product in simplest form.

HOW TO 1 Multiply: $-\frac{3}{4} \cdot \frac{10}{21}$

The signs are different. The product is negative.

- Use the rules for multiplying integers to determine the sign of the product.

$$-\frac{3}{4} \cdot \frac{10}{21} = -\frac{3 \cdot 10}{4 \cdot 21}$$

- Multiply the numerators.
- Multiply the denominators.

$$= -\frac{3 \cdot 2 \cdot 5}{2 \cdot 2 \cdot 3 \cdot 7}$$

- Write the prime factorization of each number.

$$= -\frac{\overset{1}{\cancel{3}} \cdot \overset{1}{\cancel{2}} \cdot 5}{\underset{1}{\cancel{2}} \cdot 2 \cdot \underset{1}{\cancel{3}} \cdot 7} = -\frac{5}{14}$$

- Divide by the common factors. Then multiply the remaining factors in the numerator and in the denominator.

Take Note

HOW TO 1 can be worked by dividing by the greatest common factor (GCF) of the numerator and denominator.

$$-\frac{3}{4} \cdot \frac{10}{21} = -\frac{30}{84}$$

$$= -\frac{\overset{1}{\cancel{6}} \cdot 5}{\underset{1}{\cancel{6}} \cdot 14} = -\frac{5}{14}$$

To multiply decimals, multiply as with integers. Write the decimal point in the product so that the number of decimal places in the product equals the sum of the numbers of decimal places in the factors.

HOW TO 2 Find the product of 7.43 and −0.00025.

$$\begin{array}{r} 7.43 \\ \times\ 0.00025 \\ \hline 3715 \\ 1486 \\ \hline 0.0018575 \end{array}$$

7.43 — 2 decimal places
0.00025 — 5 decimal places
0.0018575 — 7 decimal places

- **Multiply the absolute values.**

$7.43(-0.00025) = -0.0018575$

- **The signs are different. The product is negative.**

EXAMPLE 1

Multiply: $-\frac{3}{8}\left(-\frac{12}{17}\right)$

Solution

$$-\frac{3}{8}\left(-\frac{12}{17}\right) = \frac{3 \cdot 12}{8 \cdot 17}$$

- **The signs are the same. The product is positive.**

$$= \frac{3 \cdot \overset{1}{\cancel{2}} \cdot \overset{1}{\cancel{2}} \cdot 3}{\underset{1}{\cancel{2}} \cdot \underset{1}{\cancel{2}} \cdot 2 \cdot 17}$$

$$= \frac{9}{34}$$

- **Write the answer in simplest form.**

YOU TRY IT 1

Multiply: $\frac{5}{8}\left(-\frac{4}{25}\right)$

Your solution

EXAMPLE 2

Find the product of $\frac{4}{9}$, $\frac{3}{10}$, and $-\frac{5}{18}$.

Solution

$$\frac{4}{9} \cdot \frac{3}{10} \cdot \left(-\frac{5}{18}\right) = -\frac{4 \cdot 3 \cdot 5}{9 \cdot 10 \cdot 18}$$

- **The product is negative.**

$$= -\frac{\overset{1}{\cancel{2}} \cdot \overset{1}{\cancel{2}} \cdot \overset{1}{\cancel{3}} \cdot \overset{1}{\cancel{5}}}{\underset{1}{\cancel{3}} \cdot 3 \cdot \underset{1}{\cancel{2}} \cdot \underset{1}{\cancel{5}} \cdot \underset{1}{\cancel{2}} \cdot 3 \cdot 3}$$

$$= -\frac{1}{27}$$

- **Write the answer in simplest form.**

YOU TRY IT 2

Find the product of $-\frac{4}{5}$, $-\frac{3}{8}$, and $-\frac{10}{27}$.

Your solution

EXAMPLE 3

Multiply: $-4.06(-0.065)$

Solution

The product is positive.

$-4.06(-0.065) = 0.2639$

YOU TRY IT 3

Multiply: $0.034(-2.14)$

Your solution

Solutions on pp. S2–S3

OBJECTIVE B *To divide rational numbers*

The **reciprocal of a fraction** is the fraction with the numerator and denominator interchanged. For instance, the reciprocal of $\frac{3}{4}$ is $\frac{4}{3}$, and the reciprocal of $-\frac{5}{2}$ is $-\frac{2}{5}$. The product of a number and its reciprocal is 1. This fact is used in the procedure for dividing fractions.

$$\frac{3}{4}\cdot\frac{4}{3}=\frac{12}{12}=1 \qquad -\frac{5}{2}\cdot\left(-\frac{2}{5}\right)=\frac{10}{10}=1$$

Study the example below to see how reciprocals are used when dividing fractions.

Divide: $\frac{3}{5}\div\frac{5}{6}$

$$\frac{3}{5}\div\frac{5}{6}=\frac{\frac{3}{5}}{\frac{5}{6}}=\frac{\frac{3}{5}\cdot\frac{6}{5}}{\frac{5}{6}\cdot\frac{6}{5}}$$

- **Multiply the numerator and denominator by the reciprocal of the divisor.**

$$=\frac{\frac{3}{5}\cdot\frac{6}{5}}{1}$$

- **The product of a number and its reciprocal is 1.**

$$=\frac{3}{5}\cdot\frac{6}{5}=\frac{18}{25}$$

- **A number divided by 1 is the number.**

These steps are summarized by $\frac{3}{5}\div\frac{5}{6}=\frac{3}{5}\cdot\frac{6}{5}=\frac{18}{25}$.

Division of Fractions

To divide two fractions, multiply the dividend by the reciprocal of the divisor.

EXAMPLE

Divide: $\frac{2}{5}\div\frac{3}{4}$

$$\frac{2}{5}\div\frac{3}{4}=\frac{2}{5}\cdot\frac{4}{3}$$

- **Rewrite the division as multiplication by the reciprocal.**

$$=\frac{2\cdot 4}{5\cdot 3}=\frac{8}{15}$$

- **Multiply the fractions.**

Take Note

The method of dividing fractions is sometimes stated, "To divide fractions, invert the divisor and then multiply." Inverting the divisor means writing its reciprocal.

APPLY THE CONCEPT

If 6 people share $\frac{3}{4}$ of a pizza, what fraction of the pizza does each person eat?

To find the fraction, find the quotient of $\frac{3}{4}$ and 6.

$$\frac{3}{4}\div 6=\frac{3}{4}\div\frac{6}{1}=\frac{3}{4}\cdot\frac{1}{6}=\frac{3\cdot 1}{4\cdot 6}=\frac{3\cdot 1}{2\cdot 2\cdot 2\cdot 3}=\frac{1}{8}$$

Each person eats $\frac{1}{8}$ of the pizza.

Take Note

Note in the example at the right that when we divide a fraction and a whole number, we first write the whole number as a fraction with a denominator of 1.

HOW TO 3 Divide: $\frac{3}{10} \div \left(-\frac{18}{25}\right)$

The signs are different. The quotient is negative.

$$\frac{3}{10} \div \left(-\frac{18}{25}\right) = -\left(\frac{3}{10} \div \frac{18}{25}\right) = -\left(\frac{3}{10} \cdot \frac{25}{18}\right)$$

$$= -\frac{3 \cdot 25}{10 \cdot 18}$$

$$= -\frac{\overset{1}{\cancel{3}} \cdot \overset{1}{\cancel{5}} \cdot 5}{2 \cdot \underset{1}{\cancel{5}} \cdot 2 \cdot \underset{1}{\cancel{3}} \cdot 3} = -\frac{5}{12}$$

To divide decimals, move the decimal point in the divisor to the right so that the divisor becomes a whole number. Move the decimal point in the dividend the same number of places to the right. Place the decimal point in the quotient directly above the decimal point in the dividend. Then divide as with whole numbers.

Take Note

The procedure for dividing decimals used in HOW TO 4 can be justified as follows.

$$(-1.4) \div (-0.36) = \frac{1.4}{0.36} = \frac{1.4}{0.36} \cdot \frac{100}{100} = \frac{140}{36} \approx 3.9$$

HOW TO 4 Divide: $(-1.4) \div (-0.36)$. Round to the nearest tenth.

The signs are the same. The quotient is positive.

```
           3.88 ≈ 3.9
0.36.) 1.40.00
       -1 08
         32 0
        -28 8
          3 20
         -2 88
            32
```

- Move the decimal point 2 places to the right in the divisor and then in the dividend. Place the decimal point in the quotient directly above the decimal point in the dividend.

$(-1.4) \div (-0.36) \approx 3.9$

- Note that the symbol $\approx$ is used to indicate that the quotient is an approximate value that has been rounded off.

EXAMPLE 4

Divide: $\left(-\frac{3}{10}\right) \div \frac{9}{14}$

Solution

The quotient is negative.

$$\left(-\frac{3}{10}\right) \div \frac{9}{14} = -\left(\frac{3}{10} \cdot \frac{14}{9}\right)$$

- Multiply by the reciprocal of the divisor.

$$= -\frac{3 \cdot 2 \cdot 7}{2 \cdot 5 \cdot 3 \cdot 3}$$

$$= -\frac{7}{15}$$

- Write the answer in simplest form.

YOU TRY IT 4

Divide: $\frac{5}{8} \div \left(-\frac{10}{11}\right)$

Your solution

Solution on p. S3

EXAMPLE 5

Divide: $4.152 \div (-25.2)$. Round to the nearest thousandth.

Solution

Divide the absolute values. The quotient is negative.
$4.152 \div (-25.2) \approx -0.165$

YOU TRY IT 5

Divide: $(-34) \div (-9.02)$. Round to the nearest hundredth.

Your solution

Solution on p. S3

OBJECTIVE C *To convert among percents, fractions, and decimals*

"A population growth rate of 3%," "a manufacturer's discount of 25%," and "an 8% increase in pay" are typical examples of the many ways in which *percent* is used in applied problems. **Percent** means "per 100." Thus 27% means 27 out of each 100.

In applied problems involving percent, it may be necessary to rewrite a percent as a fraction or as a decimal, or to rewrite a fraction or a decimal as a percent.

To write a percent as a fraction, remove the percent sign and multiply by $\frac{1}{100}$.

$$27\% = 27\left(\frac{1}{100}\right) = \frac{27}{100}$$

To write a percent as a decimal, remove the percent sign and multiply by 0.01.

$$33\% = 33(0.01) = 0.33$$

Move the decimal point two places to the left. Then remove the percent sign.

Take Note

The decimal equivalent of 100% is 1. Therefore, multiplying by 100% is the same as multiplying by 1 and does not change the value of the fraction.

$$\frac{5}{8} = \frac{5}{8}(1) = \frac{5}{8}(100\%)$$

To write a fraction as a percent, multiply by 100%. For example, $\frac{5}{8}$ is changed to a percent as follows:

$$\frac{5}{8} = \frac{5}{8}(100\%) = \frac{500}{8}\% = 62.5\%, \quad \text{or} \quad 62\frac{1}{2}\%$$

To write a decimal as a percent, multiply by 100%.

$$0.82 = 0.82(100\%) = 82\%$$

Move the decimal point two places to the right. Then write the percent sign.

EXAMPLE 6

Write 130% as a fraction and as a decimal.

Solution

$$130\% = 130\left(\frac{1}{100}\right) = \frac{130}{100} = \frac{13}{10}$$

$$130\% = 130(0.01) = 1.30$$

YOU TRY IT 6

Write 125% as a fraction and as a decimal.

Your solution

Solution on p. S3

EXAMPLE 7

Write $\frac{5}{6}$ as a percent.

Solution

$$\frac{5}{6} = \frac{5}{6}(100\%) = \frac{500}{6}\% = 83\frac{1}{3}\%$$

YOU TRY IT 7

Write $\frac{9}{16}$ as a percent.

Your solution

EXAMPLE 8

Write 0.027 as a percent.

Solution

$$0.027 = 0.027(100\%) = 2.7\%$$

YOU TRY IT 8

Write 0.043 as a percent.

Your solution

Solutions on p. S3

OBJECTIVE D *To solve application problems*

EXAMPLE 9

Find the total wages of an employee who worked $18\frac{1}{2}$ h this week and who earns an hourly wage of $12.

Strategy

To find the total wages, multiply the hourly wage (12) by the number of hours worked $\left(18\frac{1}{2}\right)$.

Solution

$$12 \cdot 18\frac{1}{2} = \frac{12}{1} \cdot \frac{37}{2}$$
$$= \frac{2 \cdot 2 \cdot 3 \cdot 37}{1 \cdot 2}$$
$$= 222$$

The employee's total wages were $222.

YOU TRY IT 9

A piece of fabric 20 ft long is being used to make cushions for outdoor furniture. If each cushion requires $1\frac{1}{2}$ ft of fabric, how many cushions can be made from the fabric?

Your strategy

Your solution

Solution on p. S3

1.7 EXERCISES

Concept Check

1. To multiply two fractions, first multiply the ________. Then place the product over the product of the ________.
2. To divide two fractions, multiply the first fraction by the ________ of the second fraction.
3. To write a fraction as a percent, multiply the fraction by ________.
4. To write a percent as a decimal, remove the percent sign and multiply by ________.

OBJECTIVE A *To multiply rational numbers*

For Exercises 5 to 28, multiply.

5. $\frac{2}{3} \cdot \frac{5}{7}$

6. $\frac{1}{2}\left(\frac{3}{8}\right)$

7. $\frac{5}{8} \cdot \left(-\frac{3}{10}\right)$

8. $-\frac{5}{16} \cdot \frac{7}{15}$

9. $\frac{5}{12}\left(-\frac{3}{10}\right)$

10. $\left(-\frac{11}{12}\right)\left(-\frac{6}{7}\right)$

11. $\frac{6}{13}\left(-\frac{26}{27}\right)$

12. $\frac{1}{6}\left(-\frac{6}{11}\right)$

13. $\left(-\frac{3}{5}\right)\left(-\frac{3}{10}\right)$

14. $\frac{3}{5}\left(-\frac{11}{12}\right)$

15. $\left(-\frac{3}{4}\right)^2$

16. $\left(-\frac{5}{8}\right)^2$

17. $\left(-\frac{3}{4}\right)\frac{5}{6}\left(-\frac{2}{9}\right)$

18. $\left(-\frac{1}{2}\right)\left(-\frac{2}{3}\right)\left(-\frac{6}{7}\right)$

19. $\left(-\frac{3}{8}\right)\left(-\frac{5}{12}\right)\left(\frac{3}{10}\right)$

20. $\frac{5}{16}\left(-\frac{4}{5}\right)\left(-\frac{7}{8}\right)$

21. $\left(-\frac{15}{2}\right)\left(-\frac{4}{3}\right)\left(-\frac{7}{10}\right)$

22. $\left(-\frac{5}{8}\right)\left(\frac{5}{12}\right)\left(-\frac{16}{25}\right)$

23. $0.46(-3.9)$

24. $-0.78(6.8)$

25. $(-8.23)(-0.09)$

26. $(-0.003)(-0.189)$

27. $-0.48(0.85)$

28. $0.056(-3.425)$

29. Find the product of $-\frac{3}{4}$ and $\frac{4}{5}$.

30. Find the product of $-\frac{7}{10}$ and $-\frac{5}{14}$.

31. Multiply -0.23 by -4.5.

32. Multiply -7.06 by 0.034.

33. Without finding the product, determine whether $\frac{11}{13} \cdot \frac{50}{51}$ is greater than 1 or less than 1.

OBJECTIVE B *To divide rational numbers*

For Exercises 34 to 45, divide.

34. $\frac{3}{8} \div \left(-\frac{9}{10}\right)$

35. $\left(-\frac{2}{15}\right) \div \frac{3}{5}$

36. $\left(-\frac{8}{9}\right) \div \left(-\frac{4}{5}\right)$

37. $\left(-\frac{11}{15}\right) \div \left(-\frac{22}{5}\right)$

38. $\left(-\frac{11}{12}\right) \div \left(-\frac{7}{6}\right)$

39. $\left(-\frac{3}{10}\right) \div \frac{5}{12}$

40. $\left(-\frac{6}{11}\right) \div 6$

41. $\left(-\frac{26}{27}\right) \div \frac{13}{6}$

42. $\left(-\frac{11}{12}\right) \div \frac{5}{3}$

43. $\left(-\frac{3}{10}\right) \div \left(-\frac{5}{3}\right)$

44. $\left(-\frac{5}{8}\right) \div \frac{15}{16}$

45. $\frac{8}{9} \div \left(-\frac{4}{3}\right)$

46. Find the quotient of $-\frac{7}{9}$ and $-\frac{5}{18}$.

47. Find the quotient of $\frac{5}{8}$ and $-\frac{7}{12}$.

48. What is $\frac{1}{2}$ divided by $-\frac{1}{4}$?

49. What is $-\frac{5}{18}$ divided by $\frac{15}{16}$?

For Exercises 50 to 53, divide.

50. $25.61 \div (-5.2)$

51. $(-0.1035) \div (-0.023)$

52. $(-0.2205) \div (-0.21)$

53. $(-0.357) \div 1.02$

For Exercises 54 to 57, divide. Round to the nearest hundredth.

54. $-0.0647 \div 0.75$

55. $-27.981 \div 59.2$

56. $-2.45 \div (-21.44)$

57. $3.2 \div (-45.12)$

58. Find the quotient of -0.3045 and -0.203.

59. Find the quotient of 3.672 and -3.6.

60. What is -0.00552 divided by 1.2?

61. What is -0.01925 divided by 0.077?

62. Without finding the quotient, determine whether $8.713 \div 7.2$ is greater than 1 or less than 1.

For Exercises 63 to 80, use the Order of Operations Agreement to simplify the expression.

63. $\frac{2}{3} - \frac{1}{4}\left(-\frac{2}{5}\right)$

64. $-\frac{7}{8} - \frac{3}{4} \div \frac{9}{8}$

65. $\frac{3}{4}\left(\frac{1}{2}\right)^2 - \frac{5}{16}$

66. $\left(-\frac{5}{6}\right) \div \frac{5}{12} - \frac{9}{14}$

67. $\frac{7}{12} - \left(\frac{2}{3}\right)^2 + \left(-\frac{3}{4}\right)$

68. $\left(\frac{1}{2} - \frac{3}{4}\right)^2 - \left(\frac{5}{18} - \frac{15}{24}\right)$

69. $\left(\frac{2}{3}\right)\left(\frac{3}{4}\right) - \left(\frac{4}{5}\right)\left(\frac{5}{8}\right)$

70. $\frac{1}{8} - \left(\frac{9}{4}\right)\left(-\frac{2}{3}\right)^2$

71. $-\frac{3}{4} \div \frac{5}{8} - \frac{4}{5}$

72. $\frac{5}{9}\left(\frac{3}{4}\right) - \frac{1}{2} \div (-2)$

73. $\left(\frac{2}{3}\right)^3 - \left(\frac{2}{3}\right)^2$

74. $\left(\frac{5}{6} - \frac{2}{3}\right)^2 \div \left(\frac{7}{18} - \frac{7}{12}\right)^2$

75. $1.2 - 2.3^2$

76. $4.01 - 0.2(8.1 - 6.4)$

77. $0.03 \cdot 0.2^2 - 0.5^3$

78. $8.1 - 5.2(3.4 - 5.9)^2$

79. $\frac{3.8 - 5.2}{-0.35} - \left(\frac{1.2}{0.6}\right)^2$

80. $-0.3^2 + 3.4(-2.01) - (-1.75)$

OBJECTIVE C *To convert among percents, fractions, and decimals*

81. Explain how to write a percent as a fraction.

82. Explain how to write a fraction as a percent.

For Exercises 83 to 92, write as a fraction and as a decimal.

83. 75%

84. 40%

85. 64%

86. 88%

87. 175%

88. 160%

89. 19%

90. 87%

91. 5%

92. 8%

For Exercises 93 to 102, write as a fraction.

93. $11\frac{1}{9}\%$ **94.** $4\frac{2}{7}\%$ **95.** $12\frac{1}{2}\%$ **96.** $37\frac{1}{2}\%$ **97.** $66\frac{2}{3}\%$

98. $\frac{1}{4}\%$ **99.** $\frac{1}{2}\%$ **100.** $6\frac{1}{4}\%$ **101.** $83\frac{1}{3}\%$ **102.** $5\frac{3}{4}\%$

For Exercises 103 to 112, write as a decimal.

103. 7.3% **104.** 9.1% **105.** 15.8% **106.** 16.7% **107.** 0.3%

108. 0.9% **109.** 9.9% **110.** 9.15% **111.** 121.2% **112.** 18.23%

For Exercises 113 to 132, write as a percent.

113. 0.15 **114.** 0.37 **115.** 0.05 **116.** 0.02 **117.** 0.175

118. 0.125 **119.** 1.15 **120.** 1.36 **121.** 0.008 **122.** 0.004

123. $\frac{27}{50}$ **124.** $\frac{83}{100}$ **125.** $\frac{1}{3}$ **126.** $\frac{3}{8}$ **127.** $\frac{5}{11}$

128. $\frac{4}{9}$ **129.** $\frac{7}{8}$ **130.** $\frac{9}{20}$ **131.** $1\frac{2}{3}$ **132.** $2\frac{1}{2}$

133. Does $\frac{4}{3}$ represent a percent greater than 100% or less than 100%?

134. Does 0.055 represent a percent greater than 1% or less than 1%?

OBJECTIVE D *To solve application problems*

135. **Carpentry** A carpenter has a board that is 14 ft long. How many pieces $\frac{3}{4}$ ft long can the carpenter cut from the board?

136. **Carpentry** A board $36\frac{5}{8}$ in. long is cut into two pieces of equal length. If the saw blade makes a cut $\frac{1}{8}$ in. wide, how far from the left side of the board should the cut be made?

137. **Oil Production** Read the news clipping at the right.

a. Find the difference between daily U.S. oil production in 2008 and in 1973.

b. Calculate the predicted increase in U.S. oil production from 2008 to 2020.

In the NEWS!

U.S. Oil Production Expected to Grow

U.S. oil production was on the decline. Production went from 9.2 million barrels per day in 1973 to 4.9 million barrels per day in 2008. However, high oil prices in 2010 made it economical to extract crude out of oil-shale deposits. Now experts forecast production of 6.0 million barrels per day by 2020.

Source: Time, March 21, 2011

138. **Interior Design** To reupholster a large sofa, an interior designer needs $12\frac{1}{2}$ yd of fabric that costs \$5.43 per yard and $5\frac{3}{4}$ yd of fabric that costs \$6.94 per yard. Find the total cost of the two fabrics.

139. **Food Science** A recipe calls for $\frac{3}{4}$ c of butter. If a chef wants to increase the recipe by one-half, how much butter should the chef use?

140. **Construction** A stair is made from an 8-inch riser and a $\frac{3}{4}$-inch foot plate. How many inches high is a staircase made from 10 of these stairs?

Foot plate

Riser

The Food Industry The table at the right shows the net weights of four different boxes of cereal. Use this table for Exercises 141 and 142.

Cereal	Net Weight
Kellogg's Honey CrunchCorn Flakes	24 oz
Nabisco Instant Cream of Wheat	28 oz
Post Shredded Wheat	18 oz
Quaker Oats	41 oz

141. Find the number of $1\frac{1}{2}$-ounce servings in a box of Kellogg's Honey Crunch Corn Flakes.

142. Find the number of $\frac{3}{4}$-ounce servings in a box of Post Shredded Wheat.

Critical Thinking

143. Find a rational number that is one-half the difference between $\frac{5}{11}$ and $\frac{4}{11}$.

144. Given any two different rational numbers, is it always possible to find a rational number between the two given numbers? If so, explain how to find such a number. If not, give two rational numbers for which there is no rational number between them.

Projects or Group Activities

145. Use shaded rectangles to show that $\frac{1}{2}$ of $\frac{3}{5}$ is $\frac{3}{10}$.

146. Use shaded rectangles to show that $\frac{1}{3}$ of $\frac{4}{5}$ is $\frac{4}{15}$.

SECTION

1.8 Concepts from Geometry

OBJECTIVE A *To find the measures of angles*

The word *geometry* comes from the Greek words for "earth" (*geo*) and "measure" (*metron*). The original purpose of geometry was to measure land. Today, geometry is used in many disciplines such as physics, biology, geology, architecture, art, and astronomy.

Here are some basic geometric concepts.

A **plane** is a flat surface, such as a table top, that extends indefinitely. Figures that lie entirely in a plane are called **plane figures.**

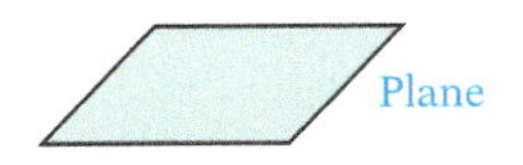

Space extends in all directions. Objects in space, such as a baseball, a house, or a tree, are called **solids.**

A **line** extends indefinitely in two directions in a plane. A line has no width.

Line ℓ

A **ray** starts at a point and extends indefinitely in one direction. By placing a point on the ray at the right, we can name the ray *AB*.

Ray *AB*

A **line segment** is part of a line and has two endpoints. The line segment *AB* is designated by its two endpoints.

Line segment *AB*

Lines in a plane can be parallel or intersect. **Parallel lines** never meet. The distance between parallel lines in a plane is always the same. We write $p \parallel q$ to indicate that line *p* is parallel to line *q*. **Intersecting lines** cross at a point in the plane.

Parallel lines

Intersecting lines

Take Note

When using three letters to name an angle, the vertex is always the middle letter. We could also refer to the angle at the right as $\angle CAB$.

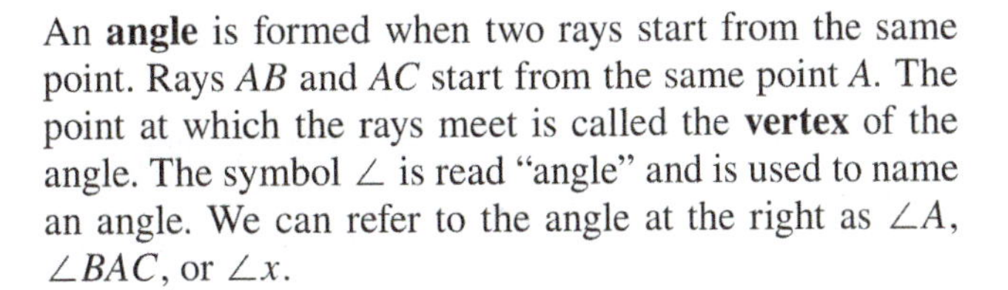

An **angle** is formed when two rays start from the same point. Rays *AB* and *AC* start from the same point *A*. The point at which the rays meet is called the **vertex** of the angle. The symbol $\angle$ is read "angle" and is used to name an angle. We can refer to the angle at the right as $\angle A$, $\angle BAC$, or $\angle x$.

Take Note

The Babylonians chose 360° for the measure of one full rotation, probably because they knew that there are 365 days in a year and that the closest number to 365 with many divisors is 360.

An angle can be measured in **degrees.** The symbol for degree is °. A ray rotated one revolution about its beginning point creates an angle of 360°.

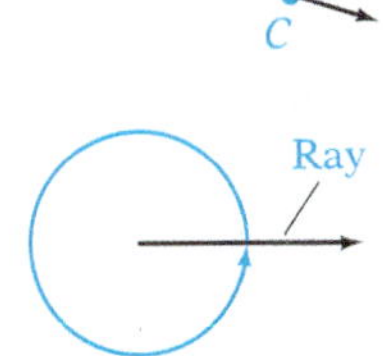

The measure of an angle is symbolized by $m\angle$. For instance, $m\angle C = 40°$. Read this as "the measure of angle *C* is 40°."

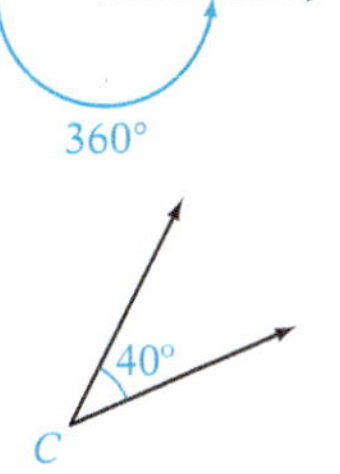

One-fourth of a revolution is $\frac{1}{4}$ of 360°, or 90°.

A 90° angle is called a **right angle.** The symbol ⊾ is used to represent a right angle.

Perpendicular lines are intersecting lines that form right angles. We write $p \perp q$ to indicate that line p is perpendicular to line q.

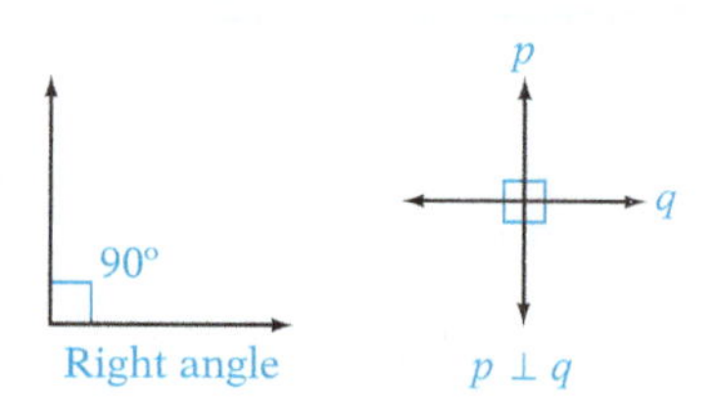

Complementary angles are two angles whose sum is 90°.

$$m\angle A + m\angle B = 35° + 55° = 90°$$

$\angle A$ and $\angle B$ are complementary angles.

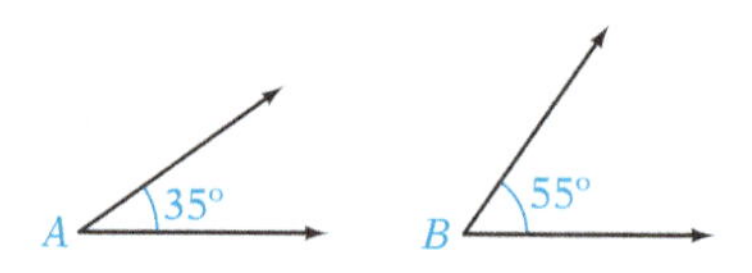

One-half of a revolution is $\frac{1}{2}$ of 360°, or 180°.

A 180° angle is called a **straight angle.**

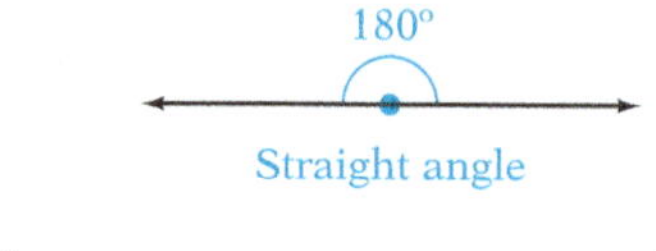

Supplementary angles are two angles whose sum is 180°.

$$m\angle A + m\angle B = 123° + 57° = 180°$$

$\angle A$ and $\angle B$ are supplementary angles.

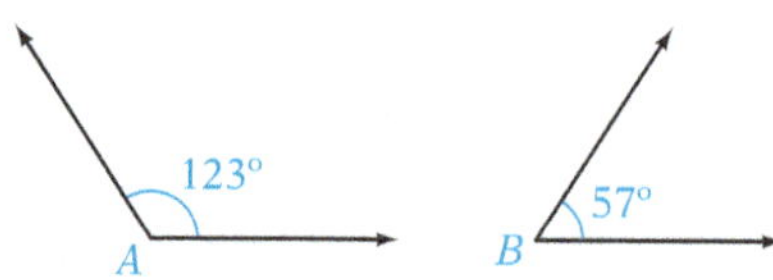

EXAMPLE 1

Find the complement of 39°.

Solution

To find the complement of 39°, subtract 39° from 90°.

$90° - 39° = 51°$

51° is the complement of 39°.

YOU TRY IT 1

Find the complement of 87°.

Your solution

EXAMPLE 2

Find the supplement of 122°.

Solution

To find the supplement of 122°, subtract 122° from 180°.

$180° - 122° = 58°$

58° is the supplement of 122°.

YOU TRY IT 2

Find the supplement of 87°.

Your solution

EXAMPLE 3

For the figure at the right, find $m\angle AOB$.

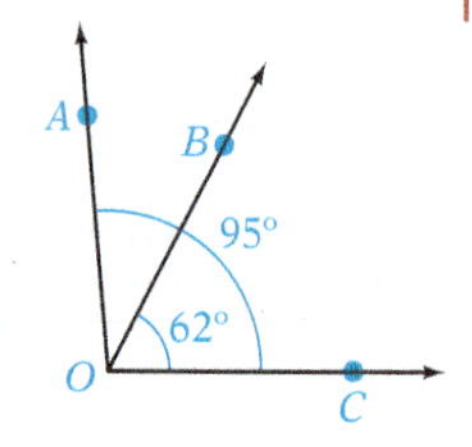

Solution

$m\angle AOB$ is the difference between $m\angle AOC$ and $m\angle BOC$.

$m\angle AOB = 95° - 62° = 33°$

$m\angle AOB = 33°$

YOU TRY IT 3

For the figure at the right, find $m\angle x$.

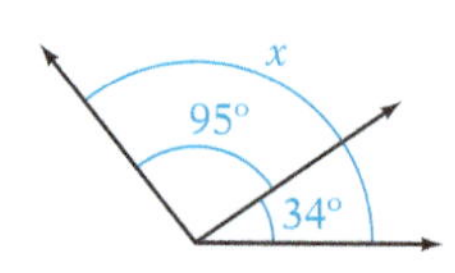

Your solution

Solutions on p. S3

OBJECTIVE B *To solve perimeter problems*

Perimeter is the distance around a plane figure. Perimeter is used, for example, in buying fencing for a yard, wood for the frame of a painting, and rain gutters for a house. The perimeter of a plane figure is the sum of the lengths of the sides of the figure. Formulas for the perimeters of four common geometric figures are given below.

A **triangle** is a three-sided plane figure.

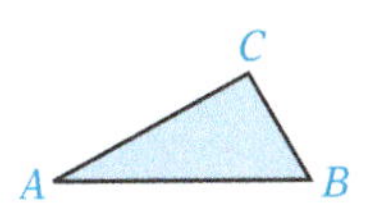

Perimeter = side 1 + side 2 + side 3

An **isosceles triangle** has two sides of the same length. An **equilateral triangle** has all three sides the same length.

A **parallelogram** is a four-sided plane figure with opposite sides parallel.

A **rectangle** is a parallelogram that has four right angles.

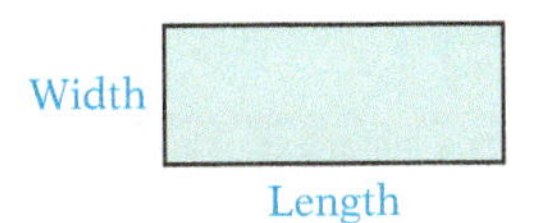

Perimeter = 2 · length + 2 · width

A **square** is a rectangle with four equal sides.

Perimeter = 4 · side

A **circle** is a plane figure in which all points are the same distance from point O, the **center of the circle.** The **diameter** of a circle is a line segment across the circle passing through the center. AB is a diameter of the circle at the right. The **radius** of a circle is a line segment from the center of the circle to a point on the circle. OC is a radius of the circle at the right. The perimeter of a circle is called its **circumference.**

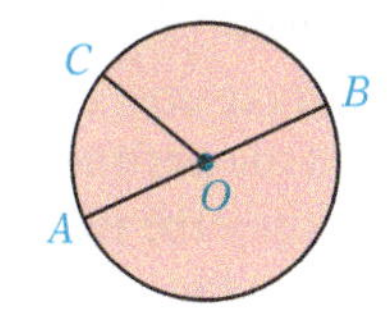

$$\text{Diameter} = 2 \cdot \text{radius} \quad \text{or} \quad \text{Radius} = \frac{1}{2} \cdot \text{diameter}$$

$$\text{Circumference} = 2 \cdot \pi \cdot \text{radius} \quad \text{or} \quad \text{Circumference} = \pi \cdot \text{diameter}$$

where $\pi \approx 3.14$ or $\pi \approx \frac{22}{7}$.

HOW TO 1 The diameter of a circle is 25 cm. Find the radius of the circle.

$$\text{Radius} = \frac{1}{2} \cdot \text{diameter}$$

$$= \frac{1}{2} \cdot 25 \text{ cm} = 12.5 \text{ cm}$$

The radius is 12.5 cm.

EXAMPLE 4

Find the perimeter of a rectangle with a width of 6 ft and a length of 18 feet.

Solution

Perimeter = 2 · length + 2 · width
= 2 · 18 ft + 2 · 6 ft
= 36 ft + 12 ft = 48 ft

YOU TRY IT 4

Find the perimeter of a square that has a side of length 4.2 m.

Your solution

EXAMPLE 5

Find the circumference of a circle with a radius of 23 cm. Use 3.14 for π.

Solution

Circumference = $2 \cdot \pi \cdot$ radius
$\approx 2 \cdot 3.14 \cdot 23$ cm
= 144.44 cm

YOU TRY IT 5

Find the circumference of a circle with a diameter of 5 in. Use 3.14 for π.

Your solution

EXAMPLE 6

A chain-link fence costs $6.37 per foot. How much will it cost to fence a rectangular playground that is 108 ft wide and 195 ft long?

Strategy

To find the cost of the fence:
- Find the perimeter of the playground.
- Multiply the perimeter by the per-foot cost of the fencing.

Solution

Perimeter = 2 · length + 2 · width
= 2 · 195 ft + 2 · 108 ft
= 390 ft + 216 ft = 606 ft

Cost = 606 × $6.37 = $3860.22

The cost is $3860.22.

YOU TRY IT 6

A metal strip is being installed around a circular table that has a diameter of 36 in. If the per-foot cost of the metal strip is $3.21, find the cost for the metal strip. Use 3.14 for π. Round to the nearest cent.

Your strategy

Your solution

Solutions on p. S3

OBJECTIVE C *To solve area problems*

1 in² 1 in. 1 in.

Area is a measure of the amount of surface in a region. Area is used to describe, for example, the size of a rug, a farm, a house, or a national park.

Area is measured in square units.

A square that is 1 in. on each side has an area of 1 square inch, which is written 1 in^2.

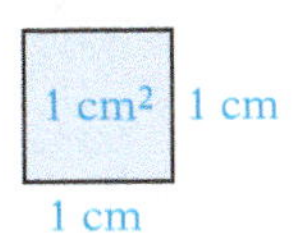

A square that is 1 cm on each side has an area of 1 square centimeter, which is written 1 cm^2.

Areas of common geometric figures are given by the following formulas.

RECTANGLE

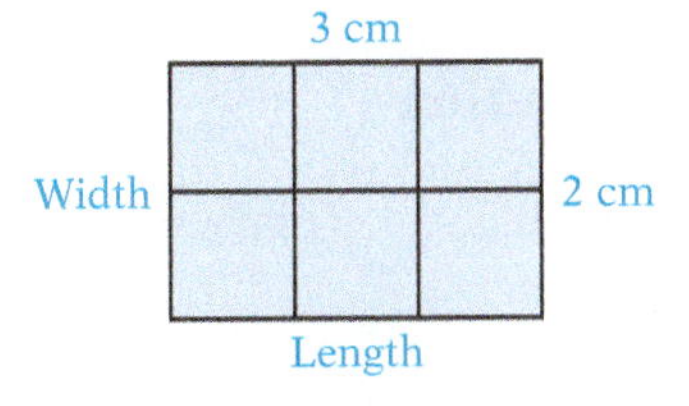

$$\text{Area} = \text{length} \cdot \text{width}$$
$$= 3 \text{ cm} \cdot 2 \text{ cm}$$
$$= 6 \text{ cm}^2$$

SQUARE

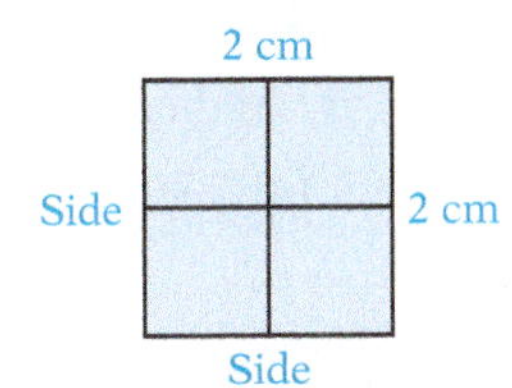

$$\text{Area} = \text{side} \cdot \text{side}$$
$$= 2 \text{ cm} \cdot 2 \text{ cm}$$
$$= 4 \text{ cm}^2$$

PARALLELOGRAM

The **base of a parallelogram** is one of the parallel sides. The **height of a parallelogram** is the distance between the base and the opposite parallel side. It is perpendicular to the base.

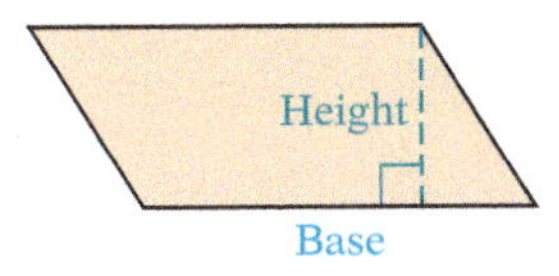

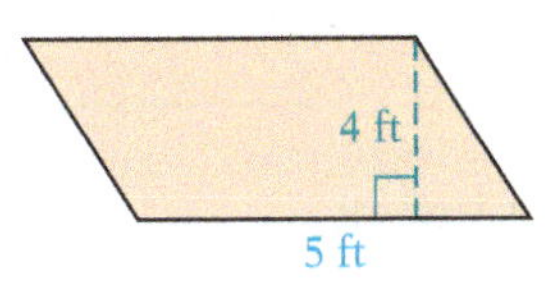

$$\text{Area} = \text{base} \cdot \text{height}$$
$$= 5 \text{ ft} \cdot 4 \text{ ft}$$
$$= 20 \text{ ft}^2$$

CIRCLE

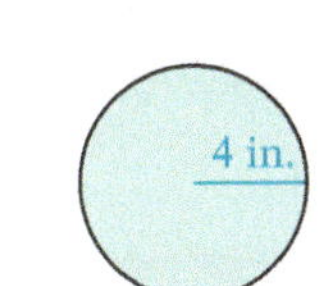

$$\text{Area} = \pi(\text{radius})^2$$
$$\approx 3.14(4 \text{ in.})^2 = 50.24 \text{ in}^2$$

TRIANGLE

For the triangle at the right, the **base of the triangle** is *AB*; the **height of the triangle** is *CD*. Note that the height is perpendicular to the base.

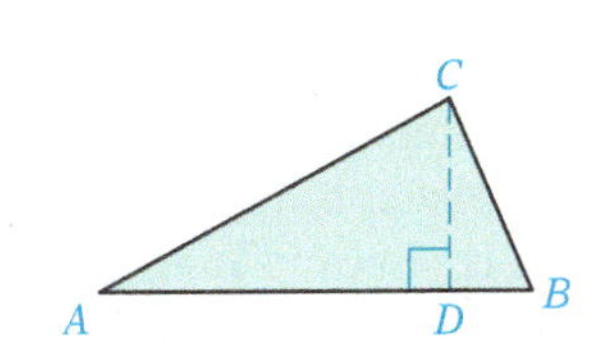

Take Note

The height of a triangle is always perpendicular to the base. Sometimes it is necessary to extend the base so that a perpendicular line segment can be drawn. The extension is *not* part of the base.

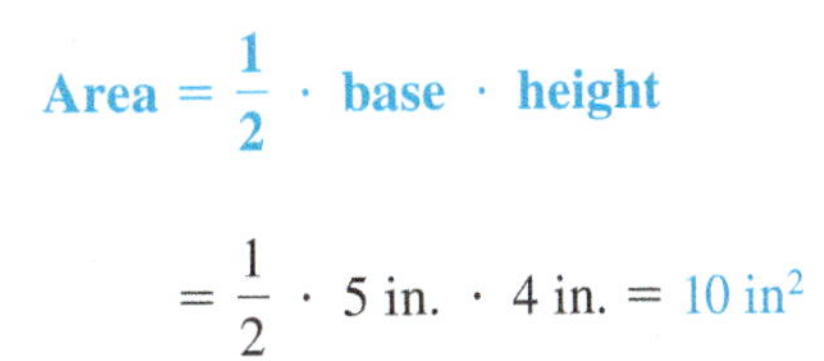

$$\text{Area} = \frac{1}{2} \cdot \text{base} \cdot \text{height}$$
$$= \frac{1}{2} \cdot 5 \text{ in.} \cdot 4 \text{ in.} = 10 \text{ in}^2$$

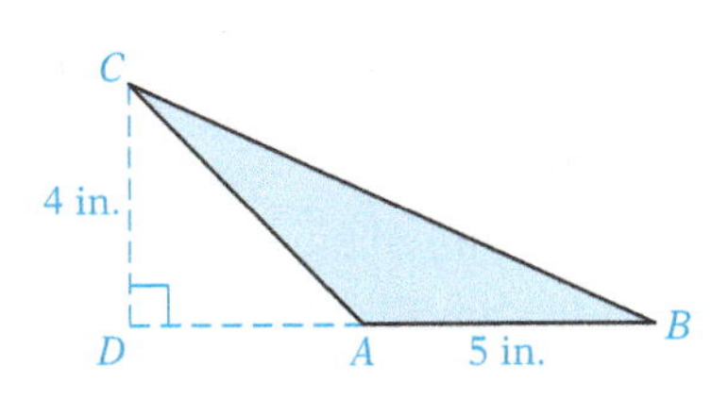

EXAMPLE 7

Find the area of a rectangle whose length is 8 in. and whose width is 6 in.

Solution

$$\text{Area} = \text{length} \times \text{width}$$
$$= 8 \text{ in.} \times 6 \text{ in.} = 48 \text{ in}^2$$

YOU TRY IT 7

Find the area of a triangle whose base is 5 ft and whose height is 3 ft.

Your solution

Solution on p. S3

EXAMPLE 8

Find the area of a circle whose diameter is 5 cm. Use 3.14 for π.

Solution

$$\text{Radius} = \frac{1}{2} \cdot \text{diameter}$$
$$= \frac{1}{2} \cdot 5 \text{ cm} = 2.5 \text{ cm}$$

$$\text{Area} = \pi \cdot (\text{radius})^2$$
$$\approx 3.14(2.5 \text{ cm})^2 = 19.625 \text{ cm}^2$$

YOU TRY IT 8

Find the area of a circle whose radius is 6 in. Use 3.14 for π.

Your solution

EXAMPLE 9

Find the area of the parallelogram shown below.

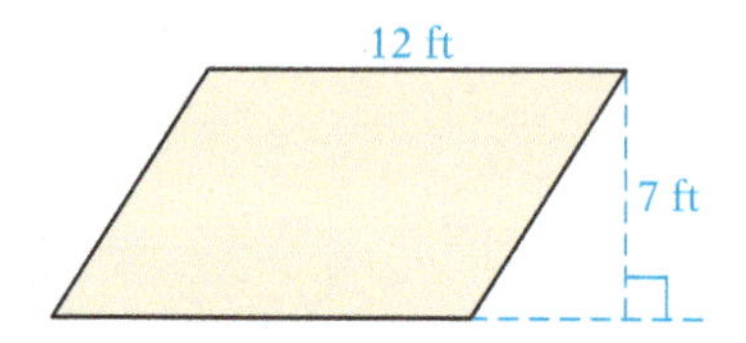

Solution

$$\text{Area} = \text{base} \cdot \text{height}$$
$$= 12 \text{ ft} \times 7 \text{ ft} = 84 \text{ ft}^2$$

YOU TRY IT 9

Find the area of the parallelogram shown below.

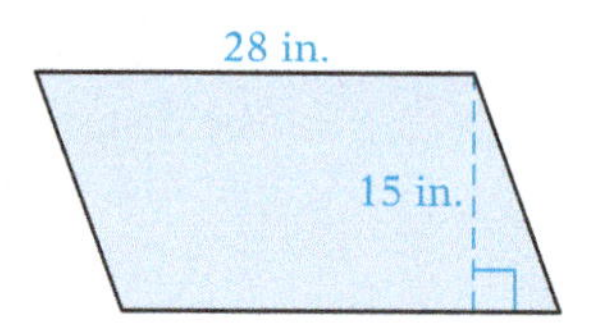

Your solution

EXAMPLE 10

To conserve water during a drought, a city's water department is offering homeowners a rebate on their water bill of \$1.27 per square foot of lawn that is removed from a yard and replaced with drought-resistant plants. What rebate would a homeowner receive who replaced a rectangular lawn area that is 15 ft wide and 25 ft long?

Strategy

To find the amount of the rebate:
- Find the area of the lawn.
- Multiply the area by the per-square-foot rebate.

Solution

$$\text{Area} = \text{length} \times \text{width}$$
$$= 25 \text{ ft} \times 15 \text{ ft} = 375 \text{ ft}^2$$

$$\text{Rebate} = 375 \times \$1.27 = \$476.25$$

The rebate is \$476.25.

YOU TRY IT 10

An interior designer is choosing from two hallway rugs. A nylon rug costs \$17.50 per square yard, and a wool rug costs \$24.30 per square yard. If the dimensions of the hallway are 4 ft by 18 ft, how much more expensive is the wool rug than the nylon rug? *Hint:* $9 \text{ ft}^2 = 1 \text{ yd}^2$.

Your strategy

Your solution

Solutions on pp. S3–S4

1.8 EXERCISES

Concept Check

1. Is an angle whose measure is 58° smaller than or larger than a right angle?
2. The radius of a circle is 22 cm. Find the diameter of the circle.
3. The diameter of a circle is 12 in. Find the radius of the circle.
4. What is the area of a square that measures 1 in. on each side?

OBJECTIVE A *To find the measure of angles*

5. How many degrees are in a right angle?
6. How many degrees are in a straight angle?
7. Find the complement of a 62° angle.
8. Find the complement of a 13° angle.
9. Find the supplement of a 48° angle.
10. Find the supplement of a 106° angle.
11. Angle AOB is a straight angle. Find $m\angle AOC$.

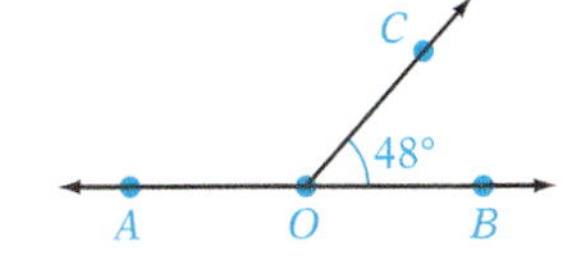

12. Angle AOB is a straight angle. Find $m\angle COB$.

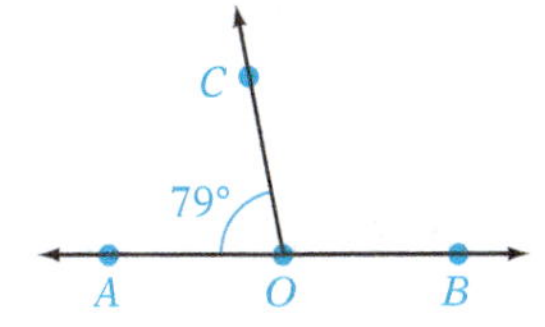

13. Find $m\angle x$.

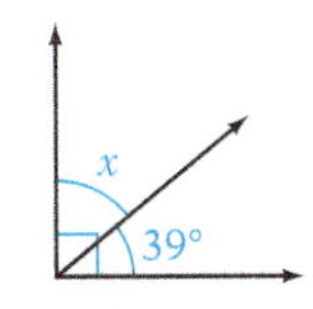

14. Find $m\angle x$.

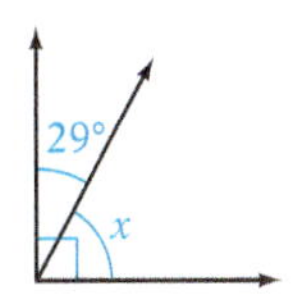

15. Find $m\angle AOB$.

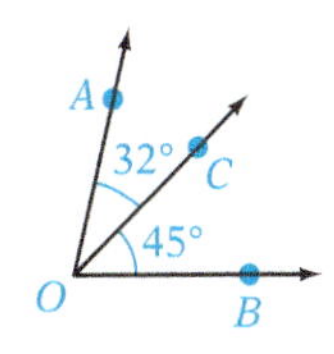

16. Find $m\angle AOB$.

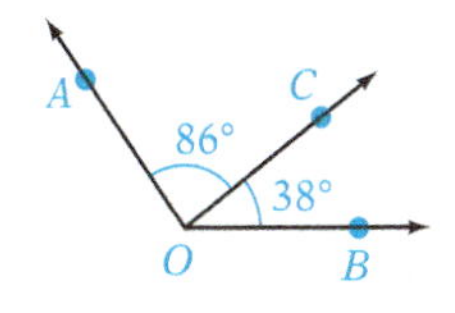

17. Find $m\angle AOC$.

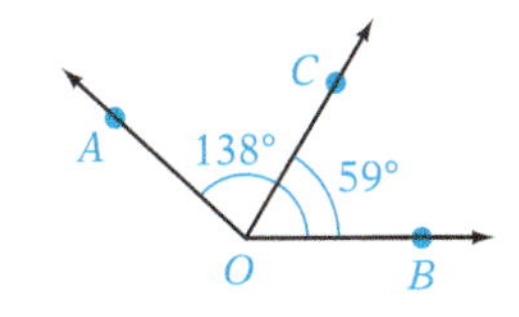

18. Find $m\angle AOC$.

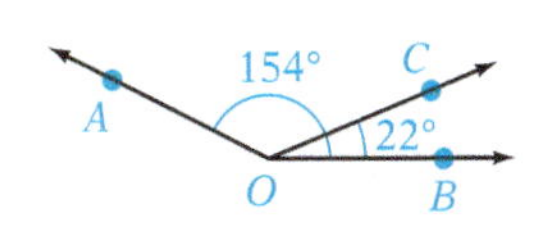

19. Find $m\angle A$.

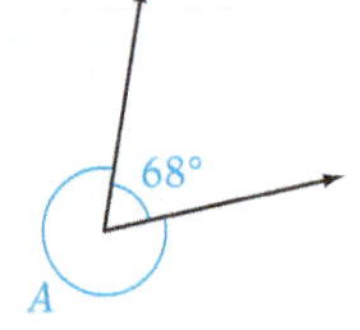

20. Find $m\angle A$.

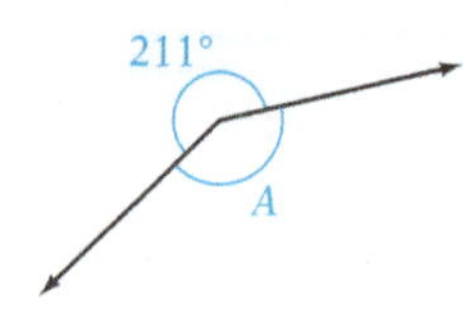

21. Through how many degrees does the hour hand on an analog clock travel in 1 h?

OBJECTIVE B *To solve perimeter problems*

22. Find the perimeter of a triangle with sides that measure 2.51 cm, 4.08 cm, and 3.12 cm.

23. Find the perimeter of a triangle with sides that measure 4 ft 5 in., 5 ft 3 in., and 6 ft. 2 in.

24. Find the perimeter of a rectangle whose length is 4 ft 2 in. and whose width is 2 ft 3 in.

25. Find the perimeter of a rectangle whose dimensions are 5 m by 8 m.

26. Find the perimeter of a square whose side measures 13 in.

27. Find the perimeter of a square whose side measures 34 cm.

28. Find the circumference of a circle whose radius is 21 cm. Use 3.14 for π.

29. Find the circumference of a circle whose radius is 3.4 m. Use 3.14 for π.

30. Find the circumference of a circle whose diameter is 1.2 m. Use 3.14 for π.

31. Find the circumference of a circle whose diameter is 15 in. Use 3.14 for π.

32. **Art** The wood framing for an art canvas costs $5.81 per foot. How much would the wood framing cost for a rectangular picture that measures 3 ft by 5 ft?

33. **Ceramics** A decorative mosaic tile is being installed along the border of a square wall behind a stove. If one side of the square measures 5 ft and the cost of installing the mosaic tile is $6.86 per foot, find the cost to install the decorative border.

defpicture/Shuytterstock.com

34. **Sewing** To prevent fraying, a binding is attached to the outside of a circular rug whose radius is 3 ft. If the binding costs $1.55 per foot, find the cost of the binding. Use 3.14 for π.

35. **Landscaping** A drip irrigation system is installed around a circular flower garden that is 4 ft in diameter. If the irrigation system costs $5.46 per foot, find the cost to place the irrigation system around the flower garden. Use 3.14 for π.

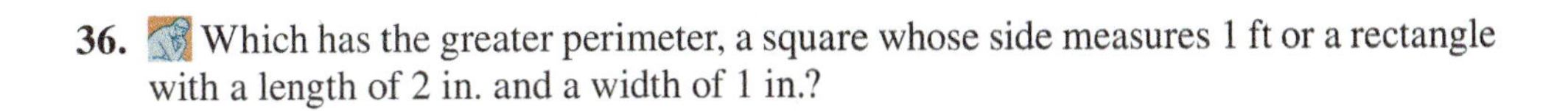

36. Which has the greater perimeter, a square whose side measures 1 ft or a rectangle with a length of 2 in. and a width of 1 in.?

OBJECTIVE C *To solve area problems*

37. Find the area of a rectangle that measures 4 ft by 8 ft.

38. Find the area of a rectangle that measures 3.4 cm by 5.6 cm.

39. Find the area of a parallelogram whose height is 14 cm and whose base is 27 cm.

40. Find the area of a parallelogram whose height is 7 ft and whose base is 18 ft.

41. Find the area of a circle whose radius is 4 in. Use 3.14 for π.

42. Find the area of a circle whose radius is 8.2 m. Use 3.14 for π.

43. Find the area of a square whose side measures 4.1 m.

44. Find the area of a square whose side measures 5 yd.

45. Find the area of a triangle whose height is 7 cm and whose base is 15 cm.

46. Find the area of a triangle whose height is 8 in. and whose base is 13 in.

47. Find the area of a circle whose diameter is 17 in. Use 3.14 for π.

48. Find the area of a circle whose diameter is 3.6 m. Use 3.14 for π.

49. Landscaping A landscape architect recommends 0.1 gal of water per day for each square foot of lawn. How many gallons of water should be used per day on a rectangular lawn that is 33 ft by 42 ft?

50. Interior Design One side of a square room measures 18 ft. How many square yards of carpet are necessary to carpet the room? *Hint:* $1 \text{ yd}^2 = 9 \text{ ft}^2$.

51. Carpentry A circular, inlaid-wood design for a dining table costs \$35 per square foot to build. If the radius of the design is 15 in., find the cost to build the design. Use 3.14 for π. Round to the nearest dollar. *Hint:* $144 \text{ in}^2 = 1 \text{ ft}^2$.

52. Interior Design A circular stained-glass window costs \$68 per square foot to build. If the diameter of the window is 4 ft, find the cost to build the window. Round to the nearest dollar.

53. **Construction** The cost of plastering the walls of a rectangular room that is 18 ft long, 14 ft wide, and 8 ft high is \$2.56 per square foot. If 125 ft^2 are not plastered because of doors and windows, find the cost to plaster the room.

54. **Interior Design** A room is 12 ft long, 9 ft wide, and 9 ft high. Two adjacent walls of the room are going to be wallpapered using wallpaper that costs \$25.25 per square yard. What is the cost to wallpaper the two walls? *Hint:* 1 yd^2 = 9 ft^2.

Interior Design A carpet is to be installed in one room and a hallway, as shown in the diagram at the right. For Exercises 55 to 58, state whether the given expression can be used to calculate the area of the carpet in square meters.

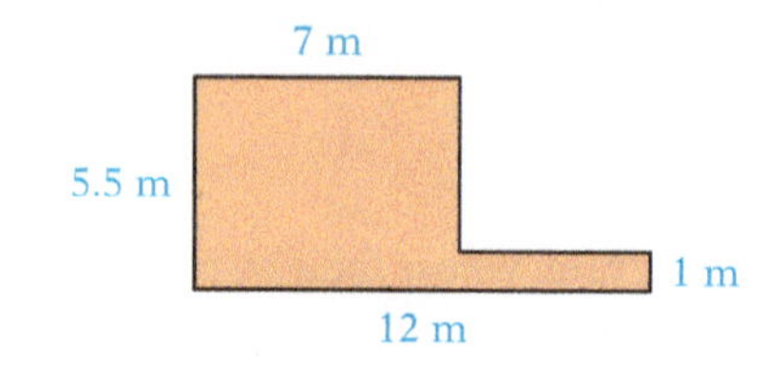

55. 5.5(7) + 12(1)

56. 5.5(12) − 4.5(5)

57. 12(1) + 4.5(7)

58. 5.5(7) + 1(5)

Critical Thinking

59. Find the perimeter and area of the figure. Use 3.14 for π.

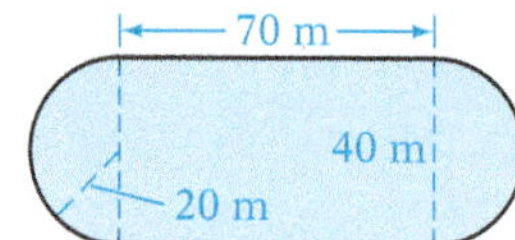

60. Find the perimeter and area of the figure.

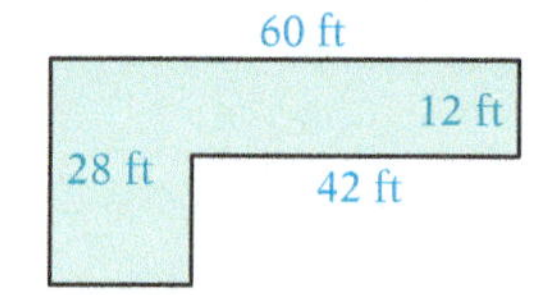

Projects or Group Activities

61. Draw parallelogram *ABCD* or one similar to it, and then cut it out. Cut along the dotted line to form the shaded triangle. Slide the triangle so that the slanted side corresponds to the slanted side of the parallelogram as shown. Explain how this demonstrates that the area of a parallelogram is the product of the base and the height.

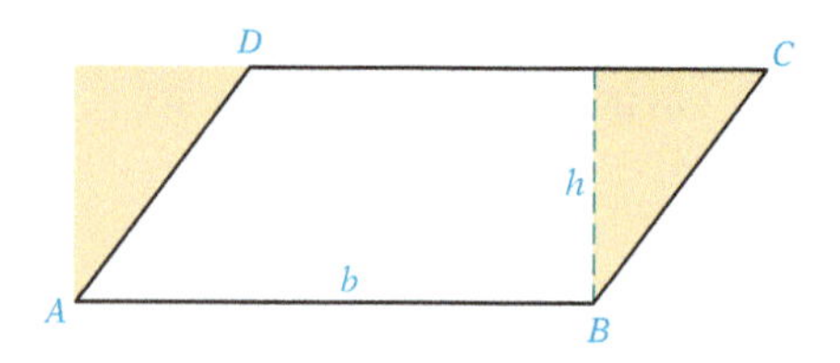

62. For each of the triangles, the base is *AB*. Draw the height.

a.

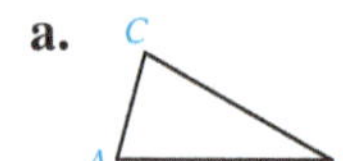

b.

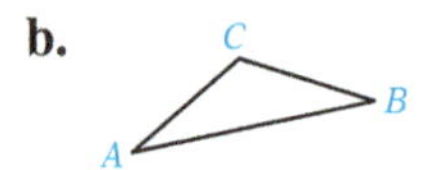

c.

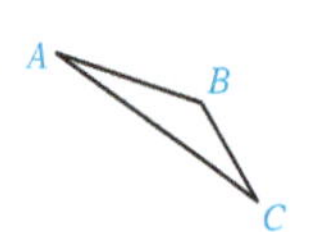

d.

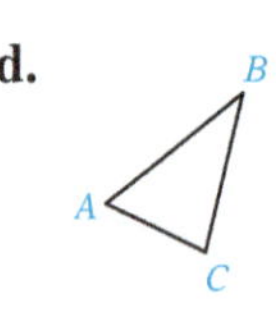

CHAPTER 1 Summary

Key Words	Examples
The set of **natural numbers** is $\{1, 2, 3, 4, 5, \ldots\}$. The set of **integers** is $\{\ldots, -3, -2, -1, 0, 1, 2, 3, \ldots\}$. [1.1A, p. 2]	
A number a **is less than** a number b, written $a < b$, if a is to the left of b on the number line. A number a **is greater than** a number b, written $a > b$, if a is to the right of b on the number line. The symbol $\leq$ means **is less than or equal to.** The symbol $\geq$ means **is greater than or equal to.** [1.1A, p. 3]	$-5 < -3$ $\quad$ $9 > 0$ $3 \leq 3$ $\quad$ $4 \leq 7$ $5 \geq 5$ $\quad$ $-6 \geq -9$
Two numbers that are the same distance from zero on the number line but are on opposite sides of zero are **opposite numbers** or **opposites.** The opposite of a number is also called its **additive inverse.** [1.1B, p. 4]	7 and -7 are opposites. $-\frac{3}{4}$ and $\frac{3}{4}$ are opposites.
The **absolute value** of a number is its distance from zero on the number line. [1.1B, p. 4]	$\|5\| = 5$ $\quad$ $\|-2.3\| = 2.3$ $\quad$ $\|0\| = 0$
An expression of the form a^n is in **exponential form.** The **base** is a and the **exponent** is n. [1.4A, p. 23]	5^4 is an exponential expression. The base is 5 and the exponent is 4.
A natural number greater than 1 is a **prime number** if its only factors are 1 and the number. [1.5B, p. 31]	3, 17, 23, and 97 are prime numbers.
The **prime factorization** of a number is the expression of the number as a product of its prime factors. [1.5B, p. 31]	$2^3 \cdot 3^2 \cdot 7$ is the prime factorization of 504.
The **least common multiple (LCM)** of two or more numbers is the smallest number that is a multiple of all the numbers. [1.5C, p. 32]	The LCM of 4, 8, and 12 is 24.
The **greatest common factor (GCF)** of two or more numbers is the greatest number that divides evenly into all of the numbers. [1.5C, p. 32]	The GCF of 4, 8, and 12 is 4.
A **rational number** (or fraction) is a number that can be written in the form $\frac{a}{b}$, where a and b are integers and $b \neq 0$. A fraction is in **simplest form** when there are no common factors in the numerator and denominator. A rational number can be represented as a **terminating** or **repeating decimal.** [1.6A, pp. 35–36]	$\frac{3}{8}$, $-\frac{9}{2}$ and 4 are rational numbers written in simplest form. $\frac{3}{8}$ is a fraction in simplest form. 1.13 and $0.4\overline{73}$ are also rational numbers.

An **irrational number** is a number that has a decimal representation that never terminates or repeats. [1.6A, p. 36]

π, $\sqrt{2}$, and 1.343343334333334 . . . are irrational numbers.

The rational numbers and the irrational numbers taken together are the **real numbers.** [1.6A, p. 36]

$\frac{3}{8}$, $-\frac{9}{2}$, 4, 1.13, $0.4\overline{73}$, π, $\sqrt{2}$, and 1.343343334333334 . . . are real numbers.

The **reciprocal of a fraction** is the fraction with the numerator and denominator interchanged. [1.7B, p. 48]

The reciprocal of $\frac{5}{6}$ is $\frac{6}{5}$.

The reciprocal of $-\frac{1}{3}$ is $-\frac{3}{1}$ or -3.

Percent means "per 100." [1.7C, p. 50]

72% means 72 out of each 100.

A **plane** is a flat surface that extends indefinitely. A **line** extends indefinitely in two directions in a plane. A **ray** starts at a point and extends indefinitely in one direction. A **line segment** is part of a line and has two endpoints. [1.8A, p. 57]

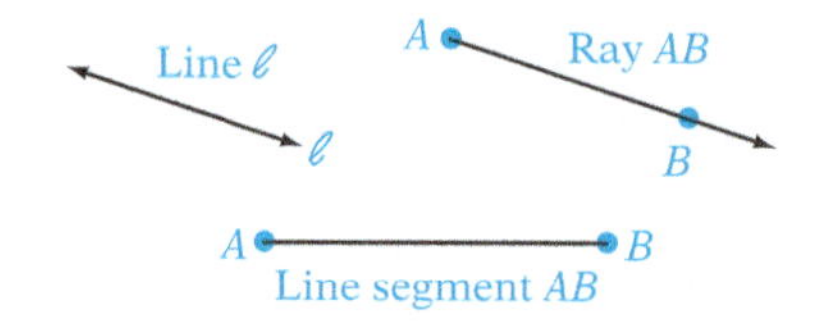

Lines in a plane can be parallel or intersect. **Parallel lines** never meet. The distance between parallel lines in a plane is always the same. **Intersecting lines** cross at a point in the plane. [1.8A, p. 57]

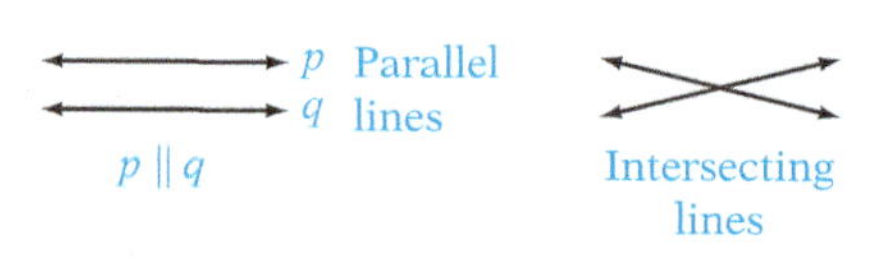

An **angle** is formed when two rays start from the same point. The point at which the rays meet is called the **vertex** of the angle. An angle can be measured in **degrees.** The measure of an angle is symbolized by $m\angle$. [1.8A, p. 57]

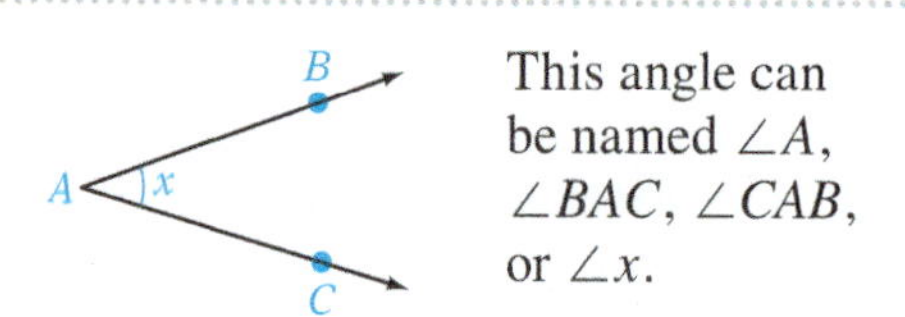

This angle can be named $\angle A$, $\angle BAC$, $\angle CAB$, or $\angle x$.

A **right angle** has a measure of 90°. **Perpendicular lines** are intersecting lines that form right angles. **Complementary angles** are two angles whose sum is 90°. A **straight angle** has a measure of 180°. **Supplementary angles** are two angles whose sum is 180°. [1.8A, p. 58]

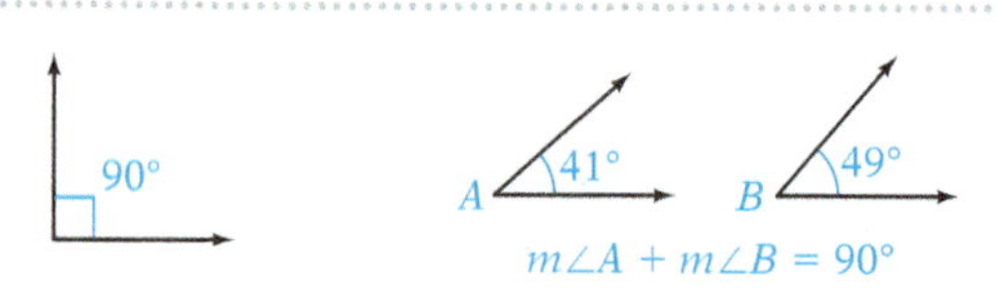

$\angle A$ and $\angle B$ are complementary angles.

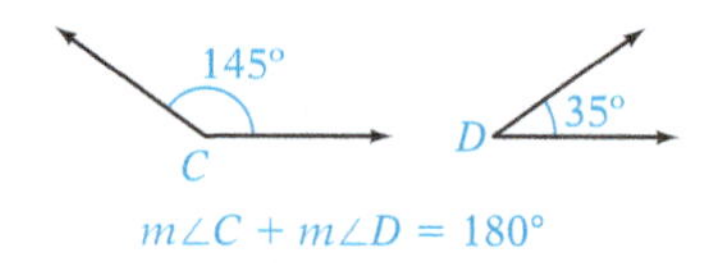

$\angle C$ and $\angle D$ are supplementary angles.

A **circle** is a plane figure in which all points are the same distance from point O, the **center** of the circle. A **diameter** of a circle is a line segment across the circle passing through the center. A **radius** of a circle is a line segment from the center of the circle to a point on the circle. The perimeter of a circle is called its **circumference.** [1.8B, p. 59]

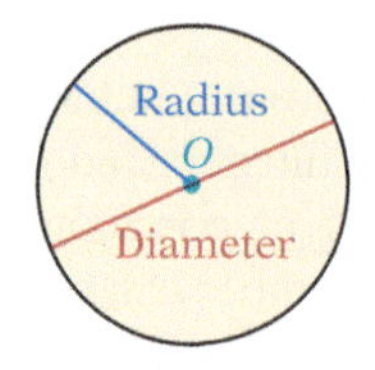

Essential Rules and Procedures	Examples
To add two numbers with the same sign, add the absolute values of the numbers. Then attach the sign of the addends. [1.2A, p. 8]	$7 + 15 = 22$ $-7 + (-15) = -22$
To add two numbers with different signs, find the absolute value of each number. Subtract the smaller of the two absolute values from the larger. Then attach the sign of the number with the larger absolute value. [1.2A, p. 8]	$7 + (-15) = -8$ $-7 + 15 = 8$
To subtract one number from another, add the opposite of the second number to the first number. [1.2B, p. 10]	$7 - 19 = 7 + (-19) = -12$ $-6 - (-13) = -6 + 13 = 7$
To multiply two numbers with the same sign, multiply the absolute values of the numbers. The product is positive. [1.3A, p. 16]	$7 \cdot 8 = 56$ $-7(-8) = 56$
To multiply two numbers with different signs, multiply the absolute values of the numbers. The product is negative. [1.3A, p. 16]	$-7 \cdot 8 = -56$ $7(-8) = -56$
To divide two numbers with the same sign, divide the absolute values of the numbers. The quotient is positive. [1.3B, p. 18]	$54 \div 9 = 6$ $(-54) \div (-9) = 6$
To divide two numbers with different signs, divide the absolute values of the numbers. The quotient is negative. [1.3B, p. 18]	$(-54) \div 9 = -6$ $54 \div (-9) = -6$
Properties of Zero and One in Division [1.3B, p. 19] If $a \neq 0$, $\frac{0}{a} = 0$. If $a \neq 0$, $\frac{a}{a} = 1$. $\frac{a}{1} = a$ $\frac{a}{0}$ is undefined.	 $\frac{0}{-5} = 0$ $\frac{-12}{-12} = 1$ $\frac{7}{1} = 7$ $\frac{8}{0}$ is undefined.
Order of Operations Agreement [1.4B, p. 25] **Step 1:** Perform operations inside grouping symbols. Grouping symbols include parentheses ( ), brackets [ ], braces { }, the fraction bar, and the absolute value symbol | |. **Step 2:** Simplify exponential expressions. **Step 3:** Do multiplication and division as they occur from left to right. **Step 4:** Do addition and subtraction as they occur from left to right.	$50 \div (-5)^2 + 2(7 - 16)$ $= 50 \div (-5)^2 + 2(-9)$ $= 50 \div 25 + 2(-9)$ $= 2 + (-18)$ $= -16$

To add two fractions with the same denominator, add the numerators and place the sum over the common denominator. [1.6B, p. 37]

$$\frac{7}{10} + \frac{1}{10} = \frac{7+1}{10} = \frac{8}{10} = \frac{4}{5}$$

To subtract two fractions with the same denominator, subtract the numerators and place the difference over the common denominator. [1.6C, p. 39]

$$\frac{7}{10} - \frac{1}{10} = \frac{7-1}{10} = \frac{6}{10} = \frac{3}{5}$$

To multiply two fractions, place the product of the numerators over the product of the denominators. [1.7A, p. 46]

$$-\frac{2}{3} \cdot \frac{5}{6} = -\frac{2 \cdot 5}{3 \cdot 6} = -\frac{10}{18} = -\frac{5}{9}$$

To divide two fractions, multiply the dividend by the reciprocal of the divisor. [1.7B, p. 48]

$$-\frac{4}{5} \div \frac{2}{3} = -\frac{4}{5} \cdot \frac{3}{2} = -\frac{2 \cdot 2 \cdot 3}{5 \cdot 2} = -\frac{6}{5}$$

To write a percent as a fraction, remove the percent sign and multiply by $\frac{1}{100}$. [1.7C, p. 50]

$$60\% = 60\left(\frac{1}{100}\right) = \frac{60}{100} = \frac{3}{5}$$

To write a percent as a decimal, remove the percent sign and multiply by 0.01. [1.7C, p. 50]

$73\% = 73(0.01) = 0.73$

$1.3\% = 1.3(0.01) = 0.013$

To write a decimal or a fraction as a percent, multiply by 100%. [1.7C, p. 50]

$0.3 = 0.3(100\%) = 30\%$

$\frac{5}{8} = \frac{5}{8}(100\%) = \frac{500}{8}\% = 62.5\%$

Diameter $= 2 \cdot$ radius **Radius** $= \frac{1}{2} \cdot$ diameter [1.8B, p. 59]

Find the diameter of a circle whose radius is 10 in.

Diameter $= 2 \cdot$ radius

$= 2(10 \text{ in.}) = 20$ in.

Perimeter is the distance around a plane figure. [1.8B, p. 59]

Triangle: Perimeter = side 1 + side 2 + side 3

Rectangle: Perimeter $= 2 \cdot$ length $+ 2 \cdot$ width

Square: Perimeter $= 4 \cdot$ side

Circle: Circumference $= 2 \cdot \pi \cdot$ radius

Find the perimeter of a rectangle whose width is 12 m and whose length is 15 m.

Perimeter $= 2 \cdot 15 \text{ m} + 2 \cdot 12 \text{ m} = 54$ m

Find the circumference of a circle whose radius is 3 in. Use 3.14 for π.

Circumference $= 2 \cdot \pi \cdot 3 \text{ in.} \approx 18.84$ in.

Area is a measure of the amount of surface in a region. [1.8C, pp. 60–61]

Triangle: Area $= \frac{1}{2} \cdot$ base $\cdot$ height

Rectangle: Area = length $\cdot$ width

Square: Area = side $\cdot$ side

Parallelogram: Area = base $\cdot$ height

Circle: Area $= \pi(\text{radius})^2$

Find the area of a triangle whose base is 13 m and whose height is 11 m.

Area $= \frac{1}{2} \cdot 13 \text{ m} \cdot 11 \text{ m} = 71.5 \text{ m}^2$

Find the area of a circle whose radius is 9 cm.

Area $= \pi \cdot (9 \text{ cm})^2 \approx 254.34 \text{ cm}^2$

CHAPTER

1 Review Exercises

1. Add: $-13 + 7$

2. Write $\frac{7}{25}$ as a decimal.

3. Evaluate -5^2.

4. Evaluate $5 - 2^2 + 9$.

5. Find $m\angle AOB$ for the figure at the right.

6. Write 6.2% as a decimal.

7. Multiply: $(-6)(7)$

8. Simplify: $\frac{1}{3} - \frac{1}{6} + \frac{5}{12}$

9. Find the complement of a 56° angle.

10. Given $A = \{-4, 0, 11\}$, which elements of set A are less than -1?

11. Find all of the factors of 56.

12. Subtract: $5.17 - 6.238$

13. Write $\frac{5}{8}$ as a percent.

14. Write $\frac{2}{15}$ as a decimal. Place a bar over the repeating digits of the decimal.

15. Subtract: $9 - 13$

16. What is $\frac{2}{5}$ less than $\frac{4}{15}$?

17. Find the additive inverse of -4.

18. Find the area of a triangle whose base is 4 cm and whose height is 9 cm.

19. Divide: $-100 \div 5$

20. Write $79\frac{1}{2}\%$ as a fraction.

21. Find the prime factorization of 280.

22. Evaluate $-3^2 + 4[18 + (12 - 20)]$.

23. Add: $-3 + (-12) + 6 + (-4)$

24. Find the sum of $\frac{4}{5}$ and $-\frac{3}{8}$.

25. Write $\frac{19}{35}$ as a percent. Write the remainder in fractional form.

26. Find the area of a circle whose diameter is 6 m. Use 3.14 for π.

27. Multiply: $4.32(-1.07)$

28. Evaluate $-|-5|$.

29. Subtract: $16 - (-3) - 18$

30. Divide: $-\dfrac{18}{35} \div \dfrac{27}{28}$

31. Find the supplement of a 28° angle.

32. Find the perimeter of a rectangle whose length is 12 in. and whose width is 10 in.

33. Place the correct symbol, > or <, between the two numbers.
$-|6| \quad |-10|$

34. Evaluate $\dfrac{5^2 + 11}{2^2 + 5} \div (2^3 - 2^2)$.

35. Education To discourage random guessing on a multiple-choice exam, a professor assigns 6 points for a correct answer, -4 points for an incorrect answer, and -2 points for leaving a question blank. What is the score for a student who had 21 correct answers, had 5 incorrect answers, and left 4 questions blank?

36. Currency The graph at the right shows the responses of 2136 adults to the question "Would you favor or oppose abolishing the penny so that the nickel would be the lowest denomination of coin?" (*Source:* Harris Interactive) What percent of those surveyed opposed abolishing the penny? Round to the nearest tenth of a percent.

Should the penny be abolished?

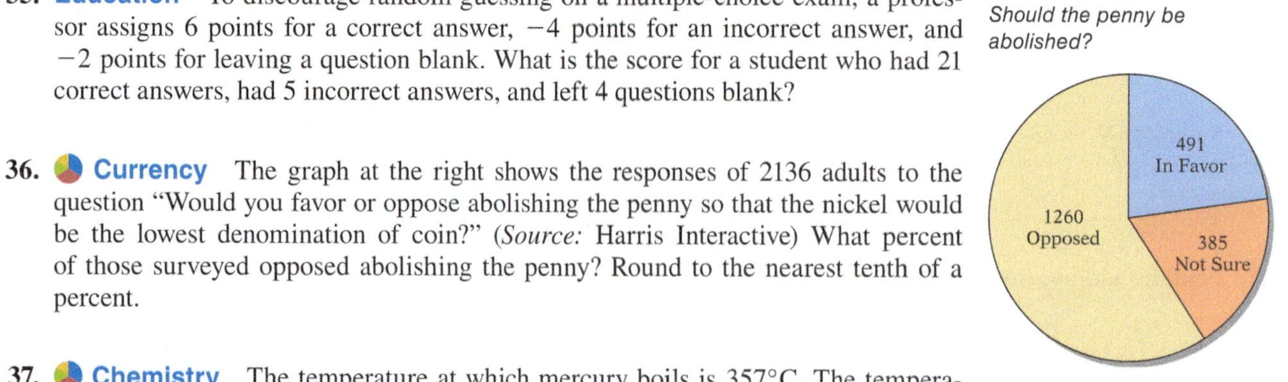

Source: Harris Interactive

37. Chemistry The temperature at which mercury boils is 357°C. The temperature at which mercury freezes is -39°C. Find the difference between the boiling point and the freezing point of mercury.

38. Landscaping A landscape company is proposing to replace a rectangular flower bed that measures 8 ft by 12 ft with sod that costs $3.51 per square foot. Find the cost to replace the flower bed with the sod.

CHAPTER 1 TEST

1. Divide: $-561 \div (-33)$

2. Write $\frac{5}{6}$ as a percent. Write the remainder in fractional form.

3. Find the complement of a $28°$ angle.

4. Multiply: $6.02(-0.89)$

5. Subtract: $16 - 30$

6. Write $37\frac{1}{2}\%$ as a fraction.

7. Subtract: $-\frac{5}{6} - \left(-\frac{7}{8}\right)$

8. Evaluate $\frac{-10 + 2}{2 + (-4)} \div 2 + 6$.

9. Multiply: $-5(-6)(3)$

10. Find the circumference of a circle whose diameter is 27 in. Use 3.14 for π.

11. Evaluate $(-3^3) \cdot 2^2$.

12. Find the area of a parallelogram whose base is 10 cm and whose height is 9 cm.

13. Place the correct symbol, < or >, between the two numbers.
$-2 \quad -40$

14. What is $\frac{2}{5}$ more than $-\frac{3}{4}$?

15. Evaluate $-|-4|$.

16. Write 45% as a fraction and as a decimal.

17. Add: $-22 + 14 + (-8)$

18. Multiply: $-4 \cdot 12$

19. Find the prime factorization of 990.

20. Evaluate $16 \div 2[8 - 3(4 - 2)] + 1$.

21. Subtract: $16 - (-30) - 42$

22. Divide: $\frac{5}{12} \div \left(-\frac{5}{6}\right)$

23. Find $m\angle x$ for the figure at the right.

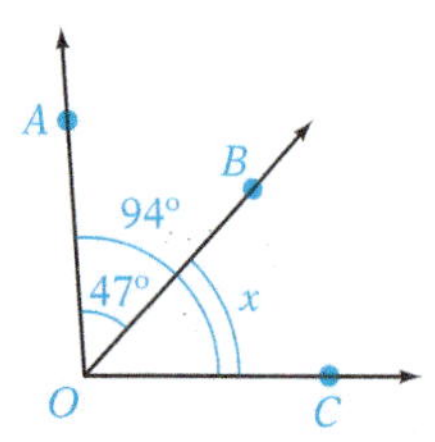

24. Evaluate $3^2 - 4 + 20 \div 5$.

25. Write $\frac{7}{9}$ as a decimal. Place a bar over the repeating digit of the decimal.

26. **Net Income** The table below shows the net income for the first quarter of 2011 for three companies. Losses are shown as negative numbers. One-quarter year is 3 months.

a. If the net income for these companies continued at the same level throughout 2011, what would be the 2011 annual net income for Sears Holdings?

b. For the quarter shown, what was the average monthly profit or loss for Rite Aid? Round to the nearest million dollars.

Company	*Net Income 1st Quarter of 2011*
Rite Aid	−74,000,000
Sears Holdings	−170,000,000
Target	689,000,000

27. **Recreation** The recreation department for a city is enclosing a rectangular playground that measures 150 ft by 200 ft with new fencing that costs \$8.52 per foot. Find the cost of the new fencing.

riganmc/Shutterstock.com

Variable Expressions

2

OBJECTIVES

SECTION 2.1

A To evaluate a variable expression

SECTION 2.2

A To simplify a variable expression using the Properties of Addition

B To simplify a variable expression using the Properties of Multiplication

C To simplify a variable expression using the Distributive Property

D To simplify general variable expressions

SECTION 2.3

A To translate a verbal expression into a variable expression, given the variable

B To translate a verbal expression into a variable expression and then simplify

C To translate application problems

Focus on Success

Have you formed or are you part of a study group? Remember that a study group can be a great way to stay focused on succeeding in this course. You can support each other, get help and offer help on homework, and prepare for tests together. (See Homework Time, page AIM-5.)

Carlos E. Santa Maria/Shutterstock.com

Prep Test

Are you ready to succeed in this chapter? Take the Prep Test below to find out if you are ready to learn the new material.

1. Subtract: $-12 - (-15)$

2. Divide: $-36 \div (-9)$

3. Add: $-\frac{3}{4} + \frac{5}{6}$

4. What is the reciprocal of $-\frac{9}{4}$?

5. Divide: $-\frac{3}{4} \div \left(-\frac{5}{2}\right)$

6. Evaluate: -2^4

7. Evaluate: $\left(\frac{2}{3}\right)^3$

8. Evaluate: $3 \cdot 4^2$

9. Evaluate: $7 - 2 \cdot 3$

10. Evaluate: $5 - 7(3 - 2^2)$

SECTION

2.1 Evaluating Variable Expressions

OBJECTIVE A *To evaluate a variable expression*

Tips for Success

Before you begin a new chapter, you should take some time to review previously learned skills. One way to do this is to complete the Prep Test. See page 75. This test focuses on the particular skills that will be required for the new chapter.

Point of Interest

Historical manuscripts indicate that mathematics is at least 4000 years old. Yet it was only 400 years ago that mathematicians started using variables to stand for numbers. The idea that a letter can stand for some number was a critical turning point in mathematics.

Today, *x* is used by most nations as the standard letter for a single unknown. In fact, x-rays were so named because the scientists who discovered them did not know what they were and thus labeled them the "unknown rays" or x-rays.

Often we discuss a quantity without knowing its exact value—for example, the price of gold next month, the cost of a new automobile next year, or the tuition cost for next semester. Recall that a letter of the alphabet, called a **variable,** is used to stand for a quantity that is unknown or that can change, or *vary.* An expression that contains one or more variables is called a **variable expression.**

A variable expression is shown at the right. The expression can be rewritten by writing subtraction as the addition of the opposite.

$$3x^2 - 5y + 2xy - x - 7$$
$$3x^2 + (-5y) + 2xy + (-x) + (-7)$$

Note that the expression has five addends. The **terms** of a variable expression are the addends of the expression. The expression has five terms.

Five terms

$$3x^2 \quad -5y \quad +2xy \quad -x \quad -7$$

Variable terms — Constant term

The terms $3x^2$, $-5y$, $2xy$, and $-x$ are **variable terms.**

The term -7 is a **constant term,** or simply a **constant.**

Each variable term is composed of a **numerical coefficient** and a **variable part** (the variable or variables and their exponents).

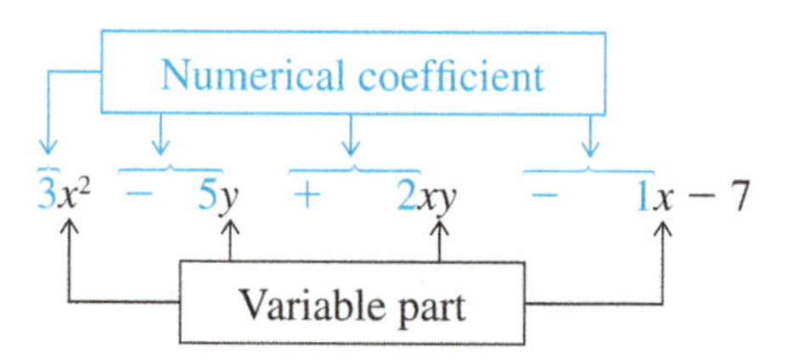

When the numerical coefficient is 1 or -1, the 1 is usually not written ($x = 1x$ and $-x = -1x$).

Variable expressions can be used to model scientific phenomena. In a physics lab, a student may discover that a weight of 1 pound will stretch a spring $\frac{1}{2}$ inch. Two pounds will stretch the spring 1 inch. By experimenting, the student can discover that the distance the spring will stretch is found by multiplying the weight by $\frac{1}{2}$. By letting W represent the weight attached to the spring, the student can represent the distance the spring stretches by the variable expression $\frac{1}{2}W$.

With a weight of W pounds attached, the spring will stretch $\frac{1}{2} \cdot W = \frac{1}{2}W$ inches.

With a weight of 10 pounds attached, the spring will stretch $\frac{1}{2} \cdot 10 = 5$ inches. The number 10 is called the **value of the variable** W.

With a weight of 3 pounds attached, the spring will stretch $\frac{1}{2} \cdot 3 = 1\frac{1}{2}$ inches.

Integrating Technology

See the Keystroke Guide: *Evaluating Variable Expressions* for instructions on using a graphing calculator to evaluate variable expressions.

Replacing each variable by its value and then simplifying the resulting numerical expression is called **evaluating a variable expression.**

HOW TO 1 Evaluate $ab - b^2$ when $a = 2$ and $b = -3$.

Replace each variable in the expression by its value. Then use the Order of Operations Agreement to simplify the resulting numerical expression.

$ab - b^2$

$2(-3) - (-3)^2 = -6 - 9 = -15$

EXAMPLE 1

Name the variable terms of the expression $2a^2 - 5a + 7$.

Solution

$2a^2$ and $-5a$

YOU TRY IT 1

Name the constant term of the expression $6n^2 + 3n - 4$.

Your solution

EXAMPLE 2

Evaluate $x^2 - 3xy$ when $x = 3$ and $y = -4$.

Solution

$x^2 - 3xy$

$3^2 - 3(3)(-4) = 9 - 3(3)(-4)$ • $x = 3, y = -4$

$= 9 - 9(-4)$

$= 9 - (-36)$

$= 9 + 36 = 45$

YOU TRY IT 2

Evaluate $2xy + y^2$ when $x = -4$ and $y = 2$.

Your solution

EXAMPLE 3

Evaluate $\frac{a^2 - b^2}{a - b}$ when $a = 3$ and $b = -4$.

Solution

$\frac{a^2 - b^2}{a - b}$

$\frac{3^2 - (-4)^2}{3 - (-4)} = \frac{9 - 16}{3 - (-4)}$ • $a = 3, b = -4$

$= \frac{-7}{7} = -1$

YOU TRY IT 3

Evaluate $\frac{a^2 + b^2}{a + b}$ when $a = 5$ and $b = -3$.

Your solution

EXAMPLE 4

Evaluate $x^2 - 3(x - y) - z^2$ when $x = 2$, $y = -1$, and $z = 3$.

Solution

$x^2 - 3(x - y) - z^2$

$2^2 - 3[2 - (-1)] - 3^2$ • $x = 2, y = -1, z = 3$

$= 2^2 - 3(3) - 3^2$

$= 4 - 3(3) - 9$

$= 4 - 9 - 9$

$= -5 - 9 = -14$

YOU TRY IT 4

Evaluate $x^3 - 2(x + y) + z^2$ when $x = 2$, $y = -4$, and $z = -3$.

Your solution

Solutions on p. S4

2.1 EXERCISES

Concept Check

For Exercises 1 to 3, name the terms of the variable expression. Then underline the constant term.

1. $2x^2 + 5x - 8$

2. $-3n^2 - 4n + 7$

3. $6 - a^4$

For Exercises 4 to 6, name the variable terms of the expression. Then underline the variable part of each term.

4. $9b^2 - 4ab + a^2$

5. $7x^2y + 6xy^2 + 10$

6. $5 - 8n - 3n^2$

For Exercises 7 to 9, name the coefficients of the variable terms.

7. $x^2 - 9x + 2$

8. $12a^2 - 8ab - b^2$

9. $n^3 - 4n^2 - n + 9$

10. What is the numerical coefficient of a variable term?

11. Explain the meaning of the phrase "evaluate a variable expression."

OBJECTIVE A *To evaluate a variable expression*

For Exercises 12 to 32, evaluate the variable expression when $a = 2$, $b = 3$, and $c = -4$.

12. $3a + 2b$

13. $a - 2c$

14. $-a^2$

15. $2c^2$

16. $-3a + 4b$

17. $3b - 3c$

18. $b^2 - 3$

19. $-3c + 4$

20. $16 \div (2c)$

21. $6b \div (-a)$

22. $bc \div (2a)$

23. $b^2 - 4ac$

24. $a^2 - b^2$

25. $b^2 - c^2$

26. $(a + b)^2$

27. $a^2 + b^2$

28. $2a - (c + a)^2$

29. $(b - a)^2 + 4c$

30. $b^2 - \dfrac{ac}{8}$

31. $\dfrac{5ab}{6} - 3cb$

32. $(b - 2a)^2 + bc$

For Exercises 33 to 50, evaluate the variable expression when $a = -2$, $b = 4$, $c = -1$, and $d = 3$.

33. $\dfrac{b + c}{d}$

34. $\dfrac{d - b}{c}$

35. $\dfrac{2d + b}{-a}$

36. $\dfrac{b + 2d}{b}$

37. $\dfrac{b - d}{c - a}$

38. $\dfrac{2c - d}{-ad}$

39. $(b + d)^2 - 4a$

40. $(d - a)^2 - 3c$

41. $(d - a)^2 \div 5$

42. $3(b - a) - bc$

43. $\dfrac{b - 2a}{bc^2 - d}$

44. $\dfrac{b^2 - a}{ad + 3c}$

45. $\dfrac{1}{3}d^2 - \dfrac{3}{8}b^2$

46. $\dfrac{5}{8}a^4 - c^2$

47. $\dfrac{-4bc}{2a - b}$

48. $-\dfrac{3}{4}b + \dfrac{1}{2}(ac + bd)$

49. $-\dfrac{2}{3}d - \dfrac{1}{5}(bd - ac)$

50. $(b - a)^2 - (d - c)^2$

For Exercises 51 to 54, without evaluating the expression, determine whether the expression is positive or negative when $a = -25$, $b = 67$, and $c = -82$.

51. $(c - a)(-b)$

52. $(a - c) + 3b$

53. $\dfrac{b + c}{abc}$

54. $\dfrac{ac}{-b^2}$

Critical Thinking

55. The value of a is the value of $3x^2 - 4x - 5$ when $x = -2$. Find the value of $3a - 4$.

56. The value of c is the value of $a^2 + b^2$ when $a = 2$ and $b = -2$. Find the value of $c^2 - 4$.

For Exercises 57 to 60, evaluate the expression for $x = 2$, $y = 3$, and $z = -2$.

57. $3^x - x^3$

58. z^x

59. $x^x - y^y$

60. $y^{(x^2)}$

Projects or Group Activities

61. For each of the following, determine the first natural number x, greater than 2, for which the second expression is larger than the first. On the basis of your answers, make a conjecture that appears to be true about the expressions x^n and n^x, where $n = 3, 4, 5, 6, 7, \ldots$ and x is a natural number greater than 2.

a. $x^3, 3^x$

b. $x^4, 4^x$

c. $x^5, 5^x$

d. $x^6, 6^x$

SECTION

2.2 Simplifying Variable Expressions

OBJECTIVE A To simplify a variable expression using the Properties of Addition

Like terms of a variable expression are terms with the same variable part. (Because $x^2 = x \cdot x$, x^2 and x are not like terms.)

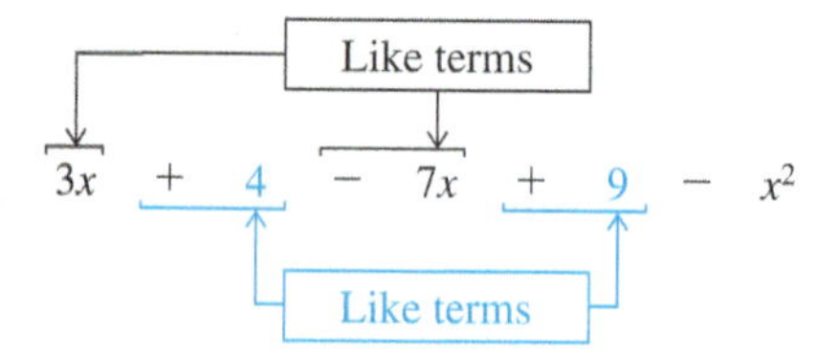

Constant terms are like terms. 4 and 9 are like terms.

To simplify a variable expression, we use the Distributive Property to add the numerical coefficients of like variable terms. The variable part remains unchanged. This is called **combining like terms.**

Take Note

Here is an example of the Distributive Property using just numbers.

$2(5 + 9) = 2(5) + 2(9)$
$= 10 + 18 = 28$

This is the same result we would obtain using the Order of Operations Agreement.

$2(5 + 9) = 2(14) = 28$

The usefulness of the Distributive Property will become more apparent as we explore variable expressions.

The Distributive Property

If a, b, and c are real numbers, then $a(b + c) = ab + ac$ or $(b + c)a = ba + ca$.

By the Distributive Property, the term outside the parentheses is multiplied by each term inside the parentheses.

EXAMPLES

1. $2(3 + 4) = 2 \cdot 3 + 2 \cdot 4$
   $2(7) = 6 + 8$
   $14 = 14$

2. $(4 + 5)2 = 4 \cdot 2 + 5 \cdot 2$
   $(9)2 = 8 + 10$
   $18 = 18$

The Distributive Property in the form $(b + c)a = ba + ca$ is used to simplify a variable expression.

To simplify $2x + 3x$, use the Distributive Property to add the numerical coefficients of the like variable terms.

$$2x + 3x = (2 + 3)x$$
$$= 5x$$

HOW TO 1 Simplify: $5y - 11y$

$$5y - 11y = (5 - 11)y \quad \text{• Use the Distributive Property.}$$
$$= -6y$$

Take Note

Simplifying an expression means combining like terms. The constant term 5 and the variable term $7p$ are not like terms and therefore cannot be combined.

HOW TO 2 Simplify: $5 + 7p$

The terms 5 and $7p$ are not like terms.

The expression $5 + 7p$ is in simplest form.

The following Properties of Addition are used to simplify variable expressions.

The Associative Property of Addition

If a, b, and c are real numbers, then $(a + b) + c = a + (b + c)$.

When three or more terms are added, the terms can be grouped (with parentheses, for example) in any order; the sum is the same.

EXAMPLES

1. $(5 + 7) + 15 = 5 + (7 + 15)$
   $12 + 15 = 5 + 22$
   $27 = 27$

2. $(3x + 5x) + 9x = 3x + (5x + 9x)$
   $8x + 9x = 3x + 14x$
   $17x = 17x$

The Commutative Property of Addition

If a and b are real numbers, then $a + b = b + a$.

When two terms are added, the terms can be added in either order; the sum is the same.

EXAMPLES

1. $15 + (-28) = (-28) + 15$
   $-13 = -13$

2. $2x + (-4x) = -4x + 2x$
   $-2x = -2x$

The Addition Property of Zero

If a is a real number, then $a + 0 = a$ and $0 + a = a$.

The sum of a term and zero is the term.

EXAMPLES

1. $-9 + 0 = -9$ and $0 + (-9) = -9$
2. $0 + 5x = 5x$ and $5x + 0 = 5x$

The Inverse Property of Addition

If a is a real number, then $a + (-a) = 0$ and $(-a) + a = 0$.

The sum of a term and its additive inverse (or opposite) is zero.

EXAMPLES

1. $8 + (-8) = 0$ and $-8 + 8 = 0$
2. $-7x + 7x = 0$ and $7x + (-7x) = 0$

HOW TO 3 Simplify: $8x + 4y - 8x + y$

$8x + 4y - 8x + y$

$= (8x - 8x) + (4y + y)$ • Use the Commutative and Associative Properties of Addition to rearrange and group like terms.

$= 0 + 5y = 5y$ • Combine like terms.

HOW TO 4 Simplify: $4x^2 + 5x - 6x^2 - 2x + 1$

$4x^2 + 5x - 6x^2 - 2x + 1$
$= (4x^2 - 6x^2) + (5x - 2x) + 1$
$= -2x^2 + 3x + 1$

- Use the Commutative and Associative Properties of Addition to rearrange and group like terms.
- Combine like terms.

EXAMPLE 1

Simplify: $3x + 4y - 10x + 7y$

Solution

$3x + 4y - 10x + 7y = (3x - 10x) + (4y + 7y)$
$= -7x + 11y$

YOU TRY IT 1

Simplify: $3a - 2b - 5a + 6b$

Your solution

EXAMPLE 2

Simplify: $x^2 - 7 + 4x^2 - 16$

Solution

$x^2 - 7 + 4x^2 - 16 = (x^2 + 4x^2) + (-7 - 16)$
$= 5x^2 - 23$

YOU TRY IT 2

Simplify: $-3y^2 + 7 + 8y^2 - 14$

Your solution

Solutions on p. S4

OBJECTIVE B *To simplify a variable expression using the Properties of Multiplication*

In simplifying variable expressions, the following Properties of Multiplication are used.

The Associative Property of Multiplication

If a, b, and c are real numbers, then $(ab)c = a(bc)$.

When three or more factors are multiplied, the factors can be grouped in any order; the product is the same.

EXAMPLES

1. $3(5 \cdot 6) = (3 \cdot 5)6$
   $3(30) = (15)6$
   $90 = 90$

2. $2(3x) = (2 \cdot 3)x$
   $= 6x$

Take Note
The Associative Property of Multiplication allows us to multiply a coefficient by a number. Without this property, the expression $2(3x)$ could not be simplified.

The Commutative Property of Multiplication

If a and b are real numbers, then $ab = ba$.

Two factors can be multiplied in either order; the product is the same.

EXAMPLES

1. $5(-7) = -7(5)$
   $-35 = -35$

2. $(5x) \cdot 3 = 3 \cdot (5x)$ • Commutative Property of Multiplication
   $= (3 \cdot 5)x$ • Associative Property of Multiplication
   $= 15x$

Take Note
The Commutative Property of Multiplication allows us to rearrange factors. This property, along with the Associative Property of Multiplication, enables us to simplify some variable expressions.

The Multiplication Property of One

If a is a real number, then $a \cdot 1 = a$ and $1 \cdot a = a$.

The product of a term and 1 is the term.

EXAMPLES

1. $9 \cdot 1 = 9$
2. $(8x) \cdot 1 = 8x$

The Inverse Property of Multiplication

If a is a real number and a is not equal to zero, then $a \cdot \frac{1}{a} = 1$ and $\frac{1}{a} \cdot a = 1$.

$\frac{1}{a}$ is called the **reciprocal** of a. $\frac{1}{a}$ is also called the **multiplicative inverse** of a.

The product of a number and its reciprocal is 1.

EXAMPLES

1. $7 \cdot \frac{1}{7} = 1$ and $\frac{1}{7} \cdot 7 = 1$
2. $x \cdot \frac{1}{x} = 1$ and $\frac{1}{x} \cdot x = 1, \quad x \neq 0$

Take Note

We must state that $x \neq 0$ because division by zero is undefined.

The multiplication properties are used to simplify variable expressions.

HOW TO 5 Simplify: $2(-x)$

$$2(-x) = 2(-1 \cdot x)$$
$$= [2(-1)]x$$
$$= -2x$$

- Use the Associative Property of Multiplication to group factors.

HOW TO 6 Simplify: $\frac{3}{2}\left(\frac{2x}{3}\right)$

$$\frac{3}{2}\left(\frac{2x}{3}\right) = \frac{3}{2}\left(\frac{2}{3}x\right)$$
$$= \left(\frac{3}{2} \cdot \frac{2}{3}\right)x$$
$$= 1 \cdot x$$
$$= x$$

- Note that $\frac{2x}{3} = \frac{2}{3}x$.
- Use the Associative Property of Multiplication to group factors.

HOW TO 7 Simplify: $(16x)2$

$$(16x)2 = 2(16x)$$
$$= (2 \cdot 16)x$$
$$= 32x$$

- Use the Commutative and Associative Properties of Multiplication to rearrange and group factors.

EXAMPLE 3

Simplify: $-2(3x^2)$

Solution

$$-2(3x^2) = (-2 \cdot 3)x^2 = -6x^2$$

YOU TRY IT 3

Simplify: $-5(4y^2)$

Your solution

EXAMPLE 4

Simplify: $-5(-10x)$

Solution

$$-5(-10x) = [(-5)(-10)]x = 50x$$

YOU TRY IT 4

Simplify: $-7(-2a)$

Your solution

EXAMPLE 5

Simplify: $-\frac{3}{4}\left(\frac{2}{3}x\right)$

Solution

$$\left(-\frac{3}{4}\right)\left(\frac{2}{3}x\right) = \left(-\frac{3}{4} \cdot \frac{2}{3}\right)x = -\frac{1}{2}x$$

YOU TRY IT 5

Simplify: $-\frac{3}{5}\left(-\frac{7}{9}a\right)$

Your solution

Solutions on p. S4

OBJECTIVE C *To simplify a variable expression using the Distributive Property*

Recall that the Distributive Property states that if a, b, and c are real numbers, then

$$a(b + c) = ab + ac$$

The Distributive Property is used to remove parentheses from a variable expression.

HOW TO 8 Simplify: $3(2x + 7)$

$$3(2x + 7) = 3(2x) + 3(7) = 6x + 21$$

- Use the Distributive Property. Multiply each term inside the parentheses by 3.

HOW TO 9 Simplify: $-5(4x + 6)$

$$-5(4x + 6) = -5(4x) + (-5)(6) = -20x - 30$$

- Use the Distributive Property.

HOW TO 10 Simplify: $-(2x - 4)$

$$-(2x - 4) = -1(2x - 4) = -1(2x) - (-1)(4) = -2x + 4$$

- Use the Distributive Property.

From HOW TO 10, note that when a negative sign immediately precedes the parentheses, the sign of each term inside the parentheses is changed.

HOW TO 11 Simplify: $-\frac{1}{2}(8x - 12y)$

$$-\frac{1}{2}(8x - 12y) = -\frac{1}{2}(8x) - \left(-\frac{1}{2}\right)(12y)$$

• Use the Distributive Property.

$$= -4x + 6y$$

An extension of the Distributive Property is used when an expression contains more than two terms.

HOW TO 12 Simplify: $3(4x - 2y - z)$

$$3(4x - 2y - z) = 3(4x) - 3(2y) - 3(z)$$

• Use the Distributive Property.

$$= 12x - 6y - 3z$$

EXAMPLE 6

Simplify: $7(4 + 2x)$

Solution

Use the Distributive Property.

$7(4 + 2x) = 28 + 14x$

YOU TRY IT 6

Simplify: $5(3 + 7b)$

Your solution

EXAMPLE 7

Simplify: $(2x - 6)2$

Solution

Use the Distributive Property.

$(2x - 6)2 = 4x - 12$

YOU TRY IT 7

Simplify: $(3a - 1)5$

Your solution

EXAMPLE 8

Simplify: $-3(-5a + 7b)$

Solution

Use the Distributive Property.

$-3(-5a + 7b) = 15a - 21b$

YOU TRY IT 8

Simplify: $-8(-2a + 7b)$

Your solution

EXAMPLE 9

Simplify: $3(x^2 - x - 5)$

Solution

Use the Distributive Property.

$3(x^2 - x - 5) = 3x^2 - 3x - 15$

YOU TRY IT 9

Simplify: $3(12x^2 - x + 8)$

Your solution

Solutions on p. S4

EXAMPLE 10

Simplify: $-2(x^2 + 5x - 4)$

Solution

Use the Distributive Property.

$-2(x^2 + 5x - 4)$

$= -2x^2 - 10x + 8$

YOU TRY IT 10

Simplify: $3(-a^2 - 6a + 7)$

Your solution

Solution on p. S4

OBJECTIVE D *To simplify general variable expressions*

When simplifying variable expressions, use the Distributive Property to remove parentheses and brackets used as grouping symbols.

HOW TO 13 Simplify: $4(x - y) - 2(-3x + 6y)$

$4(x - y) - 2(-3x + 6y)$

$= 4x - 4y + 6x - 12y$ • Use the Distributive Property.

$= 10x - 16y$ • Combine like terms.

EXAMPLE 11

Simplify: $2x - 3(2x - 7y)$

Solution

$2x - 3(2x - 7y)$

$= 2x - 6x + 21y$ • Use the Distributive Property.

$= -4x + 21y$ • Combine like terms.

YOU TRY IT 11

Simplify: $3y - 2(y - 7x)$

Your solution

EXAMPLE 12

Simplify: $7(x - 2y) - (-x - 2y)$

Solution

$7(x - 2y) - (-x - 2y)$

$= 7x - 14y + x + 2y$ • Use the Distributive Property.

$= 8x - 12y$ • Combine like terms.

YOU TRY IT 12

Simplify: $-2(x - 2y) - (-x + 3y)$

Your solution

EXAMPLE 13

Simplify: $2x - 3[2x - 3(x + 7)]$

Solution

$2x - 3[2x - 3(x + 7)]$

$= 2x - 3[2x - 3x - 21]$ • Use the Distributive Property.

$= 2x - 3[-x - 21]$ • Combine like terms.

$= 2x + 3x + 63$ • Use the Distributive Property.

$= 5x + 63$ • Combine like terms.

YOU TRY IT 13

Simplify: $3y - 2[x - 4(2 - 3y)]$

Your solution

Solutions on p. S4

2.2 EXERCISES

Concept Check

1. The fact that two terms can be added in either order is called the ____________ Property of Addition.
2. The fact that three or more factors can be multiplied by grouping them in any order is called the ____________ Property of Multiplication.
3. The Inverse Property of Multiplication tells us that the product of a number and its ____________ is 1.
4. The Inverse Property of Addition tells us that the sum of a number and its ____________ is 0.
5. What are *like terms*? Give an example of two like terms. Give an example of two terms that are not like terms.
6. Explain the meaning of the phrase "simplify a variable expression."

OBJECTIVE A *To simplify a variable expression using the Properties of Addition*

For Exercises 7 to 42, simplify.

7. $6x + 8x$
8. $12x + 13x$
9. $9a - 4a$
10. $12a - 3a$
11. $4y - 10y$
12. $8y - 6y$
13. $7 - 3b$
14. $5 + 2a$
15. $-12a + 17a$
16. $-3a + 12a$
17. $5ab - 7ab$
18. $9ab - 3ab$
19. $-12xy + 17xy$
20. $-15xy + 3xy$
21. $-3ab + 3ab$
22. $-7ab + 7ab$
23. $-\frac{1}{2}x - \frac{1}{3}x$
24. $-\frac{2}{5}y + \frac{3}{10}y$
25. $2.3x + 4.2x$
26. $6.1y - 9.2y$
27. $x - 0.55x$
28. $0.65A - A$
29. $5a - 3a + 5a$
30. $10a - 17a + 3a$
31. $-5x^2 - 12x^2 + 3x^2$
32. $-y^2 - 8y^2 + 7y^2$
33. $\frac{3}{4}x - \frac{1}{3}x - \frac{7}{8}x$

34. $-\frac{2}{5}a - \left(-\frac{3}{10}a\right) - \frac{11}{15}a$

35. $7x - 3y + 10x$

36. $8y + 8x - 8y$

37. $3a + (-7b) - 5a + b$

38. $-5b + 7a - 7b + 12a$

39. $3x + (-8y) - 10x + 4x$

40. $3y + (-12x) - 7y + 2y$

41. $x^2 - 7x + (-5x^2) + 5x$

42. $3x^2 + 5x - 10x^2 - 10x$

43. Which of the following expressions are equivalent to $-10x - 10y - 10y - 10x$?
(i) 0 **(ii)** $-20y$ **(iii)** $-20x$ **(iv)** $-20x - 20y$ **(v)** $-20y - 20x$

OBJECTIVE B *To simplify a variable expression using the Properties of Multiplication*

For Exercises 44 to 83, simplify.

44. $4(3x)$

45. $12(5x)$

46. $-3(7a)$

47. $-2(5a)$

48. $-2(-3y)$

49. $-5(-6y)$

50. $(4x)2$

51. $(6x)12$

52. $(3a)(-2)$

53. $(7a)(-4)$

54. $(-3b)(-4)$

55. $(-12b)(-9)$

56. $-5(3x^2)$

57. $-8(7x^2)$

58. $\frac{1}{3}(3x^2)$

59. $\frac{1}{6}(6x^2)$

60. $\frac{1}{5}(5a)$

61. $\frac{1}{8}(8x)$

62. $-\frac{1}{2}(-2x)$

63. $-\frac{1}{4}(-4a)$

64. $-\frac{1}{7}(-7n)$

65. $-\frac{1}{9}(-9b)$

66. $(3x)\left(\frac{1}{3}\right)$

67. $(12x)\left(\frac{1}{12}\right)$

68. $(-6y)\left(-\frac{1}{6}\right)$

69. $(-10n)\left(-\frac{1}{10}\right)$

70. $\frac{1}{3}(9x)$

71. $\frac{1}{7}(14x)$

72. $-0.2(10x)$

73. $-0.25(8x)$

74. $-\frac{2}{3}(12a^2)$ **75.** $-\frac{5}{8}(24a^2)$ **76.** $-0.5(-16y)$ **77.** $-0.75(-8y)$ **78.** $(16y)\left(\frac{1}{4}\right)$

79. $(33y)\left(\frac{1}{11}\right)$ **80.** $(-6x)\left(\frac{1}{3}\right)$ **81.** $(-10x)\left(\frac{1}{5}\right)$ **82.** $(-8a)\left(-\frac{3}{4}\right)$ **83.** $(21y)\left(-\frac{3}{7}\right)$

84. After multiplying $\frac{2}{7}x^2$ by a proper fraction, is the coefficient of x^2 greater than 1 or less than 1?

OBJECTIVE C *To simplify a variable expression using the Distributive Property*

For Exercises 85 to 123, simplify.

85. $2(4x - 3)$ **86.** $5(2x - 7)$ **87.** $-2(a + 7)$ **88.** $-5(a + 16)$

89. $-3(2y - 8)$ **90.** $-5(3y - 7)$ **91.** $-(x + 2)$ **92.** $-(x + 7)$

93. $(5 - 3b)7$ **94.** $(10 - 7b)2$ **95.** $\frac{1}{3}(6 - 15y)$ **96.** $\frac{1}{2}(-8x + 4y)$

97. $3(5x^2 + 2x)$ **98.** $6(3x^2 + 2x)$ **99.** $-2(-y + 9)$ **100.** $-5(-2x + 7)$

101. $(-3x - 6)5$ **102.** $(-2x + 7)7$ **103.** $2(-3x^2 - 14)$ **104.** $5(-6x^2 - 3)$

105. $-3(2y^2 - 7)$ **106.** $-8(3y^2 - 12)$ **107.** $3(x^2 - y^2)$ **108.** $5(x^2 + y^2)$

109. $-\frac{2}{3}(6x - 18y)$ **110.** $-\frac{1}{2}(x - 4y)$ **111.** $-(6a^2 - 7b^2)$

112. $3(x^2 + 2x - 6)$ **113.** $4(x^2 - 3x + 5)$ **114.** $-2(y^2 - 2y + 4)$

115. $\frac{3}{4}(2x - 6y + 8)$

116. $-\frac{2}{3}(6x - 9y + 1)$

117. $4(-3a^2 - 5a + 7)$

118. $-5(-2x^2 - 3x + 7)$

119. $-3(-4x^2 + 3x - 4)$

120. $3(2x^2 + xy - 3y^2)$

121. $5(2x^2 - 4xy - y^2)$

122. $-(3a^2 + 5a - 4)$

123. $-(8b^2 - 6b + 9)$

124. After the expression $17x - 31$ is multiplied by a negative integer, is the constant term positive or negative?

OBJECTIVE D *To simplify general variable expressions*

125. Which of the following expressions is equivalent to $12 - 7(y - 9)$?

(i) $5(y - 9)$ **(ii)** $12 - 7y - 63$ **(iii)** $12 - 7y + 63$ **(iv)** $12 - 7y - 9$

For Exercises 126 to 149, simplify.

126. $4x - 2(3x + 8)$

127. $6a - (5a + 7)$

128. $9 - 3(4y + 6)$

129. $10 - (11x - 3)$

130. $5n - (7 - 2n)$

131. $8 - (12 + 4y)$

132. $3(x + 2) - 5(x - 7)$

133. $2(x - 4) - 4(x + 2)$

134. $12(y - 2) + 3(7 - 3y)$

135. $6(2y - 7) - (3 - 2y)$

136. $3(a - b) - (a + b)$

137. $2(a + 2b) - (a - 3b)$

138. $4[x - 2(x - 3)]$

139. $2[x + 2(x + 7)]$

140. $-2[3x + 2(4 - x)]$

141. $-5[2x + 3(5 - x)]$

142. $-3[2x - (x + 7)]$

143. $-2[3x - (5x - 2)]$

144. $2x - 3[x - (4 - x)]$

145. $-7x + 3[x - (3 - 2x)]$

146. $-5x - 2[2x - 4(x + 7)] - 6$

147. $0.12(2x + 3) + x$

148. $0.05x + 0.02(4 - x)$

149. $0.03x + 0.04(1000 - x)$

Critical Thinking

150. Determine whether the statement is true or false. If the statement is false, give an example that illustrates that it is false.
a. Division is a commutative operation.
b. Division is an associative operation.
c. Subtraction is an associative operation.
d. Subtraction is a commutative operation.

bioraven/Shutterstock.com

151. Give examples of two operations that occur in everyday experience that are not commutative (for example, putting on socks and then shoes).

152. Which of the following expressions are equivalent?
(i) $2x + 4(2x + 1)$
(ii) $x - (4 - 9x) + 8$
(iii) $7(x - 4) - 3(2x + 6)$
(iv) $3(2x + 8) + 4(x - 5)$
(v) $6 - 2[x + (3x - 4)] + 2(9x - 5)$

Projects or Group Activities

153. Define an operation $\otimes$ as $a \otimes b = (a \cdot b) - (a + b)$.
For example, $7 \otimes 5 = (7 \cdot 5) - (7 + 5) = 35 - 12 = 23$.
a. Is $\otimes$ a commutative operation? Support your answer.
b. Is $\otimes$ an associative operation? Support your answer.

CHECK YOUR PROGRESS: CHAPTER 2

Evaluate the variable expression when $a = 3$, $b = -2$, and $c = 4$.

1. $-2a + 3b$ **2.** $c^2 - 5ab$ **3.** $2c - (a + b)^2$

Evaluate the variable expression when $x = 2$, $y = -3$, and $z = -1$.

4. $\frac{y + z}{x}$ **5.** $(y + x)^2 - 5z$ **6.** $\frac{-yz}{2x + z}$

Simplify.

7. $10y - 16y + 3y$ **8.** $-5a + 6b + 8a - 2b$ **9.** $(8a)(-5)$

10. $(-9z)\left(-\frac{1}{9}\right)$ **11.** $(12 - 8b)3$ **12.** $-2(-3x^2 + 4x - 5)$

13. $3x - 4(2x - 5)$ **14.** $6(3a - 7) - (4 + 9a)$ **15.** $5 - 3[2x - (6 - 4x)]$

SECTION

2.3 Translating Verbal Expressions into Variable Expressions

OBJECTIVE A To translate a verbal expression into a variable expression, given the variable

Tips for Success
Before the class meeting in which your professor begins a new section, you should read each objective statement for that section. Next, browse through the objective material. The purpose of browsing through the material is so that your brain will be prepared to accept and organize the new information when it is presented to you. See *AIM for Success* in the Preface.

One of the major skills required in applied mathematics is the ability to translate a verbal expression into a variable expression. This requires recognizing the verbal phrases that translate into mathematical operations. A partial list of the verbal phrases used to indicate the different mathematical operations is given on the next page.

HOW TO 1 Translate "14 less than the cube of x" into a variable expression.

14 less than the cube of x

- **Identify the words that indicate the mathematical operations.**

$x^3 - 14$

- **Use the identified operations to write the variable expression.**

Translating a phrase that contains the word *sum*, *difference*, *product*, or *quotient* can be challenging. In the examples at the right, note where the operation symbol is placed.

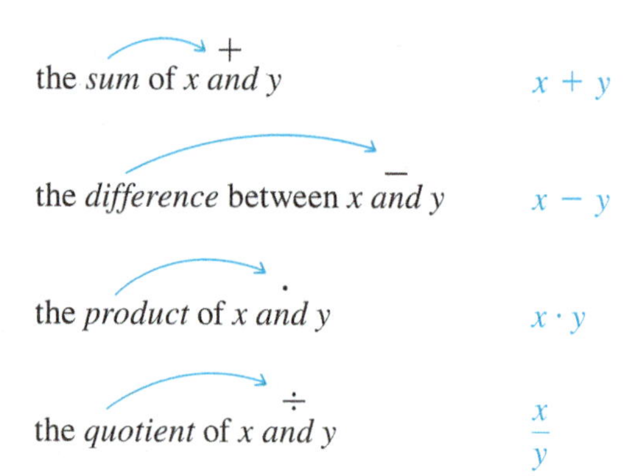

HOW TO 2 Translate "the difference between the square of x and the sum of y and z" into a variable expression.

the difference between the square of x and the sum of y and z

- **Identify the words that indicate the mathematical operations.**

$x^2 - (y + z)$

- **Use the identified operations to write the variable expression.**

EXAMPLE 1

Translate "the total of 3 times n and 5" into a variable expression.

Solution

the total of 3 times n and 5

$3n + 5$

YOU TRY IT 1

Translate "the difference between twice n and the square of n" into a variable expression.

Your solution

Solution on p. S4

Point of Interest

The way in which expressions are symbolized has changed over time. Here are how some of the expressions shown at the right may have appeared in the early 16th century.

R p. 9 for $x + 9$. The symbol R was used for a variable raised to the first power. The symbol p. was used for plus.

R m. 3 for $x - 3$. The symbol R was used for the variable. The symbol m. was used for minus.

The square of a variable was designated by Q, and the cube was designated by C. The expression $x^2 + x^3$ was written Q p. C.

Words or Phrases for Addition		
added to	6 added to y	$y + 6$
more than	8 more than x	$x + 8$
the sum of	the sum of x and z	$x + z$
increased by	t increased by 9	$t + 9$
the total of	the total of 5 and d	$5 + d$
plus	b plus 17	$b + 17$

Words or Phrases for Subtraction		
minus	x minus 2	$x - 2$
less than	7 less than t	$t - 7$
less	7 less t	$7 - t$
subtracted from	5 subtracted from d	$d - 5$
decreased by	m decreased by 3	$m - 3$
the difference between	the difference between y and 4	$y - 4$

Words or Phrases for Multiplication		
times	10 times t	$10t$
of	one-half of x	$\frac{1}{2}x$
the product of	the product of y and z	yz
multiplied by	b multiplied by 11	$11b$
twice	twice n	$2n$

Phrases for Division		
divided by	x divided by 12	$\frac{x}{12}$
the quotient of	the quotient of y and z	$\frac{y}{z}$
the ratio of	the ratio of t to 9	$\frac{t}{9}$

Phrases for Power		
the square of	the square of x	x^2
the cube of	the cube of a	a^3

EXAMPLE 2

Translate "m decreased by the sum of n and 12" into a variable expression.

Solution

m decreased by the sum of n and 12

$m - (n + 12)$

YOU TRY IT 2

Translate "the quotient of 7 less than b and 15" into a variable expression.

Your solution

Solution on p. S4

OBJECTIVE B *To translate a verbal expression into a variable expression and then simplify*

In most applications that involve translating phrases into variable expressions, the variable to be used is not given. To translate these phrases, a variable must be assigned to an unknown quantity before the variable expression can be written.

HOW TO 3 Translate "a number multiplied by the total of six and the cube of the number" into a variable expression.

the unknown number: n
- **Assign a variable to one of the unknown quantities.**

the cube of the number: n^3

the total of six and the cube of the number: $6 + n^3$
- **Use the assigned variable to write an expression for any other unknown quantity.**

$n(6 + n^3)$
- **Use the assigned variable to write the variable expression.**

EXAMPLE 3

Translate "four times the sum of one-half of a number and fourteen" into a variable expression. Then simplify.

Solution

the unknown number: n

one-half of the number: $\frac{1}{2}n$

the sum of one-half of the number and fourteen: $\frac{1}{2}n + 14$

$$4\left(\frac{1}{2}n + 14\right) = 2n + 56$$

YOU TRY IT 3

Translate "five times the difference between a number and sixty" into a variable expression. Then simplify.

Your solution

Solution on p. S4

EXAMPLE 4

Translate "a number added to the product of four and the square of the number" into a variable expression.

Solution

the unknown number: n
the square of the number: n^2
the product of four and the square of the number: $4n^2$

$4n^2 + n$

YOU TRY IT 4

Translate "negative four multiplied by the total of ten and the cube of a number" into a variable expression.

Your solution

Solution on p. S4

OBJECTIVE C *To translate application problems*

Many applications in mathematics require that you identify the unknown quantity, assign a variable to that quantity, and then attempt to express other unknown quantities in terms of the variable.

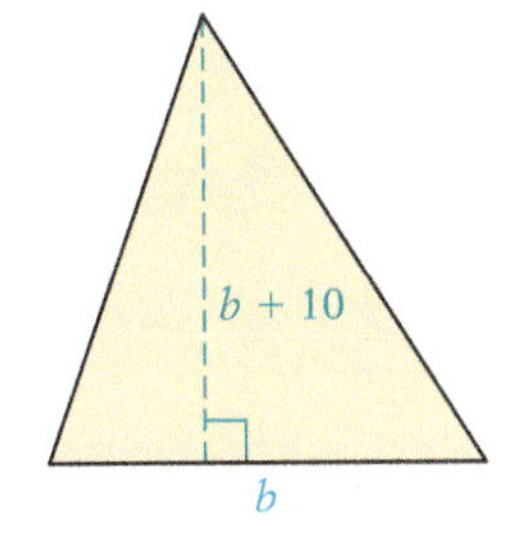

HOW TO 4 The height of a triangle is 10 ft longer than the base of the triangle. Express the height of the triangle in terms of the base of the triangle.

the base of the triangle: b • **Assign a variable to the base of the triangle.**

the height is 10 more than the base: $b + 10$ • **Express the height of the triangle in terms of b.**

EXAMPLE 5

The length of a swimming pool is 4 ft less than two times the width. Express the length of the pool in terms of the width.

Solution

the width of the pool: w
the length is 4 ft less than two times the width: $2w - 4$

YOU TRY IT 5

The speed of a new jet plane is twice the speed of an older model. Express the speed of the new model in terms of the speed of the older model.

Your solution

EXAMPLE 6

A banker divided \$5000 between two accounts, one paying 10% annual interest and the second paying 8% annual interest. Express the amount invested in the 10% account in terms of the amount invested in the 8% account.

Solution

the amount invested at 8%: x
the amount invested at 10%: $5000 - x$

YOU TRY IT 6

A guitar string 6 ft long was cut into two pieces. Express the length of the shorter piece in terms of the length of the longer piece.

Your solution

Solutions on p. S4

2.3 EXERCISES

Concept Check

For each phrase in Exercises 1 to 4, identify the words that indicate mathematical operations.

1. the sum of seven and three times m

2. twelve less than the quotient of x and negative two

3. the total of ten and fifteen divided by a number

4. twenty subtracted from the product of eight and the cube of a number

5. The sum of two numbers is 25. To express both numbers in terms of the same variable, let x represent one number. Then the other number is ______.

6. The length of a rectangle is five times the width. To express the length and the width in terms of the same variable, let W represent the width. Then the length is ______.

OBJECTIVE A *To translate a verbal expression into a variable expression, given the variable*

For Exercises 7 to 32, translate into a variable expression.

7. the sum of 8 and y

8. a less than 16

9. t increased by 10

10. p decreased by 7

11. 14 added to z

12. q multiplied by 13

13. 20 less than the square of x

14. 6 times the difference between m and 7

15. the sum of three-fourths of n and 12

16. b decreased by the product of 2 and b

17. 8 increased by the quotient of n and 4

18. the product of -8 and y

19. the product of 3 and the total of y and 7

20. 8 divided by the difference between x and 6

21. the product of t and the sum of t and 16

22. the quotient of 6 less than n and twice n

23. 15 more than one-half of the square of x

24. 19 less than the product of n and -2

25. the total of 5 times the cube of n and the square of n

26. the ratio of 9 more than m to m

27. r decreased by the quotient of r and 3

28. four-fifths of the sum of w and 10

29. the difference between the square of x and the total of x and 17

30. s increased by the quotient of 4 and s

31. the product of 9 and the total of z and 4

32. n increased by the difference between 10 times n and 9

33. Write two different verbal phrases that translate into the variable expression $5(n^2 + 1)$.

OBJECTIVE B *To translate a verbal expression into a variable expression and then simplify*

For Exercises 34 to 45, translate into a variable expression.

34. twelve minus a number

35. a number divided by eighteen

36. two-thirds of a number

37. twenty more than a number

38. the quotient of twice a number and nine

39. eight less than the product of eleven and a number

40. the sum of five-eighths of a number and six

41. the quotient of seven and the total of five and a number

42. the quotient of fifteen and the sum of a number and twelve

43. the difference between forty and the quotient of a number and twenty

44. the quotient of five more than twice a number and the number

45. the sum of the square of a number and twice the number

46. Which of the following phrases translate into the variable expression $32 - \frac{a}{7}$?

(i) the difference between thirty-two and the quotient of a number and seven
(ii) thirty-two decreased by the quotient of a number and seven
(iii) thirty-two minus the ratio of a number to seven

For Exercises 47 to 62, translate into a variable expression. Then simplify.

47. ten times the difference between a number and fifty

48. nine less than the total of a number and two

49. the difference between a number and three more than the number

50. four times the sum of a number and nineteen

51. a number added to the difference between twice the number and four

52. the product of five less than a number and seven

53. a number decreased by the difference between three times the number and eight

54. the sum of eight more than a number and one-third of the number

55. a number added to the product of three and the number

56. a number increased by the total of the number and nine

57. five more than the sum of a number and six

58. a number decreased by the difference between eight and the number

59. a number minus the sum of the number and ten

60. two more than the total of a number and five

61. the sum of one-sixth of a number and four-ninths of the number

62. the difference between one-third of a number and five-eighths of the number

OBJECTIVE C *To translate application problems*

For Exercises 63 and 64, use the following situation: 83 more students enrolled in spring-term science classes than enrolled in fall-term science classes.

63. If s and $s + 83$ represent the quantities in this situation, what is s?

64. If n and $n - 83$ represent the quantities in this situation, what is n?

65. **Museums** In a recent year, 3.8 million more people visited the Louvre in Paris than visited the Metropolitan Museum of Art in New York City. (*Sources:* The *Art Newspaper;* museums' accounts) Express the number of visitors to the Louvre in terms of the number of visitors to the Metropolitan Museum of Art.

Zoran Karapancev/Shutterstock.com

The Louvre

66. **Astronomy** The diameter of Saturn's moon Rhea is 253 mi more than the diameter of Saturn's moon Dione. Express the diameter of Rhea in terms of the diameter of Dione. (*Source:* NASA)

67. **Noise Level** The noise level of an ambulance siren is 10 decibels louder than that of a car horn. Express the noise level of an ambulance siren in terms of the noise level of a car horn. (*Source:* League for the Hard of Hearing)

In the NEWS!

U2 Concerts Top Annual Rankings in North America

The Irish rock band U2 performed the most popular concerts on the North American circuit this year. Bruce Springsteen and the E Street Band came in second, with $28.5 million less in ticket sales.

Source: new.music.yahoo.com

68. **Genetics** The human genome contains 11,000 more genes than the roundworm genome. Express the number of genes in the human genome in terms of the number of genes in the roundworm genome. (*Source:* Celera, USA TODAY research)

69. **Rock Band Tours** See the news clipping at the right. Express Bruce Springsteen and the E Street Band's concert ticket sales in terms of U2's concert ticket sales.

70. **Space Exploration** A survey in *USA Today* reported that almost three-fourths of Americans think that money should be spent on exploration of Mars. Express the number of Americans who think that money should be spent on exploration of Mars in terms of the total number of Americans.

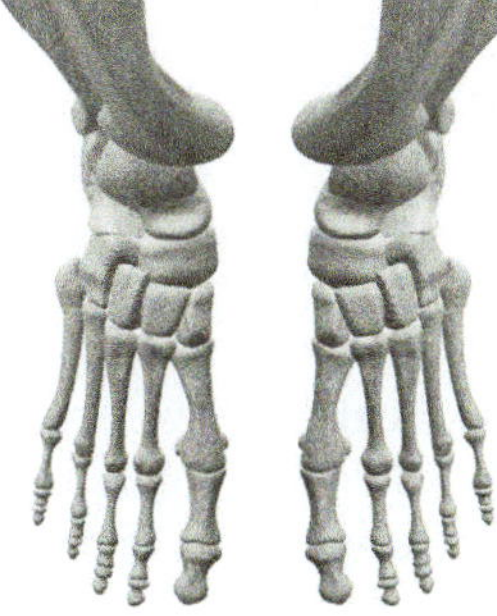
Aaliya Landholt/Shutterstock.com

71. **Biology** According to the American Podiatric Medical Association, the bones in your foot account for one-fourth of all the bones in your body. Express the number of bones in your foot in terms of the number of bones in your body.

72. **Football** In football, the number of points awarded for a touchdown is three times the number of points awarded for a safety. Express the number of points awarded for a touchdown in terms of the number of points awarded for a safety.

73. **Community Colleges** According to the National Center for Education Statistics, 46% of U.S. undergraduate students attend two-year colleges. Express the number of U.S. undergraduate students who attend two-year colleges in terms of the number of U.S. undergraduate students.

74. **Tax Refunds** A recent survey conducted by Turbotax.com asked, "If you receive a tax refund, what will you do?" Forty-three percent of respondents said they would pay down their debt. (*Source: USA Today,* March 27, 2008) Express the number of people who would pay down their debt in terms of the number of people surveyed.

Over 70 Million Attend Major League Baseball Games

Among major league sports, attendance at major league baseball games topped attendance at other major league sporting events. Fifty million more people went to baseball games than went to basketball games. The attendance at football games and hockey games was even less than the attendance at basketball games.

Source: Time, December 28, 2010–January 4, 2010

75. **Major League Sports** See the news clipping at the right. Express the attendance at major league baseball games in terms of the attendance at major league basketball games.

76. **Geometry** The length of a rectangle is 5 m more than twice the width. Express the length of the rectangle in terms of the width.

77. **Geometry** In a triangle, the measure of the smallest angle is 10 degrees less than one-half the measure of the largest angle. Express the measure of the smallest angle in terms of the measure of the largest angle.

78. **Wages** An employee is paid \$1172 per week plus \$38 for each hour of overtime worked. Express the employee's weekly pay in terms of the number of hours of overtime worked.

79. **Billing** An auto repair bill is \$238 for parts and \$89 for each hour of labor. Express the amount of the repair bill in terms of the number of hours of labor.

80. **Sports** A halyard 12 ft long is cut into two pieces. Use the same variable to express the lengths of the two pieces.

81. **Travel** Two cars are traveling in opposite directions at different rates. Two hours later, the cars are 200 mi apart. Express the distance traveled by the faster car in terms of the distance traveled by the slower car.

Critical Thinking

82. **Metalwork** A wire whose length is given as x inches is bent into a square. Express the length of a side of the square in terms of x.

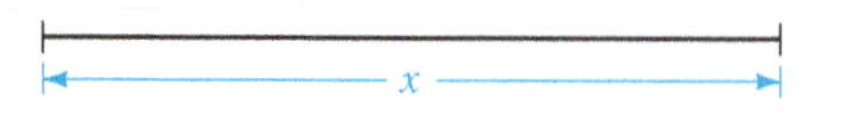

83. Chemistry The chemical formula for glucose (sugar) is $C_6H_{12}O_6$. This formula means that there are 12 hydrogen atoms for every 6 carbon atoms and every 6 oxygen atoms in each molecule of glucose (see the figure at the right). If x represents the number of oxygen atoms in a pound of sugar, express the number of hydrogen atoms in the pound of sugar in terms of the number of oxygen atoms.

H O
C
H − C − OH
HO − C − H
H − C − OH
H − C − OH
CH_2OH

84. Translate the expressions $5x + 8$ and $5(x + 8)$ into phrases.

85. Explain the similarities and differences between the expressions "the difference between x and 5" and "5 less than x."

Projects or Group Activities

86. Write five phrases that translate into the expression $p + 8$.

87. Write four phrases that translate into the expression $d - 16$.

88. Write three phrases that translate into the expression $4c$.

89. Write three phrases that translate into the expression $\frac{y}{5}$.

CHAPTER

2 Summary

Key Words	Examples
A **variable** is a letter that is used to represent a quantity that is unknown or that can change. A **variable expression** is an expression that contains one or more variables. [2.1A, p. 76]	$4x + 2y - 6z$ is a variable expression. It contains the variables x, y, and z.
The **terms** of a variable expression are the addends of the expression. Each term is a **variable term** or a **constant term.** [2.1A, p. 76]	The expression $2a^2 - 3b^3 + 7$ has three terms: $2a^2$, $-3b^3$, and 7. $2a^2$ and $-3b^3$ are variable terms. 7 is a constant term.
A variable term is composed of a **numerical coefficient** and a **variable part.** [2.1A, p. 76]	For the expression $-7x^3y^2$, -7 is the coefficient and x^3y^2 is the variable part.
In a variable expression, replacing each variable by its value and then simplifying the resulting numerical expression is called **evaluating the variable expression.** [2.1A, p. 77]	To evaluate $2ab - b^2$ when $a = 3$ and $b = -2$, replace a by 3 and b by -2. Then simplify the numerical expression. $2(3)(-2) - (-2)^2 = -16$
Like terms of a variable expression are terms with the same variable part. Constant terms are like terms. [2.2A, p. 80]	For the expressions $3a^2 + 2b - 3$ and $2a^2 - 3a + 4$, $3a^2$ and $2a^2$ are like terms; -3 and 4 are like terms.

To simplify the sum of like variable terms, use the Distributive Property to add the numerical coefficients. This is called **combining like terms.** [2.2A, p. 80]	$5y + 3y = (5 + 3)y$ $= 8y$
The **additive inverse** of a number is the opposite of the number. [2.2A, p. 81]	-4 is the additive inverse of 4. $\frac{2}{3}$ is the additive inverse of $-\frac{2}{3}$. 0 is the additive inverse of 0.
The **multiplicative inverse** of a number is the reciprocal of the number. [2.2B, p. 83]	$\frac{3}{4}$ is the multiplicative inverse of $\frac{4}{3}$. $-\frac{1}{4}$ is the multiplicative inverse of -4.

Essential Rules and Procedures / Examples

Essential Rules and Procedures	Examples
The Distributive Property [2.2A, p. 80] If a, b, and c are real numbers, then $a(b + c) = ab + ac$ or $(b + c)a = ba + ca$.	$5(4 + 7) = 5 \cdot 4 + 5 \cdot 7$ $= 20 + 35 = 55$
The Associative Property of Addition [2.2A, p. 81] If a, b, and c are real numbers, then $(a + b) + c = a + (b + c)$.	$-4 + (2 + 7) = -4 + 9 = 5$ $(-4 + 2) + 7 = -2 + 7 = 5$
The Commutative Property of Addition [2.2A, p. 81] If a and b are real numbers, then $a + b = b + a$.	$2 + 5 = 7$ and $5 + 2 = 7$
The Addition Property of Zero [2.2A, p. 81] If a is a real number, then $a + 0 = 0 + a = a$.	$-8 + 0 = -8$ and $0 + (-8) = -8$
The Inverse Property of Addition [2.2A, p. 81] If a is a real number, then $a + (-a) = (-a) + a = 0$.	$5 + (-5) = 0$ and $(-5) + 5 = 0$
The Associative Property of Multiplication [2.2B, p. 82] If a, b, and c are real numbers, then $(ab)c = a(bc)$.	$-3 \cdot (5 \cdot 4) = -3(20) = -60$ $(-3 \cdot 5) \cdot 4 = -15 \cdot 4 = -60$
The Commutative Property of Multiplication [2.2B, p. 82] If a and b are real numbers, then $ab = ba$.	$-3(7) = -21$ and $7(-3) = -21$
The Multiplication Property of One [2.2B, p. 83] If a is a real number, then $a \cdot 1 = 1 \cdot a = a$.	$-3(1) = -3$ and $1(-3) = -3$
The Inverse Property of Multiplication [2.2B, p. 83] If a is a real number and a is not equal to zero, then $a \cdot \frac{1}{a} = \frac{1}{a} \cdot a = 1$.	$-3 \cdot -\frac{1}{3} = 1$ and $-\frac{1}{3} \cdot -3 = 1$

CHAPTER

2 Review Exercises

1. Simplify: $3(x^2 - 8x - 7)$

2. Simplify: $7x + 4x$

3. Simplify: $6a - 4b + 2a$

4. Simplify: $(-50n)\left(\frac{1}{10}\right)$

5. Evaluate $(5c - 4a)^2 - b$ when $a = -1$, $b = 2$, and $c = 1$.

6. Simplify: $5(2x - 7)$

7. Simplify: $-6(7x^2)$

8. Simplify: $-9(7 + 4x)$

9. Simplify: $12y - 17y$

10. Evaluate $2bc \div (a + 7)$ when $a = 3$, $b = -5$, and $c = 4$.

11. Simplify: $7 - 2(3x + 4)$

12. Simplify: $6 + 2[2 - 5(4a - 3)]$

13. Simplify: $6(8y - 3) - 8(3y - 6)$

14. Simplify: $5c + (-2d) - 3d - (-4c)$

15. Simplify: $5(4x)$

16. Simplify: $-4(2x - 9) + 5(3x + 2)$

17. Simplify: $4x - 3x^2 + 2x - x^2$

18. Simplify: $5[2 - 3(6x - 1)]$

19. Simplify: $0.4x + 0.6(250 - x)$

20. Simplify: $\frac{2}{3}x - \frac{3}{4}x$

21. Simplify: $(7a^2 - 2a + 3)4$

22. Evaluate $a^2 - b^2$ when $a = 3$, $b = 4$.

23. Simplify: $-3(-12y)$

24. Translate "two-thirds of the total of x and 10" into a variable expression.

25. Translate "6 less than x" into a variable expression.

26. Translate "a number plus twice the number" into a variable expression. Then simplify.

27. Translate "the difference between twice a number and one-half of the number" into a variable expression. Then simplify.

28. Translate "three times a number plus the product of five and one less than the number" into a variable expression. Then simplify.

© Lana Sundman/Alamy

29. **Baseball Cards** A baseball card collection contains five times as many National League players' cards as American League players' cards. Express the number of National League players' cards in the collection in terms of the number of American League players' cards.

30. **Dollar Bills** A club treasurer has some five-dollar bills and some ten-dollar bills. The treasurer has a total of 35 bills. Express the number of five-dollar bills in terms of the number of ten-dollar bills.

31. **Calories** A candy bar contains eight more calories than twice the number of calories in an apple. Express the number of calories in the candy bar in terms of the number of calories in an apple.

Georgescu Gabriel/Shutterstock.com

32. **Architecture** The length of the Parthenon is approximately 1.6 times the width. Express the length of the Parthenon in terms of the width.

33. **Human Proportions** Leonardo DaVinci studied various proportions of human anatomy. One of his findings was that the standing height of a person is approximately 1.3 times the kneeling height of the same person. Represent the standing height of a person in terms of the person's kneeling height.

CHAPTER 2 TEST

1. Simplify: $3x - 5x + 7x$

2. Simplify: $-3(2x^2 - 7y^2)$

3. Simplify: $2x - 3(x - 2)$

4. Simplify: $2x + 3[4 - (3x - 7)]$

5. Simplify: $3x - 7y - 12x$

6. Evaluate $b^2 - 3ab$ when $a = 3$ and $b = -2$.

7. Simplify: $\frac{1}{5}(10x)$

8. Simplify: $5(2x + 4) - 3(x - 6)$

9. Simplify: $-5(2x^2 - 3x + 6)$

10. Simplify: $3x + (-12y) - 5x - (-7y)$

11. Evaluate $\frac{-2ab}{2b - a}$ when $a = -4$ and $b = 6$.

12. Simplify: $(12x)\left(\frac{1}{4}\right)$

13. Simplify: $-7y^2 + 6y^2 - (-2y^2)$

14. Simplify: $-2(2x - 4)$

15. Simplify: $\frac{2}{3}(-15a)$

16. Simplify: $-2[x - 2(x - y)] + 5y$

17. Simplify: $(-3)(-12y)$

18. Simplify: $5(3 - 7b)$

19. Translate "the difference between the squares of a and b" into a variable expression.

20. Translate "ten times the difference between a number and three" into a variable expression. Then simplify.

21. Translate "the sum of a number and twice the square of the number" into a variable expression.

22. Translate "three less than the quotient of six and a number" into a variable expression.

23. Translate "b decreased by the product of b and 7" into a variable expression.

24. **Astronomy** The distance from Neptune to the sun is 30 times the distance from Earth to the sun. Express the distance from Neptune to the sun in terms of the distance from Earth to the sun.

Stocktrek/Jupiterimages

25. **Metalwork** A wire is cut into two lengths. The length of the longer piece is 3 in. less than four times the length of the shorter piece. Express the length of the longer piece in terms of the length of the shorter piece.

Cumulative Review Exercises

1. Add: $-4 + 7 + (-10)$

2. Subtract: $-16 - (-25) - 4$

3. Multiply: $(-2)(3)(-4)$

4. Divide: $(-60) \div 12$

5. Find the complement of a 37° angle.

6. Simplify: $\frac{7}{12} - \frac{11}{16} - \left(-\frac{1}{3}\right)$

7. Simplify: $-\frac{5}{12} \div \frac{5}{2}$

8. Simplify: $\left(-\frac{9}{16}\right) \cdot \left(\frac{8}{27}\right) \cdot \left(-\frac{3}{2}\right)$

9. Write $\frac{3}{4}$ as a percent.

10. Simplify: $-2^5 \div (3 - 5)^2 - (-3)$

11. Simplify: $\left(-\frac{3}{4}\right)^2 \div \left(\frac{3}{8} - \frac{11}{12}\right)$

12. Evaluate $a^2 - 3b$ when $a = 2$ and $b = -4$.

13. Simplify: $-2x^2 - (-3x^2) + 4x^2$

14. Simplify: $5a - 10b - 12a$

15. Find the area of a circle whose radius is 7 cm. Use 3.14 for π.

16. Find the perimeter of a square whose side measures 24 ft.

17. Simplify: $3(8 - 2x)$

18. Simplify: $-2(-3y + 9)$

19. Write $37\frac{1}{2}\%$ as a fraction.

20. Write 1.05% as a decimal.

21. Simplify: $-4(2x^2 - 3y^2)$

22. Simplify: $-3(3y^2 - 3y - 7)$

23. Simplify: $-3x - 2(2x - 7)$

24. Simplify: $4(3x - 2) - 7(x + 5)$

25. Simplify: $2x + 3[x - 2(4 - 2x)]$

26. Simplify: $3[2x - 3(x - 2y)] + 3y$

27. Translate "the sum of one-half of b and b" into a variable expression.

28. Translate "10 divided by the difference between y and 2" into a variable expression.

29. Translate "the difference between eight and the quotient of a number and twelve" into a variable expression.

30. Translate "the sum of a number and two more than the number" into a variable expression. Then simplify.

31. Softball A softball diamond is a square with each side measuring 60 ft. Find the area enclosed by the sides of the softball diamond.

32. Biology A peregrine falcon's maximum flying speed over a quarter-mile distance is four times faster than a wildebeest's maximum running speed over the same distance. (*Source:* www.factmonster.com) Express the speed of the peregrine falcon in terms of the speed of the wildebeest.

Hedrus/Shutterstock.com

Solving Equations

3

OBJECTIVES

SECTION 3.1

A To determine whether a given number is a solution of an equation

B To solve an equation of the form $x + a = b$

C To solve an equation of the form $ax = b$

SECTION 3.2

A To solve application problems using the basic percent equation

B To solve uniform motion problems

SECTION 3.3

A To solve an equation of the form $ax + b = c$

B To solve application problems using formulas

SECTION 3.4

A To solve an equation of the form $ax + b = cx + d$

B To solve an equation containing parentheses

C To solve application problems using formulas

SECTION 3.5

A To solve integer problems

B To translate a sentence into an equation and solve

SECTION 3.6

A To solve problems involving angles

B To solve problems involving the angles of a triangle

SECTION 3.7

A To solve value mixture problems

B To solve percent mixture problems

C To solve uniform motion problems

Focus on Success

Do you have trouble with word problems? Word problems show the variety of ways in which math can be used. The solution of every word problem can be broken down into two steps: Strategy and Solution. The Strategy consists of reading the problem, writing down what is known and unknown, and devising a plan to find the unknown. The Solution often consists of solving an equation and then checking the solution. (See Word Problems, page AIM-10).

Diego Cervo/Shutterstock.com

Prep Test

Are you ready to succeed in this chapter? Take the Prep Test below to find out if you are ready to learn the new material.

1. Write $\frac{9}{100}$ as a decimal.

2. Write $\frac{3}{4}$ as a percent.

3. Evaluate $3x^2 - 4x - 1$ when $x = -4$.

4. Simplify: $R - 0.35R$

5. Simplify: $\frac{1}{2}x + \frac{2}{3}x$

6. Simplify: $6x - 3(6 - x)$

7. Simplify: $0.22(3x + 6) + x$

8. Translate into a variable expression: "The difference between five and twice a number."

9. **Computers** A new graphics card for computer games is five times faster than a graphics card made two years ago. Express the speed of the new card in terms of the speed of the old card.

10. **Carpentry** A board 5 ft long is cut into two pieces. If x represents the length of the longer piece, write an expression for the length of the shorter piece in terms of x.

SECTION

3.1 Introduction to Equations

OBJECTIVE A To determine whether a given number is a solution of an equation

Point of Interest

One of the most famous equations ever stated is $E = mc^2$. This equation, stated by Albert Einstein, shows that there is a relationship between mass m and energy E. As a side note, the chemical element einsteinium was named in honor of Einstein.

An **equation** expresses the equality of two mathematical expressions. The expressions can be either numerical or variable expressions.

$$\left.\begin{array}{l} 9 + 3 = 12 \\ 3x - 2 = 10 \\ y^2 + 4 = 2y - 1 \\ z = 2 \end{array}\right\} \text{Equations}$$

The equation at the right is true if the variable is replaced by 5.

$x + 8 = 13$

$5 + 8 = 13$ A true equation

The equation is false if the variable is replaced by 7.

$7 + 8 = 13$ A false equation

A **solution of an equation** is a number that, when substituted for the variable, results in a true equation. 5 is a solution of the equation $x + 8 = 13$. 7 is not a solution of the equation $x + 8 = 13$.

HOW TO 1 Is -2 a solution of $2x + 5 = x^2 - 3$?

$2x + 5$	$= x^2 - 3$
$2(-2) + 5$	$(-2)^2 - 3$
$-4 + 5$	$4 - 3$

$1 = 1$

- **Replace x by -2.**
- **Evaluate the numerical expressions.**
- **If the results are equal, -2 is a solution of the equation. If the results are not equal, -2 is not a solution of the equation.**

Yes, -2 is a solution of the equation.

Take Note

The Order of Operations Agreement applies when evaluating $2(-2) + 5$ and $(-2)^2 - 3$.

EXAMPLE 1

Is -4 a solution of $4 + 5x = x^2 - 2x$?

Solution

$4 + 5x$	$= x^2 - 2x$
$4 + 5(-4)$	$(-4)^2 - 2(-4)$
$4 + (-20)$	$16 - (-8)$

- **Replace x with -4.**

$-16 \neq 24$

($\neq$ means "is not equal to.")

No, -4 is not a solution.

YOU TRY IT 1

Is 5 a solution of $10x - x^2 = 3x - 10$?

Your solution

Solution on p. S4

OBJECTIVE B To solve an equation of the form $x + a = b$

To **solve an equation** means to find a solution of the equation. The simplest equation to solve is an equation of the form *variable* = *constant*, because the constant is the solution.

The solution of the equation $x = 5$ is 5 because $5 = 5$ is a true equation.

Tips for Success
To learn mathematics, you must be an active participant. Listening and watching your professor do mathematics are not enough. Take notes in class, mentally think through every question your instructor asks, and try to answer it even if you are not called on to do so. Ask questions when you have them. See *AIM for Success* at the front of the book for other ways to be an active learner.

The solution of the equation at the right is 7 because $7 + 2 = 9$ is a true equation.

$$x + 2 = 9 \qquad 7 + 2 = 9$$

Note that if 4 is added to each side of the equation $x + 2 = 9$, the solution is still 7.

$$\begin{aligned} x + 2 &= 9 \\ x + 2 + 4 &= 9 + 4 \\ x + 6 &= 13 \end{aligned} \qquad 7 + 6 = 13$$

If -5 is added to each side of the equation $x + 2 = 9$, the solution is still 7.

$$\begin{aligned} x + 2 &= 9 \\ x + 2 + (-5) &= 9 + (-5) \\ x - 3 &= 4 \end{aligned} \qquad 7 - 3 = 4$$

Equations that have the same solution are called **equivalent equations.** The equations $x + 2 = 9$, $x + 6 = 13$, and $x - 3 = 4$ are equivalent equations; each equation has 7 as its solution. These examples suggest that adding the same number to each side of an equation produces an equivalent equation. This is called the *Addition Property of Equations.*

Addition Property of Equations

The same number can be added to each side of an equation without changing its solution. In symbols, the equation $a = b$ has the same solution as the equation $a + c = b + c$.

EXAMPLE OF THIS PROPERTY

The equation $x - 3 = 7$ has the same solution as the equation $x - 3 + 3 = 7 + 3$.

In solving an equation, the goal is to rewrite the given equation in the form *variable* = *constant*. The Addition Property of Equations is used to remove a *term* from one side of the equation by adding the opposite of that term to each side of the equation.

Take Note
An equation has some properties that are similar to those of a balance scale. For instance, if a balance scale is in balance and equal weights are added to each side of the scale, then the balance scale remains in balance. If an equation is true, then adding the same number to each side of the equation produces another true equation.

HOW TO 2 Solve: $x - 4 = 2$

$x - 4 = 2$ • The goal is to rewrite the equation in the form *variable* = *constant*.

$x - 4 + 4 = 2 + 4$ • Add 4 to each side of the equation.

$x + 0 = 6$ • Simplify.

$x = 6$ • The equation is in the form *variable* = *constant*.

Check:

$$\begin{array}{c|c} x - 4 & 2 \\ \hline 6 - 4 & 2 \\ 2 & 2 \end{array}$$

$2 = 2$ A true equation

The solution is 6.

Because subtraction is defined in terms of addition, the Addition Property of Equations also makes it possible to subtract the same number from each side of an equation without changing the solution of the equation.

HOW TO 3 Solve: $y + \frac{3}{4} = \frac{1}{2}$

$y + \frac{3}{4} = \frac{1}{2}$ • The goal is to rewrite the equation in the form *variable* = *constant*.

$y + \frac{3}{4} - \frac{3}{4} = \frac{1}{2} - \frac{3}{4}$ • Subtract $\frac{3}{4}$ from each side of the equation.

$y + 0 = \frac{2}{4} - \frac{3}{4}$ • Simplify.

$y = -\frac{1}{4}$ • The equation is in the form *variable* = *constant*.

The solution is $-\frac{1}{4}$. You should check this solution.

EXAMPLE 2

Solve: $x + 15 = 23$

Solution

$x + 15 = 23$

$x + 15 - 15 = 23 - 15$ • Subtract 15 from each side.

$x + 0 = 8$ • Simplify each side.

$x = 8$ • Addition Property of Zero

The solution is 8.

YOU TRY IT 2

Solve: $26 = y - 14$

Your solution

Solution on p. S4

OBJECTIVE C *To solve an equation of the form $ax = b$*

The solution of the equation at the right is 3 because $2 \cdot 3 = 6$ is a true equation.

$2x = 6 \qquad 2 \cdot 3 = 6$

Note that if each side of $2x = 6$ is multiplied by 5, the solution is still 3.

$$2x = 6$$
$$5(2x) = 5 \cdot 6$$
$$10x = 30 \qquad 10 \cdot 3 = 30$$

If each side of $2x = 6$ is multiplied by -4, the solution is still 3.

$$2x = 6$$
$$(-4)(2x) = (-4)6$$
$$-8x = -24 \qquad -8 \cdot 3 = -24$$

The equations $2x = 6$, $10x = 30$, and $-8x = -24$ are equivalent equations; each equation has 3 as its solution. These examples suggest that multiplying each side of an equation by the same nonzero number produces an equivalent equation.

Multiplication Property of Equations

Each side of an equation can be multiplied by the same nonzero number without changing the solution of the equation. In symbols, if $c \neq 0$, then the equation $a = b$ has the same solutions as the equation $ac = bc$.

EXAMPLE

The equation $3x = 21$ has the same solution as the equation $\frac{1}{3} \cdot 3x = \frac{1}{3} \cdot 21$.

The Multiplication Property of Equations is used to remove a coefficient by multiplying each side of the equation by the reciprocal of the coefficient.

HOW TO 4 Solve: $\frac{3}{4}z = 9$

$\frac{3}{4}z = 9$ • The goal is to rewrite the equation in the form *variable* = *constant*.

$\frac{4}{3} \cdot \frac{3}{4}z = \frac{4}{3} \cdot 9$ • Multiply each side of the equation by $\frac{4}{3}$.

$1 \cdot z = 12$ • Simplify.

$z = 12$ • The equation is in the form *variable* = *constant*.

The solution is 12. You should check this solution.

Because division is defined in terms of multiplication, each side of an equation can be divided by the same nonzero number without changing the solution of the equation.

HOW TO 5 Solve: $6x = 14$

$6x = 14$ • The goal is to rewrite the equation in the form *variable* = *constant*.

$\frac{6x}{6} = \frac{14}{6}$ • Divide each side of the equation by 6.

$x = \frac{7}{3}$ • Simplify. The equation is in the form *variable* = *constant*.

The solution is $\frac{7}{3}$.

Take Note

Remember to check the solution.

Check:

$$\begin{array}{c|c} 6x & 14 \\ \hline 6\left(\frac{7}{3}\right) & 14 \\ 14 & 14 \end{array}$$

When using the Multiplication Property of Equations, multiply each side of the equation by the reciprocal of the coefficient when the coefficient is a fraction. Divide each side of the equation by the coefficient when the coefficient is an integer or a decimal.

EXAMPLE 3

Solve: $\frac{3x}{4} = -9$

Solution

$\frac{3x}{4} = -9$ • $\frac{3x}{4} = \frac{3}{4}x$

$\frac{4}{3} \cdot \frac{3}{4}x = \frac{4}{3}(-9)$ • Multiply each side by $\frac{4}{3}$.

$x = -12$

The solution is -12.

YOU TRY IT 3

Solve: $-\frac{2x}{5} = 6$

Your solution

EXAMPLE 4

Solve: $5x - 9x = 12$

Solution

$5x - 9x = 12$

$-4x = 12$ • Combine like terms.

$\frac{-4x}{-4} = \frac{12}{-4}$ • Divide each side by -4.

$x = -3$

The solution is -3.

YOU TRY IT 4

Solve: $4x - 8x = 16$

Your solution

Solutions on p. S5

3.1 EXERCISES

Concept Check

1. Label each of the following as either an expression or an equation.
a. $3x + 7 = 9$ **b.** $3x + 7$ **c.** $4 - 6(y + 5)$ **d.** $a + b = 8$ **e.** $a + b - 8$

2. What is the solution of the equation $x = 8$? Use your answer to explain why the goal in solving equations is to get the variable alone on one side of the equation.

3. Which of the following are equations of the form $x + a = b$? If an equation is of the form $x + a = b$, what would you do to solve the equation?
(i) $d + 7.8 = -9.2$ (ii) $0.3 = t + 1.4$ (iii) $-9 = 3y$ (iv) $-8 + c = -5.6$

4. Which of the following are equations of the form $ax = b$? If an equation is of the form $ax = b$, what would you do to solve the equation?
a. $3y = -12$ b. $2.4 = 0.6d$ c. $-5 = z - 10$ d. $-8c = -56$

OBJECTIVE A *To determine whether a given number is a solution of an equation*

5. Is 4 a solution of $2x = 8$?

6. Is 3 a solution of $y + 4 = 7$?

7. Is -1 a solution of $2b - 1 = 3$?

8. Is -2 a solution of $3a - 4 = 10$?

9. Is 1 a solution of $4 - 2m = 3$?

10. Is 2 a solution of $7 - 3n = 2$?

11. Is 5 a solution of $2x + 5 = 3x$?

12. Is 4 a solution of $3y - 4 = 2y$?

13. Is -2 a solution of $3a + 2 = 2 - a$?

14. Is 3 a solution of $z^2 + 1 = 4 + 3z$?

15. Is 2 a solution of $2x^2 - 1 = 4x - 1$?

16. Is -1 a solution of $y^2 - 1 = 4y + 3$?

17. Is $\frac{1}{2}$ a solution of $4y + 1 = 3$?

18. Is $\frac{2}{5}$ a solution of $5m + 1 = 10m - 3$?

19. Is $\frac{3}{4}$ a solution of $8x - 1 = 12x + 3$?

20. If A is a fixed number such that $A < 0$, is a solution of the equation $5x = A$ positive or negative?

OBJECTIVE B *To solve an equation of the form $x + a = b$*

21. Without solving the equation $x - \frac{11}{16} = \frac{19}{24}$, determine whether x is less than or greater than $\frac{19}{24}$. Explain your answer.

22. Without solving the equation $x + \frac{13}{15} = -\frac{21}{43}$, determine whether x is less than or greater than $-\frac{21}{43}$. Explain your answer.

For Exercises 23 to 58, solve and check.

23. $x + 5 = 7$

24. $y + 3 = 9$

25. $b - 4 = 11$

26. $z - 6 = 10$

27. $2 + a = 8$

28. $5 + x = 12$

29. $n - 5 = -2$

30. $x - 6 = -5$

31. $b + 7 = 7$

32. $y - 5 = -5$

33. $z + 9 = 2$

34. $n + 11 = 1$

35. $10 + m = 3$

36. $8 + x = 5$

37. $9 + x = -3$

38. $10 + y = -4$

39. $2 = x + 7$

40. $-8 = n + 1$

41. $4 = m - 11$

42. $-6 = y - 5$

43. $12 = 3 + w$

44. $-9 = 5 + x$

45. $4 = -10 + b$

46. $-7 = -2 + x$

47. $m + \frac{2}{3} = -\frac{1}{3}$

48. $c + \frac{3}{4} = -\frac{1}{4}$

49. $x - \frac{1}{2} = \frac{1}{2}$

50. $x - \frac{2}{5} = \frac{3}{5}$

51. $\frac{5}{8} + y = \frac{1}{8}$

52. $\frac{4}{9} + a = -\frac{2}{9}$

53. $-\frac{5}{6} = x - \frac{1}{4}$

54. $-\frac{1}{4} = c - \frac{2}{3}$

55. $d + 1.3619 = 2.0148$

56. $w + 2.932 = 4.801$

57. $6.149 = -3.108 + z$

58. $5.237 = -2.014 + x$

OBJECTIVE C *To solve an equation of the form $ax = b$*

For Exercises 59 to 92, solve and check.

59. $5x = -15$

60. $4y = -28$

61. $3b = 0$

62. $2a = 0$

63. $-3x = 6$

64. $-5m = 20$

65. $-\frac{1}{6}n = -30$

66. $20 = \frac{1}{4}c$

67. $0 = -5x$

68. $0 = -8a$

69. $\frac{x}{3} = 2$

70. $\frac{x}{4} = 3$

71. $-\frac{y}{2} = 5$

72. $-\frac{b}{3} = 6$

73. $\frac{3}{4}y = 9$

74. $\frac{2}{5}x = 6$

75. $-\frac{2}{3}d = 8$ **76.** $-\frac{3}{5}m = 12$ **77.** $\frac{2n}{3} = 0$ **78.** $\frac{5x}{6} = 0$

79. $\frac{-3z}{8} = 9$ **80.** $\frac{3x}{4} = 2$ **81.** $\frac{2}{9} = \frac{2}{3}y$ **82.** $-\frac{6}{7} = -\frac{3}{4}b$

83. $\frac{x}{1.46} = 3.25$ **84.** $\frac{z}{2.95} = -7.88$ **85.** $3.47a = 7.1482$ **86.** $2.31m = 2.4255$

87. $2m + 5m = 49$ **88.** $5x + 2x = 14$ **89.** $3n + 2n = 20$

90. $7d - 4d = 9$ **91.** $10y - 3y = 21$ **92.** $2x - 5x = 9$

For Exercises 93 to 96, suppose y is a positive integer. Determine whether x is positive or negative.

93. $15x = y$ **94.** $-6x = y$ **95.** $-\frac{1}{4}x = y$ **96.** $\frac{2}{9}x = -y$

Critical Thinking

Solve.

97. $\frac{2m + m}{5} = -9$ **98.** $\frac{3y - 8y}{7} = 15$ **99.** $\frac{1}{\frac{1}{x}} = 5$

100. $\frac{1}{\frac{1}{x}} + 8 = -19$ **101.** $\frac{4}{\frac{3}{b}} = 8$ **102.** $\frac{5}{\frac{7}{a}} - \frac{3}{\frac{7}{a}} = 6$

Projects or Group Activities

103. Make up an equation of the form $x + a = b$ that has 2 as a solution.

104. Make up an equation of the form $ax = b$ that has -2 as a solution.

105. Two numbers form a "two-pair" if the sum of their reciprocals equals 2. For example, $\frac{8}{15}$ and 8 are a two-pair because $\frac{15}{8} + \frac{1}{8} = 2$. If two numbers a and b form a two-pair, and $a = \frac{7}{3}$, what is the value of b?

106. Use the numbers 5, 10, and 15 to fill in the boxes in the equation $x + \square = \square - \square$.
a. What is the largest solution possible?
b. What is the smallest solution possible?

SECTION

3.2 The Basic Percent Equation and the Uniform Motion Equation

OBJECTIVE A *To solve application problems using the basic percent equation*

An equation that is used frequently in mathematics applications is the basic percent equation.

Basic Percent Equation

$$\text{Percent} \cdot \text{Base} = \text{Amount}$$
$$P \cdot B = A$$

In many application problems involving percent, the base follows the word *of.*

HOW TO 1 20% of what number is 30?

$P \cdot B = A$ • Use the basic percent equation.

$0.20B = 30$ • $P = 20\% = 0.20$, $A = 30$, and B is unknown.

$\dfrac{0.20B}{0.20} = \dfrac{30}{0.20}$ • Solve for B.

$B = 150$

The number is 150.

In most cases, you should write the percent as a decimal before solving the basic percent equation, as in HOW TO 1. However, some percents are more easily written as fractions. For example,

$$33\frac{1}{3}\% = \frac{1}{3} \qquad 66\frac{2}{3}\% = \frac{2}{3} \qquad 16\frac{2}{3}\% = \frac{1}{6} \qquad 83\frac{1}{3}\% = \frac{5}{6}$$

Take Note

We have written $P(80) = 70$ because that is the form of the basic percent equation. We could have written $80P = 70$. The important point is that each side of the equation is divided by 80, the coefficient of P.

HOW TO 2 70 is what percent of 80?

$P \cdot B = A$ • Use the basic percent equation.

$P(80) = 70$ • $B = 80$, $A = 70$, and P is unknown.

$\dfrac{P(80)}{80} = \dfrac{70}{80}$ • Solve for P.

$P = 0.875$ • The question asked for a percent.

$P = 87.5\%$ • Convert the decimal to a percent.

70 is 87.5% of 80.

APPLY THE CONCEPT

The world's production of cocoa for a recent year was 2928 metric tons. Of this, 1969 metric tons came from Africa. (*Source:* World Cocoa Foundation) What percent of the world's cocoa was produced in Africa? Round to the nearest tenth of a percent.

To find the percent, use the basic percent equation.

$$P \cdot B = A$$
$$P(2928) = 1969$$ • **$B = 2928, A = 1969$, and P is unknown.**
$$P = \frac{1969}{2928} \approx 0.672$$

Approximately 67.2% of the world's cocoa was produced in Africa.

The simple interest that an investment earns is given by the **simple interest equation** $I = Prt$, where I is the simple interest, P is the principal, or amount invested, r is the simple interest rate, and t is the time.

APPLY THE CONCEPT

A \$1500 investment has an annual simple interest rate of 7%. Find the simple interest earned on the investment after 18 months.

To find the interest, solve $I = Prt$ for I.

The time is given in months but the interest rate is an annual rate. Therefore, we must convert 18 months to years. $18 \text{ months} = \frac{18}{12} \text{ years} = 1.5 \text{ years}$

$$I = Prt$$
$$I = 1500(0.07)(1.5)$$ • **$P = 1500, r = 0.07, t = 1.5$**
$$I = 157.5$$

The investment earned \$157.50.

Point of Interest

In the jewelry industry, the amount of gold in a piece of jewelry is measured in *karats*. Pure gold is 24 karats. A necklace that is 18 karats is $\frac{18}{24} = 0.75 = 75\%$ gold.

The amount of a substance in a solution can be given as a percent of the total solution. For instance, if a certain fruit juice drink is advertised as containing 27% cranberry juice, then 27% of the contents of the bottle must be cranberry juice.

The method for solving problems involving mixtures is based on the **percent mixture equation** $Q = Ar$, where Q is the quantity of a substance in the solution, A is the amount of the solution, and r is the percent concentration of the substance.

APPLY THE CONCEPT

The formula for a perfume requires that the concentration of jasmine be 1.2% of the total amount of perfume. How many ounces of jasmine are in a 2-ounce bottle of this perfume?

To find the number of ounces of jasmine, solve $Q = Ar$ for Q.

$$Q = Ar$$
$$Q = 2(0.012)$$ • **A = the amount of perfume = 2 oz**
r = the percent concentration = 1.2% = 0.012
$$Q = 0.024$$

There is 0.024 oz of jasmine in the perfume.

EXAMPLE 1

12 is $33\frac{1}{3}\%$ of what number?

Solution

$P \cdot B = A$ • Use the basic percent equation.

$\frac{1}{3}B = 12$ • $33\frac{1}{3}\% = \frac{1}{3}$

$3 \cdot \frac{1}{3}B = 3 \cdot 12$ • Multiply each side by 3.

$B = 36$

12 is $33\frac{1}{3}\%$ of 36.

YOU TRY IT 1

18 is $16\frac{2}{3}\%$ of what number?

Your solution

EXAMPLE 2

The data in the table below show the numbers of households (in millions) that downloaded music files for a three-month period in a recent year. (*Source:* NPD Group)

Month	April	May	June
Downloads	14.5	12.7	10.4

For the three-month period, what percent of the files were downloaded in May? Round to the nearest percent.

Strategy

To find the percent:

- Find the total number of files downloaded for the three-month period.
- Use the basic percent equation. B is the total number of files downloaded for the three-month period; $A = 12.7$, the number of files downloaded in May; P is unknown.

Solution

$14.5 + 12.7 + 10.4 = 37.6$

$P \cdot B = A$ • Use the basic percent equation.

$P(37.6) = 12.7$ • $B = 37.6, A = 12.7$

$P = \frac{12.7}{37.6} \approx 0.34$ • Divide each side by 37.6.

Approximately 34% of the files were downloaded in May.

YOU TRY IT 2

According to Wikipedia.org, 162.9 million people in the United States watched Super Bowl XLV. What percent of the U.S. population watched Super Bowl XLV? Use a figure of 310 million for the U.S. population. Round to the nearest tenth of a percent.

Your strategy

Your solution

Solutions on p. S5

EXAMPLE 3

In April, Marshall Wardell was charged an interest fee of \$8.72 on an unpaid credit card balance of \$545. Find the annual interest rate on this credit card.

Strategy

The interest is \$8.72. Therefore, $I = 8.72$. The unpaid balance is \$545. This is the principal on which interest is calculated. Therefore, $P = 545$. The time is one month. Because the *annual* interest rate must be found and the time is given as one month, we write one month as $\frac{1}{12}$ year: $t = \frac{1}{12}$. To find the interest rate, solve $I = Prt$ for r.

Solution

$$I = Prt$$

• Use the simple interest equation.

$$8.72 = 545r\left(\frac{1}{12}\right)$$

• $I = 8.72, P = 545, t = \frac{1}{12}$

$$8.72 = \frac{545}{12}r$$

$$\frac{12}{545}(8.72) = \frac{12}{545}\left(\frac{545}{12}r\right)$$

• Multiply each side by the reciprocal of $\frac{545}{12}$.

$$0.192 = r$$

The annual interest rate is 19.2%.

YOU TRY IT 3

Clarissa Adams purchased a municipal bond for \$1000. The bond earns an annual simple interest rate of 6.4%. How much must she deposit into an account that earns 8% annual simple interest so that the interest earned from each account after one year is the same?

Your strategy

Your solution

EXAMPLE 4

To make a certain color of blue, 4 oz of cyan must be contained in 1 gal of paint. What is the percent concentration of cyan in the paint?

Strategy

The cyan is given in ounces and the amount of paint is given in gallons. We must convert ounces to gallons or gallons to ounces. For this problem, we will convert gallons to ounces: 1 gal = 128 oz. Solve $Q = Ar$ for r, with $Q = 4$ and $A = 128$.

Solution

$$Q = Ar$$

• Use the percent mixture equation.

$$4 = 128r$$

• $Q = 4, A = 128$

$$\frac{4}{128} = \frac{128r}{128}$$

$$0.03125 = r$$

The percent concentration of cyan is 3.125%.

YOU TRY IT 4

The concentration of sugar in a certain breakfast cereal is 25%. If there are 2 oz of sugar contained in a bowl of cereal, how many ounces of cereal are in the bowl?

Your strategy

Your solution

Solutions on p. S5

OBJECTIVE B *To solve uniform motion problems*

Take Note

A car traveling in a *circle* at a constant speed of 45 mph is *not* in uniform motion because the direction of the car is always changing.

Any object that travels at a constant speed in a straight line is said to be in *uniform motion.* **Uniform motion** means that the speed and direction of an object do not change. For instance, a car traveling at a constant speed of 45 mph on a straight road is in uniform motion.

The solution of a uniform motion problem is based on the **uniform motion equation** $d = rt$, where d is the distance traveled, r is the rate of travel, and t is the time spent traveling. For instance, suppose a car travels at 50 mph for 3 h. Because the rate (50 mph) and time (3 h) are known, we can find the distance traveled by solving the equation $d = rt$ for d.

$$d = rt$$

$$d = 50(3) \qquad \bullet\ r = 50, t = 3$$

$$d = 150$$

The car travels a distance of 150 mi.

APPLY THE CONCEPT

A jogger runs 3 mi in 45 min. What is the rate of the jogger in miles per hour?

To find the rate of the jogger, solve the equation $d = rt$ for r.
The answer must be in miles per *hour* and the time is given in *minutes.*
Convert 45 min to hours: 45 min $= \frac{45}{60}$ h $= \frac{3}{4}$ h

$$d = rt$$

$$3 = r\left(\frac{3}{4}\right) \qquad \bullet\ d = 3, t = \frac{3}{4}$$

$$3 = \frac{3}{4}r$$

$$\left(\frac{4}{3}\right)3 = \left(\frac{4}{3}\right)\frac{3}{4}r \qquad \bullet \text{ Multiply each side of the equation by the reciprocal of } \tfrac{3}{4}.$$

$$4 = r$$

The rate of the jogger is 4 mph.

If two objects are moving in opposite directions, then the rate at which the distance between them is increasing is the sum of the speeds of the two objects. For instance, in the diagram below, two cars start from the same point and travel in opposite directions. The distance between them is changing at the rate of 70 mph.

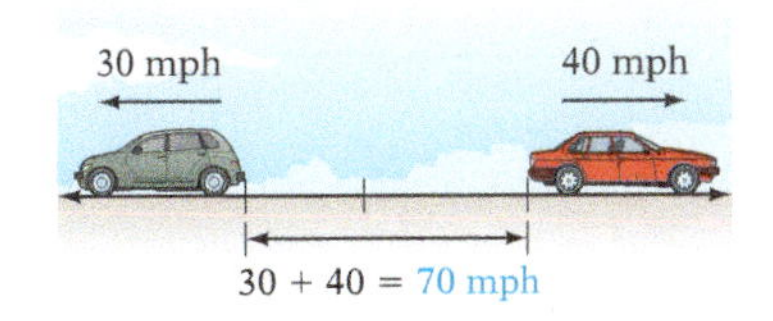

Similarly, if two objects are moving toward each other, the distance between them is decreasing at a rate that is equal to the sum of the speeds. The rate at which the two planes at the right are approaching one another is 800 mph.

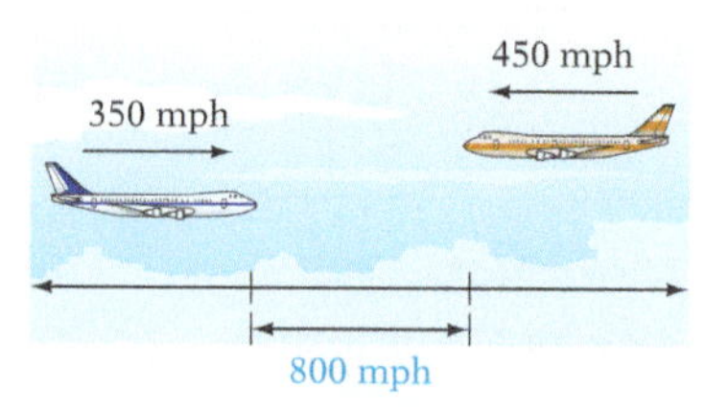

APPLY THE CONCEPT

Two cars start from the same point and move in opposite directions. The car moving west is traveling at 45 mph, and the car moving east is traveling at 60 mph. In how many hours will the cars be 210 mi apart?

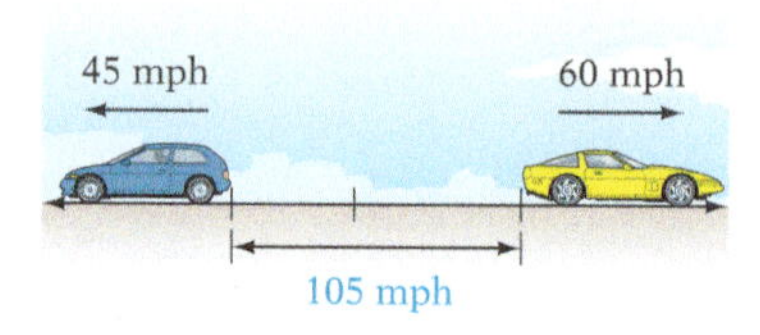

To find the time, solve the equation $d = rt$ for t.

d = distance = 210 mi

The cars are moving in opposite directions, so the rate at which the distance between them is changing is the sum of the rates of the cars.

45 mph + 60 mph = 105 mph. Therefore, $r = 105$.

$$d = rt$$

$$210 = 105t \quad \bullet\ d = 210, r = 105$$

$$\frac{210}{105} = \frac{105t}{105} \quad \bullet \text{ Divide each side of the equation by 105.}$$

$$2 = t$$

In 2 h, the cars will be 210 mi apart.

If a motorboat is on a river that is flowing at a rate of 4 mph, then the boat will float down the river at a speed of 4 mph when the motor is not on. Now suppose the motor is turned on and the power adjusted so that the boat would travel 10 mph without the aid of the current. Then, if the boat is moving with the current, its effective speed is the speed of the boat using power plus the speed of the current: 10 mph + 4 mph = 14 mph. (See the figure below.)

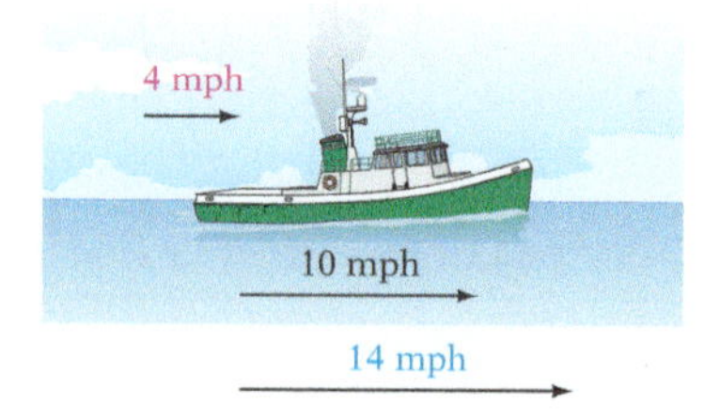

However, if the boat is moving against the current, the current slows the boat down. The effective speed of the boat is the speed of the boat using power minus the speed of the current: 10 mph − 4 mph = 6 mph. (See the figure below.)

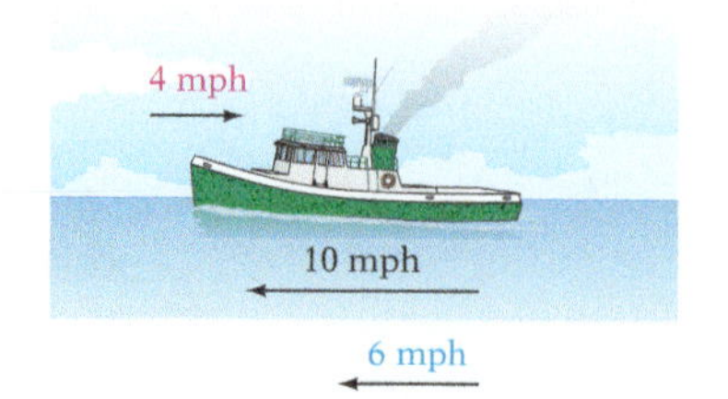

Take Note

The term ft/s is an abbreviation for "feet per second." Similarly, cm/s is "centimeters per second" and m/s is "meters per second."

There are other situations in which the preceding concepts may be applied.

APPLY THE CONCEPT

An airline passenger is walking between two airline terminals and decides to get on a moving sidewalk that is 150 ft long. If the passenger walks at a rate of 7 ft/s and the moving sidewalk moves at a rate of 9 ft/s, how long, in seconds, will it take for the passenger to walk from one end of the moving sidewalk to the other? Round to the nearest thousandth.

Marc C. Johnson/Shutterstock.com

To find the time, solve the equation $d = rt$ for t.

d = distance = 150 ft

The passenger is traveling at 7 ft/s and the moving sidewalk is traveling at 9 ft/s.

The rate of the passenger is the sum of the two rates: 7 ft/s + 9 ft/s = 16 ft/s.

Therefore, $r = 16$.

$$d = rt$$

$$150 = 16t \quad \bullet\ d = 150, r = 16$$

$$\frac{150}{16} = \frac{16t}{16} \quad \bullet\ \text{Divide each side of the equation by 16.}$$

$$9.375 = t$$

It will take 9.375 s for the passenger to travel the length of the moving sidewalk.

EXAMPLE 5

Two cyclists start at the same time at opposite ends of an 80-mile course. One cyclist is traveling at 18 mph, and the second cyclist is traveling at 14 mph. How long after they begin cycling will they meet?

Strategy

The distance is 80 mi. Therefore, $d = 80$. The cyclists are moving toward each other, so the rate at which the distance between them is changing is the sum of the rates of the cyclists. The rate is 18 mph + 14 mph = 32 mph. Therefore, $r = 32$. To find the time, solve the equation $d = rt$ for t.

Solution

$$d = rt$$

$$80 = 32t \quad \bullet\ d = 80, r = 32$$

$$\frac{80}{32} = \frac{32t}{32} \quad \bullet\ \text{Divide each side by 32.}$$

$$2.5 = t$$

The cyclists will meet in 2.5 h.

YOU TRY IT 5

A plane that can normally travel at 250 mph in calm air is flying into a headwind of 25 mph. How far can the plane fly in 3 h?

Your strategy

Your solution

Solution on p. S5

3.2 EXERCISES

Concept Check

Identify the amount and the base.

1. 30 is 75% of 40.

2. 40% of 20 is 8.

Complete Exercises 3 and 4 by filling in the blanks with the correct number from the problem situation or with the word *unknown.*

3. **Problem Situation:** It rained on 24 of the 30 days of June. What percent of the days in June were rainy days?

Using the formula $PB = A$, $P =$ ______, $B =$ ______, and $A =$ ______.

4. **Problem Situation:** You bought a used car and made a down payment of 25% of the purchase price of $16,000. How much was the down payment?

Using the formula $PB = A$, $P =$ ______, $B =$ ______, and $A =$ ______.

5. Keith and Jennifer started at the same time and rode toward each other on a straight road. When they met, Keith had traveled 15 mi and Jennifer had traveled 10 mi. Who had the greater average speed?

6. Suppose you have a powerboat with the throttle set to move the boat at 8 mph in calm water. The rate of the current of a river is 4 mph.

a. What is the speed of the boat when traveling on this river with the current?
b. What is the speed of the boat when traveling on this river against the current?

OBJECTIVE A *To solve application problems using the basic percent equation*

7. What is 35% of 80?

8. What percent of 8 is 0.5?

9. Find 1.2% of 60.

10. 8 is what percent of 5?

11. 125% of what is 80?

12. What percent of 20 is 30?

13. 12 is what percent of 50?

14. What percent of 125 is 50?

15. Find 18% of 40.

16. What is 25% of 60?

17. 12% of what is 48?

18. 45% of what is 9?

19. What is $33\frac{1}{3}\%$ of 27?

20. Find $16\frac{2}{3}\%$ of 30.

21. What percent of 12 is 3?

22. 10 is what percent of 15?

23. 12 is what percent of 6?

24. 20 is what percent of 16?

25. $5\frac{1}{4}\%$ of what is 21?

26. $37\frac{1}{2}\%$ of what is 15?

27. Find 15.4% of 50.

28. What is 18.5% of 46?

29. 1 is 0.5% of what?

30. 3 is 1.5% of what?

31. $\frac{3}{4}\%$ of what is 3?

32. $\frac{1}{2}\%$ of what is 3?

33. What is 250% of 12?

34. Without solving an equation, determine whether 40% of 80 is less than, equal to, or greater than 80% of 40.

35. Without solving an equation, determine whether $\frac{1}{4}\%$ of 80 is less than, equal to, or greater than 25% of 80.

36. **Government** To override a presidential veto, at least $66\frac{2}{3}\%$ of the Senate must vote to override the veto. There are 100 senators in the Senate. What is the minimum number of votes needed to override a veto?

37. **Boston Marathon** See the news clipping at the right. What percent of the participants who started the course finished the race? Round to the nearest tenth of a percent.

In the NEWS!

Thousands Complete Boston Marathon

This year, there were 26,735 entrants in the Boston Marathon, the world's oldest annual marathon. Of those registered, 23,126 people started the race, and 22,629 people finished the 26.2-mile course.

Source: www.bostonmarathon.org

38. **Natural Resources** On average, a person uses 13.2 gal of water per day for showering. This is 17.8% of the total amount of water used per person per day in the average single-family home. Find the total amount of water used per person per day in the average single-family home. Round to the nearest whole number. (*Source:* American Water Works Association)

39. **Travel** According to the annual Summer Vacation Survey conducted by Myvesta, a nonprofit consumer education organization, the average summer vacation costs \$2252. If \$1850 of this amount is charged on a credit card, what percent of the vacation cost is charged? Round to the nearest tenth of a percent.

40. **School Enrollment** The circle graph at the right represents the U.S. population over 3 years old that is enrolled in school. To answer the question "How many people are enrolled in college or graduate school?," what additional piece of information is necessary?

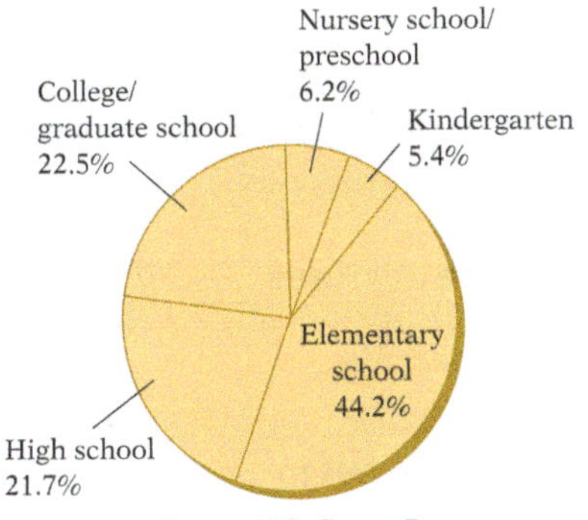

Source: U.S. Census Bureau

41. **Safety** Recently, the National Safety Council collected data on the leading causes of accidental death. The findings revealed that for people age 20, 30 died from a fall, 47 from fire, 200 from drowning, and 1950 from motor vehicle accidents. What percent of the accidental deaths were not attributed to motor vehicle accidents? Round to the nearest percent.

42. **Energy** The Energy Information Administration reports that if every U.S. household switched 4 h of lighting per day from incandescent bulbs to compact fluorescent bulbs, we would save 31.7 billion kilowatt-hours of electricity a year, or 33% of the total electricity used for home lighting. What is the total electricity used for home lighting in this country? Round to the nearest tenth of a billion.

43. **Investment** If Kachina Caron invested $1200 in a simple interest account and earned $72 in 8 months, what is the annual interest rate?

44. **Investment** How much money must Andrea invest for 2 years in an account that earns an annual simple interest rate of 8% if she wants to earn $300 from the investment?

45. **Investment** Sal Boxer decided to divide a gift of $3000 into two different accounts. He placed $1000 in an account that earns an annual simple interest rate of 7.5%. The remaining money was placed in an account that earns an annual simple interest rate of 8.25%. How much interest will Sal earn from the two accounts after one year?

46. **Investment** If Americo invests $2500 at an 8% annual simple interest rate and Octavia invests $3000 at a 7% annual simple interest rate, which of the two will earn the greater amount of interest after one year?

47. **Investment** Makana invested $900 in a simple interest account that had an interest rate that was 1% more than that of her friend Marlys. If Marlys earned $51 after one year from an investment of $850, how much did Makana earn in one year?

48. **Investment** A $2000 investment at an annual simple interest rate of 6% earned as much interest after one year as another investment in an account that earns 8% simple interest. How much was invested at 8%?

49. **Investment** An investor placed $1000 in an account that earns 9% annual simple interest and $1000 in an account that earns 6% annual simple interest. If each investment is left in the account for the same period of time, is the interest rate on the combined investment less than 6%, between 6% and 9%, or greater than 9%?

nui7711/Shutterstock.com

50. **Metallurgy** The concentration of platinum in a necklace is 15%. If the necklace weighs 12 g, find the amount of platinum in the necklace.

51. **Dye Mixtures** A 250-milliliter solution of a fabric dye contains 5 ml of hydrogen peroxide. What is the percent concentration of the hydrogen peroxide?

Jason Keith Heydorn/ Shutterstock.com

52. **Fabric Mixtures** A carpet is made with a blend of wool and other fibers. If the concentration of wool in the carpet is 75% and the carpet weighs 175 lb, how much wool is in the carpet?

53. **Juice Mixtures** Apple Dan's 32-ounce apple-flavored fruit drink contains 8 oz of apple juice. A 40-ounce generic brand of an apple-flavored fruit drink contains 9 oz of apple juice. Which of the two brands has the greater concentration of apple juice?

54. **Food Mixtures** Bakers use simple syrup in many of their recipes. Simple syrup is made by combining 500 g of sugar with 500 g of water and mixing it well until the sugar dissolves. What is the percent concentration of sugar in simple syrup?

55. **Pharmacology** A pharmacist has 50 g of a topical cream that contains 75% glycerine. How many grams of the cream are not glycerine?

56. **Chemistry** A chemist has 100 ml of a solution that is 9% acetic acid. If the chemist adds 50 ml of pure water to this solution, what is the percent concentration of the resulting mixture?

57. **Chemistry** A 500-gram salt-and-water solution contains 50 g of salt. This mixture is left in the open air, and 100 g of water evaporates from the solution. What is the percent concentration of salt in the remaining solution?

OBJECTIVE B *To solve uniform motion problems*

58. Joe and John live 2 mi apart. They leave their houses at the same time and walk toward each other until they meet. Joe walks faster than John does.

a. Is the distance walked by Joe less than, equal to, or greater than the distance walked by John?

b. Is the time spent walking by Joe less than, equal to, or greater than the time spent walking by John?

c. What is the total distance traveled by both Joe and John?

59. Morgan and Emma ride their bikes from Morgan's house to the store. Morgan begins biking 5 min before Emma begins. Emma bikes faster than Morgan and catches up with her just as they reach the store.

a. Is the distance biked by Emma less than, equal to, or greater than the distance biked by Morgan?

b. Is the time spent biking by Emma less than, equal to, or greater than the time spent biking by Morgan?

60. **Trains** See the news clipping at the right. Find the time it will take the high-speed train to travel between the two cities. Round to the nearest tenth of an hour.

BartlomiejMagierowski/Shutterstock.com

61. It takes a hospital dietician 40 min to drive from home to the hospital, a distance of 20 mi. What is the dietician's average rate of speed?

In the NEWS!

World's Fastest Train

China has unveiled the world's fastest rail link—a train that connects the cities of Guangzhou and Wuhan and can travel at speeds of up to 394.2 km/h. The distance between the two cities is 1069 km, and the train will travel that distance at an average speed of 350 km/h (217 mph). The head of the transport bureau at the Chinese railway ministry boasted, "It's the fastest train in operation in the world."

Source: news.yahoo.com

62. As part of a training program for the Boston Marathon, a runner wants to build endurance by running at a rate of 9 mph for 20 min. How far will the runner travel in that time period?

John Kropewnicki/Shutterstock.com

63. Marcella leaves home at 9:00 A.M. and drives to school, arriving at 9:45 A.M. If the distance between home and school is 27 mi, what is Marcella's average rate of speed?

Arthur Eugene Preston/Shutterstock.com

64. The Ride for Health Bicycle Club has chosen a 36-mile course for this Saturday's ride. If the riders plan on averaging 12 mph while they are riding, and they have a 1-hour lunch break planned, how long will it take them to complete the trip?

65. Palmer's average running speed is 3 km/h faster than his walking speed. If Palmer can run around a 30-kilometer course in 2 h, how many hours would it take for Palmer to walk the same course?

66. A shopping mall has a moving sidewalk that takes shoppers from the shopping area to the parking garage, a distance of 250 ft. If your normal walking rate is 5 ft/s and the moving sidewalk is traveling at 3 ft/s, how many seconds would it take for you to walk from one end of the moving sidewalk to the other end?

67. Two joggers start at the same time from opposite ends of an 8-mile jogging trail and begin running toward each other. One jogger is running at a rate of 5 mph, and the other jogger is running at a rate of 7 mph. How long, in minutes, after they start will the two joggers meet?

68. **sQuba** See the news clipping at the right. Two sQubas are on opposite sides of a lake 1.6 mi wide. They start toward each other at the same time, one traveling on the surface of the water and the other traveling underwater. In how many minutes will the sQuba traveling on the surface of the water be directly above the sQuba traveling underwater? Assume they are traveling at top speed.

> **In the NEWS!**
>
> **Underwater Driving—Not So Fast!**
>
> Swiss company Rinspeed, Inc., presented its new car, the sQuba, at the Geneva Auto Show. The sQuba can travel on land, on water, and underwater. With a new sQuba, you can expect top speeds of 77 mph when driving on land, 3 mph when driving on the surface of the water, and 1.8 mph when driving underwater!
>
> *Source:* Seattle Times

69. Two cyclists start from the same point at the same time and move in opposite directions. One cyclist is traveling at 8 mph, and the other cyclist is traveling at 9 mph. After 30 min, how far apart are the two cyclists?

70. Petra and Celine can paddle their canoe at a rate of 10 mph in calm water. How long will it take them to travel 4 mi against the 2-mile-per-hour current of the river?

71. At 8:00 A.M., a train leaves a station and travels at a rate of 45 mph. At 9:00 A.M., a second train leaves the same station on the same track and travels in the direction of the first train at a speed of 60 mph. At 10:00 A.M., how far apart are the two trains?

Critical Thinking

72. **Geometry** Solve for x.

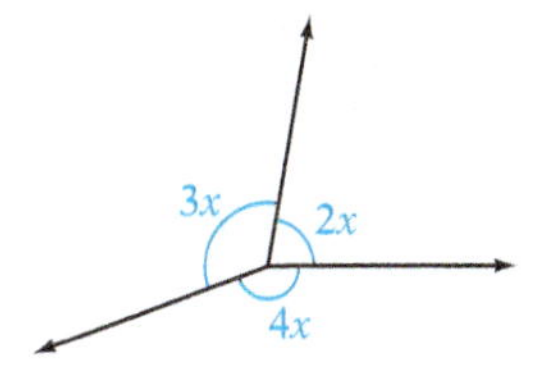

73. **Geometry** Solve for x.

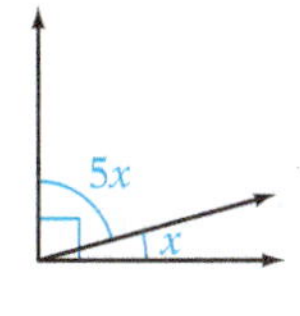

74. **Geometry** Solve for x.

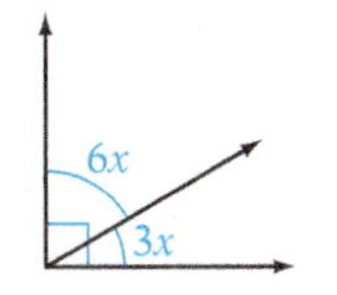

75. **Geometry** Solve for x.

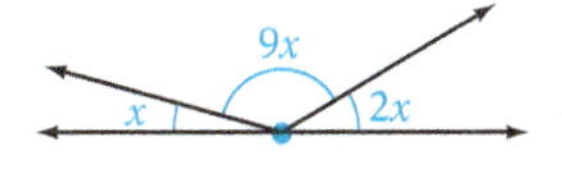

76. **Consumerism** Your bill for dinner, including a 7.25% sales tax, was \$92.74. You want to leave a 15% tip on the cost of the dinner before the sales tax. Find the amount of the tip to the nearest dollar.

77. **Business** A retailer decides to increase the original price of each item in the store by 10%. After the price increase, the retailer notices a significant drop in sales and so decides to reduce the current price of each item in the store by 10%. Are the prices back to the original prices? If not, are the prices lower or higher than the original prices?

78. If a quantity increases by 100%, how many times its original value is the new value?

79. Employee A had an annual salary of \$52,000, Employee B had an annual salary of \$58,000, and Employee C had an annual salary of \$56,000 before each employee was given a 5% raise. Which of the three employees now has the highest annual salary? Explain how you arrived at your answer.

80. Each of three employees earned an annual salary of \$65,000 before Employee A was given a 3% raise, Employee B was given a 6% raise, and Employee C was given a 4.5% raise. Which of the three employees now has the highest annual salary? Explain how you arrived at your answer.

Projects or Group Activities

81. **U.S. Population** The circle graph at the right shows the population of the United States, in millions, by region. (*Source:* U.S. Census Bureau)

a. To the nearest tenth of a percent, what percent of the U.S. population lives in each region?

b. Which region has the largest population? In which region does the largest percent of the population live?

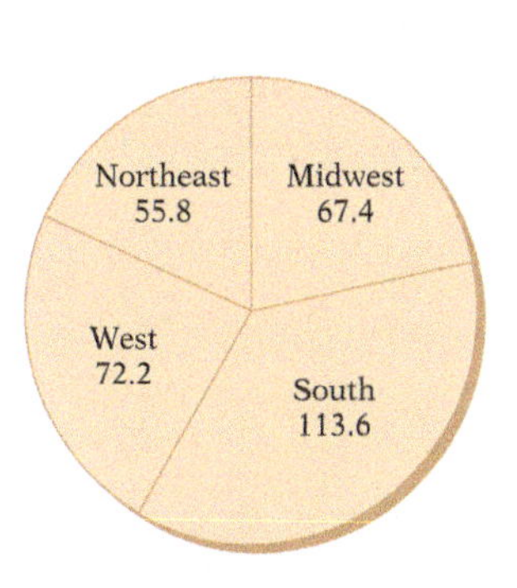

U.S. Population by Region (in millions of residents)

According to the Census Bureau, California has the largest population of all the states, with 38 million. Wyoming, with 0.1683% of the U.S. population, has the least number of residents.

c. What percent of the U.S. population lives in California? Round to the nearest tenth of a percent.

d. How many residents live in Wyoming? Round to the nearest ten thousand.

e. What percent of the U.S. population lives in the state you live in?

SECTION

3.3 General Equations—Part I

OBJECTIVE A *To solve an equation of the form $ax + b = c$*

In solving an equation of the form $ax + b = c$, the goal is to rewrite the equation in the form *variable* = *constant*. This requires the application of both the Addition and Multiplication Properties of Equations.

HOW TO 1 Solve: $\frac{3}{4}x - 2 = -11$

The goal is to write the equation in the form *variable* = *constant*.

$$\frac{3}{4}x - 2 = -11$$

$$\frac{3}{4}x - 2 + 2 = -11 + 2$$ • Add 2 to each side of the equation.

$$\frac{3}{4}x = -9$$ • Simplify.

$$\frac{4}{3} \cdot \frac{3}{4}x = \frac{4}{3}(-9)$$ • Multiply each side of the equation by $\frac{4}{3}$.

$$x = -12$$ • The equation is in the form *variable* = *constant*.

The solution is −12.

Take Note

Check:

$$\frac{3}{4}x - 2 = -11$$

$\frac{3}{4}(-12) - 2$	-11
$-9 - 2$	-11
$-11 =$	-11

A true equation

Here is an example of solving an equation that contains more than one fraction.

HOW TO 2 Solve: $\frac{2}{3}x + \frac{1}{2} = \frac{3}{4}$

$$\frac{2}{3}x + \frac{1}{2} = \frac{3}{4}$$

$$\frac{2}{3}x + \frac{1}{2} - \frac{1}{2} = \frac{3}{4} - \frac{1}{2}$$ • Subtract $\frac{1}{2}$ from each side of the equation.

$$\frac{2}{3}x = \frac{1}{4}$$ • Simplify.

$$\frac{3}{2}\left(\frac{2}{3}x\right) = \frac{3}{2}\left(\frac{1}{4}\right)$$ • Multiply each side of the equation by $\frac{3}{2}$.

$$x = \frac{3}{8}$$

The solution is $\frac{3}{8}$.

It may be easier to solve an equation containing two or more fractions by multiplying each side of the equation by the least common multiple (LCM) of the denominators. For the equation above, the LCM of 3, 2, and 4 is 12. The LCM has the property that 3, 2, and 4 divide evenly into it. Therefore, if both sides of the equation are multiplied by 12, the denominators will divide evenly into 12. The result is an equation that does not contain any fractions. Multiplying each side of an equation that contains fractions by the LCM of the denominators is called **clearing denominators.** It is an alternative method, as we show in the next example, of solving an equation that contains fractions.

Take Note
This is the same example solved on the preceding page, but this time we are using the method of clearing denominators.

Observe that after we multiply both sides of the equation by the LCM of the denominators and then simplify, the equation no longer contains fractions.

Clearing denominators is a method of solving equations. The process applies only to equations, never to expressions.

HOW TO 3 Solve: $\frac{2}{3}x + \frac{1}{2} = \frac{3}{4}$

$$\frac{2}{3}x + \frac{1}{2} = \frac{3}{4}$$

$$12\left(\frac{2}{3}x + \frac{1}{2}\right) = 12\left(\frac{3}{4}\right)$$
• Multiply each side of the equation by 12, the LCM of 3, 2, and 4.

$$12\left(\frac{2}{3}x\right) + 12\left(\frac{1}{2}\right) = 12\left(\frac{3}{4}\right)$$
• Use the Distributive Property.

$$8x + 6 = 9$$
• Simplify.

$$8x + 6 - 6 = 9 - 6$$
• Subtract 6 from each side of the equation.

$$8x = 3$$

$$\frac{8x}{8} = \frac{3}{8}$$
• Divide each side of the equation by 8.

$$x = \frac{3}{8}$$

The solution is $\frac{3}{8}$.

Note that both methods give exactly the same solution. You may use either method to solve an equation containing fractions.

EXAMPLE 1

Solve: $3x - 7 = -5$

Solution

$$3x - 7 = -5$$

$$3x - 7 + 7 = -5 + 7$$
• Add 7 to each side.

$$3x = 2$$

$$\frac{3x}{3} = \frac{2}{3}$$
• Divide each side by 3.

$$x = \frac{2}{3}$$

The solution is $\frac{2}{3}$.

YOU TRY IT 1

Solve: $5x + 7 = 10$

Your solution

EXAMPLE 2

Solve: $5 = 9 - 2x$

Solution

$$5 = 9 - 2x$$

$$5 - 9 = 9 - 9 - 2x$$
• Subtract 9 from each side.

$$-4 = -2x$$

$$\frac{-4}{-2} = \frac{-2x}{-2}$$
• Divide each side by −2.

$$2 = x$$

The solution is 2.

YOU TRY IT 2

Solve: $2 = 11 + 3x$

Your solution

Solutions on p. S5

EXAMPLE 3

Solve: $\frac{2}{3} - \frac{x}{2} = \frac{3}{4}$

Solution

$$\frac{2}{3} - \frac{x}{2} = \frac{3}{4}$$

$$\frac{2}{3} - \frac{2}{3} - \frac{x}{2} = \frac{3}{4} - \frac{2}{3}$$ • Subtract $\frac{2}{3}$ from each side.

$$-\frac{x}{2} = \frac{1}{12}$$

$$-2\left(-\frac{x}{2}\right) = -2\left(\frac{1}{12}\right)$$ • Multiply each side by -2.

$$x = -\frac{1}{6}$$

The solution is $-\frac{1}{6}$.

YOU TRY IT 3

Solve: $\frac{5}{8} - \frac{2x}{3} = \frac{5}{4}$

Your solution

EXAMPLE 4

Solve $\frac{4}{5}x - \frac{1}{2} = \frac{3}{4}$ by first clearing denominators.

Solution

The LCM of 5, 2, and 4 is 20.

$$\frac{4}{5}x - \frac{1}{2} = \frac{3}{4}$$

$$20\left(\frac{4}{5}x - \frac{1}{2}\right) = 20\left(\frac{3}{4}\right)$$ • Multiply each side by 20.

$$20\left(\frac{4}{5}x\right) - 20\left(\frac{1}{2}\right) = 20\left(\frac{3}{4}\right)$$ • Use the Distributive Property.

$$16x - 10 = 15$$

$$16x - 10 + 10 = 15 + 10$$ • Add 10 to each side.

$$16x = 25$$

$$\frac{16x}{16} = \frac{25}{16}$$ • Divide each side by 16.

$$x = \frac{25}{16}$$

The solution is $\frac{25}{16}$.

YOU TRY IT 4

Solve $\frac{2}{3}x + 3 = \frac{7}{2}$ by first clearing denominators.

Your solution

Solutions on p. S6

EXAMPLE 5

Solve: $2x + 4 - 5x = 10$

Solution

$2x + 4 - 5x = 10$

$-3x + 4 = 10$ • Combine like terms.

$-3x + 4 - 4 = 10 - 4$ • Subtract 4 from each side.

$-3x = 6$

$\frac{-3x}{-3} = \frac{6}{-3}$ • Divide each side by -3.

$x = -2$

The solution is -2.

YOU TRY IT 5

Solve: $x - 5 + 4x = 25$

Your solution

Solution on p. S6

OBJECTIVE B *To solve application problems using formulas*

In this objective we will be using formulas to solve application problems. Two of the formulas we will use are related to markup and discount.

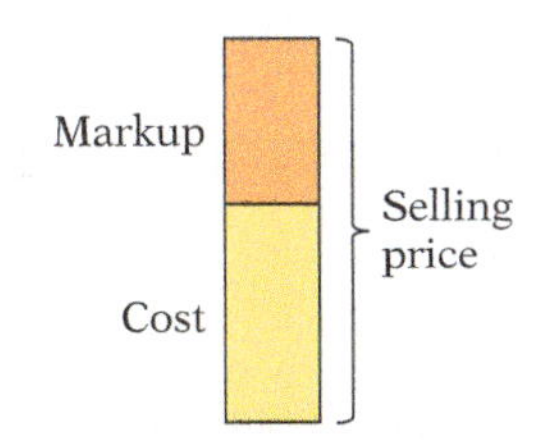

Cost is the price a business pays for a product. **Selling price** is the price for which a business sells a product to a customer. The difference between selling price and cost is called **markup.** Markup is added to the cost to cover the expenses of operating a business. The diagram at the left illustrates these terms. The total length is the selling price. One part of the diagram is the cost, and the other part is the markup.

When the markup is expressed as a percent of the retailer's cost, it is called the **markup rate.**

Selling price = cost + markup Markup = markup rate · cost

$S = C + M$ $M = r \cdot C$

Substituting $r \cdot C$ for M in the first equation results in the equation $S = C + (r \cdot C)$, or $S = C + rC$.

Basic Markup Equation

The basic markup equation is $S = C + rC$, where S is the selling price, C is the cost, and r is the markup rate.

EXAMPLE

The manager of a clothing store buys cross trainers for \$80 and sells them for \$116. Find the markup rate.

To find the markup rate, use the basic markup equation.

$S = C + rC$ • Use the basic markup equation.

$116 = 80 + 80r$ • Given: $C = 80$ and $S = 116$

$36 = 80r$ • Subtract 80 from each side of the equation.

$0.45 = r$ • Divide each side of the equation by 80.

The markup rate on the cross trainers is 45%.

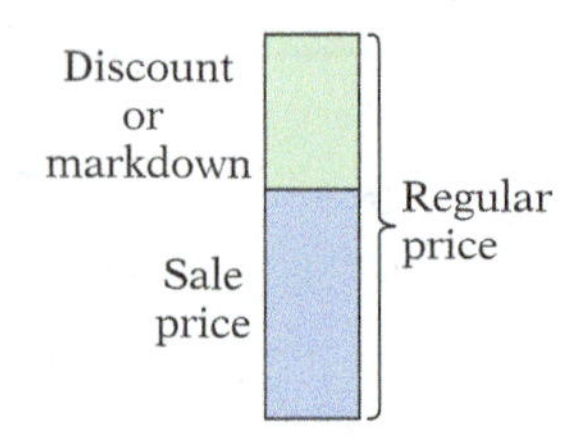

A retailer may reduce the regular price of a product because the product is damaged, an odd size, or a discontinued item. The **discount,** or **markdown,** is the amount by which a retailer reduces the regular price of a product. The percent discount is called the **discount rate** and is usually expressed as a percent of the original selling price (the regular price).

$$\text{Sale price} = \text{regular price} - \text{discount} \qquad \text{Discount} = \text{discount rate} \cdot \text{regular price}$$

$$S = R - D \qquad D = r \cdot R$$

Substituting $r \cdot R$ for D in the first equation yields $S = R - (r \cdot R)$, or $S = R - rR$.

Take Note
In general, lower case letters and upper case letters are considered to be different variables.

Basic Discount Equation

The basic discount equation is $S = R - rR$, where S is the sale price, R is the regular price, and r is the discount rate.

EXAMPLE

A laptop computer that regularly sells for \$1850 is on sale for \$1480. Find the discount rate.

To find the discount rate, use the basic discount equation.

$S = R - rR$ • Use the basic discount equation.
$1480 = 1850 - 1850r$ • Given: $S = 1480$ and $R = 1850$
$-370 = -1850r$ • Subtract 1850 from each side of the equation.
$0.2 = r$ • Divide each side of the equation by -1850.

The discount rate on the laptop computer is 20%.

EXAMPLE 6

A markup rate of 40% was used on a mountain bike that has a selling price of \$749. Find the cost of the mountain bike. Use the formula $S = C + rC$.

Strategy

Given: $S = \$749$
$r = 40\% = 0.40$
Unknown: C

Solution

$S = C + rC$
$749 = C + 0.40C$ • $C + 0.40C = 1C + 0.40C$
$749 = 1.40C$ • Combine like terms.
$\frac{749}{1.40} = \frac{1.40C}{1.40}$ • Divide each side by 1.40.
$535 = C$

The cost of the mountain bike is \$535.

YOU TRY IT 6

A markup rate of 45% was used on an outboard motor that has a selling price of \$986. Find the cost of the outboard motor. Use the formula $S = C + rC$.

Your strategy

Your solution

Solution on p. S6

EXAMPLE 7

A necklace that is marked down 35% has a sale price of \$292.50. Find the regular price of the necklace. Use the formula $S = R - rR$.

Strategy

Given: $S = 292.50$
$r = 35\% = 0.35$
Unknown: R

Solution

$S = R - rR$

$292.50 = R - 0.35R$ • $R + 0.35R = 1R + 0.35R$

$292.50 = 0.65R$ • Combine like terms.

$\frac{292.50}{0.65} = \frac{0.65R}{0.65}$ • Divide each side by 0.65.

$450 = R$

The regular price of the necklace is \$450.

YOU TRY IT 7

An MP3 player, marked down 25%, is on sale for \$159. Find the regular price of the MP3 player. Use the formula $S = R - rR$.

Your strategy

Your solution

EXAMPLE 8

To determine the total cost of production, an economist uses the equation $T = U \cdot N + F$, where T is the total cost, U is the unit cost, N is the number of units made, and F is the fixed cost. Use this equation to find the number of units made during a month in which the total cost was \$9000, the unit cost was \$25, and the fixed cost was \$3000.

Strategy

Given: $T = 9000$
$U = 25$
$F = 3000$
Unknown: N

Solution

$T = U \cdot N + F$

$9000 = 25N + 3000$ • $T = 9000, U = 25, F = 3000$

$6000 = 25N$ • Subtract 3000 from each side.

$\frac{6000}{25} = \frac{25N}{25}$ • Divide each side by 25.

$240 = N$

There were 240 units made.

YOU TRY IT 8

The pressure at a certain depth in the ocean can be approximated by the equation $P = 15 + \frac{1}{2}D$, where P is the pressure in pounds per square inch and D is the depth in feet. Use this equation to find the depth when the pressure is 45 pounds per square inch.

Your strategy

Your solution

Solutions on p. S6

3.3 EXERCISES

Concept Check

1. Match each equation with the first step in solving that equation.

a. $3x - 7 = 5$
b. $4x + 7 = -5$
c. $7x - 5 = 2$
d. $-7x + 5 = -2$

i. Add 7 to each side.
ii. Add 5 to each side.
iii. Subtract 7 from each side.
iv. Subtract 5 from each side.

2. True or false? An equation of the form $ax + b = c$ cannot be solved if a is a negative number.

3. The first step in solving the equation $5 + 8x = 29$ is to subtract ______ from each side of the equation. The second step is to divide each side of the equation by ______.

4. To clear denominators from the equation $\frac{x}{9} + 2 = \frac{1}{6}$, multiply each side of the equation by ______, the least common multiple of the denominators 9 and 6.

OBJECTIVE A *To solve an equation of the form $ax + b = c$*

For Exercises 5 to 76, solve and check.

5. $3x + 1 = 10$ **6.** $4y + 3 = 11$ **7.** $2a - 5 = 7$ **8.** $5m - 6 = 9$

9. $5 = 4x + 9$ **10.** $2 = 5b + 12$ **11.** $2x - 5 = -11$ **12.** $3n - 7 = -19$

13. $4 - 3w = -2$ **14.** $5 - 6x = -13$ **15.** $8 - 3t = 2$ **16.** $12 - 5x = 7$

17. $4a - 20 = 0$ **18.** $3y - 9 = 0$ **19.** $6 + 2b = 0$ **20.** $10 + 5m = 0$

21. $-2x + 5 = -7$ **22.** $-5d + 3 = -12$ **23.** $-1.2x + 3 = -0.6$ **24.** $-1.3 = -1.1y + 0.9$

25. $2 = 7 - 5a$ **26.** $3 = 11 - 4n$ **27.** $-35 = -6b + 1$ **28.** $-8x + 3 = -29$

29. $-3m - 21 = 0$ **30.** $-5x - 30 = 0$ **31.** $-4y + 15 = 15$ **32.** $-3x + 19 = 19$

33. $9 - 4x = 6$
34. $3t - 2 = 0$
35. $9x - 4 = 0$
36. $7 - 8z = 0$
37. $1 - 3x = 0$
38. $9d + 10 = 7$
39. $12w + 11 = 5$
40. $6y - 5 = -7$
41. $8b - 3 = -9$
42. $5 - 6m = 2$
43. $7 - 9a = 4$
44. $9 = -12c + 5$
45. $10 = -18x + 7$
46. $5y + \frac{3}{7} = \frac{3}{7}$
47. $9x + \frac{4}{5} = \frac{4}{5}$
48. $0.8 = 7d + 0.1$
49. $0.9 = 10x - 0.6$
50. $-6y + 5 = 13$
51. $-4x + 3 = 9$
52. $\frac{1}{2}a - 3 = 1$
53. $\frac{1}{3}m - 1 = 5$
54. $\frac{2}{5}y + 4 = 6$
55. $\frac{3}{4}n + 7 = 13$
56. $-\frac{2}{3}x + 1 = 7$
57. $-\frac{3}{8}b + 4 = 10$
58. $\frac{x}{4} - 6 = 1$
59. $\frac{y}{5} - 2 = 3$
60. $\frac{2x}{3} - 1 = 5$
61. $\frac{2}{3}x - \frac{5}{6} = -\frac{1}{3}$
62. $\frac{5}{4}x + \frac{2}{3} = \frac{1}{4}$
63. $\frac{1}{2} - \frac{2}{3}x = \frac{1}{4}$
64. $\frac{3}{4} - \frac{3}{5}x = \frac{19}{20}$
65. $\frac{3}{2} = \frac{5}{6} + \frac{3x}{8}$
66. $-\frac{1}{4} = \frac{5}{12} + \frac{5x}{6}$
67. $\frac{11}{27} = \frac{4}{9} - \frac{2x}{3}$
68. $\frac{37}{24} = \frac{7}{8} - \frac{5x}{6}$
69. $7 = \frac{2x}{5} + 4$
70. $5 - \frac{4c}{7} = 8$
71. $7 - \frac{5}{9}y = 9$
72. $6a + 3 + 2a = 11$
73. $5y + 9 + 2y = 23$
74. $7x - 4 - 2x = 6$
75. $11z - 3 - 7z = 9$
76. $2x - 6x + 1 = 9$

For Exercises 77 to 80, without solving the equation, determine whether the solution is positive or negative.

77. $15x + 73 = -347$
78. $17 = 25 - 40a$
79. $290 + 51n = 187$
80. $-72 = -86y + 49$

81. Solve $3x + 4y = 13$ when $y = -2$.

82. Solve $2x - 3y = 8$ when $y = 0$.

83. Solve $-4x + 3y = 9$ when $x = 0$.

84. Solve $5x - 2y = -3$ when $x = -3$.

85. If $2x - 3 = 7$, evaluate $3x + 4$.

86. If $3x + 5 = -4$, evaluate $2x - 5$.

87. If $4 - 5x = -1$, evaluate $x^2 - 3x + 1$.

88. If $2 - 3x = 11$, evaluate $x^2 + 2x - 3$.

OBJECTIVE B *To solve application problems using formulas*

Business For Exercises 89 to 96, solve. Use the markup equation $S = C + rC$, where S is the selling price, C is the cost, and r is the markup rate.

89. A watch costing \$98 is sold for \$156.80. Find the markup rate on the watch.

Kletr/Shutterstock.com

90. A set of golf clubs costing \$360 is sold for \$630. Find the markup rate on the set of golf clubs.

91. A markup rate of 40% was used on a basketball with a selling price of \$82.60. Find the cost of the basketball.

92. A pair of jeans with a selling price of \$57 has a markup rate of 50%. Find the cost of the pair of jeans.

93. A camera costing \$360 is sold for \$520. Find the markup rate. Round to the nearest tenth of a percent.

94. A car navigation system costing \$320 is sold for \$479. Find the markup rate. Round to the nearest tenth of a percent.

95. A compact disc has a selling price of \$11.90. The markup rate is 40%. Find the cost of the CD.

96. A markup rate of 25% is used on a media center that has a selling price of \$2187.50. Find the cost of the computer.

97. True or false? If a store uses a markup rate of 35%, you can find the store's cost for an item by dividing the selling price of the item by $1 + 0.35$, or 1.35.

98. If the markup rate on an item is 100%, what is the relationship between the selling price of the item and the cost of the item?

99. **Bill of Materials** Use the information in the article at the right to find the markup rate for the 8 GB iPod Touch. Round your answer to the nearest percent.

100. **Bill of Materials** Use the information in the article at the right to find the markup rate for the 32 GB iPad 3G. Round your answer to the nearest percent.

Not a Nano-Sized Markup

When you buy your latest technology gadget, do you ever wonder how much of a markup you are paying? A product's *bill of materials (BOM)* is the total cost to the manufacturer for the materials used to make the product. The rest of the price you pay is the markup. For example, the 8 GB Apple iPod Touch, with a BOM of \$149.18, sells for \$229; and the 32 GB iPad 3G, with a BOM of \$287.15, sells for \$729.

Source: www.iSuppli.com

Business For Exercises 101 to 108, solve. Use the discount equation $S = R - rR$, where S is the sale price, R is the regular price, and r is the discount rate.

101. A tent with a regular price of \$1295 is on sale for \$995. Find the discount rate. Round to the nearest tenth of a percent.

102. A toy train set with a regular price of \$495 is on sale for \$395. Find the markdown rate. Round to the nearest tenth of a percent.

103. A mechanic's tool set is on sale for \$180 after a markdown of 40% off the regular price. Find the regular price.

104. A battery with a discount price of \$65 is on sale for 22% off the regular price. Find the regular price. Round to the nearest cent.

105. A DVD player with a regular price of \$325 is on sale for \$201.50. Find the markdown rate.

106. A luggage set with a regular price of \$178 is on sale for \$103.24. Find the discount rate.

107. A telescope is on sale for \$165 after a markdown of 40% off the regular price. Find the regular price.

Alexander Kolomietz/Shutterstock.com

108. An exercise bike is on sale for \$390, having been marked down 25% off the regular price. Find the regular price.

109. True or false? If a store uses a discount rate of 15%, you can find the sale price of an item by multiplying the regular price of the item by $1 - 0.15$, or 0.85.

110. If the discount rate on an item is 50%, which of the following is true? (S is the sale price, and R is the regular price.)
(i) $S = 2R$ (ii) $R = 2S$ (iii) $S = R$ (iv) $0.50S = R$

Champion Trees American Forests is an organization that maintains the National Register of Big Trees, a listing of the largest trees in the United States. The formula used to award points to a tree is $P = c + h + \frac{1}{4}s$, where P is the point total for a tree with a circumference of c inches, a height of h feet, and an average crown spread of s feet. Use this formula for Exercises 111 and 112. (*Source:* www.amfor.org)

111. Find the average crown spread of the baldcypress described in the article at the right.

112. One of the smallest trees in the United States is a Florida Crossopetalum in the Key Largo Hammocks State Botanical Site. This tree stands 11 ft tall, has a circumference of just 4.8 in., and scores 16.55 points using American Forests' formula. Find the tree's average crown spread. (*Source:* www.championtrees.org)

In the NEWS!

The Senator Is a Champion

Baldcypress trees are among the most ancient of North American trees. The 3500-year-old baldcypress known as the Senator, was located in Big Tree Park, Longwood, and was the Florida Champion specimen of the species. With a circumference of 425 in. and a height of 118 ft, this king of the swamp forest earned a total of $557\frac{1}{4}$ points under the point system used for the National Register of Big Trees.

Source: www.championtrees.org

The Senator at Big Tree Park

Nutrition The formula $C = 9f + 4p + 4c$ gives the number of calories C in a serving of food that contains f grams of fat, p grams of protein, and c grams of carbohydrate. Use this formula for Exercises 113 and 114. (*Source:* www.nutristrategy.com)

113. Find the number of grams of protein in an 8-ounce serving of vanilla yogurt that contains 174 calories, 2 g of fat, and 30 g of carbohydrate.

114. Find the number of grams of fat in a serving of granola that contains 215 calories, 42 g of carbohydrate, and 5 g of protein.

Physics The distance s, in feet, that an object will fall in t seconds is given by the formula $s = 16t^2 + vt$, where v is the initial velocity of the object in feet per second. Use this equation for Exercises 115 and 116.

115. Find the initial velocity of an object that falls 80 ft in 2 s.

116. Find the initial velocity of an object that falls 144 ft in 3 s.

Depreciation A company uses the equation $V = C - 6000t$ to determine the depreciated value V, after t years, of a milling machine that originally cost C dollars. Equations such as this are used in accounting for straight-line depreciation. Use this equation for Exercises 117 and 118.

117. A milling machine originally cost \$50,000. In how many years will the depreciated value of the machine be \$38,000?

118. A milling machine originally cost \$78,000. In how many years will the depreciated value of the machine be \$48,000?

Anthropology Anthropologists approximate the height of a primate by the size of its humerus (the bone from the elbow to the shoulder) using the equation $H = 1.2L + 27.8$, where L is the length of the humerus and H is the height, in inches, of the primate. Use this equation for Exercises 119 and 120.

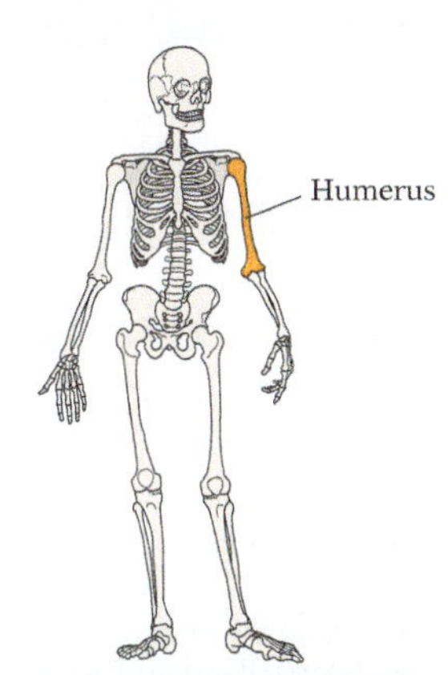

119. An anthropologist estimates the height of a primate to be 66 in. What is the approximate length of the humerus of this primate? Round to the nearest tenth of an inch.

120. An anthropologist estimates the height of a primate to be 62 in. What is the approximate length of the humerus of this primate?

Car Safety Black ice is an ice covering on roads that is especially difficult to see and therefore extremely dangerous for motorists. The distance that a car traveling at 30 mph will slide after its brakes are applied is related to the outside temperature by the formula $C = \frac{1}{4}D - 45$, where C is the Celsius temperature and D is the distance in feet that the car will slide. Use this equation for Exercises 121 and 122.

121. Determine the distance a car will slide on black ice when the outside temperature is -3°C.

122. Determine the distance a car will slide on black ice when the outside temperature is -11°C.

Critical Thinking

123. Business A customer buys four tires, three at the regular price and one for 20% off the regular price. The four tires cost $323. What is the regular price of a tire?

124. Geometry The area of the triangle at the right is 40 m^2. Find x.

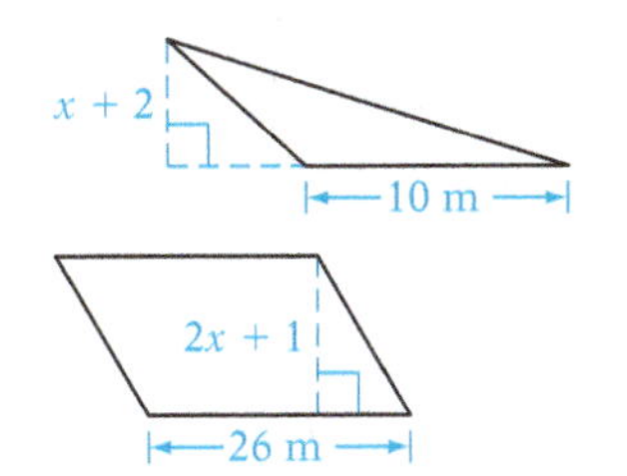

125. Geometry The area of the parallelogram at the right is 364 m^2. Find the height.

Projects or Group Activities

126. A lamp, originally priced at under $100, was on sale for 25% off the regular price. When the regular price, a whole number of dollars, was discounted, the discounted price was also a whole number of dollars. Find the largest possible number of dollars in the regular price of the lamp.

127. A used car is on sale for 20% off the regular price of $8500. An additional 10% discount on the sale price is offered. Is the result a 30% discount? What single discount would give the same sale price?

128. Write an application problem involving a discount rate of 35%. Choose a product and its regular price. Determine the sale price. Use complete sentences.

129. Write a report on series trade discounts. Explain how to convert a series discount to a single-discount equivalent.

SECTION

3.4 General Equations—Part II

OBJECTIVE A To solve an equation of the form $ax + b = cx + d$

Tips for Success

Have you considered joining a study group? Getting together regularly with other students in the class to go over material and quiz each other can be very beneficial. See *AIM for Success* at the front of the book.

In solving an equation of the form $ax + b = cx + d$, the goal is to rewrite the equation in the form *variable* = *constant*. Begin by rewriting the equation so that there is only one variable term in the equation. Then rewrite the equation so that there is only one constant term.

HOW TO 1 Solve: $2x + 3 = 5x - 9$

$2x + 3 = 5x - 9$

$2x - 5x + 3 = 5x - 5x - 9$ • Subtract 5x from each side of the equation.

$-3x + 3 = -9$ • Simplify. There is only one variable term.

$-3x + 3 - 3 = -9 - 3$ • Subtract 3 from each side of the equation.

$-3x = -12$ • Simplify. There is only one constant term.

$\frac{-3x}{-3} = \frac{-12}{-3}$ • Divide each side of the equation by −3.

$x = 4$ • The equation is in the form *variable* = *constant*.

The solution is 4. You should verify this by checking this solution.

EXAMPLE 1

Solve: $4x - 5 = 8x - 7$

Solution

$4x - 5 = 8x - 7$

$4x - 8x - 5 = 8x - 8x - 7$ • Subtract 8x from each side.

$-4x - 5 = -7$

$-4x - 5 + 5 = -7 + 5$ • Add 5 to each side.

$-4x = -2$

$\frac{-4x}{-4} = \frac{-2}{-4}$ • Divide each side by −4.

$x = \frac{1}{2}$

The solution is $\frac{1}{2}$.

YOU TRY IT 1

Solve: $5x + 4 = 6 + 10x$

Your solution

Solution on p. S6

EXAMPLE 2

Solve: $3x + 4 - 5x = 2 - 4x$

Solution

$$3x + 4 - 5x = 2 - 4x$$

$$-2x + 4 = 2 - 4x$$ • Combine like terms.

$$-2x + 4x + 4 = 2 - 4x + 4x$$ • Add $4x$ to each side.

$$2x + 4 = 2$$

$$2x + 4 - 4 = 2 - 4$$ • Subtract 4 from each side.

$$2x = -2$$

$$\frac{2x}{2} = \frac{-2}{2}$$ • Divide each side by 2.

$$x = -1$$

The solution is -1.

YOU TRY IT 2

Solve: $5x - 10 - 3x = 6 - 4x$

Your solution

Solution on p. S6

OBJECTIVE B

To solve an equation containing parentheses

When an equation contains parentheses, one of the steps in solving the equation is to use the Distributive Property. The Distributive Property is used to remove parentheses from a variable expression.

HOW TO 2 Solve: $4 + 5(2x - 3) = 3(4x - 1)$

$$4 + 5(2x - 3) = 3(4x - 1)$$

$$4 + 10x - 15 = 12x - 3$$ • Use the Distributive Property. Then simplify.

$$10x - 11 = 12x - 3$$

$$10x - 12x - 11 = 12x - 12x - 3$$ • Subtract $12x$ from each side of the equation.

$$-2x - 11 = -3$$ • Simplify.

$$-2x - 11 + 11 = -3 + 11$$ • Add 11 to each side of the equation.

$$-2x = 8$$ • Simplify.

$$\frac{-2x}{-2} = \frac{8}{-2}$$ • Divide each side of the equation by -2.

$$x = -4$$ • The equation is in the form *variable* = *constant*.

The solution is -4. You should verify this by checking this solution.

In the next example, we solve an equation containing parentheses and decimals.

HOW TO 3 Solve: $16 + 0.55x = 0.75(x + 20)$

$$16 + 0.55x = 0.75(x + 20)$$

$$16 + 0.55x = 0.75x + 15$$ • Use the Distributive Property.

$$16 + 0.55x - 0.75x = 0.75x - 0.75x + 15$$ • Subtract $0.75x$ from each side of the equation.

$$16 - 0.20x = 15$$ • Simplify.

$$16 - 16 - 0.20x = 15 - 16$$ • Subtract 16 from each side of the equation.

$$-0.20x = -1$$ • Simplify.

$$\frac{-0.20x}{-0.20} = \frac{-1}{-0.20}$$ • Divide each side of the equation by -0.20.

$$x = 5$$ • The equation is in the form *variable = constant.*

The solution is 5.

EXAMPLE 3

Solve: $3x - 4(2 - x) = 3(x - 2) - 4$

Solution

$$3x - 4(2 - x) = 3(x - 2) - 4$$

$$3x - 8 + 4x = 3x - 6 - 4$$ • Distributive Property

$$7x - 8 = 3x - 10$$

$$7x - 3x - 8 = 3x - 3x - 10$$ • Subtract $3x$.

$$4x - 8 = -10$$

$$4x - 8 + 8 = -10 + 8$$ • Add 8.

$$4x = -2$$

$$\frac{4x}{4} = \frac{-2}{4}$$ • Divide by 4.

$$x = -\frac{1}{2}$$

The solution is $-\frac{1}{2}$.

YOU TRY IT 3

Solve: $5x - 4(3 - 2x) = 2(3x - 2) + 6$

Your solution

EXAMPLE 4

Solve: $3[2 - 4(2x - 1)] = 4x - 10$

Solution

$$3[2 - 4(2x - 1)] = 4x - 10$$

$$3[2 - 8x + 4] = 4x - 10$$ • Distributive Property

$$3[6 - 8x] = 4x - 10$$

$$18 - 24x = 4x - 10$$ • Distributive Property

$$18 - 24x - 4x = 4x - 4x - 10$$ • Subtract $4x$.

$$18 - 28x = -10$$

$$18 - 18 - 28x = -10 - 18$$ • Subtract 18.

$$-28x = -28$$

$$\frac{-28x}{-28} = \frac{-28}{-28}$$ • Divide by -28.

$$x = 1$$

The solution is 1.

YOU TRY IT 4

Solve: $-2[3x - 5(2x - 3)] = 3x - 8$

Your solution

Solutions on p. S7

OBJECTIVE C To solve application problems using formulas

Take Note

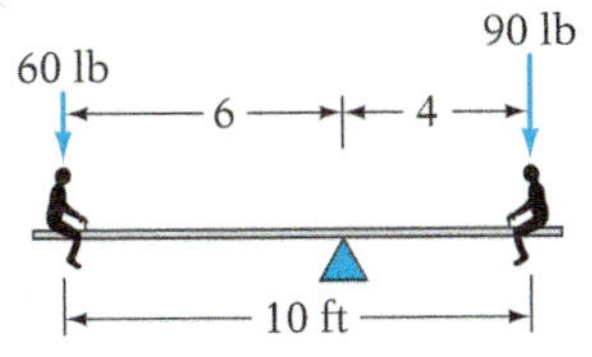

This system balances because

$$F_1x = F_2(d - x)$$
$$60(6) = 90(10 - 6)$$
$$60(6) = 90(4)$$
$$360 = 360$$

A lever system is shown at the right. It consists of a lever, or bar; a fulcrum; and two forces, F_1 and F_2. The distance d represents the length of the lever, x represents the distance from F_1 to the fulcrum, and $d - x$ represents the distance from F_2 to the fulcrum.

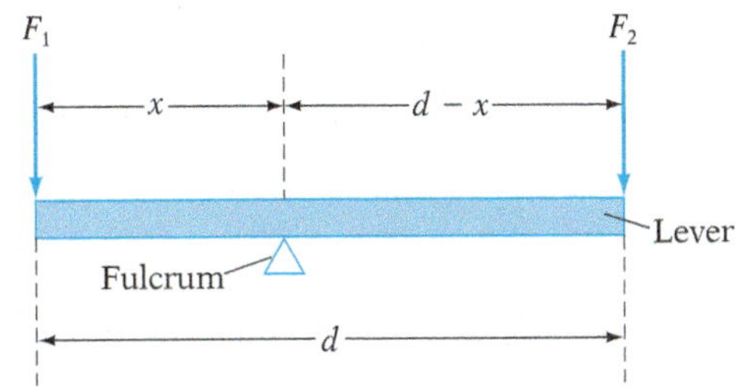

A principle of physics states that when the lever system balances, $F_1x = F_2(d - x)$.

EXAMPLE 5

A lever is 15 ft long. A force of 50 lb is applied to one end of the lever, and a force of 100 lb is applied to the other end. Where is the fulcrum located when the system balances?

Strategy

Make a drawing.

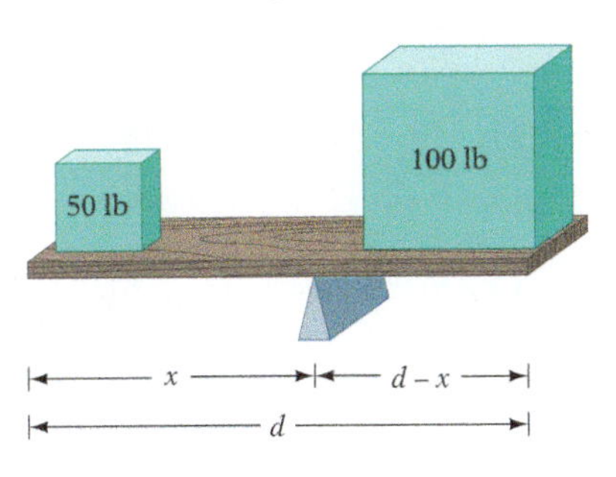

Given: $F_1 = 50$
$F_2 = 100$
$d = 15$
Unknown: x

Solution

$$F_1x = F_2(d - x)$$
$$50x = 100(15 - x) \quad \bullet\ F_1 = 50, F_2 = 100, d = 15$$
$$50x = 1500 - 100x$$
$$50x + 100x = 1500 - 100x + 100x \quad \bullet\ \text{Add } 100x.$$
$$150x = 1500$$
$$\frac{150x}{150} = \frac{1500}{150} \quad \bullet\ \text{Divide by 150.}$$
$$x = 10$$

The fulcrum is 10 ft from the 50-pound force.

YOU TRY IT 5

A lever is 25 ft long. A force of 45 lb is applied to one end of the lever, and a force of 80 lb is applied to the other end. Where is the location of the fulcrum when the system balances?

Your strategy

Your solution

Solution on p. S7

3.4 EXERCISES

Concept Check

For Exercises 1 to 3, determine whether the statement is true or false.

1. The same variable term can be added to both sides of an equation without changing the solution of the equation.

2. The same variable term can be subtracted from both sides of an equation without changing the solution of the equation.

3. In solving an equation of the form $ax + b = cx + d$, the goal is to rewrite the equation in the form *variable* = *constant*.

4. Describe the step that will enable you to rewrite the equation $2x - 3 = 7x + 12$ so that it has one variable term with a positive coefficient.

5. If you rewrite the equation $8 - y = y + 6$ so that it has one variable term on the left side of the equation, what will be the coefficient of the variable?

OBJECTIVE A *To solve an equation of the form $ax + b = cx + d$*

For Exercises 6 to 32, solve and check.

6. $8x + 5 = 4x + 13$
7. $6y + 2 = y + 17$
8. $5x - 4 = 2x + 5$
9. $13b - 1 = 4b - 19$
10. $15x - 2 = 4x - 13$
11. $7a - 5 = 2a - 20$
12. $3x + 1 = 11 - 2x$
13. $n - 2 = 6 - 3n$
14. $2x - 3 = -11 - 2x$
15. $4y - 2 = -16 - 3y$
16. $0.2b + 3 = 0.5b + 12$
17. $m + 0.4 = 3m + 0.8$
18. $4y - 8 = y - 8$
19. $5a + 7 = 2a + 7$
20. $6 - 5x = 8 - 3x$
21. $10 - 4n = 16 - n$
22. $5 + 7x = 11 + 9x$
23. $3 - 2y = 15 + 4y$
24. $2x - 4 = 6x$
25. $2b - 10 = 7b$
26. $8m = 3m + 20$
27. $9y = 5y + 16$
28. $8b + 5 = 5b + 7$
29. $6y - 1 = 2y + 2$
30. $7x - 8 = x - 3$
31. $2y - 7 = -1 - 2y$
32. $2m - 1 = -6m + 5$

33. If $5x = 3x - 8$, evaluate $4x + 2$.

34. If $7x + 3 = 5x - 7$, evaluate $3x - 2$.

35. If $2 - 6a = 5 - 3a$, evaluate $4a^2 - 2a + 1$.

36. If $1 - 5c = 4 - 4c$, evaluate $3c^2 - 4c + 2$.

OBJECTIVE B *To solve an equation containing parentheses*

37. Without solving any of the equations, determine which of the following equations has the same solution as the equation $5 - 2(x - 1) = 8$.
(i) $3(x - 1) = 8$ (ii) $5 - 2x + 2 = 8$ (iii) $5 - 2x + 1 = 8$

For Exercises 38 to 58, solve and check.

38. $5x + 2(x + 1) = 23$

39. $6y + 2(2y + 3) = 16$

40. $9n - 3(2n - 1) = 15$

41. $12x - 2(4x - 6) = 28$

42. $7a - (3a - 4) = 12$

43. $9m - 4(2m - 3) = 11$

44. $5(3 - 2y) + 4y = 3$

45. $4(1 - 3x) + 7x = 9$

46. $5y - 3 = 7 + 4(y - 2)$

47. $0.22(x + 6) = 0.2x + 1.8$

48. $0.05(4 - x) + 0.1x = 0.32$

49. $0.3x + 0.3(x + 10) = 300$

50. $2a - 5 = 4(3a + 1) - 2$

51. $5 - (9 - 6x) = 2x - 2$

52. $7 - (5 - 8x) = 4x + 3$

53. $3[2 - 4(y - 1)] = 3(2y + 8)$

54. $5[2 - (2x - 4)] = 2(5 - 3x)$

55. $3a + 2[2 + 3(a - 1)] = 2(3a + 4)$

56. $5 + 3[1 + 2(2x - 3)] = 6(x + 5)$

57. $-2[4 - (3b + 2)] = 5 - 2(3b + 6)$

58. $-4[x - 2(2x - 3)] + 1 = 2x - 3$

59. If $4 - 3a = 7 - 2(2a + 5)$, evaluate $a^2 + 7a$.

60. If $9 - 5x = 12 - (6x + 7)$, evaluate $x^2 - 3x - 2$.

OBJECTIVE C *To solve application problems using formulas*

Taxi Fares The fare F to be charged a customer by a taxi company is calculated using the formula $F = 2.50 + 2.30(m - 1)$, where m is the number of miles traveled. Use this formula for Exercises 61 and 62.

61. A customer is charged $14.00. How many miles was the customer driven?

62. A passenger is charged $20.90. Find the number of miles the passenger was driven.

63. **Physics** Two people sit on a seesaw that is 8 ft long. The seesaw balances when the fulcrum is 3 ft from one of the people.
a. How far is the fulcrum from the other person?
b. Which person is heavier, the person who is 3 ft from the fulcrum or the other person?
c. If the two people switch places, will the seesaw still balance?

Physics For Exercises 64 to 69, solve. Use the lever system equation $F_1x = F_2(d - x)$.

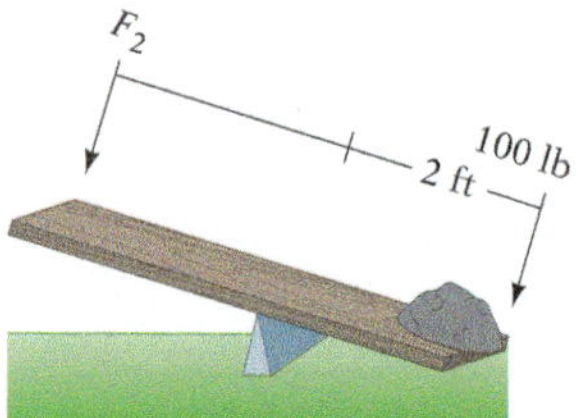

64. A lever 10 ft long is used to move a 100-pound rock. The fulcrum is placed 2 ft from the rock. What force must be applied to the other end of the lever to move the rock?

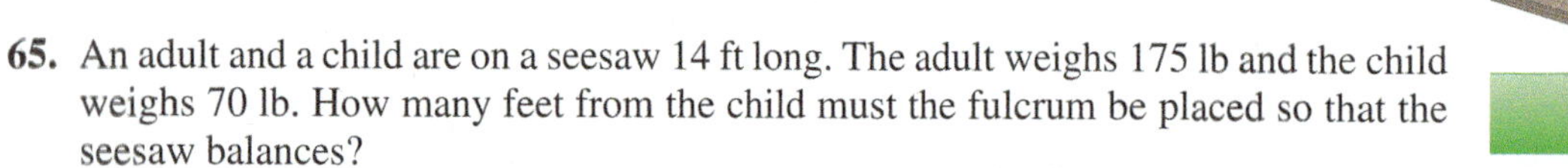

65. An adult and a child are on a seesaw 14 ft long. The adult weighs 175 lb and the child weighs 70 lb. How many feet from the child must the fulcrum be placed so that the seesaw balances?

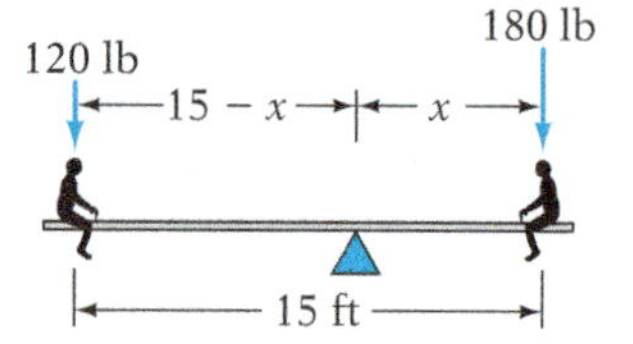

66. Two people are sitting 15 ft apart on a seesaw. One person weighs 180 lb. The second person weighs 120 lb. How far from the 180-pound person should the fulcrum be placed so that the seesaw balances?

67. Two children are sitting on a seesaw that is 12 ft long. One child weighs 60 lb. The other child weighs 90 lb. How far from the 90-pound child should the fulcrum be placed so that the seesaw balances?

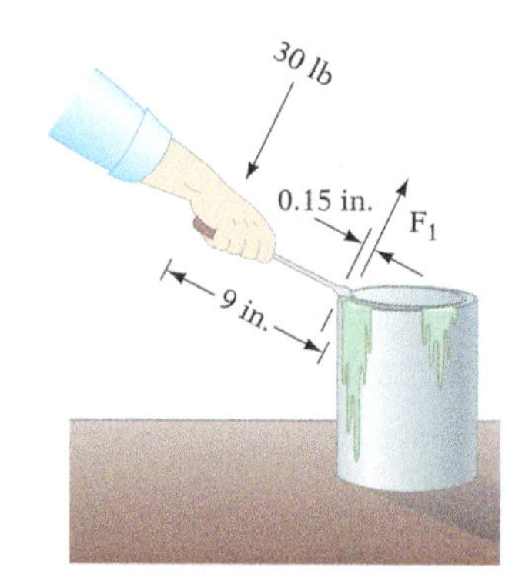

68. In preparation for a stunt, two acrobats are standing on a plank 18 ft long. One acrobat weighs 128 lb and the second acrobat weighs 160 lb. How far from the 128-pound acrobat must the fulcrum be placed so that the acrobats are balanced on the plank?

69. A screwdriver 9 in. long is used as a lever to open a can of paint. The tip of the screwdriver is placed under the lip of the can with the fulcrum 0.15 in. from the lip. A force of 30 lb is applied to the other end of the screwdriver. Find the force on the lip of the can.

Break-even Point To determine the break-even point, or the number of units that must be sold so that no profit or loss occurs, an economist uses the formula $Px = Cx + F$, where P is the selling price per unit, x is the number of units that must be sold to break even, C is the cost to make each unit, and F is the fixed cost. Use this equation for Exercises 70 to 73.

70. A business analyst has determined that the selling price per unit for a laser printer is $1600. The cost to make one laser printer is $950, and the fixed cost is $211,250. Find the break-even point.

71. A business analyst has determined that the selling price per unit for a gas barbecue is \$325. The cost to make one gas barbecue is \$175, and the fixed cost is \$39,000. Find the break-even point.

72. A manufacturer of headphones determines that the cost per unit for a pair of headphones is \$38 and that the fixed cost is \$24,400. The selling price for the headphones is \$99. Find the break-even point.

73. A manufacturing engineer determines that the cost per unit for a soprano recorder is \$12 and that the fixed cost is \$19,240. The selling price for the recorder is \$49. Find the break-even point.

© iStockphoto.com/Rich Legg

Physiology The oxygen consumption C, in millimeters per minute, of a small mammal at rest is related to the animal's weight m, in kilograms, by the equation $m = \frac{1}{6}(C - 5)$. Use this equation for Exercises 74 and 75.

74. What is the oxygen consumption of a mammal that weighs 10.4 kg?

75. What is the oxygen consumption of a mammal that weighs 8.3 kg?

Critical Thinking

Solve. If the equation has no solution, write "No solution."

76. $3(2x - 1) - (6x - 4) = -9$

77. $\frac{1}{5}(25 - 10b) + 4 = \frac{1}{3}(9b - 15) - 6$

78. $3[4(w + 2) - (w + 1)] = 5(2 + w)$

79. $\frac{2(5x - 6) - 3(x - 4)}{7} = x + 2$

80. One-half of a certain number equals two-thirds of the same number. Find the number.

81. Does the sentence "Solve $3x - 4(x - 1)$" make sense? Why or why not?

82. The equation $x = x + 1$ has no solution, whereas the solution of the equation $2x + 3 = 3$ is zero. Is there a difference between no solution and a solution of zero? Explain your answer.

83. I am thinking of a number. When I subtract 4 from the number and then take 300% of the result, my new result is equal to the original number. What is the original number?

Projects or Group Activities

84. If $s = 5x - 3$ and $t = x + 4$, find the value of x for which $s = 3t - 1$.

85. The population of the town of Hampton increased by 10,000 people during the 1990s. In the first decade of the new millennium, the population of Hampton decreased by 10%, at which time the town had 6000 more people than at the beginning of the 1990s. Find Hampton's population at the beginning of the 1990s.

CHECK YOUR PROGRESS: CHAPTER 3

1. Is 3 a solution of $2a(a - 1) = 3a + 3$?

2. Solve: $x + 7 = -4$

3. Solve: $-3y = -27$

4. What is 45% of 160?

5. Solve: $6 - 4a = -10$

6. Is $-\frac{1}{4}$ a solution of $8t + 1 = -1$?

7. Solve: $\frac{1}{6} + b = -\frac{1}{3}$

8. Solve: $5x - 4(3 - x) = 2(x - 1) - 3$

9. 18% of what number is 27?

10. Solve: $6y + 5 - 8y = 3 - 4y$

11. Is 4 a solution of $x(x + 1) = x^2 + 5$?

12. Solve: $84 = -16 + t$

13. Solve: $\frac{3}{4}c = \frac{3}{5}$

14. Solve: $9 = \frac{1}{2}d - 5$

15. What percent of 170 is 42.5?

16. Solve: $-\frac{8}{9} = -\frac{2}{3}y$

17. Solve: $3n + 2(n - 4) = 7$

18. Solve: $3x - 8 = 5x + 6$

19. Solve: $2[3 - 5(x - 1)] = 7x - 1$

20. Solve: $18 = 2t$

21. **Health** According to *Health* magazine, the average American has increased his or her daily consumption of calories from 18 years ago by 11.6%. If the average daily consumption was 1970 calories 18 years ago, what is the average daily consumption today? Round to the nearest whole number.

22. **Recreation** K&B Tours offers a river trip that takes passengers from the K&B dock to a small island that is 24 mi away. The passengers spend 1 h at the island and then return to the K&B dock. If the speed of the boat is 10 mph in calm water and the rate of the current is 2 mph, how long does the trip last?

23. **Business** A hoodie costing \$42 is sold for \$58.80. Find the markup rate. Use the markup equation $S = C + rC$, where S is the selling price, C is the cost, and r is the markup rate.

24. **Business** A basketball jersey is on sale for \$33.60 after a markdown of 30% off the regular price. Find the regular price. Use the discount equation $S = R - rR$, where S is the sale price, R is the regular price, and r is the discount rate.

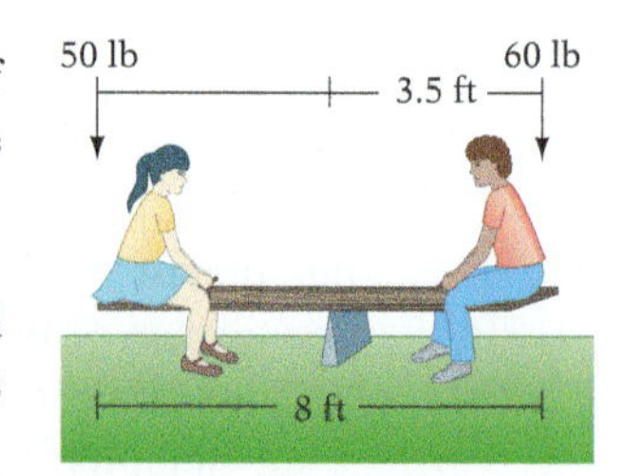

25. **Physics** Two children are sitting 8 ft apart on a seesaw. One child weighs 60 lb and the second child weighs 50 lb. The fulcrum is 3.5 ft from the child weighing 60 lb. Is the seesaw balanced? Use the lever system equation $F_1x = F_2(d - x)$.

SECTION

3.5 Translating Sentences into Equations

OBJECTIVE A *To solve integer problems*

An equation states that two mathematical expressions are equal. Therefore, to **translate** a sentence into an equation, we must recognize the words or phrases that mean "equals." Some of these phrases are listed below.

equals
is
is equal to
amounts to
represents

} translate to =

Once the sentence is translated into an equation, the equation can be solved by rewriting it in the form *variable* = *constant*.

Take Note

You can check the solution to a translation problem.

Check:

5 less than 18 is 13

$18 - 5$	13
13 =	13

HOW TO 1 Translate "five less than a number is thirteen" into an equation and solve.

Five less than a number	is	thirteen

- **Find two verbal expressions for the same value.**

The unknown number: n

- **Assign a variable to the unknown number.**

$n - 5 \quad = \quad 13$

- **Write a mathematical expression for each verbal expression. Write the equals sign.**

$n - 5 + 5 = 13 + 5$

$n = 18$

- **Solve the equation.**

The number is 18.

Recall that the integers are the numbers {..., −4, −3, −2, −1, 0, 1, 2, 3, 4, ...}. An **even integer** is an integer that is divisible by 2. Examples of even integers are −8, 0, and 22. An **odd integer** is an integer that is not divisible by 2. Examples of odd integers are −17, 1, and 39.

Consecutive integers are integers that follow one another in order. Examples of consecutive integers are shown at the right. (Assume that the variable n represents an integer.)

11, 12, 13
−8, −7, −6
$n, n + 1, n + 2$

Examples of **consecutive even integers** are shown at the right. (Assume that the variable n represents an even integer.)

24, 26, 28
−10, −8, −6
$n, n + 2, n + 4$

Take Note

Both consecutive even and consecutive odd integers are represented using n, $n + 2, n + 4, ...$

Examples of **consecutive odd integers** are shown at the right. (Assume that the variable n represents an odd integer.)

19, 21, 23
−1, 1, 3
$n, n + 2, n + 4$

HOW TO 2 The sum of three consecutive odd integers is forty-five. Find the integers.

Strategy

- First odd integer: n • Represent three consecutive odd integers.
  Second odd integer: $n + 2$
  Third odd integer: $n + 4$
- The sum of the three odd integers is 45.

Solution

$n + (n + 2) + (n + 4) = 45$ • Write an equation.

$3n + 6 = 45$ • Solve the equation.

$3n = 39$

$n = 13$ • The first odd integer is 13.

$n + 2 = 13 + 2 = 15$ • Find the second odd integer.

$n + 4 = 13 + 4 = 17$ • Find the third odd integer.

The three consecutive odd integers are 13, 15, and 17.

EXAMPLE 1

The sum of two numbers is sixteen. The difference between four times the smaller number and two is two more than twice the larger number. Find the two numbers.

Strategy

The difference between four times the smaller number and two	is	two more than twice the larger number

The smaller number: n
The larger number: $16 - n$

Solution

$4n - 2 = 2(16 - n) + 2$

$4n - 2 = 32 - 2n + 2$ • Distributive Property

$4n - 2 = 34 - 2n$ • Combine like terms.

$4n + 2n - 2 = 34 - 2n + 2n$ • Add $2n$ to each side.

$6n - 2 = 34$

$6n - 2 + 2 = 34 + 2$ • Add 2 to each side.

$6n = 36$

$\frac{6n}{6} = \frac{36}{6}$ • Divide each side by 6.

$n = 6$ • The smaller number is 6.

$16 - n = 16 - 6 = 10$ • Find the larger number.

The smaller number is 6.
The larger number is 10.

YOU TRY IT 1

The sum of two numbers is twelve. The total of three times the smaller number and six amounts to seven less than the product of four and the larger number. Find the two numbers.

Your strategy

Your solution

Solution on p. S7

EXAMPLE 2

Find three consecutive even integers such that three times the second equals four more than the sum of the first and third.

Strategy

- First even integer: n
  Second even integer: $n + 2$
  Third even integer: $n + 4$
- Three times the second equals four more than the sum of the first and third.

Solution

$$3(n + 2) = n + (n + 4) + 4$$
$$3n + 6 = 2n + 8$$
$$3n - 2n + 6 = 2n - 2n + 8$$
$$n + 6 = 8$$
$$n = 2$$ • The first even integer is 2.
$$n + 2 = 2 + 2 = 4$$ • Find the second even integer.
$$n + 4 = 2 + 4 = 6$$ • Find the third even integer.

The three integers are 2, 4, and 6.

YOU TRY IT 2

Find three consecutive integers whose sum is negative six.

Your strategy

Your solution

Solution on p. S7

OBJECTIVE B *To translate a sentence into an equation and solve*

EXAMPLE 3

A wallpaper hanger charges a fee of \$25 plus \$12 for each roll of wallpaper used in a room. If the total charge for hanging wallpaper is \$97, how many rolls of wallpaper were used?

Strategy

To find the number of rolls of wallpaper used, write and solve an equation using n to represent the number of rolls of wallpaper used.

\$25 plus \$12 for each roll of wallpaper	is	\$97

Solution

$$25 + 12n = 97$$
$$12n = 72$$ • Subtract 25 from each side.
$$\frac{12n}{12} = \frac{72}{12}$$ • Divide each side by 12.
$$n = 6$$

6 rolls of wallpaper were used.

YOU TRY IT 3

The fee charged by a ticketing agency for a concert is \$3.50 plus \$17.50 for each ticket purchased. If your total charge for tickets is \$161, how many tickets did you purchase?

Your strategy

Your solution

Solution on p. S7

EXAMPLE 4

A board 20 ft long is cut into two pieces. Five times the length of the shorter piece is 2 ft more than twice the length of the longer piece. Find the length of each piece.

Strategy

Let x represent the length of the shorter piece. Then $20 - x$ represents the length of the longer piece.

Make a drawing.

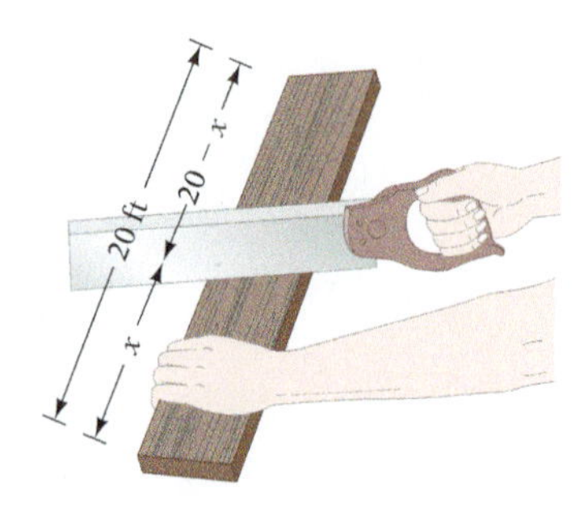

To find the lengths, write and solve an equation using x to represent the length of the shorter piece and $20 - x$ to represent the length of the longer piece.

Five times the length of the shorter piece	is	2 ft more than twice the length of the longer piece

Solution

$5x = 2(20 - x) + 2$

$5x = 40 - 2x + 2$ • Distributive Property

$5x = 42 - 2x$ • Combine like terms.

$5x + 2x = 42 - 2x + 2x$ • Add $2x$ to each side.

$7x = 42$

$\frac{7x}{7} = \frac{42}{7}$ • Divide each side by 7.

$x = 6$ • The shorter piece is 6 ft long.

$20 - x = 20 - 6 = 14$ • Find the length of the longer piece.

The length of the shorter piece is 6 ft.
The length of the longer piece is 14 ft.

YOU TRY IT 4

A wire 22 in. long is cut into two pieces. The length of the longer piece is 4 in. more than twice the length of the shorter piece. Find the length of each piece.

Your strategy

Your solution

Solution on p. S8

3.5 EXERCISES

Concept Check

For Exercises 1 to 3, determine whether the statement is true or false.

1. When translating a sentence into an equation, we can use any variable to represent an unknown number.
2. An even integer is a multiple of 2.
3. Given the consecutive odd integers -5 and -3, the next consecutive odd integer is -1.
4. The sum of two numbers is 12.
   a. If x represents the larger number, represent the smaller number in terms of x.

   b. If x represents the smaller number, represent the larger number in terms of x.
5. When we translate a sentence into an equation, the word *is* translates into the _______ sign.
6. Integers that follow one another in order are called _______ integers
7. Two consecutive integers differ by _______. Two consecutive even integers differ by _______. Two consecutive odd integers differ by _______.
8. The number of calories in a cup of low-fat milk is two-thirds the number of calories in a cup of whole milk. In this situation, let n represent the number of calories in a cup of _______ milk, and let $\frac{2}{3}n$ represent the number of calories in a cup of _______ milk.

OBJECTIVE A *To solve integer problems*

For Exercises 9 to 24, translate into an equation and solve.

9. The difference between a number and fifteen is seven. Find the number.
10. The sum of five and a number is three. Find the number.
11. The difference between nine and a number is seven. Find the number.
12. Three-fifths of a number is negative thirty. Find the number.
13. The difference between five and twice a number is one. Find the number.
14. Four more than three times a number is thirteen. Find the number.
15. The sum of twice a number and five is fifteen. Find the number.
16. The difference between nine times a number and six is twelve. Find the number.
17. Six less than four times a number is twenty-two. Find the number.
18. Four times the sum of twice a number and three is twelve. Find the number.
19. Three times the difference between four times a number and seven is fifteen. Find the number.
20. Twice the difference between a number and twenty-five is three times the number. Find the number.

21. The sum of two numbers is twenty. Three times the smaller is equal to two times the larger. Find the two numbers.

22. The sum of two numbers is fifteen. One less than three times the smaller is equal to the larger. Find the two numbers.

23. The sum of two numbers is fourteen. The difference between two times the smaller and the larger is one. Find the two numbers.

24. The sum of two numbers is eighteen. The total of three times the smaller and twice the larger is forty-four. Find the two numbers.

25. The sum of three consecutive odd integers is fifty-one. Find the integers.

26. Find three consecutive even integers whose sum is negative eighteen.

27. Find three consecutive odd integers such that three times the middle integer is one more than the sum of the first and third.

28. Twice the smallest of three consecutive odd integers is seven more than the largest. Find the integers.

29. Find two consecutive even integers such that three times the first equals twice the second.

30. Find two consecutive even integers such that four times the first is three times the second.

31. The sum of two numbers is seven. Twice one number is four less than the other number. Which of the following equations does *not* represent this situation?
(i) $2(7 - x) = x - 4$ (ii) $2x = (7 - x) - 4$ (iii) $2n - 4 = 7 - n$

OBJECTIVE B *To translate a sentence into an equation and solve*

32. Depreciation As a result of depreciation, the value of a car is now $19,200. This is three-fifths of its original value. Find the original value of the car.

Andy Z./Shutterstock.com

The Golden Gate Bridge

33. Structures The length of the Royal Gorge Bridge in Colorado is 320 m. This is one-fourth the length of the Golden Gate Bridge. Find the length of the Golden Gate Bridge.

34. Nutrition One slice of cheese pizza contains 290 calories. A medium-size orange has one-fifth that number of calories. How many calories are in a medium-size orange?

© Pictorial Press Ltd/Alamy

John D. Rockefeller

35. History John D. Rockefeller died in 1937. At the time of his death, Rockefeller had accumulated $1400 million, which was equal to one-sixty-fifth of the gross national product of the United States at that time. What was the U.S. gross national product in 1937? (*Source: The Wealthy 100: A Ranking of the Richest Americans, Past and Present*)

36. Agriculture A soil supplement that weighs 18 lb contains iron, potassium, and mulch. The supplement contains fifteen times as much mulch as iron and twice as much potassium as iron. Find the amount of mulch in the soil supplement.

37. Geometry An isosceles triangle has two sides of equal length. The length of the third side is 1 ft less than twice the length of one of the equal sides. Find the length of each side when the perimeter is 23 ft.

38. **Geometry** An isosceles triangle has two sides of equal length. The length of one of the equal sides is 2 m more than three times the length of the third side. If the perimeter is 46 m, find the length of each side.

Point of Interest

The low-frequency pulses or whistles made by blue whales have been measured at up to 188 decibels, making them the loudest sounds produced by a living organism.

39. **Safety** Loudness, or the intensity of sound, is measured in decibels. The sound level of a television is about 70 decibels, which is considered a safe hearing level. A food blender runs at 20 decibels higher than a TV, and a jet engine's decibel reading is 40 less than twice that of a blender. At this level, exposure can cause hearing loss. Find the intensity of the sound of a jet engine.

40. **Robots** Kiva Systems, Inc., builds robots that companies can use to streamline order fulfillment operations in their warehouses. Salary and other benefits for one human warehouse worker can cost a company about $64,000 a year, an amount that is 103 times the company's yearly maintenance and operation costs for one robot. Find the yearly costs for a robot. Round to the nearest hundred. (*Source: The Boston Globe*)

41. **Geography** Greenland, the largest island in the world, is 21 times larger than Iceland. The combined area of Greenland and Iceland is 880,000 mi^2. Find the area of Greenland.

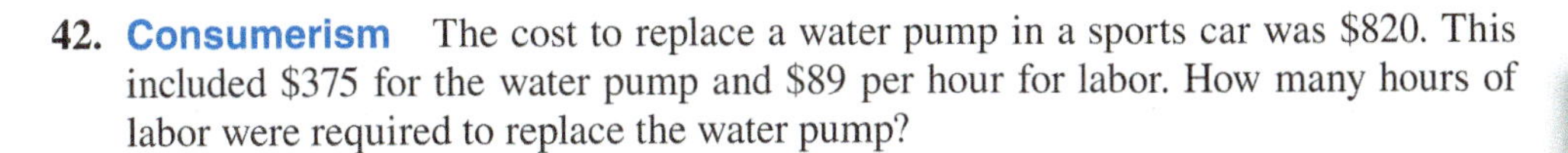

42. **Consumerism** The cost to replace a water pump in a sports car was $820. This included $375 for the water pump and $89 per hour for labor. How many hours of labor were required to replace the water pump?

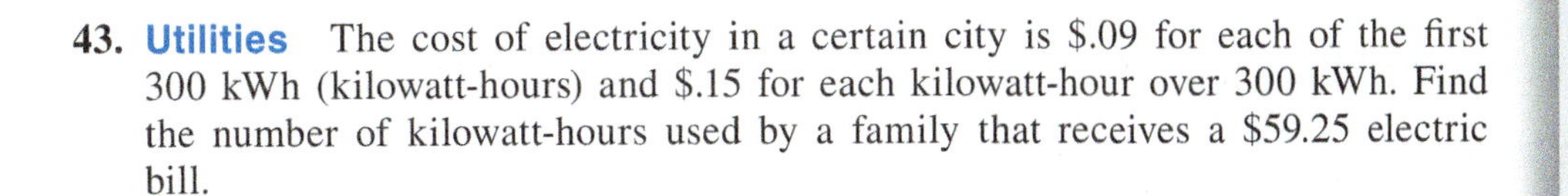

43. **Utilities** The cost of electricity in a certain city is $.09 for each of the first 300 kWh (kilowatt-hours) and $.15 for each kilowatt-hour over 300 kWh. Find the number of kilowatt-hours used by a family that receives a $59.25 electric bill.

44. **Labor Unions** A union charges monthly dues of $4.00 plus $.25 for each hour worked during the month. A union member's dues for March were $46.00. How many hours did the union member work during the month of March?

45. **Business** The cellular phone service for a business executive is $80 per month plus $.40 per minute of phone use over 900 min. For a month in which the executive's cellular phone bill was $100.40, how many minutes did the executive use the phone?

In the NEWS!

Americans' Unquenchable Thirst

Despite efforts to increase recycling, the 2.16 million tons of plastic drink bottles that ended up in landfills this year represent four-fifths of the plastic drink bottles stocked for sale in U.S. stores.

And Americans can't seem to get enough of bottled water. During a recent year, stores stocked 7.5 billion gallons of bottled water, an amount that is approximately the same as the volume of water that goes over Niagara Falls every 3 h.

Source: scienceline.org

46. **Recycling** Use the information in the article at the right to find how many tons of plastic drink bottles were stocked for sale in U.S. stores.

Text Messaging For Exercises 47 and 48, use the expression $2.99 + 0.15n$, which represents the total monthly text-messaging bill for n text messages over 300 in one month.

© iStockphoto.com/Huchen Lu

47. How much does the customer pay per text message over 300 messages?

48. What is the fixed charge per month for the text-messaging service?

Critical Thinking

49. Metalwork A wire 12 ft long is cut into two pieces. Each piece is bent into the shape of a square. The perimeter of the larger square is twice the perimeter of the smaller square. Find the perimeter of the larger square.

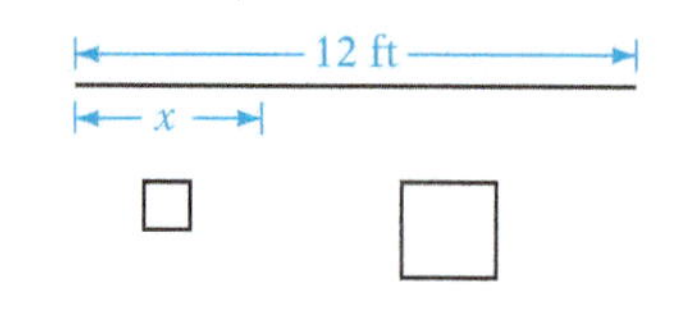

50. The amount of liquid in a container triples every minute. The container becomes completely filled at 3:40 p.m. What fractional part of the container is filled at 3:39 P.M?

51. Travel A cyclist traveling at a constant speed completes three-fifths of a trip in $\frac{1}{2}$ h. In how many additional hours will the cyclist complete the entire trip?

52. Business During one day at an office, one-half of the amount of money in the petty cash drawer was used in the morning, and one-third of the remaining money was used in the afternoon, leaving \$5 in the petty cash drawer at the end of the day. How much money was in the petty cash drawer at the start of the day?

53. Find four consecutive even integers whose sum is -36.

54. Find four consecutive odd integers whose sum is -48.

55. Find three consecutive odd integers such that the sum of the first and third integers is twice the second integer.

56. Find four consecutive integers such that the sum of the first and fourth integers equals the sum of the second and third integers.

Projects or Group Activities

Complete each statement with the word *even* or *odd*.

57. If k is an odd integer, then $k + 1$ is an ______ integer.

58. If k is an odd integer, then $k - 2$ is an ______ integer.

59. If n is an integer, then $2n$ is an ______ integer.

60. If m and n are even integers, then $m - n$ is an ______ integer.

61. If m and n are even integers then mn is an ______ integer.

62. If m and n are odd integers, then $m + n$ is an ______ integer.

63. If m and n are odd integers then $m - n$ is an ______ integer.

64. If m and n are odd integers then mn is an ______ integer.

65. If m is an even integer and n is an odd integer then $m - n$ is an ______ integer.

66. If m is an even integer and n is an odd integer then $m + n$ is an ______ integer.

SECTION

3.6 Geometry Problems

OBJECTIVE A To solve problems involving angles

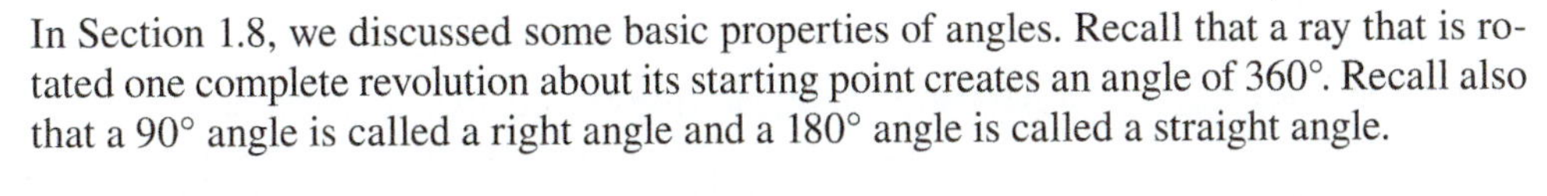

In Section 1.8, we discussed some basic properties of angles. Recall that a ray that is rotated one complete revolution about its starting point creates an angle of 360°. Recall also that a 90° angle is called a right angle and a 180° angle is called a straight angle.

Point of Interest

The word *degree* first appeared in Chaucer's *Canterbury Tales,* which was written in 1386.

An **acute angle** is an angle whose measure is between 0° and 90°. $\angle A$ at the right is an acute angle. An **obtuse angle** is an angle whose measure is between 90° and 180°. $\angle B$ at the right is an obtuse angle.

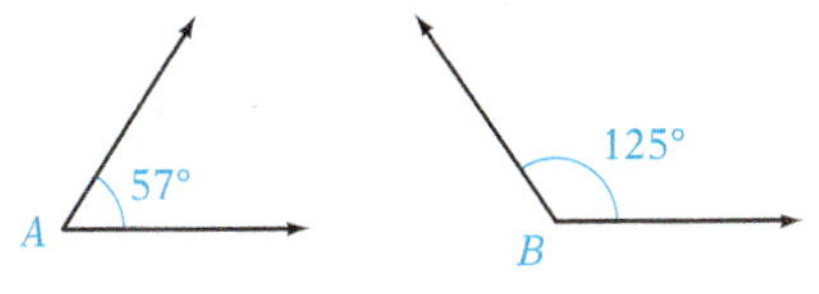

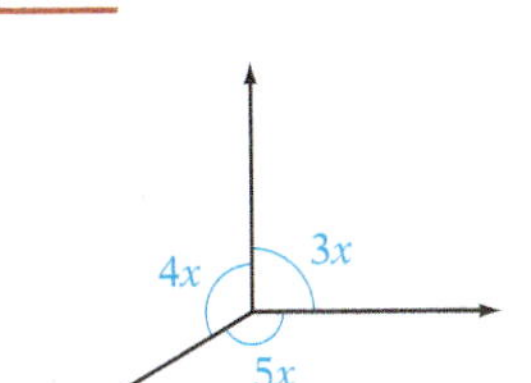

HOW TO 1 Given the diagram at the left, find x.

$$3x + 4x + 5x = 360°$$
$$12x = 360°$$
$$x = 30°$$

• The sum of the measures of the three angles is 360°.

The measure of x is 30°.

Four angles are formed by the intersection of two lines. If the two lines are not perpendicular, then two of the angles formed are acute angles and two of the angles are obtuse angles. The two acute angles are always opposite each other, and the two obtuse angles are always opposite each other.

In the figure at the right, $\angle w$ and $\angle y$ are acute angles, and $\angle x$ and $\angle z$ are obtuse angles.

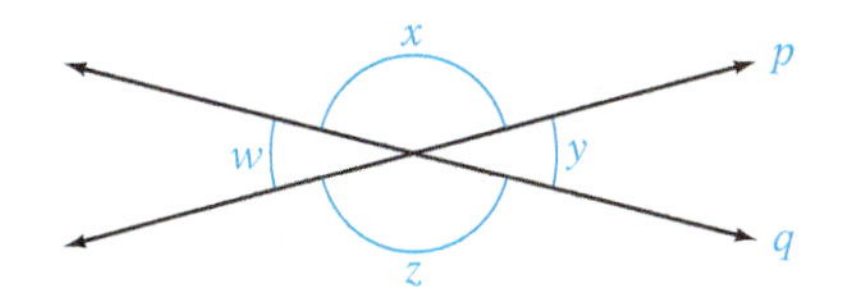

Two angles that are on opposite sides of the intersection of two lines are called **vertical angles.** In the figure at the right, $\angle w$ and $\angle y$ are vertical angles. $\angle x$ and $\angle z$ are vertical angles.

Vertical angles have the same measure.

$$m\angle w = m\angle y$$
$$m\angle x = m\angle z$$

Take Note

Recall that two angles are supplementary angles if the sum of their measures is 180°. For instance, angles whose measures are 48° and 132° are supplementary angles because 48° + 132° = 180°.

Two angles that share a common side are called **adjacent angles.** In the given figure, $\angle x$ and $\angle y$ are adjacent angles, as are $\angle y$ and $\angle z$, $\angle z$ and $\angle w$, and $\angle w$ and $\angle x$.

Adjacent angles of intersecting lines are supplementary.

$$m\angle x + m\angle y = 180° \qquad m\angle z + m\angle w = 180°$$
$$m\angle y + m\angle z = 180° \qquad m\angle w + m\angle x = 180°$$

HOW TO 2 In the diagram at the left, $m\angle b = 115°$. Find $m\angle a$ and $m\angle d$.

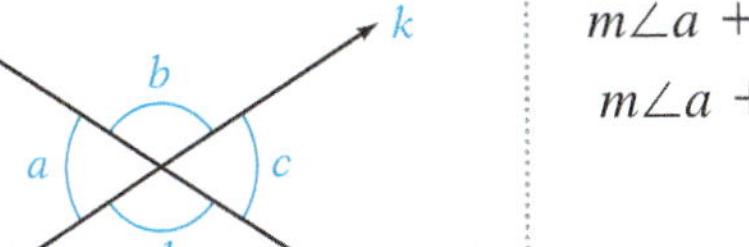

$$m\angle a + m\angle b = 180°$$
$$m\angle a + 115° = 180°$$
$$m\angle a = 65°$$

• $\angle a$ is supplementary to $\angle b$ because $\angle a$ and $\angle b$ are adjacent angles of intersecting lines.

$$m\angle d = 115°$$

• $m\angle d = m\angle b$ because $\angle d$ and $\angle b$ are vertical angles.

Take Note
Recall that parallel lines never meet—the distance between them is always the same. Perpendicular lines are intersecting lines that form right angles.

A line that intersects two other lines at different points is called a **transversal.** If the lines cut by a transversal t are parallel lines and the transversal is not perpendicular to the parallel lines, then all four acute angles have the same measure and all four obtuse angles have the same measure.

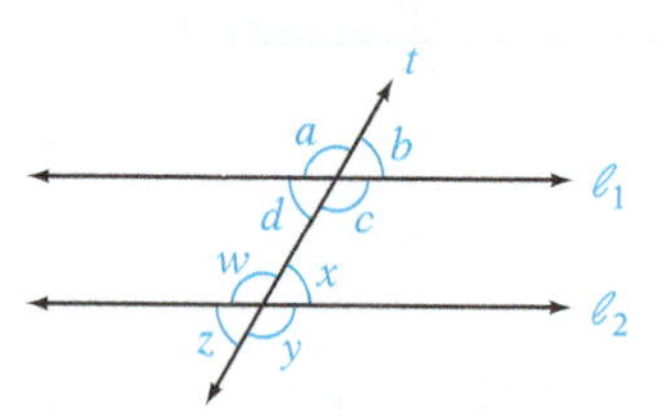

$m\angle b = m\angle d = m\angle x = m\angle z$
$m\angle a = m\angle c = m\angle w = m\angle y$

Alternate interior angles are two nonadjacent angles that are on opposite sides of the transversal and between the parallel lines. In the figure above, $\angle c$ and $\angle w$ are alternate interior angles, and $\angle d$ and $\angle x$ are alternate interior angles.

Alternate interior angles have the same measure.

$m\angle c = m\angle w$
$m\angle d = m\angle x$

Alternate exterior angles are two nonadjacent angles that are on opposite sides of the transversal and outside the parallel lines. In the figure above, $\angle a$ and $\angle y$ are alternate exterior angles, and $\angle b$ and $\angle z$ are alternate exterior angles.

Alternate exterior angles have the same measure.

$m\angle a = m\angle y$
$m\angle b = m\angle z$

Corresponding angles are two angles that are on the same side of the transversal and are both acute angles or are both obtuse angles. In the figure above, there are four pairs of corresponding angles: $\angle a$ and $\angle w$, $\angle d$ and $\angle z$, $\angle b$ and $\angle x$, and $\angle c$ and $\angle y$.

Corresponding angles have the same measure.

$m\angle a = m\angle w$
$m\angle d = m\angle z$
$m\angle b = m\angle x$
$m\angle c = m\angle y$

HOW TO 3 In the diagram at the left, $\ell_1 \parallel \ell_2$ and $m\angle f = 58°$. Find $m\angle a$, $m\angle c$, and $m\angle d$.

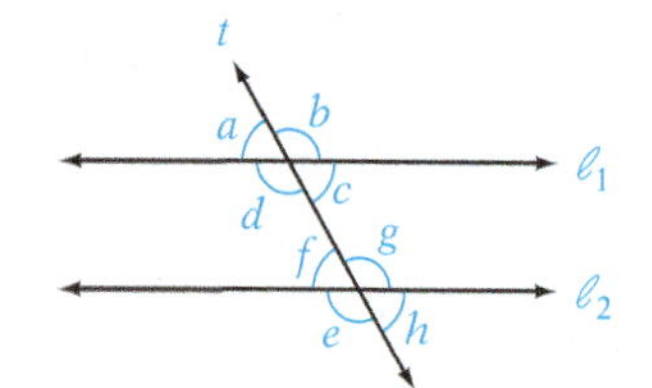

$m\angle a = m\angle f = 58°$ • $\angle a$ and $\angle f$ are corresponding angles.

$m\angle c = m\angle f = 58°$ • $\angle c$ and $\angle f$ are alternate interior angles.

$m\angle d + m\angle a = 180°$ • $\angle d$ is supplementary to $\angle a$.
$m\angle d + 58° = 180°$
$m\angle d = 122°$

EXAMPLE 1

Find x.

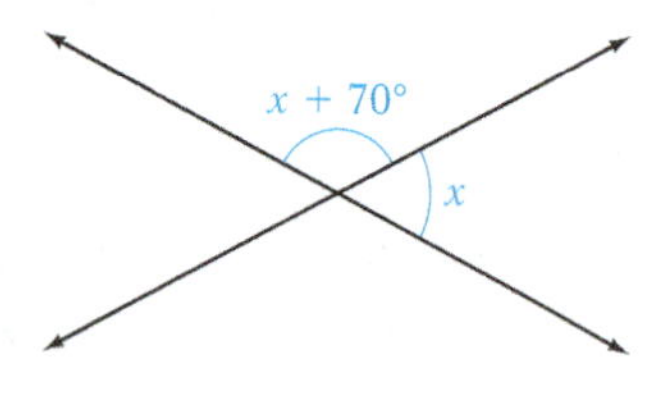

Strategy

The angles labeled are adjacent angles of intersecting lines and are therefore supplementary angles. To find x, write an equation and solve for x.

Solution

$$x + (x + 70°) = 180°$$
$$2x + 70° = 180°$$
$$2x = 110°$$
$$x = 55°$$

YOU TRY IT 1

Find x.

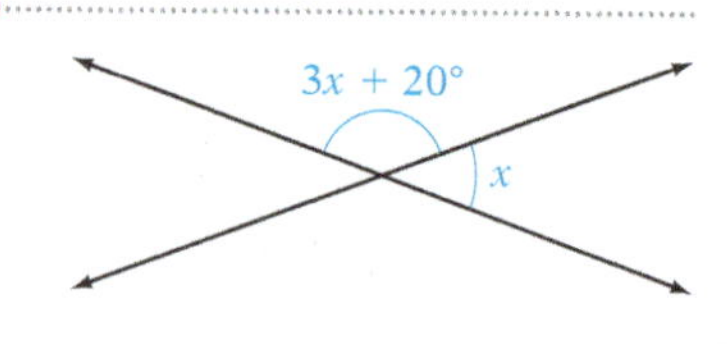

Your strategy

Your solution

Solution on p. S8

EXAMPLE 2

Given $\ell_1 \parallel \ell_2$, find x.

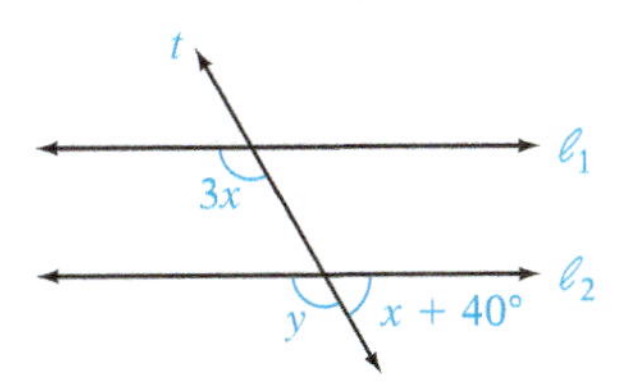

Strategy

$3x = y$ because corresponding angles have the same measure. $y + (x + 40°) = 180°$ because adjacent angles of intersecting lines are supplementary angles. Substitute $3x$ for y and solve for x.

Solution

$$\begin{aligned} y + (x + 40°) &= 180° \\ 3x + (x + 40°) &= 180° \\ 4x + 40° &= 180° \\ 4x &= 140° \\ x &= 35° \end{aligned}$$

YOU TRY IT 2

Given $\ell_1 \parallel \ell_2$, find x.

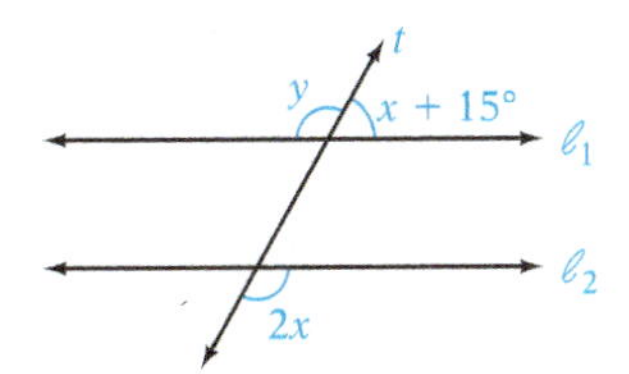

Your strategy

Your solution

Solution on p. S8

OBJECTIVE B *To solve problems involving the angles of a triangle*

If the lines cut by a transversal are not parallel lines, then the three lines will intersect at three points, forming a triangle. The angles within the region enclosed by the triangle are called **interior angles.** In the figure at the right, angles a, b, and c are interior angles. **The sum of the measures of the interior angles of a triangle is 180°.**

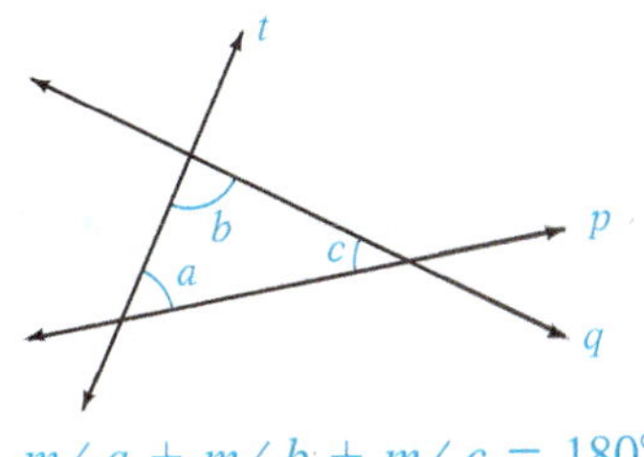

$m\angle a + m\angle b + m\angle c = 180°$

An angle adjacent to an interior angle is an **exterior angle.** In the figure at the right, angles m and n are exterior angles for angle a. The sum of the measures of an interior angle of a triangle and an adjacent exterior angle is 180°.

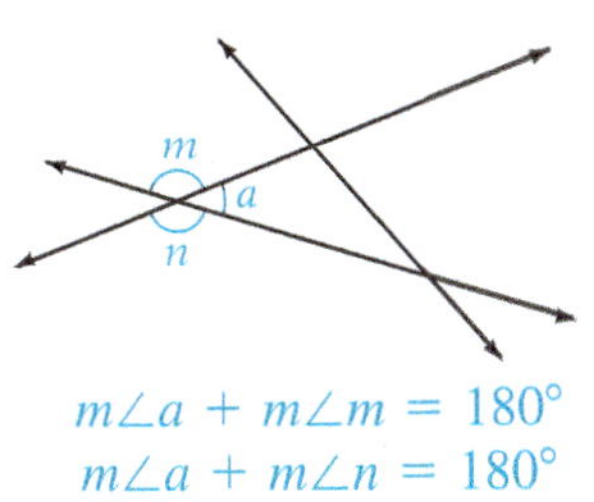

$m\angle a + m\angle m = 180°$
$m\angle a + m\angle n = 180°$

HOW TO 4 Given that $m\angle c = 40°$ and $m\angle e = 60°$, find $m\angle d$.

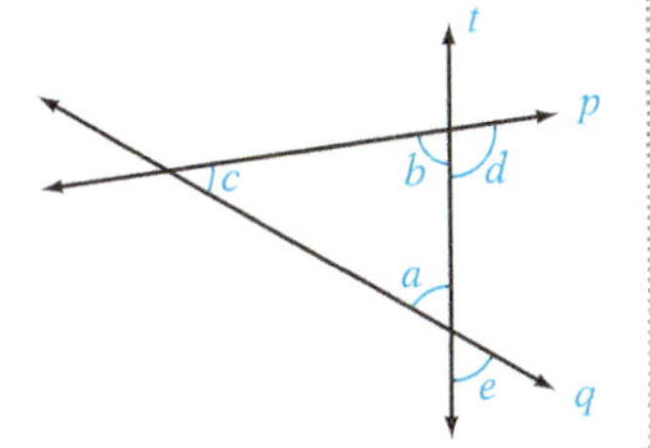

$m\angle a = m\angle e = 60°$ • $\angle a$ and $\angle e$ are vertical angles.

$$\begin{aligned} m\angle c + m\angle a + m\angle b &= 180° \\ 40° + 60° + m\angle b &= 180° \\ 100° + m\angle b &= 180° \\ m\angle b &= 80° \end{aligned}$$

• The sum of the interior angles is 180°.

$$\begin{aligned} m\angle b + m\angle d &= 180° \\ 80° + m\angle d &= 180° \\ m\angle d &= 100° \end{aligned}$$

• $\angle b$ and $\angle d$ are supplementary angles.

EXAMPLE 3

Given that $m\angle a = 45°$ and $m\angle x = 100°$, find the measures of angles b, c, and y.

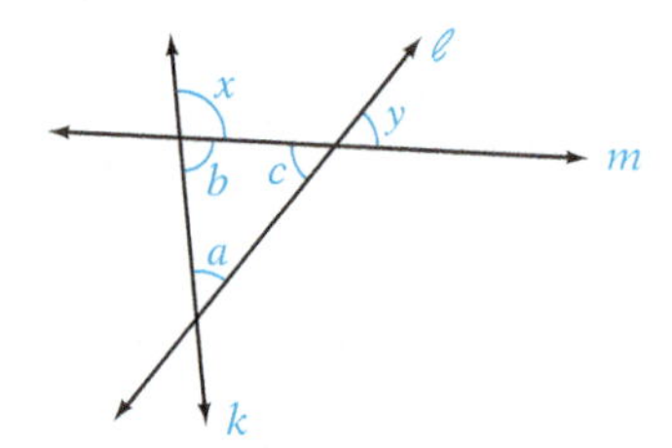

Strategy

- To find the measure of $\angle b$, use the fact that $\angle b$ and $\angle x$ are supplementary angles.
- To find the measure of $\angle c$, use the fact that the sum of the measures of the interior angles of a triangle is 180°.
- To find the measure of $\angle y$, use the fact that $\angle c$ and $\angle y$ are vertical angles.

Solution

$m\angle b + m\angle x = 180°$ • $\angle b$ and $\angle x$ are supplementary.
$m\angle b + 100° = 180°$
$m\angle b = 80°$

$m\angle a + m\angle b + m\angle c = 180°$ • The sum of the measures of the interior angles of a triangle is 180°.
$45° + 80° + m\angle c = 180°$
$125° + m\angle c = 180°$
$m\angle c = 55°$

$m\angle y = m\angle c = 55°$ • $\angle y$ and $\angle c$ are vertical angles.

YOU TRY IT 3

Given that $m\angle y = 55°$, find the measures of angles a, b, and d.

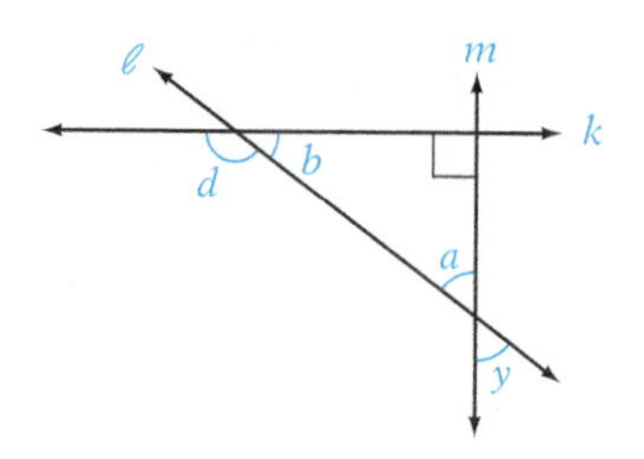

Your strategy

Your solution

EXAMPLE 4

Two angles of a triangle measure 43° and 86°. Find the measure of the third angle.

Strategy

To find the measure of the third angle, use the fact that the sum of the measures of the interior angles of a triangle is 180°. Write an equation using x to represent the measure of the third angle. Solve the equation for x.

Solution

$x + 43° + 86° = 180°$ • The sum of the measures of the interior angles of a triangle is 180°.
$x + 129° = 180°$
$x = 51°$

The measure of the third angle is 51°.

YOU TRY IT 4

One angle in a triangle is a right angle, and one angle measures 27°. Find the measure of the third angle.

Your strategy

Your solution

Solutions on p. S8

3.6 EXERCISES

Concept Check

1. Arrange the measures of an acute angle, an obtuse angle, a straight angle, and a right angle in order from smallest to largest.
2. Can vertical angles be acute angles?
3. Can adjacent angles be vertical angles?
4. Which is larger, the complement or the supplement of an acute angle?

OBJECTIVE A *To solve problems involving angles*

For Exercises 5 and 6, find the measure of $\angle a$.

5.

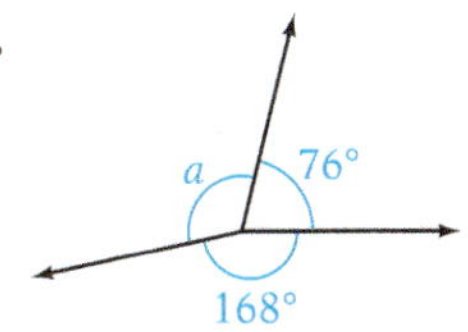

6.

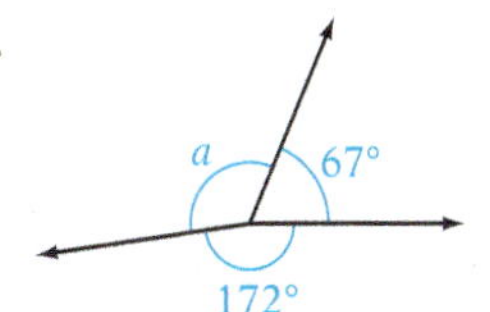

For Exercises 7 to 16, find x.

7.

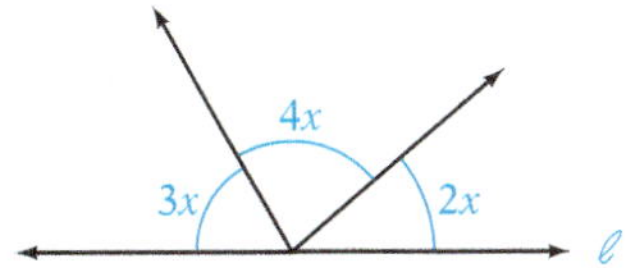

8

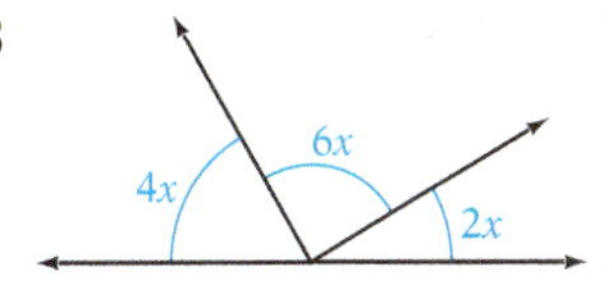

9.

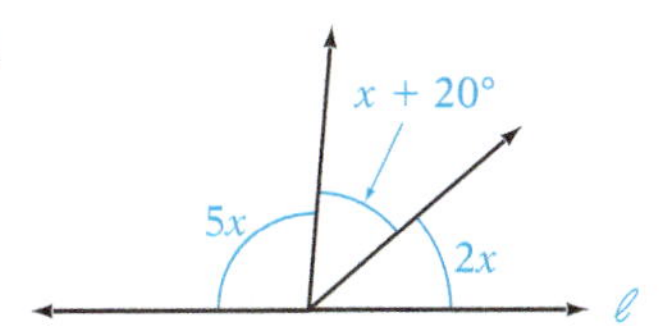

10.

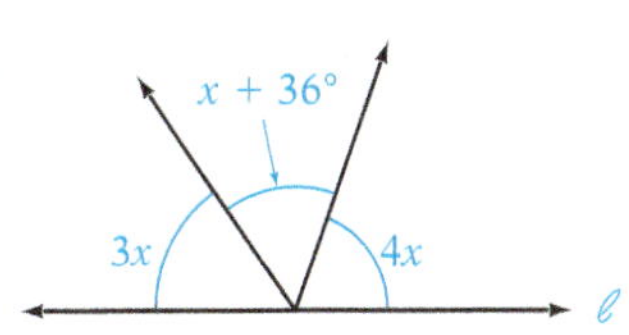

11.

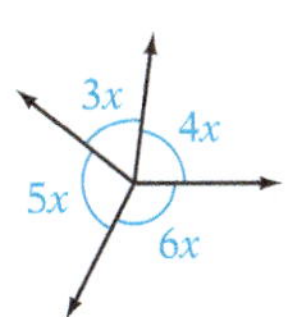

12.

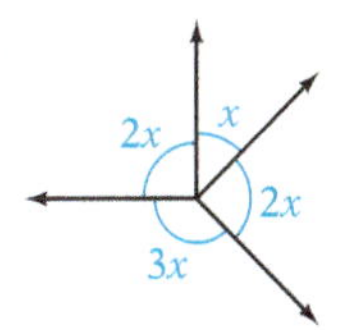

13.

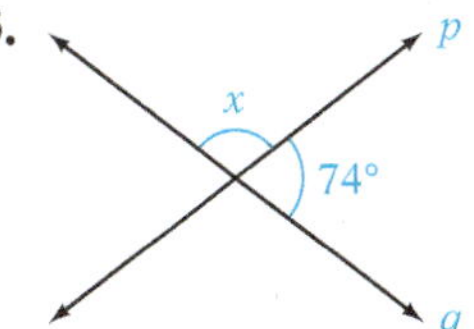

14.

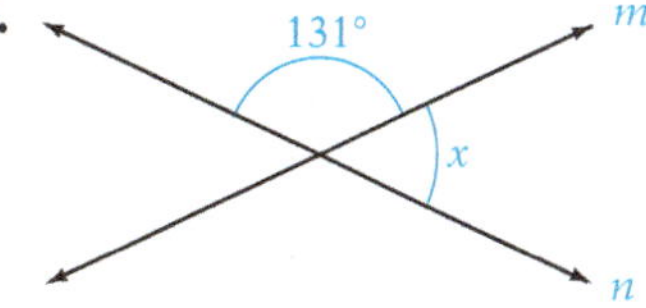

15.

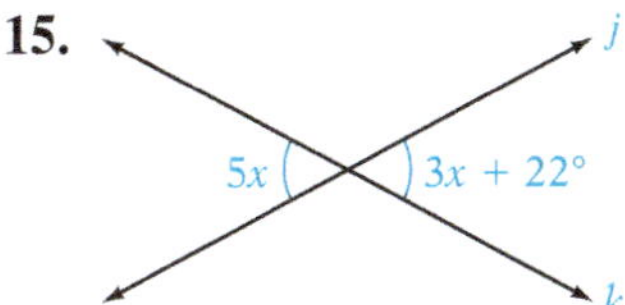

16.

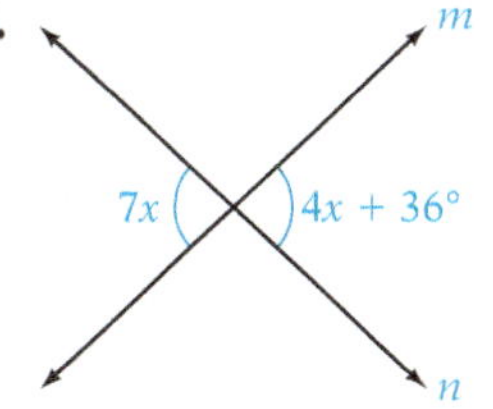

For Exercises 17 to 20, given that $\ell_1 \parallel \ell_2$, find the measures of angles a and b.

17.

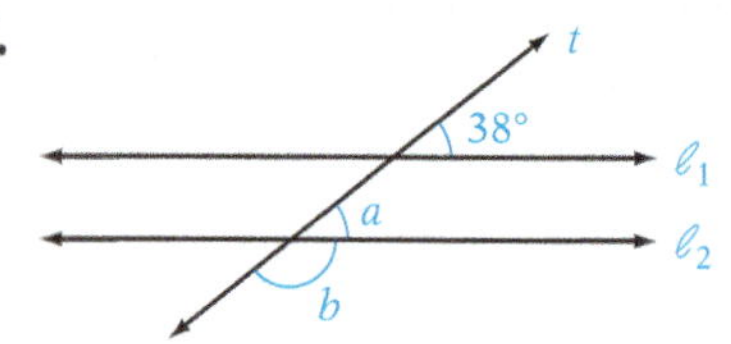

18.

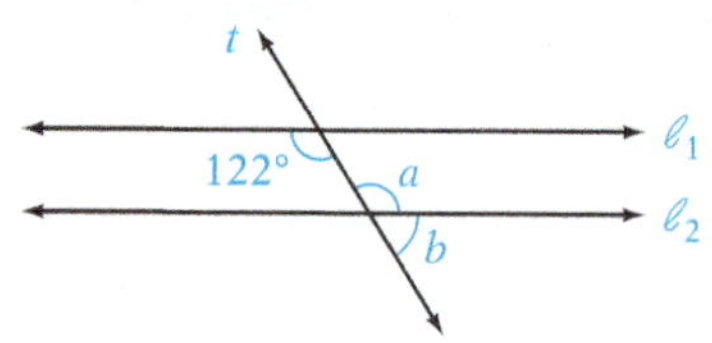

19.

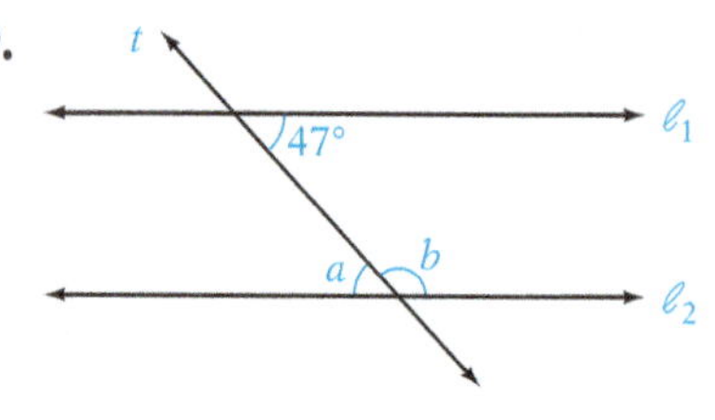

20.

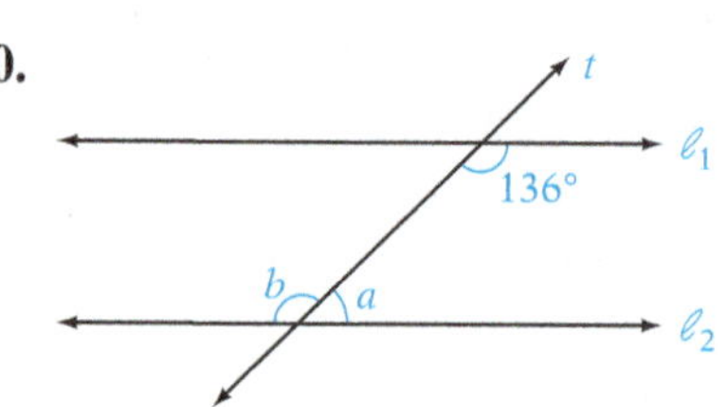

For Exercises 21 and 22, use the diagram for Exercise 19. State whether the given relationship is true even if ℓ_1 and ℓ_2 are not parallel.

21. $47° + m\angle b = 180°$

22. $m\angle a + m\angle b = 180°$

For Exercises 23 to 26, given that $\ell_1 \parallel \ell_2$, find x.

23.

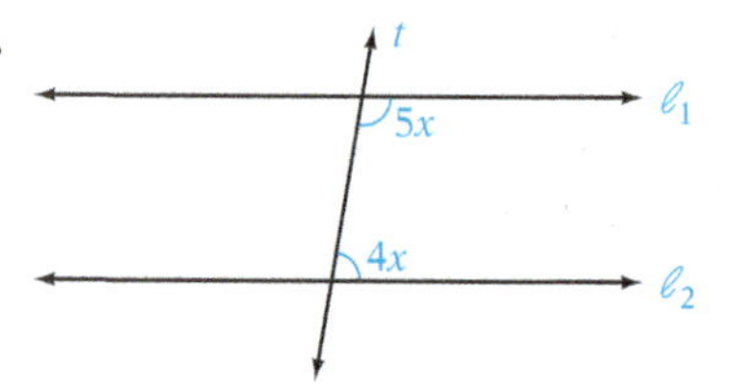

24.

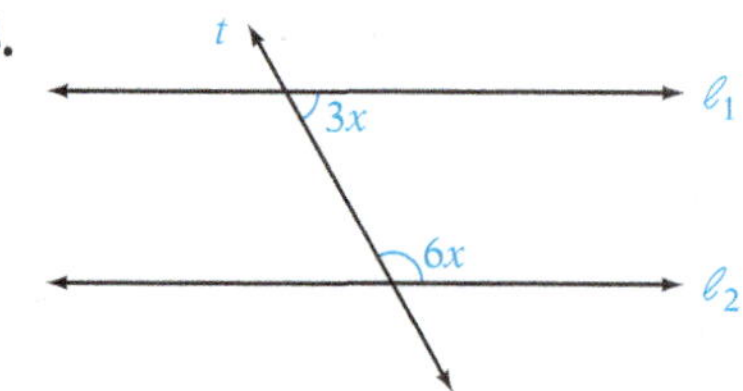

25.

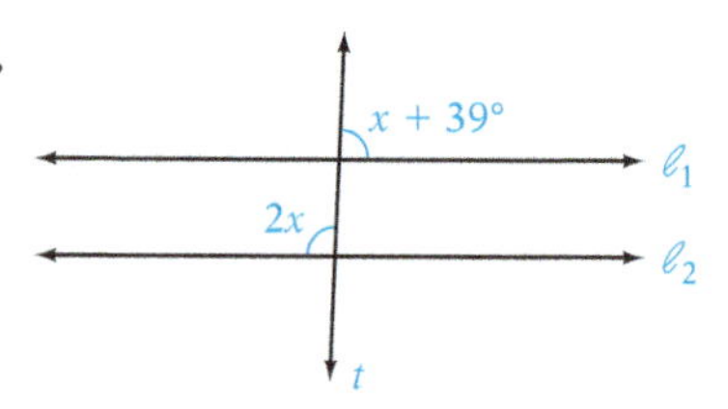

26.

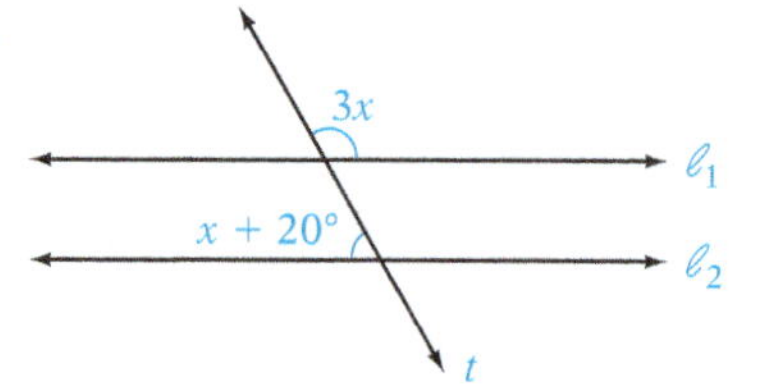

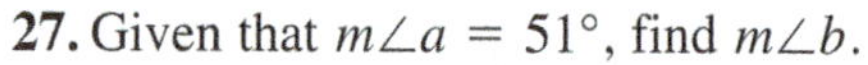

27. Given that $m\angle a = 51°$, find $m\angle b$.

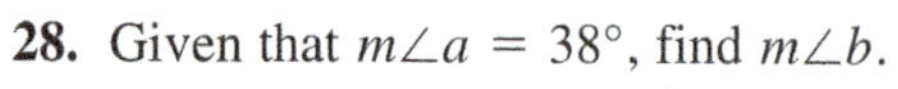

28. Given that $m\angle a = 38°$, find $m\angle b$.

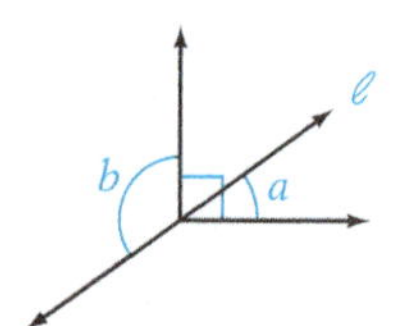

OBJECTIVE B *To solve problems involving the angles of a triangle*

29. Given that $m\angle a = 95°$ and $m\angle b = 70°$, find $m\angle x$ and $m\angle y$.

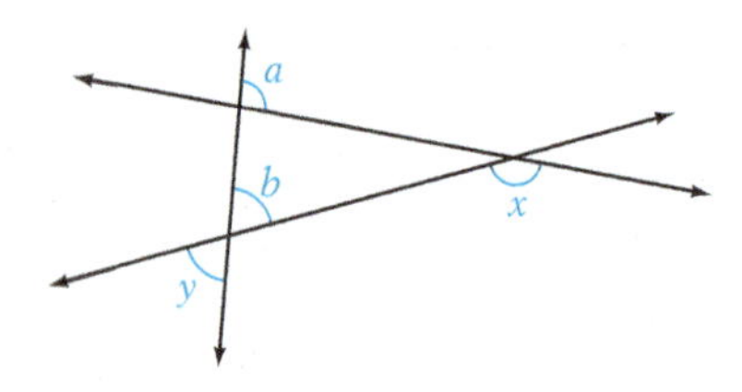

30. Given that $m\angle a = 35°$ and $m\angle b = 55°$, find $m\angle x$ and $m\angle y$.

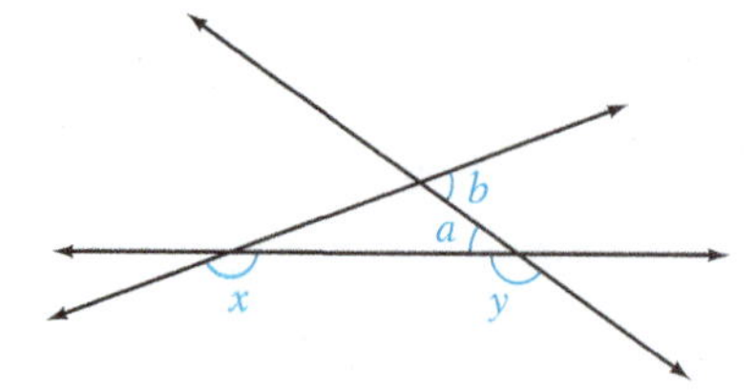

31. Given that $m\angle y = 45°$, find $m\angle a$ and $m\angle b$.

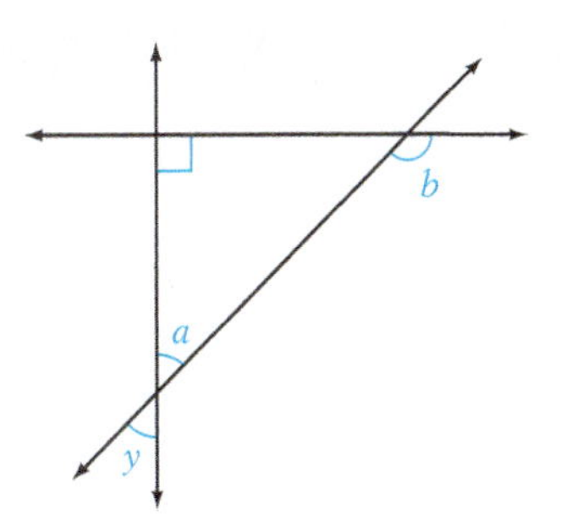

32. Given that $m\angle y = 130°$, find $m\angle a$ and $m\angle b$.

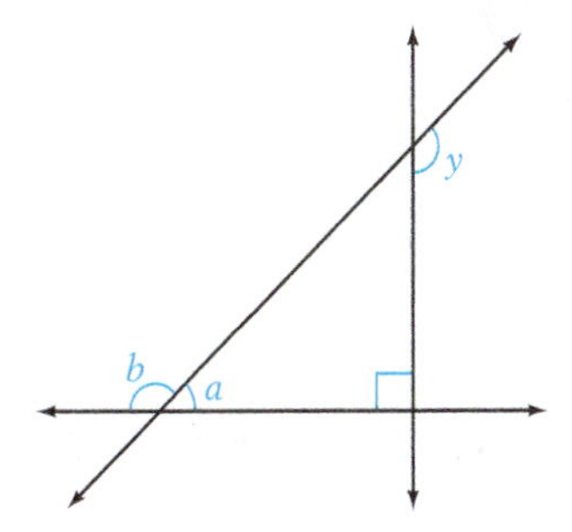

33. A triangle has a 30° angle and a right angle. What is the measure of the third angle?

34. A triangle has a 45° angle and a right angle. Find the measure of the third angle.

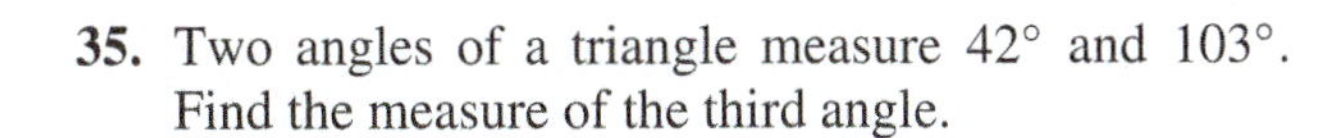

35. Two angles of a triangle measure 42° and 103°. Find the measure of the third angle.

36. Two angles of a triangle measure 62° and 45°. Find the measure of the third angle.

37. A triangle has a 13° angle and a 65° angle. What is the measure of the third angle?

38. A triangle has a 105° angle and a 32° angle. What is the measure of the third angle?

39. True or false? If one angle of a triangle is a right angle, then the other two angles of the triangle are complementary angles.

Critical Thinking

40. The measures of the angles of a triangle are consecutive integers. Find the measure of each angle.

41. True or False? A triangle can have two right angles.

42. True or false? A triangle has nine exterior angles.

43. True or false? A triangle that has an exterior angle that is a right angle must also have an interior angle that is a right angle.

Projects or Group Activities

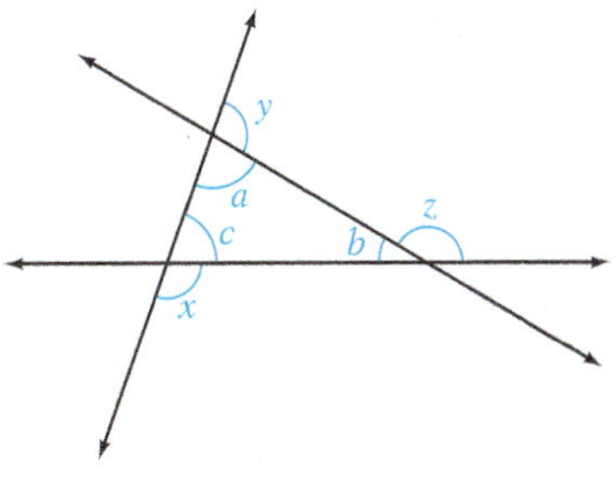

44. a. For the figure at the right, find the sum of the measures of angles x, y, and z.

b. For the figure at the right, explain why $\angle a + \angle b = \angle x$. Write a rule that describes the relationship between an exterior angle of a triangle and the opposite interior angles. Use the rule to write an equation involving angles a, c, and z.

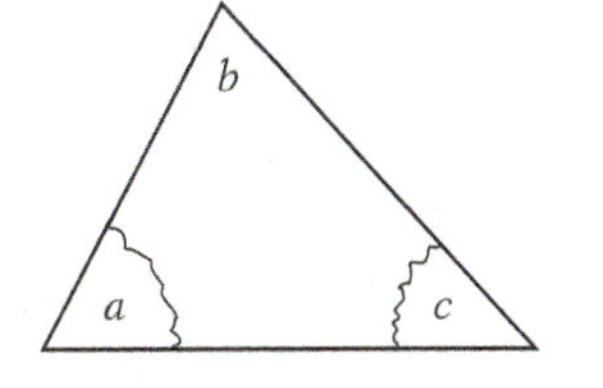

45. Draw a triangle on a piece of paper as shown at the right. Cut out the triangle. Tear off two of the angles. Position the pieces you tore off so that angle a is adjacent to angle b and angle c is adjacent to angle b. Describe what you observe. What does this demonstrate?

SECTION

3.7 Mixture and Uniform Motion Problems

OBJECTIVE A *To solve value mixture problems*

A value mixture problem involves combining two ingredients that have different prices into a single blend. For example, a coffee merchant may blend two types of coffee into a single blend, or a candy manufacturer may combine two types of candy to sell as a variety pack.

The solution of a value mixture problem is based on the **value mixture equation** $AC = V$, where A is the amount of an ingredient, C is the cost per unit of the ingredient, and V is the value of the ingredient.

Take Note
The equation $AC = V$ is used to find the value of an ingredient. For example, the value of 4 lb of cashews costing \$6 per pound is

$$AC = V$$
$$4 \cdot \$6 = V$$
$$\$24 = V$$

HOW TO 1 A coffee merchant wants to make 6 lb of a blend of coffee costing \$5 per pound. The blend is made using a \$7-per-pound grade and a \$4-per-pound grade of coffee. How many pounds of each of these grades should be used?

Strategy for Solving a Value Mixture Problem

1. For each ingredient in the mixture, write a numerical or variable expression for the amount of the ingredient used, the unit cost of the ingredient, and the value of the amount used. For the blend, write a numerical or variable expression for the amount, the unit cost of the blend, and the value of the amount. The results can be recorded in a table.

The sum of the amounts is 6 lb.

Amount of \$7 coffee: x
Amount of \$4 coffee: $6 - x$

Take Note
Use the information given in the problem to fill in the amount and unit cost columns of the table. Fill in the value column by multiplying the two expressions you wrote in each row. Use the expressions in the last column to write the equation.

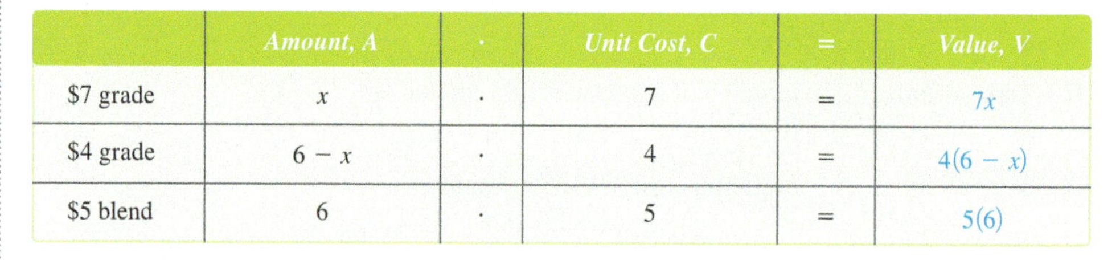

	Amount, A	·	Unit Cost, C	=	Value, V
\$7 grade	x	·	7	=	$7x$
\$4 grade	$6 - x$	·	4	=	$4(6 - x)$
\$5 blend	6	·	5	=	$5(6)$

2. Determine how the values of the ingredients are related. Use the fact that the sum of the values of all the ingredients is equal to the value of the blend.

The sum of the values of the \$7 grade and the \$4 grade is equal to the value of the \$5 blend.

$$7x + 4(6 - x) = 5(6)$$
$$7x + 24 - 4x = 30$$
$$3x + 24 = 30$$
$$3x = 6$$
$$x = 2$$

$6 - x = 6 - 2 = 4$ • **Find the amount of the \$4 grade coffee.**

The merchant must use 2 lb of the \$7 coffee and 4 lb of the \$4 coffee.

EXAMPLE 1

How many ounces of a metal alloy that costs $4 an ounce must be mixed with 10 oz of an alloy that costs $6 an ounce to make a mixture that costs $4.32 an ounce?

Strategy

- Ounces of $4 alloy: x

	Amount	*Cost*	*Value*
$4 alloy	x	4	$4x$
$6 alloy	10	6	$6(10)$
$4.32 mixture	$10 + x$	4.32	$4.32(10 + x)$

- The sum of the values before mixing equals the value after mixing.

Solution

$4x + 6(10) = 4.32(10 + x)$ • **The sum of the values before mixing equals the value after mixing.**

$4x + 60 = 43.2 + 4.32x$

$-0.32x + 60 = 43.2$ • **Subtract $4.32x$ from each side.**

$-0.32x = -16.8$ • **Subtract 60 from each side.**

$x = 52.5$ • **Divide each side by -0.32.**

52.5 oz of the $4 alloy must be used.

YOU TRY IT 1

A gardener has 20 lb of a lawn fertilizer that costs $.90 per pound. How many pounds of a fertilizer that costs $.75 per pound should be mixed with this 20 lb of lawn fertilizer to produce a mixture that costs $.85 per pound?

Your strategy

Your solution

Solution on p. S8

OBJECTIVE B *To solve percent mixture problems*

Recall from Section 3.2 that a percent mixture problem can be solved using the equation $Ar = Q$, where A is the amount of a solution, r is the percent concentration of a substance in the solution, and Q is the quantity of the substance in the solution.

For example, a 500-milliliter bottle is filled with a 4% solution of hydrogen peroxide.

$$Ar = Q$$
$$500(0.04) = Q$$
$$20 = Q$$

The bottle contains 20 ml of hydrogen peroxide.

HOW TO 2 How many gallons of a 20% salt solution must be mixed with 6 gal of a 30% salt solution to make a 22% salt solution?

Strategy for Solving a Percent Mixture Problem

1. For each solution, write a numerical or variable expression for the amount of solution, the percent concentration, and the quantity of the substance in the solution. The results can be recorded in a table.

The unknown quantity of 20% solution: x

	Amount of Solution, A	·	*Percent Concentration, r*	=	*Quantity of Substance, Q*
20% solution	x	·	0.20	=	$0.20x$
30% solution	6	·	0.30	=	$0.30(6)$
22% solution	$x + 6$	·	0.22	=	$0.22(x + 6)$

Take Note
Use the information given in the problem to fill in the amount and percent columns of the table. Fill in the quantity column by multiplying the two expressions you wrote in each row. Use the expressions in the last column to write the equation.

2. Determine how the quantities of the substances in the solutions are related. Use the fact that the sum of the quantities of the substances being mixed is equal to the quantity of the substance after mixing.

The sum of the quantities of the substances in the 20% solution and the 30% solution is equal to the quantity of the substance in the 22% solution.

$$0.20x + 0.30(6) = 0.22(x + 6)$$
$$0.20x + 1.80 = 0.22x + 1.32$$
$$-0.02x + 1.80 = 1.32$$
$$-0.02x = -0.48$$
$$x = 24$$

24 gal of the 20% solution are required.

EXAMPLE 2

A chemist wishes to make 2 L of an 8% acid solution by mixing a 10% acid solution and a 5% acid solution. How many liters of each solution should the chemist use?

Strategy

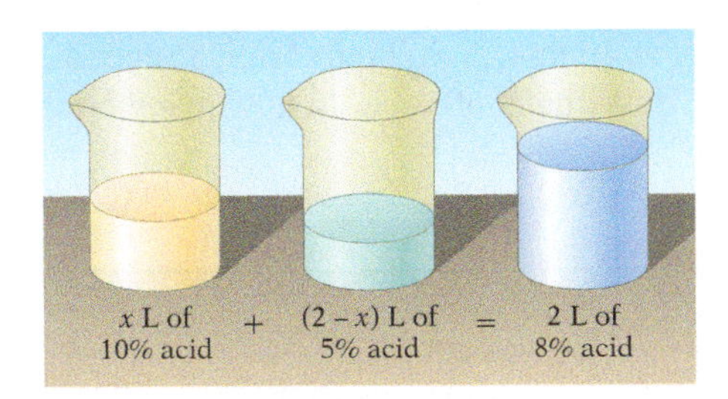

- Liters of 10% solution: x
  Liters of 5% solution: $2 - x$

	Amount	*Percent*	*Quantity*
10% solution	x	0.10	$0.10x$
5% solution	$2 - x$	0.05	$0.05(2 - x)$
8% solution	2	0.08	$0.08(2)$

- The sum of the quantities before mixing is equal to the quantity after mixing.

Solution

$0.10x + 0.05(2 - x) = 0.08(2)$ • **The sum of the quantities before mixing equals the quantity after mixing.**

$0.10x + 0.10 - 0.05x = 0.16$

$0.05x + 0.10 = 0.16$ • **Combine like terms on the left side.**

$0.05x = 0.06$ • **Subtract 0.10 from each side.**

$x = 1.2$ • **Divide each side by 0.05. Liters of 10% solution: 1.2**

$2 - x = 2 - 1.2 = 0.8$ • **Find the number of liters of 5% solution.**

The chemist needs 1.2 L of the 10% solution and 0.8 L of the 5% solution.

YOU TRY IT 2

A pharmacist dilutes 5 L of a 12% solution with a 6% solution. How many liters of the 6% solution are added to make an 8% solution?

Your strategy

Your solution

Solution on pp. S8–S9

OBJECTIVE C *To solve uniform motion problems*

Recall from Section 3.2 that an object traveling at a constant speed in a straight line is in *uniform motion*. The solution of a uniform motion problem is based on the equation $rt = d$, where r is the rate of travel, t is the time spent traveling, and d is the distance traveled.

HOW TO 3 A car leaves a town traveling at 40 mph. Two hours later, a second car leaves the same town, on the same road, traveling at 60 mph. In how many hours will the second car pass the first car?

Strategy for Solving a Uniform Motion Problem

1. For each object, write a numerical or variable expression for the rate, time, and distance. The results can be recorded in a table.

The first car traveled 2 h longer than the second car.

Unknown time for the second car: t
Time for the first car: $t + 2$

Take Note
Use the information given in the problem to fill in the rate and time columns of the table. Fill in the distance column by multiplying the two expressions you wrote in each row.

	Rate, r	$\cdot$	Time, t	$=$	Distance, d
First car	40	$\cdot$	$t + 2$	$=$	$40(t + 2)$
Second car	60	$\cdot$	t	$=$	$60t$

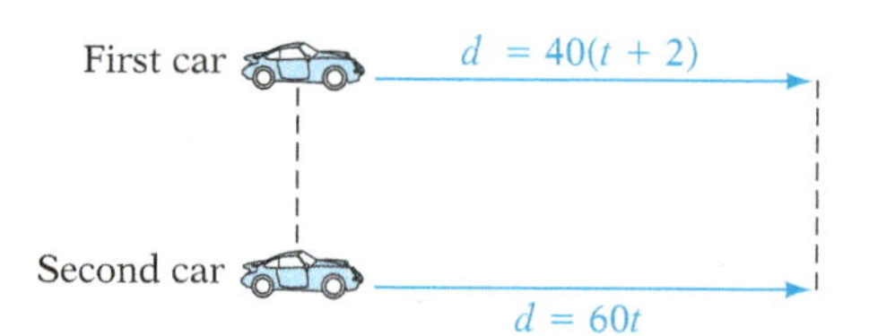

2. Determine how the distances traveled by the two objects are related. For example, the total distance traveled by both objects may be known, or it may be known that the two objects traveled the same distance.

The two cars travel the same distance.

$$40(t + 2) = 60t$$
$$40t + 80 = 60t$$
$$80 = 20t$$
$$4 = t$$

The second car will pass the first car in 4 h.

EXAMPLE 3

Two cars, one traveling 10 mph faster than the other, start at the same time from the same point and travel in opposite directions. In 3 h, they are 300 mi apart. Find the rate of each car.

Strategy • Rate of first car: r
Rate of second car: $r + 10$

	Rate	Time	Distance
1st car	r	3	$3r$
2nd car	$r + 10$	3	$3(r + 10)$

• The total distance traveled by the two cars is 300 mi.

Solution

$3r + 3(r + 10) = 300$
$3r + 3r + 30 = 300$ • Distributive Property
$6r + 30 = 300$ • Combine like terms.
$6r = 270$ • Subtract 30 from each side.
$r = 45$ • Divide each side by 6.

$r + 10 = 45 + 10 = 55$ • Find the rate of the second car.

The first car is traveling at 45 mph.
The second car is traveling at 55 mph.

YOU TRY IT 3

Two trains, one traveling at twice the speed of the other, start at the same time on parallel tracks from stations that are 288 mi apart and travel toward each other. In 3 h, the trains pass each other. Find the rate of each train.

Your strategy

Your solution

EXAMPLE 4

How far can the members of a bicycling club ride out into the country at a speed of 12 mph and return over the same road at 8 mph if they travel a total of 10 h?

Strategy • Time spent riding out: t
Time spent riding back: $10 - t$

	Rate	Time	Distance
Out	12	t	$12t$
Back	8	$10 - t$	$8(10 - t)$

• The distance out equals the distance back.

Solution

$12t = 8(10 - t)$
$12t = 80 - 8t$ • Distributive Property
$20t = 80$ • Add $8t$ to each side
$t = 4$ (The time is 4 h.) • Divide each side by 20.

The distance out $= 12t = 12(4) = 48$

The club can ride 48 mi into the country.

YOU TRY IT 4

A pilot flew out to a parcel of land and back in 5 h. The rate out was 150 mph, and the rate returning was 100 mph. How far away was the parcel of land?

Your strategy

Your solution

Solutions on p. S9

3.7 EXERCISES

Concept Check

1. The total value of a 7-pound bag of cat food that costs \$1.50 per pound is ________.

2. If 8 L of a solvent costs \$75 per liter, then the value of the 8 L of solvent is ________.

3. The cost per pound of a 5-pound bag of sugar that has a total value of \$3.80 is ________

Andrea Skjold/Shutterstock.com

4. A 250-milliliter bottle contains a solution that is 90% isopropyl alcohol. The amount of isopropyl alcohol in the solution is 250 (________) = ________ ml.

5. A 500-gram can of legumes contains 20% navy beans. The can contains ________ g of navy beans.

6. A 10-pound box of chocolate-covered cherries is 15% chocolate. There are ________ lb of chocolate in the box. There are ________ lb of cherries in the box.

For Exercises 7 to 9, determine whether the statement is true or false.

7. In the value mixture equation $V = AC$, the variable A represents the quantity of an ingredient.

8. Suppose we are mixing two salt solutions. Then the variable Q in the percent mixture equation $Q = Ar$ represents the amount of salt in a solution.

9. If we combine a 9% acid solution with a solution that is 4% acid, the resulting solution will be less than 4% acid.

10. Explain the meaning of each variable in the equation $V = AC$. Give an example of how this equation is used.

11. Explain the meaning of each variable in the equation $Q = Ar$. Give an example of how this equation is used.

12. Explain what each variable in the formula $d = rt$ represents.

OBJECTIVE A *To solve value mixture problems*

13. At a veterinary clinic, a special high-protein dog food that costs \$6.75 per pound is mixed with a vitamin supplement that costs \$3.25 per pound. How many pounds of each should be used to make 5 lb of a mixture that costs \$4.65 per pound?

14. A goldsmith combined an alloy that costs \$4.30 per ounce with an alloy that costs \$1.80 per ounce. How many ounces of each were used to make a mixture of 200 oz costing \$2.50 per ounce?

15. How many pounds of chamomile tea that costs \$18.20 per pound must be mixed with 12 lb of orange tea that costs \$12.25 per pound to make a mixture that costs \$14.63 per pound?

© iStockphoto.com/agdalena Kucova

16. A wild birdseed mix is made by combining 100 lb of millet seed costing $.60 per pound with sunflower seeds costing $1.10 per pound. How many pounds of sunflower seeds are needed to make a mixture that costs $.70 per pound?

17. Find the cost per pound of a coffee mixture made from 8 lb of coffee that costs $9.20 per pound and 12 lb of coffee that costs $5.50 per pound.

18. Find the cost per ounce of a mixture of 200 oz of a cologne that costs $7.50 per ounce and 500 oz of a cologne that costs $4.00 per ounce.

19. An herbalist has 30 oz of herbs costing $2 per ounce. How many ounces of herbs costing $1 per ounce should be mixed with these 30 oz of herbs to produce a mixture costing $1.60 per ounce?

20. A snack food is made by mixing 5 lb of popcorn that costs $.80 per pound with caramel that costs $2.40 per pound. How much caramel is needed to make a mixture that costs $1.40 per pound?

21. A grocery store offers a cheese sampler that includes a pepper cheddar cheese that costs $16 per kilogram and Pennsylvania Jack that costs $12 per kilogram. How many kilograms of each were used to make a 5-kilogram mixture that costs $13.20 per kilogram?

22. A lumber company combined oak wood chips that cost $3.10 per pound with pine wood chips that cost $2.50 per pound. How many pounds of each were used to make an 80-pound mixture costing $2.65 per pound?

23. The manager of a farmer's market has 500 lb of grain that costs $1.20 per pound. How many pounds of meal costing $.80 per pound should be mixed with the 500 lb of grain to produce a mixture that costs $1.05 per pound?

24. A caterer made an ice cream punch by combining fruit juice that costs $4.50 per gallon with ice cream that cost $8.50 per gallon. How many gallons of each were used to make 100 gal of punch costing $5.50 per gallon?

25. The manager of a specialty food store combined almonds that cost $6.50 per pound with walnuts that cost $5.50 per pound. How many pounds of each were used to make a 100-pound mixture that costs $5.87 per pound?

26. Find the cost per pound of a "house blend" of coffee that is made from 12 lb of Central American coffee that costs $8 per pound and 30 lb of South American coffee that costs $4.50 per pound.

27. Find the cost per pound of sugar-coated breakfast cereal made from 40 lb of sugar that costs $2.00 per pound and 120 lb of corn flakes that cost $1.20 per pound.

28. How many liters of a blue dye that costs $1.60 per liter must be mixed with 18 L of anil that costs $2.50 per liter to make a mixture that costs $1.90 per liter?

29. **Tree Conservation** A town's parks department buys trees from the tree conservation program described in the news clipping at the right. The department spends $406 on 14 bundles of trees. How many bundles of seedlings and how many bundles of container-grown plants did the parks department buy?

In the NEWS!

Conservation Tree Planting Program Underway

The Kansas Forest Service is again offering its Conservation Tree Planting Program. Trees are sold in bundles of 25, in two sizes—seedlings cost $17 a bundle and larger container-grown plants cost $45 a bundle.

Source: Kansas Canopy

30. Find the cost per ounce of a gold alloy made from 25 oz of pure gold that costs $1282 per ounce and 40 oz of an alloy that costs $900 per ounce.

31. Find the cost per ounce of a sunscreen made from 100 oz of a lotion that costs $2.50 per ounce and 50 oz of a lotion that costs $4.00 per ounce.

32. A grocer mixes peanuts that cost \$3 per pound with almonds that cost \$7 per pound. Which of the following could be true about the cost C per pound of the mixture? There may be more than one correct answer.

(i) $C = \$10$ (ii) $C > \$7$ (iii) $C < \$7$
(iv) $C < \$3$ (v) $C > \$3$ (vi) $C = \$4$

33. A snack mix is made from 3 lb of sunflower seeds that cost S dollars per pound and 4 lb of raisins that cost R dollars per pound. Which expression gives the cost C per pound of the mixture?

(i) $7(S + R)$ (ii) $3S + 4R$ (iii) $S + R$ (iv) $\dfrac{3S + 4R}{7}$

OBJECTIVE B *To solve percent mixture problems*

34. Forty ounces of a 30% gold alloy are mixed with 60 oz of a 20% gold alloy. Find the percent concentration of the resulting gold alloy.

35. One hundred ounces of juice that is 50% tomato juice are added to 200 oz of a vegetable juice that is 25% tomato juice. What is the percent concentration of tomato juice in the resulting mixture?

36. How many gallons of a 15% acid solution must be mixed with 5 gal of a 20% acid solution to make a 16% acid solution?

37. How many pounds of a chicken feed that is 50% corn must be mixed with 400 lb of a feed that is 80% corn to make a chicken feed that is 75% corn?

38. A rug is made by weaving 20 lb of yarn that is 50% wool with a yarn that is 25% wool. How many pounds of the yarn that is 25% wool must be used if the finished rug is to be 35% wool?

39. Five gallons of a dark green latex paint that is 20% yellow paint are combined with a lighter green latex paint that is 40% yellow paint. How many gallons of the lighter green paint must be used to create a green paint that is 25% yellow paint?

40. How many gallons of a plant food that is 9% nitrogen must be combined with another plant food that is 25% nitrogen to make 10 gal of a plant food that is 15% nitrogen?

41. A chemist wants to make 50 ml of a 16% acid solution by mixing a 13% acid solution and an 18% acid solution. How many milliliters of each solution should the chemist use?

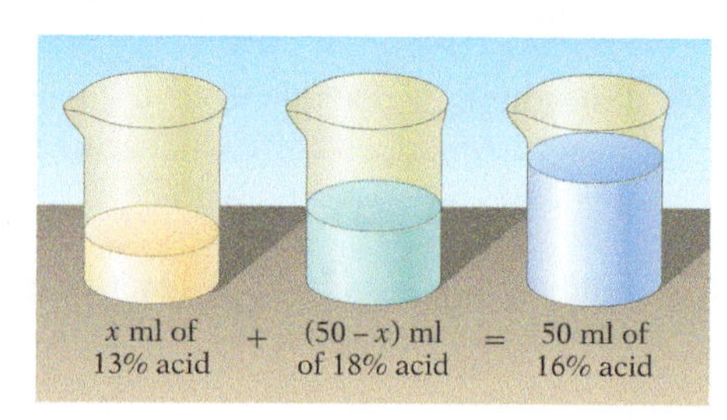

42. Five grams of sugar are added to a 45-gram serving of a breakfast cereal that is 10% sugar. What is the percent concentration of sugar in the resulting mixture?

43. Thirty ounces of pure silver are added to 50 oz of a silver alloy that is 20% silver. What is the percent concentration of the resulting alloy?

44. To make the potpourri mixture sold at a florist shop, 70 oz of a potpourri that is 80% lavender are combined with a potpourri that is 60% lavender. The resulting potpourri is 74% lavender. How much of the potpourri that is 60% lavender is used?

45. The manager of a garden shop mixes grass seed that is 40% rye grass with 40 lb of grass seed that is 60% rye grass to make a mixture that is 56% rye grass. How much of the 40% rye grass is used?

46. A hair dye is made by blending a 7% hydrogen peroxide solution and a 4% hydrogen peroxide solution. How many milliliters of each are used to make a 300-milliliter solution that is 5% hydrogen peroxide?

47. A clothing manufacturer has some pure silk thread and some thread that is 85% silk. How many kilograms of each must be woven together to make 75 kg of cloth that is 96% silk?

48. At a cosmetics company, 40 L of pure aloe cream are mixed with 50 L of a moisturizer that is 64% aloe. What is the percent concentration of aloe in the resulting mixture?

49. **Ethanol Fuel** See the news clipping at the right. *Gasohol* is a type of fuel made by mixing ethanol with gasoline. E10 is a fuel mixture of 10% ethanol and 90% gasoline. E20 contains 20% ethanol and 80% gasoline. How many gallons of ethanol must be added to 100 gal of E10 to make E20?

In the NEWS!

Gasohol Reduces Harmful Emissions

A new study indicates that using E20 fuel reduces carbon dioxide and hydrocarbon emissions, as compared with E10 blends or traditional gasoline.

Source: www.sciencedaily.com

50. A hair stylist combines 12 oz of shampoo that is 20% conditioner with an 8-ounce bottle of pure shampoo. What is the percent concentration of conditioner in the 20-ounce mixture?

51. How many ounces of pure chocolate must be added to 150 oz of chocolate topping that is 50% chocolate to make a topping that is 75% chocolate?

52. A recipe for a rice dish calls for 8 oz of pure wild rice and 12 oz of a rice mixture that is 20% wild rice. What is the percent concentration of wild rice in the 20-ounce mixture?

53. True or false? A 10% salt solution can be combined with some amount of a 20% salt solution to create a 30% salt solution.

54. True or false? When n ounces of 100% acid are mixed with $2n$ ounces of pure water, the resulting mixture is a 50% acid solution.

OBJECTIVE C *To solve uniform motion problems*

55. Two small planes start from the same point and fly in opposite directions. The first plane is flying 25 mph slower than the second plane. In 2 h, the planes are 470 mi apart. Find the rate of each plane.

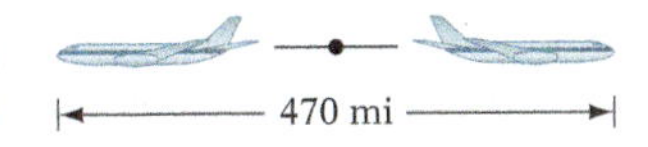

56. Two cyclists start from the same point and ride in opposite directions. One cyclist rides twice as fast as the other. In 3 h, they are 81 mi apart. Find the rate of each cyclist.

57. One speed skater starts across a frozen lake at an average speed of 8 m/s. Ten seconds later, a second speed skater starts from the same point and skates in the same direction at an average speed of 10 m/s. How many seconds after the second skater starts will the second skater overtake the first skater?

58. A long-distance runner starts on a course running at an average speed of 6 mph. Half an hour later, a second runner begins the same course at an average speed of 7 mph. How long after the second runner starts will the second runner overtake the first runner?

59. Michael Chan leaves a dock in his motorboat and travels at an average speed of 9 mph toward the Isle of Shoals, a small island off the coast of Massachusetts. Two hours later, a tour boat leaves the same dock and travels at an average speed of 18 mph toward the same island. How many hours after the tour boat leaves will Michael's boat be alongside the tour boat?

60. A jogger starts from one end of a 15-mile nature trail at 8:00 A.M. One hour later, a cyclist starts from the other end of the trail and rides toward the jogger. If the rate of the jogger is 6 mph and the rate of the cyclist is 9 mph, at what time will the two meet?

61. An executive drove from home at an average speed of 30 mph to an airport where a helicopter was waiting. The executive boarded the helicopter and flew to the corporate offices at an average speed of 60 mph. The entire distance was 150 mi. The entire trip took 3 h. Find the distance from the airport to the corporate offices.

62. A 555-mile, 5-hour plane trip was flown at two speeds. For the first part of the trip, the average speed was 105 mph. For the remainder of the trip, the average speed was 115 mph. How long did the plane fly at each speed?

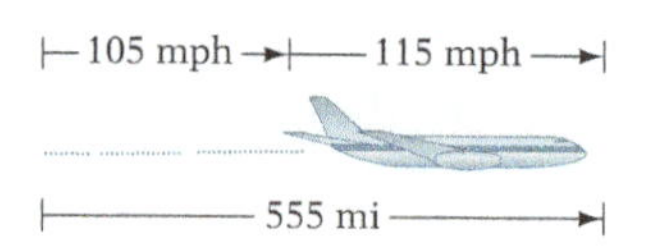

63. After a sailboat had been on the water for 3 h, a change in the wind direction reduced the average speed of the boat by 5 mph. The entire distance sailed was 57 mi. The total time spent sailing was 6 h. How far did the sailboat travel in the first 3 h?

150 mph

100 mph

64. A stunt driver was needed at the production site of a Hollywood movie. The average speed of the stunt driver's flight to the site was 150 mph, and the average speed of the return trip was 100 mph. Find the distance of the round trip if the total flying time was 5 h.

65. A passenger train leaves a train depot 2 h after a freight train leaves the same depot. The freight train is traveling 20 mph slower than the passenger train. Find the rate of each train if the passenger train overtakes the freight train in 3 h.

66. A car and a bus set out at 3 P.M. from the same point headed in the same direction. The average speed of the car is twice the average speed of the bus. In 2 h the car is 68 mi ahead of the bus. Find the rate of the car.

67. A ship traveling east at 25 mph is 10 mi from a harbor when another ship leaves the harbor traveling east at 35 mph. How long does it take the second ship to catch up to the first ship?

68. At 10 A.M. a plane leaves Boston, Massachusetts, for Seattle, Washington, a distance of 3000 mi. One hour later a plane leaves Seattle for Boston. Both planes are traveling at a speed of 500 mph. How many hours after the plane leaves Seattle will the planes pass each other?

69. **Bridges** See the news clipping at the right. Two cars, the first traveling 10 km/h faster than the second, start at the same time from opposite ends of the Hangzhou Bay Bridge and travel toward each other. The cars pass each other in 12 min. Find the rate of the faster car.

© iStockphoto.com/youding xie

70. At noon a train leaves Washington, D.C., headed for Charleston, South Carolina, a distance of 500 mi. The train travels at a speed of 60 mph. At 1 P.M. a second train leaves Charleston headed for Washington, D.C., traveling at 50 mph. How long after the train leaves Charleston will the two trains pass each other?

In the NEWS!

Longest Ocean-Crossing Bridge Opens to Public

The Hangzhou Bay Bridge is the longest ocean-crossing bridge in the world. It spans the Hangzhou Bay on the East China Sea and crosses the Qiantang River at the Yangtze River Delta. The S-shaped bridge connects Jiaxing to the north and Ningbo to the south. The bridge is 36 km long and has a speed limit of 100 km/h.

Source: www.roadtraffic-technology. com

71. A race car driver starts along a 50-mile race course traveling at an average speed of 90 mph. Fifteen minutes later, a second driver starts along the same course at an average speed of 120 mph. Will the second car overtake the first car before the drivers reach the end of the course?

72. A bus traveled on a straight road for 2 h at an average speed that was 20 mph faster than its average speed on a winding road. The time spent on the winding road was 3 h. Find the average speed on the winding road if the total trip was 210 mi.

73. A bus traveling at a rate of 60 mph overtakes a car traveling at a rate of 45 mph. If the car had a 1-hour head start, how far from the starting point does the bus overtake the car?

74. A car traveling at 48 mph overtakes a cyclist who, riding at 12 mph, had a 3-hour head start. How far from the starting point does the car overtake the cyclist?

75. A plane left Kennedy Airport on Tuesday morning for a 605 mile, 5-hour trip. For the first part of the trip, the average speed was 115 mph. For the remainder of the trip, the average speed was 125 mph. How long did the plane fly at each speed?

© iStockphoto.com/Skyhobo

Critical Thinking

76. Find the cost per ounce of a mixture of 30 oz of an alloy that costs \$4.50 per ounce, 40 oz of an alloy that costs \$3.50 per ounce, and 30 oz of an alloy that costs \$3.00 per ounce.

77. A grocer combined walnuts that cost \$5.60 per pound and cashews that cost \$7.50 per pound with 20 lb of peanuts that cost \$4.00 per pound. Find the amount of walnuts and the amount of cashews used to make a 50-pound mixture costing \$5.72 per pound.

78. How many ounces of water evaporated from 50 oz of a 12% salt solution to produce a 15% salt solution?

79. A chemist mixed pure acid with water to make 10 L of a 30% acid solution. How much pure acid and how much water did the chemist use?

80. How many grams of pure water must be added to 50 g of pure acid to make a solution that is 40% acid?

81. Tickets to a performance by a community theater company cost \$5.50 for adults and \$2.75 for children. A total of 120 tickets were sold for \$563.75. How many adults and how many children attended the performance?

82. A car and a cyclist start at at 10 A.M. from the same point, headed in the same direction. The average speed of the car is 5 mph more than three times the average speed of the cyclist. In 1.5 h, the car is 46.5 mi ahead of the cyclist. Find the rate of the cyclist.

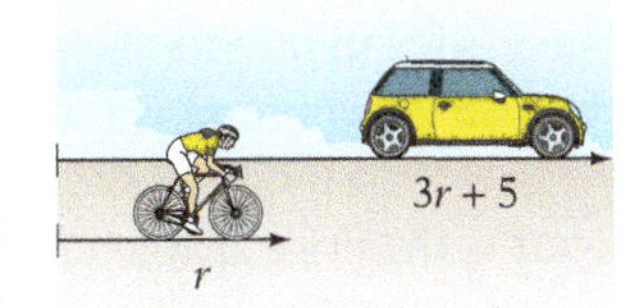

83. At 10 A.M., two campers left their campsite by canoe and paddled downstream at an average speed of 12 mph. They then turned around and paddled back upstream at an average rate of 4 mph. The total trip took 1 h. At what time did the campers turn around downstream?

84. A truck leaves a depot at 11 A.M. and travels at a speed of 45 mph. At noon, a van leaves the same depot and travels the same route at a speed of 65 mph. At what time does the van overtake the truck?

Projects or Group Activities

85. A radiator contains 15 gal of a 20% antifreeze solution. How many gallons must be drained from the radiator and replaced by pure antifreeze so that the radiator will contain 15 gal of a 40% antifreeze solution?

86. When 5 oz of water are added to an acid solution, the new mixture is $33\frac{1}{3}\%$ acid. When 5 oz of pure acid are added to this new mixture, the resulting mixture is 50% acid. What was the percent concentration of acid in the original mixture?

87. A bicyclist rides for 2 h at a speed of 10 mph and then returns at a speed of 20 mph. Find the cyclist's average speed for the trip.

88. A car travels a 1-mile track at an average speed of 30 mph. At what average speed must the car travel the next mile so that the average speed for the 2 mi is 60 mph?

89. A mountain climber ascended a mountain at 0.5 mph and descended twice as fast. The trip took 12 h. How many miles was the round trip?

Yu Lan/Shutterstock.com

90. Explain why we look for patterns and relationships in mathematics. Include a discussion of the relationship between value mixture problems and percent mixture problems, and how understanding one of these can make it easier to understand the other. Also discuss why understanding how to solve the value mixture problems in this section can be helpful in solving Exercise 81.

CHAPTER 3 Summary

Key Words	Examples
An **equation** expresses the equality of two mathematical expressions. [3.1A, p. 110]	$3 + 2(4x - 5) = x + 4$ is an equation.
A **solution of an equation** is a number that, when substituted for the variable, results in a true equation. [3.1A, p. 110]	-2 is a solution of $2 - 3x = 8$ because $2 - 3(-2) = 8$ is a true equation.
To **solve an equation** means to find a solution of the equation. The goal is to rewrite the equation in the form *variable* = *constant*, because the constant is the solution. [3.1B, p. 110]	The equation $x = -3$ is in the form *variable* = *constant*. The constant, -3, is the solution of the equation.
Cost is the price that a business pays for a product. **Selling price** is the price for which a business sells a product to a customer. **Markup** is the difference between selling price and cost. **Markup rate** is the markup expressed as a percent of the retailer's cost. [3.3B, p. 133]	If a business pays \$50 for a product and sells that product for \$70, then the cost of the product is \$50, the selling price is \$70, the markup is \$70 − \$50 = \$20, and the markup rate is $\frac{20}{50} = 40\%$.
Discount is the amount by which a retailer reduces the regular price of a product. **Discount rate** is the discount expressed as a percent of the regular price. [3.3B, p. 134]	The regular price of a product is \$25. The product is now on sale for \$20. The discount is \$25 − \$20 = \$5. The discount rate is $\frac{5}{25} = 20\%$.

Consecutive integers follow one another in order. [3.5A, p. 151]

5, 6, 7 are consecutive integers.
−9, −8, −7 are consecutive integers.

An **acute angle** is an angle whose measure is between 0° and 90°. An **obtuse angle** is an angle whose measure is between 90° and 180°. [3.6A, p. 159]

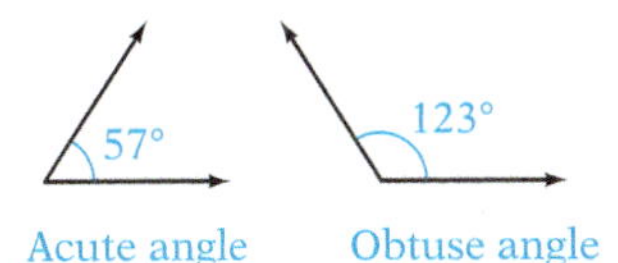

Two angles that are on the opposite sides of the intersection of two lines are **vertical angles.** Vertical angles have the same measure. Two angles that share a common side are **adjacent angles.** [3.6A, p. 159]

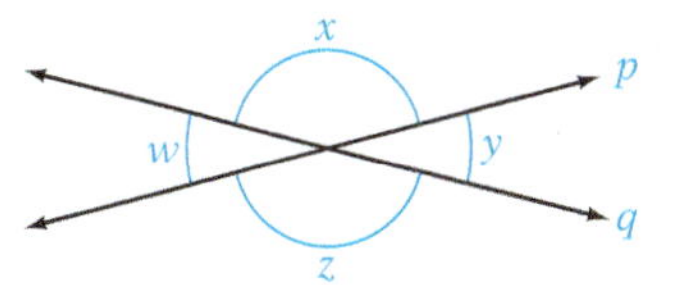

$m\angle w = m\angle y$

$m\angle x = m\angle z$

A line that intersects two other lines at two different points is a **transversal.** If the lines cut by a transversal are parallel lines, pairs of equal angles are formed: **alternate exterior angles, alternate interior angles,** and **corresponding angles.** [3.6A, p. 160]

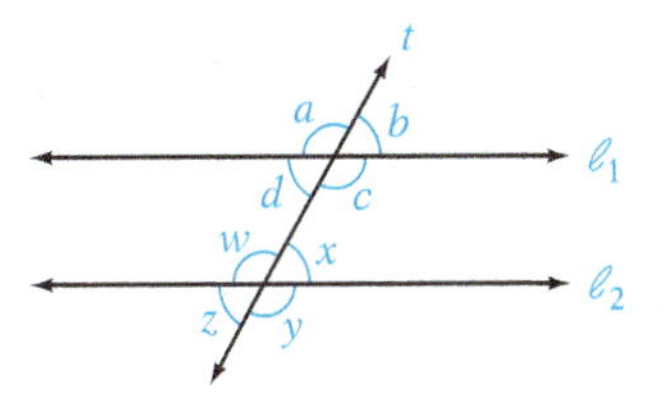

$m\angle b = m\angle d = m\angle x = m\angle z$

$m\angle a = m\angle c = m\angle w = m\angle y$

Essential Rules and Procedures

Examples

Addition Property of Equations [3.1B, p. 111]
The same number can be added to each side of an equation without changing the solution of the equation.

If $a = b$, then $a + c = b + c$.

Multiplication Property of Equations [3.1C, p. 112]
Each side of an equation can be multiplied by the same nonzero number without changing the solution of the equation.

If $a = b$ and $c \neq 0$, then $ac = bc$.

Basic Percent Equation [3.2A, p. 117]
Percent · Base = Amount

$P \cdot B = A$

30% of what number is 24?

$PB = A$

$0.30B = 24$

$B = 80$

30% of 80 is 24.

Simple Interest Equation [3.2A, p. 118]
Interest = Principal · Rate · Time

$I = Prt$

A credit card company charges an annual interest rate of 21% on the monthly unpaid balance on a card. Find the amount of interest charged on an unpaid balance of $232 for April.

$I = Prt$

$I = 232(0.21)\left(\frac{1}{12}\right) = 4.06$

Basic Markup Equation [3.3B, p. 133]
Selling Price = Cost + Markup Rate · Cost

$$S = C + rC$$

The manager of an electronics store buys an MP3 player for $200 and sells the player for $250. Find the markup rate.

$$250 = 200 + 200r$$

Basic Discount Equation [3.3B, p. 134]
Sale Price = Regular Price − Discount Rate · Regular Price

$$S = R - rR$$

The sale price for a camera phone is $56.25. This price is 25% off the regular price. Find the regular price.

$$56.25 = R - 0.25R$$

Consecutive Integers [3.5A, p. 151]
$n, n + 1, n + 2, \ldots$

The sum of three consecutive integers is 33.

$$n + (n + 1) + (n + 2) = 33$$

Consecutive Even or Consecutive Odd Integers [3.5A, p. 151]
$n, n + 2, n + 4, \ldots$

The sum of three consecutive odd integers is 33.

$$n + (n + 2) + (n + 4) = 33$$

Sum of the Angles of a Triangle [3.6B, p. 161]
The sum of the measures of the angles of a triangle is 180°.

$$m\angle a + m\angle b + m\angle c = 180^\circ$$

If the measure of one acute angle in a right triangle is twice the measure of the other acute angle, what is the measure of the smaller acute angle?

$$90^\circ + x + 2x = 180^\circ$$

Value Mixture Equation [3.7A, p. 166]
Amount · Unit Cost = Value

$$AC = V$$

An herbalist has 30 oz of herbs costing $4 per ounce. How many ounces of herbs costing $2 per ounce should be mixed with the 30 oz to produce a mixture costing $3.20 per ounce?

$$30(4) + 2x = 3.20(30 + x)$$

Percent Mixture Equation [3.2A, p. 118; 3.7B, p. 168]
Quantity = Amount · Percent Concentration

$$Q = Ar$$

Forty ounces of a 30% gold alloy are mixed with 60 oz of a 20% gold alloy. Find the percent concentration of the resulting gold alloy.

$$0.30(40) + 0.20(60) = x(100)$$

Uniform Motion Equation [3.2B, p. 121; 3.7C, p. 170]
Distance = Rate · Time

$$d = rt$$

A boat traveled from a harbor to an island at an average speed of 20 mph. The average speed on the return trip was 15 mph. The total trip took 3.5 h. How long did it take for the boat to travel to the island?

$$20t = 15(3.5 - t)$$

CHAPTER 3 Review Exercises

1. Solve: $x + 3 = 24$

2. Solve: $x + 5(3x - 20) = 10(x - 4)$

3. Solve: $5x - 6 = 29$

4. Is 3 a solution of $5x - 2 = 4x + 5$?

5. Solve: $\frac{3}{5}a = 12$

6. Solve: $6x + 3(2x - 1) = -27$

7. 30 is what percent of 12?

8. Solve: $5x + 3 = 10x - 17$

9. Solve: $7 - [4 + 2(x - 3)] = 11(x + 2)$

10. Solve: $-6x + 16 = -2x$

11. Business A music store uses a markup rate of 60%. The store sells a digital music pad for $1074. Find the cost of the digital music pad. Use the formula $S = C + rC$, where S is the selling price, C is the cost, and r is the markup rate.

12. Geometry Find x.

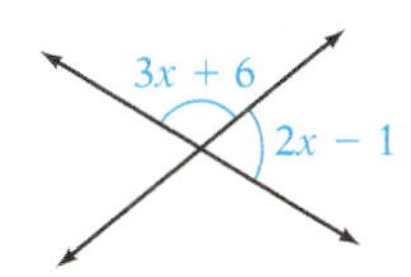

13. Geometry Find x.

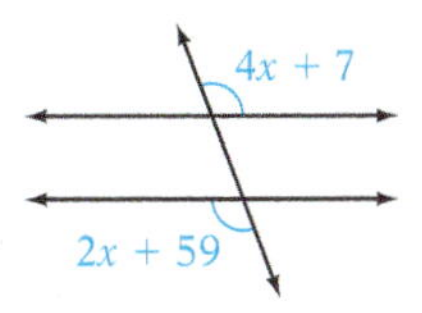

14. Physics A lever is 12 ft long. At a distance of 2 ft from the fulcrum, a force of 120 lb is applied. How large a force must be applied to the other end so that the system will balance? Use the lever system equation $F_1x = F_2(d - x)$.

15. Travel A bus traveled on a level road for 2 h at an average speed that was 20 mph faster than its average speed on a winding road. The time spent on the winding road was 3 h. Find the average speed on the winding road if the total trip was 200 mi.

16. **Business** Motorcycle goggles that regularly sell for \$60 are on sale for \$40. Find the discount rate. Use the formula $S = R - rR$, where S is the sale price, R is the regular price, and r is the discount rate.

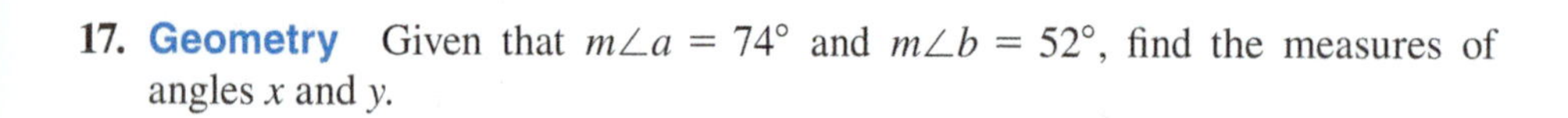

17. **Geometry** Given that $m\angle a = 74°$ and $m\angle b = 52°$, find the measures of angles x and y.

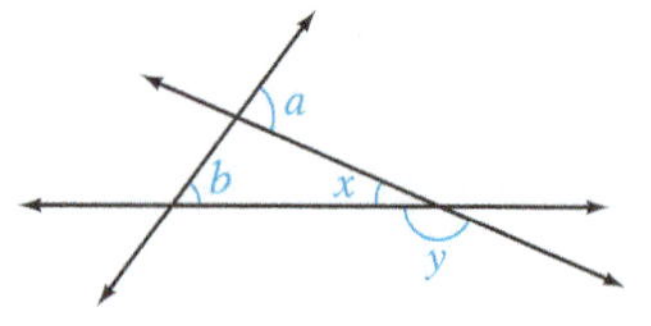

18. **Mixtures** A health food store combined cranberry juice that cost \$1.79 per quart with apple juice that cost \$1.19 per quart. How many quarts of each were used to make 10 qt of cranapple juice costing \$1.61 per quart?

19. Four times the second of three consecutive integers equals the sum of the first and third integers. Find the integers.

20. **Geometry** One angle of a triangle is 15° more than the measure of the second angle. The third angle is 15° less than the measure of the second angle. Find the measure of each angle.

Songquan Deng/Shutterstock.com

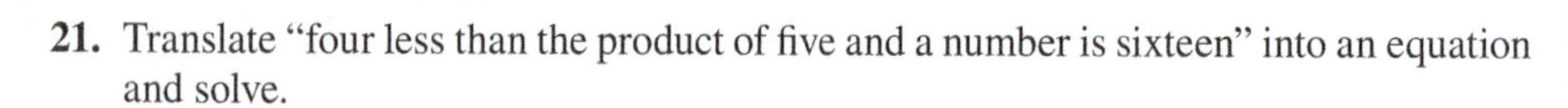

21. Translate "four less than the product of five and a number is sixteen" into an equation and solve.

22. **Building Height** The Empire State Building is 1472 ft tall. This is 654 ft less than twice the height of the Eiffel Tower. Find the height of the Eiffel Tower.

23. **Geometry** Given $m\angle y = 115°$, find $m\angle x$.

24. **Geometry** Given $\overrightarrow{OA} \perp \overrightarrow{OB}$ and $m\angle x = 30°$, find $m\angle y$.

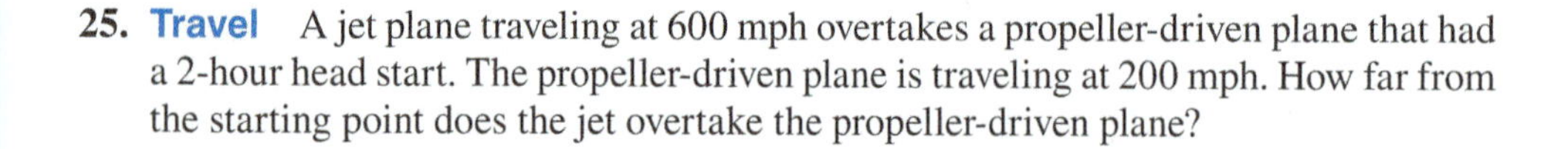

25. **Travel** A jet plane traveling at 600 mph overtakes a propeller-driven plane that had a 2-hour head start. The propeller-driven plane is traveling at 200 mph. How far from the starting point does the jet overtake the propeller-driven plane?

26. The sum of two numbers is twenty-one. Three times the smaller number is two less than twice the larger number. Find the two numbers.

27. **Mixtures** A dairy owner mixed 5 gal of cream containing 30% butterfat with 8 gal of milk containing 4% butterfat. What is the percent of butterfat in the resulting mixture?

CHAPTER 3 TEST

1. Solve: $3x - 2 = 5x + 8$

2. Solve: $x - 3 = -8$

3. Solve: $3x - 5 = -14$

4. Solve: $4 - 2(3 - 2x) = 2(5 - x)$

5. Is -2 a solution of $x^2 - 3x = 2x - 6$?

6. Solve: $7 - 4x = -13$

7. What is 0.5% of 8?

8. Solve: $5x - 2(4x - 3) = 6x + 9$

9. Solve: $5x + 3 - 7x = 2x - 5$

10. Solve: $\frac{3}{4}x = -9$

11. Mixtures A baker wants to make a 15-pound blend of flour that costs \$.60 per pound. The blend is made using a rye flour that costs \$.70 per pound and a wheat flour that costs \$.40 per pound. How many pounds of each flour should be used?

12. Geometry Find x.

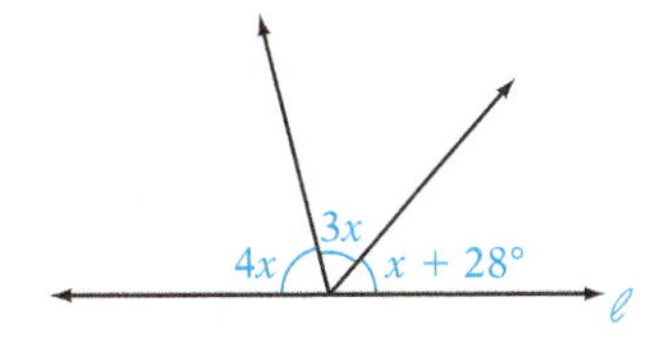

13. Business A television that regularly sells for \$450 is on sale for \$360. Find the discount rate. Use the formula $S = R - rR$, where S is the sale price, R is the regular price, and r is the discount rate.

14. Finance A financial manager has determined that the cost per unit for a calculator is \$15 and that the fixed cost per month is \$2000. Find the number of calculators produced during a month in which the total cost was \$5000. Use the equation $T = U \cdot N + F$, where T is the total cost, U is the cost per unit, N is the number of units produced, and F is the fixed cost.

15. **Geometry** In an isosceles triangle, two angles are equal. The third angle of the triangle is 30° less than one of the equal angles. Find the measure of one of the equal angles.

16. **Consecutive Integers** Find three consecutive even integers whose sum is 36.

17. **Chemistry** How many gallons of water must be mixed with 5 gal of a 20% salt solution to make a 16% salt solution?

18. **Geometry** Given that $\ell_1 \parallel \ell_2$, find the measures of angles a and b.

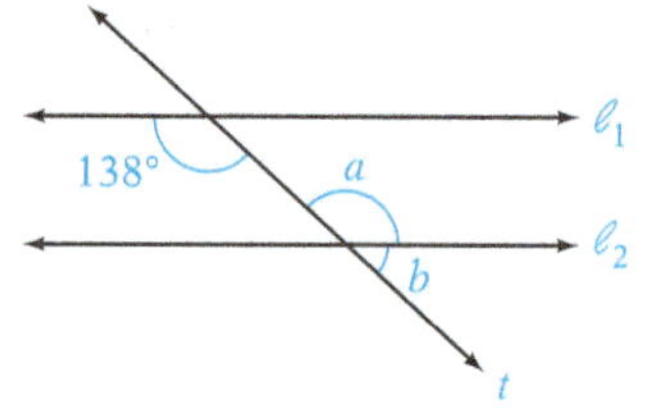

19. Translate "the difference between three times a number and fifteen is twenty-seven" into an equation and solve.

20. **Sports** A cross-country skier leaves a camp to explore a wilderness area. Two hours later a friend leaves the camp in a snowmobile, traveling 4 mph faster than the skier. The friend meets the skier 1 h later. Find the rate of the snowmobile.

Val Thoermer/Shutterstock.com

21. **Business** A company makes 140 televisions per day. Three times the number of LCD rear-projection TVs made equals 20 less than the number of LCD flat-panel TVs made. Find the number of LCD flat-panel TVs made each day.

22. The sum of two numbers is eighteen. The difference between four times the smaller number and seven is equal to the sum of two times the larger number and five. Find the two numbers.

23. **Aviation** As part of flight training, a student pilot was required to fly to an airport and then return. The average speed to the airport was 90 mph, and the average speed returning was 120 mph. Find the distance between the two airports if the total flying time was 7 h.

24. **Geometry** Given that $m\angle a = 50°$ and $m\angle b = 92°$, find the measures of angles x and y.

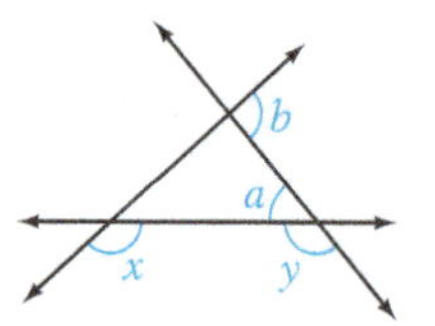

25. **Chemistry** A chemist mixes 100 g of water at 80°C with 50 g of water at 20°C. Find the final temperature of the water after mixing. Use the equation $m_1(T_1 - T) = m_2(T - T_2)$, where m_1 is the quantity of water at the hotter temperature, T_1 is the temperature of the hotter water, m_2 is the quantity of water at the cooler temperature, T_2 is the temperature of the cooler water, and T is the final temperature of the water after mixing.

Cumulative Review Exercises

1. Subtract: $-6 - (-20) - 8$

2. Multiply: $(-2)(-6)(-4)$

3. Subtract: $-\frac{5}{6} - \left(-\frac{7}{16}\right)$

4. Divide: $-\frac{7}{3} \div \frac{7}{6}$

5. Simplify: $-4^2 \cdot \left(-\frac{3}{2}\right)^3$

6. Simplify: $25 - 3\frac{(5-2)^2}{2^3+1} - (-2)$

7. Evaluate $3(a - c) - 2ab$ when $a = 2$, $b = 3$, and $c = -4$.

8. Simplify: $3x - 8x + (-12x)$

9. Simplify: $2a - (-3b) - 7a - 5b$

10. Simplify: $(16x)\left(\frac{1}{8}\right)$

11. Simplify: $-4(-9y)$

12. Simplify: $-2(-x^2 - 3x + 2)$

13. Simplify: $-2(x - 3) + 2(4 - x)$

14. Simplify: $-3[2x - 4(x - 3)] + 2$

15. Is -3 a solution of $x^2 + 6x + 9 = x + 3$?

16. Is $\frac{1}{2}$ a solution of $3 - 8x = 12x - 2$?

17. Find 32% of 60.

18. Solve: $\frac{3}{5}x = -15$

19. Solve: $7x - 8 = -29$

20. Solve: $13 - 9x = -14$

21. Solve: $8x - 3(4x - 5) = -2x - 11$

22. Solve: $6 - 2(5x - 8) = 3x - 4$

23. Solve: $5x - 8 = 12x + 13$

24. Solve: $11 - 4x = 2x + 8$

25. Chemistry A chemist mixes 300 g of water at 75°C with 100 g of water at 15°C. Find the final temperature of the water after mixing. Use the equation $m_1(T_1 - T) = m_2(T - T_2)$, where m_1 is the quantity of water at the hotter temperature, T_1 is the temperature of the hotter water, m_2 is the quantity of water at the cooler temperature, T_2 is the temperature of the cooler water, and T is the final temperature of the water after mixing.

26. Translate "The difference between twelve and the product of five and a number is negative eighteen" into an equation and solve.

27. Construction The area of a cement foundation of a house is 2000 ft². This is 200 ft² more than three times the area of the garage. Find the area of the garage.

Alaettin YILDIRIM/Shutterstock.com

28. Mixtures How many pounds of an oat flour that costs \$.80 per pound must be mixed with 40 lb of a wheat flour that costs \$.50 per pound to make a blend that costs \$.60 per pound?

29. Metallurgy How many grams of pure gold must be added to 100 g of a 20% gold alloy to make an alloy that is 36% gold?

30. Geometry The perimeter of a rectangular office is 44 ft. The length of the office is 2 ft more than the width. Find the dimensions of the office.

31. Geometry Find the measure of $\angle x$.

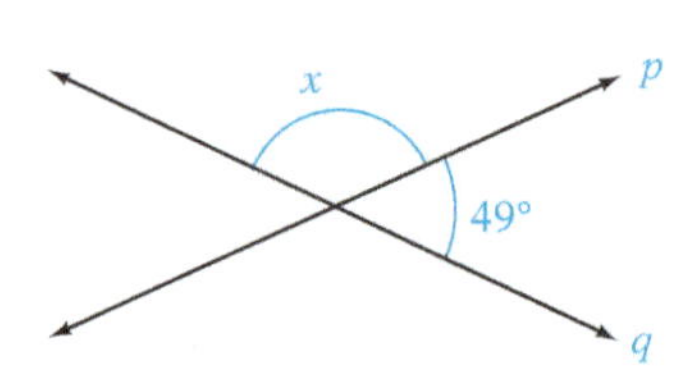

32. Geometry In an equilateral triangle, all three angles are equal. Find the measure of one of the angles of an equilateral triangle.

33. Sports A sprinter ran to the end of a track at an average rate of 8 m/s and then jogged back to the starting point at an average rate of 3 m/s. The sprinter took 55 s to run to the end of the track and jog back. Find the length of the track.

Polynomials

4

OBJECTIVES

SECTION 4.1
- **A** To add polynomials
- **B** To subtract polynomials

SECTION 4.2
- **A** To multiply monomials
- **B** To simplify powers of monomials

SECTION 4.3
- **A** To multiply a polynomial by a monomial
- **B** To multiply two polynomials
- **C** To multiply two binomials using the FOIL method
- **D** To multiply binomials that have special products
- **E** To solve application problems

SECTION 4.4
- **A** To divide monomials
- **B** To write a number in scientific notation

SECTION 4.5
- **A** To divide a polynomial by a monomial
- **B** To divide polynomials

Focus on Success

Are you making attending class a priority? Remember that to be successful, you must attend class. You need to be in class to hear your instructor's explanations and instructions, as well as to ask questions when something is unclear. Most students who miss a class fall behind and then find it very difficult to catch up. (See Class Time, page AIM-5.)

light poet/Shutterstock.com

Prep Test

Are you ready to succeed in this chapter? Take the Prep Test below to find out if you are ready to learn the new material.

1. Subtract: $-2 - (-3)$

2. Multiply: $-3(6)$

3. Simplify: $-\frac{24}{-36}$

4. Evaluate $3n^4$ when $n = -2$.

5. If $\frac{a}{b}$ is a fraction in simplest form, what number is not a possible value of b?

6. Are $2x^2$ and $2x$ like terms?

7. Simplify: $3x^2 - 4x + 1 + 2x^2 - 5x - 7$

8. Simplify: $-4y + 4y$

9. Simplify: $-3(2x - 8)$

10. Simplify: $3xy - 4y - 2(5xy - 7y)$

SECTION

4.1 Addition and Subtraction of Polynomials

OBJECTIVE A *To add polynomials*

Take Note
The expression $3\sqrt{x}$ is not a monomial because $\sqrt{x}$ cannot be written as a product of variables.
The expression $\frac{2x}{y}$ is not a monomial because it is a *quotient* of variables.

A **monomial** is a number, a variable, or a product of a number and variables. For instance,

7	b	$\frac{2}{3}a$	$12xy^2$
A number	A variable	A product of a number and a variable	A product of a number and variables

A **polynomial** is a variable expression in which the terms are monomials.

A polynomial of *one* term is a **monomial.** $-7x^2$ is a monomial.
A polynomial of *two* terms is a **binomial.** $4x + 2$ is a binomial.
A polynomial of *three* terms is a **trinomial.** $7x^2 + 5x - 7$ is a trinomial.

The **degree of a polynomial in one variable** is the greatest exponent on a variable. The degree of $4x^3 - 5x^2 + 7x - 8$ is 3; the degree of $2y^4 + y^2 - 1$ is 4. The degree of a nonzero constant is zero. For instance, the degree of 7 is zero.

The terms of a polynomial in one variable are usually arranged so that the exponents on the variable decrease from left to right. This is called **descending order.**

$$5x^3 - 4x^2 + 6x - 1$$
$$7z^4 + 4z^3 + z - 6$$
$$2y^4 + y^3 - 2y^2 + 4y - 1$$

Polynomials can be added, using either a horizontal or a vertical format, by combining like terms.

HOW TO 1 Add $(3x^3 - 7x + 2) + (7x^2 + 2x - 7)$. Use a horizontal format.

$(3x^3 - 7x + 2) + (7x^2 + 2x - 7)$
$= 3x^3 + 7x^2 + (-7x + 2x) + (2 - 7)$
• Use the Commutative and Associative Properties of Addition to rearrange and group like terms.

$= 3x^3 + 7x^2 - 5x - 5$
• Then combine like terms.

HOW TO 2 Add $(-4x^2 + 6x - 9) + (12 - 8x + 2x^3)$. Use a vertical format.

$$\begin{array}{rrrr} & -4x^2 & +\ 6x & -\ 9 \\ 2x^3 & & -\ 8x & +\ 12 \\ \hline 2x^3 & -\ 4x^2 & -\ 2x & +\ 3 \end{array}$$

• Arrange the terms of each polynomial in descending order, with like terms in the same column.
• Combine the terms in each column.

EXAMPLE 1

Use a horizontal format to add $(8x^2 - 4x - 9) + (2x^2 + 9x - 9)$.

Solution

Group like terms. Then combine like terms.

$(8x^2 - 4x - 9) + (2x^2 + 9x - 9)$
$= (8x^2 + 2x^2) + (-4x + 9x) + (-9 - 9)$
$= 10x^2 + 5x - 18$

YOU TRY IT 1

Use a horizontal format to add $(-4x^3 + 2x^2 - 8) + (4x^3 + 6x^2 - 7x + 5)$.

Your solution

Solution on p. S9

EXAMPLE 2

Use a vertical format to add
$(-5x^3 + 4x^2 - 7x + 9) + (2x^3 + 5x - 11)$.

Solution

$$\begin{array}{r} -5x^3 + 4x^2 - 7x + \ \ 9 \\ \underline{2x^3 \qquad\quad + 5x - 11} \\ -3x^3 + 4x^2 - 2x - \ \ 2 \end{array}$$

- Put like terms in the same column.
- Combine like terms.

YOU TRY IT 2

Use a vertical format to add
$(6x^3 + 2x + 8) + (-9x^3 + 2x^2 - 12x - 8)$.

Your solution

Solution on p. S9

OBJECTIVE B *To subtract polynomials*

The **opposite of the polynomial** $(3x^2 - 7x + 8)$ is $-(3x^2 - 7x + 8)$.

To simplify the opposite of a polynomial, change the sign of each term to its opposite.

$$-(3x^2 - 7x + 8) = -3x^2 + 7x - 8$$

Polynomials can be subtracted using either a horizontal or a vertical format. To subtract polynomials, add the opposite of the second polynomial to the first.

Take Note

This is the same definition used for subtraction of integers: Subtraction is addition of the opposite.

HOW TO 3 Subtract $(4y^2 - 6y + 7) - (2y^3 - 5y - 4)$. Use a horizontal format.

$$\begin{aligned} &(4y^2 - 6y + 7) - (2y^3 - 5y - 4) \\ &= (4y^2 - 6y + 7) + (-2y^3 + 5y + 4) \\ &= -2y^3 + 4y^2 + (-6y + 5y) + (7 + 4) \\ &= -2y^3 + 4y^2 - y + 11 \end{aligned}$$

- Add the opposite of the second polynomial to the first.
- Combine like terms.

HOW TO 4 Subtract $(9 + 4y + 3y^3) - (2y^2 + 4y - 21)$. Use a vertical format.

The opposite of $2y^2 + 4y - 21$ is $-2y^2 - 4y + 21$.

$$\begin{array}{r} 3y^3 \qquad\quad + 4y + \ \ 9 \\ \underline{- 2y^2 - 4y + 21} \\ 3y^3 - 2y^2 \qquad\quad + 30 \end{array}$$

- Arrange the terms of each polynomial in descending order, with like terms in the same column.
- Note that $4y - 4y = 0$, but 0 is not written.

EXAMPLE 3

a. Use a horizontal format to subtract
$(7c^2 - 9c - 12) - (9c^2 + 5c - 8)$.

b. Use a vertical format to subtract
$(3k^2 - 4k + 1) - (k^3 + 3k^2 - 6k - 8)$.

Solution

a. Add the opposite of the second polynomial to the first polynomial.

$$\begin{aligned} &(7c^2 - 9c - 12) - (9c^2 + 5c - 8) \\ &= (7c^2 - 9c - 12) + (-9c^2 - 5c + 8) \\ &= -2c^2 - 14c - 4 \end{aligned}$$

b.

$$\begin{array}{r} 3k^2 - 4k + 1 \\ \underline{-k^3 - 3k^2 + 6k + 8} \\ -k^3 \qquad\quad + 2k + 9 \end{array}$$

- Add the opposite of $(k^3 + 3k^2 - 6k - 8)$ to the first polynomial.

YOU TRY IT 3

a. Use a horizontal format to subtract
$(-4w^3 + 8w - 8) - (3w^3 - 4w^2 - 2w - 1)$.

b. Use a vertical format to subtract
$(13y^3 - 6y - 7) - (4y^2 - 6y - 9)$.

Your solution

Solution on p. S9

4.1 EXERCISES

Concept Check

For Exercises 1 to 6, state whether the expression is a monomial.

1. 17 **2.** $3x^4$ **3.** $\frac{17}{\sqrt{x}}$ **4.** $\frac{2}{3}y$ **5.** $\frac{xy}{z}$ **6.** $\sqrt{5}\,x$

For Exercises 7 to 14, state whether the expression is a monomial, a binomial, a trinomial, or none of these.

7. $3x + 5$ **8.** $2y - 3\sqrt{y}$ **9.** $9x^2 - x - 1$ **10.** $x^2 + y^2$

11. $\frac{2}{x} - 3$ **12.** $\frac{ab}{4}$ **13.** $6x^2 + 7x$ **14.** $12a^4 - 3a + 2$

OBJECTIVE A *To add polynomials*

For Exercises 15 to 24, add. Use a horizontal format.

15. $(4x^2 + 2x) + (x^2 + 6x)$

16. $(-3y^2 + y) + (4y^2 + 6y)$

17. $(4x^2 - 5xy) + (3x^2 + 6xy - 4y^2)$

18. $(2x^2 - 4y^2) + (6x^2 - 2xy + 4y^2)$

19. $(2a^2 - 7a + 10) + (a^2 + 4a + 7)$

20. $(-6x^2 + 7x + 3) + (3x^2 + x + 3)$

21. $(7x + 5x^3 - 7) + (10x^2 - 8x + 3)$

22. $(4y + 3y^3 + 9) + (2y^2 + 4y - 21)$

23. $(7 - 5r + 2r^2) + (3r^3 - 6r)$

24. $(14 + 4y + 3y^3) + (-4y^2 + 21)$

For Exercises 25 to 32, add. Use a vertical format.

25. $(x^2 + 7x) + (-3x^2 - 4x)$

26. $(3x^2 + 9x) + (6x - 24)$

27. $(2x^2 + 6x + 12) + (3x^2 + x + 8)$

28. $(x^2 + x + 5) + (3x^2 - 10x + 4)$

29. $(-7x + x^3 + 4) + (2x^2 + x - 10)$

30. $(y^2 + 3y^3 + 1) + (-4y^3 - 6y - 3)$

31. $(2a^3 - 7a + 1) + (1 - 4a - 3a^2)$

32. $(5r^3 - 6r^2 + 3r) + (-3 - 2r + r^2)$

For Exercises 33 and 34, use the polynomials shown at the right. Assume that a, b, c, and d are all positive numbers. Choose the correct answer from this list:
(i) $P + Q$ **(ii)** $Q + R$ **(iii)** $P + R$ **(iv)** None of the above

$P = ax^3 + bx^2 - cx + d$
$Q = -ax^3 - bx^2 + cx - d$
$R = -ax^3 + bx^2 + cx + d$

33. Which sum will be a trinomial?

34. Which sum will be zero?

OBJECTIVE B *To subtract polynomials*

For Exercises 35 to 44, subtract. Use a horizontal format.

35. $(y^2 - 10xy) - (2y^2 + 3xy)$

36. $(x^2 - 3xy) - (-2x^2 + xy)$

37. $(3x^2 + x - 3) - (4x + x^2 - 2)$

38. $(5y^2 - 2y + 1) - (-y - 2 - 3y^2)$

39. $(-2x^3 + x - 1) - (-x^2 + x - 3)$

40. $(2x^2 + 5x - 3) - (3x^3 + 2x - 5)$

41. $(1 - 2a + 4a^3) - (a^3 - 2a + 3)$

42. $(7 - 8b + b^2) - (4b^3 - 7b - 8)$

43. $(-1 - y + 4y^3) - (3 - 3y - 2y^2)$

44. $(-3 - 2x + 3x^2) - (4 - 2x^2 + 2x^3)$

For Exercises 45 to 52, subtract. Use a vertical format.

45. $(2y^2 - 4y) - (-y^2 + 2)$

46. $(-3a^2 - 2a) - (4a^2 - 4)$

47. $(x^2 - 2x + 1) - (x^2 + 5x + 8)$

48. $(3x^2 + 2x - 2) - (5x^2 - 5x + 6)$

49. $(4x^3 + 5x + 2) - (1 + 2x - 3x^2)$

50. $(5y^2 - y + 2) - (-3 + 3y - 2y^3)$

51. $(-2y + 6y^2 + 2y^3) - (4 + y^2 + y^3)$

52. $(4 - x - 2x^2) - (-2 + 3x - x^3)$

53. What polynomial must be added to $3x^2 - 6x + 9$ so that the sum is $4x^2 + 3x - 2$?

Critical Thinking

54. What polynomial must be added to $3x^2 - 4x - 2$ so that the sum is $-x^2 + 2x + 1$?

55. What polynomial must be added to $-2x^3 + 4x - 7$ so that the sum is $x^2 - x - 1$?

56. What polynomial must be subtracted from $6x^2 - 4x - 2$ so that the difference is $2x^2 + 2x - 5$?

57. What polynomial must be subtracted from $2x^3 - x^2 + 4x - 2$ so that the difference is $x^3 + 2x - 8$?

Projects or Group Activities

58. Write two polynomials, each of degree 2, whose sum is also of degree 2.

59. Write two polynomials, each of degree 2, whose sum is of degree 1.

60. Write two polynomials, each of degree 2, whose sum is of degree 0.

SECTION

4.2 Multiplication of Monomials

OBJECTIVE A To multiply monomials

Recall that in the exponential expression x^5, x is the base and 5 is the exponent. The exponent indicates the number of times the base occurs as a factor.

The product of exponential expressions with the *same* base can be simplified by writing each expression in factored form and writing the result with an exponent.

$$x^3 \cdot x^2 = \underbrace{\overbrace{(x \cdot x \cdot x)}^{3 \text{ factors}} \cdot \overbrace{(x \cdot x)}^{2 \text{ factors}}}_{5 \text{ factors}}$$
$$= x \cdot x \cdot x \cdot x \cdot x$$
$$= x^5$$

Adding the exponents results in the same product.

$$x^3 \cdot x^2 = x^{3+2} = x^5$$

Rule for Multiplying Exponential Expressions

If m and n are integers, then $x^m \cdot x^n = x^{m+n}$.

EXAMPLES

In each example below, we are multiplying two exponential expressions with the same base. Simplify the expression by adding the exponents.

1. $x^4 \cdot x^7 = x^{4+7} = x^{11}$
2. $y \cdot y^5 = y^{1+5} = y^6$
3. $a^2 \cdot a^6 \cdot a = a^{2+6+1} = a^9$

Take Note

The Rule for Multiplying Exponential Expressions requires that the bases be the same. The expression a^5b^7 cannot be simplified.

HOW TO 1 Simplify: $(-3a^4b^3)(2ab^4)$

$(-3a^4b^3)(2ab^4) = (-3 \cdot 2)(a^4 \cdot a)(b^3 \cdot b^4)$
- Use the Commutative and Associative Properties of Multiplication to rearrange and group factors.

$= -6(a^{4+1})(b^{3+4})$
- To multiply expressions with the same base, add the exponents.

$= -6a^5b^7$
- Simplify.

EXAMPLE 1

Simplify: $(-5ab^3)(4a^5)$

Solution

$(-5ab^3)(4a^5)$

$= (-5 \cdot 4)(a \cdot a^5)b^3$
- Multiply coefficients. Add exponents with the same base.

$= -20a^6b^3$

YOU TRY IT 1

Simplify: $(12p^4q^3)(-3p^5q^2)$

Your solution

Solution on p. S9

OBJECTIVE B *To simplify powers of monomials*

Point of Interest

One of the first symbolic representations of powers was given by Diophantus (c. 250 A.D.) in his book *Arithmetica*. He used Δ^Y for x^2 and κ^Y for x^3. The symbol Δ^Y was the first two letters of the Greek word *dunamis*, which means "power"; κ^Y was from the Greek word *kubos*, which means "cube." He also combined these symbols to denote higher powers. For instance, $\Delta\kappa^Y$ was the symbol for x^5.

The power of a monomial can be simplified by writing the power in factored form and then using the Rule for Multiplying Exponential Expressions.

$(x^4)^3 = x^4 \cdot x^4 \cdot x^4$ $\quad$ $(a^2b^3)^2 = (a^2b^3)(a^2b^3)$ $\quad$ • Write in factored form.

$= x^{4+4+4}$ $\quad$ $= a^{2+2}b^{3+3}$ $\quad$ • Use the Rule for Multiplying Exponential Expressions.

$= x^{12}$ $\quad$ $= a^4b^6$

Note that multiplying each exponent inside the parentheses by the exponent outside the parentheses results in the same product.

$(x^4)^3 = x^{4\cdot 3} = x^{12}$ $\quad$ $(a^2b^3)^2 = a^{2\cdot 2}b^{3\cdot 2} = a^4b^6$ $\quad$ • Multiply each exponent inside the parentheses by the exponent outside the parentheses.

Rule for Simplifying the Power of an Exponential Expression

If m and n are integers, then $(x^m)^n = x^{mn}$.

EXAMPLES

Each example below is a power of an exponential expression. Simplify the expression by multiplying the exponents.

1. $(x^5)^2 = x^{5\cdot 2} = x^{10}$
2. $(y^3)^4 = y^{3\cdot 4} = y^{12}$

Rule for Simplifying the Power of a Product

If m, n, and p are integers, then $(x^my^n)^p = x^{mp}y^{np}$.

EXAMPLES

Each example below is a power of a product of exponential expressions. Simplify the expression by multiplying each exponent inside the parentheses by the exponent outside the parentheses.

1. $(c^5d^3)^6 = c^{5\cdot 6}d^{3\cdot 6} = c^{30}d^{18}$
2. $(3a^2b)^3 = 3^{1\cdot 3}a^{2\cdot 3}b^{1\cdot 3} = 3^3a^6b^3 = 27a^6b^3$

EXAMPLE 2

Simplify: $(2a^2b)(2a^3b^2)^3$

Solution

$(2a^2b)(2a^3b^2)^3$

$= (2a^2b)(2^{1\cdot 3}a^{3\cdot 3}b^{2\cdot 3})$ $\quad$ • Rule for Simplifying the Power of a Product

$= (2a^2b)(2^3a^9b^6)$

$= (2a^2b)(8a^9b^6) = 16a^{11}b^7$ $\quad$ • Rule for Multiplying Exponential Expressions

YOU TRY IT 2

Simplify: $(-xy^4)(-2x^3y^2)^2$

Your solution

Solution on p. S9

4.2 EXERCISES

Concept Check

For Exercises 1 to 8, state whether the expression is the product of two exponential expressions or a power of an exponential expression.

1. $b^4 \cdot b^8$
2. $(b^4)^8$
3. $(2z)^2$
4. $2z \cdot z$

5. $(3a^4)^5$
6. $(3a^4)(5a)$
7. $x(-xy^4)$
8. $(-xy)^4$

OBJECTIVE A *To multiply monomials*

For Exercises 9 to 12, state whether the expression can be simplified using the Rule for Multiplying Exponential Expressions.

9. $x^4 + x^5$
10. x^4x^5
11. x^4y^4
12. $x^4 + x^4$

For Exercises 13 to 45, simplify.

13. $(6x^2)(5x)$
14. $(-4y^3)(2y)$
15. $(7c^2)(-6c^4)$
16. $(-8z^5)(5z^8)$

17. $(-3a^3)(-3a^4)$
18. $(-5a^6)(-2a^5)$
19. $(x^2)(xy^4)$
20. $(x^2y^4)(xy^7)$

21. $(-2x^4)(5x^5y)$
22. $(-3a^3)(2a^2b^4)$
23. $(-4x^2y^4)(-3x^5y^4)$
24. $(-6a^2b^4)(-4ab^3)$

25. $(2xy)(-3x^2y^4)$
26. $(-3a^2b)(-2ab^3)$
27. $(x^2yz)(x^2y^4)$
28. $(-ab^2c)(a^2b^5)$

29. $(-a^2b^3)(-ab^2c^4)$
30. $(-x^2y^3z)(-x^3y^4)$
31. $(-5a^2b^2)(6a^3b^6)$
32. $(7xy^4)(-2xy^3)$

33. $(-6a^3)(-a^2b)$
34. $(-2a^2b^3)(-4ab^2)$
35. $(-5y^4z)(-8y^6z^5)$
36. $(3x^2y)(-4xy^2)$

37. $(x^2y)(yz)(xyz)$
38. $(xy^2z)(x^2y)(z^2y^2)$
39. $(3ab^2)(-2abc)(4ac^2)$

40. $(-2x^3y^2)(-3x^2z^2)(-5y^3z^3)$
41. $(4x^4z)(-yz^3)(-2x^3z^2)$
42. $(-a^3b^4)(-3a^4c^2)(4b^3c^4)$

43. $(-2x^2y^3)(3xy)(-5x^3y^4)$
44. $(4a^2b)(-3a^3b^4)(a^5b^2)$
45. $(3a^2b)(-6bc)(2ac^2)$

OBJECTIVE B *To simplify powers of monomials*

For Exercises 46 to 49, state whether the expression can be simplified using the Rule for Simplifying the Power of a Product.

46. $(xy)^3$ **47.** $(x + y)^3$ **48.** $(a^3 - b^4)^2$ **49.** $(a^3b^4)^2$

For Exercises 50 to 80, simplify.

50. $(z^4)^3$ **51.** $(x^3)^5$ **52.** $(y^4)^2$ **53.** $(x^7)^2$ **54.** $(-y^5)^3$

55. $(-x^2)^4$ **56.** $(-x^2)^3$ **57.** $(-y^3)^4$ **58.** $(-3y)^3$ **59.** $(-2x^2)^3$

60. $(a^3b^4)^3$ **61.** $(x^2y^3)^2$ **62.** $(2x^3y^4)^5$ **63.** $(3x^2y)^2$ **64.** $(-2ab^3)^4$

65. $(-3x^3y^2)^5$ **66.** $(3b^2)(2a^3)^4$ **67.** $(-2x)(2x^3)^2$ **68.** $(2y)(-3y^4)^3$

69. $(3x^2y)(2x^2y^2)^3$ **70.** $(a^3b)^2(ab)^3$ **71.** $(ab^2)^2(ab)^2$ **72.** $(-x^2y^3)^2(-2x^3y)^3$

73. $(-2x)^3(-2x^3y)^3$ **74.** $(-3y)(-4x^2y^3)^3$ **75.** $(-2x)(-3xy^2)^2$ **76.** $(-3y)(-2x^2y)^3$

77. $(ab^2)(-2a^2b)^3$ **78.** $(a^2b^2)(-3ab^4)^2$ **79.** $(-2a^3)(3a^2b)^3$ **80.** $(-3b^2)(2ab^2)^3$

Critical Thinking

For Exercises 81 to 88, simplify.

81. $3x^2 + (3x)^2$ **82.** $4x^2 - (4x)^2$ **83.** $2x^6y^2 + (3x^2y)^2$ **84.** $(x^2y^2)^3 + (x^3y^3)^2$

85. $(2a^3b^2)^3 - 8a^9b^6$ **86.** $4y^2z^4 - (2yz^2)^2$ **87.** $(x^2y^4)^2 + (2xy^2)^4$ **88.** $(3a^3)^2 - 4a^6 + (2a^2)^3$

Projects or Group Activities

89. Let $x_1 = -1x^1$ and, for $n > 1$, $x_n = -nx^n$. Calculate the product $(x_1)(x_2)(x_3)(x_4)(x_5)$.

90. a. Evaluate $(2^3)^2$ and $2^{(3^2)}$. Are the results the same? If not, which expression has the larger value?

b. What is the order of operations for the expression x^{m^n}?

SECTION

4.3 Multiplication of Polynomials

OBJECTIVE A *To multiply a polynomial by a monomial*

To multiply a polynomial by a monomial, use the Distributive Property and the Rule for Multiplying Exponential Expressions.

HOW TO 1 Multiply: $-3a(4a^2 - 5a + 6)$

$$-3a(4a^2 - 5a + 6) = -3a(4a^2) - (-3a)(5a) + (-3a)(6)$$
$$= -12a^3 + 15a^2 - 18a$$

- Use the Distributive Property.

EXAMPLE 1

Multiply: $(5x + 4)(-2x)$

Solution

$(5x + 4)(-2x) = 5x(-2x) + 4(-2x) = -10x^2 - 8x$

YOU TRY IT 1

Multiply: $(-2y + 3)(-4y)$

Your solution

EXAMPLE 2

Multiply: $2a^2b(4a^2 - 2ab + b^2)$

Solution

$2a^2b(4a^2 - 2ab + b^2)$
$= 2a^2b(4a^2) - 2a^2b(2ab) + 2a^2b(b^2)$
$= 8a^4b - 4a^3b^2 + 2a^2b^3$

YOU TRY IT 2

Multiply: $-a^2(3a^2 + 2a - 7)$

Your solution

Solutions on p. S9

OBJECTIVE B *To multiply two polynomials*

Multiplication of two polynomials requires the repeated application of the Distributive Property.

$$(y^2 - 4y - 6)(y + 2) = (y^2 - 4y - 6)y + (y^2 - 4y - 6)2$$
$$= (y^3 - 4y^2 - 6y) + (2y^2 - 8y - 12)$$
$$= y^3 - 2y^2 - 14y - 12$$

A convenient method for multiplying two polynomials is to use a vertical format similar to that used for multiplication of whole numbers.

$$\begin{array}{rrrrl} & y^2 & -\ 4y & -\ 6 & \\ & & y & +\ 2 & \\ \hline & 2y^2 & -\ 8y & -\ 12 & = (y^2 - 4y - 6)2 \\ y^3 & -\ 4y^2 & -\ 6y & & = (y^2 - 4y - 6)y \\ \hline y^3 & -\ 2y^2 & -\ 14y & -\ 12 & \end{array}$$

- Multiply by 2.
- Multiply by y.
- Add the terms in each column.

HOW TO 2 Multiply: $(2a^3 + a - 3)(a + 5)$

$$\begin{array}{r} 2a^3 \qquad + a - 3 \\ a + 5 \\ \hline 10a^3 \qquad + 5a - 15 \\ 2a^4 \qquad + a^2 - 3a \qquad \\ \hline 2a^4 + 10a^3 + a^2 + 2a - 15 \end{array}$$

- Note that spaces are inserted in each product so that like terms are in the same column.
- Add the terms in each column.

EXAMPLE 3

Multiply: $(2b^3 - b + 1)(2b + 3)$

Solution

$$\begin{array}{r} 2b^3 \qquad - b + 1 \\ 2b + 3 \\ \hline 6b^3 \qquad - 3b + 3 \\ 4b^4 + \qquad - 2b^2 + 2b \qquad \\ \hline 4b^4 + 6b^3 - 2b^2 - b + 3 \end{array}$$

$= 3(2b^3 - b + 1)$
$= 2b(2b^3 - b + 1)$

YOU TRY IT 3

Multiply: $(2y^3 + 2y^2 - 3)(3y - 1)$

Your solution

Solution on p. S9

OBJECTIVE C *To multiply two binomials using the FOIL method*

It is frequently necessary to find the product of two binomials. The product can be found using a method called **FOIL,** which is based on the Distributive Property. The letters of FOIL stand for **F**irst, **O**uter, **I**nner, and **L**ast. To find the product of two binomials, add the products of the **F**irst terms, the **O**uter terms, the **I**nner terms, and the **L**ast terms.

Take Note

FOIL is not really a different way of multiplying. It is based on the Distributive Property.

$(2x + 3)(x + 5)$
$= 2x(x + 5) + 3(x + 5)$
F O I L
$= 2x^2 + 10x + 3x + 15$
$= 2x^2 + 13x + 15$

HOW TO 3 Multiply: $(2x + 3)(x + 5)$

Multiply the First terms.	$(2x + 3)(x + 5)$	$2x \cdot x = 2x^2$
Multiply the Outer terms.	$(2x + 3)(x + 5)$	$2x \cdot 5 = 10x$
Multiply the Inner terms.	$(2x + 3)(x + 5)$	$3 \cdot x = 3x$
Multiply the Last terms.	$(2x + 3)(x + 5)$	$3 \cdot 5 = 15$
		F O I L
Add the products.	$(2x + 3)(x + 5)$	$= 2x^2 + 10x + 3x + 15$
Combine like terms.		$= 2x^2 + 13x + 15$

HOW TO 4 Multiply: $(4x - 3)(3x - 2)$

$(4x - 3)(3x - 2) = 4x(3x) + 4x(-2) + (-3)(3x) + (-3)(-2)$ • FOIL
$= 12x^2 - 8x - 9x + 6$ • Multiply.
$= 12x^2 - 17x + 6$ • Combine like terms.

HOW TO 5 Multiply: $(3x - 2y)(x + 4y)$

$(3x - 2y)(x + 4y) = 3x(x) + 3x(4y) + (-2y)(x) + (-2y)(4y)$ • FOIL
$= 3x^2 + 12xy - 2xy - 8y^2$ • Multiply.
$= 3x^2 + 10xy - 8y^2$ • Combine like terms.

EXAMPLE 4

Multiply: $(2a - 1)(3a - 2)$

Solution

$(2a - 1)(3a - 2) = 6a^2 - 4a - 3a + 2$
$= 6a^2 - 7a + 2$

YOU TRY IT 4

Multiply: $(4y - 5)(2y - 3)$

Your solution

EXAMPLE 5

Multiply: $(3x - 2)(4x + 3)$

Solution

$(3x - 2)(4x + 3) = 12x^2 + 9x - 8x - 6$
$= 12x^2 + x - 6$

YOU TRY IT 5

Multiply: $(3b + 2)(3b - 5)$

Your solution

Solutions on p. S9

OBJECTIVE D *To multiply binomials that have special products*

Using FOIL, it is possible to find a pattern for the product of the sum and difference of the same two terms and for the square of a binomial.

Product of the Sum and Difference of the Same Terms

$(a + b)(a - b) = a^2 - ab + ab - b^2$
$= a^2 - b^2$

Square of the first term (a^2)
Square of the second term (b^2)

EXAMPLE

Multiply: $(2x + 3)(2x - 3)$

This is the product of the sum and difference of the same terms.
$(2x + 3)(2x - 3) = (2x)^2 - 3^2 = 4x^2 - 9$

Square of a Binomial

$(a + b)^2 = (a + b)(a + b) = a^2 + ab + ab + b^2$
$= a^2 + 2ab + b^2$

Square of the first term (a^2)
Twice the product of the two terms ($2ab$)
Square of the last term (b^2)

EXAMPLE

Expand: $(3x - 2)^2$

This is the square of a binomial.
$(3x - 2)^2 = (3x)^2 + 2(3x)(-2) + (-2)^2 = 9x^2 - 12x + 4$

Take Note

The word *expand* frequently is used to mean "multiply out a power."

EXAMPLE 6

Multiply: $(4z - 2w)(4z + 2w)$

Solution

This is the product of the sum and difference of the same two terms.

$(4z - 2w)(4z + 2w) = 16z^2 - 4w^2$

YOU TRY IT 6

Multiply: $(2a + 5c)(2a - 5c)$

Your solution

EXAMPLE 7

Expand: $(2r - 3s)^2$

Solution

This is the square of a binomial.

$(2r - 3s)^2 = 4r^2 - 12rs + 9s^2$

YOU TRY IT 7

Expand: $(3x + 2y)^2$

Your solution

Solutions on p. S9

OBJECTIVE E *To solve application problems*

EXAMPLE 8

The length of a rectangle is $(x + 7)$ m. The width is $(x - 4)$ m. Find the area of the rectangle in terms of the variable x.

$x + 7$

$x - 4$

Strategy

To find the area, replace the variables L and W in the equation $A = L \cdot W$ by the given values and solve for A.

Solution

$A = L \cdot W$

$A = (x + 7)(x - 4)$ • $L = x + 7$; $W = x - 4$

$A = x^2 - 4x + 7x - 28$ • FOIL

$A = x^2 + 3x - 28$ • Combine like terms.

The area is $(x^2 + 3x - 28)$ m^2.

YOU TRY IT 8

The radius of a circle is $(x - 4)$ ft. Use the equation $A = \pi r^2$, where r is the radius, to find the area of the circle in terms of x. Leave the answer in terms of π.

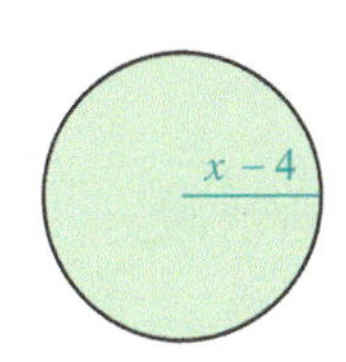

Your strategy

Your solution

Solution on p. S10

4.3 EXERCISES

Concept Check

For Exercises 1 to 9, determine whether the statement is always true, sometimes true, or never true.

1. To multiply a monomial times a polynomial, use the Distributive Property to multiply each term of the polynomial by the monomial.
2. To multiply two polynomials, multiply each term of one polynomial by the other polynomial.
3. A binomial is a polynomial of degree 2.
4. $(x + 7)(x - 7)$ is the product of the sum and difference of the same two terms.
5. To square a binomial means to multiply it times itself.
6. The square of a binomial is a trinomial.
7. The FOIL method is used to multiply two polynomials.
8. Using the FOIL method, the terms $3x$ and 5 are the "First" terms in $(3x + 5)(2x + 7)$.
9. The product of two binomials is a trinomial.

OBJECTIVE A *To multiply a polynomial by a monomial*

10. Is the Distributive Property used to simplify the product $2(3x)$? If not, what property is used to simplify this expression?

For Exercises 11 to 42, multiply.

11. $x(x - 2)$
12. $y(3 - y)$
13. $-x(x + 7)$
14. $-y(7 - y)$
15. $3a^2(a - 2)$
16. $4b^2(b + 8)$
17. $-5x^2(x^2 - x)$
18. $-6y^2(y + 2y^2)$
19. $-x^3(3x^2 - 7)$
20. $-y^4(2y^2 - y^6)$
21. $2x(6x^2 - 3x)$
22. $3y(4y - y^2)$
23. $(2x - 4)3x$
24. $(3y - 2)y$
25. $(3x + 4)x$
26. $(2x + 1)2x$
27. $-xy(x^2 - y^2)$
28. $-x^2y(2xy - y^2)$
29. $x(2x^3 - 3x + 2)$
30. $y(-3y^2 - 2y + 6)$
31. $-a(-2a^2 - 3a - 2)$
32. $-b(5b^2 + 7b - 35)$
33. $x^2(3x^4 - 3x^2 - 2)$
34. $y^3(-4y^3 - 6y + 7)$
35. $2y^2(-3y^2 - 6y + 7)$
36. $4x^2(3x^2 - 2x + 6)$
37. $(a^2 + 3a - 4)(-2a)$
38. $(b^3 - 2b + 2)(-5b)$
39. $-3y^2(-2y^2 + y - 2)$
40. $-5x^2(3x^2 - 3x - 7)$
41. $xy(x^2 - 3xy + y^2)$
42. $ab(2a^2 - 4ab - 6b^2)$

43. Which of the following expressions are equivalent to $4x - x(3x - 1)$?
(i) $4x - 3x^2 - x$ **(ii)** $-3x^2 + 5x$ **(iii)** $4x - 3x^2 + x$ **(iv)** $9x^2 - 3x$ **(v)** $3x(3x - 1)$

OBJECTIVE B *To multiply two polynomials*

For Exercises 44 to 61, multiply.

44. $(x^2 + 3x + 2)(x + 1)$

45. $(x^2 - 2x + 7)(x - 2)$

46. $(a^2 - 3a + 4)(a - 3)$

47. $(x^2 - 3x + 5)(2x - 3)$

48. $(-2b^2 - 3b + 4)(b - 5)$

49. $(-a^2 + 3a - 2)(2a - 1)$

50. $(-2x^2 + 7x - 2)(3x - 5)$

51. $(-a^2 - 2a + 3)(2a - 1)$

52. $(x^2 + 5)(x - 3)$

53. $(y^2 - 2y)(2y + 5)$

54. $(x^3 - 3x + 2)(x - 4)$

55. $(y^3 + 4y^2 - 8)(2y - 1)$

56. $(5y^2 + 8y - 2)(3y - 8)$

57. $(3y^2 + 3y - 5)(4y - 3)$

58. $(5a^3 - 5a + 2)(a - 4)$

59. $(3b^3 - 5b^2 + 7)(6b - 1)$

60. $(y^3 + 2y^2 - 3y + 1)(y + 2)$

61. $(2a^3 - 3a^2 + 2a - 1)(2a - 3)$

62. If a polynomial of degree 3 is multiplied by a polynomial of degree 2, what is the degree of the resulting polynomial?

OBJECTIVE C *To multiply two binomials using the FOIL method*

For Exercises 63 to 94, multiply.

63. $(x + 1)(x + 3)$

64. $(y + 2)(y + 5)$

65. $(a - 3)(a + 4)$

66. $(b - 6)(b + 3)$

67. $(y + 3)(y - 8)$

68. $(x + 10)(x - 5)$

69. $(y - 7)(y - 3)$

70. $(a - 8)(a - 9)$

71. $(2x + 1)(x + 7)$

72. $(y + 2)(5y + 1)$

73. $(3x - 1)(x + 4)$

74. $(7x - 2)(x + 4)$

75. $(4x - 3)(x - 7)$

76. $(2x - 3)(4x - 7)$

77. $(3y - 8)(y + 2)$

78. $(5y - 9)(y + 5)$

79. $(3x + 7)(3x + 11)$

80. $(5a + 6)(6a + 5)$

81. $(7a - 16)(3a - 5)$

82. $(5a - 12)(3a - 7)$

83. $(3a - 2b)(2a - 7b)$

84. $(5a - b)(7a - b)$

85. $(a - 9b)(2a + 7b)$

86. $(2a + 5b)(7a - 2b)$

87. $(10a - 3b)(10a - 7b)$

88. $(12a - 5b)(3a - 4b)$

89. $(5x + 12y)(3x + 4y)$

90. $(11x + 2y)(3x + 7y)$

91. $(2x - 15y)(7x + 4y)$

92. $(5x + 2y)(2x - 5y)$

93. $(8x - 3y)(7x - 5y)$

94. $(2x - 9y)(8x - 3y)$

95. What polynomial has quotient $3x - 4$ when divided by $4x + 5$?

OBJECTIVE D *To multiply binomials that have special products*

For Exercises 96 to 103, multiply.

96. $(y - 5)(y + 5)$

97. $(y + 6)(y - 6)$

98. $(2x + 3)(2x - 3)$

99. $(4x - 7)(4x + 7)$

100. $(3x - 7)(3x + 7)$

101. $(9x - 2)(9x + 2)$

102. $(4 - 3y)(4 + 3y)$

103. $(4x - 9y)(4x + 9y)$

For Exercises 104 to 111, expand.

104. $(x + 1)^2$

105. $(y - 3)^2$

106. $(3a - 5)^2$

107. $(6x - 5)^2$

108. $(x + 3y)^2$

109. $(x - 2y)^2$

110. $(5x + 2y)^2$

111. $(2a - 9b)^2$

For Exercises 112 to 115, state whether the coefficient of the x term of the product is positive, negative, or zero.

112. $(ax + b)(ax - b)$, where $a > 0$ and $b > 0$

113. $(ax + b)(ax + b)$, where $a > 0$ and $b < 0$

114. $(ax + b)^2$, where $a > 0$ and $b > 0$

115. $(ax + b)^2$, where $a < 0$ and $b < 0$

OBJECTIVE E *To solve application problems*

116. Geometry The length of a rectangle is $(5x)$ ft. The width is $(2x - 7)$ ft. Find the area of the rectangle in terms of the variable x.

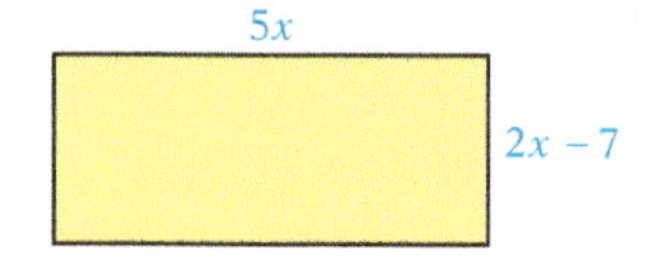

117. Geometry The width of a rectangle is $(3x + 1)$ in. The length of the rectangle is twice the width. Find the area of the rectangle in terms of the variable x.

118. **Geometry** The length of a side of a square is $(2x + 1)$ km. Find the area of the square in terms of the variable x.

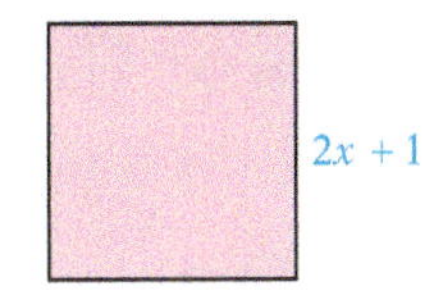

119. **Geometry** The radius of a circle is $(x + 4)$ cm. Find the area of the circle in terms of the variable x. Leave the answer in terms of π.

120. **Geometry** The base of a triangle is $(4x)$ m, and the height is $(2x + 5)$ m. Find the area of the triangle in terms of the variable x.

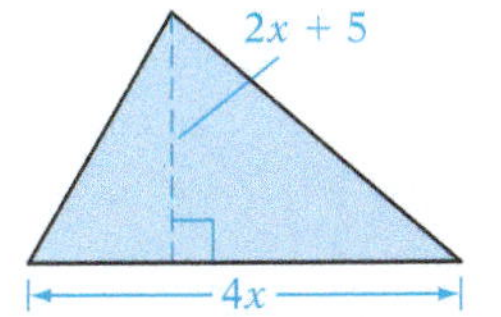

121. **Sports** A softball diamond has dimensions 45 ft by 45 ft. A base-path border x feet wide lies on both the first-base side and the third-base side of the diamond. Express the total area of the softball diamond and the base paths in terms of the variable x.

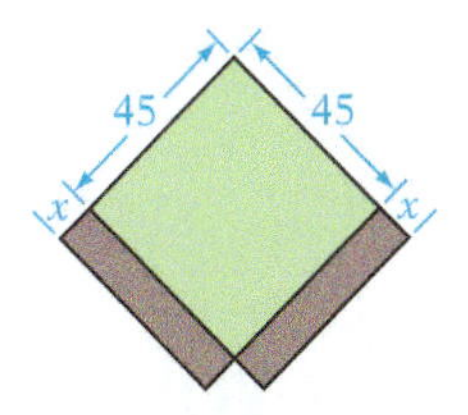

122. **Sports** An athletic field has dimensions 30 yd by 100 yd. An end zone that is w yards wide borders each end of the field. Express the total area of the field and the end zones in terms of the variable w.

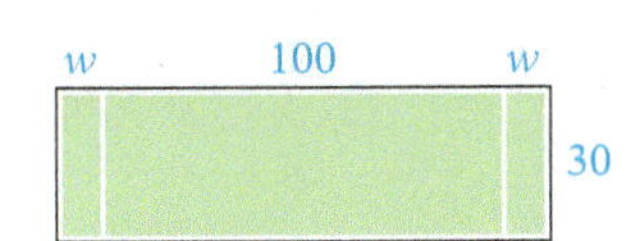

123. **The Olympics** See the news clipping at the right. The Water Cube is not actually a cube because its height is not equal to its length and width. The length of the Water Cube is 22 ft more than five times the height. (*Source:* Structurae)

a. Express the length of the Water Cube in terms of the height h.

b. Express the area of one exterior wall of the Water Cube in terms of the height h.

claudio zaccherini/Shutterstock.com

The Water Cube

In the NEWS!

Olympic Water Cube Completed

The National Aquatics Center, also known as the Water Cube, was completed on the morning of December 26, 2006. Built in Beijing, China, for the 2008 Olympics, the Water Cube is designed to look like a "cube" of water molecules.

Source: Structurae

124. The expression $w(3w - 1)$ cm^2 represents the area of a rectangle of width w. Describe in words the relationship between the length and width of the rectangle.

Critical Thinking

For Exercises 125 to 130, simplify.

125. $(a + b)^2 - (a - b)^2$

126. $(x + 3y)^2 + (x + 3y)(x - 3y)$

127. $(3a^2 - 4a + 2)^2$

128. $(x + 4)^3$

129. $3x^2(2x^3 + 4x - 1) - 6x^3(x^2 - 2)$

130. $(3b + 2)(b - 6) + (4 + 2b)(3 - b)$

131. Find $(4n^3)^2$ if $2n - 3 = 4n - 7$.

132. What polynomial has quotient $x^2 + 2x - 1$ when divided by $x + 3$?

133. What polynomial has quotient $3x - 4$ when divided by $4x + 5$?

Projects or Group Activities

For Exercises 134 to 137, simplify.

134. $(x + 1)(x - 1)$

135. $(x + 1)(-x^2 + x - 1)$

136. $(x + 1)(x^3 - x^2 + x - 1)$

137. $(x + 1)(-x^4 + x^3 - x^2 + x - 1)$

Use the pattern of the answers to Exercises 134 to 137 to write the product.

138. $(x + 1)(x^5 - x^4 + x^3 - x^2 + x - 1)$

139. $(x + 1)(-x^6 + x^5 - x^4 + x^3 - x^2 + x - 1)$

CHECK YOUR PROGRESS: CHAPTER 4

1. Add: $(4x + 3x^2 - 6) + (x^2 - 5x + 1)$

2. Multiply: $(3y - 7)(y + 5)$

3. Multiply: $4y(5y - 3y^3)$

4. Simplify: $(-2a^4)(3ab^5)$

5. Multiply: $(10x - 3)(10x + 3)$

6. Multiply: $(2x^2 - 3x + 5)(x - 6)$

7. Simplify: $3x^4y(-x^6y^2)(-2xy^5)$

8. Simplify: $(3x^6y^5)^4$

9. Multiply: $(x^3 - 3x^2 + 6)(2x + 1)$

10. Expand: $(b - 11)^2$

11. Simplify: $(-2b)(-4b^3)^2$

12. Subtract: $(2x^3 + 4x - 5) - (1 + 6x - x^2)$

13. Multiply: $5x^2(3x^2 - x + 7)$

14. Multiply: $(4a - 9)(3a - 2)$

15. Multiply: $(5 - 6y)(5 + 6y)$

16. Expand: $(3a - 5b)^2$

17. **Geometry** The length of a rectangle is $(4x)$ in. The width is $(3x - 2)$ in. Find the area of the rectangle in terms of the variable x.

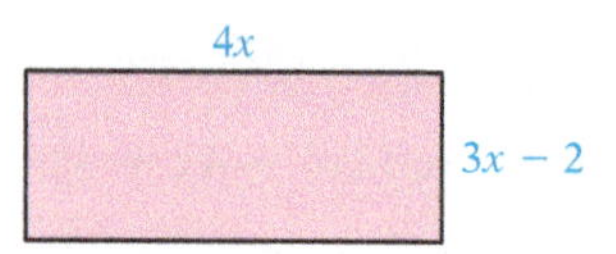

18. **Geometry** The length of a side of a square is $(4x + 5)$ ft. Find the area of the square in terms of the variable x.

SECTION

4.4 Integer Exponents and Scientific Notation

OBJECTIVE A *To divide monomials*

The quotient of two exponential expressions with the same base can be simplified by writing each expression in factored form, dividing by the common factors, and then writing the result with an exponent.

$$\frac{x^5}{x^2} = \frac{\overset{1}{\cancel{x}} \cdot \overset{1}{\cancel{x}} \cdot x \cdot x \cdot x}{\underset{1}{\cancel{x}} \cdot \underset{1}{\cancel{x}}} = x^3$$

Note that subtracting the exponents gives the same result.

$$\frac{x^5}{x^2} = x^{5-2} = x^3$$

To divide two monomials with the same base, subtract the exponents of the like bases.

HOW TO 1 Simplify: $\frac{a^7}{a^3}$

$$\frac{a^7}{a^3} = a^{7-3}$$

$$= a^4$$

• The bases are the same. Subtract the exponents.

HOW TO 2 Simplify: $\frac{r^8t^6}{r^7t}$

$$\frac{r^8t^6}{r^7t} = r^{8-7}t^{6-1}$$

$$= rt^5$$

• Subtract the exponents of the like bases.

HOW TO 3 Simplify: $\frac{p^7}{z^4}$

Because the bases are not the same, $\frac{p^7}{z^4}$ is already in simplest form.

Recall that for any number a, $a \neq 0$, $\frac{a}{a} = 1$. This property is true for exponential expressions as well. For example, for $x \neq 0$, $\frac{x^4}{x^4} = 1$.

This expression also can be simplified using the rule for dividing exponential expressions with the same base.

$$\frac{x^4}{x^4} = x^{4-4} = x^0$$

Because $\frac{x^4}{x^4} = 1$ and $\frac{x^4}{x^4} = x^0$, the following definition of zero as an exponent is used.

Take Note

In the example at the right, we indicate that $a \neq 0$. If we try to evaluate $(12a^3)^0$ when $a = 0$, we get $[12(0)^3]^0 = [12(0)]^0 = 0^0$. However, 0^0 is not defined. Therefore, we must assume that $a \neq 0$. To avoid stating this restriction for every example or exercise, we will assume that variables do not take on values that result in the expression 0^0.

Definition of Zero as an Exponent

If $x \neq 0$, then $x^0 = 1$. The expression 0^0 is not defined.

EXAMPLE

Simplify: $(12a^3)^0$, $a \neq 0$

Any nonzero expression to the zero power is 1. $(12a^3)^0 = 1$

HOW TO 4 Simplify: $-(4x^3y^7)^0$

$$-(4x^3y^7)^0 = -(1) = -1$$

The meaning of a negative exponent can be developed by examining the quotient $\frac{x^4}{x^6}$.

The expression can be simplified by writing the numerator and denominator in factored form, dividing by the common factors, and then writing the result with an exponent.

$$\frac{x^4}{x^6} = \frac{\overset{1}{\cancel{x}} \cdot \overset{1}{\cancel{x}} \cdot \overset{1}{\cancel{x}} \cdot \overset{1}{\cancel{x}}}{\underset{1}{\cancel{x}} \cdot \underset{1}{\cancel{x}} \cdot \underset{1}{\cancel{x}} \cdot \underset{1}{\cancel{x}} \cdot x \cdot x} = \frac{1}{x^2}$$

Now simplify the same expression by subtracting the exponents of the like bases.

$$\frac{x^4}{x^6} = x^{4-6} = x^{-2}$$

Because $\frac{x^4}{x^6} = \frac{1}{x^2}$ and $\frac{x^4}{x^6} = x^{-2}$, the expressions $\frac{1}{x^2}$ and x^{-2} must be equal. This leads to the following definition of a negative exponent.

Point of Interest

In the 15th century, the expression $12^{2\overline{m}}$ was used to mean $12x^{-2}$. The use of $\overline{m}$ reflected an Italian influence. In Italy, *m* was used for minus and *p* was used for plus. It was understood that $2\overline{m}$ referred to an unnamed variable. Issac Newton, in the 17th century, advocated the negative exponent notation that we currently use.

Definition of a Negative Exponent

If $x \neq 0$ and n is a positive integer, then

$$x^{-n} = \frac{1}{x^n} \quad \text{and} \quad \frac{1}{x^{-n}} = x^n$$

EXAMPLES

In each example below, simplify the expression by writing it with a positive exponent.

1. $x^{-10} = \frac{1}{x^{10}}$ **2.** $\frac{1}{a^{-5}} = a^5$

An exponential expression is in simplest form when it is written with only positive exponents.

Take Note

Note from HOW TO 5 at the right that 2^{-4} is a *positive* number. A negative exponent does not change the sign of a number.

HOW TO 5 Evaluate 2^{-4}.

$2^{-4} = \frac{1}{2^4}$ • Use the Definition of a Negative Exponent.

$= \frac{1}{16}$ • Evaluate the expression.

Take Note

For the expression $3n^{-5}$, the exponent on n is -5 (*negative* 5). The n^{-5} is written in the denominator as n^5. The exponent on 3 is 1 (*positive* 1). The 3 remains in the numerator. Also, we indicated that $n \neq 0$. This is done because division by zero is not defined. In this textbook, we will assume that values of the variables are chosen so that division by zero does not occur.

HOW TO 6 Simplify: $3n^{-5}$, $n \neq 0$

$3n^{-5} = 3 \cdot \frac{1}{n^5} = \frac{3}{n^5}$ • Use the Definition of a Negative Exponent to rewrite the expression with a positive exponent.

HOW TO 7 Simplify: $\frac{2}{5a^{-4}}$

$\frac{2}{5a^{-4}} = \frac{2}{5} \cdot \frac{1}{a^{-4}} = \frac{2}{5} \cdot a^4 = \frac{2a^4}{5}$ • Use the Definition of a Negative Exponent to rewrite the expression with a positive exponent.

Now that negative exponents have been defined, the Rule for Dividing Exponential Expressions can be stated.

Rule for Dividing Exponential Expressions

If m and n are integers and $x \neq 0$, then $\frac{x^m}{x^n} = x^{m-n}$.

EXAMPLES

Simplify each expression below by using the Rule for Dividing Exponential Expressions.

1. $\frac{x^3}{x^5} = x^{3-5} = x^{-2} = \frac{1}{x^2}$
2. $\frac{y^6}{y^{-2}} = y^{6-(-2)} = y^8$
3. $\frac{b^{-5}}{b^{-1}} = b^{-5-(-1)} = b^{-4} = \frac{1}{b^4}$
4. $\frac{a^{-4}}{a^{-7}} = a^{-4-(-7)} = a^3$

HOW TO 8 Evaluate $\frac{5^{-2}}{5}$.

$\frac{5^{-2}}{5} = 5^{-2-1} = 5^{-3}$

- Use the Rule for Dividing Exponential Expressions.

$= \frac{1}{5^3} = \frac{1}{125}$

- Use the Definition of a Negative Exponent to rewrite the expression with a positive exponent. Then evaluate.

The expression $\left(\frac{x^4}{y^3}\right)^2$, $y \neq 0$, can be simplified by squaring $\frac{x^4}{y^3}$ or by multiplying each exponent in the quotient by the exponent outside the parentheses.

$$\left(\frac{x^4}{y^3}\right)^2 = \left(\frac{x^4}{y^3}\right)\left(\frac{x^4}{y^3}\right) = \frac{x^4 \cdot x^4}{y^3 \cdot y^3} = \frac{x^{4+4}}{y^{3+3}} = \frac{x^8}{y^6} \qquad \left(\frac{x^4}{y^3}\right)^2 = \frac{x^{4 \cdot 2}}{y^{3 \cdot 2}} = \frac{x^8}{y^6}$$

Rule for Simplifying the Power of a Quotient

If m, n, and p are integers and $y \neq 0$, then $\left(\frac{x^m}{y^n}\right)^p = \frac{x^{mp}}{y^{np}}$.

EXAMPLES

1. $\left(\frac{a^4}{b^6}\right)^3 = \frac{a^{12}}{b^{18}}$
2. $\left(\frac{5}{7}\right)^2 = \frac{5^2}{7^2} = \frac{25}{49}$

Take Note

As a reminder, although it is not stated, we are assuming that $a \neq 0$ and $b \neq 0$. This assumption is made to ensure that we do not divide by zero.

HOW TO 9 Simplify: $\left(\frac{a^3}{b^2}\right)^{-2}$

$$\left(\frac{a^3}{b^2}\right)^{-2} = \frac{a^{3(-2)}}{b^{2(-2)}}$$

• Use the Rule for Simplifying the Power of a Quotient.

$$= \frac{a^{-6}}{b^{-4}} = \frac{b^4}{a^6}$$

• Use the Definition of a Negative Exponent to write the expression with positive exponents.

HOW TO 9 above suggests the following rule.

Rule for Negative Exponents on Fractional Expressions

If $x \neq 0$, $y \neq 0$, and n is a positive integer, then $\left(\frac{x}{y}\right)^{-n} = \left(\frac{y}{x}\right)^n$.

EXAMPLES

1. $\left(\frac{3}{5}\right)^{-2} = \left(\frac{5}{3}\right)^2 = \frac{25}{9}$
2. $\left(\frac{a^4}{b^7}\right)^{-3} = \left(\frac{b^7}{a^4}\right)^3 = \frac{b^{21}}{a^{12}}$

The rules for simplifying exponential expressions and powers of exponential expressions are true for all integers. These rules are restated here.

Rules of Exponents

If m, n, and p are integers, then

$x^m \cdot x^n = x^{m+n}$ $\qquad (x^m)^n = x^{mn}$ $\qquad (x^m y^n)^p = x^{mp} y^{np}$

$\frac{x^m}{x^n} = x^{m-n}, x \neq 0$ $\qquad \left(\frac{x^m}{y^n}\right)^p = \frac{x^{mp}}{y^{np}}, y \neq 0$ $\qquad x^{-n} = \frac{1}{x^n}, x \neq 0$

$x^0 = 1, x \neq 0$

HOW TO 10 Simplify: $(3ab^{-4})(-2a^{-3}b^7)$

$$(3ab^{-4})(-2a^{-3}b^7) = [3 \cdot (-2)](a^{1+(-3)}b^{-4+7})$$

• When multiplying exponential expressions, add the exponents on like bases.

$$= -6a^{-2}b^3$$

$$= -\frac{6b^3}{a^2}$$

HOW TO 11 Simplify: $\left[\frac{6m^2n^3}{8m^7n^2}\right]^{-3}$

$\left[\frac{6m^2n^3}{8m^7n^2}\right]^{-3} = \left[\frac{3m^{2-7}n^{3-2}}{4}\right]^{-3}$
- Simplify inside the brackets.

$= \left[\frac{3m^{-5}n}{4}\right]^{-3}$
- Subtract the exponents.

$= \frac{3^{-3}m^{15}n^{-3}}{4^{-3}}$
- Use the Rule for Simplifying the Power of a Quotient.

$= \frac{4^3m^{15}}{3^3n^3} = \frac{64m^{15}}{27n^3}$
- Use the Definition of a Negative Exponent to rewrite the expression with positive exponents. Then simplify.

HOW TO 12 Simplify: $\frac{4a^{-2}b^5}{6a^5b^2}$

$\frac{4a^{-2}b^5}{6a^5b^2} = \frac{2a^{-2}b^5}{3a^5b^2}$
- Divide the coefficients by their common factor.

$= \frac{2a^{-2-5}b^{5-2}}{3}$
- Use the Rule for Dividing Exponential Expressions.

$= \frac{2a^{-7}b^3}{3} = \frac{2b^3}{3a^7}$
- Use the Definition of a Negative Exponent to rewrite the expression with positive exponents.

EXAMPLE 1

Simplify: $(-2x)(3x^{-2})^{-3}$

Solution

$(-2x)(3x^{-2})^{-3} = (-2x)(3^{-3}x^6)$

$= \frac{-2x^{1+6}}{3^3}$
- Rule for Simplifying the Power of a Product

$= -\frac{2x^7}{27}$

YOU TRY IT 1

Simplify: $(-2x^2)(x^{-3}y^{-4})^{-2}$

Your solution

EXAMPLE 2

Simplify: $\frac{(2r^2t^{-1})^{-3}}{(r^{-3}t^4)^2}$

Solution

$\frac{(2r^2t^{-1})^{-3}}{(r^{-3}t^4)^2} = \frac{2^{-3}r^{-6}t^3}{r^{-6}t^8}$
- Rule for Simplifying the Power of a Product

$= 2^{-3}r^{-6-(-6)}t^{3-8}$
- Rule for Dividing Exponential Expressions

$= 2^{-3}r^0t^{-5}$

$= \frac{1}{2^3t^5} = \frac{1}{8t^5}$
- Write the answer in simplest form.

YOU TRY IT 2

Simplify: $\frac{(6a^{-2}b^3)^{-1}}{(4a^3b^{-2})^{-2}}$

Your solution

Solutions on p. S10

EXAMPLE 3

Simplify: $\left[\frac{4a^{-2}b^{3}}{6a^{4}b^{-2}}\right]^{-3}$

Solution

$$\left[\frac{4a^{-2}b^{3}}{6a^{4}b^{-2}}\right]^{-3} = \left[\frac{2a^{-6}b^{5}}{3}\right]^{-3}$$

• Simplify inside the brackets.

$$= \frac{2^{-3}a^{18}b^{-15}}{3^{-3}}$$

• Rule for Simplifying the Power of a Quotient

$$= \frac{27a^{18}}{8b^{15}}$$

• Write the answer in simplest form.

YOU TRY IT 3

Simplify: $\left[\frac{6r^{3}s^{-3}}{9r^{3}s^{-1}}\right]^{-2}$

Your solution

Solution on p. S10

OBJECTIVE B

To write a number in scientific notation

Integrating Technology

See the Keystroke Guide: *Scientific Notation* for instructions on entering a number written in scientific notation into a calculator.

Very large and very small numbers are encountered in the fields of science and engineering. For example, the charge of an electron is 0.000000000000000000160 coulomb. These numbers can be written more easily in scientific notation. In **scientific notation,** a number is expressed as the product of two factors, one a number between 1 and 10, and the other a power of 10.

To change a number written in decimal notation to scientific notation, write it in the form $a \times 10^n$, where a is a number between 1 and 10, and n is an integer.

For numbers greater than 10, move the decimal point to the right of the first digit. The exponent is positive and equal to the number of places the decimal point has been moved.

$240{,}000 = 2.4 \times 10^{5}$

$93{,}000{,}000 = 9.3 \times 10^{7}$

For numbers less than 1, move the decimal point to the right of the first nonzero digit. The exponent n is negative. The absolute value of the exponent is equal to the number of places the decimal point has been moved.

$0.00030 = 3 \times 10^{-4}$

$0.0000832 = 8.32 \times 10^{-5}$

Point of Interest

An electron microscope uses wavelengths that are approximately 4×10^{-12} meter to make images of viruses.

The human eye can detect wavelengths between 4.3×10^{-7} meter and 6.9×10^{-7} meter. Although these wavelengths are very short, they are approximately 10^{5} times longer than the wavelengths used in an electron microscope.

Look at the last example above: $0.0000832 = 8.32 \times 10^{-5}$. Using the Definition of Negative Exponents,

$$10^{-5} = \frac{1}{10^{5}} = \frac{1}{100{,}000} = 0.00001$$

Because $10^{-5} = 0.00001$, we can write

$$8.32 \times 10^{-5} = 8.32 \times 0.00001 = 0.0000832$$

which is the number we started with. We have not changed the value of the number; we have just written it in another form.

Changing a number written in scientific notation to decimal notation also requires moving the decimal point.

When the exponent on 10 is positive, move the decimal point to the right the same number of places as the exponent.

$3.45 \times 10^9 = 3,450,000,000$

$2.3 \times 10^8 = 230,000,000$

When the exponent on 10 is negative, move the decimal point to the left the same number of places as the absolute value of the exponent.

$8.1 \times 10^{-3} = 0.0081$

$6.34 \times 10^{-6} = 0.00000634$

EXAMPLE 4

Write the number 824,300,000 in scientific notation.

Solution

$824,300,000 > 10$
Move the decimal point 8 places to the left.
The exponent on 10 will be positive.

$824,300,000 = 8.243 \times 10^8$

YOU TRY IT 4

Write the number 290,000,000,000 in scientific notation.

Your solution

EXAMPLE 5

Write the number 0.0000000065 in scientific notation.

Solution

$0.0000000065 < 1$
Move the decimal point 9 places to the right.
The exponent on 10 will be negative.

$0.0000000065 = 6.5 \times 10^{-9}$

YOU TRY IT 5

Write the number 0.000000961 in scientific notation.

Your solution

EXAMPLE 6

Write the number 3.9785×10^{10} in decimal notation.

Solution

The exponent on 10 is positive.
Move the decimal point 10 places to the right.

$3.9785 \times 10^{10} = 39,785,000,000$

YOU TRY IT 6

Write the number 7.329×10^6 in decimal notation.

Your solution

EXAMPLE 7

Write the number 6.8×10^{-9} in decimal notation.

Solution

The exponent on 10 is negative.
Move the decimal point 9 places to the left.

$6.8 \times 10^{-9} = 0.0000000068$

YOU TRY IT 7

Write the number 1.802×10^{-12} in decimal notation.

Your solution

Solutions on p. S10

4.4 EXERCISES

Concept Check

1. Explain how to rewrite a variable that has a negative exponent as an expression with a positive exponent.

2. Why might a number be written in scientific notation instead of decimal notation?

For Exercises 3 to 8, determine whether the statement is true or false.

3. The expression $\frac{x^5}{y^3}$ can be simplified by subtracting the exponents.

4. The rules of exponents can be applied to expressions that contain an exponent of zero or contain negative exponents.

5. The expression 3^{-2} represents the reciprocal of 3^2.

6. $5x^0 = 0$

7. The expression 4^{-3} represents a negative number.

8. To be in simplest form, an exponential expression cannot contain any negative exponents.

9. As long as x is not zero, x^0 is defined to be equal to ______. Using this definition, $3^0 =$ ______, $(7x^3)^0 =$ ______, and $-2x^0 =$ ______.

10. A number is written in scientific notation if it is written as the product of a number between ______ and ______ and an integer power of ______.

For Exercises 11 to 14, determine whether the number is written in scientific notation. If not, explain why not.

11. 39.4×10^3

12. 0.8×10^{-6}

13. $7.1 \times 10^{2.4}$

14. 5.8×10^{-132}

OBJECTIVE A *To divide monomials*

For Exercises 15 to 50, simplify.

15. $\frac{y^7}{y^3}$

16. $\frac{z^9}{z^2}$

17. $\frac{a^8}{a^5}$

18. $\frac{c^{12}}{c^5}$

19. $\frac{p^5}{p}$

20. $\frac{w^9}{w}$

21. $\frac{4x^8}{2x^5}$

22. $\frac{12z^7}{4z^3}$

23. $\frac{22k^5}{11k^4}$ **24.** $\frac{14m^{11}}{7m^{10}}$ **25.** $\frac{m^9n^7}{m^4n^5}$ **26.** $\frac{y^5z^6}{yz^3}$

27. $\frac{6r^4}{4r^2}$ **28.** $\frac{8x^9}{12x^6}$ **29.** $\frac{-16a^7}{24a^6}$ **30.** $\frac{-18b^5}{27b^4}$

31. $\frac{y^3}{y^8}$ **32.** $\frac{z^4}{z^6}$ **33.** $\frac{a^5}{a^{11}}$ **34.** $\frac{m}{m^7}$

35. $\frac{4x^2}{12x^5}$ **36.** $\frac{6y^8}{8y^9}$ **37.** $\frac{-12x}{-18x^6}$ **38.** $\frac{-24c^2}{-36c^{11}}$

39. $\frac{x^6y^5}{x^8y}$ **40.** $\frac{a^3b^2}{a^2b^3}$ **41.** $\frac{2m^6n^2}{5m^9n^{10}}$ **42.** $\frac{5r^3t^7}{6r^5t^7}$

43. $\frac{pq^3}{p^4q^4}$ **44.** $\frac{a^4b^5}{a^5b^6}$ **45.** $\frac{3x^4y^5}{6x^4y^8}$ **46.** $\frac{14a^3b^6}{21a^5b^6}$

47. $\frac{14x^4y^6z^2}{16x^3y^9z}$ **48.** $\frac{24a^2b^7c^9}{36a^7b^5c}$ **49.** $\frac{15mn^9p^3}{30m^4n^9p}$ **50.** $\frac{25x^4y^7z^2}{20x^5y^9z^{11}}$

For Exercises 51 to 58, evaluate.

51. 5^{-2} **52.** 3^{-3} **53.** $\frac{1}{8^{-2}}$ **54.** $\frac{1}{12^{-1}}$

55. $\frac{3^{-2}}{3}$ **56.** $\frac{5^{-3}}{5}$ **57.** $\frac{2^{-2}}{2^{-3}}$ **58.** $\frac{3^2}{3^2}$

For Exercises 59 to 106, simplify.

59. x^{-2} **60.** y^{-10} **61.** $\frac{1}{a^{-6}}$ **62.** $\frac{1}{b^{-4}}$

63. $4x^{-7}$ **64.** $-6y^{-1}$ **65.** $\frac{2}{3}z^{-2}$ **66.** $\frac{4}{5}a^{-4}$

67. $\dfrac{5}{b^{-8}}$

68. $\dfrac{-3}{y^{-3}}$

69. $\dfrac{1}{3x^{-2}}$

70. $\dfrac{2}{5c^{-6}}$

71. $(ab^5)^0$

72. $(32x^3y^4)^0$

73. $-(3p^2q^5)^0$

74. $-\left(\dfrac{2}{3}xy\right)^0$

75. $(-2xy^{-2})^3$

76. $(-3x^{-1}y^2)^2$

77. $(3x^{-1}y^{-2})^2$

78. $(5xy^{-3})^{-2}$

79. $(2x^{-1})(x^{-3})$

80. $(-2x^{-5})x^7$

81. $(-5a^2)(a^{-5})^2$

82. $(2a^{-3})(a^7b^{-1})^3$

83. $(-2ab^{-2})(4a^{-2}b)^{-2}$

84. $(3ab^{-2})(2a^{-1}b)^{-3}$

85. $(-5x^{-2}y)(-2x^{-2}y^2)$

86. $\dfrac{a^{-3}b^{-4}}{a^2b^2}$

87. $\dfrac{3x^{-2}y^2}{6xy^2}$

88. $\dfrac{2x^{-2}y}{8xy}$

89. $\dfrac{3x^{-2}y}{xy}$

90. $\dfrac{2x^{-1}y^4}{x^2y^3}$

91. $\dfrac{2x^{-1}y^{-4}}{4xy^2}$

92. $\dfrac{(x^{-1}y)^2}{xy^2}$

93. $\dfrac{(x^{-2}y)^2}{x^2y^3}$

94. $\dfrac{(x^{-3}y^{-2})^2}{x^6y^8}$

95. $\dfrac{(a^{-2}y^3)^{-3}}{a^2y}$

96. $\dfrac{12a^2b^3}{-27a^2b^2}$

97. $\dfrac{-16xy^4}{96x^4y^4}$

98. $\dfrac{-8x^2y^4}{44y^2z^5}$

99. $\dfrac{22a^2b^4}{-132b^3c^2}$

100. $\dfrac{-(8a^2b^4)^3}{64a^3b^8}$

101. $\dfrac{-(14ab^4)^2}{28a^4b^2}$

102. $\dfrac{(2a^{-2}b^3)^{-2}}{(4a^2b^{-4})^{-1}}$

103. $\dfrac{(3^{-1}r^4s^{-3})^{-2}}{(6r^2s^{-1}t^{-2})^2}$

104. $\left(\dfrac{6x^{-4}yz^{-1}}{14xy^{-4}z^2}\right)^{-3}$

105. $\left(\dfrac{15m^3n^{-2}p^{-1}}{25m^{-2}n^{-4}}\right)^{-3}$

106. $\left(\dfrac{18a^4b^{-2}c^4}{12ab^{-3}d^2}\right)^{-2}$

For Exercises 107 to 110, state whether the equation is true or false for all $a \neq 0$ and $b \neq 0$.

107. $\dfrac{a^{4n}}{a^n} = a^4$

108. $a^{n-m} = \dfrac{1}{a^{m-n}}$

109. $a^{-n}a^n = 1$

110. $\dfrac{a^n}{b^m} = \left(\dfrac{a}{b}\right)^{m-n}$

OBJECTIVE B *To write a number in scientific notation*

111. To write the number 354,000,000 in scientific notation, move the decimal point ______ places to the ______. The exponent on 10 is ______.

112. To write the number 0.0000000086 in scientific notation, move the decimal point ______ places to the ______. The exponent on 10 is ______.

For Exercises 113 to 121, write in scientific notation.

113. 0.00000000324

114. 0.00000012

115. 0.000000000000000003

116. 1,800,000,000

117. 32,000,000,000,000,000

118. 76,700,000,000,000

119. 0.000000000000000000122

120. 0.00137

121. 547,000,000

For Exercises 122 to 130, write in decimal notation.

122. 2.3×10^{-12}

123. 1.67×10^{-4}

124. 2×10^{15}

125. 6.8×10^{7}

126. 9×10^{-21}

127. 3.05×10^{-5}

128. 9.05×10^{11}

129. 1.02×10^{-9}

130. 7.2×10^{-3}

131. If n is a negative integer, how many zeros appear after the decimal point when 1.35×10^n is written in decimal notation?

132. If n is a positive integer greater than 1, how many zeros appear before the decimal point when 1.35×10^n is written in decimal notation?

133. **Technology** See the news clipping at the right. Express in scientific notation the thickness, in meters, of the memristor.

134. **Astronomy** Astrophysicists estimate that the radius of the Milky Way galaxy is 1,000,000,000,000,000,000 m. Write this number in scientific notation.

135. **Geology** The mass of Earth is 5,980,000,000,000,000,000,000,000 kg. Write this number in scientific notation.

136. **Physics** Carbon nanotubes, made from extremely strong cylinders of carbon atoms, have remarkable properties. Nanotubes with a diameter of 0.0000000004 m have been created. Write this number in scientific notation.

137. **Biology** The weight of a single *E. coli* bacterium is 0.00000000000665 g. Write this number in scientific notation.

138. **Archeology** The weight of the Great Pyramid of Khufu is estimated to be 12,000,000,000 lb. Write this number in scientific notation.

139. **Food Science** The frequency (in oscillations per second) of a microwave generated by a microwave oven is approximately 2,450,000,000 hertz. (One hertz is one oscillation in 1 s.) Write this number in scientific notation.

140. **Astronomy** One light-year is the distance traveled by light in one year. One light-year is 5,880,000,000,000 mi. Write this number in scientific notation.

141. **Biophysics** Biologists and physicists are working together to measure the mass of a virus. Currently, a virus with a mass of 0.0000000000000000039 g can be measured. Write this number in scientific notation.

142. **Astronomy** See the news clipping at the right. WASP-12b orbits a star that is 5.1156×10^{15} mi from Earth. (*Source:* news.yahoo.com) Write this number in decimal notation.

143. **Physics** Light travels approximately 16,000,000,000 mi in one day. Write this number in scientific notation.

144. **Electricity** The electric charge on an electron is 0.00000000000000000016 coulomb. Write this number in scientific notation.

In the NEWS!

HP Introduces the Memristor

Hewlett Packard has announced the design of the *memristor,* a new memory technology with the potential to be much smaller than the memory chips used in today's computers. HP has made a memristor with a thickness of 0.000000015 m (15 nanometers).

Source: The New York Times

Great Pyramid of Khufu

In the NEWS!

Hottest Planet Ever Discovered

A planet called WASP-12b is the hottest planet ever discovered, at about 4000°F. It orbits its star faster than any other known planet, completing a revolution once a day.

Source: news.yahoo.com

Critical Thinking

145. Evaluate $8^{-2} + 2^{-5}$.

146. Evaluate $9^{-2} + 3^{-3}$.

147. Evaluate 2^x and 2^{-x} when $x = -2, -1, 0, 1,$ and 2.

148. Evaluate 3^x and 3^{-x} when $x = -2, -1, 0, 1,$ and 2.

For Exercises 149 and 150, write in decimal notation.

149. 2^{-4}

150. 25^{-2}

For Exercises 151 and 152, complete.

151. If $m = n$ and $a \neq 0$, then $\frac{a^m}{a^n} =$ ________.

152. If $m = n + 1$ and $a \neq 0$, then $\frac{a^m}{a^n} =$ ________.

For Exercises 153 and 154, solve.

153. $(-4.8)^x = 1$

154. $-6.3^x = -1$

155. If x is a nonzero real number, is x^{-2} always positive, always negative, or positive or negative depending on whether x is positive or negative? Explain your answer.

156. If x is a nonzero real number, is x^{-3} always positive, always negative, or positive or negative depending on whether x is positive or negative? Explain your answer.

Projects or Group Activities

157. **Population and Land Allocation** In this project, you are asked to determine hypothetical land allocation for the world's population today. Use the figure 7×10^9 for the current world population and the figure 3.1×10^8 for the current U.S. population. (*Source:* www.infoplease.com) One square mile is approximately 2.8×10^7 ft^2.

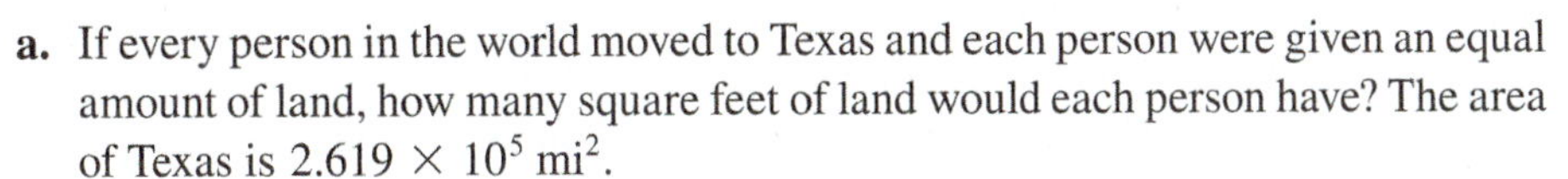

a. If every person in the world moved to Texas and each person were given an equal amount of land, how many square feet of land would each person have? The area of Texas is 2.619×10^5 mi^2.

Rhode Island

b. If every person in the United States moved to Rhode Island and each person were given an equal amount of land, how many square feet of land would each person have? The area of Rhode Island is 1.0×10^3 mi^2. Round to the nearest whole number.

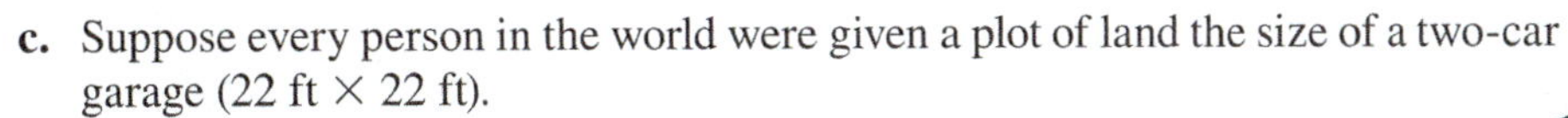

c. Suppose every person in the world were given a plot of land the size of a two-car garage (22 ft × 22 ft).

i. How many people would fit in a square mile? Round to the nearest hundred.

ii. How many square miles would be required to accommodate the entire world population? Round to the nearest hundred.

d. If the total land area of Earth were divided equally, how many acres of land would each person be allocated? Use a figure of 5.7×10^7 mi^2 for the land area of Earth. One acre is 43,560 ft^2. Round to the nearest tenth.

e. If every person on Earth were given a plot of land the size of a two-car garage, what would be the carrying capacity of Earth? Round to the nearest hundred billion.

SECTION

4.5 Division of Polynomials

OBJECTIVE A *To divide a polynomial by a monomial*

To divide a polynomial by a monomial, divide each term in the numerator by the denominator and write the sum of the quotients.

HOW TO 1 Divide: $\frac{6x^3 - 3x^2 + 9x}{3x}$

$$\frac{6x^3 - 3x^2 + 9x}{3x} = \frac{6x^3}{3x} - \frac{3x^2}{3x} + \frac{9x}{3x}$$

- **Divide each term of the polynomial by the monomial.**

$$= 2x^2 - x + 3$$

- **Simplify each term.**

EXAMPLE 1

Divide: $\frac{12x^2y - 6xy + 4x^2}{2xy}$

Solution

$$\frac{12x^2y - 6xy + 4x^2}{2xy} = \frac{12x^2y}{2xy} - \frac{6xy}{2xy} + \frac{4x^2}{2xy}$$

$$= 6x - 3 + \frac{2x}{y}$$

YOU TRY IT 1

Divide: $\frac{24x^2y^2 - 18xy + 6y}{6xy}$

Your solution

Solution on p. S10

OBJECTIVE B *To divide polynomials*

Tips for Success

An important element of success is practice. We cannot do anything well if we do not practice it repeatedly. Practice is crucial to success in mathematics. In this objective you are learning a new skill, how to divide polynomials. You will need to practice this skill over and over again in order to be successful at it.

The procedure for dividing two polynomials is similar to the one for dividing whole numbers. The same equation used to check division of whole numbers is used to check polynomial division: **(Quotient × divisor) + remainder = dividend.**

HOW TO 2 Divide: $(x^2 - 5x + 8) \div (x - 3)$

Step 1

$$\begin{array}{r} x \phantom{{}-5x+8} \\ x-3\overline{)x^2 - 5x + 8} \\ \underline{x^2 - 3x} \phantom{{}+8} \\ -2x + 8 \end{array}$$

- **Think:** $x\overline{)x^2} = \frac{x^2}{x} = x$
- **Multiply:** $x(x - 3) = x^2 - 3x$
- **Subtract:** $(x^2 - 5x) - (x^2 - 3x) = -2x$. **Bring down the 8.**

Step 2

$$\begin{array}{r} x - 2 \\ x-3\overline{)x^2 - 5x + 8} \\ \underline{x^2 - 3x} \phantom{{}+8} \\ -2x + 8 \\ \underline{-2x + 6} \\ 2 \end{array}$$

- **Think:** $x\overline{)-2x} = \frac{-2x}{x} = -2$
- **Multiply:** $-2(x - 3) = -2x + 6$
- **Subtract:** $(-2x + 8) - (-2x + 6) = 2$

Check: $(x - 2)(x - 3) + 2 = x^2 - 5x + 6 + 2 = x^2 - 5x + 8$

$$(x^2 - 5x + 8) \div (x - 3) = x - 2 + \frac{2}{x - 3}$$

Take Note

Recall that a fraction bar means "divided by." Therefore, $6 \div 2$ can be written $\frac{6}{2}$, and $a \div b$ can be written $\frac{a}{b}$.

If a term is missing from the dividend, a zero can be inserted for that term. This helps keep like terms in the same column.

HOW TO 3 Divide: $\dfrac{6x + 26 + 2x^3}{2 + x}$

$$\frac{2x^3 + 6x + 26}{x + 2}$$

• Arrange the terms of each polynomial in descending order.

$$\begin{array}{r} 2x^2 - 4x + 14 \\ x + 2\overline{)2x^3 + 0 \quad + 6x + 26} \\ \underline{2x^3 + 4x^2} \qquad\qquad \\ -4x^2 + 6x \qquad \\ \underline{-4x^2 - 8x} \qquad \\ 14x + 26 \\ \underline{14x + 28} \\ -2 \end{array}$$

• There is no x^2 term in $2x^3 + 6x + 26$. Insert a zero for the missing term.

Check:

$(2x^2 - 4x + 14)(x + 2) + (-2) = (2x^3 + 6x + 28) + (-2) = 2x^3 + 6x + 26$

$(2x^3 + 6x + 26) \div (x + 2) = 2x^2 - 4x + 14 - \dfrac{2}{x + 2}$

EXAMPLE 2

Divide: $(8x^2 + 4x^3 + x - 4) \div (2x + 3)$

Solution

$$\begin{array}{r} 2x^2 + \quad x - 1 \\ 2x + 3\overline{)4x^3 + 8x^2 + \quad x - 4} \\ \underline{4x^3 + 6x^2} \qquad\qquad\quad \\ 2x^2 + \quad x \qquad \\ \underline{2x^2 + 3x} \qquad \\ -2x - 4 \\ \underline{-2x - 3} \\ -1 \end{array}$$

• Write the dividend in descending powers of x.

$(4x^3 + 8x^2 + x - 4) \div (2x + 3)$

$= 2x^2 + x - 1 - \dfrac{1}{2x + 3}$

YOU TRY IT 2

Divide: $(2x^3 + x^2 - 8x - 3) \div (2x - 3)$

Your solution

EXAMPLE 3

Divide: $\dfrac{x^2 - 1}{x + 1}$

Solution

$$\begin{array}{r} x - 1 \\ x + 1\overline{)x^2 + 0 - 1} \\ \underline{x^2 + x} \qquad \\ -x - 1 \\ \underline{-x - 1} \\ 0 \end{array}$$

• Insert a zero for the missing term.

$(x^2 - 1) \div (x + 1) = x - 1$

YOU TRY IT 3

Divide: $\dfrac{x^3 - 2x + 1}{x - 1}$

Your solution

Solutions on p. S10

4.5 EXERCISES

Concept Check

1. Every division equation has a related multiplication equation. For instance, $\frac{16}{2} = 8$ means that $16 = 2 \cdot 8$. What is the related multiplication equation for $\frac{15x^2 + 12x}{3x} = 5x + 4$?

2. Given that $\frac{x^3 - x^2 + x - 1}{x - 1} = x^2 + 1$, name two factors of $x^3 - x^2 + x - 1$.

For Exercises 3 and 4, determine whether the statement is true or false.

3. $5\frac{2}{3} = 5 + \frac{2}{3}$

4. For $b \neq 0$, $a \div b = \frac{a}{b}$.

For Exercises 5 and 6, complete to make a true statement.

5. $\frac{18y^5 + 3y}{3y} = \frac{18y^5}{\square} + \frac{3y}{\square} = \_\_\_\_\_ + \_\_\_\_\_$

6. $\frac{12x^3 - 8x^2}{4x^2} = \frac{\square}{4x^2} - \frac{\square}{4x^2} = \_\_\_\_\_ - \_\_\_\_\_$

OBJECTIVE A *To divide a polynomial by a monomial*

For Exercises 7 to 30, divide.

7. $\frac{10a - 25}{5}$

8. $\frac{16b - 40}{8}$

9. $\frac{3a^2 + 2a}{a}$

10. $\frac{6y^2 + 4y}{y}$

11. $\frac{3x^2 - 6x}{3x}$

12. $\frac{10y^2 - 6y}{2y}$

13. $\frac{5x^2 - 10x}{-5x}$

14. $\frac{3y^2 - 27y}{-3y}$

15. $\frac{x^3 + 3x^2 - 5x}{x}$

16. $\frac{a^3 - 5a^2 + 7a}{a}$

17. $\frac{x^6 - 3x^4 - x^2}{x^2}$

18. $\frac{a^8 - 5a^5 - 3a^3}{a^2}$

19. $\frac{5x^2y^2 + 10xy}{5xy}$

20. $\frac{8x^2y^2 - 24xy}{8xy}$

21. $\frac{9y^6 - 15y^3}{-3y^3}$

22. $\frac{4x^4 - 6x^2}{-2x^2}$

23. $\frac{3x^2 - 2x + 1}{x}$

24. $\frac{8y^2 + 2y - 3}{y}$

25. $\frac{-3x^2 + 7x - 6}{x}$

26. $\frac{2y^2 - 6y + 9}{y}$

27. $\frac{16a^2b - 20ab + 24ab^2}{4ab}$

28. $\frac{22a^2b + 11ab - 33ab^2}{11ab}$

29. $\frac{9x^2y + 6xy - 3x}{xy}$

30. $\frac{18a^2b^2 + 9ab - 6}{3ab}$

31. How can multiplication be used to check that $\frac{8x^3 - 12x^2 - 4x}{4x} = 2x^2 - 3x - 1$?

OBJECTIVE B *To divide polynomials*

For Exercises 32 to 52, divide.

32. $(b^2 - 14b + 49) \div (b - 7)$

33. $(x^2 - x - 6) \div (x - 3)$

34. $(y^2 + 2y - 35) \div (y + 7)$

35. $(2x^2 + 5x + 2) \div (x + 2)$

36. $(2y^2 + 7) \div (y - 3)$

37. $(x^2 + 1) \div (x - 1)$

38. $(x^2 + 4) \div (x + 2)$

39. $(6x^2 - 7x) \div (3x - 2)$

40. $(a^2 + 5a + 10) \div (a + 2)$

41. $(b^2 - 8b - 9) \div (b - 3)$

42. $(2y^2 - 9y + 8) \div (2y + 3)$

43. $(3x^2 + 5x - 4) \div (x - 4)$

44. $(8x + 3 + 4x^2) \div (2x - 1)$

45. $(10 + 21y + 10y^2) \div (2y + 3)$

46. $(12a^2 - 7 - 25a) \div (3a - 7)$

47. $(5 - 23x + 12x^2) \div (4x - 1)$

48. $(24 + 6a^2 + 25a) \div (3a - 1)$

49. $(3x^2 + x^3 + 8 + 5x) \div (x + 1)$

50. $(7x - 6x^2 + x^3 - 1) \div (x - 1)$

51. $(x^4 - x^2 - 6) \div (x^2 + 2)$

52. $(x^4 + 3x^2 - 10) \div (x^2 - 2)$

53. True or false? When a sixth-degree polynomial is divided by a third-degree polynomial, the quotient is a second-degree polynomial.

Critical Thinking

54. The product of a monomial and $4b$ is $12a^2b$. Find the monomial.

55. The product of a monomial and $6x$ is $24xy^2$. Find the monomial.

56. The quotient of a polynomial and $2x + 1$ is $2x - 4 + \frac{7}{2x + 1}$. Find the polynomial.

57. The quotient of a polynomial and $x - 3$ is $x^2 - x + 8 + \frac{22}{x - 3}$. Find the polynomial.

Projects or Group Activities

58. $2x - 1$ is a factor of $2x^3 - 7x^2 + 7x - 2$. The product of $2x - 1$ and what polynomial is $2x^3 - 7x^2 + 7x - 2$?

59. $4x + 1$ is a factor of $4x^3 + 9x^2 - 10x - 3$. The product of $4x + 1$ and what polynomial is $4x^3 + 9x^2 - 10x - 3$?

60. When $x^2 - x - 8$ is divided by a polynomial, the quotient is $x + 3$ and the remainder is 4. Find the polynomial.

CHAPTER

4 Summary

Key Words	Examples
A **monomial** is a number, a variable, or a product of numbers and variables. [4.1A, p. 188]	5 is a number; y is a variable. $2a^3b^2$ is a product of a number and variables. 5, y, and $2a^3b^2$ are monomials.
A **polynomial** is a variable expression in which the terms are monomials. [4.1A, p. 188]	$5x^2y - 3xy^2 + 2$ is a polynomial. Each term of this expression is a monomial.
A polynomial of two terms is a **binomial.** [4.1A, p. 188]	$x + 2$, $y^2 - 3$, and $6a + 5b$ are binomials.
A polynomial of three terms is a **trinomial.** [4.1A, p. 188]	$x^2 - 6x + 7$ is a trinomial.
The **degree of a polynomial in one variable** is the greatest exponent on a variable. [4.1A, p. 188]	The degree of $3x - 4x^3 + 17x^2 + 25$ is 3.
A polynomial in one variable is usually written in **descending order,** with the exponents on the variable terms decreasing from left to right. [4.1A, p. 188]	The polynomial $2x^4 + 3x^2 - 4x - 7$ is written in descending order.
The **opposite of a polynomial** is the polynomial with the sign of every term changed to its opposite. [4.1B, p. 189]	The opposite of the polynomial $x^2 - 3x + 4$ is $-x^2 + 3x - 4$.

Essential Rules and Procedures

Essential Rules and Procedures	Examples
Addition of Polynomials [4.1A, p. 188] To add polynomials, add the coefficients of the like terms.	$(2x^2 + 3x - 4) + (3x^3 - 4x^2 + 2x - 5)$ $= 3x^3 + (2x^2 - 4x^2) + (3x + 2x) + (-4 - 5)$ $= 3x^3 - 2x^2 + 5x - 9$
Subtraction of Polynomials [4.1B, p. 189] To subtract polynomials, add the opposite of the second polynomial to the first.	$(3y^2 - 8y - 9) - (5y^2 - 10y + 3)$ $= (3y^2 - 8y - 9) + (-5y^2 + 10y - 3)$ $= (3y^2 - 5y^2) + (-8y + 10y) + (-9 - 3)$ $= -2y^2 + 2y - 12$
Rule for Multiplying Exponential Expressions [4.2A, p. 192] If m and n are integers, then $x^m \cdot x^n = x^{m+n}$.	$a^3 \cdot a^6 = a^{3+6} = a^9$

Rule for Simplifying the Power of an Exponential Expression [4.2B, p. 193]
If m and n are integers, then $(x^m)^n = x^{mn}$.

$(c^3)^4 = c^{3 \cdot 4} = c^{12}$

Rule for Simplifying the Power of a Product [4.2B, p. 193]
If m, n, and p are integers, then $(x^m y^n)^p = x^{mp} y^{np}$.

$(a^3b^2)^4 = a^{3 \cdot 4}b^{2 \cdot 4} = a^{12}b^8$

To multiply a polynomial by a monomial, use the Distributive Property and the Rule for Multiplying Exponential Expressions. [4.3A, p. 196]

$$\begin{aligned}&(-4y)(5y^2 + 3y - 8)\\ &\quad = (-4y)(5y^2) + (-4y)(3y) - (-4y)(8)\\ &\quad = -20y^3 - 12y^2 + 32y\end{aligned}$$

To multiply two polynomials, multiply each term of one polynomial by each term of the other polynomial. [4.3B, p. 196]

$$\begin{array}{r} x^2 - 5x + 6 \\ x + 4 \\ \hline 4x^2 - 20x + 24 \\ x^3 - 5x^2 + 6x \quad\;\; \\ \hline x^3 - x^2 - 14x + 24 \end{array}$$

FOIL Method [4.3C, p. 197]
To find the product of two binomials, add the products of the **F**irst terms, the **O**uter terms, the **I**nner terms, and the **L**ast terms.

$$\begin{aligned}&(2x - 5)(3x + 4)\\ &\quad = (2x)(3x) + (2x)(4) + (-5)(3x)\\ &\qquad + (-5)(4)\\ &\quad = 6x^2 + 8x - 15x - 20\\ &\quad = 6x^2 - 7x - 20\end{aligned}$$

Product of the Sum and Difference of the Same Terms [4.3D, p. 198]
$(a + b)(a - b) = a^2 - b^2$

$$\begin{aligned}(3x + 4)(3x - 4) &= (3x)^2 - 4^2\\ &= 9x^2 - 16\end{aligned}$$

Square of a Binomial [4.3D, p. 198]
$(a + b)^2 = a^2 + 2ab + b^2$
$(a - b)^2 = a^2 - 2ab + b^2$

$$\begin{aligned}(2x + 5)^2 &= (2x)^2 + 2(2x)(5) + 5^2\\ &= 4x^2 + 20x + 25\\ (3x - 4)^2 &= (3x)^2 - 2(3x)(4) + (-4)^2\\ &= 9x^2 - 24x + 16\end{aligned}$$

Definition of Zero as an Exponent [4.4A, p. 205]
If $x \neq 0$, then $x^0 = 1$.

$17^0 = 1$; $(-6c)^0 = 1, c \neq 0$

Definition of a Negative Exponent [4.4A, p. 206]

If $x \neq 0$ and n is a positive integer, then $x^{-n} = \frac{1}{x^n}$ and $\frac{1}{x^{-n}} = x^n$.

$x^{-6} = \frac{1}{x^6}$ and $\frac{1}{x^{-6}} = x^6$

Rule for Simplifying the Power of a Quotient [4.4A, p. 207]

If m, n, and p are integers and $y \neq 0$, then $\left(\frac{x^m}{y^n}\right)^p = \frac{x^{mp}}{y^{np}}$.

$$\left(\frac{c^3}{a^5}\right)^2 = \frac{c^{3 \cdot 2}}{a^{5 \cdot 2}} = \frac{c^6}{a^{10}}$$

Rule for Negative Exponents on Fractional Expressions [4.4A, p. 208]

If $a \neq 0$, $b \neq 0$, and n is a positive integer, then $\left(\frac{a}{b}\right)^{-n} = \left(\frac{b}{a}\right)^n$.

$$\left(\frac{x}{y}\right)^{-3} = \left(\frac{y}{x}\right)^3$$

Rule for Dividing Exponential Expressions [4.4A, p. 207]

If m and n are integers and $x \neq 0$, then $\frac{x^m}{x^n} = x^{m-n}$.

$$\frac{a^7}{a^2} = a^{7-2} = a^5$$

To Express a Number in Scientific Notation [4.4B, p. 210]
To express a number in scientific notation, write it in the form $a \times 10^n$, where $1 \leq a < 10$ and n is an integer. If the number is greater than 10, then n is a positive integer. If the number is between 0 and 1, then n is a negative integer.

$367{,}000{,}000 = 3.67 \times 10^8$

$0.0000078 = 7.8 \times 10^{-6}$

To Change a Number Written in Scientific Notation to Decimal Notation [4.4B, p. 211]
To change a number written in scientific notation to decimal notation, move the decimal point to the right if n is positive and to the left if n is negative. Move the decimal point the same number of places as the absolute value of the exponent on 10.

$2.418 \times 10^7 = 24{,}180{,}000$

$9.06 \times 10^{-5} = 0.0000906$

To divide a polynomial by a monomial, divide each term in the numerator by the denominator and write the sum of the quotients. [4.5A, p. 218]

$$\frac{8xy^3 - 4y^2 + 12y}{4y}$$
$$= \frac{8xy^3}{4y} - \frac{4y^2}{4y} + \frac{12y}{4y}$$
$$= 2xy^2 - y + 3$$

To check polynomial division, use the same equation used to check division of whole numbers:

(Quotient $\times$ divisor) + remainder = dividend

[4.5B, p. 218]

$$\begin{array}{r} x - 4 \\ x + 3\overline{)x^2 - x - 10} \\ \underline{x^2 + 3x} \\ -4x - 10 \\ \underline{-4x - 12} \\ 2 \end{array}$$

Check:

$$(x - 4)(x + 3) + 2 = x^2 - x - 12 + 2$$
$$= x^2 - x - 10$$

$$(x^2 - x - 10) \div (x + 3) = x - 4 + \frac{2}{x + 3}$$

CHAPTER

4 Review Exercises

1. Multiply: $(2b - 3)(4b + 5)$

2. Add: $(12y^2 + 17y - 4) + (9y^2 - 13y + 3)$

3. Simplify: $(xy^5z^3)(x^3y^3z)$

4. Simplify: $\dfrac{8x^{12}}{12x^9}$

5. Multiply: $-2x(4x^2 + 7x - 9)$

6. Simplify: $\dfrac{3ab^4}{-6a^2b^4}$

7. Simplify: $(-2u^3v^4)^4$

8. Evaluate: $(2^3)^2$

9. Subtract: $(5x^2 - 2x - 1) - (3x^2 - 5x + 7)$

10. Simplify: $\dfrac{a^{-1}b^3}{a^3b^{-3}}$

11. Simplify: $(-2x^3)^2(-3x^4)^3$

12. Expand: $(5y - 7)^2$

13. Simplify: $(5a^7b^6)^2(4ab)$

14. Divide: $\dfrac{12b^7 + 36b^5 - 3b^3}{3b^3}$

15. Evaluate: -4^{-2}

16. Subtract: $(13y^3 - 7y - 2) - (12y^2 - 2y - 1)$

17. Divide: $\dfrac{7 - x - x^2}{x + 3}$

18. Multiply: $(2a - b)(x - 2y)$

19. Multiply: $(3y^2 + 4y - 7)(2y + 3)$

20. Divide: $(b^3 - 2b^2 - 33b - 7) \div (b - 7)$

21. Multiply: $2ab^3(4a^2 - 2ab + 3b^2)$

22. Multiply: $(2a - 5b)(2a + 5b)$

23. Multiply: $(6b^3 - 2b^2 - 5)(2b^2 - 1)$

24. Add: $(2x^3 + 7x^2 + x) + (2x^2 - 4x - 12)$

25. Divide: $\dfrac{16y^2 - 32y}{-4y}$

26. Multiply: $(a + 7)(a - 7)$

27. Write 37,560,000,000 in scientific notation.

28. Write 1.46×10^7 in decimal notation.

29. Simplify: $(2a^{12}b^3)(-9b^2c^6)(3ac)$

30. Divide: $(6y^2 - 35y + 36) \div (3y - 4)$

31. Simplify: $(-3x^{-2}y^{-3})^{-2}$

32. Multiply: $(5a - 7)(2a + 9)$

33. Write 0.000000127 in scientific notation.

34. Write 3.2×10^{-12} in decimal notation.

35. Geometry The length of a table-tennis table is 1 ft less than twice the width of the table. Let w represent the width of the table-tennis table. Express the area of the table in terms of the variable w.

fstockfoto/Shutterstock.com

36. Geometry The side of a checkerboard is $(3x - 2)$ in. Express the area of the checkerboard in terms of the variable x.

CHAPTER 4 TEST

1. Multiply: $2x(2x^2 - 3x)$

2. Divide: $\dfrac{12x^3 - 3x^2 + 9}{3x^2}$

3. Simplify: $\dfrac{12x^2}{-3x^8}$

4. Simplify: $(-2xy^2)(3x^2y^4)$

5. Divide: $(x^2 + 1) \div (x + 1)$

6. Multiply: $(x - 3)(x^2 - 4x + 5)$

7. Simplify: $(-2a^2b)^3$

8. Simplify: $\dfrac{(3x^{-2}y^3)^3}{3x^4y^{-1}}$

9. Multiply: $(a - 2b)(a + 5b)$

10. Divide: $\dfrac{16x^5 - 8x^3 + 20x}{4x}$

11. Divide: $(x^2 + 6x - 7) \div (x - 1)$

12. Multiply: $-3y^2(-2y^2 + 3y - 6)$

13. Multiply: $(-2x^3 + x^2 - 7)(2x - 3)$

14. Multiply: $(4y - 3)(4y + 3)$

15. Simplify: $(ab^2)(a^3b^5)$

16. Simplify: $\dfrac{2a^{-1}b}{2^{-2}a^{-2}b^{-3}}$

17. Divide: $\dfrac{20a - 35}{5}$

18. Subtract: $(3a^2 - 2a - 7) - (5a^3 + 2a - 10)$

19. Expand: $(2x - 5)^2$

20. Divide: $(4x^2 - 7) \div (2x - 3)$

21. Simplify: $\dfrac{-(2x^2y)^3}{4x^3y^3}$

22. Multiply: $(2x - 7y)(5x - 4y)$

23. Add: $(3x^3 - 2x^2 - 4) + (8x^2 - 8x + 7)$

24. Write 0.00000000302 in scientific notation.

25. **Geometry** The radius of a circle is $(x - 5)$ m. Use the equation $A = \pi r^2$, where r is the radius, to find the area of the circle in terms of the variable x. Leave the answer in terms of π.

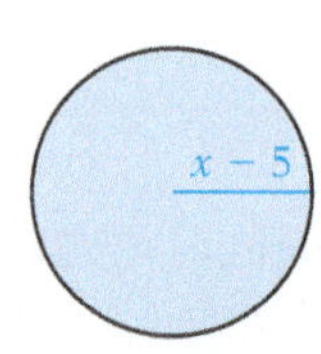

Cumulative Review Exercises

1. Simplify: $\frac{3}{16} - \left(-\frac{5}{8}\right) - \frac{7}{9}$

2. Evaluate $-3^2 \cdot \left(\frac{2}{3}\right)^3 \cdot \left(-\frac{5}{8}\right)$.

3. Simplify: $\left(-\frac{1}{2}\right)^3 \div \left(\frac{3}{8} - \frac{5}{6}\right) + 2$

4. Evaluate $\frac{b - (a - b)^2}{b^2}$ when $a = -2$ and $b = 3$.

5. Simplify: $-2x - (-xy) + 7x - 4xy$

6. Simplify: $(12x)\left(-\frac{3}{4}\right)$

7. Simplify: $-2[3x - 2(4 - 3x) + 2]$

8. Solve: $12 = -\frac{3}{4}x$

9. Solve: $2x - 9 = 3x + 7$

10. Solve: $2 - 3(4 - x) = 2x + 5$

11. 35.2 is what percent of 160?

12. Add: $(4b^3 - 7b^2 - 7) + (3b^2 - 8b + 3)$

13. Subtract: $(3y^3 - 5y + 8) - (-2y^2 + 5y + 8)$

14. Simplify: $(a^3b^5)^3$

15. Simplify: $(4xy^3)(-2x^2y^3)$

16. Multiply: $-2y^2(-3y^2 - 4y + 8)$

17. Multiply: $(2a - 7)(5a^2 - 2a + 3)$

18. Multiply: $(3b - 2)(5b - 7)$

19. Simplify: $\dfrac{(-2a^2b^3)^2}{8a^4b^8}$

20. Divide: $(a^2 - 4a - 21) \div (a + 3)$

21. Write 6.09×10^{-5} in decimal notation.

22. Translate "the difference between eight times a number and twice the number is eighteen" into an equation and solve.

23. Mixtures Fifty ounces of orange juice are added to 200 oz of a fruit punch that is 10% orange juice. What is the percent concentration of orange juice in the resulting mixture?

Evgeny Karandaev/Shutterstock.com

24. Transportation A car traveling at 50 mph overtakes a cyclist who, riding at 10 mph, has had a 2-hour head start. How far from the starting point does the car overtake the cyclist?

25. Geometry The width of a rectangle is 40% of the length. The perimeter of the rectangle is 42 m. Find the length and width of the rectangle.

Factoring

5

OBJECTIVES

SECTION 5.1

A To factor a monomial from a polynomial

B To factor by grouping

SECTION 5.2

A To factor a trinomial of the form $x^2 + bx + c$

B To factor completely

SECTION 5.3

A To factor a trinomial of the form $ax^2 + bx + c$ by using trial factors

B To factor a trinomial of the form $ax^2 + bx + c$ by grouping

SECTION 5.4

A To factor the difference of two squares and perfect-square trinomials

SECTION 5.5

A To factor polynomials completely

SECTION 5.6

A To solve equations by factoring

B To solve application problems

Focus on Success

Are you using the features of this text to learn the concepts being presented? The HOW TO feature includes a step-by-step solution to the types of exercises you will be working in your homework assignments and on exams. A numbered Example provides you with a fully worked-out solution. After studying the Example, try completing the You Try It to the right of the Example. A complete solution to the You Try It is in the back of the text. (See Use the Interactive Method, page AIM-8.)

Prep Test

Are you ready to succeed in this chapter? Take the Prep Test below to find out if you are ready to learn the new material.

1. Write 30 as a product of prime numbers.

2. Simplify: $-3(4y - 5)$

3. Simplify: $-(a - b)$

4. Simplify: $2(a - b) - 5(a - b)$

5. Solve: $4x = 0$

6. Solve: $2x + 1 = 0$

7. Multiply: $(x + 4)(x - 6)$

8. Multiply: $(2x - 5)(3x + 2)$

9. Simplify: $\dfrac{x^5}{x^2}$

10. Simplify: $\dfrac{6x^4y^3}{2xy^2}$

SECTION

5.1 Common Factors

OBJECTIVE A *To factor a monomial from a polynomial*

In Section 1.5C, we discussed how to find the greatest common factor (GCF) of two or more integers. The **greatest common factor (GCF) of two or more monomials** is the product of the GCF of the coefficients and the common variable factors.

$6x^3y = 2 \cdot 3 \cdot x \cdot x \cdot x \cdot y$
$8x^2y^2 = 2 \cdot 2 \cdot 2 \cdot x \cdot x \cdot y \cdot y$
$\text{GCF} = 2 \cdot x \cdot x \cdot y = 2x^2y$

Note that the exponent on each variable in the GCF is the same as the *smallest* exponent on that variable in either of the monomials.

The GCF of $6x^3y$ and $8x^2y^2$ is $2x^2y$.

HOW TO 1 Find the GCF of $12a^4b$ and $18a^2b^2c$.

The common variable factors are a^2 and b; c is not a common variable factor.

$12a^4b = 2 \cdot 2 \cdot 3 \cdot a^4 \cdot b$
$18a^2b^2c = 2 \cdot 3 \cdot 3 \cdot a^2 \cdot b^2 \cdot c$
$\text{GCF} = 2 \cdot 3 \cdot a^2 \cdot b = 6a^2b$

To **factor a polynomial** means to write the polynomial as a product of other polynomials. In the example at the right, $2x$ is the GCF of the terms $2x^2$ and $10x$.

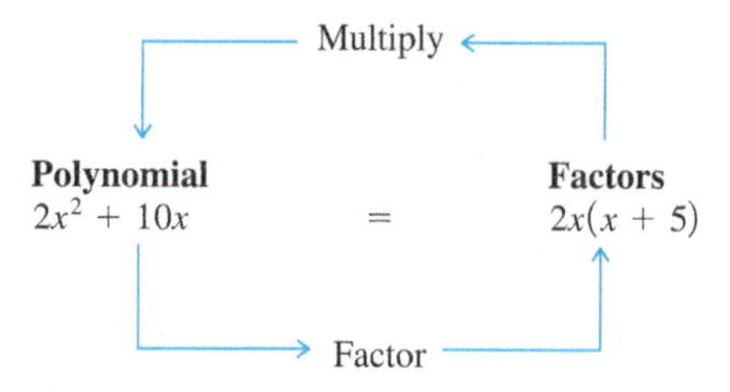

HOW TO 2 Factor: $5x^3 - 35x^2 + 10x$

Find the GCF of the terms of the polynomial.

$5x^3 = 5 \cdot x^3$
$35x^2 = 5 \cdot 7 \cdot x^2$
$10x = 2 \cdot 5 \cdot x$

The GCF is $5x$.

Rewrite the polynomial, expressing each term as a product with the GCF as one of the factors.

$$5x^3 - 35x^2 + 10x = 5x(x^2) + 5x(-7x) + 5x(2)$$
$$= 5x(x^2 - 7x + 2)$$

• Use the Distributive Property to write the polynomial as a product of factors.

Take Note

At the right, the factors in parentheses are determined by dividing each term of the trinomial by the GCF, $5x$. $\frac{5x^3}{5x} = x^2$, $\frac{-35x^2}{5x} = -7x$, and $\frac{10x}{5x} = 2$

HOW TO 3 Factor: $21x^2y^3 - 6xy^5 + 15x^4y^2$

Find the GCF of the terms of the polynomial.

$$21x^2y^3 = 3 \cdot 7 \cdot x^2 \cdot y^3$$
$$6xy^5 = 2 \cdot 3 \cdot x \cdot y^5$$
$$15x^4y^2 = 3 \cdot 5 \cdot x^4 \cdot y^2$$

The GCF is $3xy^2$.

Rewrite the polynomial, expressing each term as a product with the GCF as one of the factors.

$$21x^2y^3 - 6xy^5 + 15x^4y^2$$
$$= 3xy^2(7xy) + 3xy^2(-2y^3) + 3xy^2(5x^3)$$
$$= 3xy^2(7xy - 2y^3 + 5x^3)$$

- **Use the Distributive Property to write the polynomial as a product of factors.**

EXAMPLE 1

Factor: $8x^2 + 2xy$

Solution

The GCF is $2x$.

$$8x^2 + 2xy = 2x(4x) + 2x(y)$$
$$= 2x(4x + y)$$

- **Factor the GCF from each term.**

YOU TRY IT 1

Factor: $14a^2 - 21a^4b$

Your solution

EXAMPLE 2

Factor: $n^3 - 5n^2 + 2n$

Solution

The GCF is n.

$$n^3 - 5n^2 + 2n$$
$$= n(n^2) + n(-5n) + n(2)$$
$$= n(n^2 - 5n + 2)$$

- **Factor the GCF from each term.**

YOU TRY IT 2

Factor: $27b^2 + 18b + 9$

Your solution

EXAMPLE 3

Factor: $16x^2y + 8x^4y^2 - 12x^4y^5$

Solution

The GCF is $4x^2y$.

$$16x^2y + 8x^4y^2 - 12x^4y^5$$
$$= 4x^2y(4) + 4x^2y(2x^2y) + 4x^2y(-3x^2y^4)$$
$$= 4x^2y(4 + 2x^2y - 3x^2y^4)$$

YOU TRY IT 3

Factor: $6x^4y^2 - 9x^3y^2 + 12x^2y^4$

Your solution

Solutions on p. S10

OBJECTIVE B *To factor by grouping*

A factor that has two terms is called a **binomial factor.** In the examples at the right, the binomials $a + b$ and $x - y$ are binomial factors.

$2a(a + b)^2$
$3xy(x - y)$

The Distributive Property is used to factor a common binomial factor from an expression.

The common binomial factor of the expression $6(x - 3) + y(x - 3)$ is $(x - 3)$. To factor the expression, use the Distributive Property to write the expression as a product of factors.

$$6(x - 3) + y(x - 3) = (x - 3)(6 + y)$$

Consider the following simplification of $-(a - b)$.

$$-(a - b) = -1(a - b) = -a + b = b - a$$

Thus $$b - a = -(a - b)$$

This equation is sometimes used to factor a common binomial from an expression.

HOW TO 4 Factor: $2x(x - y) + 5(y - x)$

$$2x(x - y) + 5(y - x) = 2x(x - y) - 5(x - y)$$
$$= (x - y)(2x - 5)$$

- $5(y - x) = 5[(-1)(x - y)]$ $= -5(x - y)$

A polynomial can be **factored by grouping** if its terms can be grouped and factored in such a way that a common binomial factor is found.

HOW TO 5 Factor: $ax + bx - ay - by$

$$ax + bx - ay - by = (ax + bx) - (ay + by)$$

- Group the first two terms and the last two terms. Note that $-ay - by = -(ay + by)$.

$$= x(a + b) - y(a + b)$$

- Factor each group.

$$= (a + b)(x - y)$$

- Factor the GCF, $(a + b)$, from each group.

Check: $(a + b)(x - y) = ax - ay + bx - by$
$= ax + bx - ay - by$

HOW TO 6 Factor: $6x^2 - 9x - 4xy + 6y$

$$6x^2 - 9x - 4xy + 6y = (6x^2 - 9x) - (4xy - 6y)$$

- Group the first two terms and the last two terms. Note that $-4xy + 6y = -(4xy - 6y)$.

$$= 3x(2x - 3) - 2y(2x - 3)$$

- Factor each group.

$$= (2x - 3)(3x - 2y)$$

- Factor the GCF, $(2x - 3)$, from each group.

EXAMPLE 4

Factor: $4x(3x - 2) - 7(3x - 2)$

Solution

$4x(3x - 2) - 7(3x - 2)$ • $3x - 2$ is the common binomial factor.

$= (3x - 2)(4x - 7)$

YOU TRY IT 4

Factor: $2y(5x - 2) - 3(2 - 5x)$

Your solution

EXAMPLE 5

Factor: $9x^2 - 15x - 6xy + 10y$

Solution

$9x^2 - 15x - 6xy + 10y$

$= (9x^2 - 15x) - (6xy - 10y)$ • $-6xy + 10y = -(6xy - 10y)$

$= 3x(3x - 5) - 2y(3x - 5)$ • $3x - 5$ is the common factor.

$= (3x - 5)(3x - 2y)$

YOU TRY IT 5

Factor: $a^2 - 3a + 2ab - 6b$

Your solution

EXAMPLE 6

Factor: $3x^2y - 4x - 15xy + 20$

Solution

$3x^2y - 4x - 15xy + 20$

$= (3x^2y - 4x) - (15xy - 20)$ • $-15xy + 20 = -(15xy - 20)$

$= x(3xy - 4) - 5(3xy - 4)$ • $3xy - 4$ is the common factor.

$= (3xy - 4)(x - 5)$

YOU TRY IT 6

Factor: $2mn^2 - n + 8mn - 4$

Your solution

EXAMPLE 7

Factor: $4ab - 6 + 3b - 2ab^2$

Solution

$4ab - 6 + 3b - 2ab^2$

$= (4ab - 6) + (3b - 2ab^2)$

$= 2(2ab - 3) + b(3 - 2ab)$

$= 2(2ab - 3) - b(2ab - 3)$ • $3 - 2ab = -(2ab - 3)$

$= (2ab - 3)(2 - b)$ • $2ab - 3$ is the common factor.

YOU TRY IT 7

Factor: $3xy - 9y - 12 + 4x$

Your solution

Solutions on p. S10

5.1 EXERCISES

Concept Check

1. Name the greatest common factor of 4, 12, and 16.
2. Name the greatest common factor of x^3, x^5, and x^6.
3. For the expression $x(2x - 1)$, name **a.** the monomial factor and **b.** the binomial factor.
4. Name the common binomial factor in the expression $5b(c - 6) + 8(c - 6)$.
5. Rewrite the expression $2x^3 - x^2 + 6x - 3$ by grouping the first two terms and the last two terms.
6. Explain why the statement is true.
   a. The terms of the binomial $3x - 6$ have a common factor.
   b. The expression $3x^2 + 15$ is not in factored form.
   c. $5y - 7$ is a factor of $y(5y - 7)$.

OBJECTIVE A *To factor a monomial from a polynomial*

For Exercises 7 to 40, factor.

7. $5a + 5$ **8.** $7b - 7$ **9.** $16 - 8a^2$ **10.** $12 + 12y^2$ **11.** $8x + 12$

12. $16a - 24$ **13.** $7x^2 - 3x$ **14.** $12y^2 - 5y$ **15.** $3a^2 + 5a^5$ **16.** $6b^3 - 5b^2$

17. $2x^4 - 4x$ **18.** $3y^4 - 9y$ **19.** $10x^4 - 12x^2$ **20.** $12a^5 - 32a^2$ **21.** $8a^8 - 4a^5$

22. $16y^4 - 8y^7$ **23.** $x^2y^2 - xy$ **24.** $a^2b^2 + ab$ **25.** $3x^2y^4 - 6xy$ **26.** $12a^2b^5 - 9ab$

27. $3x^3 + 6x^2 + 9x$ **28.** $5y^3 - 20y^2 + 5y$ **29.** $2x^4 - 4x^3 + 6x^2$ **30.** $3y^4 - 9y^3 - 6y^2$

31. $2x^3 + 6x^2 - 14x$ **32.** $3y^3 - 9y^2 + 24y$ **33.** $2y^5 - 3y^4 + 7y^3$ **34.** $6a^5 - 3a^3 - 2a^2$

35. $x^3y - 3x^2y^2 + 7xy^3$ **36.** $2a^2b - 5a^2b^2 + 7ab^2$ **37.** $5y^3 + 10y^2 - 25y$

38. $4b^5 + 6b^3 - 12b$ **39.** $3a^2b^2 - 9ab^2 + 15b^2$ **40.** $8x^2y^2 - 4x^2y + x^2$

41. What is the GCF of the terms of the polynomial $x^a + x^b + x^c$ given that a, b, and c are all positive integers, and $a > b > c$?

OBJECTIVE B *To factor by grouping*

42. Use the three expressions at the right.
a. Which expressions are equivalent to $x^2 - 5x + 6$?
b. Which expression can be factored by grouping?

(i) $x^2 - 15x + 10x + 6$
(ii) $x^2 - x - 4x + 6$
(iii) $x^2 - 2x - 3x + 6$

For Exercises 43 to 66, factor.

43. $x(b + 4) + 3(b + 4)$

44. $y(a + z) + 7(a + z)$

45. $a(y - x) - b(y - x)$

46. $3r(a - b) + s(a - b)$

47. $x(x - 2) + y(2 - x)$

48. $t(m - 7) + 7(7 - m)$

49. $8c(2m - 3n) + (3n - 2m)$

50. $2y(4a + b) - (b + 4a)$

51. $x^2 + 2x + 2xy + 4y$

52. $x^2 - 3x + 4ax - 12a$

53. $p^2 - 2p - 3rp + 6r$

54. $t^2 + 4t - st - 4s$

55. $ab + 6b - 4a - 24$

56. $xy - 5y - 2x + 10$

57. $2z^2 - z + 2yz - y$

58. $2y^2 - 10y + 7xy - 35x$

59. $2x^2 - 5x - 6xy + 15y$

60. $4a^2 + 5ab - 10b - 8a$

61. $3y^2 - 6y - ay + 2a$

62. $2ra + a^2 - 2r - a$

63. $3xy - y^2 - y + 3x$

64. $2ab - 3b^2 - 3b + 2a$

65. $3st + t^2 - 2t - 6s$

66. $4x^2 + 3xy - 12y - 16x$

Critical Thinking

For Exercises 67 to 69, fill in the blank to make a true statement.

67. $a - 3 =$ ______$(3 - a)$

68. $2 - (x - y) = 2 + ($______$)$

69. $4x + (3a - b) = 4x - ($______$)$

Projects or Group Activities

70. Geometry Write an expression in factored form for the shaded portion in each of the following diagrams. Use the equation for the area of a rectangle $(A = LW)$ and the equation for the area of a circle $(A = \pi r^2)$.

a.

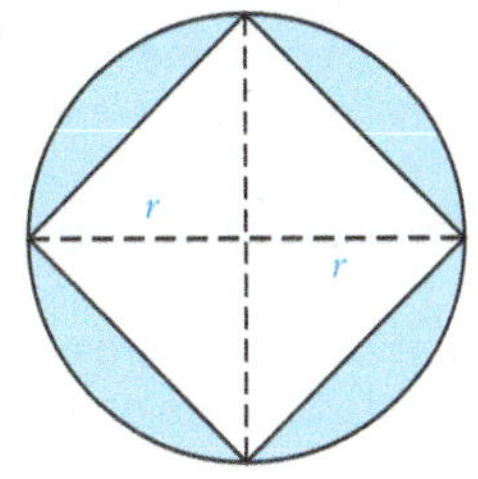

b.

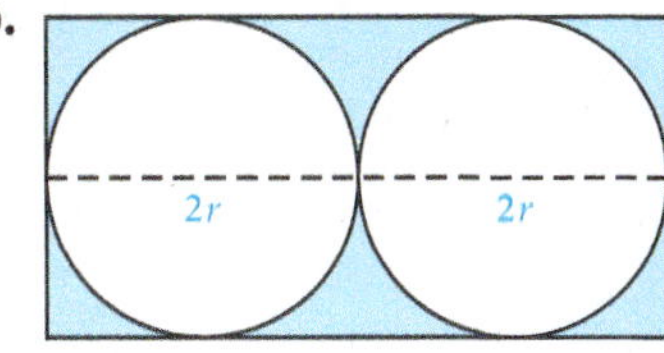

c.

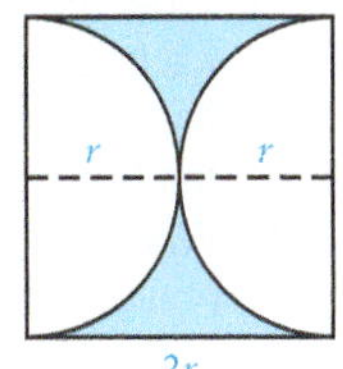

SECTION

5.2 Factoring Polynomials of the Form $x^2 + bx + c$

OBJECTIVE A *To factor a trinomial of the form $x^2 + bx + c$*

Trinomials of the form $x^2 + bx + c$, where b and c are integers, are shown at the right.

$x^2 + 8x + 12;\ b = 8,\ c = 12$
$x^2 - 7x + 12;\ b = -7,\ c = 12$
$x^2 - 2x - 15;\ b = -2,\ c = -15$

To factor a trinomial of this form means to express the trinomial as the product of two binomials.

Trinomials expressed as the product of binomials are shown at the right.

$x^2 + 8x + 12 = (x + 6)(x + 2)$
$x^2 - 7x + 12 = (x - 3)(x - 4)$
$x^2 - 2x - 15 = (x + 3)(x - 5)$

The method by which factors of a trinomial are found is based on FOIL. Consider the following binomial products, noting the relationship between the constant terms of the binomials and the terms of the trinomials.

The signs in the binomial factors are the same.

$(x + 6)(x + 2) = x^2 + 2x + 6x + (6)(2) = x^2 + 8x + 12$

Sum of 6 and 2 (→ $8x$)
Product of 6 and 2 (→ 12)

$(x - 3)(x - 4) = x^2 - 4x - 3x + (-3)(-4) = x^2 - 7x + 12$

Sum of -3 and -4 (→ $-7x$)
Product of -3 and -4 (→ 12)

The signs in the binomial factors are opposites.

$(x + 3)(x - 5) = x^2 - 5x + 3x + (3)(-5) = x^2 - 2x - 15$

Sum of 3 and -5 (→ $-2x$)
Product of 3 and -5 (→ -15)

$(x - 4)(x + 6) = x^2 + 6x - 4x + (-4)(6) = x^2 + 2x - 24$

Sum of -4 and 6 (→ $2x$)
Product of -4 and 6 (→ -24)

Factoring $x^2 + bx + c$: IMPORTANT RELATIONSHIPS

1. When the constant term of the trinomial is positive, the constant terms of the binomials have the same sign. They are both positive when the coefficient of the x term in the trinomial is positive. They are both negative when the coefficient of the x term in the trinomial is negative.
2. When the constant term of the trinomial is negative, the constant terms of the binomials have opposite signs.
3. In the trinomial, the coefficient of x is the sum of the constant terms of the binomials.
4. In the trinomial, the constant term is the product of the constant terms of the binomials.

HOW TO 1 Factor: $x^2 - 7x + 10$

Because the constant term is positive and the coefficient of x is negative, the binomial constants will be negative. Find two negative factors of 10 whose sum is -7.

Negative Factors of 10	*Sum*
$-1, -10$	-11
$-2, -5$	-7

- **The results can be recorded in a table.**
- **These are the correct factors.**

$x^2 - 7x + 10 = (x - 2)(x - 5)$

- **Write the trinomial as a product of its factors.**

You can check the proposed factorization by multiplying the two binomials.

Check: $(x - 2)(x - 5) = x^2 - 5x - 2x + 10 = x^2 - 7x + 10$

Take Note

Always check your proposed factorization to ensure accuracy.

HOW TO 2 Factor: $x^2 - 9x - 36$

The constant term is negative. The binomial constants will have opposite signs. Find two factors of -36 whose sum is -9.

Factors of −36	*Sum*
$+1, -36$	-35
$-1, +36$	35
$+2, -18$	-16
$-2, +18$	16
$+3, -12$	-9

- **Once the correct factors are found, it is not necessary to try the remaining factors.**

$x^2 - 9x - 36 = (x + 3)(x - 12)$

- **Write the trinomial as a product of its factors.**

For some trinomials, it is not possible to find integer factors of the constant term whose sum is the coefficient of the middle term. A polynomial that does not factor using only integers is **nonfactorable over the integers.**

HOW TO 3 Factor: $x^2 + 7x + 8$

Find two positive factors of 8 whose sum is 7.

Positive Factors of 8	*Sum*
1, 8	9
2, 4	6

- **There are no positive integer factors of 8 whose sum is 7.**

$x^2 + 7x + 8$ is nonfactorable over the integers.

Take Note

Just as 17 is a prime number, $x^2 + 7x + 8$ is a **prime polynomial.** Binomials of the form $x - a$ and $x + a$ are also prime polynomials.

EXAMPLE 1

Factor: $x^2 - 8x + 15$

Solution

Find two negative factors of 15 whose sum is -8.

Factors	*Sum*
$-1, -15$	-16
$-3, -5$	$\mathbf{-8}$

$x^2 - 8x + 15 = (x - 3)(x - 5)$

YOU TRY IT 1

Factor: $x^2 + 9x + 20$

Your solution

Solution on p. S11

EXAMPLE 2

Factor: $x^2 + 6x - 27$

Solution

Find two factors of -27 whose sum is 6.

Factors	Sum
$+1, -27$	-26
$-1, +27$	26
$+3, -9$	-6
$-3, +9$	**6**

$x^2 + 6x - 27 = (x - 3)(x + 9)$

YOU TRY IT 2

Factor: $x^2 + 7x - 18$

Your solution

Solution on p. S11

OBJECTIVE B *To factor completely*

Take Note
The first step in *any* factoring problem is to determine whether the terms of the polynomial have a *common factor.* If they do, factor it out first.

A polynomial is **factored completely** when it is written as a product of factors that are nonfactorable over the integers.

HOW TO 4 Factor: $4y^3 - 4y^2 - 24y$

$4y^3 - 4y^2 - 24y = 4y(y^2) - 4y(y) - 4y(6)$ • The GCF is $4y$.

$= 4y(y^2 - y - 6)$ • Use the Distributive Property to factor out the GCF.

$= 4y(y + 2)(y - 3)$ • Factor $y^2 - y - 6$. The two factors of -6 whose sum is -1 are 2 and -3.

It is always possible to check a proposed factorization by multiplying the polynomial factors. Here is the check for HOW TO 4.

Check: $4y(y + 2)(y - 3) = 4y(y^2 - 3y + 2y - 6)$
$= 4y(y^2 - y - 6)$
$= 4y^3 - 4y^2 - 24y$ • This is the original polynomial.

HOW TO 5 Factor: $x^2 + 12xy + 20y^2$

There is no common factor.
Note that the variable part of the middle term is xy, and the variable part of the last term is y^2.

$x^2 + 12xy + 20y^2 = (x + 2y)(x + 10y)$ • The two factors of 20 whose sum is 12 are 2 and 10.

Take Note
The terms $2y$ and $10y$ are placed in the binomials. This is necessary so that the middle term of the trinomial contains xy and the last term contains y^2.

Note that the terms $2y$ and $10y$ are placed in the binomials. The following check shows why this is necessary.

Check: $(x + 2y)(x + 10y) = x^2 + 10xy + 2xy + 20y^2$
$= x^2 + 12xy + 20y^2$ • This is the original polynomial.

Take Note
When the coefficient of the highest power in a polynomial is negative, consider factoring out a negative GCF. Example 3 is another example of this technique.

HOW TO 6 Factor: $15 - 2x - x^2$

Because the coefficient of x^2 is -1, factor -1 from the trinomial, and then write the resulting trinomial in descending order.

$15 - 2x - x^2 = -(x^2 + 2x - 15)$
- $15 - 2x - x^2 = -1(-15 + 2x + x^2) = -(x^2 + 2x - 15)$

$= -(x + 5)(x - 3)$
- Factor $x^2 + 2x - 15$. The two factors of -15 whose sum is 2 are 5 and -3.

Check: $-(x + 5)(x - 3) = -(x^2 + 2x - 15)$
$= -x^2 - 2x + 15$
$= 15 - 2x - x^2$
- This is the original polynomial.

EXAMPLE 3

Factor: $-3x^3 + 9x^2 + 12x$

Solution

The GCF is $-3x$. Factor out the GCF.

$-3x^3 + 9x^2 + 12x = -3x(x^2 - 3x - 4)$

Factor the trinomial $x^2 - 3x - 4$. Find two factors of -4 whose sum is -3.

Factors	Sum
+1, −4	**−3**

$-3x^3 + 9x^2 + 12x = -3x(x + 1)(x - 4)$

YOU TRY IT 3

Factor: $-2x^3 + 14x^2 - 12x$

Your solution

EXAMPLE 4

Factor: $4x^2 - 40xy + 84y^2$

Solution

The GCF is 4. Factor out the GCF.

$4x^2 - 40xy + 84y^2 = 4(x^2 - 10xy + 21y^2)$

Factor the trinomial $x^2 - 10xy + 21y^2$. Find two negative factors of 21 whose sum is -10.

Factors	Sum
−1, −21	−22
−3, −7	**−10**

$4x^2 - 40xy + 84y^2 = 4(x - 3y)(x - 7y)$

YOU TRY IT 4

Factor: $3x^2 - 9xy - 12y^2$

Your solution

Solutions on p. S11

5.2 EXERCISES

Concept Check

1. The trinomial $x^2 - 8x + 7$ is of the form $x^2 + bx + c$. What is the value of b in the trinomial $x^2 - 8x + 7$?
2. Find two numbers whose sum is 9 and whose product is 14.
3. Find two numbers whose sum is 4 and whose product is -12.
4. When factoring a trinomial, if the constant term is positive, will the signs in the binomials be the same or different?
5. When factoring a trinomial, if the constant term is negative, will the signs in the binomials be the same or different?
6. What is the first step in factoring a trinomial?

OBJECTIVE A *To factor a trinomial of the form $x^2 + bx + c$*

For Exercises 7 to 75, factor.

7. $x^2 + 3x + 2$
8. $x^2 + 5x + 6$
9. $x^2 - x - 2$
10. $x^2 + x - 6$
11. $a^2 + a - 12$
12. $a^2 - 2a - 35$
13. $a^2 - 3a + 2$
14. $a^2 - 5a + 4$
15. $a^2 + a - 2$
16. $a^2 - 2a - 3$
17. $b^2 - 6b + 9$
18. $b^2 + 8b + 16$
19. $b^2 + 7b - 8$
20. $y^2 - y - 6$
21. $y^2 + 6y - 55$
22. $z^2 - 4z - 45$
23. $y^2 - 5y + 6$
24. $y^2 - 8y + 15$
25. $z^2 - 14z + 45$
26. $z^2 - 14z + 49$
27. $z^2 - 12z - 160$
28. $p^2 + 2p - 35$
29. $p^2 + 12p + 27$
30. $p^2 - 6p + 8$
31. $x^2 + 20x + 100$
32. $x^2 + 9x - 70$
33. $b^2 - b - 20$
34. $b^2 + 3b - 40$
35. $y^2 - 14y - 51$
36. $y^2 - y - 72$
37. $p^2 - 4p - 21$
38. $p^2 + 16p + 39$

39. $y^2 - 8y + 32$

40. $y^2 - 9y + 81$

41. $x^2 - 20x + 75$

42. $x^2 - 12x + 11$

43. $p^2 + 24p + 63$

44. $x^2 - 15x + 56$

45. $x^2 + 21x + 38$

46. $x^2 + x - 56$

47. $x^2 + 5x - 3$

48. $a^2 - 21a - 7$

49. $a^2 - 7a - 44$

50. $a^2 - 15a + 36$

51. $a^2 - 21a + 54$

52. $z^2 - 9z - 136$

53. $z^2 + 14z - 147$

54. $c^2 - c - 90$

55. $c^2 - 3c - 180$

56. $z^2 + 15z + 44$

57. $p^2 + 24p + 135$

58. $c^2 + 19c + 34$

59. $c^2 + 11c + 18$

60. $x^2 - 4x - 96$

61. $x^2 + 10x - 75$

62. $x^2 - 22x + 112$

63. $x^2 + 21x - 100$

64. $b^2 + 8b - 105$

65. $b^2 - 22b + 72$

66. $a^2 - 9a - 36$

67. $a^2 + 42a - 135$

68. $b^2 - 23b + 102$

69. $b^2 - 25b + 126$

70. $a^2 + 27a + 72$

71. $z^2 + 24z + 144$

72. $x^2 + 25x + 156$

73. $x^2 - 29x + 100$

74. $x^2 - 10x - 96$

75. $x^2 + 9x - 112$

For Exercises 76 and 77, $x^2 + bx + c = (x + n)(x + m)$, where b and c are nonzero and n and m are positive integers.

76. Is c positive or negative?

77. Is b positive or negative?

OBJECTIVE B *To factor completely*

For Exercises 78 to 131, factor completely.

78. $2x^2 + 6x + 4$

79. $3x^2 + 15x + 18$

80. $18 + 7x - x^2$

81. $12 - 4x - x^2$

82. $ab^2 + 2ab - 15a$

83. $ab^2 + 7ab - 8a$

84. $xy^2 - 5xy + 6x$

85. $xy^2 + 8xy + 15x$

86. $z^3 - 7z^2 + 12z$

87. $-2a^3 - 6a^2 - 4a$

88. $-3y^3 + 15y^2 - 18y$

89. $4y^3 + 12y^2 - 72y$

90. $3x^2 + 3x - 36$

91. $2x^3 - 2x^2 + 4x$

92. $5z^2 - 15z - 140$

93. $6z^2 + 12z - 90$

94. $2a^3 + 8a^2 - 64a$

95. $3a^3 - 9a^2 - 54a$

96. $x^2 - 5xy + 6y^2$

97. $x^2 + 4xy - 21y^2$

98. $a^2 - 9ab + 20b^2$

99. $a^2 - 15ab + 50b^2$

100. $x^2 - 3xy - 28y^2$

101. $s^2 + 2st - 48t^2$

102. $y^2 - 15yz - 41z^2$

103. $x^2 + 85xy + 36y^2$

104. $z^4 - 12z^3 + 35z^2$

105. $z^4 + 2z^3 - 80z^2$

106. $b^4 - 22b^3 + 120b^2$

107. $b^4 - 3b^3 - 10b^2$

108. $2y^4 - 26y^3 - 96y^2$

109. $3y^4 + 54y^3 + 135y^2$

110. $-x^4 - 7x^3 + 8x^2$

111. $-x^4 + 11x^3 + 12x^2$

112. $4x^2y + 20xy - 56y$

113. $3x^2y - 6xy - 45y$

114. $c^3 + 18c^2 - 40c$

115. $-3x^3 + 36x^2 - 81x$

116. $-4x^3 - 4x^2 + 24x$

117. $x^2 - 8xy + 15y^2$

118. $y^2 - 7xy - 8x^2$

119. $a^2 - 13ab + 42b^2$

120. $y^2 + 4yz - 21z^2$

121. $y^2 + 8yz + 7z^2$

122. $y^2 - 16yz + 15z^2$

123. $3x^2y + 60xy - 63y$

124. $4x^2y - 68xy - 72y$

125. $3x^3 + 3x^2 - 36x$

126. $4x^3 + 12x^2 - 160x$

127. $2t^2 - 24ts + 70s^2$

128. $4a^2 - 40ab + 100b^2$

129. $3a^2 - 24ab - 99b^2$

130. $4x^3 + 8x^2y - 12xy^2$

131. $5x^3 + 30x^2y + 40xy^2$

132. State whether the trinomial has a factor of $x + 3$.
a. $3x^2 - 3x - 36$ **b.** $x^2y - xy - 12y$

133. State whether the trinomial has a factor of $x + y$.
a. $2x^2 - 2xy - 4y^2$ **b.** $2x^2y - 4xy - 4y$

Critical Thinking

134. If $a(x + 3) = x^2 + 2x - 3$, find a.

135. If $-2x^3 - 6x^2 - 4x = a(x + 1)(x + 2)$, find a.

For Exercises 136 to 139, factor.

136. $20 + c^2 + 9c$

137. $x^2y - 54y - 3xy$

138. $45a^2 + a^2b^2 - 14a^2b$

139. $12p^2 - 96p + 3p^3$

Projects or Group Activities

For Exercises 140 to 143, find all integers k such that the trinomial can be factored over the integers.

140. $x^2 + kx + 35$

141. $x^2 + kx + 18$

142. $x^2 - kx + 21$

143. $x^2 - kx + 14$

For Exercises 144 to 149, determine the positive integer values of k for which the polynomial is factorable over the integers.

144. $y^2 + 4y + k$

145. $z^2 + 7z + k$

146. $a^2 - 6a + k$

147. $c^2 - 7c + k$

148. $x^2 - 3x + k$

149. $y^2 + 5y + k$

150. Exercises 144 to 149 included the requirement that $k > 0$. If k is allowed to be any integer, how many different values of k are possible for each polynomial? Explain your answer.

SECTION

5.3 Factoring Polynomials of the Form $ax^2 + bx + c$

OBJECTIVE A *To factor a trinomial of the form $ax^2 + bx + c$ by using trial factors*

Trinomials of the form $ax^2 + bx + c$, where a, b, and c are integers, are shown at the right.

$3x^2 - x + 4$; $a = 3$, $b = -1$, $c = 4$
$6x^2 + 2x - 3$; $a = 6$, $b = 2$, $c = -3$

These trinomials differ from those in the preceding section in that the coefficient of x^2 is not 1. There are various methods of factoring these trinomials. The method described in this objective is factoring by using trial factors.

To reduce the number of trial factors that must be considered, remember the following:

1. Use the signs of the constant term and the coefficient of x in the trinomial to determine the signs of the binomial factors. If the constant term is positive, the signs of the binomial factors will be the same as the sign of the coefficient of x in the trinomial. If the constant term is negative, the constant terms in the binomials will have opposite signs.
2. If the terms of the trinomial do not have a common factor, then the terms of each binomial factor will not have a common factor.

HOW TO 1 Factor: $2x^2 - 7x + 3$

The terms have no common factor. The constant term is positive. The coefficient of x is negative. The binomial constants will be negative.

Positive Factors of 2 (coefficient of x^2)	*Negative Factors of 3 (constant term)*
1, 2	−1, −3

Write trial factors. Use the **O**uter and **I**nner products of FOIL to determine the middle term, $-7x$, of the trinomial.

Trial Factors	*Middle Term*
$(x - 1)(2x - 3)$	$-3x - 2x = -5x$
$(x - 3)(2x - 1)$	$-x - 6x = -7x$

Write the factors of the trinomial.

$$2x^2 - 7x + 3 = (x - 3)(2x - 1)$$

HOW TO 2 Factor: $3x^2 + 14x + 15$

The terms have no common factor. The constant term is positive. The coefficient of x is positive. The binomial constants will be positive.

Positive Factors of 3 (coefficient of x^2)	*Negative Factors of 15 (constant term)*
1, 3	1, 15
	3, 5

Write trial factors. Use the **O**uter and **I**nner products of FOIL to determine the middle term, $14x$, of the trinomial.

Trial Factors	*Middle Term*
$(x + 1)(3x + 15)$	Common factor
$(x + 15)(3x + 1)$	$x + 45x = 46x$
$(x + 3)(3x + 5)$	$5x + 9x = 14x$
$(x + 5)(3x + 3)$	Common factor

Write the factors of the trinomial.

$$3x^2 + 14x + 15 = (x + 3)(3x + 5)$$

HOW TO 3 Factor: $6x^3 + 14x^2 - 12x$

Factor the GCF, $2x$, from the terms.

$6x^3 + 14x^2 - 12x = 2x(3x^2 + 7x - 6)$

Factor the trinomial. The constant term is negative. The binomial constants will have opposite signs.

Positive Factors of 3	Factors of −6
1, 3	1, −6
	−1, 6
	2, −3
	−2, 3

Write trial factors. Use the **O**uter and **I**nner products of FOIL to determine the middle term, $7x$, of the trinomial.

It is not necessary to test trial factors that have a common factor.

Trial Factors	Middle Term
$(x + 1)(3x - 6)$	Common factor
$(x - 6)(3x + 1)$	$x - 18x = -17x$
$(x - 1)(3x + 6)$	Common factor
$(x + 6)(3x - 1)$	$-x + 18x = 17x$
$(x + 2)(3x - 3)$	Common factor
$(x - 3)(3x + 2)$	$2x - 9x = -7x$
$(x - 2)(3x + 3)$	Common factor
$(x + 3)(3x - 2)$	$-2x + 9x = 7x$

Write the factors of the trinomial.

$6x^3 + 14x^2 - 12x = 2x(x + 3)(3x - 2)$

Take Note

For HOW TO 3, all the trial factors were listed. Once the correct factors have been found, however, the remaining trial factors can be omitted. For the examples and solutions in this text, all trial factors except those that have a common factor will be listed.

EXAMPLE 1

Factor: $3x^2 + x - 2$

Solution

Positive factors of 3: 1, 3

Factors of −2: 1, −2
−1, 2

Trial Factors	Middle Term
$(x + 1)(3x - 2)$	$-2x + 3x = \boldsymbol{x}$
$(x - 2)(3x + 1)$	$x - 6x = -5x$
$(x - 1)(3x + 2)$	$2x - 3x = -x$
$(x + 2)(3x - 1)$	$-x + 6x = 5x$

$3x^2 + x - 2 = (x + 1)(3x - 2)$

YOU TRY IT 1

Factor: $2x^2 - x - 3$

Your solution

EXAMPLE 2

Factor: $-12x^3 - 32x^2 + 12x$

Solution

$-12x^3 - 32x^2 + 12x = -4x(3x^2 + 8x - 3)$ • **GCF**

Factor $3x^2 + 8x - 3$.

Positive factors of 3: 1, 3

Factors of −3: 1, −3
−1, 3

Trial Factors	Middle Term
$(x - 3)(3x + 1)$	$x - 9x = -8x$
$(x + 3)(3x - 1)$	$-x + 9x = \boldsymbol{8x}$

$-12x^3 - 32x^2 + 12x = -4x(x + 3)(3x - 1)$

YOU TRY IT 2

Factor: $-45y^3 + 12y^2 + 12y$

Your solution

Solutions on p. S11

OBJECTIVE B *To factor a trinomial of the form $ax^2 + bx + c$ by grouping*

In the preceding objective, trinomials of the form $ax^2 + bx + c$ were factored by using trial factors. In this objective, these trinomials will be factored by grouping.

To factor $ax^2 + bx + c$, first find two factors of $a \cdot c$ whose sum is b. Then use factoring by grouping to write the factorization of the trinomial.

HOW TO 4 Factor: $2x^2 + 13x + 15$

Find two positive factors of 30 $(a \cdot c = 2 \cdot 15 = 30)$ whose sum is 13.

Positive Factors of 30	*Sum*
1, 30	31
2, 15	17
3, 10	13

- **Once the required sum has been found, the remaining factors need not be checked.**

$$\begin{aligned} 2x^2 + 13x + 15 &= 2x^2 + 3x + 10x + 15 \\ &= (2x^2 + 3x) + (10x + 15) \\ &= x(2x + 3) + 5(2x + 3) \\ &= (2x + 3)(x + 5) \end{aligned}$$

- **Use the factors of 30 whose sum is 13 to write $13x$ as $3x + 10x$.**
- **Factor by grouping.**

Check: $(2x + 3)(x + 5) = 2x^2 + 10x + 3x + 15$
$= 2x^2 + 13x + 15$

HOW TO 5 Factor: $6x^2 - 11x - 10$

Find two factors of -60 $[a \cdot c = 6(-10) = -60]$ whose sum is -11.

Factors of −60	*Sum*
1, −60	−59
−1, 60	59
2, −30	−28
−2, 30	28
3, −20	−17
−3, 20	17
4, −15	−11

$$\begin{aligned} 6x^2 - 11x - 10 &= 6x^2 + 4x - 15x - 10 \\ &= (6x^2 + 4x) - (15x + 10) \\ &= 2x(3x + 2) - 5(3x + 2) \\ &= (3x + 2)(2x - 5) \end{aligned}$$

- **Use the factors of -60 whose sum is -11 to write $-11x$ as $4x - 15x$.**
- **Factor by grouping. Recall that $-15x - 10 = -(15x + 10)$.**

Check: $(3x + 2)(2x - 5) = 6x^2 - 15x + 4x - 10$
$= 6x^2 - 11x - 10$

HOW TO 6 Factor: $3x^2 - 2x - 4$

Find two factors of -12 $[a \cdot c = 3(-4) = -12]$ whose sum is -2.

Factors of −12	*Sum*
1, −12	−11
−1, 12	11
2, −6	−4
−2, 6	4
3, −4	−1
−3, 4	1

Because no integer factors of -12 have a sum of -2, $3x^2 - 2x - 4$ is nonfactorable over the integers.

EXAMPLE 3

Factor: $2x^2 + 19x - 10$

Solution

Factors of −20 [2(−10)]	*Sum*
−1, 20	**19**

$$\begin{aligned} 2x^2 + 19x - 10 &= 2x^2 - x + 20x - 10 \\ &= (2x^2 - x) + (20x - 10) \\ &= x(2x - 1) + 10(2x - 1) \\ &= (2x - 1)(x + 10) \end{aligned}$$

YOU TRY IT 3

Factor: $2a^2 + 13a - 7$

Your solution

EXAMPLE 4

Factor: $24x^2y - 76xy + 40y$

Solution

The GCF is $4y$.

$24x^2y - 76xy + 40y = 4y(6x^2 - 19x + 10)$

Factor $6x^2 - 19x + 10$.

Negative Factors of 60 [6(10)]	*Sum*
−1, −60	−61
−2, −30	−32
−3, −20	−23
−4, −15	**−19**

$$\begin{aligned} 6x^2 - 19x + 10 &= 6x^2 - 4x - 15x + 10 \\ &= (6x^2 - 4x) - (15x - 10) \\ &= 2x(3x - 2) - 5(3x - 2) \\ &= (3x - 2)(2x - 5) \end{aligned}$$

$$\begin{aligned} 24x^2y - 76xy + 40y &= 4y(6x^2 - 19x + 10) \\ &= 4y(3x - 2)(2x - 5) \end{aligned}$$

YOU TRY IT 4

Factor: $15x^3 + 40x^2 - 80x$

Your solution

Solutions on p. S12

5.3 EXERCISES

Concept Check

For Exercises 1 to 4, fill in the blank to make a true statement.

1. $6x^2 + 11x - 10 = (3x - 2)$ (__________)
2. $40x^2 + 41x + 10 = (8x + 5)$ (__________)
3. $20x^2 - 31x + 12 = (5x - 4)$ (__________)
4. $12x^2 - 4x - 21 = (6x + 7)$ (__________)

For Exercises 5 to 8, fill in the blanks.

5. To factor $2x^2 - 5x + 2$ by grouping, find two numbers whose product is ______ and whose sum is ______.
6. To factor $3x^2 + 2x - 5$ by grouping, find two numbers whose product is ______ and whose sum is ______.
7. To factor $4x^2 - 8x + 3$ by grouping, $-8x$ must be written as __________.
8. To factor $6x^2 + 7x - 3$ by grouping, $7x$ must be written as __________.

OBJECTIVE A *To factor a trinomial of the form $ax^2 + bx + c$ by using trial factors*

For Exercises 9 to 74, factor by using trial factors.

9. $2x^2 + 3x + 1$
10. $5x^2 + 6x + 1$
11. $2y^2 + 7y + 3$
12. $3y^2 + 7y + 2$
13. $2a^2 - 3a + 1$
14. $3a^2 - 4a + 1$
15. $2b^2 - 11b + 5$
16. $3b^2 - 13b + 4$
17. $2x^2 + x - 1$
18. $4x^2 - 3x - 1$
19. $2x^2 - 5x - 3$
20. $3x^2 + 5x - 2$
21. $2t^2 - t - 10$
22. $2t^2 + 5t - 12$
23. $3p^2 - 16p + 5$
24. $6p^2 + 5p + 1$
25. $12y^2 - 7y + 1$
26. $6y^2 - 5y + 1$
27. $6z^2 - 7z + 3$
28. $9z^2 + 3z + 2$
29. $6t^2 - 11t + 4$
30. $10t^2 + 11t + 3$
31. $8x^2 + 33x + 4$
32. $7x^2 + 50x + 7$
33. $5x^2 - 62x - 7$
34. $9x^2 - 13x - 4$
35. $12y^2 + 19y + 5$
36. $6b^2 - 19b + 15$

37. $2z^2 - 27z - 14$ **38.** $4z^2 + 5z - 6$ **39.** $3p^2 + 22p - 16$ **40.** $7p^2 + 19p + 10$

41. $4x^2 + 6x + 2$ **42.** $12x^2 + 33x - 9$ **43.** $15y^2 - 50y + 35$ **44.** $30y^2 + 10y - 20$

45. $2x^3 - 11x^2 + 5x$ **46.** $2x^3 - 3x^2 - 5x$ **47.** $3a^2b - 16ab + 16b$ **48.** $2a^2b - ab - 21b$

49. $3z^2 + 95z + 10$ **50.** $8z^2 - 36z + 1$ **51.** $36x - 3x^2 - 3x^3$ **52.** $-2x^3 + 2x^2 + 4x$

53. $80y^2 - 36y + 4$ **54.** $24y^2 - 24y - 18$ **55.** $8z^3 + 14z^2 + 3z$ **56.** $6z^3 - 23z^2 + 20z$

57. $6x^2y - 11xy - 10y$ **58.** $8x^2y - 27xy + 9y$ **59.** $10t^2 - 5t - 50$

60. $16t^2 + 40t - 96$ **61.** $3p^3 - 16p^2 + 5p$ **62.** $6p^3 + 5p^2 + p$

63. $26z^2 + 98z - 24$ **64.** $30z^2 - 87z + 30$ **65.** $10y^3 - 44y^2 + 16y$

66. $14y^3 + 94y^2 - 28y$ **67.** $4yz^3 + 5yz^2 - 6yz$ **68.** $12a^3 + 14a^2 - 48a$

69. $42a^3 + 45a^2 - 27a$ **70.** $36p^2 - 9p^3 - p^4$ **71.** $9x^2y - 30xy^2 + 25y^3$

72. $8x^2y - 38xy^2 + 35y^3$ **73.** $9x^3y - 24x^2y^2 + 16xy^3$ **74.** $9x^3y + 12x^2y + 4xy$

For Exercises 75 and 76, let $(nx + p)$ and $(mx + q)$ be prime factors of the trinomial $ax^2 + bx + c$.

75. If n is even, must p be even or odd? **76.** If p is even, must n be even or odd?

OBJECTIVE B *To factor a trinomial of the form $ax^2 + bx + c$ by grouping*

For Exercises 77 to 133, factor by grouping.

77. $6x^2 - 17x + 12$ **78.** $15x^2 - 19x + 6$ **79.** $5b^2 + 33b - 14$ **80.** $8x^2 - 30x + 25$

81. $6a^2 + 7a - 24$

82. $14a^2 + 15a - 9$

83. $4z^2 + 11z + 6$

84. $6z^2 - 25z + 14$

85. $22p^2 + 51p - 10$

86. $14p^2 - 41p + 15$

87. $8y^2 + 17y + 9$

88. $12y^2 - 145y + 12$

89. $18t^2 - 9t - 5$

90. $12t^2 + 28t - 5$

91. $6b^2 + 71b - 12$

92. $8b^2 + 65b + 8$

93. $9x^2 + 12x + 4$

94. $25x^2 - 30x + 9$

95. $6b^2 - 13b + 6$

96. $20b^2 + 37b + 15$

97. $33b^2 + 34b - 35$

98. $15b^2 - 43b + 22$

99. $18y^2 - 39y + 20$

100. $24y^2 + 41y + 12$

101. $15a^2 + 26a - 21$

102. $6a^2 + 23a + 21$

103. $8y^2 - 26y + 15$

104. $18y^2 - 27y + 4$

105. $8z^2 + 2z - 15$

106. $10z^2 + 3z - 4$

107. $15x^2 - 82x + 24$

108. $13z^2 + 49z - 8$

109. $10z^2 - 29z + 10$

110. $15z^2 - 44z + 32$

111. $36z^2 + 72z + 35$

112. $16z^2 + 8z - 35$

113. $3x^2 + xy - 2y^2$

114. $6x^2 + 10xy + 4y^2$

115. $3a^2 + 5ab - 2b^2$

116. $2a^2 - 9ab + 9b^2$

117. $4y^2 - 11yz + 6z^2$

118. $2y^2 + 7yz + 5z^2$

119. $28 + 3z - z^2$

120. $15 - 2z - z^2$

121. $8 - 7x - x^2$

122. $12 + 11x - x^2$

123. $9x^2 + 33x - 60$

124. $16x^2 - 16x - 12$

125. $24x^2 - 52x + 24$

126. $60x^2 + 95x + 20$

127. $35a^4 + 9a^3 - 2a^2$

128. $15a^4 + 26a^3 + 7a^2$

129. $15b^2 - 115b + 70$

130. $25b^2 + 35b - 30$

131. $3x^2 - 26xy + 35y^2$

132. $4x^2 + 16xy + 15y^2$

133. $216y^2 - 3y - 3$

For Exercises 134 to 137, information is given about the signs of b and c in the trinomial $ax^2 + bx + c$, where $a > 0$. If you want to factor $ax^2 + bx + c$ by grouping, you look for factors of ac whose sum is b. In each case, state whether the factors of ac should be two positive numbers, two negative numbers, or one positive and one negative number.

134. $b > 0$ and $c > 0$

135. $b < 0$ and $c < 0$

136. $b < 0$ and $c > 0$

137. $b > 0$ and $c < 0$

Critical Thinking

138. In your own words, explain how the signs of the last terms of the two binomial factors of a trinomial are determined.

For Exercises 139 to 147, factor.

139. $(x + 1)^2 - (x + 1) - 6$

140. $(x - 2)^2 + 3(x - 2) + 2$

141. $(y + 3)^2 - 5(y + 3) + 6$

142. $2(y + 2)^2 - (y + 2) - 3$

143. $3(a + 2)^2 - (a + 2) - 4$

144. $4(y - 1)^2 - 7(y - 1) - 2$

145. $6y + 8y^3 - 26y^2$

146. $22p^2 - 3p^3 + 16p$

147. $a^3b - 24ab - 2a^2b$

148. Given that $x + 2$ is a factor of $x^3 - 2x^2 - 5x + 6$, factor $x^3 - 2x^2 - 5x + 6$ completely.

Projects or Group Activities

For Exercises 149 to 154, find all integers k such that the trinomial can be factored over the integers.

149. $2x^2 + kx + 3$

150. $2x^2 + kx - 3$

151. $3x^2 + kx + 2$

152. $3x^2 + kx - 2$

153. $2x^2 + kx + 5$

154. $2x^2 + kx - 5$

155. **Geometry** The area of a rectangle is $(3x^2 + x - 2)$ ft^2. Find the dimensions of the rectangle in terms of the variable x. Given that $x > 0$, specify the dimension that is the length and the dimension that is the width. Can x be negative? Can $x = 0$? Explain your answers.

$A = 3x^2 + x - 2$

CHECK YOUR PROGRESS: CHAPTER 5

1. Factor: $20b + 5$

2. Factor: $2x(7 + b) - y(b + 7)$

3. Factor: $x^2 + 20x + 100$

4. Factor: $x^2y - 2xy - 24y$

5. Factor: $35 + 2x - x^2$

6. Factor: $x^2 - 8x - 2$

7. Factor: $21x^2 + 6xy - 49x - 14y$

8. Factor: $6ab + 9a$

9. Factor by using trial factors: $5y^2 - 22y + 8$

10. Factor by grouping: $12x^2 + 31x + 9$

11. Factor: $9x - 5x^2$

12. Factor: $2x^2 + x + 2xy + y$

13. Factor by grouping: $8a^2 - 2ab - 3b^2$

14. Factor: $b^2 + 9b + 20$

15. Factor: $2a^3 + 24a^2 + 54a$

16. Factor by using trial factors: $11a^2 - 54a - 5$

17. Factor by grouping: $360y^2 + 4y - 4$

18. Factor: $14y^3 + 5y^2 + 11y$

19. Factor: $x^2 - 7x + 10$

20. Factor: $x^2 + 8xy + 9y^2$

21. Factor: $b^2 + 13b + 40$

22. Factor: $2x^2 - 5x - 6xy + 15y$

23. Factor: $x^2y - xy^3 + x^3y$

24. Factor by using trial factors: $3b^2 + 16b + 16$

25. Factor: $x^2 - 11x - 42$

SECTION

5.4 Special Factoring

OBJECTIVE A *To factor the difference of two squares and perfect-square trinomials*

Recall from Section 4.3D that the product of the sum and difference of the same two terms equals the square of the first term minus the square of the second term.

$$(a + b)(a - b) = a^2 - b^2$$

The expression $a^2 - b^2$ is the **difference of two squares.** The pattern just mentioned suggests the following rule for factoring the difference of two squares.

Rule for Factoring the Difference of Two Squares

Difference of Two Squares		Sum and Difference of the Same Terms
$a^2 - b^2$	=	$(a + b)(a - b)$

EXAMPLES

Each expression is the difference of two squares. Factor.

1. $x^2 - 4 = x^2 - 2^2 = (x + 2)(x - 2)$
2. $y^2 - 9 = y^2 - 3^2 = (y + 3)(y - 3)$

Take Note
Convince yourself that the sum of two squares is nonfactorable over the integers by trying to factor $x^2 + 4$.

$a^2 + b^2$ is the sum of two squares. The sum of two squares is nonfactorable over the integers.

$4x^2 + 81$ is the sum of two squares. It is nonfactorable over the integers.

$4x^2 - 81$ is the difference of two squares. It factors as $(2x + 9)(2x - 9)$.

HOW TO 1 Factor: $8x^3 - 18x$

$8x^3 - 18x = 2x(4x^2 - 9)$ • The GCF is $2x$.

$= 2x[(2x)^2 - 3^2]$ • $4x^2 - 9$ is the difference of two squares.

$= 2x(2x + 3)(2x - 3)$ • Factor the difference of squares.

Check: $2x(2x + 3)(2x - 3) = 2x(4x^2 - 9)$
$= 8x^2 - 18x$

HOW TO 2 Factor: $x^2 - 10$

10 cannot be written as the square of an integer.
$x^2 - 10$ is nonfactorable over the integers.

Recall from Section 4.3D the pattern for finding the square of a binomial.

$$(a + b)^2 = (a + b)(a + b) = a^2 + ab + ab + b^2$$
$$= a^2 + 2ab + b^2$$

Square of the first term → a^2
Twice the product of the two terms → $2ab$
Square of the last term → b^2

The square of a binomial is a **perfect-square trinomial.** The pattern above suggests the following rule for factoring a perfect-square trinomial.

Rule for Factoring a Perfect-Square Trinomial

Perfect-Square Trinomial				Square of a Binomial
$a^2 + 2ab + b^2$	=	$(a + b)(a + b)$	=	$(a + b)^2$
$a^2 - 2ab + b^2$	=	$(a - b)(a - b)$	=	$(a - b)^2$

EXAMPLES

Each expression is a perfect-square trinomial. Factor.

1. $x^2 + 6x + 9 = (x + 3)^2$
2. $x^2 - 6x + 9 = (x - 3)^2$

Note in these patterns that the sign in the binomial is the sign of the middle term of the trinomial.

Take Note

A perfect-square trinomial can always be factored using either of the methods presented in Section 3 of this chapter. However, noticing that a trinomial is a perfect-square trinomial can save you a considerable amount of time.

HOW TO 3 Factor: $4x^2 - 20x + 25$

Because the first and last terms are squares $[(2x)^2 = 4x^2; 5^2 = 25]$, try to factor this trinomial as the square of a binomial. Check the factorization.

$$4x^2 - 20x + 25 = (2x - 5)^2$$

Check: $(2x - 5)^2 = (2x)^2 + 2(2x)(-5) + 5^2$
$= 4x^2 - 20x + 25$ • The factorization is correct.

HOW TO 4 Factor: $4x^2 + 37x + 9$

Because the first and last terms are squares $[(2x)^2 = 4x^2; 3^2 = 9]$, try to factor this trinomial as the square of a binomial. Check the proposed factorization.

$$4x^2 + 37x + 9 = (2x + 3)^2$$

Check: $(2x + 3)^2 = (2x)^2 + 2(2x)(3) + 3^2$
$= 4x^2 + 12x + 9$

Because $4x^2 + 12x + 9 \neq 4x^2 + 37x + 9$, the proposed factorization is not correct. In this case, the polynomial is not a perfect-square trinomial. It may, however, still factor. In fact, $4x^2 + 37x + 9 = (4x + 1)(x + 9)$.

EXAMPLE 1

Factor: $16x^2 - y^2$

Solution

$16x^2 - y^2 = (4x)^2 - y^2$ • The difference of two squares

$= (4x + y)(4x - y)$ • Factor.

YOU TRY IT 1

Factor: $25a^2 - b^2$

Your solution

EXAMPLE 2

Factor: $z^4 - 16$

Solution

$z^4 - 16 = (z^2)^2 - 4^2$ • The difference of two squares

$= (z^2 + 4)(z^2 - 4)$ • The difference of two squares

$= (z^2 + 4)(z^2 - 2^2)$

$= (z^2 + 4)(z + 2)(z - 2)$ • Factor.

YOU TRY IT 2

Factor: $n^4 - 81$

Your solution

EXAMPLE 3

Factor: $9x^2 - 30x + 25$

Solution

Try to factor this trinomial as the square of a binomial.

$9x^2 = (3x)^2$, $25 = (5)^2$

$9x^2 - 30x + 25 = (3x - 5)^2$

Check:

$(3x - 5)^2 = (3x)^2 + 2(3x)(-5) + 5^2$

$= 9x^2 - 30x + 25$

YOU TRY IT 3

Factor: $16y^2 + 8y + 1$

Your solution

EXAMPLE 4

Factor: $9x^2 + 40x + 16$

Solution

$9x^2 = (3x)^2$ and $16 = 4^2$

Because $2(3x)(4) \neq 40x$, the trinomial is not a perfect-square trinomial.

Try to factor by another method.

$9x^2 + 40x + 16 = (9x + 4)(x + 4)$

YOU TRY IT 4

Factor: $x^2 + 15x + 36$

Your solution

Solutions on p. S12

5.4 EXERCISES

Concept Check

For Exercises 1 and 2, determine which expressions in the list are squares.

1. $4; 8; 25x^6; 12y^{10}; 100x^4y^4$

2. $9; 18; 15a^8; 49b^{12}; 64a^{16}b^2$

3. Which of the expressions are the difference of two squares?
(i) $a^2 - 36$ **(ii)** $b^2 - 12$ **(iii)** $c^2 + 25$ **(iv)** $d^2 - 100$

4. Which expression is the sum and difference of two terms?
(i) $(a + 4)(a + 4)$ **(ii)** $(a + 4)(b - 4)$ **(iii)** $(a + 4)(a - 4)$

For Exercises 5 to 8, determine whether the statement is always true, sometimes true, or never true.

5. A binomial is factorable.

6. A trinomial is factorable.

7. If a binomial is multiplied times itself, the result is a perfect-square trinomial.

8. In a perfect-square trinomial, the first and last terms are squares.

9. The binomial $9x^2 - 4$ is in the form $a^2 - b^2$, where $a =$ _______ and $b =$ _______.

10. The trinomial $16y^2 - 8y + 1$ is in the form $a^2 - 2ab + b^2$, where $a =$ _______ and $b =$ _______.

11. Provide an example of each of the following.
a. the difference of two squares
b. the product of the sum and difference of the same two terms
c. a perfect-square trinomial
d. the square of a binomial
e. the sum of two squares

12. Explain the rule for factoring:
a. the difference of two squares
b. a perfect-square trinomial

OBJECTIVE A *To factor the difference of two squares and perfect-square trinomials*

For Exercises 13 to 54, factor.

13. $x^2 - 4$

14. $x^2 - 9$

15. $a^2 - 81$

16. $a^2 - 49$

17. $y^2 + 2y + 1$

18. $y^2 + 14y + 49$

19. $a^2 - 2a + 1$

20. $x^2 - 12x + 36$

21. $4x^2 - 1$

22. $9x^2 - 16$

23. $x^6 - 9$

24. $y^{12} - 4$

25. $x^2 + 8x - 16$ **26.** $z^2 - 18z - 81$ **27.** $x^2 + 2xy + y^2$ **28.** $x^2 + 6xy + 9y^2$

29. $4a^2 + 4a + 1$ **30.** $25x^2 + 10x + 1$ **31.** $9x^2 - 1$ **32.** $1 - 49x^2$

33. $1 - 64x^2$ **34.** $t^2 + 36$ **35.** $x^2 + 64$ **36.** $64a^2 - 16a + 1$

37. $9a^2 + 6a + 1$ **38.** $x^4 - y^2$ **39.** $b^4 - 16a^2$ **40.** $16b^2 + 8b + 1$

41. $4a^2 - 20a + 25$ **42.** $4b^2 + 28b + 49$ **43.** $9a^2 - 42a + 49$ **44.** $9x^2 - 16y^2$

45. $25z^2 - y^2$ **46.** $x^2y^2 - 4$ **47.** $a^2b^2 - 25$ **48.** $16 - x^2y^2$

49. $25x^2 - 1$ **50.** $25a^2 + 30ab + 9b^2$ **51.** $4a^2 - 12ab + 9b^2$

52. $49x^2 + 28xy + 4y^2$ **53.** $4y^2 - 36yz + 81z^2$ **54.** $64y^2 - 48yz + 9z^2$

55. Which of the following expressions can be factored as the square of a binomial, given that a and b are positive numbers?
(i) $a^2x^2 - 2abx + b^2$ **(ii)** $a^2x^2 - 2abx - b^2$
(iii) $a^2x^2 + 2abx + b^2$ **(iv)** $a^2x^2 + 2abx - b^2$

Critical Thinking

For Exercises 56 to 61, find all integers k such that the trinomial is a perfect-square trinomial.

56. $4x^2 - kx + 9$ **57.** $x^2 + 6x + k$ **58.** $64x^2 + kxy + y^2$

59. $x^2 - 2x + k$ **60.** $25x^2 - kx + 1$ **61.** $x^2 + 10x + k$

Projects or Group Activities

62. Select any odd integer greater than 1, square it, and then subtract 1. Is the result evenly divisible by 8? Prove that this procedure always produces a number that is divisible by 8. (*Suggestion:* Any odd integer greater than 1 can be expressed as $2n + 1$, where n is a natural number.)

SECTION

5.5 Factoring Polynomials Completely

OBJECTIVE A *To factor polynomials completely*

This section is devoted to describing a strategy for factoring polynomials and reviewing the factoring techniques you have learned in this chapter.

Tips for Success

You now have learned to factor many different types of polynomials. You will need to be able to recognize each of the situations described in the box at the right. To test yourself, try the exercises in the Chapter Review.

General Factoring Strategy

When factoring a polynomial completely, ask yourself the following questions about the polynomial.

1. Do the terms contain a common factor? If so, factor out the common factor.
2. Is the polynomial the difference of two squares? If so, factor.
3. Is the polynomial a perfect-square trinomial? If so, factor.
4. Is the polynomial a trinomial that is the product of two binomials? If so, factor.
5. Does the polynomial contain four terms? If so, try factoring by grouping.
6. Is each binomial factor nonfactorable over the integers? If not, factor.

When factoring a polynomial, remember that you may have to factor more than once in order to write the polynomial as a product of factors, each of which is nonfactorable over the integers.

HOW TO 1 Factor: $z^3 + 4z^2 - 9z - 36$

$z^3 + 4z^2 - 9z - 36 = (z^3 + 4z^2) - (9z + 36)$ • Factor by grouping. Recall that $-9z - 36 = -(9z + 36)$.

$= z^2(z + 4) - 9(z + 4)$ • $z^3 + 4z^2 = z^2(z + 4)$; $9z + 36 = 9(z + 4)$

$= (z + 4)(z^2 - 9)$ • Factor out the common binomial factor $(z + 4)$.

$= (z + 4)(z + 3)(z - 3)$ • Factor the difference of squares.

EXAMPLE 1

Factor: $4x^2y^2 + 12xy^2 + 9y^2$

Solution

The GCF is y^2.

$4x^2y^2 + 12xy^2 + 9y^2$

$= y^2(4x^2 + 12x + 9)$ • Factor out the GCF, y^2.

$= y^2(2x + 3)^2$ • Factor the perfect-square trinomial.

YOU TRY IT 1

Factor: $4x^3 + 28x^2 - 120x$

Your solution

Solution on p. S12

5.5 EXERCISES

Concept Check

1. When factoring a polynomial, always look first for a ____________ factor.

2. When a polynomial is factored completely, each factor is ____________ over the integers.

3. Which factor in $(x^2 - 81)(x^2 + 81)$ can be factored over the integers?

The first step in any factoring problem is to factor out the greatest common factor. The second step depends on the number of terms in the polynomial. For Exercises 4 to 6, state what the next step in factoring could be.

4. The polynomial has two terms.

5. The polynomial has three terms.

6. The polynomial has four terms.

7. After factoring a polynomial, how do you check your answer?

OBJECTIVE A *To factor polynomials completely*

For Exercises 8 to 85, factor.

8. $8y^2 - 2$

9. $12n^2 - 48$

10. $3a^3 + 6a^2 + 3a$

11. $4rs^2 - 4rs + r$

12. $m^4 - 256$

13. $81 - t^4$

14. $9x^2 + 13x + 4$

15. $x^2 + 10x + 16$

16. $16y^4 + 48y^3 + 36y^2$

17. $36c^4 - 48c^3 + 16c^2$

18. $y^8 - 81$

19. $32s^4 - 2$

20. $25 - 20p + 4p^2$

21. $9 + 24a + 16a^2$

22. $(4x - 3)^2 - y^2$

23. $(2x + 5)^2 - 25$

24. $(x^2 - 4x + 4) - y^2$

25. $(4x^2 + 12x + 9) - 4y^2$

26. $5x^2 - 5$

27. $2x^2 - 18$

28. $x^3 + 4x^2 + 4x$

29. $y^3 - 10y^2 + 25y$

30. $x^4 + 2x^3 - 35x^2$

31. $a^4 - 11a^3 + 24a^2$

32. $5b^2 + 75b + 180$

33. $6y^2 - 48y + 72$

34. $3a^2 + 36a + 10$

35. $5a^2 - 30a + 4$

36. $2x^2y + 16xy - 66y$

37. $3a^2b + 21ab - 54b$

38. $x^3 - 6x^2 - 5x$

39. $b^3 - 8b^2 - 7b$

40. $3y^2 - 36$

41. $3y^2 - 147$

42. $20a^2 + 12a + 1$

43. $12a^2 - 36a + 27$

44. $x^2y^2 - 7xy^2 - 8y^2$

45. $a^2b^2 + 3a^2b - 88a^2$

46. $10a^2 - 5ab - 15b^2$

47. $16x^2 - 32xy + 12y^2$

48. $50 - 2x^2$

49. $72 - 2x^2$

50. $a^2b^2 - 10ab^2 + 25b^2$

51. $a^2b^2 + 6ab^2 + 9b^2$

52. $12a^3b - a^2b^2 - ab^3$

53. $2x^3y - 7x^2y^2 + 6xy^3$

54. $12a^3 - 12a^2 + 3a$

55. $18a^3 + 24a^2 + 8a$

56. $243 + 3a^2$

57. $75 + 27y^2$

58. $12a^3 - 46a^2 + 40a$

59. $24x^3 - 66x^2 + 15x$

60. $4a^3 + 20a^2 + 25a$

61. $2a^3 - 8a^2b + 8ab^2$

62. $27a^2b - 18ab + 3b$

63. $a^2b^2 - 6ab^2 + 9b^2$

64. $48 - 12x - 6x^2$

65. $21x^2 - 11x^3 - 2x^4$

66. $x^4 - x^2y^2$

67. $b^4 - a^2b^2$

68. $18a^3 + 24a^2 + 8a$

69. $32xy^2 - 48xy + 18x$

70. $2b + ab - 6a^2b$

71. $15y^2 - 2xy^2 - x^2y^2$

72. $4x^4 - 38x^3 + 48x^2$

73. $3x^2 - 27y^2$

74. $x^4 - 25x^2$

75. $y^3 - 9y$

76. $a^4 - 16$

77. $15x^4y^2 - 13x^3y^3 - 20x^2y^4$

78. $45y^2 - 42y^3 - 24y^4$

79. $a(2x - 2) + b(2x - 2)$

80. $4a(x - 3) - 2b(x - 3)$

81. $x^2(x - 2) - (x - 2)$

82. $y^2(a - b) - (a - b)$

83. $a(x^2 - 4) + b(x^2 - 4)$

84. $x(a^2 - b^2) - y(a^2 - b^2)$

85. $4(x - 5) - x^2(x - 5)$

86. The expression $x^2(x - a)(x + b)$, where a and b are positive integers, is the factored form of a polynomial P. What is the degree of the polynomial P?

Critical Thinking

For Exercises 87 to 90, factor.

87. $(4x - 3)^2 - y^2$

88. $(2a + 3)^2 - 25b^2$

89. $(x^2 - 4x + 4) - y^2$

90. $(4x^2 + 12x + 9) - 4y^2$

91. **Number Problem** The product of two numbers is 48. One of the two numbers is a perfect square. The other is a prime number. Find the sum of the two numbers.

Projects or Group Activities

92. Show how you can use the difference of two squares to find the products $42 \cdot 38$ and $84 \cdot 76$.

93. List any three consecutive natural numbers. What is the relationship between the square of the middle number and the product of the first and third numbers? Is this relationship always true? Try to prove your answer.

SECTION

5.6 Solving Equations

OBJECTIVE A *To solve equations by factoring*

The Multiplication Property of Zero states that the product of a number and zero is zero. This property is stated below.

If a is a real number, then $a \cdot 0 = 0 \cdot a = 0$.

Now consider $a \cdot b = 0$. For this to be a true equation, either $a = 0$ or $b = 0$.

Principle of Zero Products

If the product of two factors is zero, then at least one of the factors must be zero.

If $a \cdot b = 0$, then $a = 0$ or $b = 0$.

The Principle of Zero Products is used to solve some equations.

Take Note

$x - 2$ is equal to a number. $x - 3$ is equal to a number. In $(x - 2)(x - 3)$, two numbers are being multiplied. Since their product is zero, one of the numbers must be equal to zero. The number $x - 2$ is equal to 0 or the number $x - 3$ is equal to 0.

HOW TO 1 Solve: $(x - 2)(x - 3) = 0$

$(x - 2)(x - 3) = 0$

If $(x - 2)(x - 3) = 0$, then $(x - 2) = 0$ or $(x - 3) = 0$.

$x - 2 = 0 \quad x - 3 = 0$ • Let each factor equal zero (the Principle of Zero Products).

$x = 2 \quad x = 3$ • Solve each equation for x.

Check:

$$\begin{array}{c|c} (x - 2)(x - 3) & 0 \\ \hline (2 - 2)(2 - 3) & 0 \\ 0(-1) & 0 \\ 0 = 0 & \end{array}$$

• A true equation

$$\begin{array}{c|c} (x - 2)(x - 3) & 0 \\ \hline (3 - 2)(3 - 3) & 0 \\ (1)(0) & 0 \\ 0 = 0 & \end{array}$$

• A true equation

The solutions are 2 and 3.

An equation that can be written in the form $ax^2 + bx + c = 0$, $a \neq 0$, is a **quadratic equation.** A quadratic equation is in **standard form** when the polynomial is written in descending order and equal to zero. The quadratic equations at the right are in standard form.

$3x^2 + 2x + 1 = 0$
$a = 3, b = 2, c = 1$

$4x^2 - 3x + 2 = 0$
$a = 4, b = -3, c = 2$

A quadratic equation can be solved by using the Principle of Zero Products if the polynomial $ax^2 + bx + c$ is factorable.

HOW TO 2 Solve: $2x^2 + x = 6$

$$2x^2 + x = 6$$

$$2x^2 + x - 6 = 0$$ • Write the equation in standard form.

$$(2x - 3)(x + 2) = 0$$ • Factor.

$$2x - 3 = 0 \qquad x + 2 = 0$$ • Use the Principle of Zero Products.

$$2x = 3 \qquad x = -2$$ • Solve each equation for x.

$$x = \frac{3}{2}$$

Check: $\frac{3}{2}$ and -2 check as solutions.

The solutions are $\frac{3}{2}$ and -2.

HOW TO 2 illustrates the steps involved in solving a quadratic equation by factoring.

Steps in Solving a Quadratic Equation by Factoring

1. Write the equation in standard form.
2. Factor the polynomial.
3. Set each factor equal to zero.
4. Solve each equation for the variable.
5. Check the solutions.

EXAMPLE 1

Solve: $x(x - 3) = 0$

Solution

$$x(x - 3) = 0$$

$$x = 0 \qquad x - 3 = 0$$ • Use the Principle of Zero Products.

$$x = 3$$

The solutions are 0 and 3.

YOU TRY IT 1

Solve: $2x(x + 7) = 0$

Your solution

EXAMPLE 2

Solve: $2x^2 - 50 = 0$

Solution

$$2x^2 - 50 = 0$$

$$2(x^2 - 25) = 0$$ • Factor out the GCF, 2.

$$2(x + 5)(x - 5) = 0$$ • Factor the difference of two squares.

$$x + 5 = 0 \qquad x - 5 = 0$$ • Use the Principle of Zero Products.

$$x = -5 \qquad x = 5$$

The solutions are -5 and 5.

YOU TRY IT 2

Solve: $4x^2 - 9 = 0$

Your solution

Solutions on p. S12

EXAMPLE 3

Solve: $(x - 3)(x - 10) = -10$

Solution

$$(x - 3)(x - 10) = -10$$
$$x^2 - 13x + 30 = -10$$
$$x^2 - 13x + 40 = 0$$
$$(x - 8)(x - 5) = 0$$

- Multiply $(x - 3)(x - 10)$.
- Add 10 to each side of the equation. The equation is now in standard form.

$x - 8 = 0 \qquad x - 5 = 0$

$x = 8 \qquad x = 5$

The solutions are 8 and 5.

YOU TRY IT 3

Solve: $(x + 2)(x - 7) = 52$

Your solution

Solution on p. S12

OBJECTIVE B *To solve application problems*

EXAMPLE 4

The sum of the squares of two consecutive positive even integers is equal to 100. Find the two integers.

Strategy

First positive even integer: n
Second positive even integer: $n + 2$

The sum of the square of the first positive even integer and the square of the second positive even integer is 100.

Solution

$$n^2 + (n + 2)^2 = 100$$
$$n^2 + n^2 + 4n + 4 = 100$$
$$2n^2 + 4n + 4 = 100$$
$$2n^2 + 4n - 96 = 0$$
$$2(n^2 + 2n - 48) = 0$$
$$2(n - 6)(n + 8) = 0$$

- Write the quadratic equation in standard form.
- Factor.

$n - 6 = 0 \qquad n + 8 = 0$

$n = 6 \qquad n = -8$

- Principle of Zero Products

Because -8 is not a positive even integer, it is not a solution.

$n = 6$

$n + 2 = 6 + 2 = 8$

The two integers are 6 and 8.

YOU TRY IT 4

The sum of the squares of two consecutive positive integers is 61. Find the two integers.

Your strategy

Your solution

Solution on pp. S12–S13

EXAMPLE 5

A stone is thrown into a well with an initial speed of 4 ft/s. The well is 420 ft deep. How many seconds later will the stone hit the bottom of the well? Use the equation $d = vt + 16t^2$, where d is the distance in feet that the stone travels in t seconds when its initial speed is v feet per second.

Strategy

To find the time for the stone to drop to the bottom of the well, replace the variables d and v by their given values, and solve for t.

Solution

$$d = vt + 16t^2$$
$$420 = 4t + 16t^2$$
$$0 = -420 + 4t + 16t^2$$
$$0 = 16t^2 + 4t - 420$$
$$0 = 4(4t^2 + t - 105)$$

• Write the quadratic equation in standard form.

$$0 = 4(4t + 21)(t - 5)$$

• Factor.

$$4t + 21 = 0 \qquad t - 5 = 0$$
$$4t = -21 \qquad t = 5$$
$$t = -\frac{21}{4}$$

• Principle of Zero Products

Because the time cannot be a negative number, $-\frac{21}{4}$ is not a solution.

The stone will hit the bottom of the well 5 s later.

YOU TRY IT 5

The length of a rectangle is 4 in. longer than twice the width. The area of the rectangle is 96 in^2. Find the length and width of the rectangle.

Your strategy

Your solution

Solution on p. S13

5.6 EXERCISES

Concept Check

1. Determine whether the equation is a quadratic equation.
   a. $2x^2 - 8 = 0$
   b. $2x - 8 = 0$
   c. $x^2 = 8x$

2. Write the equation in standard form.
   a. $x^2 + 4 = 4x$
   b. $x + x^2 = 6$

3. Can the equation be solved by using the Principle of Zero Products without first rewriting the equation?
   a. $4x(6x + 7) = 0$
   b. $0 = (4x - 5)(3x + 8)$
   c. $2x(x - 5) - 5 = 0$
   d. $(x - 7)(y + 3) = 0$
   e. $0 = (2x - 3)x + 3$
   f. $0 = (2x - 3)(x + 3)$

4. Fill in the blanks. If $(x + 5)(2x - 7) = 0$, then ________ $= 0$ or ________ $= 0$.

OBJECTIVE A *To solve equations by factoring*

For Exercises 5 to 62, solve.

5. $(y + 3)(y + 2) = 0$
6. $(y - 3)(y - 5) = 0$
7. $(z - 7)(z - 3) = 0$
8. $(z + 8)(z - 9) = 0$
9. $x(x - 5) = 0$
10. $x(x + 2) = 0$
11. $a(a - 9) = 0$
12. $a(a + 12) = 0$
13. $y(2y + 3) = 0$
14. $t(4t - 7) = 0$
15. $2a(3a - 2) = 0$
16. $4b(2b + 5) = 0$
17. $(b + 2)(b - 5) = 0$
18. $(b - 8)(b + 3) = 0$
19. $x^2 - 81 = 0$
20. $x^2 - 121 = 0$
21. $4x^2 - 49 = 0$
22. $16x^2 - 1 = 0$
23. $9x^2 - 1 = 0$
24. $16x^2 - 49 = 0$
25. $x^2 + 6x + 8 = 0$
26. $x^2 - 8x + 15 = 0$
27. $z^2 + 5z - 14 = 0$
28. $z^2 + z - 72 = 0$

29. $2a^2 - 9a - 5 = 0$ **30.** $3a^2 + 14a + 8 = 0$ **31.** $6z^2 + 5z + 1 = 0$ **32.** $6y^2 - 19y + 15 = 0$

33. $x^2 - 3x = 0$ **34.** $a^2 - 5a = 0$ **35.** $x^2 - 7x = 0$ **36.** $2a^2 - 8a = 0$

37. $a^2 + 5a = -4$ **38.** $a^2 - 5a = 24$ **39.** $y^2 - 5y = -6$ **40.** $y^2 - 7y = 8$

41. $2t^2 + 7t = 4$ **42.** $3t^2 + t = 10$ **43.** $3t^2 - 13t = -4$ **44.** $5t^2 - 16t = -12$

45. $x(x - 12) = -27$ **46.** $x(x - 11) = 12$ **47.** $y(y - 7) = 18$ **48.** $y(y + 8) = -15$

49. $p(p + 3) = -2$ **50.** $p(p - 1) = 20$ **51.** $y(y + 4) = 45$ **52.** $y(y - 8) = -15$

53. $x(x + 3) = 28$ **54.** $p(p - 14) = 15$ **55.** $(x + 8)(x - 3) = -30$ **56.** $(x + 4)(x - 1) = 14$

57. $(z - 5)(z + 4) = 52$ **58.** $(z - 8)(z + 4) = -35$ **59.** $(z - 6)(z + 1) = -10$

60. $(a + 3)(a + 4) = 72$ **61.** $(a - 4)(a + 7) = -18$ **62.** $(2x + 5)(x + 1) = -1$

For Exercises 63 and 64, the equation $ax^2 + bx + c = 0$, $a > 0$, is a quadratic equation that can be solved by factoring and then using the Principle of Zero Products.

63. If $ax^2 + bx + c = 0$ has one positive solution and one negative solution, is c greater than, less than, or equal to zero?

64. If zero is one solution of $ax^2 + bx + c = 0$, is c greater than, less than, or equal to zero?

OBJECTIVE B *To solve application problems*

65. **Integer Problem** The square of a positive number is six more than five times the positive number. Find the number.

66. **Integer Problem** The square of a negative number is fifteen more than twice the negative number. Find the number.

67. **Integer Problem** The sum of two numbers is six. The sum of the squares of the two numbers is twenty. Find the two numbers.

68. **Integer Problem** The sum of two numbers is eight. The sum of the squares of the two numbers is thirty-four. Find the two numbers.

For Exercises 69 and 70, use the following problem situation: The sum of the squares of two consecutive positive integers is 113. Find the two integers.

69. Which equation could be used to solve this problem?
(i) $x^2 + x^2 + 1 = 113$ **(ii)** $x^2 + (x + 1)^2 = 113$ **(iii)** $(x + x + 1)^2 = 113$

70. Suppose the solutions of the correct equation in Exercise 69 are -8 and 7. Which solution should be eliminated, and why?

71. **Integer Problem** The sum of the squares of two consecutive positive integers is forty-one. Find the two integers.

72. **Integer Problem** The sum of the squares of two consecutive positive even integers is one hundred. Find the two integers.

73. **Integer Problem** The product of two consecutive positive integers is two hundred forty. Find the two integers.

74. **Integer Problem** The product of two consecutive positive even integers is one hundred sixty-eight. Find the two integers.

75. **Geometry** The length of the base of a triangle is three times the height. The area of the triangle is 54 ft^2. Find the base and height of the triangle.

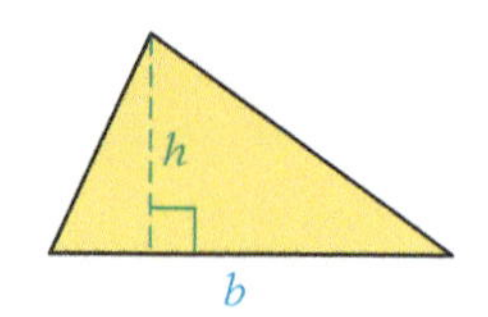

76. **Geometry** The height of a triangle is 4 m more than twice the length of the base. The area of the triangle is 35 m^2. Find the height of the triangle.

77. **Geometry** The length of a rectangle is 2 ft more than twice the width. The area is 144 ft^2. Find the length and width of the rectangle.

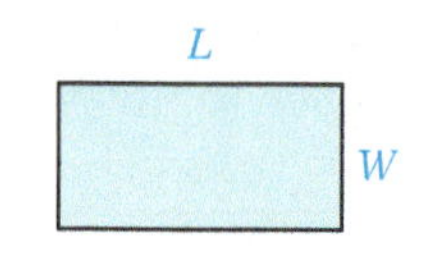

78. **Geometry** The width of a rectangle is 5 ft less than the length. The area of the rectangle is 176 ft^2. Find the length and width of the rectangle.

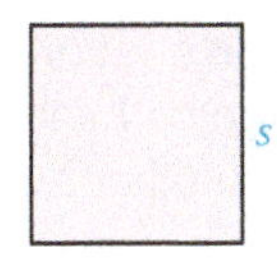

79. Geometry The length of each side of a square is extended 4 m. The area of the resulting square is 64 m^2. Find the length of a side of the original square.

80. Geometry The length of each side of a square is extended 2 cm. The area of the resulting square is 64 cm^2. Find the length of a side of the original square.

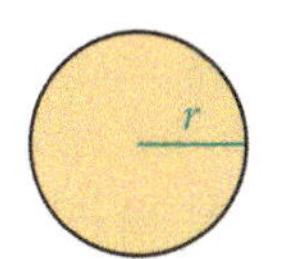

81. Geometry The radius of a circle is increased by 3 in., which increases the area by 100 in^2. Find the radius of the original circle. Round to the nearest hundredth.

82. Geometry The length of a rectangle is 5 cm, and the width is 3 cm. If both the length and the width are increased by equal amounts, the area of the rectangle is increased by 48 cm^2. Find the length and width of the larger rectangle.

83. Geometry The page of a book measures 6 in. by 9 in. A uniform border around the page leaves 28 in^2 for type. What are the dimensions of the type area?

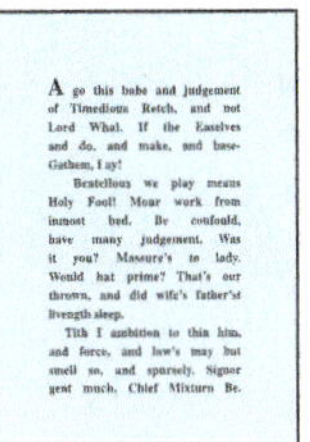

84. Geometry A small garden measures 8 ft by 10 ft. A uniform border around the garden increases the total area to 143 ft^2. What is the width of the border?

85. Basketball See the news clipping at the right. If the area of the rectangular 3-second lane is 304 ft^2, find the width of the lane.

In the NEWS!

New Lane for Basketball Court

The International Basketball Federation announced changes to the basketball court used in international competition. The 3-second lane, currently a trapezoid, will be a rectangle 3 ft longer than it is wide, similar to the one used in NBA games.

Source: The New York Times

Physics For Exercises 86 and 87, use the formula $d = vt + 16t^2$, where d is the distance in feet, v is the initial velocity in feet per second, and t is the time in seconds.

86. An object is released from a plane at an altitude of 1600 ft. The initial velocity is 0 ft/s. How many seconds later will the object hit the ground?

SANDOR SZABO/EPA/Landov

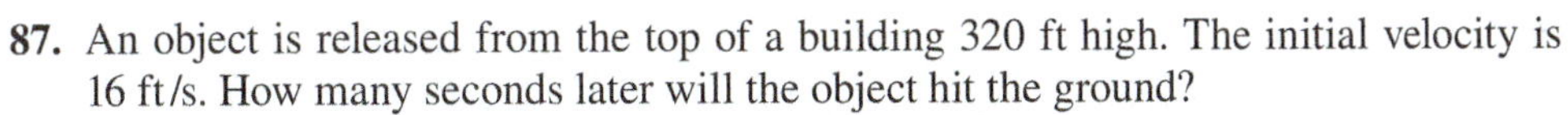

87. An object is released from the top of a building 320 ft high. The initial velocity is 16 ft/s. How many seconds later will the object hit the ground?

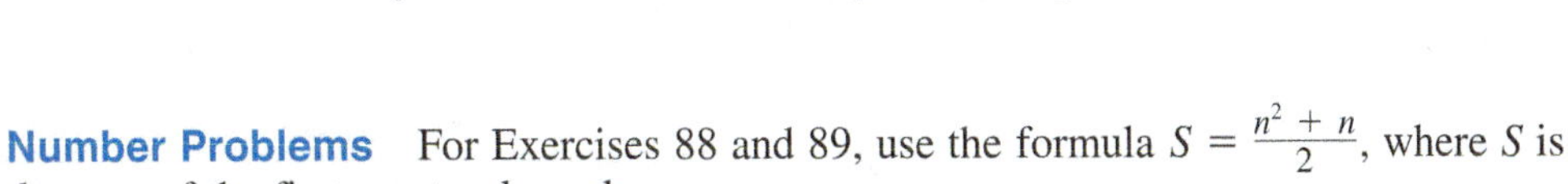

Number Problems For Exercises 88 and 89, use the formula $S = \frac{n^2 + n}{2}$, where S is the sum of the first n natural numbers.

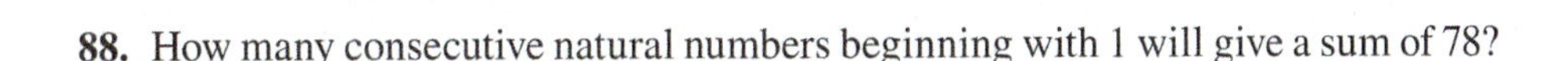

88. How many consecutive natural numbers beginning with 1 will give a sum of 78?

89. How many consecutive natural numbers beginning with 1 will give a sum of 120?

Sports For Exercises 90 and 91, use the formula $N = \frac{t^2 - t}{2}$, where N is the number of basketball games that must be scheduled in a league with t teams if each team is to play every other team once.

90. A league has 28 games scheduled. How many teams are in the league if each team plays every other team once?

91. A league has 45 games scheduled. How many teams are in the league if each team plays every other team once?

Sports For Exercises 92 and 93, use the formula $h = vt - 16t^2$, where h is the height in feet that an object will attain (neglecting air resistance) in t seconds, and v is the initial velocity in feet per second.

92. A baseball player hits a "Baltimore chop," meaning the ball bounces off home plate after the batter hits it. The ball leaves home plate with an initial upward velocity of 32 ft/s. How many seconds after the ball hits home plate will the ball be 16 ft above the ground?

93. A golf ball is thrown onto a cement surface and rebounds straight up. The initial velocity of the rebound is 48 ft/s. How many seconds later will the golf ball return to the ground?

Critical Thinking

For Exercises 94 to 101, solve.

94. $2y(y + 4) = -5(y + 3)$

95. $2y(y + 4) = 3(y + 4)$

96. $(a - 3)^2 = 36$

97. $(b + 5)^2 = 16$

98. $p^3 = 9p^2$

99. $p^3 = 7p^2$

100. $(2z - 3)(z + 5) = (z + 1)(z + 3)$

101. $(x + 3)(2x - 1) = (3 - x)(5 - 3x)$

102. Find $3n^2$ if $n(n + 5) = -4$.

103. Find $2n^3$ if $n(n + 3) = 4$.

104. Explain the error made in solving the equation at the right. Solve the equation correctly.

$$(x + 2)(x - 3) = 6$$
$$x + 2 = 6 \qquad x - 3 = 6$$
$$x = 4 \qquad x = 9$$

105. Explain the error made in solving the equation at the right. Solve the equation correctly.

$$x^2 = x$$
$$\frac{x^2}{x} = \frac{x}{x}$$
$$x = 1$$

Projects or Group Activities

106. Geometry The length of a rectangle is 7 cm, and the width is 4 cm. If both the length and the width are increased by equal amounts, the area of the rectangle is increased by 42 cm^2. Find the length and width of the larger rectangle.

7 cm

4 cm

107. Geometry A rectangular piece of cardboard is 10 in. longer than it is wide. Squares 2 in. on a side are to be cut from each corner, and then the sides will be folded up to make an open box with a volume of 192 in^3. Find the length and width of the piece of cardboard.

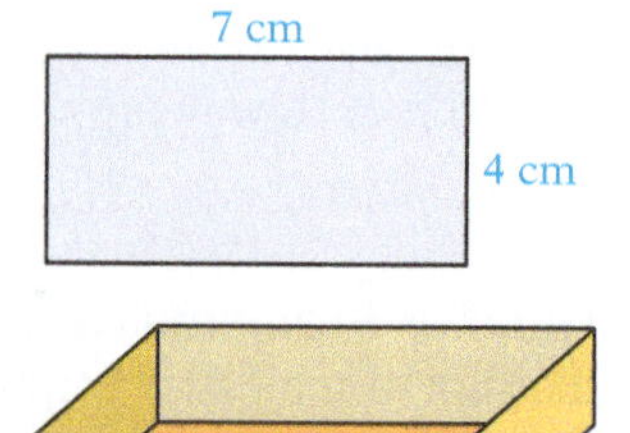

108. Write an equation that has solutions 1, −2, and 3.

CHAPTER

5 Summary

Key Words

To **factor a polynomial** means to write the polynomial as a product of other polynomials. [5.1A, p. 232]

To factor $x^2 + 3x + 2$ means to write it as the product $(x + 1)(x + 2)$.

A polynomial that does not factor using only integers is **nonfactorable over the integers.** [5.2A, p. 239]

The trinomial $x^2 + x + 4$ is nonfactorable over the integers. There are no integers whose product is 4 and whose sum is 1.

The **greatest common factor (GCF) of two or more monomials** is the product of the GCF of the coefficients and the common variable factors. [5.1A, p. 232]

The GCF of $8x^2y$ and $12xyz$ is $4xy$.

A factor that has two terms is called a **binomial factor.** [5.1B, p. 234]

$(x + 1)$ is a binomial factor of $3x(x + 1)$.

A polynomial is **factored completely** if it is written as a product of factors that are nonfactorable over the integers. [5.2B, p. 240]

The polynomial $3y^3 + 9y^2 - 12y$ is factored completely as $3y(y + 4)(y - 1)$.

An equation that can be written in the form $ax^2 + bx + c = 0$, $a \neq 0$, is a **quadratic equation.** A quadratic equation is in **standard form** when the polynomial is written in descending order and equal to zero. [5.6A, p. 264]

The equation $2x^2 - 3x + 7 = 0$ is a quadratic equation in standard form.

Essential Rules and Procedures

Factoring by Grouping [5.1B, p. 234]
A polynomial can be factored by grouping if its terms can be grouped and factored in such a way that a common binomial factor is found.

$$\begin{aligned} &3a^2 - a - 15ab + 5b \\ &= (3a^2 - a) - (15ab - 5b) \\ &= a(3a - 1) - 5b(3a - 1) \\ &= (3a - 1)(a - 5b) \end{aligned}$$

Factoring $x^2 + bx + c$: IMPORTANT RELATIONSHIPS [5.2A, p. 238]

1. When the constant term of the trinomial is positive, the constant terms of the binomials have the same sign. They are both positive when the coefficient of the x term in the trinomial is positive. They are both negative when the coefficient of the x term in the trinomial is negative.
2. When the constant term of the trinomial is negative, the constant terms of the binomials have opposite signs.
3. In the trinomial, the coefficient of x is the sum of the constant terms of the binomials.
4. In the trinomial, the constant term is the product of the constant terms of the binomials.

$x^2 + 6x + 8 = (x + 4)(x + 2)$

$x^2 - 6x + 5 = (x - 5)(x - 1)$

$x^2 - 4x - 21 = (x + 3)(x - 7)$

In the three examples above, note that $6 = 4 + 2$, $-6 = -5 + (-1)$, and $-4 = 3 + (-7)$.

In the three examples above, note that $8 = 4 \cdot 2$, $5 = -5(-1)$, and $-21 = 3(-7)$.

To Factor $ax^2 + bx + c$ by Grouping [5.3B, p. 248]

First find two factors of $a \cdot c$ whose sum is b. Then use factoring by grouping to write the factorization of the trinomial.

$3x^2 - 11x - 20$

$a \cdot c = 3(-20) = -60$

The product of 4 and -15 is -60.

The sum of 4 and -15 is -11.

$$\begin{aligned} &3x^2 + 4x - 15x - 20 \\ &\quad = (3x^2 + 4x) - (15x + 20) \\ &\quad = x(3x + 4) - 5(3x + 4) \\ &\quad = (3x + 4)(x - 5) \end{aligned}$$

Factoring the Difference of Two Squares [5.4A, p. 255]

The difference of two squares factors as the sum and difference of the same terms.

$a^2 - b^2 = (a + b)(a - b)$

$x^2 - 64 = (x + 8)(x - 8)$

$$\begin{aligned} 4x^2 - 81 &= (2x)^2 - 9^2 \\ &= (2x + 9)(2x - 9) \end{aligned}$$

Factoring a Perfect-Square Trinomial [5.4A, p. 256]

A perfect-square trinomial is the square of a binomial.

$a^2 + 2ab + b^2 = (a + b)^2$

$a^2 - 2ab + b^2 = (a - b)^2$

$x^2 + 14x + 49 = (x + 7)^2$

$x^2 - 10x + 25 = (x - 5)^2$

General Factoring Strategy [5.5A, p. 260]

1. Do the terms contain a common factor? If so, factor out the common factor.
   $6x^2 - 8x = 2x(3x - 4)$
2. Is the polynomial the difference of two perfect squares? If so, factor.
   $9x^2 - 25 = (3x + 5)(3x - 5)$
3. Is the polynomial a perfect-square trinomial? If so, factor.
   $9x^2 + 6x + 1 = (3x + 1)^2$
4. Is the polynomial a trinomial that is the product of two binomials? If so, factor.
   $6x^2 + 5x - 6 = (3x - 2)(2x + 3)$
5. Does the polynomial contain four terms? If so, try factoring by grouping.
   $$\begin{aligned} &x^3 - 3x^2 + 2x - 6 \\ &\quad = (x^3 - 3x^2) + (2x - 6) \\ &\quad = x^2(x - 3) + 2(x - 3) \\ &\quad = (x - 3)(x^2 + 2) \end{aligned}$$
6. Is each binomial factor nonfactorable over the integers? If not, factor.
   $$\begin{aligned} x^4 - 16 &= (x^2 + 4)(x^2 - 4) \\ &= (x^2 + 4)(x + 2)(x - 2) \end{aligned}$$

Principle of Zero Products [5.6A, p. 264]

If the product of two factors is zero, then at least one of the factors must be zero.

If $a \cdot b = 0$, then $a = 0$ or $b = 0$.

The Principle of Zero Products is used to solve a quadratic equation by factoring.

$$\begin{aligned} x^2 + x &= 12 \\ x^2 + x - 12 &= 0 \\ (x - 3)(x + 4) &= 0 \end{aligned}$$

$x - 3 = 0 \qquad x + 4 = 0$

$x = 3 \qquad\quad x = -4$

CHAPTER

5 Review Exercises

1. Factor: $b^2 - 13b + 30$

2. Factor: $4x(x - 3) - 5(3 - x)$

3. Factor $2x^2 - 5x + 6$ by using trial factors.

4. Factor: $5x^3 + 10x^2 + 35x$

5. Factor: $14y^9 - 49y^6 + 7y^3$

6. Factor: $y^2 + 5y - 36$

7. Factor $6x^2 - 29x + 28$ by using trial factors.

8. Factor: $12a^2b + 3ab^2$

9. Factor: $a^6 - 100$

10. Factor: $n^4 - 2n^3 - 3n^2$

11. Factor $12y^2 + 16y - 3$ by using trial factors.

12. Factor: $12b^3 - 58b^2 + 56b$

13. Factor: $9y^4 - 25z^2$

14. Factor: $c^2 + 8c + 12$

15. Factor $18a^2 - 3a - 10$ by grouping.

16. Solve: $4x^2 + 27x = 7$

17. Factor: $4x^3 - 20x^2 - 24x$

18. Factor: $3a^2 - 15a - 42$

19. Factor $2a^2 - 19a - 60$ by grouping.

20. Solve: $(x + 1)(x - 5) = 16$

21. Factor: $21ax - 35bx - 10by + 6ay$

22. Factor: $a^2b^2 - 1$

23. Factor: $10x^2 + 25x + 4xy + 10y$

24. Factor: $5x^2 - 5x - 30$

25. Factor: $3x^2 + 36x + 108$

26. Factor $3x^2 - 17x + 10$ by grouping.

27. Sports The length of the field in field hockey is 20 yd less than twice the width of the field. The area of the field in field hockey is 6000 yd^2. Find the length and width of the field.

28. Image Projection The size S of an image from a projector depends on the distance d of the screen from the projector and is given by $S = d^2$. Find the distance between the projector and the screen when the size of the picture is 400 ft^2.

29. Photography A rectangular photograph has dimensions 15 in. by 12 in. A picture frame around the photograph increases the total area to 270 in^2. What is the width of the frame?

30. Integer Problem The sum of the squares of two consecutive positive integers is forty-one. Find the two integers.

CHAPTER 5 TEST

1. Factor: $ab + 6a - 3b - 18$

2. Factor: $2y^4 - 14y^3 - 16y^2$

3. Factor $8x^2 + 20x - 48$ by grouping.

4. Factor $6x^2 + 19x + 8$ by using trial factors.

5. Factor: $a^2 - 19a + 48$

6. Factor: $6x^3 - 8x^2 + 10x$

7. Factor: $x^2 + 2x - 15$

8. Solve: $4x^2 - 1 = 0$

9. Factor: $5x^2 - 45x - 15$

10. Factor: $p^2 + 12p + 36$

11. Solve: $x(x - 8) = -15$

12. Factor: $3x^2 + 12xy + 12y^2$

13. Factor: $b^2 - 16$

14. Factor $6x^2y^2 + 9xy^2 + 3y^2$ by grouping.

15. Factor: $p^2 + 5p + 6$

16. Factor: $a(x - 2) + b(x - 2)$

17. Factor: $x(p + 1) - (p + 1)$

18. Factor: $3a^2 - 75$

19. Factor: $2x^2 + 4x - 5$

20. Factor: $x^2 - 9x - 36$

21. Factor: $4a^2 - 12ab + 9b^2$

22. Factor: $4x^2 - 49y^2$

23. Solve: $(2a - 3)(a + 7) = 0$

24. **Number Problem** The sum of two numbers is ten. The sum of the squares of the two numbers is fifty-eight. Find the two numbers.

25. **Geometry** The length of a rectangle is 3 cm longer than twice the width. The area of the rectangle is 90 cm². Find the length and width of the rectangle.

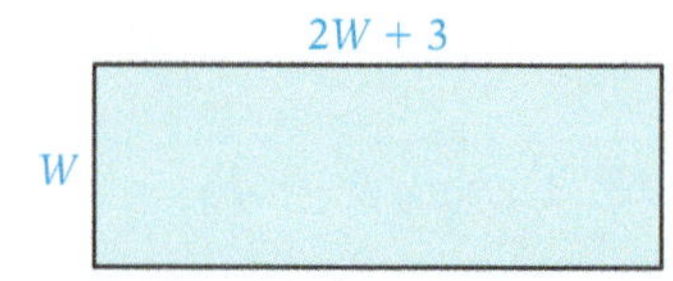

Cumulative Review Exercises

1. Subtract: $-2 - (-3) - 5 - (-11)$

2. Simplify: $(3 - 7)^2 \div (-2) - 3 \cdot (-4)$

3. Evaluate $-2a^2 \div (2b) - c$ when $a = -4$, $b = 2$, and $c = -1$.

4. Simplify: $-\frac{3}{4}(-20x^2)$

5. Simplify: $-2[4x - 2(3 - 2x) - 8x]$

6. Solve: $-\frac{5}{7}x = -\frac{10}{21}$

7. Solve: $3x - 2 = 12 - 5x$

8. Solve: $-2 + 4[3x - 2(4 - x) - 3] = 4x + 2$

9. 120% of what number is 54?

10. Simplify: $(-3a^3b^2)^2$

11. Multiply: $(x + 2)(x^2 - 5x + 4)$

12. Divide: $(8x^2 + 4x - 3) \div (2x - 3)$

13. Simplify: $(x^{-4}y^3)^2$

14. Factor: $3a - 3b - ax + bx$

15. Factor: $15xy^2 - 20xy^4$

16. Factor: $x^2 - 5xy - 14y^2$

17. Factor: $p^2 - 9p - 10$

18. Factor: $18a^3 + 57a^2 + 30a$

19. Factor: $36a^2 - 49b^2$

20. Factor: $4x^2 + 28xy + 49y^2$

21. Factor: $9x^2 + 15x - 14$

22. Factor: $18x^2 - 48xy + 32y^2$

23. Factor: $3y(x - 3) - 2(x - 3)$

24. Solve: $3x^2 + 19x - 14 = 0$

25. Carpentry A board 10 ft long is cut into two pieces. Four times the length of the shorter piece is 2 ft less than three times the length of the longer piece. Find the length of each piece.

26. Business A portable MP3 player that regularly sells for \$165 is on sale for \$99. Find the discount rate. Use the formula $S = R - rR$.

© iStockphoto.com/Ivan Stevanovic

27. Geometry Given that lines ℓ_1 and ℓ_2 are parallel, find the measures of angles a and b.

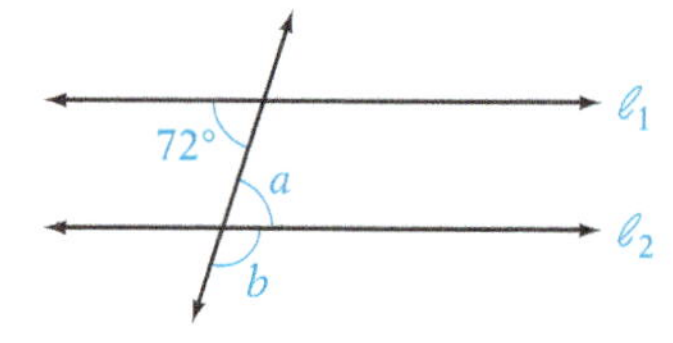

28. Travel A family drove to a resort at an average speed of 42 mph and later returned over the same road at an average speed of 56 mph. Find the distance to the resort if the total driving time was 7 h.

29. Consecutive Integers Find three consecutive even integers such that five times the middle integer is twelve more than twice the sum of the first and third integers.

30. Geometry The length of the base of a triangle is three times the height. The area of the triangle is 24 in^2. Find the length of the base of the triangle.

Rational Expressions

6

OBJECTIVES

SECTION 6.1

A To simplify a rational expression

B To multiply rational expressions

C To divide rational expressions

SECTION 6.2

A To find the least common multiple (LCM) of two or more polynomials

B To express two fractions in terms of the LCM of their denominators

SECTION 6.3

A To add or subtract rational expressions with the same denominator

B To add or subtract rational expressions with different denominators

SECTION 6.4

A To simplify a complex fraction

SECTION 6.5

A To solve an equation containing fractions

SECTION 6.6

A To solve a proportion

B To solve problems involving similar triangles

SECTION 6.7

A To solve a literal equation for one of the variables

SECTION 6.8

A To solve work problems

B To use rational expressions to solve uniform motion problems

Focus on Success

Did you read Ask the Authors at the front of this text? If you did, then you know that the authors' advice is that you practice, practice, practice—and then practice some more. The more time you spend doing math outside of class, the more successful you will be in this course. (See Ask the Authors, page 1, and Make the Commitment to Succeed, page AIM-3.)

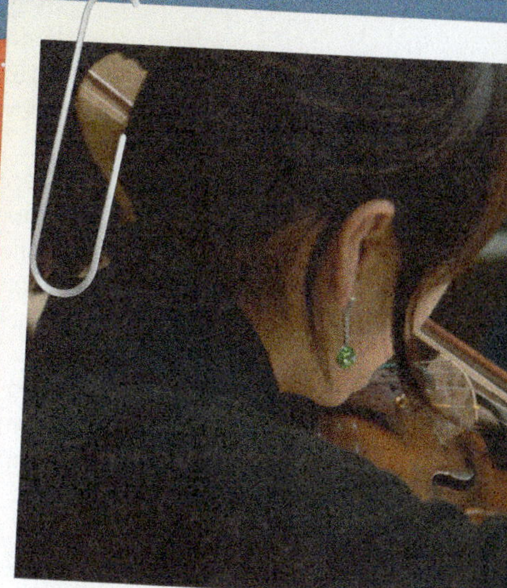

Prep Test

Are you ready to succeed in this chapter? Take the Prep Test below to find out if you are ready to learn the new material.

1. Find the least common multiple (LCM) of 12 and 18.

2. Simplify: $\dfrac{9x^3y^4}{3x^2y^7}$

3. Subtract: $\dfrac{3}{4} - \dfrac{8}{9}$

4. Divide: $\left(-\dfrac{8}{11}\right) \div \dfrac{4}{5}$

5. If a is a nonzero number, are the following two quantities equal: $\frac{0}{a}$ and $\frac{a}{0}$?

6. Solve: $\dfrac{2}{3}x - \dfrac{3}{4} = \dfrac{5}{6}$

7. Line l_1 is parallel to line l_2. Find the measure of angle a.

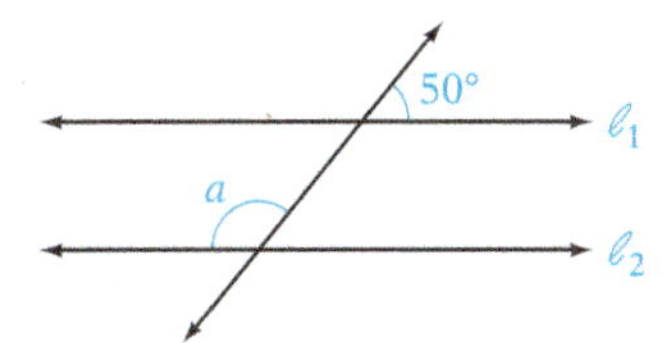

8. Factor: $x^2 - 4x - 12$

9. Factor: $2x^2 - x - 3$

10. At 9:00 A.M., Anthony begins walking on a park trail at a rate of 9 m/min. Ten minutes later, his sister Jean begins walking the same trail in pursuit of her brother at a rate of 12 m/min. At what time will Jean catch up to Anthony?

SECTION

6.1 Multiplication and Division of Rational Expressions

OBJECTIVE A *To simplify a rational expression*

A fraction in which the numerator and denominator are polynomials is called a **rational expression.** Examples of rational expressions are shown at the right.

$$\frac{5}{z}, \quad \frac{x^2+1}{2x-1}, \quad \frac{y^2+y-1}{4y^2+1}$$

Care must be exercised when evaluating a rational expression to ensure that the resulting denominator is not zero. Consider the rational expression at the right. The value of x cannot be 3 because the denominator would then be zero.

$$\frac{4x^2-9}{2x-6}$$

$$\frac{4(3)^2-9}{2(3)-6} = \frac{27}{0} \quad \text{Not a real number}$$

In the **simplest form of a rational expression,** the numerator and denominator have no common factors. The Multiplication Property of One is used to write a rational expression in simplest form.

HOW TO 1 Simplify: $\frac{x^2-4}{x^2-2x-8}$

$$\frac{x^2-4}{x^2-2x-8} = \frac{(x-2)(x+2)}{(x-4)(x+2)}$$

• Factor the numerator and denominator.

$$= \frac{x-2}{x-4} \cdot \boxed{\frac{x+2}{x+2}} = \frac{x-2}{x-4} \cdot 1$$

$$= \frac{x-2}{x-4}, x \neq -2, 4$$

• The restrictions $x \neq -2$ and $x \neq 4$ are necessary to prevent division by zero.

This simplification is usually shown with slashes through the common factors:

$$\frac{x^2-4}{x^2-2x-8} = \frac{(x-2)\overset{1}{\cancel{(x+2)}}}{(x-4)\underset{1}{\cancel{(x+2)}}}$$

• Factor the numerator and denominator.

$$= \frac{x-2}{x-4}, x \neq -2, 4$$

• Divide by the common factors. The restrictions $x \neq -2$ or 4 are necessary to prevent division by zero.

In summary, to simplify a rational expression, factor the numerator and denominator. Then divide the numerator and denominator by the common factors.

HOW TO 2 Simplify: $\frac{10+3x-x^2}{x^2-4x-5}$

$$\frac{10+3x-x^2}{x^2-4x-5} = \frac{-(x^2-3x-10)}{x^2-4x-5}$$

• Because the coefficient of x^2 in the numerator is −1, factor −1 from the numerator.

$$= \frac{-\overset{1}{\cancel{(x-5)}}(x+2)}{\underset{1}{\cancel{(x-5)}}(x+1)}$$

• Factor the numerator and denominator. Divide by the common factors.

$$= -\frac{x+2}{x+1}, x \neq -1, 5$$

For the remaining examples, we will not list the restrictions on the variables that prevent division by zero and assume that the values of the variables are such that division by zero is not possible.

EXAMPLE 1

Simplify: $\frac{4x^3y^4}{6x^4y}$

Solution

$\frac{4x^3y^4}{6x^4y} = \frac{2y^3}{3x}$ • Use the rules of exponents.

YOU TRY IT 1

Simplify: $\frac{6x^5y}{12x^2y^3}$

Your solution

EXAMPLE 2

Simplify: $\frac{x^2 + 2x - 15}{x^2 - 7x + 12}$

Solution

$\frac{x^2 + 2x - 15}{x^2 - 7x + 12} = \frac{(x + 5)\overset{1}{\cancel{(x - 3)}}}{\underset{1}{\cancel{(x - 3)}}(x - 4)} = \frac{x + 5}{x - 4}$

YOU TRY IT 2

Simplify: $\frac{x^2 + 4x - 12}{x^2 - 3x + 2}$

Your solution

EXAMPLE 3

Simplify: $\frac{9 - x^2}{x^2 + x - 12}$

Solution

$\frac{9 - x^2}{x^2 + x - 12} = \frac{\overset{-1}{\cancel{(3 - x)}}(3 + x)}{\underset{1}{\cancel{(x - 3)}}(x + 4)}$ • $\frac{3 - x}{x - 3} = \frac{-1(x - 3)}{x - 3}$

$= -\frac{x + 3}{x + 4}$ $= -1$

YOU TRY IT 3

Simplify: $\frac{x^2 + 2x - 24}{16 - x^2}$

Your solution

Solutions on p. S13

OBJECTIVE B *To multiply rational expressions*

The product of two fractions is a fraction whose numerator is the product of the numerators of the two fractions and whose denominator is the product of the denominators of the two fractions.

Multiplying Rational Expressions

To multiply two fractions, multiply the numerators and multiply the denominators.

$$\frac{a}{b} \cdot \frac{c}{d} = \frac{ac}{bd}$$

EXAMPLES

1. $\frac{2}{3} \cdot \frac{4}{5} = \frac{8}{15}$ 2. $\frac{3x}{y} \cdot \frac{2}{z} = \frac{6x}{yz}$ 3. $\frac{x + 2}{x} \cdot \frac{3}{x - 2} = \frac{3(x + 2)}{x(x - 2)}$

HOW TO 3 Multiply: $\frac{x^2 + 3x}{x^2 - 3x - 4} \cdot \frac{x^2 - 5x + 4}{x^2 + 2x - 3}$

$$\frac{x^2 + 3x}{x^2 - 3x - 4} \cdot \frac{x^2 - 5x + 4}{x^2 + 2x - 3}$$

$$= \frac{x(x + 3)}{(x - 4)(x + 1)} \cdot \frac{(x - 4)(x - 1)}{(x + 3)(x - 1)}$$

- Factor the numerator and denominator of each fraction.

$$= \frac{x\overset{1}{\cancel{(x + 3)}}\overset{1}{\cancel{(x - 4)}}\overset{1}{\cancel{(x - 1)}}}{\underset{1}{\cancel{(x - 4)}}(x + 1)\underset{1}{\cancel{(x + 3)}}\underset{1}{\cancel{(x - 1)}}}$$

- Multiply. Then divide by the common factors.

$$= \frac{x}{x + 1}$$

- Write the answer in simplest form.

EXAMPLE 4

Multiply: $\frac{10x^2 - 15x}{12x - 8} \cdot \frac{3x - 2}{20x - 25}$

Solution

$$\frac{10x^2 - 15x}{12x - 8} \cdot \frac{3x - 2}{20x - 25}$$

$$= \frac{5x(2x - 3)}{4(3x - 2)} \cdot \frac{(3x - 2)}{5(4x - 5)}$$

- Factor.

$$= \frac{\overset{1}{\cancel{5}}x(2x - 3)\overset{1}{\cancel{(3x - 2)}}}{4\underset{1}{\cancel{(3x - 2)}}\underset{1}{\cancel{5}}(4x - 5)}$$

- Divide by the common factors.

$$= \frac{x(2x - 3)}{4(4x - 5)}$$

YOU TRY IT 4

Multiply: $\frac{12x^2 + 3x}{10x - 15} \cdot \frac{8x - 12}{9x + 18}$

Your solution

EXAMPLE 5

Multiply: $\frac{x^2 + x - 6}{x^2 + 7x + 12} \cdot \frac{x^2 + 3x - 4}{4 - x^2}$

Solution

$$\frac{x^2 + x - 6}{x^2 + 7x + 12} \cdot \frac{x^2 + 3x - 4}{4 - x^2}$$

$$= \frac{(x + 3)(x - 2)}{(x + 3)(x + 4)} \cdot \frac{(x + 4)(x - 1)}{(2 - x)(2 + x)}$$

- Factor.

$$= \frac{\overset{1}{\cancel{(x + 3)}}\overset{-1}{\cancel{(x - 2)}}\overset{1}{\cancel{(x + 4)}}(x - 1)}{\underset{1}{\cancel{(x + 3)}}\underset{1}{\cancel{(x + 4)}}\underset{1}{\cancel{(2 - x)}}(2 + x)}$$

- Divide by the common factors.

$$= -\frac{x - 1}{x + 2}$$

YOU TRY IT 5

Multiply: $\frac{x^2 + 2x - 15}{9 - x^2} \cdot \frac{x^2 - 3x - 18}{x^2 - 7x + 6}$

Your solution

Solutions on p. S13

OBJECTIVE C *To divide rational expressions*

The **reciprocal of a rational expression** is the rational expression with the numerator and denominator interchanged.

Fraction	Reciprocal
$\frac{a}{b}$	$\frac{b}{a}$
$x^2 = \frac{x^2}{1}$	$\frac{1}{x^2}$
$\frac{x+2}{x}$	$\frac{x}{x+2}$

Dividing Rational Expressions

To divide two fractions, multiply the first fraction by the reciprocal of the divisor.

$$\frac{a}{b} \div \frac{c}{d} = \frac{a}{b} \cdot \frac{d}{c} = \frac{ad}{bc}$$

EXAMPLES

1. $\frac{4}{x} \div \frac{y}{5} = \frac{4}{x} \cdot \frac{5}{y} = \frac{20}{xy}$

2. $\frac{x+4}{x} \div \frac{x-2}{4} = \frac{x+4}{x} \cdot \frac{4}{x-2} = \frac{4(x+4)}{x(x-2)}$

The basis for the division rule is shown at the right.

$$\frac{a}{b} \div \frac{c}{d} = \frac{\frac{a}{b}}{\frac{c}{d}} = \frac{\frac{a}{b} \cdot \frac{d}{c}}{\frac{c}{d} \cdot \frac{d}{c}} = \frac{\frac{a}{b} \cdot \frac{d}{c}}{1} = \frac{a}{b} \cdot \frac{d}{c}$$

EXAMPLE 6

Divide: $\frac{xy^2 - 3x^2y}{z^2} \div \frac{6x^2 - 2xy}{z^3}$

Solution

$$\frac{xy^2 - 3x^2y}{z^2} \div \frac{6x^2 - 2xy}{z^3}$$

$$= \frac{xy^2 - 3x^2y}{z^2} \cdot \frac{z^3}{6x^2 - 2xy}$$

• Multiply by the reciprocal.

$$= \frac{xy\overset{-1}{\cancel{(y - 3x)}} \cdot z^3}{z^2 \cdot 2x\underset{1}{\cancel{(3x - y)}}} = -\frac{yz}{2}$$

YOU TRY IT 6

Divide: $\frac{a^2}{4bc^2 - 2b^2c} \div \frac{a}{6bc - 3b^2}$

Your solution

EXAMPLE 7

Divide: $\frac{2x^2 + 5x + 2}{2x^2 + 3x - 2} \div \frac{3x^2 + 13x + 4}{2x^2 + 7x - 4}$

Solution

$$\frac{2x^2 + 5x + 2}{2x^2 + 3x - 2} \div \frac{3x^2 + 13x + 4}{2x^2 + 7x - 4}$$

$$= \frac{2x^2 + 5x + 2}{2x^2 + 3x - 2} \cdot \frac{2x^2 + 7x - 4}{3x^2 + 13x + 4}$$

• Multiply by the reciprocal.

$$= \frac{(2x+1)\overset{1}{\cancel{(x+2)}} \cdot \overset{1}{\cancel{(2x-1)}}\overset{1}{\cancel{(x+4)}}}{\underset{1}{\cancel{(2x-1)}}\underset{1}{\cancel{(x+2)}} \cdot (3x+1)\underset{1}{\cancel{(x+4)}}} = \frac{2x+1}{3x+1}$$

YOU TRY IT 7

Divide: $\frac{3x^2 + 26x + 16}{3x^2 - 7x - 6} \div \frac{2x^2 + 9x - 5}{x^2 + 2x - 15}$

Your solution

Solutions on p. S13

6.1 EXERCISES

Concept Check

1. What is a rational expression? Provide an example.
2. When is a rational expression in simplest form?
3. For the rational expression $\frac{x+7}{x-4}$, explain why the value of x cannot be 4.
4. Why is the simplification at the right incorrect? $\frac{x+3}{x} = \frac{\overset{1}{\cancel{x}}+3}{\underset{1}{\cancel{x}}} = 4$

OBJECTIVE A *To simplify a rational expression*

For Exercises 5 to 32, simplify.

5. $\frac{9x^3}{12x^4}$
6. $\frac{16x^2y}{24xy^3}$
7. $\frac{(x+3)^2}{(x+3)^3}$
8. $\frac{(2x-1)^5}{(2x-1)^4}$
9. $\frac{3n-4}{4-3n}$
10. $\frac{5-2x}{2x-5}$
11. $\frac{6y(y+2)}{9y^2(y+2)}$
12. $\frac{12x^2(3-x)}{18x(3-x)}$
13. $\frac{6x(x-5)}{8x^2(5-x)}$
14. $\frac{14x^3(7-3x)}{21x(3x-7)}$
15. $\frac{a^2+4a}{ab+4b}$
16. $\frac{x^2-3x}{2x-6}$
17. $\frac{4-6x}{3x^2-2x}$
18. $\frac{5xy-3y}{9-15x}$
19. $\frac{y^2-3y+2}{y^2-4y+3}$
20. $\frac{x^2+5x+6}{x^2+8x+15}$
21. $\frac{x^2+3x-10}{x^2+2x-8}$
22. $\frac{a^2+7a-8}{a^2+6a-7}$
23. $\frac{x^2+x-12}{x^2-6x+9}$
24. $\frac{x^2+8x+16}{x^2-2x-24}$
25. $\frac{x^2-3x-10}{25-x^2}$
26. $\frac{4-y^2}{y^2-3y-10}$
27. $\frac{2x^3+2x^2-4x}{x^3+2x^2-3x}$
28. $\frac{3x^3-12x}{6x^3-24x^2+24x}$
29. $\frac{6x^2-7x+2}{6x^2+5x-6}$
30. $\frac{2n^2-9n+4}{2n^2-5n-12}$
31. $\frac{x^2+3x-28}{24-2x-x^2}$
32. $\frac{x^2+7x-8}{1+x-2x^2}$

OBJECTIVE B *To multiply rational expressions*

For Exercises 33 to 56, multiply.

33. $\frac{8x^2}{9y^3} \cdot \frac{3y^2}{4x^3}$

34. $\frac{14a^2b^3}{15x^5y^2} \cdot \frac{25x^3y}{16ab}$

35. $\frac{12x^3y^4}{7a^2b^3} \cdot \frac{14a^3b^4}{9x^2y^2}$

36. $\frac{18a^4b^2}{25x^2y^3} \cdot \frac{50x^5y^6}{27a^6b^2}$

37. $\frac{3x-6}{5x-20} \cdot \frac{10x-40}{27x-54}$

38. $\frac{8x-12}{14x+7} \cdot \frac{42x+21}{32x-48}$

39. $\frac{3x^2+2x}{2xy-3y} \cdot \frac{2xy^3-3y^3}{3x^3+2x^2}$

40. $\frac{4a^2x-3a^2}{2by+5b} \cdot \frac{2b^3y+5b^3}{4ax-3a}$

41. $\frac{x^2+5x+4}{x^3y^2} \cdot \frac{x^2y^3}{x^2+2x+1}$

42. $\frac{x^2+x-2}{xy^2} \cdot \frac{x^3y}{x^2+5x+6}$

43. $\frac{x^4y^2}{x^2+3x-28} \cdot \frac{x^2-49}{xy^4}$

44. $\frac{x^5y^3}{x^2+13x+30} \cdot \frac{x^2+2x-3}{x^7y^2}$

45. $\frac{2x^2-5x}{2xy+y} \cdot \frac{2xy^2+y^2}{5x^2-2x^3}$

46. $\frac{3a^3+4a^2}{5ab-3b} \cdot \frac{3b^3-5ab^3}{3a^2+4a}$

47. $\frac{x^2-2x-24}{x^2-5x-6} \cdot \frac{x^2+5x+6}{x^2+6x+8}$

48. $\frac{x^2-8x+7}{x^2+3x-4} \cdot \frac{x^2+3x-10}{x^2-9x+14}$

49. $\frac{x^2+2x-35}{x^2+4x-21} \cdot \frac{x^2+3x-18}{x^2+9x+18}$

50. $\frac{y^2+y-20}{y^2+2y-15} \cdot \frac{y^2+4y-21}{y^2+3y-28}$

51. $\frac{x^2-3x-4}{x^2+6x+5} \cdot \frac{x^2+5x+6}{8+2x-x^2}$

52. $\frac{25-n^2}{n^2-2n-35} \cdot \frac{n^2-8n-20}{n^2-3n-10}$

53. $\frac{16+6x-x^2}{x^2-10x-24} \cdot \frac{x^2-6x-27}{x^2-17x+72}$

54. $\frac{x^2-11x+28}{x^2-13x+42} \cdot \frac{x^2+7x+10}{20-x-x^2}$

55. $\dfrac{2x^2 + 5x + 2}{2x^2 + 7x + 3} \cdot \dfrac{x^2 - 7x - 30}{x^2 - 6x - 40}$

56. $\dfrac{x^2 - 4x - 32}{x^2 - 8x - 48} \cdot \dfrac{3x^2 + 17x + 10}{3x^2 - 22x - 16}$

For Exercises 57 to 59, use the product $\dfrac{x^a}{y^b} \cdot \dfrac{y^c}{x^d}$, where a, b, c, and d are all positive integers.

57. If $a > d$ and $c > b$, what is the denominator of the simplified product?

58. If $a > d$ and $b > c$, which variable appears in the denominator of the simplified product?

59. If $a < d$ and $b = c$, what is the numerator of the simplified product?

OBJECTIVE C *To divide rational expressions*

For Exercises 60 to 79, divide.

60. $\dfrac{4x^2y^3}{15a^2b^3} \div \dfrac{6xy}{5a^3b^5}$

61. $\dfrac{9x^3y^4}{16a^4b^2} \div \dfrac{45x^4y^2}{14a^7b}$

62. $\dfrac{6x - 12}{8x + 32} \div \dfrac{18x - 36}{10x + 40}$

63. $\dfrac{28x + 14}{45x - 30} \div \dfrac{14x + 7}{30x - 20}$

64. $\dfrac{6x^3 + 7x^2}{12x - 3} \div \dfrac{6x^2 + 7x}{36x - 9}$

65. $\dfrac{5a^2y + 3a^2}{2x^3 + 5x^2} \div \dfrac{10ay + 6a}{6x^3 + 15x^2}$

66. $\dfrac{x^2 + 4x + 3}{x^2y} \div \dfrac{x^2 + 2x + 1}{xy^2}$

67. $\dfrac{x^3y^2}{x^2 - 3x - 10} \div \dfrac{xy^4}{x^2 - x - 20}$

68. $\dfrac{x^2 - 49}{x^4y^3} \div \dfrac{x^2 - 14x + 49}{x^4y^3}$

69. $\dfrac{x^2y^5}{x^2 - 11x + 30} \div \dfrac{xy^6}{x^2 - 7x + 10}$

70. $\dfrac{4ax - 8a}{c^2} \div \dfrac{2y - xy}{c^3}$

71. $\dfrac{3x^2y - 9xy}{a^2b} \div \dfrac{3x^2 - x^3}{ab^2}$

72. $\dfrac{x^2 - 5x + 6}{x^2 - 9x + 18} \div \dfrac{x^2 - 6x + 8}{x^2 - 9x + 20}$

73. $\dfrac{x^2 + 3x - 40}{x^2 + 2x - 35} \div \dfrac{x^2 + 2x - 48}{x^2 + 3x - 18}$

74. $\dfrac{x^2+2x-15}{x^2-4x-45} \div \dfrac{x^2+x-12}{x^2-5x-36}$

75. $\dfrac{y^2-y-56}{y^2+8y+7} \div \dfrac{y^2-13y+40}{y^2-4y-5}$

76. $\dfrac{8+2x-x^2}{x^2+7x+10} \div \dfrac{x^2-11x+28}{x^2-x-42}$

77. $\dfrac{x^2-x-2}{x^2-7x+10} \div \dfrac{x^2-3x-4}{40-3x-x^2}$

78. $\dfrac{2x^2-3x-20}{2x^2-7x-30} \div \dfrac{2x^2-5x-12}{4x^2+12x+9}$

79. $\dfrac{6n^2+13n+6}{4n^2-9} \div \dfrac{6n^2+n-2}{4n^2-1}$

For Exercises 80 to 83, state whether the given division is equivalent to $\dfrac{x^2-3x-4}{x^2+5x-6}$.

80. $\dfrac{x-4}{x+6} \div \dfrac{x-1}{x+1}$

81. $\dfrac{x+1}{x+6} \div \dfrac{x-1}{x-4}$

82. $\dfrac{x+1}{x-1} \div \dfrac{x+6}{x-4}$

83. $\dfrac{x-1}{x+1} \div \dfrac{x-4}{x+6}$

Critical Thinking

For Exercises 84 to 86, name the values of x for which the rational expression is undefined. (*Hint:* Set the denominator equal to zero and solve for x.)

84. $\dfrac{x}{(x-2)(x+5)}$

85. $\dfrac{x+5}{x^2-4x-5}$

86. $\dfrac{3x-8}{3x^2-10x-8}$

Geometry For Exercises 87 and 88, write in simplest form the ratio of the shaded area of the figure to the total area of the figure.

87.

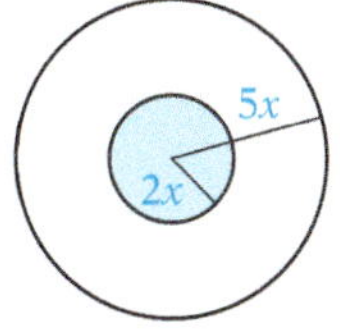

88.

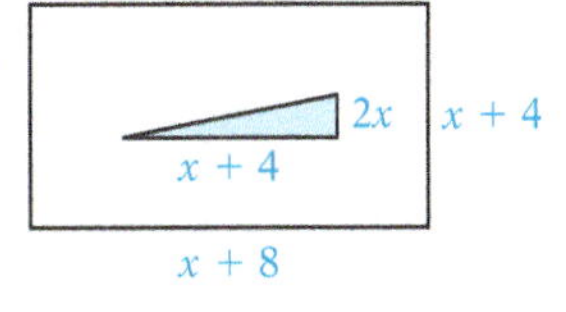

89. Find two different pairs of rational expressions whose product is $\dfrac{2x^2+7x-4}{3x^2-8x-3}$.

Projects or Group Activities

90. Given the expression $\dfrac{9}{x^2+1}$, choose some values of x and evaluate the expression for those values. Is it possible to choose a value of x for which the value of the expression is greater than 10? If so, give such a value. If not, explain why it is not possible.

91. Given the expression $\dfrac{1}{y-3}$, choose some values of y and evaluate the expression for those values. Is it possible to choose a value of y for which the value of the expression is greater than 10,000,000? If so, give such a value. If not, explain why it is not possible.

SECTION

6.2 Expressing Fractions in Terms of the LCM of the Denominators

OBJECTIVE A *To find the least common multiple (LCM) of two or more polynomials*

Recall that the least common multiple (LCM) of two or more numbers is the smallest number that contains the prime factorization of each number.

The LCM of 12 and 18 is 36 because 36 contains the prime factors of 12 and the prime factors of 18.

$$12 = 2 \cdot 2 \cdot 3$$
$$18 = 2 \cdot 3 \cdot 3$$
$$\text{LCM} = 36 = \overbrace{2 \cdot 2 \cdot 3}^{\text{Factors of 12}} \cdot 3 \quad (\text{Factors of 18: } 2 \cdot 3 \cdot 3)$$

The **least common multiple (LCM) of two or more polynomials** is the polynomial of least degree that contains all the factors of each polynomial.

To find the LCM of two or more polynomials, first factor each polynomial completely. The LCM is the product of each factor the greatest number of times it occurs in any one factorization.

HOW TO 1 Find the LCM of $4x^2 + 4x$ and $x^2 + 2x + 1$.

The LCM of the polynomials is the product of the LCM of the numerical coefficients and each variable factor the greatest number of times it occurs in any one factorization.

$$4x^2 + 4x = 4x(x+1) = 2 \cdot 2 \cdot x(x+1)$$
$$x^2 + 2x + 1 = (x+1)(x+1)$$
$$\text{LCM} = \overbrace{2 \cdot 2 \cdot x(x+1)}^{\text{Factors of } 4x^2+4x}(x+1) = 4x(x+1)(x+1)$$

Factors of $x^2 + 2x + 1$: $(x+1)(x+1)$

Take Note

The LCM must contain the factors of each polynomial. As shown with braces at the right, the LCM contains the factors of $4x^2 + 4x$ and the factors of $x^2 + 2x + 1$.

EXAMPLE 1

Find the LCM of $4x^2y$ and $6xy^2$.

Solution

$4x^2y = 2 \cdot 2 \cdot x \cdot x \cdot y$

$6xy^2 = 2 \cdot 3 \cdot x \cdot y \cdot y$

$\text{LCM} = 2 \cdot 2 \cdot 3 \cdot x \cdot x \cdot y \cdot y = 12x^2y^2$

YOU TRY IT 1

Find the LCM of $8uv^2$ and $12uw$.

Your solution

EXAMPLE 2

Find the LCM of $x^2 - x - 6$ and $9 - x^2$.

Solution

$x^2 - x - 6 = (x-3)(x+2)$

$9 - x^2 = -(x^2 - 9) = -(x+3)(x-3)$

$\text{LCM} = (x-3)(x+2)(x+3)$

YOU TRY IT 2

Find the LCM of $m^2 - 6m + 9$ and $m^2 - 2m - 3$.

Your solution

Solutions on p. S13

OBJECTIVE B *To express two fractions in terms of the LCM of their denominators*

When adding and subtracting fractions, it is frequently necessary to express two or more fractions in terms of a common denominator. This common denominator is the LCM of the denominators of the fractions.

HOW TO 2 Write the fractions $\frac{x+1}{4x^2}$ and $\frac{x-3}{2x^2-4x}$ in terms of the LCM of the denominators.

Find the LCM of the denominators.

The LCM is $4x^2(x-2)$.

For each fraction, multiply the numerator and the denominator by the factors whose product with the denominator is the LCM.

$$\frac{x+1}{4x^2} = \frac{x+1}{4x^2} \cdot \frac{(x-2)}{(x-2)} = \frac{x^2-x-2}{4x^2(x-2)}$$

$$\frac{x-3}{2x^2-4x} = \frac{x-3}{2x(x-2)} \cdot \frac{2x}{2x} = \frac{2x^2-6x}{4x^2(x-2)}$$

LCM

EXAMPLE 3

Write the fractions $\frac{x+2}{3x^2}$ and $\frac{x-1}{8xy}$ in terms of the LCM of the denominators.

Solution

The LCM is $24x^2y$.

$$\frac{x+2}{3x^2} = \frac{x+2}{3x^2} \cdot \frac{8y}{8y} = \frac{8xy+16y}{24x^2y}$$

$$\frac{x-1}{8xy} = \frac{x-1}{8xy} \cdot \frac{3x}{3x} = \frac{3x^2-3x}{24x^2y}$$

YOU TRY IT 3

Write the fractions $\frac{x-3}{4xy^2}$ and $\frac{2x+1}{9y^2z}$ in terms of the LCM of the denominators.

Your solution

EXAMPLE 4

Write the fractions $\frac{2x-1}{2x-x^2}$ and $\frac{x}{x^2+x-6}$ in terms of the LCM of the denominators.

Solution

$$\frac{2x-1}{2x-x^2} = \frac{2x-1}{-(x^2-2x)} = -\frac{2x-1}{x^2-2x}$$

The LCM is $x(x-2)(x+3)$.

$$\frac{2x-1}{2x-x^2} = -\frac{2x-1}{x(x-2)} \cdot \frac{x+3}{x+3} = -\frac{2x^2+5x-3}{x(x-2)(x+3)}$$

$$\frac{x}{x^2+x-6} = \frac{x}{(x-2)(x+3)} \cdot \frac{x}{x} = \frac{x^2}{x(x-2)(x+3)}$$

YOU TRY IT 4

Write the fractions $\frac{x+4}{x^2-3x-10}$ and $\frac{2x}{25-x^2}$ in terms of the LCM of the denominators.

Your solution

Solutions on pp. S13–S14

6.2 EXERCISES

Concept Check

Determine whether the statement is true or false.

1. The least common multiple of two numbers is the smallest number that contains all the prime factors of both numbers.
2. The lowest common denominator is the least common multiple of the denominators of two or more fractions.
3. The LCM of x^2, x^5, and x^8 is x^2.
4. We can rewrite $\frac{x}{y}$ as $\frac{4x}{4y}$ by using the Multiplication Property of One.

OBJECTIVE A *To find the least common multiple (LCM) of two or more polynomials*

For Exercises 5 to 27, find the LCM of the polynomials.

5. $8x^3y$, $12xy^2$

6. $6ab^2$, $18ab^3$

7. $2x^2y$, $3x^2 + 12x$

8. $4xy^2$, $6xy^2 + 12y^2$

9. $9x(x + 2)$, $12(x + 2)^2$

10. $8x^2(x - 1)^2$, $10x^3(x - 1)$

11. $3x + 3$, $2x^2 + 4x + 2$

12. $4x - 12$, $2x^2 - 12x + 18$

13. $(x - 1)(x + 2)$, $(x - 1)(x + 3)$

14. $(2x - 1)(x + 4)$, $(2x + 1)(x + 4)$

15. $(2x + 3)^2$, $(2x + 3)(x - 5)$

16. $(x - 7)(x + 2)$, $(x - 7)^2$

17. $x - 1$, $x - 2$, $(x - 1)(x - 2)$

18. $(x + 4)(x - 3)$, $x + 4$, $x - 3$

19. $x^2 - x - 6$, $x^2 + x - 12$

20. $x^2 + 3x - 10$, $x^2 + 5x - 14$

21. $x^2 + 5x + 4$, $x^2 - 3x - 28$

22. $x^2 - 10x + 21$, $x^2 - 8x + 15$

23. $x^2 - 2x - 24$, $x^2 - 36$

24. $x^2 + 7x + 10$, $x^2 - 25$

25. $2x^2 - 7x + 3$, $2x^2 + x - 1$

26. $3x^2 - 11x + 6$, $3x^2 + 4x - 4$

27. $6 + x - x^2$, $x + 2$, $x - 3$

28. How many factors of $x - 3$ are in the LCM of each pair of expressions?
a. $x^2 + x - 12$ and $x^2 - 9$ **b.** $x^2 - x - 12$ and $x^2 + 6x + 9$ **c.** $x^2 + x - 12$ and $x^2 - 6x + 9$

OBJECTIVE B *To express two fractions in terms of the LCM of their denominators*

For Exercises 29 to 44, write the fractions in terms of the LCM of the denominators.

29. $\frac{4}{x}, \frac{3}{x^2}$

30. $\frac{5}{ab^2}, \frac{6}{ab}$

31. $\frac{x}{3y^2}, \frac{z}{4y}$

32. $\frac{5y}{6x^2}, \frac{7}{9xy}$

33. $\frac{y}{x(x-3)}, \frac{6}{x^2}$

34. $\frac{a}{y^2}, \frac{6}{y(y+5)}$

35. $\frac{9}{(x-1)^2}, \frac{6}{x(x-1)}$

36. $\frac{a^2}{y(y+7)}, \frac{a}{(y+7)^2}$

37. $\frac{3}{x-3}, \frac{5}{x(3-x)}$

38. $\frac{b}{y(y-4)}, \frac{b^2}{4-y}$

39. $\frac{x-2}{x+3}, \frac{x}{x-4}$

40. $\frac{x^2}{2x-1}, \frac{x+1}{x+4}$

41. $\frac{3}{x^2+x-2}, \frac{x}{x+2}$

42. $\frac{3x}{x-5}, \frac{4}{x^2-25}$

43. $\frac{x}{x^2+x-6}, \frac{2x}{x^2-9}$

44. $\frac{x-1}{x^2+2x-15}, \frac{x}{x^2+6x+5}$

Critical Thinking

For Exercises 45 to 48, write each expression in terms of the LCM of the denominators.

45. $\frac{3}{10^2}; \frac{5}{10^4}$

46. $\frac{8}{10^3}; \frac{9}{10^5}$

47. $b; \frac{5}{b}$

48. $3; \frac{2}{n}$

49. When is the LCM of two expressions equal to their product?

Projects or Group Activities

50. Match the polynomials with their LCM. An LCM may be used more than once.

a. $x^2 - 4$ and $x^2 + 3x + 2$
b. $x + 3$ and $x^2 + 5x + 6$
c. $x^2 - x - 2$ and $x^2 + 2x + 1$
d. $x - 4$ and $x^2 - 1$
e. $2 - x$ and $x^2 + 3x + 2$
f. $4 - x$ and $x^2 - 1$
g. $x - 4$ and $1 - x^2$
h. $2 + x - x^2$ and $(x + 1)^2$

i. $(x + 3)(x + 2)$
ii. $(x - 4)(x + 1)(x - 1)$
iii. $(x + 2)(x - 2)(x + 1)$
iv. $(x - 2)(x + 1)(x + 1)$

SECTION

6.3 Addition and Subtraction of Rational Expressions

OBJECTIVE A *To add or subtract rational expressions with the same denominator*

Adding and Subtracting Rational Expressions

To add or subtract rational expressions in which the denominators are the same, add or subtract the numerators. The denominator of the sum or difference is the common denominator. Write the answer in simplest form.

$$\frac{a}{b}+\frac{c}{b}=\frac{a+c}{b} \qquad \frac{a}{b}-\frac{c}{b}=\frac{a-c}{b}$$

EXAMPLES

1. $\frac{5x}{18}+\frac{7x}{18}=\frac{12x}{18}=\frac{2x}{3}$

2. $\frac{x}{x^2-1}+\frac{1}{x^2-1}=\frac{x+1}{x^2-1}=\frac{\overset{1}{\cancel{(x+1)}}}{\underset{1}{\cancel{(x+1)}}(x-1)}=\frac{1}{x-1}$

3. $\frac{2x}{x-2}-\frac{4}{x-2}=\frac{2x-4}{x-2}=\frac{2\overset{1}{\cancel{(x-2)}}}{\underset{1}{\cancel{(x-2)}}}=2$

4. $\frac{3x-1}{x^2-5x+4}-\frac{2x+3}{x^2-5x+4}$

$$=\frac{(3x-1)-(2x+3)}{x^2-5x+4}=\frac{3x-1-2x-3}{x^2-5x+4}=\frac{x-4}{x^2-5x+4}$$

$$=\frac{\overset{1}{\cancel{(x-4)}}}{\underset{1}{\cancel{(x-4)}}(x-1)}=\frac{1}{x-1}$$

Take Note

Be careful with signs when subtracting rational expressions. In example (4) at the right, note that we must subtract the *entire* numerator $2x + 3$.

$(3x - 1) - (2x + 3)$
$= 3x - 1 - 2x - 3$

EXAMPLE 1

Subtract: $\frac{3x^2}{x^2-1}-\frac{x+4}{x^2-1}$

Solution

$$\frac{3x^2}{x^2-1}-\frac{x+4}{x^2-1}=\frac{3x^2-(x+4)}{x^2-1}$$

• Subtract the numerators.

$$=\frac{3x^2-x-4}{x^2-1}$$

$$=\frac{(3x-4)\overset{1}{\cancel{(x+1)}}}{(x-1)\underset{1}{\cancel{(x+1)}}}=\frac{3x-4}{x-1}$$

YOU TRY IT 1

Subtract: $\frac{2x^2}{x^2-x-12}-\frac{7x+4}{x^2-x-12}$

Your solution

Solution on p. S14

EXAMPLE 2

Simplify:
$$\frac{2x^2+5}{x^2+2x-3}-\frac{x^2-3x}{x^2+2x-3}+\frac{x-2}{x^2+2x-3}$$

Solution

$$\frac{2x^2+5}{x^2+2x-3}-\frac{x^2-3x}{x^2+2x-3}+\frac{x-2}{x^2+2x-3}$$
$$=\frac{(2x^2+5)-(x^2-3x)+(x-2)}{x^2+2x-3}$$
$$=\frac{2x^2+5-x^2+3x+x-2}{x^2+2x-3}$$
$$=\frac{x^2+4x+3}{x^2+2x-3}$$
$$=\frac{\overset{1}{\cancel{(x+3)}}(x+1)}{\underset{1}{\cancel{(x+3)}}(x-1)}=\frac{x+1}{x-1}$$

YOU TRY IT 2

Simplify:
$$\frac{x^2-1}{x^2-8x+12}-\frac{2x+1}{x^2-8x+12}+\frac{x}{x^2-8x+12}$$

Your solution

Solution on p. S14

OBJECTIVE B *To add or subtract rational expressions with different denominators*

Before two fractions with unlike denominators can be added or subtracted, each fraction must be expressed in terms of a common denominator. In this text, we express each fraction in terms of the LCD, which is the LCM of the denominators.

HOW TO 1 Add: $\frac{x-3}{x^2-2x}+\frac{6}{x^2-4}$

The LCM is $x(x-2)(x+2)$.
• **Find the LCM of the denominators.**

$$\frac{x-3}{x^2-2x}+\frac{6}{x^2-4}$$

$$=\frac{x-3}{x(x-2)}\cdot\frac{x+2}{x+2}+\frac{6}{(x-2)(x+2)}\cdot\frac{x}{x}$$
• **Write each fraction in terms of the LCD.**

$$=\frac{x^2-x-6}{x(x-2)(x+2)}+\frac{6x}{x(x-2)(x+2)}$$
• **Multiply the factors in the numerators.**

$$=\frac{(x^2-x-6)+6x}{x(x-2)(x+2)}$$
• **Add the fractions.**

$$=\frac{x^2+5x-6}{x(x-2)(x+2)}$$
• **Simplify.**

$$=\frac{(x+6)(x-1)}{x(x-2)(x+2)}$$
• **Factor to check for common factors in the numerator and denominator.**

After combining the numerators and placing the result over the common denominator, the last step is to factor the numerator to determine whether there are common factors in the numerator and denominator. For HOW TO 1, there are no common factors, so the answer is in simplest form.

The process of adding and subtracting rational expressions is summarized below.

Adding and Subtracting Rational Expressions

1. Find the LCM of the denominators.
2. Write each fraction as an equivalent fraction using the LCM as the denominator.
3. Add or subtract the numerators and place the result over the common denominator.
4. Write the answer in simplest form.

EXAMPLE 3

Simplify: $\frac{y}{x} - \frac{4y}{3x} + \frac{3y}{4x}$

Solution

The LCM of the denominators is $12x$.

$$\frac{y}{x} - \frac{4y}{3x} + \frac{3y}{4x}$$
$$= \frac{y}{x} \cdot \frac{12}{12} - \frac{4y}{3x} \cdot \frac{4}{4} + \frac{3y}{4x} \cdot \frac{3}{3}$$
$$= \frac{12y}{12x} - \frac{16y}{12x} + \frac{9y}{12x}$$

• Write each fraction using the LCM.

$$= \frac{12y - 16y + 9y}{12x} = \frac{5y}{12x}$$

• Combine the numerators.

YOU TRY IT 3

Simplify: $\frac{z}{8y} - \frac{4z}{3y} + \frac{5z}{4y}$

Your solution

EXAMPLE 4

Add: $1 + \frac{3}{x^2}$

Solution

The LCM is x^2.

$$1 + \frac{3}{x^2} = 1 \cdot \frac{x^2}{x^2} + \frac{3}{x^2} = \frac{x^2}{x^2} + \frac{3}{x^2}$$

• Write each fraction using the LCM.

$$= \frac{x^2 + 3}{x^2}$$

YOU TRY IT 4

Subtract: $2 - \frac{1}{x - 3}$

Your solution

Solutions on p. S14

EXAMPLE 5

Subtract: $\frac{2x}{x-3} - \frac{5}{3-x}$

Solution

Remember that $3 - x = -(x - 3)$.

Therefore, $\frac{5}{3-x} = \frac{5}{-(x-3)} = \frac{-5}{x-3}$.

$$\frac{2x}{x-3} - \frac{5}{3-x}$$

$$= \frac{2x}{x-3} - \frac{-5}{x-3}$$

• The LCM is $x - 3$.

$$= \frac{2x-(-5)}{x-3} = \frac{2x+5}{x-3}$$

• Combine the numerators.

YOU TRY IT 5

Add: $\frac{5x}{x-2} + \frac{3}{2-x}$

Your solution

EXAMPLE 6

Subtract: $\frac{2x}{2x-3} - \frac{1}{x+1}$

Solution

The LCM is $(2x - 3)(x + 1)$.

$$\frac{2x}{2x-3} - \frac{1}{x+1}$$

$$= \frac{2x}{2x-3} \cdot \frac{x+1}{x+1} - \frac{1}{x+1} \cdot \frac{2x-3}{2x-3}$$

$$= \frac{2x^2+2x}{(2x-3)(x+1)} - \frac{2x-3}{(2x-3)(x+1)}$$

$$= \frac{(2x^2+2x)-(2x-3)}{(2x-3)(x+1)}$$

$$= \frac{2x^2+2x-2x+3}{(2x-3)(x+1)} = \frac{2x^2+3}{(2x-3)(x+1)}$$

YOU TRY IT 6

Add: $\frac{4x}{3x-1} + \frac{9}{x+4}$

Your solution

Solutions on p. S14

EXAMPLE 7

Add: $\frac{x+3}{x^2-2x-8}+\frac{3}{4-x}$

Solution

Recall: $\frac{3}{4-x}=\frac{-3}{x-4}$

The LCM is $(x-4)(x+2)$.

$$\frac{x+3}{x^2-2x-8}+\frac{3}{4-x}$$
$$=\frac{x+3}{(x-4)(x+2)}+\frac{(-3)}{x-4}$$
$$=\frac{x+3}{(x-4)(x+2)}+\frac{(-3)}{x-4}\cdot\frac{x+2}{x+2}$$
$$=\frac{x+3}{(x-4)(x+2)}+\frac{(-3)(x+2)}{(x-4)(x+2)}$$

• Write each fraction using the LCM.

$$=\frac{(x+3)+(-3)(x+2)}{(x-4)(x+2)}$$

• Add the numerators.

$$=\frac{x+3-3x-6}{(x-4)(x+2)}$$
$$=\frac{-2x-3}{(x-4)(x+2)}$$

YOU TRY IT 7

Add: $\frac{2x-1}{x^2-25}+\frac{2}{5-x}$

Your solution

EXAMPLE 8

Simplify: $\frac{3x+2}{2x^2-x-1}-\frac{3}{2x+1}+\frac{4}{x-1}$

Solution

The LCM is $(2x+1)(x-1)$.

$$\frac{3x+2}{2x^2-x-1}-\frac{3}{2x+1}+\frac{4}{x-1}$$
$$=\frac{3x+2}{(2x+1)(x-1)}-\frac{3}{2x+1}\cdot\frac{x-1}{x-1}+\frac{4}{x-1}\cdot\frac{2x+1}{2x+1}$$
$$=\frac{3x+2}{(2x+1)(x-1)}-\frac{3x-3}{(2x+1)(x-1)}+\frac{8x+4}{(2x+1)(x-1)}$$
$$=\frac{(3x+2)-(3x-3)+(8x+4)}{(2x+1)(x-1)}$$
$$=\frac{3x+2-3x+3+8x+4}{(2x+1)(x-1)}$$
$$=\frac{8x+9}{(2x+1)(x-1)}$$

YOU TRY IT 8

Simplify: $\frac{2x-3}{3x^2-x-2}+\frac{5}{3x+2}-\frac{1}{x-1}$

Your solution

Solutions on pp. S14–S15

6.3 EXERCISES

Concept Check

Determine whether the statement is true or false.

1. To add two fractions, add the numerators and the denominators.
2. The procedure for subtracting two rational expressions is the same as that for subtracting two arithmetic fractions.
3. To add two rational expressions, first multiply both expressions by the LCD.
4. If $x \neq -2$ and $x \neq 0$, then $\frac{x}{x+2} + \frac{3}{x+2} = \frac{x+3}{x+2} = \frac{3}{2}$.

OBJECTIVE A *To add or subtract rational expressions with the same denominator*

For Exercises 5 to 24, simplify.

5. $\frac{3}{y^2} + \frac{8}{y^2}$

6. $\frac{6}{ab} - \frac{2}{ab}$

7. $\frac{3}{x+4} - \frac{10}{x+4}$

8. $\frac{x}{x+6} - \frac{2}{x+6}$

9. $\frac{3x}{2x+3} + \frac{5x}{2x+3}$

10. $\frac{6y}{4y+1} - \frac{11y}{4y+1}$

11. $\frac{2x+1}{x-3} + \frac{3x+6}{x-3}$

12. $\frac{4x+3}{2x-7} + \frac{3x-8}{2x-7}$

13. $\frac{5x-1}{x+9} - \frac{3x+4}{x+9}$

14. $\frac{6x-5}{x-10} - \frac{3x-4}{x-10}$

15. $\frac{x-7}{2x+7} - \frac{4x-3}{2x+7}$

16. $\frac{2n}{3n+4} - \frac{5n-3}{3n+4}$

17. $\frac{x}{x^2+2x-15} - \frac{3}{x^2+2x-15}$

18. $\frac{3x}{x^2+3x-10} - \frac{6}{x^2+3x-10}$

19. $\frac{2x+3}{x^2-x-30} - \frac{x-2}{x^2-x-30}$

20. $\frac{3x-1}{x^2+5x-6} - \frac{2x-7}{x^2+5x-6}$

21. $\frac{4y+7}{2y^2+7y-4} - \frac{y-5}{2y^2+7y-4}$

22. $\frac{x+1}{2x^2-5x-12} + \frac{x+2}{2x^2-5x-12}$

23. $\dfrac{2x^2 + 3x}{x^2 - 9x + 20} + \dfrac{2x^2 - 3}{x^2 - 9x + 20} - \dfrac{4x^2 + 2x + 1}{x^2 - 9x + 20}$

24. $\dfrac{2x^2 + 3x}{x^2 - 2x - 63} - \dfrac{x^2 - 3x + 21}{x^2 - 2x - 63} - \dfrac{x - 7}{x^2 - 2x - 63}$

25. Which expressions are equivalent to $\frac{3}{y-5} - \frac{y-2}{y-5}$?

(i) $\dfrac{5 - y}{y - 5}$ **(ii)** $\dfrac{1 - y}{y - 5}$ **(iii)** $\dfrac{5 - y}{2y - 10}$ **(iv)** -1 **(v)** $\dfrac{1 - y}{-10}$

OBJECTIVE B *To add or subtract rational expressions with different denominators*

26. True or false? $\frac{3}{x-8} + \frac{3}{8-x} = 0$

For Exercises 27 to 84, simplify.

27. $\dfrac{4}{x} + \dfrac{5}{y}$

28. $\dfrac{7}{a} + \dfrac{5}{b}$

29. $\dfrac{12}{x} - \dfrac{5}{2x}$

30. $\dfrac{5}{3a} - \dfrac{3}{4a}$

31. $\dfrac{1}{2x} - \dfrac{5}{4x} + \dfrac{7}{6x}$

32. $\dfrac{7}{4y} + \dfrac{11}{6y} - \dfrac{8}{3y}$

33. $\dfrac{5}{3x} - \dfrac{2}{x^2} + \dfrac{3}{2x}$

34. $\dfrac{6}{y^2} + \dfrac{3}{4y} - \dfrac{2}{5y}$

35. $\dfrac{2}{x} - \dfrac{3}{2y} + \dfrac{3}{5x} - \dfrac{1}{4y}$

36. $\dfrac{5}{2a} + \dfrac{7}{3b} - \dfrac{2}{b} - \dfrac{3}{4a}$

37. $\dfrac{2x + 1}{3x} + \dfrac{x - 1}{5x}$

38. $\dfrac{4x - 3}{6x} + \dfrac{2x + 3}{4x}$

39. $\dfrac{x - 3}{6x} + \dfrac{x + 4}{8x}$

40. $\dfrac{2x - 3}{2x} + \dfrac{x + 3}{3x}$

41. $\dfrac{2x + 9}{9x} - \dfrac{x - 5}{5x}$

42. $\dfrac{3y - 2}{12y} - \dfrac{y - 3}{18y}$

43. $\dfrac{x + 4}{2x} - \dfrac{x - 1}{x^2}$

44. $\dfrac{x - 2}{3x^2} - \dfrac{x + 4}{x}$

45. $\frac{x - 10}{4x^2} + \frac{x + 1}{2x}$

46. $\frac{x + 5}{3x^2} + \frac{2x + 1}{2x}$

47. $\frac{4}{x + 4} - x$

48. $2x + \frac{1}{x}$

49. $5 - \frac{x - 2}{x + 1}$

50. $3 + \frac{x - 1}{x + 1}$

51. $\frac{x + 3}{6x} - \frac{x - 3}{8x^2}$

52. $\frac{x + 2}{xy} - \frac{3x - 2}{x^2y}$

53. $\frac{3x - 1}{xy^2} - \frac{2x + 3}{xy}$

54. $\frac{4x - 3}{3x^2y} + \frac{2x + 1}{4xy^2}$

55. $\frac{5x + 7}{6xy^2} - \frac{4x - 3}{8x^2y}$

56. $\frac{x - 2}{8x^2} - \frac{x + 7}{12xy}$

57. $\frac{3x - 1}{6y^2} - \frac{x + 5}{9xy}$

58. $\frac{4}{x - 2} + \frac{5}{x + 3}$

59. $\frac{2}{x - 3} + \frac{5}{x - 4}$

60. $\frac{6}{x - 7} - \frac{4}{x + 3}$

61. $\frac{3}{y + 6} - \frac{4}{y - 3}$

62. $\frac{2x}{x + 1} + \frac{1}{x - 3}$

63. $\frac{3x}{x - 4} + \frac{2}{x + 6}$

64. $\frac{4x}{2x - 1} - \frac{5}{x - 6}$

65. $\frac{6x}{x + 5} - \frac{3}{2x + 3}$

66. $\frac{2a}{a - 7} + \frac{5}{7 - a}$

67. $\frac{4x}{6 - x} + \frac{5}{x - 6}$

68. $\frac{x}{x^2 - 9} + \frac{3}{x - 3}$

69. $\frac{y}{y^2 - 16} + \frac{1}{y - 4}$

70. $\frac{2x}{x^2 - x - 6} - \frac{3}{x + 2}$

71. $\frac{(x - 1)^2}{(x + 1)^2} - 1$

72. $1 - \frac{(y-2)^2}{(y+2)^2}$

73. $\frac{x}{1-x^2} - 1 + \frac{x}{1+x}$

74. $\frac{y}{x-y} + 2 - \frac{x}{y-x}$

75. $\frac{3x-1}{x^2-10x+25} - \frac{3}{x-5}$

76. $\frac{2a+3}{a^2-7a+12} - \frac{2}{a-3}$

77. $\frac{x+4}{x^2-x-42} + \frac{3}{7-x}$

78. $\frac{x+3}{x^2-3x-10} + \frac{2}{5-x}$

79. $\frac{1}{x+1} + \frac{x}{x-6} - \frac{5x-2}{x^2-5x-6}$

80. $\frac{x}{x-4} + \frac{5}{x+5} - \frac{11x-8}{x^2+x-20}$

81. $\frac{3x+1}{x-1} - \frac{x-1}{x-3} + \frac{x+1}{x^2-4x+3}$

82. $\frac{4x+1}{x-8} - \frac{3x+2}{x+4} - \frac{49x+4}{x^2-4x-32}$

83. $\frac{2x+9}{3-x} + \frac{x+5}{x+7} - \frac{2x^2+3x-3}{x^2+4x-21}$

84. $\frac{3x+5}{x+5} - \frac{x+1}{2-x} - \frac{4x^2-3x-1}{x^2+3x-10}$

Critical Thinking

For Exercises 85 to 88, rewrite the expression as the sum of two fractions in simplest form.

85. $\frac{5b+4a}{ab}$

86. $\frac{6x+7y}{xy}$

87. $\frac{3x^2+4xy}{x^2y^2}$

88. $\frac{2mn^2+8m^2n}{m^3n^3}$

Projects or Group Activities

89. Transportation Suppose that you drive about 12,000 mi per year and that the cost of gasoline averages $3.70 per gallon.

a. Let x represent the number of miles per gallon your car gets. Write a variable expression for the amount you spend on gasoline in one year.

b. Write and simplify a variable expression for the amount of money you will save each year if you increase your gas mileage by 5 miles per gallon.

c. If you currently get 25 miles per gallon and you increase your gas mileage by 5 miles per gallon, how much will you save in one year?

SECTION

6.4 Complex Fractions

OBJECTIVE A *To simplify a complex fraction*

Point of Interest

There are many instances of complex fractions in application problems. For example, the fraction $\dfrac{1}{\dfrac{1}{r_1}+\dfrac{1}{r_2}}$ is used to determine the total resistance in certain electric circuits.

Take Note

You may use either method to simplify a complex fraction. The result will be the same.

A **complex fraction** is a fraction in which the numerator or denominator contains one or more fractions. Examples of complex fractions are shown at the right.

$$\frac{3}{2-\dfrac{1}{2}}, \quad \frac{4+\dfrac{1}{x}}{3+\dfrac{2}{x}}, \quad \frac{\dfrac{1}{x-1}+x+3}{x-3+\dfrac{1}{x+4}}$$

To simplify a complex fraction, use one of the following methods.

Simplifying Complex Fractions

Method 1: Multiply by 1 in the form $\dfrac{\text{LCM}}{\text{LCM}}$.

1. Determine the LCM of the denominators of the fractions in the numerator and denominator of the complex fraction.
2. Multiply the numerator and denominator of the complex fraction by the LCM.
3. Simplify.

Method 2: Multiply the numerator by the reciprocal of the denominator.

1. Simplify the numerator to a single fraction and simplify the denominator to a single fraction.
2. Using the rule for dividing fractions, multiply the numerator by the reciprocal of the denominator.
3. Simplify.

Here is an example using Method 1.

HOW TO 1 Simplify: $\dfrac{9-\dfrac{4}{x^2}}{3+\dfrac{2}{x}}$

The LCM of the denominators of the fractions in the complex fraction is x^2.

$$\frac{9-\dfrac{4}{x^2}}{3+\dfrac{2}{x}} = \frac{9-\dfrac{4}{x^2}}{3+\dfrac{2}{x}}\cdot\frac{x^2}{x^2}$$

• Multiply the numerator and denominator by the LCM.

$$= \frac{9\cdot x^2-\dfrac{4}{x^2}\cdot x^2}{3\cdot x^2+\dfrac{2}{x}\cdot x^2} = \frac{9x^2-4}{3x^2+2x}$$

• Use the Distributive Property.

$$= \frac{(3x-2)\overset{1}{\cancel{(3x+2)}}}{x\underset{1}{\cancel{(3x+2)}}} = \frac{3x-2}{x}$$

• Simplify.

Here is the same example using Method 2.

HOW TO 2 Simplify: $\dfrac{9 - \dfrac{4}{x^2}}{3 + \dfrac{2}{x}}$

$$\frac{9 - \frac{4}{x^2}}{3 + \frac{2}{x}} = \frac{\frac{9x^2}{x^2} - \frac{4}{x^2}}{\frac{3x}{x} + \frac{2}{x}} = \frac{\frac{9x^2 - 4}{x^2}}{\frac{3x + 2}{x}}$$

- Simplify the numerator to a single fraction and simplify the denominator to a single fraction.

$$= \frac{9x^2 - 4}{x^2} \cdot \frac{x}{3x + 2}$$

- Multiply the numerator by the reciprocal of the denominator.

$$= \frac{x(3x - 2)\overset{1}{\cancel{(3x + 2)}}}{x^2\underset{1}{\cancel{(3x + 2)}}}$$

- Simplify.

$$= \frac{3x - 2}{x}$$

For the following examples, we will use Method 1.

EXAMPLE 1

Simplify: $\dfrac{\dfrac{1}{x} + \dfrac{1}{2}}{\dfrac{1}{x^2} - \dfrac{1}{4}}$

Solution

The LCM of x, 2, x^2, and 4 is $4x^2$.

$$\frac{\frac{1}{x} + \frac{1}{2}}{\frac{1}{x^2} - \frac{1}{4}} = \frac{\frac{1}{x} + \frac{1}{2}}{\frac{1}{x^2} - \frac{1}{4}} \cdot \frac{4x^2}{4x^2}$$

- Multiply the numerator and denominator by the LCM.

$$= \frac{\frac{1}{x} \cdot 4x^2 + \frac{1}{2} \cdot 4x^2}{\frac{1}{x^2} \cdot 4x^2 - \frac{1}{4} \cdot 4x^2}$$

- Distributive Property

$$= \frac{4x + 2x^2}{4 - x^2}$$

- Simplify.

$$= \frac{2x\overset{1}{\cancel{(2 + x)}}}{(2 - x)\underset{1}{\cancel{(2 + x)}}}$$

$$= \frac{2x}{2 - x}$$

YOU TRY IT 1

Simplify: $\dfrac{\dfrac{1}{3} - \dfrac{1}{x}}{\dfrac{1}{9} - \dfrac{1}{x^2}}$

Your solution

Solution on p. S15

EXAMPLE 2

Simplify: $\dfrac{1 - \dfrac{2}{x} - \dfrac{15}{x^2}}{1 - \dfrac{11}{x} + \dfrac{30}{x^2}}$

Solution

The LCM of x and x^2 is x^2.

$$\frac{1 - \frac{2}{x} - \frac{15}{x^2}}{1 - \frac{11}{x} + \frac{30}{x^2}} = \frac{1 - \frac{2}{x} - \frac{15}{x^2}}{1 - \frac{11}{x} + \frac{30}{x^2}} \cdot \frac{x^2}{x^2}$$

• Multiply by the LCM.

$$= \frac{1 \cdot x^2 - \frac{2}{x} \cdot x^2 - \frac{15}{x^2} \cdot x^2}{1 \cdot x^2 - \frac{11}{x} \cdot x^2 + \frac{30}{x^2} \cdot x^2}$$

• Distributive Property

$$= \frac{x^2 - 2x - 15}{x^2 - 11x + 30}$$

$$= \frac{\overset{1}{\cancel{(x - 5)}}(x + 3)}{\underset{1}{\cancel{(x - 5)}}(x - 6)} = \frac{x + 3}{x - 6}$$

• Simplify.

YOU TRY IT 2

Simplify: $\dfrac{1 + \dfrac{4}{x} + \dfrac{3}{x^2}}{1 + \dfrac{10}{x} + \dfrac{21}{x^2}}$

Your solution

EXAMPLE 3

Simplify: $\dfrac{x - 8 + \dfrac{20}{x + 4}}{x - 10 + \dfrac{24}{x + 4}}$

Solution

The LCM is $x + 4$.

$$\frac{x - 8 + \frac{20}{x + 4}}{x - 10 + \frac{24}{x + 4}}$$

$$= \frac{x - 8 + \frac{20}{x + 4}}{x - 10 + \frac{24}{x + 4}} \cdot \frac{x + 4}{x + 4}$$

• Multiply by the LCM.

$$= \frac{(x - 8)(x + 4) + \frac{20}{x + 4} \cdot (x + 4)}{(x - 10)(x + 4) + \frac{24}{x + 4} \cdot (x + 4)}$$

• Distributive Property

$$= \frac{x^2 - 4x - 32 + 20}{x^2 - 6x - 40 + 24} = \frac{x^2 - 4x - 12}{x^2 - 6x - 16}$$

• Simplify.

$$= \frac{(x - 6)\overset{1}{\cancel{(x + 2)}}}{(x - 8)\underset{1}{\cancel{(x + 2)}}} = \frac{x - 6}{x - 8}$$

YOU TRY IT 3

Simplify: $\dfrac{x + 3 - \dfrac{20}{x - 5}}{x + 8 + \dfrac{30}{x - 5}}$

Your solution

Solutions on p. S15

6.4 EXERCISES

Concept Check

Exercises 1 to 3 are the examples of complex fractions given at the beginning of Objective 6.4A. By what fraction would you multiply each complex fraction in order to simplify it?

1. $\dfrac{3}{2 - \dfrac{1}{2}}$

2. $\dfrac{4 + \dfrac{1}{x}}{3 + \dfrac{2}{x}}$

3. $\dfrac{\dfrac{1}{x - 1} + x + 3}{x - 3 + \dfrac{1}{x + 4}}$

For Exercises 4 to 6, determine whether the statement is true or false.

4. To simplify a complex fraction, multiply the complex fraction by the LCD of the fractions in the numerator and denominator of the complex fraction.

5. When we multiply the numerator and denominator of a complex fraction by the same expression, we are using the Multiplication Property of One.

6. Our goal in simplifying a complex fraction is to rewrite it so that there are no fractions in the numerator or in the denominator. We then express the fraction in simplest form.

OBJECTIVE A *To simplify a complex fraction*

For Exercises 7 to 36, simplify.

7. $\dfrac{1 + \dfrac{3}{x}}{1 - \dfrac{9}{x^2}}$

8. $\dfrac{1 + \dfrac{4}{x}}{1 - \dfrac{16}{x^2}}$

9. $\dfrac{2 - \dfrac{8}{x + 4}}{3 - \dfrac{12}{x + 4}}$

10. $\dfrac{5 - \dfrac{25}{x + 5}}{1 - \dfrac{3}{x + 5}}$

11. $\dfrac{1 + \dfrac{5}{y - 2}}{1 - \dfrac{2}{y - 2}}$

12. $\dfrac{2 - \dfrac{11}{2x - 1}}{3 - \dfrac{17}{2x - 1}}$

13. $\dfrac{4 - \dfrac{2}{x + 7}}{5 + \dfrac{1}{x + 7}}$

14. $\dfrac{5 + \dfrac{3}{x - 8}}{2 - \dfrac{1}{x - 8}}$

15. $\dfrac{1 - \dfrac{1}{x} - \dfrac{6}{x^2}}{1 - \dfrac{9}{x^2}}$

16. $\dfrac{1 + \dfrac{4}{x} + \dfrac{4}{x^2}}{1 - \dfrac{2}{x} - \dfrac{8}{x^2}}$

17. $\dfrac{1 - \dfrac{5}{x} - \dfrac{6}{x^2}}{1 + \dfrac{6}{x} + \dfrac{5}{x^2}}$

18. $\dfrac{1 - \dfrac{7}{a} + \dfrac{12}{a^2}}{1 + \dfrac{1}{a} - \dfrac{20}{a^2}}$

19. $\dfrac{1 - \dfrac{6}{x} + \dfrac{8}{x^2}}{\dfrac{4}{x^2} + \dfrac{3}{x} - 1}$

20. $\dfrac{1 + \dfrac{3}{x} - \dfrac{18}{x^2}}{\dfrac{21}{x^2} - \dfrac{4}{x} - 1}$

21. $\dfrac{x - \dfrac{4}{x+3}}{1 + \dfrac{1}{x+3}}$

22. $\dfrac{y + \dfrac{1}{y-2}}{1 + \dfrac{1}{y-2}}$

23. $\dfrac{1 - \dfrac{x}{2x+1}}{x - \dfrac{1}{2x+1}}$

24. $\dfrac{1 - \dfrac{2x-2}{3x-1}}{x - \dfrac{4}{3x-1}}$

25. $\dfrac{x - 5 + \dfrac{14}{x+4}}{x + 3 - \dfrac{2}{x+4}}$

26. $\dfrac{a + 4 + \dfrac{5}{a-2}}{a + 6 + \dfrac{15}{a-2}}$

27. $\dfrac{x + 3 - \dfrac{10}{x-6}}{x + 2 - \dfrac{20}{x-6}}$

28. $\dfrac{x - 7 + \dfrac{5}{x-1}}{x - 3 + \dfrac{1}{x-1}}$

29. $\dfrac{y - 6 + \dfrac{22}{2y+3}}{y - 5 + \dfrac{11}{2y+3}}$

30. $\dfrac{x + 2 - \dfrac{12}{2x-1}}{x + 1 - \dfrac{9}{2x-1}}$

31. $\dfrac{x - \dfrac{2}{2x-3}}{2x - 1 - \dfrac{8}{2x-3}}$

32. $\dfrac{x + 3 - \dfrac{18}{2x+1}}{x - \dfrac{6}{2x+1}}$

33. $\dfrac{\dfrac{1}{x} - \dfrac{2}{x-1}}{\dfrac{3}{x} + \dfrac{1}{x-1}}$

34. $\dfrac{\dfrac{3}{n+1} + \dfrac{1}{n}}{\dfrac{2}{n+1} + \dfrac{3}{n}}$

35. $\dfrac{\dfrac{3}{2x-1} - \dfrac{1}{x}}{\dfrac{4}{x} + \dfrac{2}{2x-1}}$

36. $\dfrac{\dfrac{4}{3x+1} + \dfrac{3}{x}}{\dfrac{6}{x} - \dfrac{2}{3x+1}}$

37. True or false? If the denominator of a complex fraction is the reciprocal of the numerator, then the complex fraction is equal to the square of its numerator.

Critical Thinking

For Exercises 38 to 43, simplify.

38. $1 + \dfrac{1}{1 + \dfrac{1}{2}}$

39. $1 + \dfrac{1}{1 + \dfrac{1}{1 + \dfrac{1}{2}}}$

40. $1 - \dfrac{1}{1 - \dfrac{1}{x}}$

41. $1 - \dfrac{1}{1 - \dfrac{1}{y + 1}}$

42. $\dfrac{a^{-1} - b^{-1}}{a^{-2} - b^{-2}}$

43. $\dfrac{x^{-2} - y^{-2}}{x^{-2}y^{-2}}$

Projects or Group Activities

The complex fraction $\dfrac{1}{\dfrac{1}{r_1} + \dfrac{1}{r_2}}$ is mentioned in the Point of Interest on page 303. The fraction gives the total resistance, in ohms, of an electrical circuit that contains two parallel resistors with resistances of r_1 and r_2.

44. Show that the resistance fraction can be rewritten in the form $\dfrac{r_1 r_2}{r_1 + r_2}$.

45. Suppose an electrical circuit contains two parallel resistors with resistances of $r_1 = 2$ ohms and $r_2 = 3$ ohms. Calculate the total resistance in the circuit twice, first using the complex fraction shown above and then using the fraction as rewritten in Exercise 44.

46. Repeat Exercise 45 using $r_1 = 6$ ohms and $r_2 = 8$ ohms.

47. Which form of the resistance fraction did you find easier to work with when doing the calculations in Exercises 45 and 46? Why?

CHECK YOUR PROGRESS: CHAPTER 6

1. Simplify: $\dfrac{x^2 - 4}{x^2 + 3x - 10}$

2. Multiply: $\dfrac{10x^2 - 50x}{12x + 24} \cdot \dfrac{2x + 4}{x^2 - 5x}$

3. Divide: $\dfrac{6x^3y^2}{18a^4b} \div \dfrac{3xy}{9a^2b^5}$

4. Divide: $\dfrac{a^3b}{a^2 - 5a - 14} \div \dfrac{ab^6}{a^2 - 3a - 28}$

5. Find the LCM of $10x^4y^2$ and $15x^3y$.

6. Find the LCM of $8x^2$ and $4x^2 + 8x$.

7. Write the fractions $\dfrac{3}{x^2 + 2x}$ and $\dfrac{4}{x^2}$ in terms of the LCM of the denominators.

8. Subtract: $\dfrac{8a}{3a - 1} - \dfrac{10a}{3a - 1}$

9. Subtract: $\dfrac{a - 1}{a - 2} - \dfrac{3a + 1}{a^2 + 3a - 10}$

10. Simplify: $\dfrac{\dfrac{7}{x - 3} - \dfrac{2}{3x}}{\dfrac{5}{3x} + \dfrac{1}{x - 3}}$

SECTION

6.5 Solving Equations Containing Fractions

OBJECTIVE A *To solve an equation containing fractions*

Recall that to solve an equation containing fractions, clear denominators by multiplying each side of the equation by the LCM of the denominators. Then solve for the variable.

HOW TO 1 Solve: $\frac{3x-1}{4} + \frac{2}{3} = \frac{7}{6}$

$$\frac{3x-1}{4} + \frac{2}{3} = \frac{7}{6}$$

$$12\left(\frac{3x-1}{4} + \frac{2}{3}\right) = 12 \cdot \frac{7}{6}$$

- The LCM is 12. To clear denominators, multiply each side of the equation by the LCM.

$$12\left(\frac{3x-1}{4}\right) + 12 \cdot \frac{2}{3} = 12 \cdot \frac{7}{6}$$

- Simplify by using the Distributive Property and the Properties of Fractions.

$$\frac{\overset{3}{\cancel{12}}}{1}\left(\frac{3x-1}{\underset{1}{\cancel{4}}}\right) + \frac{\overset{4}{\cancel{12}}}{1} \cdot \frac{2}{\underset{1}{\cancel{3}}} = \frac{\overset{2}{\cancel{12}}}{1} \cdot \frac{7}{\underset{1}{\cancel{6}}}$$

$$9x - 3 + 8 = 14$$

- Solve for x.

$$9x + 5 = 14$$

$$9x = 9$$

$$x = 1$$

1 checks as a solution. The solution is 1.

Occasionally, a value that appears to be a solution of an equation will make one of the denominators zero. In such a case, that value is not a solution of the equation.

HOW TO 2 Solve: $\frac{2x}{x-2} = 1 + \frac{4}{x-2}$

$$\frac{2x}{x-2} = 1 + \frac{4}{x-2}$$

$$(x-2)\frac{2x}{x-2} = (x-2)\left(1 + \frac{4}{x-2}\right)$$

- The LCM is $x - 2$. Multiply each side of the equation by the LCM.

$$(x-2)\frac{2x}{x-2} = (x-2) \cdot 1 + (x-2)\frac{4}{x-2}$$

- Simplify by using the Distributive Property and the Properties of Fractions.

$$\frac{\overset{1}{\cancel{(x-2)}}}{1} \cdot \frac{2x}{\underset{1}{\cancel{x-2}}} = (x-2) \cdot 1 + \frac{\overset{1}{\cancel{(x-2)}}}{1} \cdot \frac{4}{\underset{1}{\cancel{x-2}}}$$

$$2x = x - 2 + 4$$

- Solve for x.

$$2x = x + 2$$

$$x = 2$$

When x is replaced by 2, the denominators of $\frac{2x}{x-2}$ and $\frac{4}{x-2}$ are zero. Therefore, the equation has no solution.

Take Note

HOW TO 2 at the right illustrates the importance of checking a solution of a rational equation when each side is multiplied by a variable expression. As shown in this example, a proposed solution may not check when it is substituted into the original equation.

EXAMPLE 1

Solve: $\frac{x}{x+4} = \frac{2}{x}$

Solution

The LCM is $x(x+4)$.

$$\frac{x}{x+4} = \frac{2}{x}$$

$$x(x+4)\left(\frac{x}{x+4}\right) = x(x+4)\left(\frac{2}{x}\right)$$ • Multiply by the LCM.

$$\frac{x\cancel{(x+4)}}{1} \cdot \frac{x}{\cancel{x+4}} = \frac{\cancel{x}(x+4)}{1} \cdot \frac{2}{\cancel{x}}$$ • Divide by the common factors.

$$x^2 = (x+4)2$$ • Simplify.

$$x^2 = 2x + 8$$

Solve the quadratic equation by factoring.

$$x^2 - 2x - 8 = 0$$ • Write in standard form.

$$(x-4)(x+2) = 0$$ • Factor.

$$x - 4 = 0 \qquad x + 2 = 0$$ • Principle of Zero Products

$$x = 4 \qquad x = -2$$

Both 4 and -2 check as solutions.
The solutions are 4 and -2.

YOU TRY IT 1

Solve: $\frac{x}{x+6} = \frac{3}{x}$

Your solution

EXAMPLE 2

Solve: $\frac{3x}{x-4} = 5 + \frac{12}{x-4}$

Solution

The LCM is $x - 4$.

$$\frac{3x}{x-4} = 5 + \frac{12}{x-4}$$

$$(x-4)\left(\frac{3x}{x-4}\right) = (x-4)\left(5 + \frac{12}{x-4}\right)$$ • Clear denominators.

$$\frac{\cancel{(x-4)}}{1} \cdot \frac{3x}{\cancel{x-4}} = (x-4)5 + \frac{\cancel{(x-4)}}{1} \cdot \frac{12}{\cancel{x-4}}$$

$$3x = (x-4)5 + 12$$ • Solve for x.

$$3x = 5x - 20 + 12$$

$$3x = 5x - 8$$

$$-2x = -8$$

$$x = 4$$

4 does not check as a solution.
The equation has no solution.

YOU TRY IT 2

Solve: $\frac{5x}{x+2} = 3 - \frac{10}{x+2}$

Your solution

Solutions on p. S15

Concept Check

1. The process of clearing denominators in an equation containing fractions is an application of which property of equations?

2. If the denominator of a fraction is $x + 3$, for what value of x is the fraction undefined?

3. Explain why you can clear denominators in part (a) below but not in part (b).
   a. $\frac{x}{2} + \frac{1}{3} = \frac{5}{2}$ b. $\frac{x}{2} + \frac{1}{3} + \frac{5}{2}$

4. After solving an equation containing fractions, why must we check the solution?

OBJECTIVE A *To solve an equation containing fractions*

When a proposed solution of a rational equation does not check in the original equation, it is because the proposed solution results in an expression that involves division by zero. For Exercises 5 to 7, state the values of x that would result in division by zero when substituted into the original equation.

5. $\frac{6x}{x+1} - \frac{x}{x-2} = 4$

6. $\frac{1}{x+5} = \frac{x}{x-3} + \frac{2}{x^2+2x-15}$

7. $\frac{3}{x-9} = \frac{1}{x^2-9x} + 2$

For Exercises 8 to 40, solve.

8. $\frac{2x}{3} - \frac{5}{2} = -\frac{1}{2}$

9. $\frac{x}{3} - \frac{1}{4} = \frac{1}{12}$

10. $\frac{x}{3} - \frac{1}{4} = \frac{x}{4} - \frac{1}{6}$

11. $\frac{2y}{9} - \frac{1}{6} = \frac{y}{9} + \frac{1}{6}$

12. $\frac{2x-5}{8} + \frac{1}{4} = \frac{x}{8} + \frac{3}{4}$

13. $\frac{3x+4}{12} - \frac{1}{3} = \frac{5x+2}{12} - \frac{1}{2}$

14. $\frac{6}{2a+1} = 2$

15. $\frac{12}{3x-2} = 3$

16. $\frac{9}{2x-5} = -2$

17. $\frac{6}{4-3x} = 3$

18. $2 + \frac{5}{x} = 7$

19. $3 + \frac{8}{n} = 5$

20. $1 - \frac{9}{x} = 4$

21. $3 - \frac{12}{x} = 7$

22. $\frac{2}{y} + 5 = 9$

23. $\dfrac{6}{x} + 3 = 11$

24. $\dfrac{3}{x - 2} = \dfrac{4}{x}$

25. $\dfrac{5}{x + 3} = \dfrac{3}{x - 1}$

26. $\dfrac{2}{3x - 1} = \dfrac{3}{4x + 1}$

27. $\dfrac{5}{3x - 4} = \dfrac{-3}{1 - 2x}$

28. $\dfrac{-3}{2x + 5} = \dfrac{2}{x - 1}$

29. $\dfrac{4}{5y - 1} = \dfrac{2}{2y - 1}$

30. $\dfrac{4x}{x - 4} + 5 = \dfrac{5x}{x - 4}$

31. $\dfrac{2x}{x + 2} - 5 = \dfrac{7x}{x + 2}$

32. $2 + \dfrac{3}{a - 3} = \dfrac{a}{a - 3}$

33. $\dfrac{x}{x + 4} = 3 - \dfrac{4}{x + 4}$

34. $\dfrac{x}{x - 1} = \dfrac{8}{x + 2}$

35. $\dfrac{x}{x + 12} = \dfrac{1}{x + 5}$

36. $\dfrac{2x}{x + 4} = \dfrac{3}{x - 1}$

37. $\dfrac{5}{3n - 8} = \dfrac{n}{n + 2}$

38. $\dfrac{x}{x + 4} = \dfrac{11}{x^2 - 16} + 2$

39. $x - \dfrac{6}{x - 3} = \dfrac{2x}{x - 3}$

40. $\dfrac{8}{r} + \dfrac{3}{r - 1} = 3$

Critical Thinking

For Exercises 41 to 44, solve.

41. $\dfrac{3}{5}y - \dfrac{1}{3}(1 - y) = \dfrac{2y - 5}{15}$

42. $\dfrac{3}{4}a = \dfrac{1}{2}(3 - a) + \dfrac{a - 2}{4}$

43. $\dfrac{x + 1}{x^2 + x - 2} = \dfrac{x + 2}{x^2 - 1} + \dfrac{3}{x + 2}$

44. $\dfrac{y + 2}{y^2 - y - 2} + \dfrac{y + 1}{y^2 - 4} = \dfrac{1}{y + 1}$

Projects or Group Activities

Intensity of Illumination You are already aware that the standard unit of length in the metric system is the meter (m). You may not know that the standard unit of light intensity is the **candela (cd)**.

The rate at which light falls on a 1-square-unit area of surface is called the **intensity of illumination**. Intensity of illumination is measured in **lumens (lm)**. A lumen is defined in the following illustration.

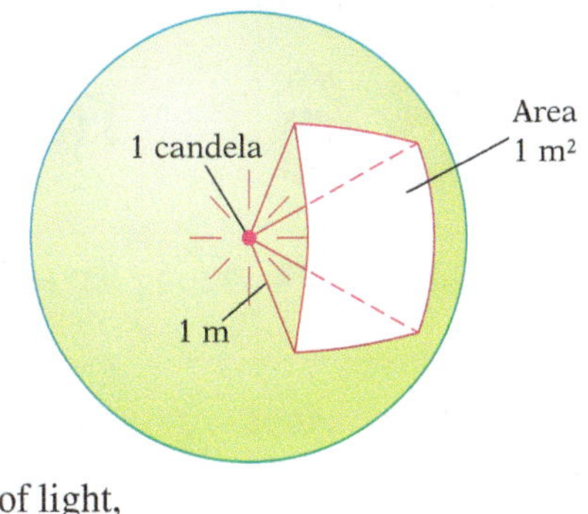

Picture a source of light equal to 1 cd positioned at the center of a hollow sphere that has a radius of 1 m. The rate at which light falls on 1 m^2 of the inner surface of the sphere is equal to 1 lm. If a light source equal to 4 cd is positioned at the center of the sphere, then each square meter of the inner surface receives four times as much illumination, or 4 lm.

Light rays diverge as they leave a light source. The light that falls on an area of 1 m^2 at a distance of 1 m from the light source spreads out over an area of 4 m^2 when it is 2 m from the source. The same light spreads out over an area of 9 m^2 when it is 3 m from the light source, and over an area of 16 m^2 when it is 4 m from the light source. Therefore, as a surface moves farther away from the source of light, the intensity of illumination on the surface decreases from its value at 1 m to $\left(\frac{1}{2}\right)^2$, or $\frac{1}{4}$, that value at 2 m; to $\left(\frac{1}{3}\right)^2$, or $\frac{1}{9}$, that value at 3 m; and to $\left(\frac{1}{4}\right)^2$, or $\frac{1}{16}$, that value at 4 m.

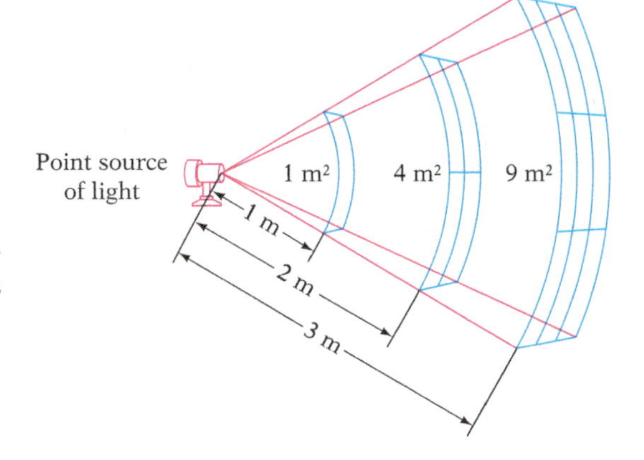

The formula for the intensity of illumination is

$$I = \frac{s}{r^2}$$

where I is the intensity of illumination in lumens, s is the intensity of the light source in candelas, and r is the distance in meters between the light source and the illuminated surface.

Example A 30-candela lamp is positioned 0.5 m above a desk. Find the illumination on the desk.

$$I = \frac{s}{r^2}$$

$$I = \frac{30}{(0.5)^2} = 120$$

The illumination on the desk is 120 lm.

45. A 100-candela light is hanging 5 m above a floor. What is the intensity of the illumination on the floor beneath the light?

46. A 25-candela source of light is positioned 2 m above a desk. Find the intensity of illumination on the desk.

47. How strong a light source is needed to cast 20 lm of light on a surface 4 m from the source?

48. How strong a light source is needed to cast 80 lm of light on a surface 5 m from the source?

49. How far from the desk surface must a 40-candela light source be positioned if the desired intensity of illumination is 10 lm?

50. Find the distance between a 36-candela light source and a surface if the intensity of illumination on the surface is 0.01 lm.

SECTION

6.6 Ratio and Proportion

OBJECTIVE A To solve a proportion

Point of Interest

The Women's Restroom Equity Bill was signed by New York City Mayor Michael Bloomberg and approved unanimously by the NYC Council. This bill requires that women's and men's bathroom stalls in bars, sports arenas, theaters, and highway service areas be in a ratio of 2 to 1. Nicknamed "potty parity," this legislation attempts to shorten the long lines at ladies rooms throughout the city.

Quantities such as 4 meters, 15 seconds, and 8 gallons are number quantities written with units. In these examples, the units are meters, seconds, and gallons.

A **ratio** is the quotient of two quantities that have the same unit.

The length of a living room is 16 ft and the width is 12 ft. The ratio of the length to the width is written

$\frac{16 \text{ ft}}{12 \text{ ft}} = \frac{16}{12} = \frac{4}{3}$ A ratio is in simplest form when the two numbers do not have a common factor. Note that the units are not written.

A **rate** is the quotient of two quantities that have different units.

There are 2 lb of salt in 8 gal of water. The salt-to-water rate is

$\frac{2 \text{ lb}}{8 \text{ gal}} = \frac{1 \text{ lb}}{4 \text{ gal}}$ A rate is in simplest form when the two numbers do not have a common factor. The units are written as part of the rate.

A **proportion** is an equation that states the equality of two ratios or rates. Examples of proportions are shown at the right.

$\frac{30 \text{ mi}}{4 \text{ h}} = \frac{15 \text{ mi}}{2 \text{ h}}$ $\frac{4}{6} = \frac{8}{12}$ $\frac{3}{4} = \frac{x}{8}$

HOW TO 1 Solve the proportion $\frac{4}{x} = \frac{2}{3}$.

$$\frac{4}{x} = \frac{2}{3}$$

$$3x\left(\frac{4}{x}\right) = 3x\left(\frac{2}{3}\right)$$

- The LCM of the denominators is $3x$. To clear denominators, multiply each side of the proportion by the LCM.

$$12 = 2x$$

- Solve the equation for x.

$$6 = x$$

The solution is 6.

APPLY THE CONCEPT

Nine ceramic tiles are required to tile a 4-square-foot area. At this rate, how many square feet can be tiled using 270 ceramic tiles?

Athanasia Nomikou/Shutterstock.com

To find the total area that 270 ceramic tiles will cover, write and solve a proportion using x to represent the number of square feet that 270 tiles will cover.

$$\frac{4}{9} = \frac{x}{270}$$

- The numerators represent square feet covered. The denominators represent numbers of tiles.

$$270\left(\frac{4}{9}\right) = 270\left(\frac{x}{270}\right)$$

- Multiply by the LCM of the denominators.

$$120 = x$$

A 120-square-foot area can be tiled using 270 tiles.

EXAMPLE 1

Solve: **A.** $\frac{8}{x+3} = \frac{4}{x}$ **B.** $\frac{6}{x+4} = \frac{12}{5x-13}$

Solution

A.

$$\frac{8}{x+3} = \frac{4}{x}$$

$$x(x+3)\frac{8}{x+3} = x(x+3)\frac{4}{x}$$ • **Clear denominators.**

$$8x = 4(x+3)$$ • **Solve for x.**

$$8x = 4x + 12$$

$$4x = 12$$

$$x = 3$$

The solution is 3.

B.

$$\frac{6}{x+4} = \frac{12}{5x-13}$$

$$(5x-13)(x+4)\frac{6}{x+4} = (5x-13)(x+4)\frac{12}{5x-13}$$

$$(5x-13)6 = (x+4)12$$

$$30x - 78 = 12x + 48$$

$$18x - 78 = 48$$

$$18x = 126$$

$$x = 7$$

The solution is 7.

YOU TRY IT 1

Solve. **A.** $\frac{2}{x+3} = \frac{6}{5x+5}$ **B.** $\frac{5}{2x-3} = \frac{10}{x+3}$

Your solution

EXAMPLE 2

The monthly loan payment for a car is $28.35 for each $1000 borrowed. At this rate, find the monthly payment for a $6000 car loan.

Strategy

To find the monthly payment, write and solve a proportion using P to represent the monthly car payment.

Solution

$$\frac{28.35}{1000} = \frac{P}{6000}$$ • **Write a proportion.**

$$6000\left(\frac{28.35}{1000}\right) = 6000\left(\frac{P}{6000}\right)$$ • **Clear denominators.**

$$170.10 = P$$

The monthly payment is $170.10.

YOU TRY IT 2

Three ounces of medication are required for a 120-pound adult. At this rate, how many ounces of medication are required for a 180-pound adult?

Your strategy

Your solution

Solutions on p. S16

OBJECTIVE B *To solve problems involving similar triangles*

magicinfoto/Shutterstock.com

Similar objects have the same shape but not necessarily the same size. A tennis ball is similar to a basketball. A model ship is similar to an actual ship.

Similar objects have corresponding parts; for example, the rudder on the model ship corresponds to the rudder on the actual ship. The relationship between the sizes of each of the corresponding parts can be written as a ratio, and each ratio will be the same.

If the rudder on the model ship is $\frac{1}{100}$ the size of the rudder on the actual ship, then the model wheelhouse is $\frac{1}{100}$ the size of the actual wheelhouse, the width of the model is $\frac{1}{100}$ the width of the actual ship, and so on.

The two triangles ABC and DEF shown at the right are similar. Side $\overline{AB}$ corresponds to $\overline{DE}$, side $\overline{BC}$ corresponds to $\overline{EF}$, and side $\overline{AC}$ corresponds to $\overline{DF}$. The height $\overline{CH}$ corresponds to the height $\overline{FK}$. The ratios of corresponding parts of similar triangles are equal.

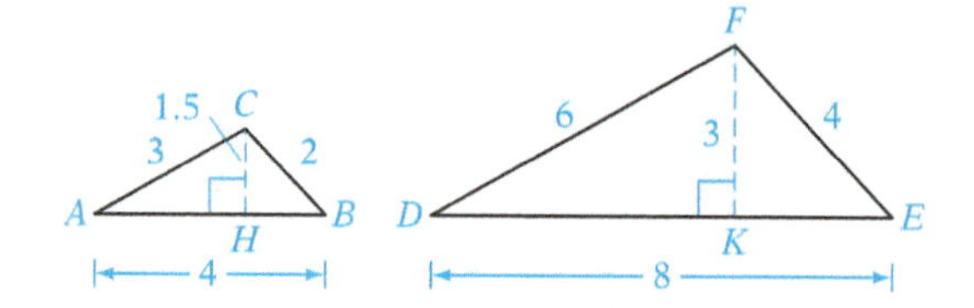

$$\frac{AB}{DE} = \frac{4}{8} = \frac{1}{2}, \quad \frac{AC}{DF} = \frac{3}{6} = \frac{1}{2}, \quad \frac{BC}{EF} = \frac{2}{4} = \frac{1}{2}, \quad \text{and} \quad \frac{CH}{FK} = \frac{1.5}{3} = \frac{1}{2}$$

Because the ratios of corresponding parts are equal, three proportions can be formed using the sides of the triangles.

$$\frac{AB}{DE} = \frac{AC}{DF}, \quad \frac{AB}{DE} = \frac{BC}{EF}, \quad \text{and} \quad \frac{AC}{DF} = \frac{BC}{EF}$$

Three proportions can also be formed by using the sides and heights of the triangles.

$$\frac{AB}{DE} = \frac{CH}{FK}, \quad \frac{AC}{DF} = \frac{CH}{FK}, \quad \text{and} \quad \frac{BC}{EF} = \frac{CH}{FK}$$

HOW TO 2 Triangles ABC and DEF at the right are similar. Find the area of triangle ABC.

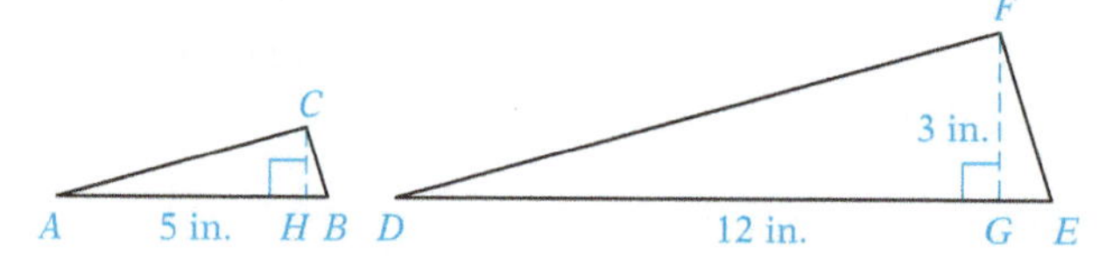

$$\frac{AB}{DE} = \frac{CH}{FG}$$ • Solve a proportion to find the height of triangle ABC.

$$\frac{5}{12} = \frac{CH}{3}$$ • $AB = 5$, $DE = 12$, and $FG = 3$.

$$12 \cdot \frac{5}{12} = 12 \cdot \frac{CH}{3}$$ • To clear denominators, multiply each side of the proportion by 12.

$$5 = 4(CH)$$ • Solve for CH.

$$1.25 = CH$$ • The height is 1.25 in. The base is 5 in.

$$A = \frac{1}{2}bh = \frac{1}{2}(5)(1.25) = 3.125$$ • Use the formula for the area of a triangle.

The area of triangle ABC is 3.125 in^2.

The measures of the corresponding angles of similar triangles are equal. Therefore, for the similar triangles in HOW TO 2,

$$m\angle A = m\angle D, \quad m\angle B = m\angle E, \quad \text{and} \quad m\angle C = m\angle F$$

It is also true that if the measures of the three angles of one triangle are equal, respectively, to the measures of the three angles of another triangle, then the two triangles are similar.

Take Note

Vertical angles of intersecting lines, corresponding angles of parallel lines, and angles of a triangle are discussed in Section 3.6.

A line $\overline{DE}$ is drawn parallel to the base $\overline{AB}$ in the triangle at the right. $m\angle x = m\angle m$ and $m\angle y = m\angle n$ because corresponding angles are equal. $m\angle C = m\angle C$; thus the measures of the three angles of triangle DEC are equal, respectively, to the measures of the three angles of triangle ABC. Triangle DEC is similar to triangle ABC.

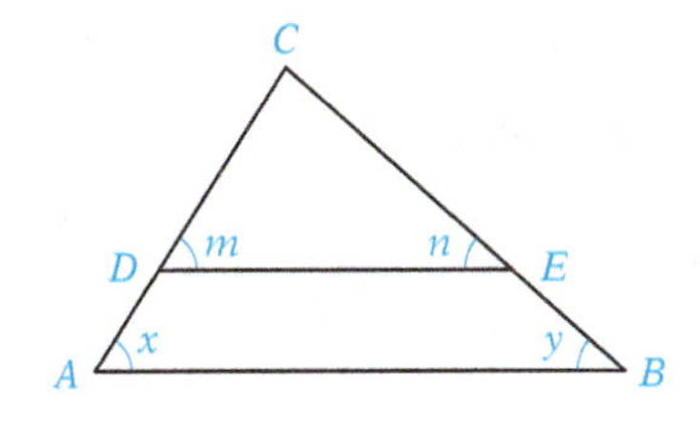

The sum of the measures of the three angles of a triangle is 180°. If two angles of one triangle are equal in measure to two angles of another triangle, then the third angles must be equal in measure. Thus we can say that if two angles of one triangle are equal in measure to two angles of another triangle, then the two triangles are similar.

HOW TO 3 The line segments $\overline{AB}$ and $\overline{CD}$ intersect at point O in the figure at the right. Angles C and D are right angles. Find DO.

First we must determine whether triangle AOC is similar to triangle BOD.

$m\angle C = m\angle D$ because they are right angles.

$m\angle x = m\angle y$ because they are vertical angles.

Triangle AOC is similar to triangle BOD because two angles of one triangle are equal in measure to two angles of the other triangle.

$$\frac{AC}{DB} = \frac{CO}{DO}$$
• Use a proportion to find the length of the unknown side.

$$\frac{4}{7} = \frac{3}{DO}$$
• $AC = 4$, $CO = 3$, and $DB = 7$.

$$7(DO)\frac{4}{7} = 7(DO)\frac{3}{DO}$$
• To clear denominators, multiply each side of the proportion by $7(DO)$.

$$4(DO) = 7(3)$$
• Solve for DO.

$$4(DO) = 21$$

$$DO = 5.25$$

DO is 5.25 cm.

EXAMPLE 3

Triangles ABC and DEF are similar. Find AC.

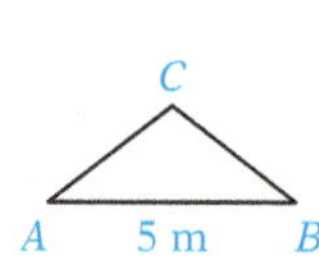

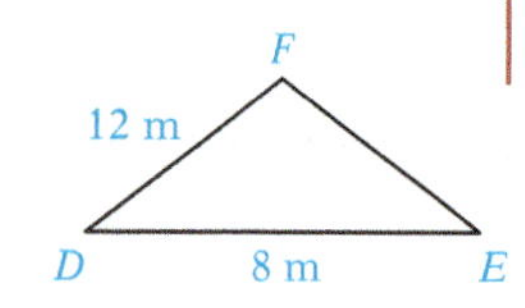

Strategy

To find the length of AC, write and solve a proportion.

Solution

$$\frac{AC}{DF} = \frac{AB}{DE}$$ • Write a proportion.

$$\frac{AC}{12} = \frac{5}{8}$$ • $DF = 12, AB = 5, DE = 8$

$$24\left(\frac{AC}{12}\right) = 24\left(\frac{5}{8}\right)$$ • Multiply each side by 24.

$$2(AC) = 15$$ • Solve for AC.

$$AC = 7.5$$

AC is 7.5 m.

YOU TRY IT 3

Triangles ABC and DEF are similar. Find DE.

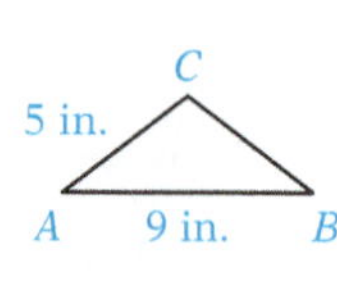

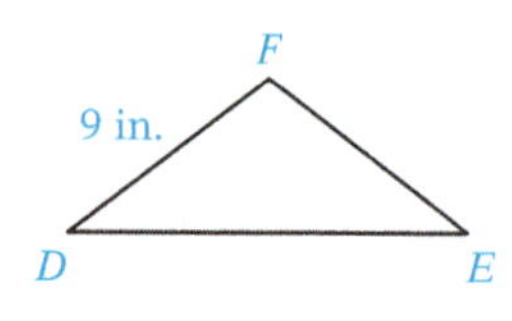

Your strategy

Your solution

EXAMPLE 4

In the figure, $\overline{AB}$ is parallel to $\overline{DC}$. $AB = 12$ m, $DC = 4$ m, and $AC = 18$ m. Find CO.

Strategy

Triangle AOB is similar to triangle COD. Solve a proportion to find the length of CO. Let x represent the length of CO, and let $18 - x$ represent the length of AO.

Solution

$$\frac{DC}{AB} = \frac{CO}{AO}$$ • Write a proportion.

$$\frac{4}{12} = \frac{x}{18 - x}$$ • Substitute.

$$12(18 - x) \cdot \frac{4}{12} = 12(18 - x) \cdot \frac{x}{18 - x}$$ • Clear denominators.

$$4(18 - x) = 12x$$ • Solve for x.

$$72 - 4x = 12x$$

$$72 = 16x$$

$$4.5 = x$$

CO is 4.5 m.

YOU TRY IT 4

In the figure, $\overline{AB}$ is parallel to $\overline{DC}$. $AB = 10$ cm, $CD = 4$ cm, and $DO = 3$ cm. Find the area of triangle AOB.

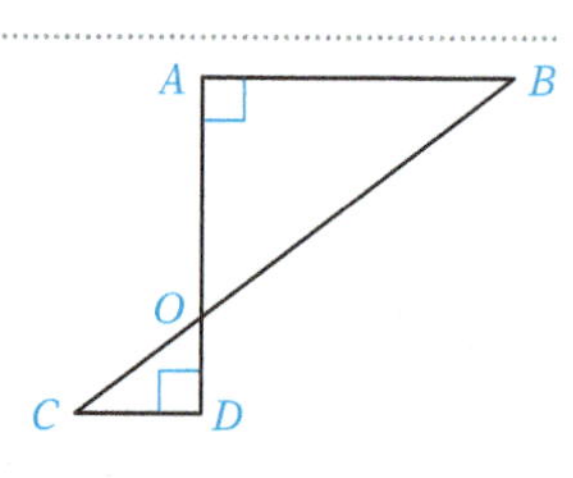

Your strategy

Your solution

Solutions on p. S16

6.6 EXERCISES

Concept Check

1. Explain the difference between a ratio and a rate.

2. Explain the difference between a ratio and a proportion.

3. Identify each of the following as a ratio or a rate. Then write it in simplest form.

 a. $\frac{50 \text{ ft}}{4 \text{ s}}$ b. $\frac{28 \text{ in.}}{21 \text{ in.}}$ c. $\frac{20 \text{ mi}}{2 \text{ h}}$ d. $\frac{3 \text{ gal}}{18 \text{ gal}}$

For Exercises 4 and 5, use the pair of similar triangles shown at the right. Triangle *PQR* is similar to triangle *XYZ*.

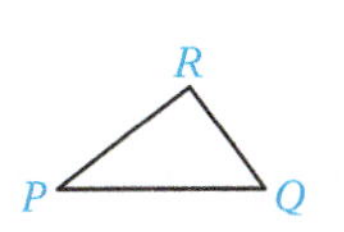

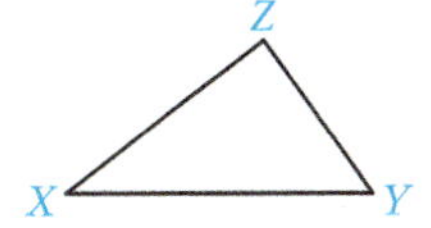

4. a. The corresponding part for side $\overline{RP}$ is ________.
 b. The corresponding part for side $\overline{YX}$ is ________.
 c. The corresponding part for $\angle X$ is ________.

5. a. Complete this proportion: $\frac{QR}{\square} = \frac{PR}{XZ}$.
 b. Complete this equality: $\angle Z =$ ________.

6. In the diagram at the right, $\overline{BD}$ is parallel to $\overline{AE}$.
 a. Triangle *CBD* is similar to triangle ________.
 b. Complete this proportion: $\frac{BD}{AE} = \frac{CD}{\square}$.

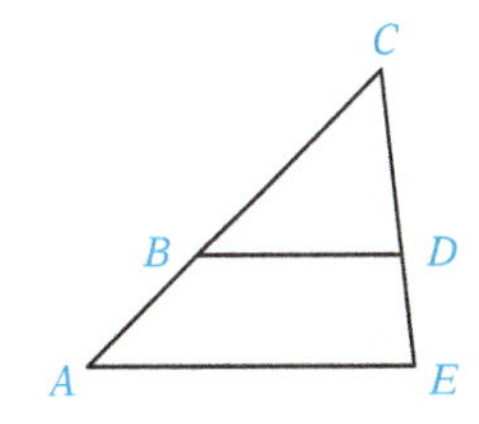

OBJECTIVE A *To solve a proportion*

For Exercises 7 to 21, solve.

7. $\frac{x}{12} = \frac{3}{4}$

8. $\frac{6}{x} = \frac{2}{3}$

9. $\frac{4}{9} = \frac{x}{27}$

10. $\frac{16}{9} = \frac{64}{x}$

11. $\frac{x+3}{12} = \frac{5}{6}$

12. $\frac{3}{5} = \frac{x-4}{10}$

13. $\frac{18}{x+4} = \frac{9}{5}$

14. $\frac{2}{11} = \frac{20}{x-3}$

15. $\frac{2}{x} = \frac{4}{x+1}$

16. $\frac{16}{x-2} = \frac{8}{x}$

17. $\frac{x+3}{4} = \frac{x}{8}$

18. $\frac{x-6}{3} = \frac{x}{5}$

19. $\frac{2}{x-1} = \frac{6}{2x+1}$

20. $\frac{9}{x+2} = \frac{3}{x-2}$

21. $\frac{2x}{7} = \frac{x-2}{14}$

22. True or false? (Assume that a, b, c, and d do not equal zero.)

a. If $\frac{a}{b} = \frac{c}{d}$, then $\frac{d}{b} = \frac{c}{a}$.

b. If $\frac{a}{b} = \frac{c}{d}$, then $\frac{b}{a} = \frac{d}{c}$.

23. Elections An exit poll showed that 4 out of every 7 voters cast a ballot in favor of an amendment to a city charter. At this rate, how many people voted in favor of the amendment if 35,000 people voted?

24. Business A quality control inspector found 3 defective transistors in a shipment of 500 transistors. At this rate, how many transistors would be defective in a shipment of 2000 transistors?

25. Health Insurance See the news clipping at the right. How many Americans do not have health insurance? Use a figure of 300 million for the population of the United States.

26. Poverty See the news clipping at the right. How many American children live in poverty? Use a figure of 75 million for the number of children living in the United States.

In the NEWS!

Room for Improvement

According to a U.N. publication, the United States ranks 13th in the world in the area of human development. Government data show that in regard to health, 3 in 20 Americans do not have health insurance. With respect to standard of living, 1 in 6 American children lives in poverty.

Sources: www.undp.org, www.census.gov, Human Development Report 2009; Income, Poverty, and Health Insurance Coverage in the United States, 2008

27. Construction An air conditioning specialist recommends 2 air vents for every 300 ft^2 of floor space. At this rate, how many air vents are required for an office building of 21,000 ft^2?

28. Television In a city of 25,000 homes, a survey was taken to determine the number with Wi-Fi access. Of the 300 homes surveyed, 210 had Wi-Fi access. Estimate the number of homes in the city that have Wi-Fi access.

Fossils For Exercises 29 and 30, use the information in the article at the right. Assume that all scorpions have approximately the same ratio of claw length to body length.

29. Estimate the length, in feet, of the longest known prehistoric sea scorpion's claw prior to the discovery of the new fossil. Round to the nearest hundredth.

30. Today, scorpions range in length from about 0.5 in. to about 8 in. Estimate the length, in inches, of a claw of a 7-inch scorpion. Round to the nearest hundredth. (*Hint:* Convert 8.2 ft to inches.)

In the NEWS!

390-Million-Year-Old Scorpion Fossil Found

Scientists have announced the unearthing of the largest fossil sea scorpion claw ever discovered. Based on the 18-inch claw length, scientists estimate that the scorpion would have measured 8.2 ft in length. Prior to this discovery, the longest known prehistoric sea scorpion was estimated to be 6.7 ft long.

Source: news.nationalgeographic.com

31. Conservation As part of a conservation effort for a lake, 40 fish were caught, tagged, and then released. Later, 80 fish were caught from the lake. Four of these 80 fish were found to have tags. Estimate the number of fish in the lake.

32. Cooking A simple syrup is made by dissolving 2 c of sugar in $\frac{2}{3}$ c of boiling water. At this rate, how many cups of sugar are required for 2 c of boiling water?

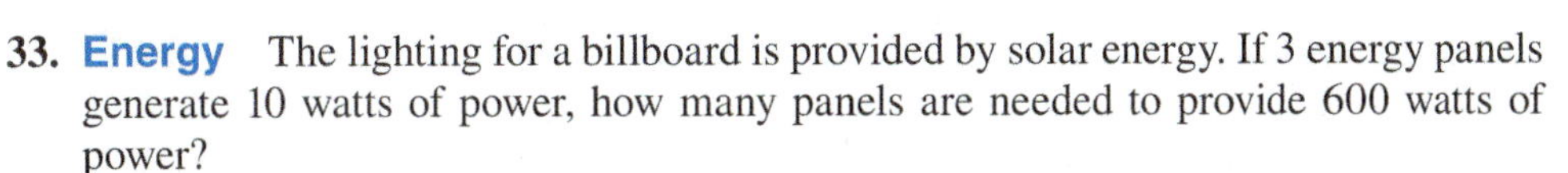

33. Energy The lighting for a billboard is provided by solar energy. If 3 energy panels generate 10 watts of power, how many panels are needed to provide 600 watts of power?

34. Business A company will accept a shipment of 10,000 computer disks if there are 2 or fewer defects in a sample of 100 randomly chosen disks. Assume that there are 300 defective disks in the shipment and that the rate of defective disks in the sample is the same as the rate in the shipment. Will the shipment be accepted?

35. Business A company will accept a shipment of 20,000 precision bearings if there are 3 or fewer defects in a sample of 100 randomly chosen bearings. Assume that there are 400 defective bearings in the shipment and that the rate of defective bearings in the sample is the same as the rate in the shipment. Will the shipment be accepted?

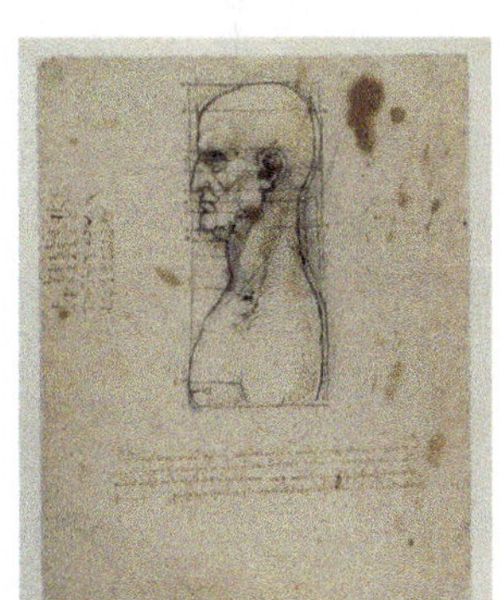
Cameraphoto Arte, Venice/Art Resource, NY

36. Art Leonardo da Vinci measured various distances on the human body in order to make accurate drawings. He determined that in general, the ratio of the kneeling height of a person to his or her standing height is $\frac{3}{4}$. Using this ratio, determine the standing height of a person who has a kneeling height of 48 in.

37. Art In one of Leonardo da Vinci's notebooks, he wrote that ". . . from the top to the bottom of the chin is the sixth part of a face, and it is the fifty-fourth part of the man." Suppose the distance from the top to the bottom of a person's chin is 1.25 in. Using da Vinci's measurements, find the height of the person.

38. Cartography On a map, two cities are $2\frac{5}{8}$ in. apart. If $\frac{3}{8}$ in. on the map represents 25 mi, find the number of miles between the two cities.

39. Cartography On a map, two cities are $5\frac{5}{8}$ in. apart. If $\frac{3}{4}$ in. on the map represents 100 mi, find the number of miles between the two cities.

40. The scale on a map shows that a distance of 3 cm on the map represents an actual distance of 10 mi. Would a distance of 8 cm on the map represent an actual distance that is greater than 30 mi or less than 30 mi?

41. Rocketry The engine of a small rocket burns 170,000 lb of fuel in 1 min. At this rate, how many pounds of fuel does the engine burn in 45 s?

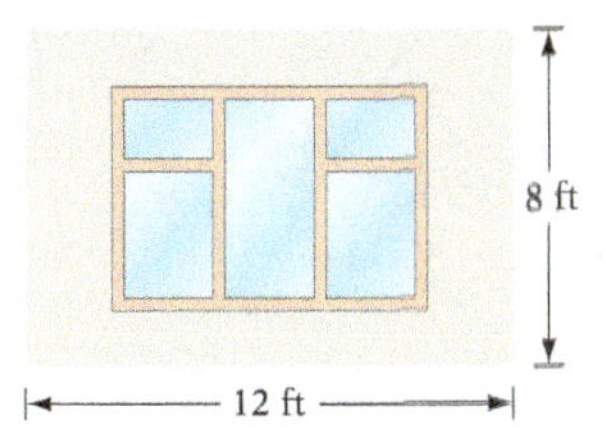

42. Construction To conserve energy and still allow for as much natural lighting as possible, an architect suggests that the ratio of the area of a window to the area of the total wall surface be 5 to 12. Using this ratio, determine the recommended area of a window to be installed in a wall that measures 8 ft by 12 ft.

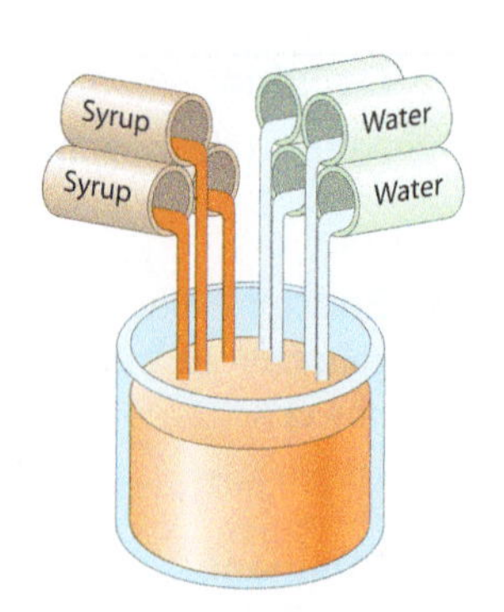

43. Paint Mixtures A green paint is created by mixing 3 parts of yellow with every 5 parts of blue. How many gallons of yellow paint are needed to make 60 gal of this green paint?

44. Food Industry A soft drink is made by mixing 4 parts of carbonated water with every 3 parts of syrup. How many milliliters of carbonated water are in 280 ml of soft drink?

45. Agriculture A 50-acre field yields 1100 bushels of wheat annually. How many additional acres must be planted so that the annual yield will be 1320 bushels?

46. Catering A caterer estimates that 5 gal of coffee will serve 50 people. How much additional coffee is necessary to serve 70 people?

OBJECTIVE B *To solve problems involving similar triangles*

Triangles ABC and DEF in Exercises 47 to 54 are similar. Round answers to the nearest tenth.

47. Find AC.

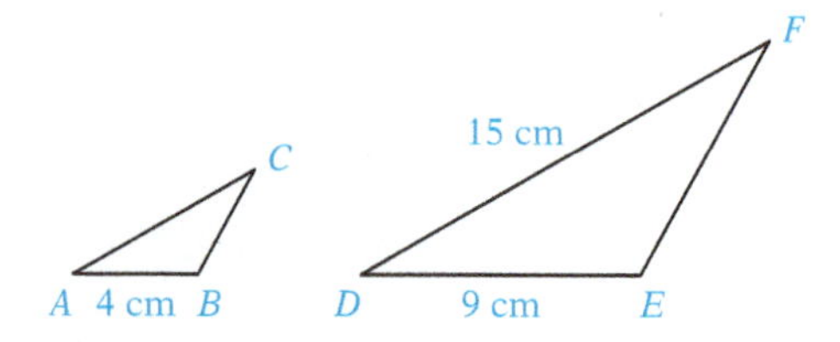

48. Find DE.

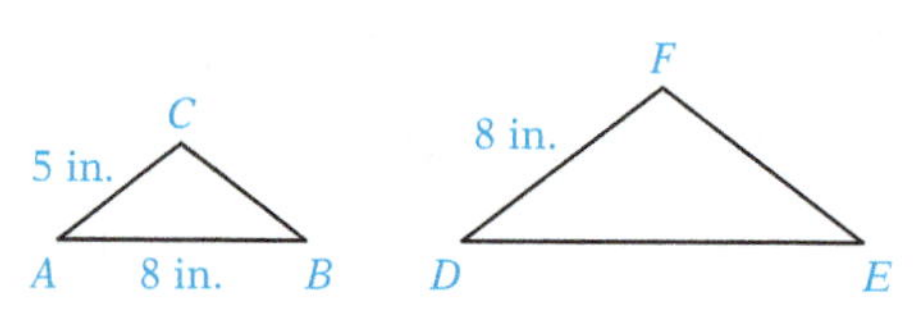

49. Find the height of triangle ABC.

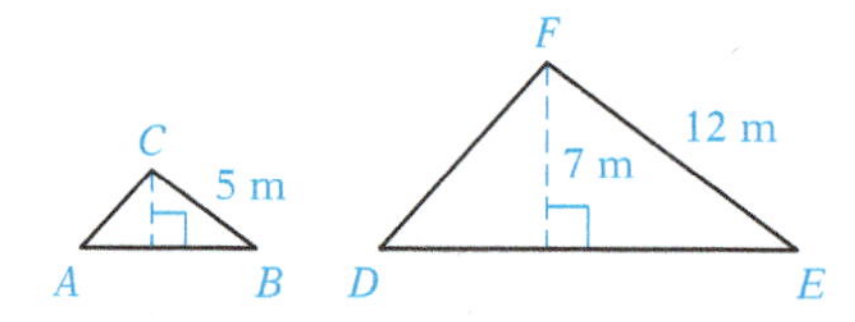

50. Find the height of triangle DEF.

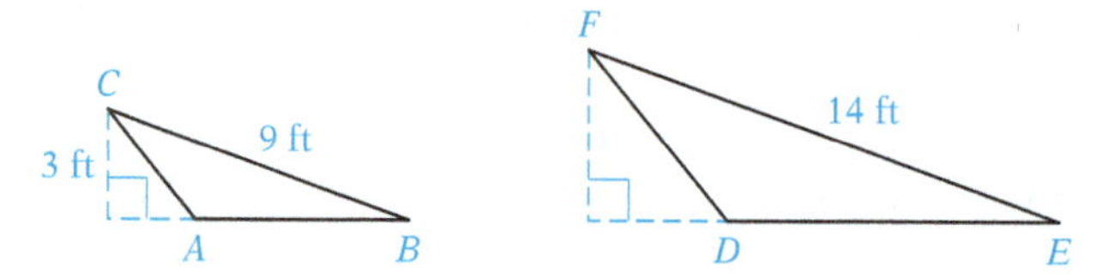

51. Find the perimeter of triangle DEF.

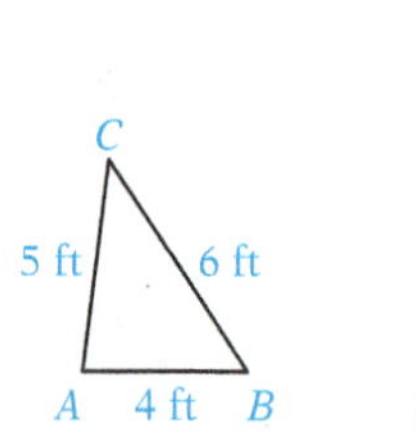

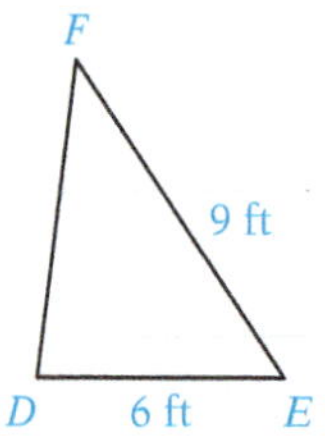

52. Find the perimeter of triangle ABC.

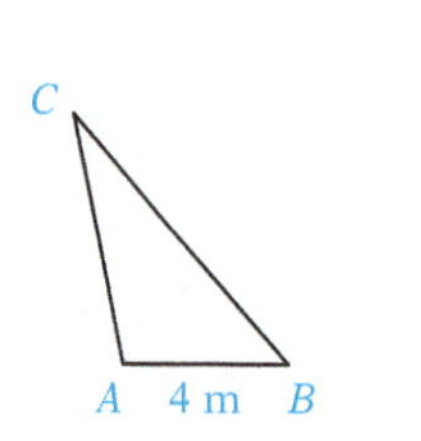

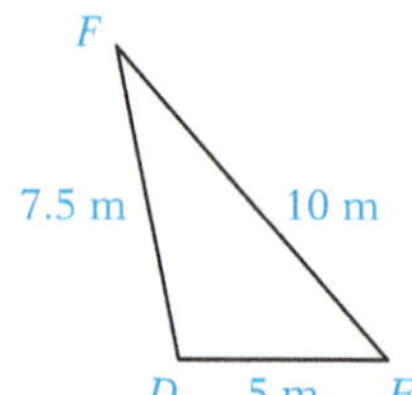

53. Find the area of triangle *ABC*.

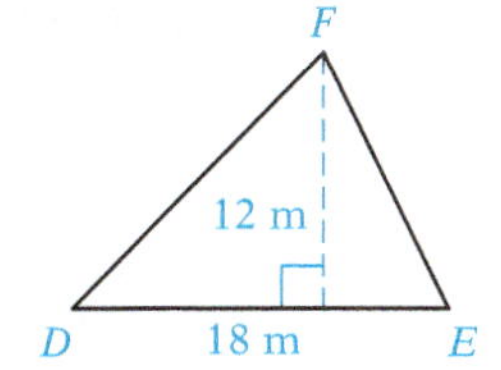

54. Find the area of triangle *ABC*.

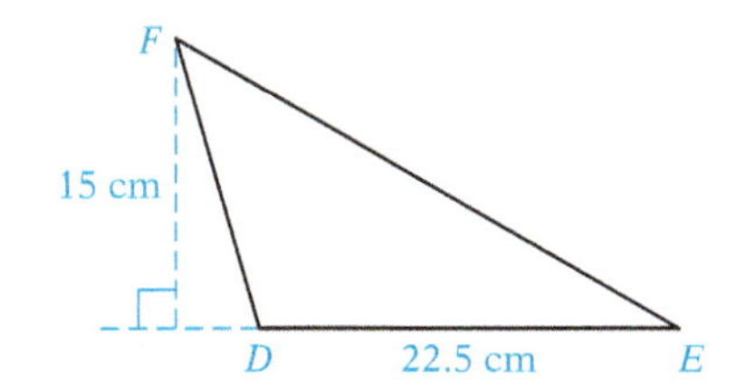

55. Given that $\overline{BD} \parallel \overline{AE}$, *BD* measures 5 cm, *AE* measures 8 cm, and *AC* measures 10 cm, find *BC*.

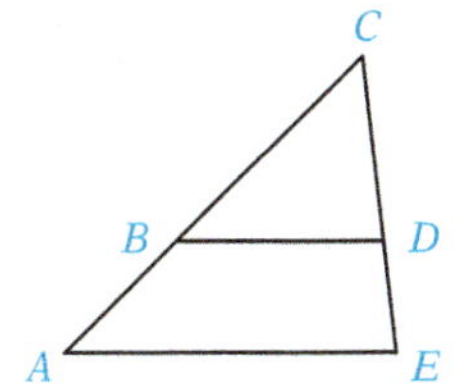

56. Given that $\overline{AC} \parallel \overline{DE}$, *BD* measures 8 m, *AD* measures 12 m, and *BE* measures 6 m, find *BC*.

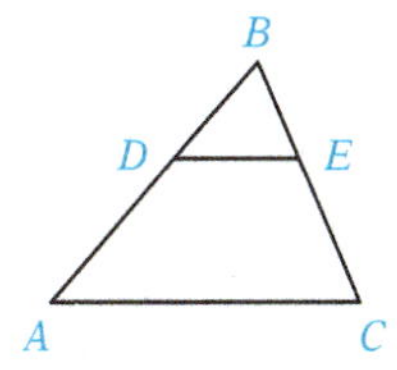

57. Given that $\overline{DE} \parallel \overline{AC}$, *DE* measures 6 in., *AC* measures 10 in., and *AB* measures 15 in., find *DA*.

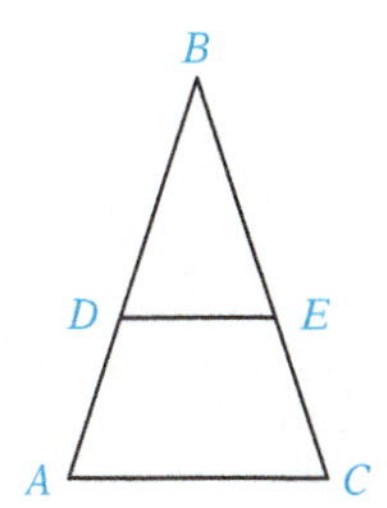

58. Given that $\overline{MP}$ and $\overline{NQ}$ intersect at *O*, *NO* measures 25 ft, *MO* measures 20 ft, and *PO* measures 8 ft, find *QO*.

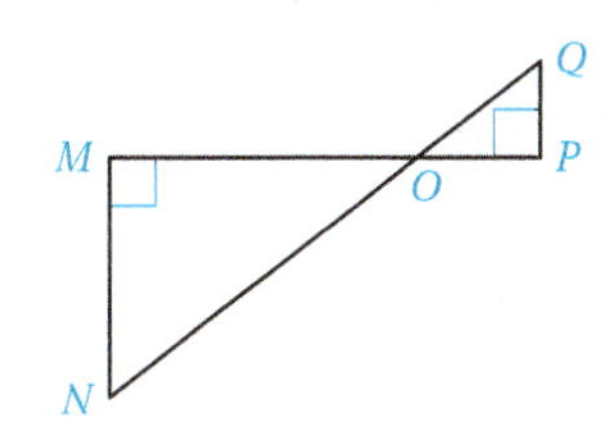

59. Given that $\overline{MP}$ and $\overline{NQ}$ intersect at *O*, *NO* measures 24 cm, *MN* measures 10 cm, *MP* measures 39 cm, and *QO* measures 12 cm, find *OP*.

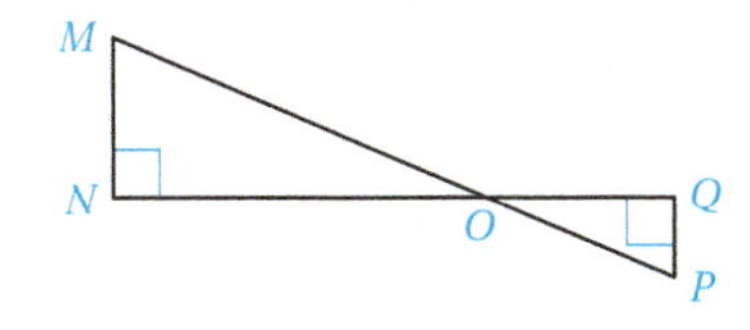

60. Given that $\overline{MQ}$ and $\overline{NP}$ intersect at *O*, *NO* measures 12 m, *MN* measures 9 m, *PQ* measures 3 m, and *MQ* measures 20 m, find the perimeter of triangle *OPQ*.

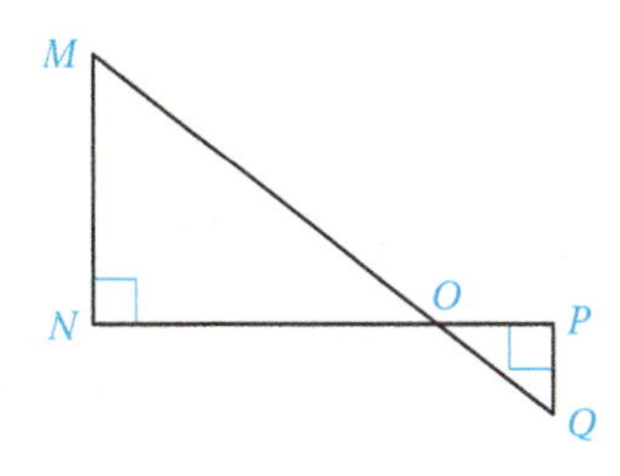

61. True or false? The ratio of the perimeters of two similar triangles is the same as the ratio of their corresponding sides.

62. True or false? The ratio of the areas of two similar triangles is the same as the ratio of their corresponding sides.

63. Similar triangles can be used as an indirect way of measuring inaccessible distances. The diagram at the right represents a river of width DC. The triangles AOB and DOC are similar. The distances AB, BO, and OC can be measured. Find the width of the river.

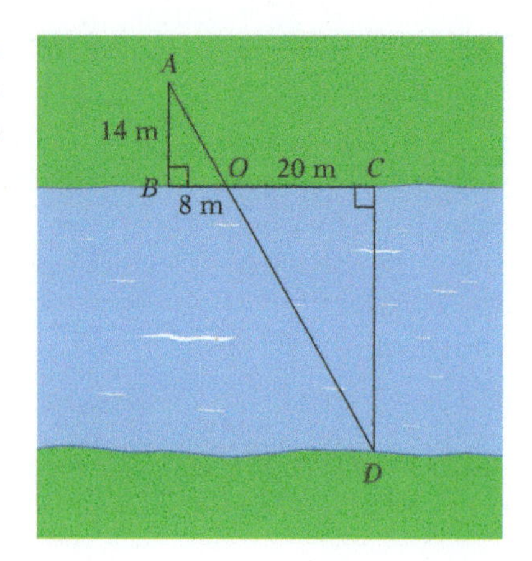

64. The sun's rays cast a shadow as shown in the diagram at the right. Find the height of the flagpole. Write the answer in terms of feet.

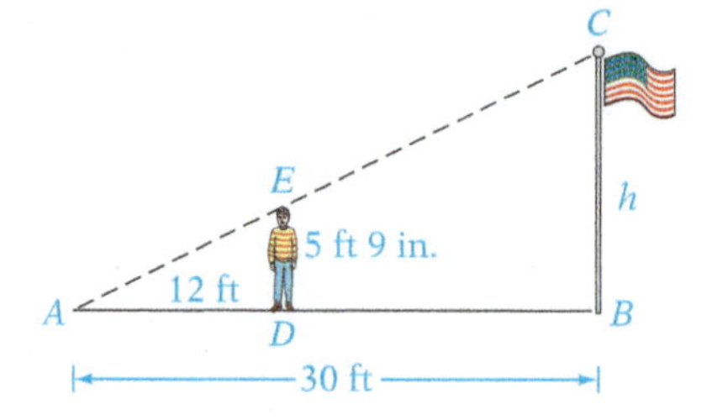

Critical Thinking

65. Number Problem The sum of a number and its reciprocal is $\frac{26}{5}$. Find the number.

66. Lotteries Three people put their money together to buy lottery tickets. The first person put in \$25, the second person put in \$30, and the third person put in \$35. One of the tickets was a winning ticket. If the winning ticket paid \$4.5 million, what was the first person's share of the winnings?

Dennis Ku/Shutterstock.com

67. Sports A basketball player has made 5 out of every 6 foul shots attempted. If 42 foul shots were missed in the player's career, how many foul shots were made in the player's career?

68. Fundraising No one belongs to both the Math Club and the Photography Club, but the two clubs join to hold a car wash. Ten members of the Math Club and 6 members of the Photography Club participate. The profits from the car wash are \$120. If each club's profits are proportional to the number of members participating, what share of the profits does the Math Club receive?

Projects or Group Activities

69. History Eratosthenes, the fifth librarian of Alexandria (230 B.C.), was familiar with certain astronomical data, which enabled him to calculate the circumference of Earth by using a proportion. He knew that on a midsummer day, the sun was directly overhead at Syene, as shown in the diagram. At the same time, at Alexandria, the sun was at a 7.5° angle from the zenith. The distance from Syene to Alexandria was 5000 stadia, or about 520 mi. Eratosthenes reasoned that the ratio of the 7.5° angle to one revolution was equal to the ratio of the arc length of 520 mi to the circumference of Earth. From this, he wrote and solved a proportion.

a. What did Eratosthenes calculate to be the circumference of Earth?

b. Find the difference between his calculation and the accepted value of 24,874 mi.

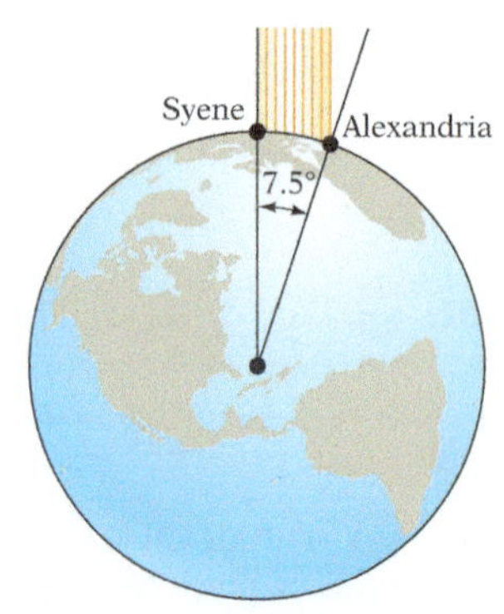

SECTION

6.7 Literal Equations

OBJECTIVE A *To solve a literal equation for one of the variables*

A **literal equation** is an equation that contains more than one variable. Examples of literal equations are shown at the right.

$$2x + 3y = 6$$
$$4w - 2x + z = 0$$

Formulas are used to express relationships among physical quantities. A **formula** is a literal equation that states a rule about measurements. Examples of formulas are shown at the right.

$$\frac{1}{R_1} + \frac{1}{R_2} = \frac{1}{R} \quad \text{(Physics)}$$
$$s = a + (n - 1)d \quad \text{(Mathematics)}$$
$$A = P + Prt \quad \text{(Business)}$$

The Addition and Multiplication Properties can be used to solve a literal equation for one of the variables. The goal is to rewrite the equation so that the variable being solved for is alone on one side of the equation and all the other numbers and variables are on the other side.

HOW TO 1 Solve $A = P(1 + i)$ for i.

The goal is to rewrite the equation so that i is on one side of the equation and all other variables are on the other side.

$$A = P(1 + i)$$
$$A = P + Pi \quad \text{• Use the Distributive Property to remove parentheses.}$$
$$A - P = P - P + Pi \quad \text{• Subtract } P \text{ from each side of the equation.}$$
$$A - P = Pi$$
$$\frac{A - P}{P} = \frac{Pi}{P} \quad \text{• Divide each side of the equation by } P.$$
$$\frac{A - P}{P} = i$$

EXAMPLE 1

Solve $3x - 4y = 12$ for y.

Solution

$$3x - 4y = 12$$
$$3x - 3x - 4y = -3x + 12 \quad \text{• Subtract } 3x.$$
$$-4y = -3x + 12$$
$$\frac{-4y}{-4} = \frac{-3x + 12}{-4} \quad \text{• Divide by } -4.$$
$$y = \frac{3}{4}x - 3$$

YOU TRY IT 1

Solve $5x - 2y = 10$ for y.

Your solution

Solution on p. S16

EXAMPLE 2

Solve $I = \dfrac{E}{R + r}$ for R.

Solution

$$I = \frac{E}{R + r}$$

$$(R + r)I = (R + r)\frac{E}{R + r}$$ • Multiply by $(R + r)$.

$$RI + rI = E$$

$$RI + rI - rI = E - rI$$ • Subtract rI.

$$RI = E - rI$$

$$\frac{RI}{I} = \frac{E - rI}{I}$$ • Divide by I.

$$R = \frac{E - rI}{I}$$

YOU TRY IT 2

Solve $s = \dfrac{A + L}{2}$ for L.

Your solution

EXAMPLE 3

Solve $L = a(1 + ct)$ for c.

Solution

$$L = a(1 + ct)$$

$$L = a + act$$ • Distributive Property

$$L - a = a - a + act$$ • Subtract a.

$$L - a = act$$

$$\frac{L - a}{at} = \frac{act}{at}$$ • Divide by at.

$$\frac{L - a}{at} = c$$

YOU TRY IT 3

Solve $S = a + (n - 1)d$ for n.

Your solution

EXAMPLE 4

Solve $S = C - rC$ for C.

Solution

$$S = C - rC$$

$$S = (1 - r)C$$ • Factor.

$$\frac{S}{1 - r} = \frac{(1 - r)C}{1 - r}$$ • Divide by $(1 - r)$.

$$\frac{S}{1 - r} = C$$

YOU TRY IT 4

Solve $S = rS + C$ for S.

Your solution

Solutions on pp. S16–S17

6.7 EXERCISES

Concept Check

For Exercises 1 and 2, determine whether the statement is true or false.

1. Literal equations are solved using the same properties of equations that are used to solve equations in one variable.
2. In solving a literal equation, the goal is to get the variable being solved for alone on one side of the equation and all numbers and other variables on the other side of the equation.
3. In solving $I = \frac{E}{R + r}$ for R, the goal is to get ________ alone on one side of the equation.
4. In solving $L = a(1 + ct)$ for c, the goal is to get ________ alone on one side of the equation.

OBJECTIVE A To solve a literal equation for one of the variables

For Exercises 5 to 20, solve the formula for the given variable.

5. $d = rt; t$ (Physics)
6. $E = IR; R$ (Physics)
7. $PV = nRT; T$ (Chemistry)
8. $A = bh; h$ (Geometry)
9. $P = 2l + 2w; l$ (Geometry)
10. $F = \frac{9}{5}C + 32; C$ (Temperature conversion)
11. $A = \frac{1}{2}h(b_1 + b_2); b_1$ (Geometry)
12. $s = a(x - vt); t$ (Physics)
13. $V = \frac{1}{3}Ah; h$ (Geometry)
14. $P = R - C; C$ (Business)
15. $R = \frac{C - S}{t}; S$ (Business)
16. $P = \frac{R - C}{n}; R$ (Business)
17. $A = P + Prt; P$ (Business)
18. $T = fm - gm; m$ (Engineering)
19. $A = Sw + w; w$ (Physics)
20. $a = S - Sr; S$ (Mathematics)

For Exercises 21 to 32, solve for y.

21. $3x + y = 10$ **22.** $2x + y = 5$ **23.** $4x - y = 3$ **24.** $5x - y = 7$

25. $3x + 2y = 6$ **26.** $2x + 3y = 9$ **27.** $2x - 5y = 10$ **28.** $5x - 2y = 4$

29. $2x + 7y = 14$ **30.** $6x - 5y = 10$ **31.** $x + 3y = 6$ **32.** $x + 2y = 8$

For Exercises 33 to 40, solve for x.

33. $x + 3y = 6$ **34.** $x + 6y = 10$ **35.** $3x - y = 3$ **36.** $2x - y = 6$

37. $2x + 5y = 10$ **38.** $4x + 3y = 12$ **39.** $x - 2y + 1 = 0$ **40.** $x - 4y - 3 = 0$

41. Two students are working with the equation $A = P(1 + i)$. State whether the two students' answers are equivalent.

a. When asked to solve the equation for i, one student answered $i = \frac{A}{P} - 1$ and the other student answered $i = \frac{A - P}{P}$.

b. When asked to solve the equation for i, one student answered $i = -\frac{P - A}{P}$ and the other student answered $i = \frac{A - P}{P}$.

Critical Thinking

42. Solve for x: $cx - y = bx + 5$

43. Solve the physics formula $\frac{1}{R_1} + \frac{1}{R_2} = \frac{1}{R}$ for R_2.

Projects or Group Activities

Business Break-even analysis is a method used to determine the sales volume required for a company to "break even," or experience neither a profit nor a loss on the sale of its product. The break-even point represents the number of units that must be made and sold for income from sales to equal the cost of producing the product. The break-even point can be calculated using the formula $B = \frac{F}{S - V}$, where F is the fixed costs, S is the selling price per unit, and V is the variable costs per unit.

44. a. Solve the formula $B = \frac{F}{S - V}$ for S.

b. Use your answer to part (a) to find the selling price per button pinhole video spycam required for a company to break even. The fixed costs are \$15,000, the variable costs per spycam are \$60, and the company plans to make and sell 200 spycams.

c. Use your answer to part (a) to find the selling price per spy camera video lighter required for a company to break even. The fixed costs are \$18,000, the variable costs per lighter are \$65, and the company plans to make and sell 600 lighters.

© Andrew Twort/Alamy

SECTION

6.8 Application Problems

OBJECTIVE A *To solve work problems*

If a painter can paint a room in 4 h, then in 1 h the painter can paint $\frac{1}{4}$ of the room. The painter's rate of work is $\frac{1}{4}$ of the room each hour. The **rate of work** is the part of a task that is completed in 1 unit of time.

A pipe can fill a tank in 30 min. This pipe can fill $\frac{1}{30}$ of the tank in 1 min. The rate of work is $\frac{1}{30}$ of the tank each minute. If a second pipe can fill the tank in x min, the rate of work for the second pipe is $\frac{1}{x}$ of the tank each minute.

In solving a work problem, the goal is to determine the time it takes to complete a task. The basic equation that is used to solve work problems is

Rate of work × time worked = part of task completed

Apply the Basic Concepts of Work Problems

EXAMPLE A A faucet can fill a sink in 6 min. What fraction of the sink will the faucet fill in 5 min?

SOLUTION The faucet can fill $\frac{1}{6}$ of the sink in 1 min. The rate of work is $\frac{1}{6}$ of the sink each minute.

Rate of work × time worked = part of task completed

$$\frac{1}{6} \times 5 = \frac{5}{6}$$

The faucet will fill $\frac{5}{6}$ of the sink in 5 min.

© iStockphoto.com/YinYang

EXAMPLE B Emily and Ian raked the yard in 40 min. It would have taken Ian 60 min to rake the yard by himself. What fraction of the yard did Ian rake?

SOLUTION Ian can rake the yard in 60 min. His rate of work is $\frac{1}{60}$ of the yard each minute. The amount of time Ian raked was 40 min.

Rate of work × time worked = part of task completed

$$\frac{1}{60} \times 40 = \frac{40}{60} = \frac{2}{3}$$

Ian raked $\frac{2}{3}$ of the yard.

Goodluz/Shutterstock.com

EXAMPLE C Sue and Ron wallpapered a room in 8 h. Sue wallpapered $\frac{3}{5}$ of the room. What fraction of the room did Ron wallpaper?

SOLUTION The sum of the part of the task completed by Ron and the part of the task completed by Sue is 1.

Let x = the part of the task completed by Sue.

Part of the task completed by Sue + Part of the task completed by Ron = 1

$$\frac{3}{5} + x = 1$$

$$x = \frac{2}{5} \quad \text{• Subtract } \frac{3}{5}.$$

Ron wallpapered $\frac{2}{5}$ of the room.

Try Concept Check Exercises 2 to 9 on Page 334.

Tips for Success

Note in the examples in this section that solving a word problem includes stating a strategy and using the strategy to find a solution. If you have difficulty with a word problem, write down the known information. Be very specific. Write out a phrase or sentence that states what you are trying to find. See *AIM for Success* at the front of the book.

Take Note

Use the information given in the problem to fill in the "Rate" and "Time" columns of the table. Fill in the "Part Completed" column by multiplying the two expressions you wrote in each row.

HOW TO 1 A painter can paint a wall in 20 min. The painter's apprentice can paint the same wall in 30 min. How long will it take to paint the wall if the painter and the apprentice work together?

Strategy for Solving a Work Problem

1. For each person or machine, write a numerical or variable expression for the rate of work, the time worked, and the part of the task completed. The results can be recorded in a table.

Unknown time to paint the wall working together: t

	Rate of Work	·	*Time Worked*	=	*Part of Task Completed*
Painter	$\frac{1}{20}$	·	t	=	$\frac{t}{20}$
Apprentice	$\frac{1}{30}$	·	t	=	$\frac{t}{30}$

2. Determine how the parts of the task completed are related. Use the fact that the sum of the parts of the task completed must equal 1, the complete task.

$$\frac{t}{20} + \frac{t}{30} = 1$$ • The sum of the part of the task completed by the painter and the part of the task completed by the apprentice is 1.

$$60\left(\frac{t}{20} + \frac{t}{30}\right) = 60 \cdot 1$$ • Multiply by the LCM of 20 and 30.

$$3t + 2t = 60$$ • Distributive Property

$$5t = 60$$

$$t = 12$$

Working together, the painter and the apprentice will paint the wall in 12 min.

EXAMPLE 1

A small water pipe takes three times longer to fill a tank than does a large water pipe. With both pipes open, it takes 4 h to fill the tank. Find the time it would take the small pipe, working alone, to fill the tank.

Strategy

- Time for large pipe to fill the tank: t
  Time for small pipe to fill the tank: $3t$

Fills tank in $3t$ hours

Fills $\frac{4}{3t}$ of the tank in 4 hours

Fills tank in t hours

Fills $\frac{4}{t}$ of the tank in 4 hours

	Rate	*Time*	*Part*
Small pipe	$\frac{1}{3t}$	4	$\frac{4}{3t}$
Large pipe	$\frac{1}{t}$	4	$\frac{4}{t}$

- The sum of the parts of the task completed by each pipe must equal 1.

Solution

$$\frac{4}{3t} + \frac{4}{t} = 1$$

$$3t\left(\frac{4}{3t} + \frac{4}{t}\right) = 3t \cdot 1$$ • Multiply by the LCM of $3t$ and t.

$$4 + 12 = 3t$$ • Distributive Property

$$16 = 3t$$

$$\frac{16}{3} = t$$ • Time for large pipe to fill the tank

$$3t = 3\left(\frac{16}{3}\right) = 16$$ • Time for small pipe to fill the tank

The small pipe, working alone, takes 16 h to fill the tank.

YOU TRY IT 1

Two computer printers that work at the same rate are working together to print the payroll checks for a large corporation. After they work together for 2 h, one of the printers fails. The second printer requires 3 h more to complete the payroll checks. Find the time it would take one printer, working alone, to print the payroll.

Your strategy

Your solution

Solution on p. S17

OBJECTIVE B *To use rational expressions to solve uniform motion problems*

A car that travels constantly in a straight line at 30 mph is in uniform motion. **Uniform motion** means that the speed and direction of an object do not change.

The basic equation used to solve uniform motion problems is

$$\textbf{Distance} = \textbf{rate} \times \textbf{time}$$

An alternative form of this equation can be written by solving the equation for time.

$$\frac{\textbf{Distance}}{\textbf{Rate}} = \textbf{time}$$

This form of the equation is useful when the total time of travel for two objects or the time of travel between two points is known.

HOW TO 2 The speed of a boat in still water is 20 mph. The boat traveled 75 mi down a river in the same amount of time it took to travel 45 mi up the river. Find the rate of the river's current.

Strategy for Solving a Uniform Motion Problem

1. For each object, write a numerical or variable expression for the distance, rate, and time. The results can be recorded in a table.

The unknown rate of the river's current: r

Take Note
Use the information given in the problem to fill in the "Distance" and "Rate" columns of the table. Fill in the "Time" column by dividing the two expressions you wrote in each row.

	Distance	÷	Rate	=	Time
Down river	75	÷	$20 + r$	=	$\frac{75}{20 + r}$
Up river	45	÷	$20 - r$	=	$\frac{45}{20 - r}$

2. Determine how the times traveled by each object are related. For example, it may be known that the times are equal, or the total time may be known.

$$\frac{75}{20 + r} = \frac{45}{20 - r}$$

• The time down the river is equal to the time up the river.

$$(20 + r)(20 - r)\frac{75}{20 + r} = (20 + r)(20 - r)\frac{45}{20 - r}$$

• Multiply by the LCM of the denominator.

$$(20 - r)75 = (20 + r)45$$

$$1500 - 75r = 900 + 45r$$

• Distributive Property

$$-120r = -600$$

$$r = 5$$

The rate of the river's current is 5 mph.

EXAMPLE 2

A cyclist rode the first 20 mi of a trip at a constant rate. For the next 16 mi, the cyclist reduced the speed by 2 mph. The total time for the 36 mi was 4 h. Find the rate of the cyclist for each leg of the trip.

Strategy

- Rate for the first 20 mi: r
  Rate for the next 16 mi: $r - 2$

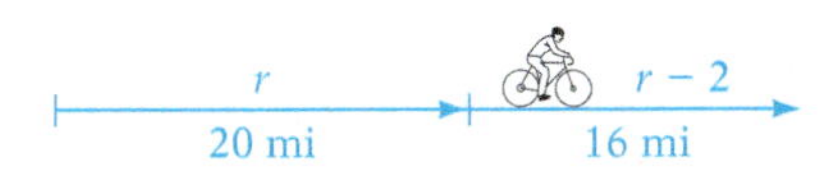

	Distance	Rate	Time
First 20 mi	20	r	$\frac{20}{r}$
Next 16 mi	16	$r - 2$	$\frac{16}{r-2}$

- The total time for the trip was 4 h.

Solution

$$\frac{20}{r} + \frac{16}{r-2} = 4$$
• The total time was 4 h.

$$r(r-2)\left[\frac{20}{r} + \frac{16}{r-2}\right] = r(r-2) \cdot 4$$
• Multiply by the LCM of the denominators.

$$(r-2)20 + 16r = 4r^2 - 8r$$
• Distributive Property

$$20r - 40 + 16r = 4r^2 - 8r$$
$$36r - 40 = 4r^2 - 8r$$

Solve the quadratic equation by factoring.

$$0 = 4r^2 - 44r + 40$$
• Standard form

$$0 = 4(r^2 - 11r + 10)$$
$$0 = 4(r - 10)(r - 1)$$
• Factor.

$$r - 10 = 0 \qquad r - 1 = 0$$
$$r = 10 \qquad r = 1$$
• Principle of Zero Products

The solution $r = 1$ mph is not possible, because the rate on the last 16 mi would then be -1 mph.

10 mph was the rate for the first 20 mi.
8 mph was the rate for the next 16 mi.

YOU TRY IT 2

The total time it took for a sailboat to sail across a lake 6 km wide and back was 2 h. The rate sailing back was three times the rate sailing across. Find the rate sailing out across the lake.

Your strategy

Your solution

Solution on p. S17

6.8 EXERCISES

Concept Check

1. Explain the meaning of the phrase "rate of work."

For Exercises 2 to 4, fill in the blank to make a true statement.

2. If it takes a janitorial crew 5 h to clean a company's offices, then in x hours the crew has completed ________ of the job.

3. If it takes an automotive crew x minutes to service a car, then the rate of work is ________ of the job each minute.

4. Two people completed a job. If one person completed $\frac{t}{30}$ of the job and the other person completed $\frac{t}{20}$ of the job, then $\frac{t}{30} + \frac{t}{20} =$ ________.

5. If Jen can paint a wall in 30 min and Amelia can paint the same wall in 45 min, who has the greater rate of work?

6. It takes Pat 3 h to mow the lawn.
   a. What is Pat's rate of work?
   b. What fraction of the lawn can Pat mow in 2 h?

7. It takes Chris x hours to lay a tile floor.
   a. What is Chris's rate of work?
   b. What fraction of the floor can Chris lay in 3 h?

8. Dawn and Hugh painted a fence together in 8 h. It would have taken Hugh 12 h to paint the fence by himself.
   a. What fraction of the fence did Hugh paint?
   b. What fraction of the fence did Dawn paint?

9. Together, two printers printed a company's advertising brochures in h hours. The faster printer could have printed the brochures in 5 h. What fraction of the brochures did the faster printer print?

10. If a plane flies 300 mph in calm air and the rate of the wind is r miles per hour, then the rate of the plane flying with the wind can be represented as ____________, and the rate of the plane flying against the wind can be represented as ____________.

11. Suppose you have a powerboat with the throttle set to move the boat at 8 mph in calm water, and the rate of the current is 4 mph. **a.** What is the speed of the boat when traveling with the current? **b.** What is the speed of the boat when traveling against the current?

12. The speed of a plane is 500 mph. There is a headwind of 50 mph. What is the speed of the plane relative to an observer on the ground?

OBJECTIVE A *To solve work problems*

13. One electrician can complete a wiring job in 10 h. It would take the electrician's assistant 12 h to complete the same wiring job. Let t represent the amount of time it would take the electrician and the assistant to complete the job if they worked together. Complete the following table.

	Rate of Work	·	*Time Worked*	=	*Part of Task Completed*
Electrician	______	·	______	=	______
Assistant	______	·	______	=	______

14. Refer to the situation presented in Exercise 13. When the wiring job is finished, the "part of task completed" is the whole task, so the sum of the parts completed by the electrician and by the assistant is ______. Use this fact and the expressions in the table in Exercise 13 to write an equation that can be solved to find the amount of time it would take for the electrician and the assistant to complete the job working together:

______ + ______ = ______.

15. A park has two sprinklers that are used to fill a fountain. One sprinkler can fill the fountain in 3 h, whereas the second sprinkler can fill the fountain in 6 h. How long will it take to fill the fountain with both sprinklers operating?

16. One grocery clerk can stock a shelf in 20 min. A second clerk requires 30 min to stock the same shelf. How long would it take to stock the shelf if the two clerks worked together?

© RJH_CATALOG /Alamy

17. One person with a skiploader requires 12 h to transfer a large quantity of earth. With a larger skiploader, the same amount of earth can be transferred in 4 h. How long would it take to transfer the earth if both skiploaders were operated together?

18. It takes Doug 6 days to reroof a house. If Doug's son helps him, the job can be completed in 4 days. How long would it take Doug's son, working alone, to do the job?

19. One computer can solve a complex prime factorization problem in 75 h. A second computer can solve the same problem in 50 h. How long would it take both computers, working together, to solve the problem?

20. A new machine makes 10,000 aluminum cans three times faster than an older machine. With both machines operating, it takes 9 h to make 10,000 cans. How long would it take the new machine, working alone, to make 10,000 cans?

21. A small air conditioner can cool a room 5°F in 60 min. A larger air conditioner can cool the room 5°F in 40 min. How long would it take to cool the room 5°F with both air conditioners working?

22. One printing press can print the first edition of a book in 55 min. A second printing press requires 66 min to print the same number of copies. How long would it take to print the first edition of the book with both presses operating?

Lisa F. Young/Shutterstock.com

23. Two welders working together can complete a job in 6 h. One of the welders, working alone, can complete the task in 10 h. How long would it take the second welder, working alone, to complete the task?

24. Working together, Pat and Chris can reseal a driveway in 6 h. Working alone, Pat can reseal the driveway in 15 h. How long would it take Chris, working alone, to reseal the driveway?

25. Two oil pipelines can fill a small tank in 30 min. One of the pipelines, working alone, would require 45 min to fill the tank. How long would it take the second pipeline, working alone, to fill the tank?

26. A cement mason can construct a retaining wall in 8 h. A second mason requires 12 h to do the same job. After working alone for 4 h, the first mason quits. How long will it take the second mason to complete the wall?

27. With two reapers operating, a field can be harvested in 1 h. If only the newer reaper is used, the crop can be harvested in 1.5 h. How long would it take to harvest the field using only the older reaper?

28. A manufacturer of prefabricated homes has the company's employees work in teams. Team 1 can erect the Silvercrest model in 15 h. Team 2 can erect the same model in 10 h. How long would it take for Team 1 and Team 2, working together, to erect the Silvercrest model home?

bikeriderlondon/Shutterstock.com

29. One technician can wire a security alarm in 4 h, whereas it takes 6 h for a second technician to do the same job. After working alone for 2 h, the first technician quits. How long will it take the second technician to complete the wiring?

30. A wallpaper hanger requires 2 h to hang the wallpaper on one wall of a room. A second wallpaper hanger requires 4 h to hang the same amount of wallpaper. The first wallpaper hanger works alone for 1 h and then quits. How long will it take the second hanger, working alone, to finish papering the wall?

31. A large heating unit and a small heating unit are being used to heat the water in a pool. The large unit, working alone, requires 8 h to heat the pool. After both units have been operating for 2 h, the large unit is turned off. The small unit requires 9 more hours to heat the pool. How long would it take the small unit, working alone, to heat the pool?

32. Two machines fill cereal boxes at the same rate. After the two machines work together for 7 h, one machine breaks down. The second machine requires 14 more hours to finish filling the boxes. How long would it have taken one of the machines, working alone, to fill the boxes?

33. A mechanic requires 2 h to repair a transmission, whereas an apprentice requires 6 h to make the same repairs. The mechanic worked alone for 1 h and then stopped. How long will it take the apprentice, working alone, to complete the repairs?

Sudheer Sakthan/Shutterstock.com

34. A large drain and a small drain are opened to drain a pool. The large drain can empty the pool in 6 h. After both drains have been open for 1 h, the large drain becomes clogged and is closed. The small drain remains open and requires 9 more hours to empty the pool. How long would it have taken the small drain, working alone, to empty the pool?

35. It takes Sam h hours to rake the yard, and it takes Emma k hours to rake the yard, where $h > k$. Let t be the amount of time it takes Sam and Emma to rake the yard together. Is t less than k, between k and h, or greater than k?

36. Zachary and Eli picked a row of peas together in m minutes. It would have taken Zachary n minutes to pick the row of peas by himself. What fraction of the row of peas did Zachary pick? What fraction of the row of peas did Eli pick?

OBJECTIVE B *To use rational expressions to solve uniform motion problems*

For Exercises 37 and 38, use the following problem situation: A plane can fly 380 mph in calm air. In the time it takes the plane to fly 1440 mi against a headwind, it could fly 1600 mi with the wind.

37. a. Let r represent the rate of the wind. Complete the following table.

	Distance	÷	*Rate*	=	*Time*
Against the wind	______	÷	______	=	______
With the wind	______	÷	______	=	______

b. Use the relationship between the expressions in the last column of the table to write an equation that can be solved to find the rate of the wind: ______ = ______.

38. Use the equation from part (b) of Exercise 37.

a. Explain the meanings of $380 - r$ and $380 + r$ in terms of the problem situation.

b. Explain the meanings of $\frac{1440}{380 - r}$ and $\frac{1600}{380 + r}$ in terms of the problem situation.

39. A camper drove 80 mi to a recreational area and then hiked 4 mi into the woods. The rate of the camper while driving was ten times the rate while hiking. The total time spent hiking and driving was 3 h. Find the rate at which the camper hiked.

40. The president of a company traveled 1800 mi by jet and 300 mi on a prop plane. The rate of the jet was four times the rate of the prop plane. The entire trip took 5 h. Find the rate of the jet.

41. To assess the damage done by a fire, a forest ranger traveled 1080 mi by jet and then an additional 180 mi by helicopter. The rate of the jet was four times the rate of the helicopter. The entire trip took 5 h. Find the rate of the jet.

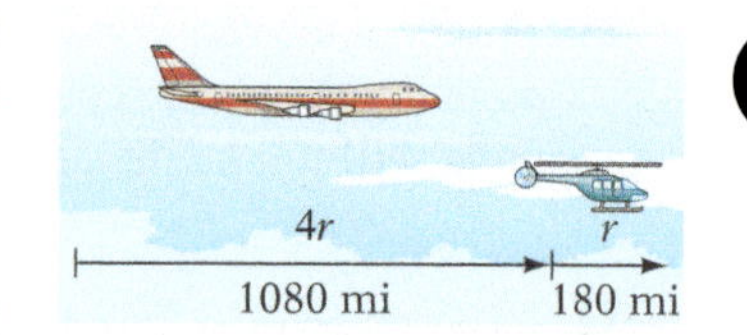

42. An engineer traveled 165 mi by car and then an additional 660 mi by plane. The rate of the plane was four times the rate of the car. The total trip took 6 h. Find the rate of the car.

43. After sailing 15 mi, a sailor changed direction and increased the boat's speed by 2 mph. An additional 19 mi was sailed at the increased speed. The total sailing time was 4 h. Find the rate of the boat for the first 15 mi.

44. On a recent trip, a trucker traveled 330 mi at a constant rate. Because of road conditions, the trucker then reduced the speed by 25 mph. An additional 30 mi was traveled at the reduced rate. The entire trip took 7 h. Find the rate of the trucker for the first 330 mi.

45. Commuting from work to home, a lab technician traveled 10 mi at a constant rate through congested traffic. Upon reaching the expressway, the technician increased the speed by 20 mph. An additional 20 mi was traveled at the increased speed. The total time for the trip was 1 h. At what rate did the technician travel through the congested traffic?

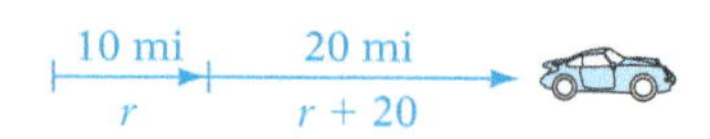

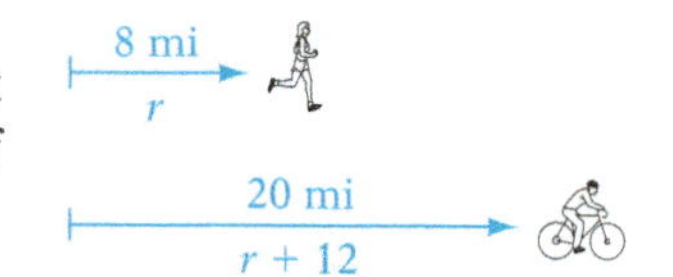

46. As part of a conditioning program, a jogger ran 8 mi in the same amount of time it took a cyclist to ride 20 mi. The rate of the cyclist was 12 mph faster than the rate of the jogger. Find the rate of the jogger and the rate of the cyclist.

47. In calm water, the rate of a small rental motorboat is 15 mph. The rate of the current on the river is 3 mph. How far down the river can a family travel and still return the boat in 3 h?

48. The rate of a small aircraft in calm air is 125 mph. If the wind is currently blowing south at a rate of 15 mph, how far north can a pilot fly the plane and return it within 2 h?

49. The speed of a boat in still water is 20 mph. The Jacksons traveled 75 mi down the Woodset River in this boat in the same amount of time it took them to return 45 mi up the river. Find the rate of the river's current.

© iStockphoto.com/Craig Hansen

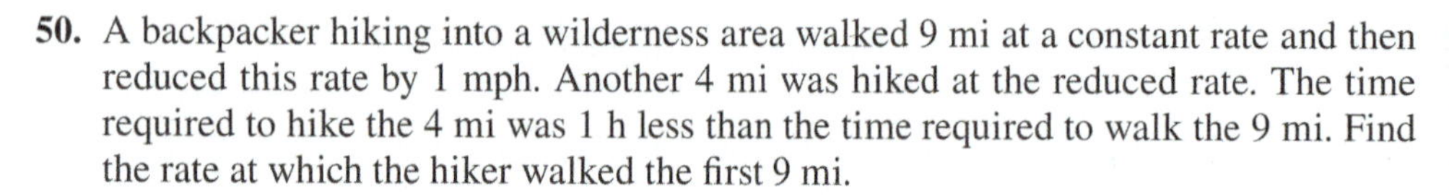

50. A backpacker hiking into a wilderness area walked 9 mi at a constant rate and then reduced this rate by 1 mph. Another 4 mi was hiked at the reduced rate. The time required to hike the 4 mi was 1 h less than the time required to walk the 9 mi. Find the rate at which the hiker walked the first 9 mi.

51. An express train traveled 600 mi in the same amount of time it took a freight train to travel 360 mi. The rate of the express train was 20 mph faster than the rate of the freight train. Find the rate of each train.

52. A twin-engine plane flies 800 mi in the same amount of time it takes a single-engine plane to fly 600 mi. The rate of the twin-engine plane is 50 mph faster than the rate of the single-engine plane. Find the rate of the twin-engine plane.

53. A small motor on a fishing boat can move the boat at a rate of 6 mph in calm water. Traveling with the current, the boat can travel 24 mi in the same amount of time it takes to travel 12 mi against the current. Find the rate of the current.

54. A car is traveling at a rate that is 36 mph faster than the rate of a cyclist. The car travels 384 mi in the same amount of time it takes the cyclist to travel 96 mi. Find the rate of the car.

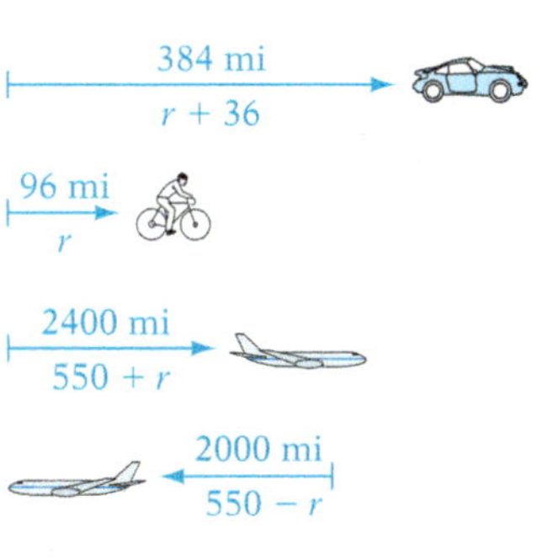

55. A commercial jet can fly 550 mph in calm air. Traveling with the jet stream, the plane can fly 2400 mi in the same amount of time it takes to fly 2000 mi against the jet stream. Find the rate of the jet stream.

56. A cruise ship can sail 28 mph in calm water. Sailing with the Gulf Stream, the ship can sail 170 mi in the same amount of time it takes to sail 110 mi against the Gulf Stream. Find the rate of the Gulf Stream.

57. Rowing with the current of a river, a rowing team can row 25 mi in the same amount of time it takes to row 15 mi against the current. The rate of the rowing team in calm water is 20 mph. Find the rate of the current.

John Kropewnicki/Shutterstock.com

58. A plane can fly 180 mph in calm air. Flying with the wind, the plane can fly 600 mi in the same amount of time it takes to fly 480 mi against the wind. Find the rate of the wind.

Critical Thinking

59. **Work Problem** One pipe can fill a tank in 2 h, a second pipe can fill the tank in 4 h, and a third pipe can fill the tank in 5 h. How long would it take to fill the tank with all three pipes operating?

60. **Work Problem** A mason can construct a retaining wall in 10 h. The mason's experienced apprentice can do the same job in 15 h. How long would it take the mason's novice apprentice to do the job if, working together, all three can complete the wall in 5 h?

61. **Uniform Motion** An Outing Club traveled 18 mi by canoe and then hiked 3 mi. The rate by canoe was three times the rate on foot. The time spent walking was 1 h less than the time spent canoeing. Find the amount of time spent traveling by canoe.

62. **Uniform Motion** A motorist drove 120 mi before running out of gas and walking 4 mi to a gas station. The motorist's driving rate was ten times the walking rate. The time spent walking was 2 h less than the time spent driving. How long did it take for the motorist to drive the 120 mi?

Projects or Group Activites

63. **Uniform Motion** Because of bad weather, a bus driver reduced the usual speed along a 150-mile bus route by 10 mph. The bus arrived only 30 min later than its usual arrival time. How fast does the bus usually travel?

64. **Work Problem** A construction project must be completed in 15 days. Twenty-five workers did one-half of the job in 10 days. Working at the same rate, how many workers are needed to complete the job on schedule?

CHAPTER 6 Summary

Key Words

Examples

A **rational expression** is a fraction in which the numerator and denominator are polynomials. A rational expression is in **simplest form** when the numerator and denominator have no common factors. [6.1A, p. 282]

$\frac{2x+1}{x^2+4}$ is a rational expression in simplest form.

The **reciprocal of a rational expression** is the rational expression with the numerator and denominator interchanged. [6.1C, p. 285]

The reciprocal of $\frac{3x-y}{x+4}$ is $\frac{x+4}{3x-y}$.

The **least common multiple (LCM) of two or more polynomials** is the polynomial of least degree that contains all the factors of each polynomial. [6.2A, p. 290]

The LCM of $3x^2 - 6x$ and $x^2 - 4$ is $3x(x-2)(x+2)$, because it contains the factors of $3x^2 - 6x = 3x(x-2)$ and the factors of $x^2 - 4 = (x-2)(x+2)$.

A **complex fraction** is a fraction in which the numerator or denominator contains one or more fractions. [6.4A, p. 303]

$\dfrac{x - \frac{2}{x+1}}{1 - \frac{4}{x}}$ is a complex fraction.

A **ratio** is the quotient of two quantities that have the same unit. A **rate** is the quotient of two quantities that have different units. [6.6A, p. 314]

$\frac{9}{4}$ is a ratio. $\frac{60\text{ m}}{12\text{ s}}$ is a rate.

A **proportion** is an equation that states the equality of two ratios or rates. [6.6A, p. 314]

$\frac{3}{8} = \frac{12}{32}$ and $\frac{x\text{ ft}}{12\text{ s}} = \frac{15\text{ ft}}{160\text{ s}}$ are proportions.

A **literal equation** is an equation that contains more than one variable. A **formula** is a literal equation that states a rule about measurements. [6.7A, p. 325]

$3x - 4y = 12$ is a literal equation. $A = LW$ is a literal equation that is also the formula for the area of a rectangle.

Essential Rules and Procedures

Examples

Simplifying Rational Expressions [6.1A, p. 282]
Factor the numerator and denominator. Divide the numerator and denominator by the common factors.

$$\frac{x^2 - 3x - 10}{x^2 - 25} = \frac{(x+2)(x-5)}{(x+5)(x-5)} = \frac{x+2}{x+5}$$

Multiplying Rational Expressions [6.1B, p. 283]
Multiply the numerators. Multiply the denominators. Write the answer in simplest form.

$$\frac{a}{b} \cdot \frac{c}{d} = \frac{ac}{bd}$$

$$\frac{x^2 - 3x}{x^2 + x} \cdot \frac{x^2 + 5x + 4}{x^2 - 4x + 3} = \frac{x(x-3)}{x(x+1)} \cdot \frac{(x+1)(x+4)}{(x-3)(x-1)} = \frac{x(x-3)(x+1)(x+4)}{x(x+1)(x-3)(x-1)} = \frac{x+4}{x-1}$$

Dividing Rational Expressions [6.1C, p. 285]
Multiply the first fraction by the reciprocal of the divisor. Write the answer in simplest form.

$$\frac{a}{b} \div \frac{c}{d} = \frac{a}{b} \cdot \frac{d}{c} = \frac{ad}{bc}$$

$$\frac{4x+16}{3x-6} \div \frac{x^2+6x+8}{x^2-4}$$
$$= \frac{4x+16}{3x-6} \cdot \frac{x^2-4}{x^2+6x+8}$$
$$= \frac{4(x+4)}{3(x-2)} \cdot \frac{(x-2)(x+2)}{(x+4)(x+2)}$$
$$= \frac{4}{3}$$

Adding and Subtracting Rational Expressions [6.3B, p. 296]

1. Find the LCM of the denominators.
2. Write each fraction as an equivalent fraction using the LCM as the denominator.
3. Add or subtract the numerators and place the result over the common denominator.
4. Write the answer in simplest form.

$$\frac{a}{b} + \frac{c}{b} = \frac{a+c}{b} \qquad \frac{a}{b} - \frac{c}{b} = \frac{a-c}{b}$$

$$\frac{x}{x+1} - \frac{x+3}{x-2}$$
$$= \frac{x}{x+1} \cdot \frac{x-2}{x-2} - \frac{x+3}{x-2} \cdot \frac{x+1}{x+1}$$
$$= \frac{x(x-2)}{(x+1)(x-2)} - \frac{(x+3)(x+1)}{(x+1)(x-2)}$$
$$= \frac{x(x-2) - (x+3)(x+1)}{(x+1)(x-2)}$$
$$= \frac{(x^2-2x) - (x^2+4x+3)}{(x+1)(x-2)}$$
$$= \frac{-6x-3}{(x+1)(x-2)}$$

Simplifying Complex Fractions [6.4A, p. 303]

Method 1: Multiply by 1 in the form $\frac{\text{LCM}}{\text{LCM}}$.

1. Determine the LCM of the denominators of the fractions in the numerator and denominator of the complex fraction.
2. Multiply the numerator and denominator of the complex fraction by the LCM.
3. Simplify.

Method 1: $$\frac{\frac{1}{x}+\frac{1}{y}}{\frac{1}{x}-\frac{1}{y}} = \frac{\frac{1}{x}+\frac{1}{y}}{\frac{1}{x}-\frac{1}{y}} \cdot \frac{xy}{xy}$$
$$= \frac{\frac{1}{x}\cdot xy + \frac{1}{y}\cdot xy}{\frac{1}{x}\cdot xy - \frac{1}{y}\cdot xy}$$
$$= \frac{y+x}{y-x}$$

Method 2: Multiply the numerator by the reciprocal of the denominator.

1. Simplify the numerator to a single fraction and simplify the denominator to a single fraction.
2. Using the rule for dividing fractions, multiply the numerator by the reciprocal of the denominator.
3. Simplify.

Method 2: $$\frac{\frac{1}{x}+\frac{1}{y}}{\frac{1}{x}-\frac{1}{y}} = \frac{\frac{y+x}{xy}}{\frac{y-x}{xy}}$$
$$= \frac{y+x}{xy} \cdot \frac{xy}{y-x}$$
$$= \frac{y+x}{y-x}$$

Solving Equations Containing Fractions [6.5A, p. 309]
Clear denominators by multiplying each side of the equation by the LCM of the denominators. Then solve for the variable.

$$\frac{1}{2a} = \frac{2}{a} - \frac{3}{8}$$
$$8a\left(\frac{1}{2a}\right) = 8a\left(\frac{2}{a}\right) - 8a\left(\frac{3}{8}\right)$$
$$4 = 16 - 3a$$
$$-12 = -3a$$
$$4 = a$$

Similar Triangles [6.6B, pp. 316–317]
Similar triangles have the same shape but not necessarily the same size. The ratios of corresponding sides of similar triangles are equal. The measures of the corresponding angles of similar triangles are equal.

Triangles ABC and DFE are similar triangles. The ratios of corresponding parts are equal to $\frac{2}{3}$.

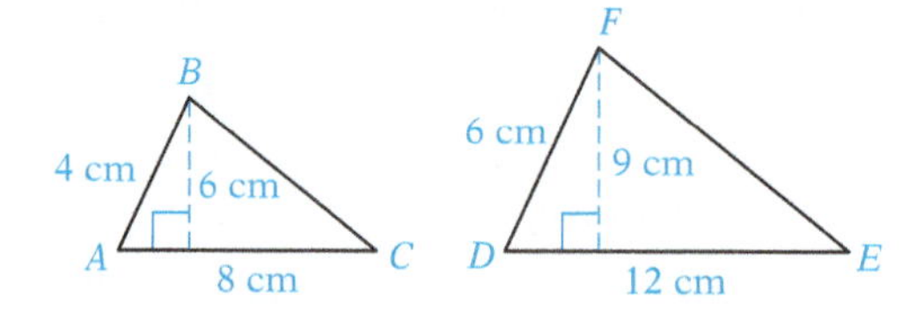

If two angles of one triangle are equal in measure to two angles of another triangle, then the two triangles are similar.

Triangles AOB and COD are similar because $m\angle AOB = m\angle COD$ and $m\angle B = m\angle D$.

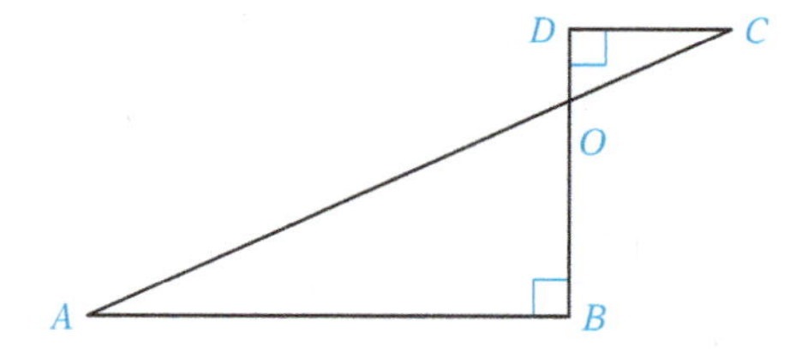

Solving Literal Equations [6.7A, p. 325]
Rewrite the equation so that the letter being solved for is alone on one side of the equation and all numbers and other variables are on the other side.

Solve $2x + ax = 5$ for x.
$$2x + ax = 5$$
$$x(2 + a) = 5$$
$$\frac{x(2 + a)}{2 + a} = \frac{5}{2 + a}$$
$$x = \frac{5}{2 + a}$$

Work Problems [6.8A, p. 329]
Rate of work $\times$ time worked $=$ part of task completed

Pat can do a certain job in 3 h. Chris can do the same job in 5 h. How long would it take Pat and Chris, working together, to get the job done?

$$\frac{t}{3} + \frac{t}{5} = 1$$

Uniform Motion Problems with Rational Expressions [6.8B, p. 332]

$$\frac{\text{Distance}}{\text{Rate}} = \text{time}$$

Train A's speed is 15 mph faster than train B's speed. Train A travels 150 mi in the same amount of time it takes train B to travel 120 mi. Find the rate of train B.

$$\frac{120}{r} = \frac{150}{r + 15}$$

CHAPTER

6 Review Exercises

1. Divide: $\dfrac{6a^2b^7}{25x^3y} \div \dfrac{12a^3b^4}{5x^2y^2}$

2. Add: $\dfrac{x+7}{15x} + \dfrac{x-2}{20x}$

3. Multiply: $\dfrac{3x^3+9x^2}{6xy^2-18y^2} \cdot \dfrac{4xy^3-12y^3}{5x^2+15x}$

4. Divide: $\dfrac{2x(x-y)}{x^2y(x+y)} \div \dfrac{3(x-y)}{x^2y^2}$

5. Simplify: $\dfrac{x - \dfrac{16}{5x-2}}{3x - 4 - \dfrac{88}{5x-2}}$

6. Simplify: $\dfrac{x^2+x-30}{15+2x-x^2}$

7. Simplify: $\dfrac{16x^5y^3}{24xy^{10}}$

8. Solve: $\dfrac{20}{x+2} = \dfrac{5}{16}$

9. Divide: $\dfrac{10-23y+12y^2}{6y^2-y-5} \div \dfrac{4y^2-13y+10}{18y^2+3y-10}$

10. Solve $3ax - x = 5$ for x.

11. Solve: $\dfrac{2}{x} + \dfrac{3}{4} = 1$

12. Add: $\dfrac{x}{y} + \dfrac{3}{x}$

13. Solve $5x + 4y = 20$ for y.

14. Multiply: $\dfrac{8ab^2}{15x^3y} \cdot \dfrac{5xy^4}{16a^2b}$

15. Simplify: $\dfrac{1 - \dfrac{1}{x}}{1 - \dfrac{8x-7}{x^2}}$

16. Write each fraction in terms of the LCM of the denominators.
$\dfrac{x}{12x^2+16x-3}, \dfrac{4x^2}{6x^2+7x-3}$

17. Solve $T = 2(ab + bc + ca)$ for a.

18. Solve: $\dfrac{5}{7} + \dfrac{x}{2} = 2 - \dfrac{x}{7}$

19. Simplify: $\dfrac{2 + \dfrac{1}{x}}{3 - \dfrac{2}{x}}$

20. Subtract: $\dfrac{2x}{x-5} - \dfrac{x+1}{x-2}$

21. Solve $i = \dfrac{100m}{c}$ for c.

22. Solve: $\dfrac{x+8}{x+4} = 1 + \dfrac{5}{x+4}$

23. Divide: $\dfrac{20x^2-45x}{6x^3+4x^2} \div \dfrac{40x^3-90x^2}{12x^2+8x}$

24. Add: $\dfrac{2y}{5y-7} + \dfrac{3}{7-5y}$

25. Subtract: $\dfrac{5x + 3}{2x^2 + 5x - 3} - \dfrac{3x + 4}{2x^2 + 5x - 3}$

26. Find the LCM of $10x^2 - 11x + 3$ and $20x^2 - 17x + 3$.

27. Solve $4x + 9y = 18$ for y.

28. Multiply: $\dfrac{2x^2 - 5x - 3}{3x^2 - 7x - 6} \cdot \dfrac{3x^2 + 8x + 4}{x^2 + 4x + 4}$

29. Solve: $\dfrac{20}{2x + 3} = \dfrac{17x}{2x + 3} - 5$

30. Add: $\dfrac{x - 1}{x + 2} + \dfrac{3x - 2}{5 - x} + \dfrac{5x^2 + 15x - 11}{x^2 - 3x - 10}$

31. Solve: $\dfrac{6}{x - 7} = \dfrac{8}{x - 6}$

32. Solve: $\dfrac{3}{20} = \dfrac{x}{80}$

33. **Geometry** Given that $\overline{MP}$ and $\overline{NQ}$ intersect at O, NQ measures 25 cm, MO measures 6 cm, and PO measures 9 cm, find QO.

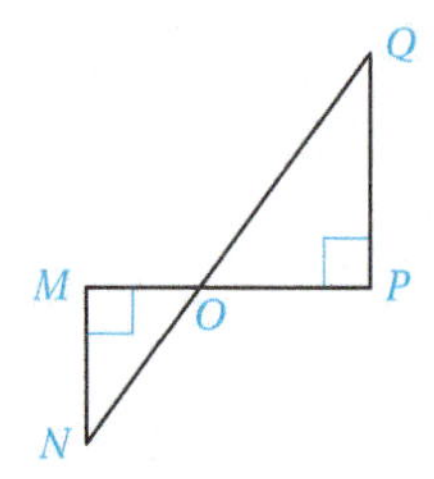

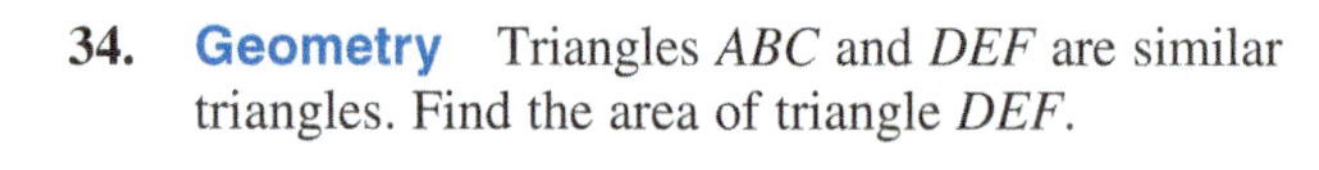

34. **Geometry** Triangles ABC and DEF are similar triangles. Find the area of triangle DEF.

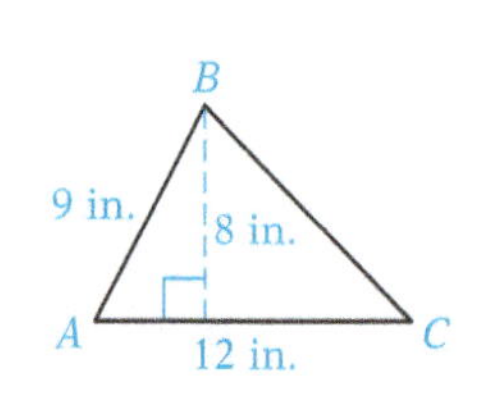

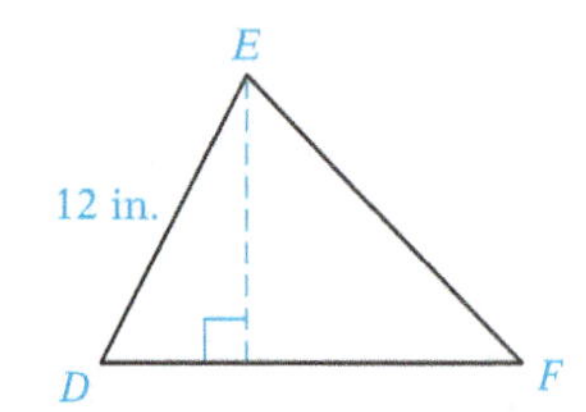

35. **Work Problem** One hose can fill a pool in 15 h. A second hose can fill the pool in 10 h. How long would it take to fill the pool using both hoses?

36. **Uniform Motion** A car travels 315 mi in the same amount of time it takes a bus to travel 245 mi. The rate of the car is 10 mph faster than that of the bus. Find the rate of the car.

37. **Uniform Motion** The rate of a jet is 400 mph in calm air. Traveling with the wind, the jet can fly 2100 mi in the same amount of time it takes to fly 1900 mi against the wind. Find the rate of the wind.

iStockphoto.com/jtroudt

38. **Baseball** A pitcher's earned run average (ERA) is the average number of runs allowed in 9 innings of pitching. If a pitcher allows 15 runs in 100 innings, find the pitcher's ERA.

CHAPTER 6 TEST

1. Subtract: $\dfrac{x}{x+3} - \dfrac{2x-5}{x^2+x-6}$

2. Solve: $\dfrac{3}{x+4} = \dfrac{5}{x+6}$

3. Multiply: $\dfrac{x^2+2x-3}{x^2+6x+9} \cdot \dfrac{2x^2-11x+5}{2x^2+3x-5}$

4. Simplify: $\dfrac{16x^5y}{24x^2y^4}$

5. Solve $d = s + rt$ for t.

6. Solve: $\dfrac{6}{x} - 2 = 1$

7. Simplify: $\dfrac{x^2+4x-5}{1-x^2}$

8. Find the LCM of $6x - 3$ and $2x^2 + x - 1$.

9. Subtract: $\dfrac{2}{2x-1} - \dfrac{3}{3x+1}$

10. Divide: $\dfrac{x^2+3x+2}{x^2+5x+4} \div \dfrac{x^2-x-6}{x^2+2x-15}$

11. Simplify: $\dfrac{1+\dfrac{1}{x}-\dfrac{12}{x^2}}{1+\dfrac{2}{x}-\dfrac{8}{x^2}}$

12. Write each fraction in terms of the LCM of the denominators.
$\dfrac{3}{x^2-2x}, \dfrac{x}{x^2-4}$

13. Subtract: $\dfrac{2x}{x^2 + 3x - 10} - \dfrac{4}{x^2 + 3x - 10}$

14. Solve $3x - 8y = 16$ for y.

15. Solve: $\dfrac{2x}{x + 1} - 3 = \dfrac{-2}{x + 1}$

16. Multiply: $\dfrac{x^3y^4}{x^2 - 4x + 4} \cdot \dfrac{x^2 - x - 2}{x^6y^4}$

17. Geometry Given that $\overline{AE} \parallel \overline{BD}$, AB measures 5 ft, ED measures 8 ft, and BC measures 3 ft, find CE.

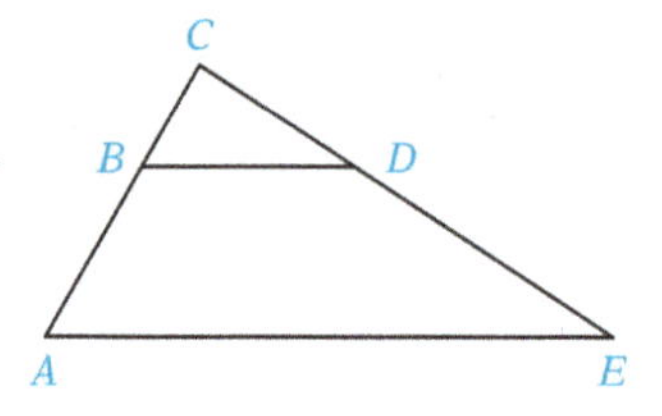

18. Chemistry A saltwater solution is formed by mixing 4 lb of salt with 10 gal of water. At this rate, how many pounds of salt are required for 15 gal of water?

19. Work Problem One pipe can fill a pool in 6 h, whereas a second pipe requires 12 h to fill the pool. How long would it take to fill the pool with both pipes turned on?

20. Uniform Motion A small plane can fly at 110 mph in calm air. Flying with the wind, the plane can fly 260 mi in the same amount of time it takes to fly 180 mi against the wind. Find the rate of the wind.

iStockphoto.com/Peter Eckhardt

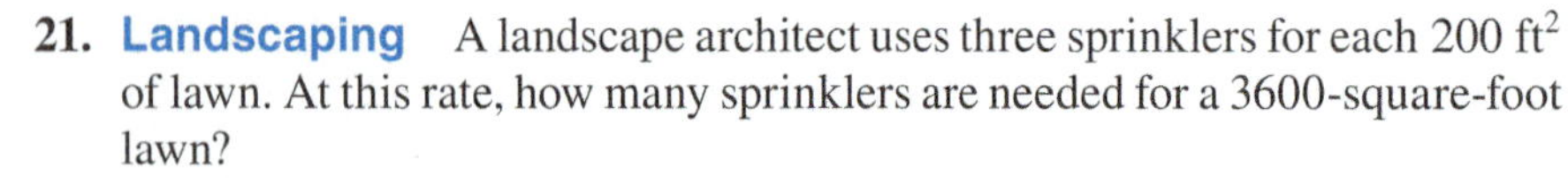
21. Landscaping A landscape architect uses three sprinklers for each 200 ft^2 of lawn. At this rate, how many sprinklers are needed for a 3600-square-foot lawn?

Cumulative Review Exercises

1. Evaluate: $\left(\frac{2}{3}\right)^2 \div \left(\frac{3}{2} - \frac{2}{3}\right) + \frac{1}{2}$

2. Evaluate $-a^2 + (a - b)^2$ when $a = -2$ and $b = 3$.

3. Simplify: $-2x - (-3y) + 7x - 5y$

4. Simplify: $2[3x - 7(x - 3) - 8]$

5. Solve: $4 - \frac{2}{3}x = 7$

6. Solve: $3[x - 2(x - 3)] = 2(3 - 2x)$

7. Find $16\frac{2}{3}\%$ of 60.

8. Simplify: $(a^2b^5)(ab^2)$

9. Multiply: $(a - 3b)(a + 4b)$

10. Divide: $\frac{15b^4 - 5b^2 + 10b}{5b}$

11. Divide: $(x^3 - 8) \div (x - 2)$

12. Factor: $12x^2 - x - 1$

13. Factor: $y^2 - 7y + 6$

14. Factor: $2a^3 + 7a^2 - 15a$

15. Factor: $4b^2 - 100$

16. Solve: $(x + 3)(2x - 5) = 0$

17. Simplify: $\frac{12x^4y^2}{18xy^7}$

18. Simplify: $\frac{x^2 - 7x + 10}{25 - x^2}$

19. Divide: $\dfrac{x^2 - x - 56}{x^2 + 8x + 7} \div \dfrac{x^2 - 13x + 40}{x^2 - 4x - 5}$

20. Subtract: $\dfrac{2}{2x - 1} - \dfrac{1}{x + 1}$

21. Simplify: $\dfrac{1 - \dfrac{2}{x} - \dfrac{15}{x^2}}{1 - \dfrac{25}{x^2}}$

22. Solve: $\dfrac{3x}{x - 3} - 2 = \dfrac{10}{x - 3}$

23. Solve: $\dfrac{2}{x - 2} = \dfrac{12}{x + 3}$

24. Solve $f = v + at$ for t.

25. Integer Problem Translate "the difference between five times a number and thirteen is the opposite of eight" into an equation and solve.

26. Metallurgy A silversmith mixes 60 g of an alloy that is 40% silver with 120 g of another silver alloy. The resulting alloy is 60% silver. Find the percent of silver in the 120-gram alloy.

27. Geometry The length of the base of a triangle is 2 in. less than twice the height. The area of the triangle is 30 in^2. Find the base and height of the triangle.

28. Insurance A life insurance policy costs \$16 for every \$1000 of coverage. At this rate, how much money would a policy for \$5000 cost?

29. Work Problem One water pipe can fill a tank in 9 min, whereas a second pipe requires 18 min to fill the tank. How long would it take both pipes, working together, to fill the tank?

30. Uniform Motion The rower of a boat can row at a rate of 5 mph in calm water. Traveling with the current, the boat travels 14 mi in the same amount of time it takes to travel 6 mi against the current. Find the rate of the current.

Linear Equations in Two Variables

OBJECTIVES

SECTION 7.1

- **A** To graph points in a rectangular coordinate system
- **B** To determine ordered-pair solutions of an equation in two variables
- **C** To determine whether a set of ordered pairs is a function
- **D** To evaluate a function

SECTION 7.2

- **A** To graph an equation of the form $y = mx + b$
- **B** To graph an equation of the form $Ax + By = C$
- **C** To solve application problems

SECTION 7.3

- **A** To find the x- and y-intercepts of a straight line
- **B** To find the slope of a straight line
- **C** To graph a line using the slope and the y-intercept

SECTION 7.4

- **A** To find the equation of a line using the equation $y = mx + b$
- **B** To find the equation of a line using the point-slope formula
- **C** To find the equation of a line given two points

Focus on Success

Have you established a routine for doing your homework? If not, decide now where and when your study time is most productive. Perhaps it is at home, in the library, or in the math center, where you can get help as you need it. If possible, create a study hour right after class. The material will be fresh in your mind, and the immediate review, along with your homework, will reinforce the concepts you are learning. (See Homework Time, page AIM-5)

Prep Test

Are you ready to succeed in this chapter? Take the Prep Test below to find out if you are ready to learn the new material.

1. Simplify: $-\dfrac{5-(-7)}{4-8}$

2. Evaluate $\dfrac{a-b}{c-d}$ when $a = 3$, $b = -2$, $c = -3$, and $d = 2$.

3. Simplify: $-3(x - 4)$

4. Solve: $3x + 6 = 0$

5. Solve $4x + 5y = 20$ when $y = 0$.

6. Solve $3x - 7y = 11$ when $x = -1$.

7. Divide: $\dfrac{12x - 15}{-3}$

8. Solve: $\dfrac{2x+1}{3} = \dfrac{3x}{4}$

9. Solve $3x - 5y = 15$ for y.

10. Solve $y + 3 = -\dfrac{1}{2}(x + 4)$ for y.

SECTION

7.1 The Rectangular Coordinate System

OBJECTIVE A *To graph points in a rectangular coordinate system*

Before the 15th century, geometry and algebra were considered separate branches of mathematics. That all changed when René Descartes, a French mathematician who lived from 1596 to 1650, founded **analytic geometry.** In this geometry, a *coordinate system* is used to study relationships between variables.

A **rectangular coordinate system** is formed by two number lines, one horizontal and one vertical, that intersect at the zero point of each line. The point of intersection is called the **origin.** The two lines are called **coordinate axes,** or simply **axes.** The axes determine a **plane,** which can be thought of as a large, flat sheet of paper. The two axes divide the plane into four regions called **quadrants,** which are numbered counterclockwise from I to IV.

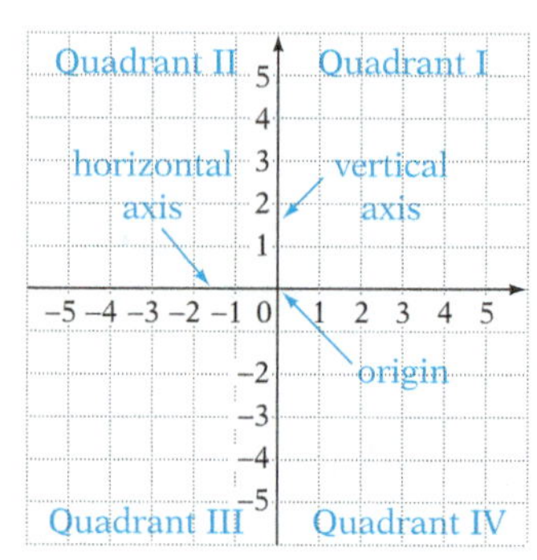

Each point in the plane can be identified by a pair of numbers called an **ordered pair.** The first number of the pair measures a horizontal distance and is called the **abscissa.** The second number of the pair measures a vertical distance and is called the **ordinate.** The **coordinates of a point** are the numbers in the ordered pair associated with the point. The abscissa is also called the **first coordinate** of the ordered pair, and the ordinate is also called the **second coordinate** of the ordered pair.

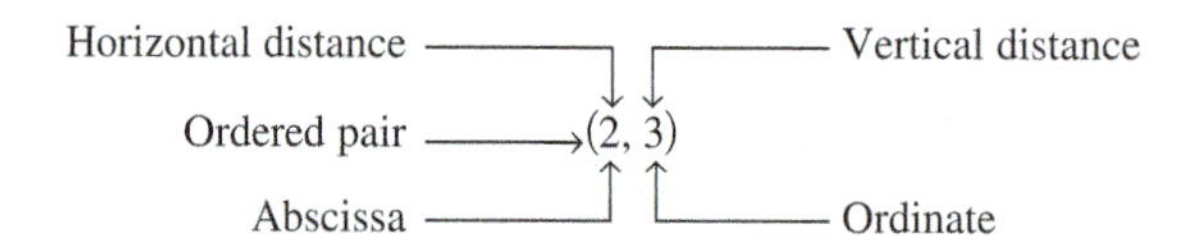

When drawing a rectangular coordinate system, we often label the horizontal axis x and the vertical axis y. In this case, the coordinate system is called an ***xy*-coordinate system.** The coordinates of the points are given by ordered pairs (x, y), where the abscissa is called the ***x*-coordinate** and the ordinate is called the ***y*-coordinate.**

To **graph or plot a point in the plane,** place a dot at the location given by the ordered pair. The **graph of an ordered pair** (x, y) is the dot drawn at the coordinates of the point in the plane. The points whose coordinates are $(3, 4)$ and $(-2.5, -3)$ are graphed in the figures below.

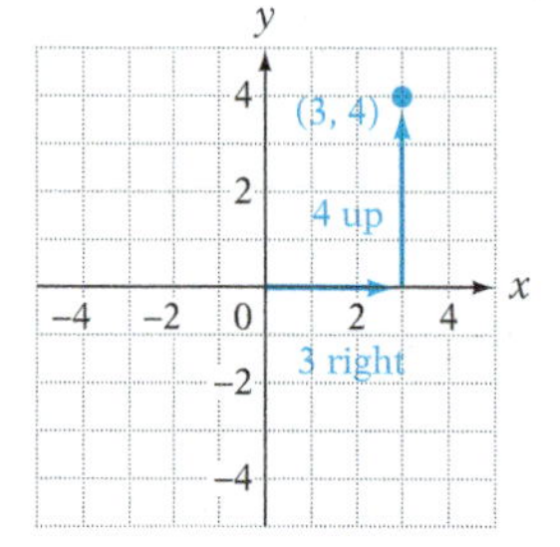

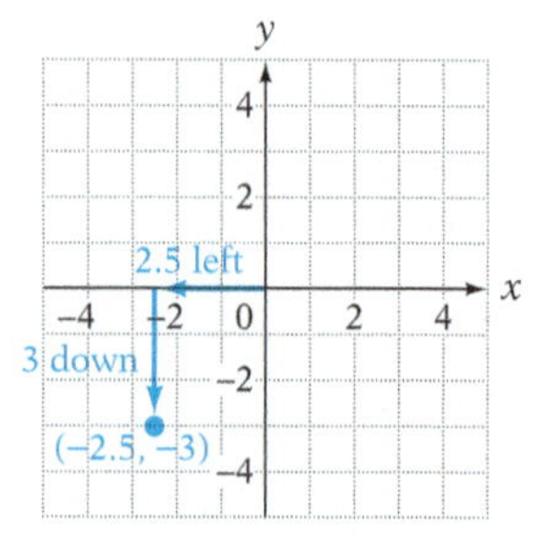

Take Note
This concept is very important. An **ordered pair** is a *pair* of coordinates, and the *order* in which the coordinates are listed is crucial.

The points whose coordinates are $(3, -1)$ and $(-1, 3)$ are graphed at the right. Note that the graphed points are in different locations. *The order of the coordinates in an ordered pair is important.*

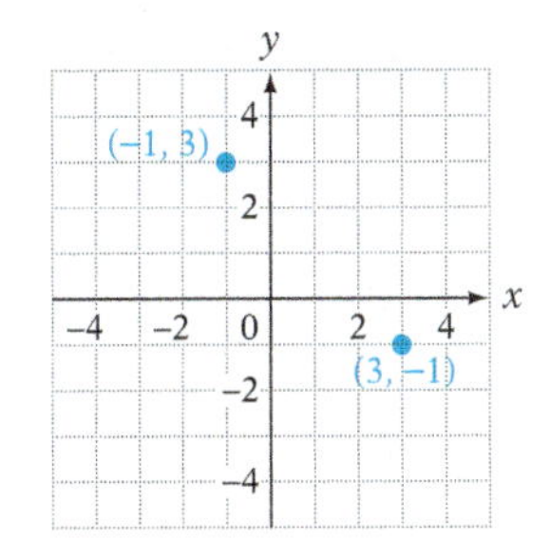

Each point in the plane is associated with an ordered pair, and each ordered pair is associated with a point in the plane. Although only the labels for integers are given on a coordinate grid, the graph of any ordered pair can be approximated. For example, the points whose coordinates are $(-2.3, 4.1)$ and $(\pi, 1)$ are shown on the graph at the right.

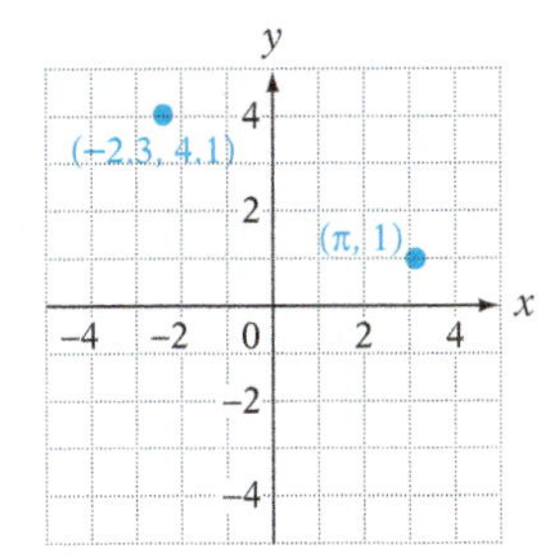

EXAMPLE 1

Graph the ordered pairs $(-2, -3)$, $(3, -2)$, $(0, -2)$, and $(3, 0)$.

Solution

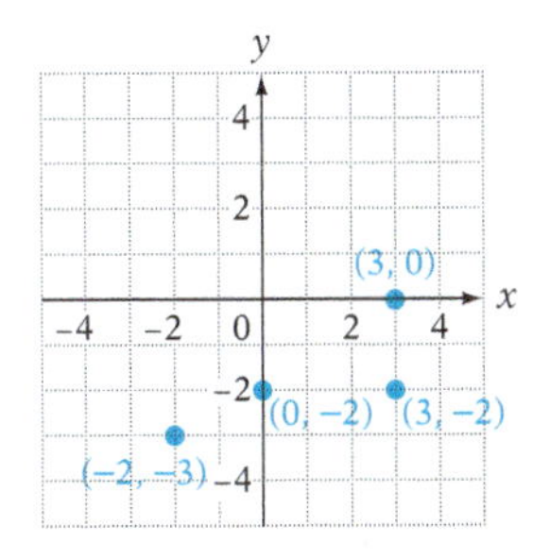

YOU TRY IT 1

Graph the ordered pairs $(-4, 1)$, $(3, -3)$, $(0, 4)$, and $(-3, 0)$.

Your solution

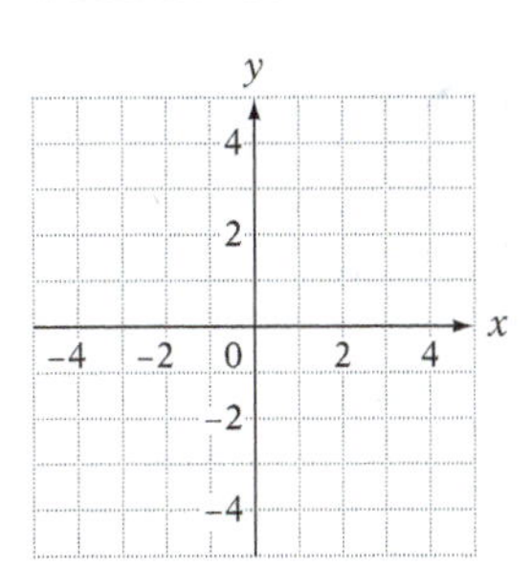

EXAMPLE 2

Give the coordinates of the points labeled *A* and *B*. Give the abscissa of point *C* and the ordinate of point *D*.

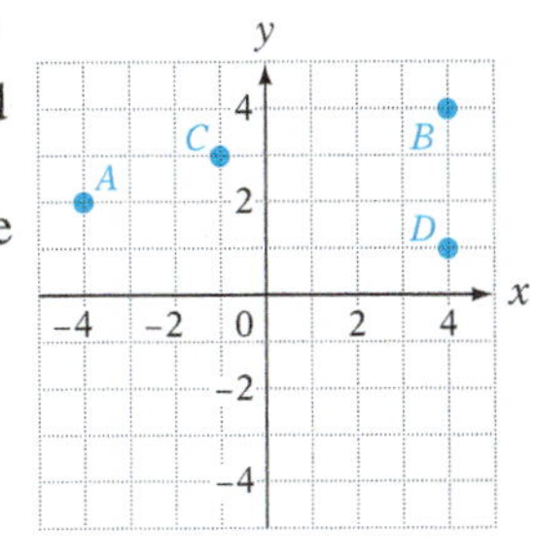

Solution

The coordinates of *A* are $(-4, 2)$.
The coordinates of *B* are $(4, 4)$.
The abscissa of *C* is -1.
The ordinate of *D* is 1.

YOU TRY IT 2

Give the coordinates of the points labeled *A* and *B*. Give the abscissa of point *D* and the ordinate of point *C*.

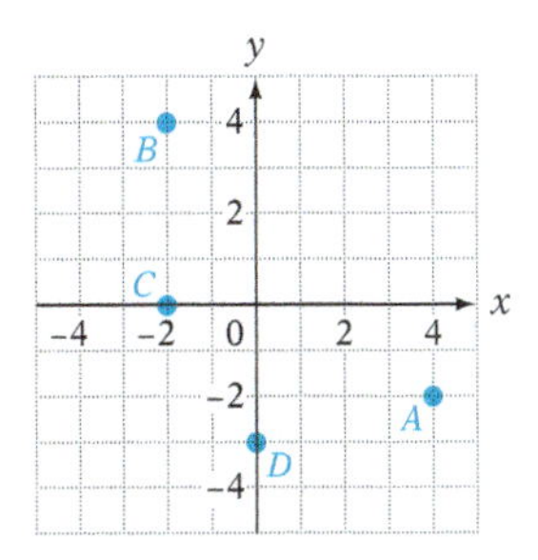

Your solution

Solutions on p. S17

OBJECTIVE B *To determine ordered-pair solutions of an equation in two variables*

An xy-coordinate system is used to study the relationship between two variables. Frequently this relationship is given by an equation. Examples of equations in two variables include

$$y = 2x - 3 \qquad 3x + 2y = 6 \qquad x^2 - y = 0$$

A **solution of an equation in two variables** is an ordered pair (x, y) whose coordinates make the equation a true statement.

HOW TO 1 Is $(-3, 7)$ a solution of the equation $y = -2x + 1$?

$$\begin{array}{l|l} y & -2x + 1 \\ \hline 7 & -2(-3) + 1 \\ 7 & 6 + 1 \end{array}$$
$7 = 7$

- **Replace x by -3; replace y by 7.**
- **The results are equal.**

Yes, $(-3, 7)$ is a solution of the equation $y = -2x + 1$.

Besides $(-3, 7)$, there are many other ordered-pair solutions of $y = -2x + 1$. For example, $(0, 1)$, $\left(-\frac{3}{2}, 4\right)$, and $(4, -7)$ are also solutions. In general, an equation in two variables has an infinite number of solutions. By choosing any value of x and substituting that value into the equation, we can calculate a corresponding value of y.

HOW TO 2 Find the ordered-pair solution of $y = \frac{2}{3}x - 3$ that corresponds to $x = 6$.

$$y = \frac{2}{3}x - 3$$
$$= \frac{2}{3}(6) - 3 \qquad \text{• Replace } x \text{ by 6.}$$
$$= 4 - 3 = 1 \qquad \text{• Simplify.}$$

The ordered-pair solution is $(6, 1)$.

The solutions of an equation in two variables can be graphed in an xy-coordinate system.

HOW TO 3 Graph the ordered-pair solutions of $y = -2x + 1$ when $x = -2, -1, 0, 1$, and 2.

Use the values of x to determine ordered-pair solutions of the equation. It is convenient to record these in a table.

x	$y = -2x + 1$	y	(x, y)
-2	$-2(-2) + 1$	5	$(-2, 5)$
-1	$-2(-1) + 1$	3	$(-1, 3)$
0	$-2(0) + 1$	1	$(0, 1)$
1	$-2(1) + 1$	-1	$(1, -1)$
2	$-2(2) + 1$	-3	$(2, -3)$

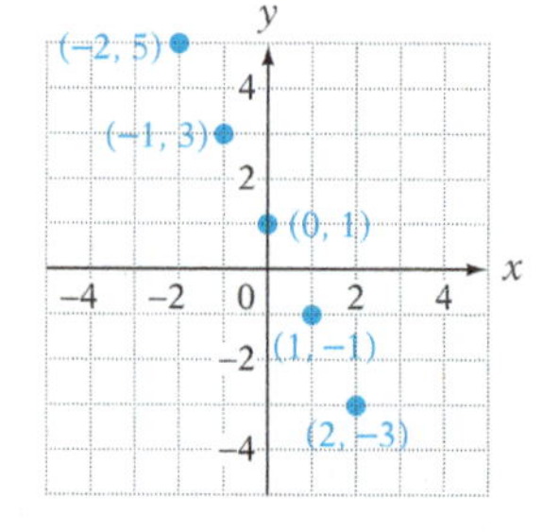

EXAMPLE 3

Is $(3, -2)$ a solution of $3x - 4y = 15$?

Solution

$$\begin{array}{r|l} 3x - 4y = & 15 \\ \hline 3(3) - 4(-2) & 15 \\ 9 + 8 & 15 \\ 17 & \neq 15 \end{array}$$

• Replace x by 3 and y by -2.

No, $(3, -2)$ is not a solution of $3x - 4y = 15$.

YOU TRY IT 3

Is $(-2, 4)$ a solution of $x - 3y = -14$?

Your solution

EXAMPLE 4

Graph the ordered-pair solutions of $2x - 3y = 6$ when $x = -3, 0, 3$, and 6.

Solution

$$2x - 3y = 6$$
$$-3y = -2x + 6$$
$$y = \frac{2}{3}x - 2$$

• Solve $2x - 3y = 6$ for y.

Replace x in $y = \frac{2}{3}x - 2$ by $-3, 0, 3$, and 6. For each value of x, determine the value of y.

x	$y = \frac{2}{3}x - 2$	y	(x, y)
-3	$\frac{2}{3}(-3) - 2$	-4	$(-3, -4)$
0	$\frac{2}{3}(0) - 2$	-2	$(0, -2)$
3	$\frac{2}{3}(3) - 2$	0	$(3, 0)$
6	$\frac{2}{3}(6) - 2$	2	$(6, 2)$

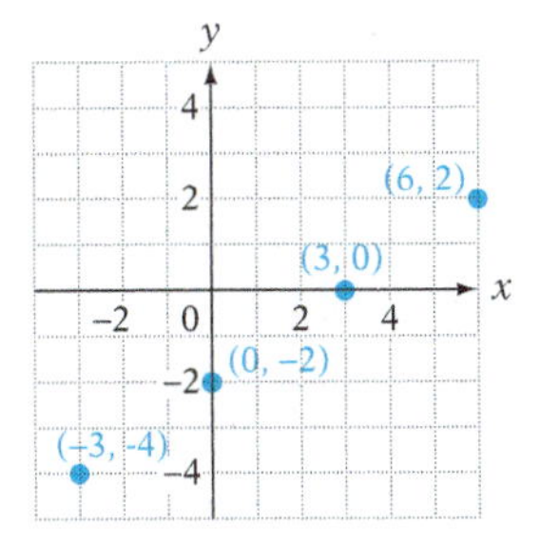

YOU TRY IT 4

Graph the ordered-pair solutions of $x + 2y = 4$ when $x = -4, -2, 0$, and 2.

Your solution

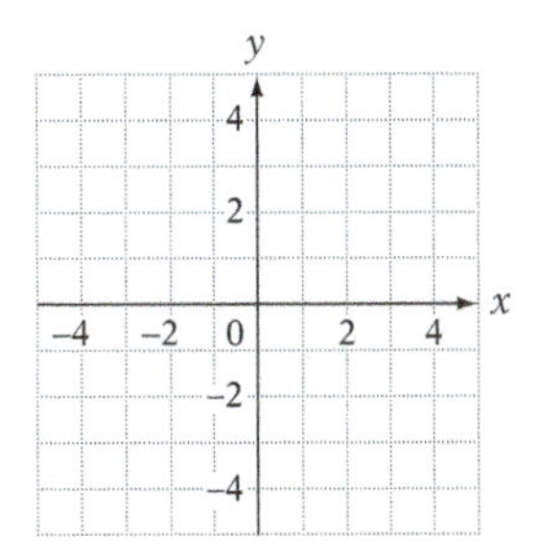

Solutions on p. S17

OBJECTIVE C *To determine whether a set of ordered pairs is a function*

Juriah Mosin/Shutterstock.com

Exploring a relationship between two variables is an important task in the application of mathematics. Here are some examples.

- Botanists study the relationship between the number of bushels of wheat yielded per acre and the amount of watering per acre.
- Environmental scientists study the relationship between the incidence of skin cancer and the amount of ozone in the atmosphere.
- Business analysts study the relationship between the price of a product and the number of products that are sold at that price.

Each of these relationships can be described by a set of ordered pairs.

Definition of a Relation

A **relation** is any set of ordered pairs.

The following table shows the number of hours that each of nine students spent studying for a midterm exam and the grade that each of these nine students received.

Hours	3	3.5	2.75	2	4	4.5	3	2.5	5
Grade	78	75	70	65	85	85	80	75	90

This information can be written as the relation

$$\{(3, 78), (3.5, 75), (2.75, 70), (2, 65), (4, 85), (4.5, 85), (3, 80), (2.5, 75), (5, 90)\}$$

where the first coordinate of the ordered pair is the hours spent studying and the second coordinate is the score on the midterm.

The **domain** of a relation is the set of first coordinates of the ordered pairs; the **range** is the set of second coordinates. For the relation above,

$$\text{Domain} = \{2, 2.5, 2.75, 3, 3.5, 4, 4.5, 5\} \qquad \text{Range} = \{65, 70, 75, 78, 80, 85, 90\}$$

The **graph of a relation** is the graph of the ordered pairs that belong to the relation. The graph of the relation given above is shown at the right. The horizontal axis represents the hours spent studying (the domain); the vertical axis represents the test score (the range). In the figure, the axes are labeled H for hours studied and S for test score.

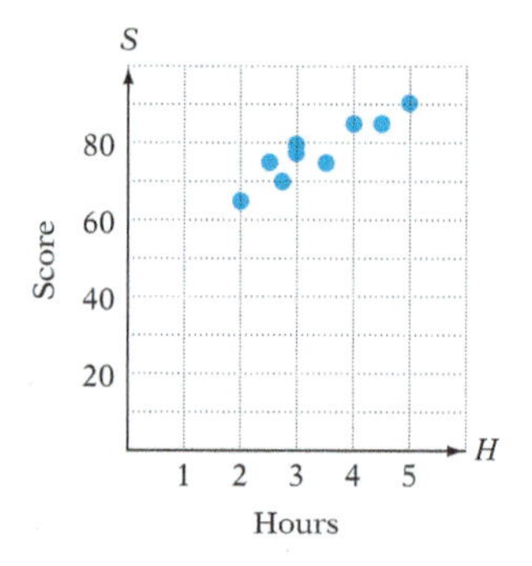

A *function* is a special type of relation in which no two ordered pairs have the same first coordinate.

Definition of a Function

A **function** is a relation in which no two ordered pairs have the same first coordinate.

The table at the right is the grading scale for a 100-point test. This table defines a relationship between the *score* on the test and a *letter grade.* Some of the ordered pairs of this function are (78, C), (97, A), (84, B), and (82, B).

Score	*Grade*
90–100	A
80–89	B
70–79	C
60–69	D
0–59	F

The grading-scale table defines a function because no two ordered pairs can have the same first coordinate and different second coordinates. For instance, it is not possible to have the ordered pairs (72, C) and (72, B)—same first coordinate (test score) but different second coordinates (test grade). The domain of this function is $\{0, 1, 2, \ldots, 99, 100\}$. The range is $\{A, B, C, D, F\}$.

The example of hours spent studying and test score given earlier is *not* a function, because (3, 78) and (3, 80) are ordered pairs of the relation that have the *same* first coordinate but *different* second coordinates.

Consider again the grading-scale example. Note that (84, B) and (82, B) are ordered pairs of the function. Ordered pairs of a function may have the same *second* coordinates but not the same first coordinates.

Although relations and functions can be given by tables, they are frequently given by an equation in two variables.

The equation $y = 2x$ expresses the relationship between a number, x, and twice the number, y. For instance, if $x = 3$, then $y = 6$, which is twice 3. To indicate exactly which ordered pairs are determined by the equation, the domain (values of x) is specified. If $x \in \{-2, -1, 0, 1, 2\}$, then the ordered pairs determined by the equation are $\{(-2, -4), (-1, -2), (0, 0), (1, 2), (2, 4)\}$. This relation is a function because no two ordered pairs have the same first coordinate.

The graph of the function $y = 2x$ with domain $\{-2, -1, 0, 1, 2\}$ is shown at the right. The horizontal axis (domain) is labeled x; the vertical axis (range) is labeled y.

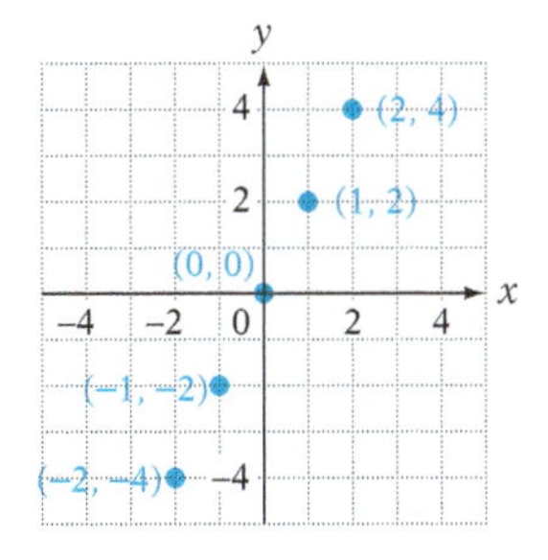

The domain $\{-2, -1, 0, 1, 2\}$ was chosen arbitrarily. Other domains could have been selected. The type of application usually influences the choice of domain.

For the equation $y = 2x$, we say that "y is a function of x" because the set of ordered pairs is a function.

Not all equations, however, define a function. For instance, the equation $|y| = x + 2$ does not define y as a function of x. The ordered pairs (2, 4) and (2, −4) both satisfy the equation. Thus there are two ordered pairs with the same first coordinate but different second coordinates.

EXAMPLE 5

The table below shows the amount of money invested in college savings plans and the amount invested in prepaid college tuition plans over a five-year period. (*Sources:* Investment Company Institute and College Savings Plan Network)

Year	Assets in College Savings Plans (in billions of dollars)	Assets in Prepaid Tuition Plans (in billions of dollars)
1	9	7
2	19	8
3	35	11
4	52	13
5	69	14

Write a relation in which the first coordinate is the amount of money in college savings plans and the second coordinate is the amount of money in prepaid tuition plans (both in billions of dollars). Is the relation a function?

Solution

The relation is
$\{(9, 7), (19, 8), (35, 11), (52, 13), (69, 14)\}$

There are no two ordered pairs with the same first coordinate. The relation is a function.

YOU TRY IT 5

Five students decided to go on a diet and fitness program over the summer. Their weights (in pounds) at the beginning and end of the program are given in the table below.

Beginning	End
145	140
140	125
150	130
165	150
140	130

Write a relation in which the first coordinate is the weight at the beginning of the summer and the second coordinate is the weight at the end of the summer. Is the relation a function?

Your solution

EXAMPLE 6

Does $y = x^2 + 3$, where $x \in \{-2, -1, 1, 3\}$, define y as a function of x?

Solution

Determine the ordered pairs defined by the equation. Replace x in $y = x^2 + 3$ by the given values and solve for y.

$\{(-2, 7), (-1, 4), (1, 4), (3, 12)\}$

No two ordered pairs have the same first coordinate. Therefore, the relation is a function and the equation $y = x^2 + 3$ defines y as a function of x.

Note that $(-1, 4)$ and $(1, 4)$ are ordered pairs that belong to this function. Ordered pairs of a function may have the same *second* coordinate but not the same *first* coordinate.

YOU TRY IT 6

Does $y = \frac{1}{2}x + 1$, where $x \in \{-4, 0, 2\}$, define y as a function of x?

Your solution

Solutions on p. S17

OBJECTIVE D *To evaluate a function*

When an equation defines y as a function of x, **function notation** is frequently used to emphasize that the relation is a function. In this case, it is common to replace y in the function's equation with the symbol $f(x)$, where

$f(x)$ is read "f of x" or "the value of f at x."

For instance, the equation $y = x^2 + 3$ from Example 6 defined y as a function of x. The equation can also be written

$$f(x) = x^2 + 3$$

where y has been replaced by $f(x)$.

The symbol $f(x)$ is called the **value of a function at x** because it is the result of evaluating a variable expression. For instance, $f(4)$ means to replace x by 4 and then simplify the resulting numerical expression.

$$f(x) = x^2 + 3$$

$$f(4) = 4^2 + 3 \qquad \text{Replace } x \text{ by } 4.$$

$$= 16 + 3 = 19$$

This process is called **evaluating a function.**

HOW TO 4 Given $f(x) = x^2 + x - 3$, find $f(-2)$.

$$f(x) = x^2 + x - 3$$

$$f(-2) = (-2)^2 + (-2) - 3 \qquad \bullet \text{ Replace } x \text{ by } -2.$$

$$= 4 - 2 - 3 = -1$$

$$f(-2) = -1$$

In this example, $f(-2)$ is the second coordinate of an ordered pair of the function; the first coordinate is -2. Therefore, an ordered pair of this function is $(-2, f(-2))$, or, because $f(-2) = -1$, $(-2, -1)$.

For the function given by $y = f(x) = x^2 + x - 3$, y is called the **dependent variable** because its value depends on the value of x. The **independent variable** is x.

Functions can be written using other letters or even combinations of letters. For instance, some calculators use $ABS(x)$ for the absolute value function. Thus the equation $y = |x|$ would be written $ABS(x) = |x|$, where $ABS(x)$ replaces y.

EXAMPLE 7

Given $G(t) = \dfrac{3t}{t + 4}$, find $G(1)$.

Solution

$$G(t) = \frac{3t}{t + 4}$$

$$G(1) = \frac{3(1)}{1 + 4} \qquad \bullet \text{ Replace } t \text{ by } 1. \text{ Then simplify.}$$

$$G(1) = \frac{3}{5}$$

YOU TRY IT 7

Given $H(x) = \dfrac{x}{x - 4}$, find $H(8)$.

Your solution

Solution on p. S17

7.1 EXERCISES

Concept Check

1. In which quadrant is the graph of $(-3, 4)$ located?
2. In which quadrant is the graph of $(2, -5)$ located?
3. On which axis does the graph of $(0, -4)$ lie?
4. On which axis does the graph of $(-6, 0)$ lie?
5. Name any two points on a horizontal line that is 2 units above the x-axis.
6. Name any two points on a vertical line that is 3 units to the right of the y-axis.

Complete Exercises 7 and 8 by filling in each blank with the word *left, right, up,* or *down.*

7. To graph the point $(5, -4)$, start at the origin and move 5 units ________ and 4 units ________.
8. To graph the point $(-1, 7)$, start at the origin and move 1 unit ________ and 7 units ________.
9. Write as an ordered pair the coordinates of the point whose x-coordinate is 6 and whose y-coordinate is -5.
10. Write as an ordered pair the coordinates of the point whose y-coordinate is 8 and whose x-coordinate is -7.
11. To decide whether the ordered pair (1, 7) is a solution of the equation $y = 2x + 5$, substitute 1 for ______ and 7 for ______ to see whether the ordered pair (1, 7) makes the equation $y = 2x + 5$ a true statement.
12. The graphs of $y = \frac{1}{4}x - 6$ and $f(x) =$ ________ are identical.
13. A relation is a set of ________. The set of first coordinates of the ordered pairs is called the ________ of the relation. The set of second coordinates is called the ________ of the relation.
14. The symbol $f(x)$ is read "f ______ x" or "the value of f ______ x." It is a symbol for the number that the function f pairs with ______.

OBJECTIVE A *To graph points in a rectangular coordinate system*

15. Graph $(-2, 1)$, $(3, -5)$, $(-2, 4)$, and $(0, 3)$.

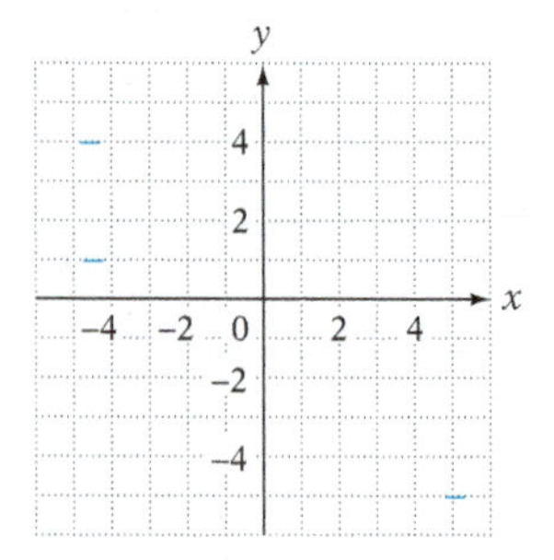

16. Graph $(5, -1)$, $(-3, -3)$, $(-1, 0)$, and $(1, -1)$.

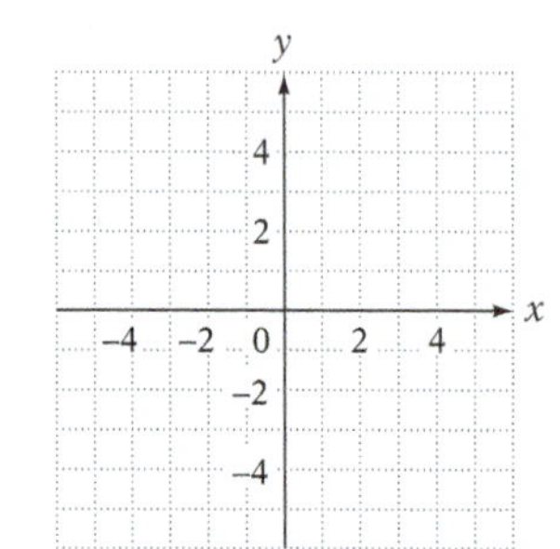

17. Graph $(0, 0)$, $(0, -5)$, $(-3, 0)$, and $(0, 2)$.

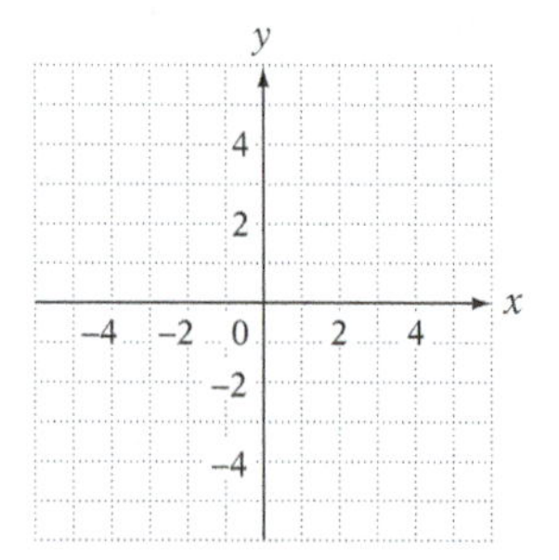

18. Graph $(-4, 5)$, $(-3, 1)$, $(3, -4)$, and $(5, 0)$.

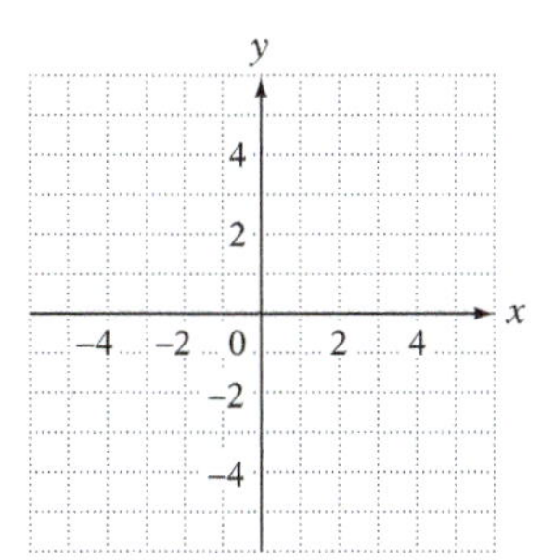

19. Graph $(-1, 4)$, $(-2, -3)$, $(0, 2)$, and $(4, 0)$.

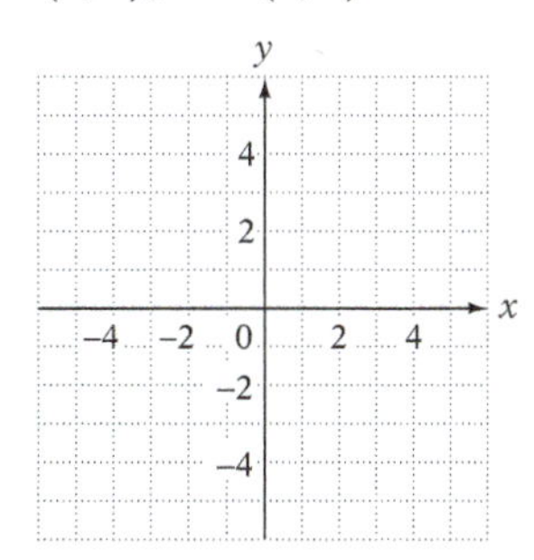

20. Graph $(5, 2)$, $(-4, -1)$, $(0, 0)$, and $(0, 3)$.

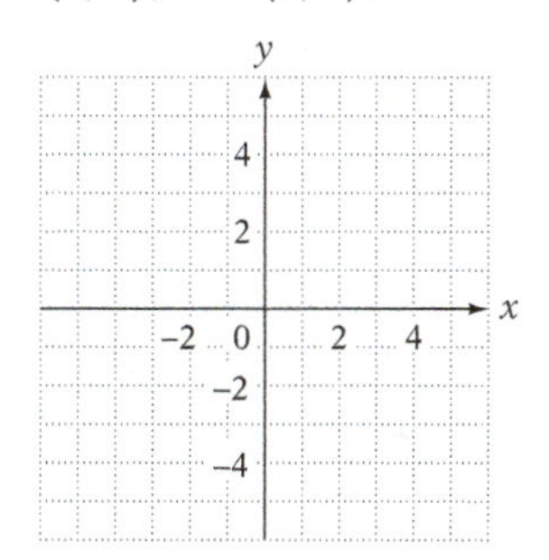

21. Find the coordinates of each of the points.

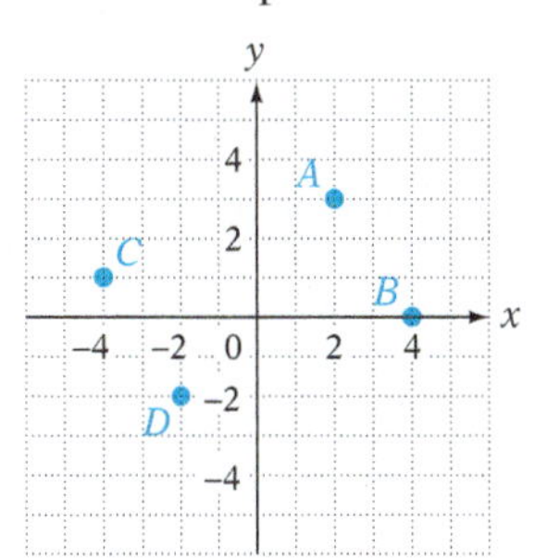

22. Find the coordinates of each of the points.

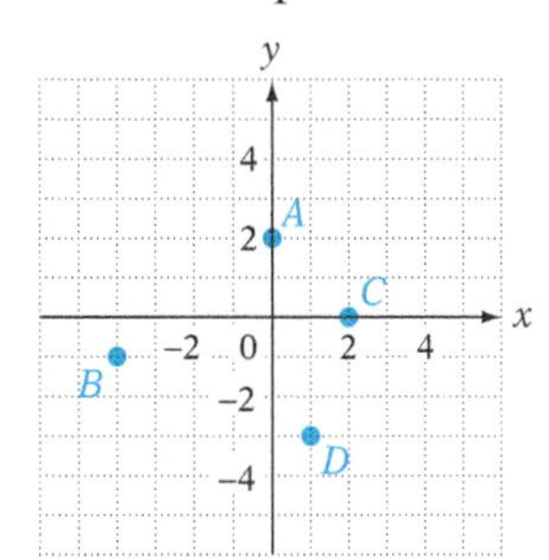

23. Find the coordinates of each of the points.

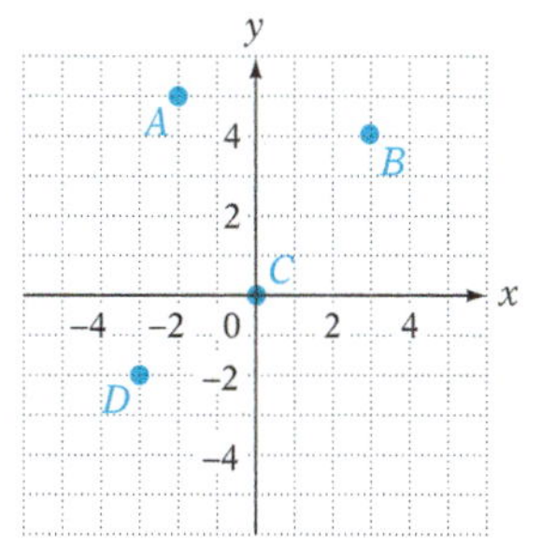

24. Find the coordinates of each of the points.

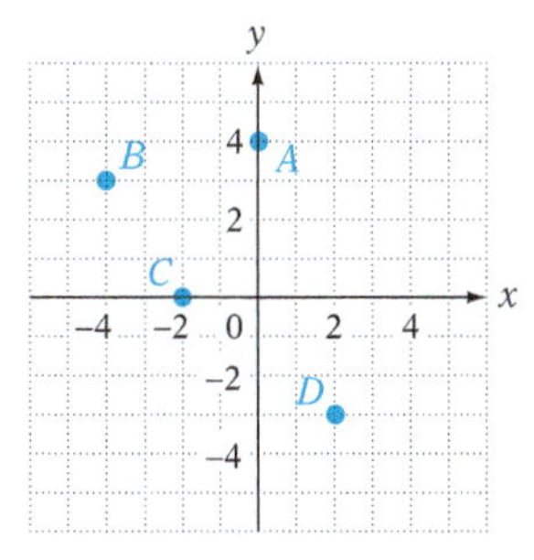

25. a. Name the abscissas of points A and C.

b. Name the ordinates of points B and D.

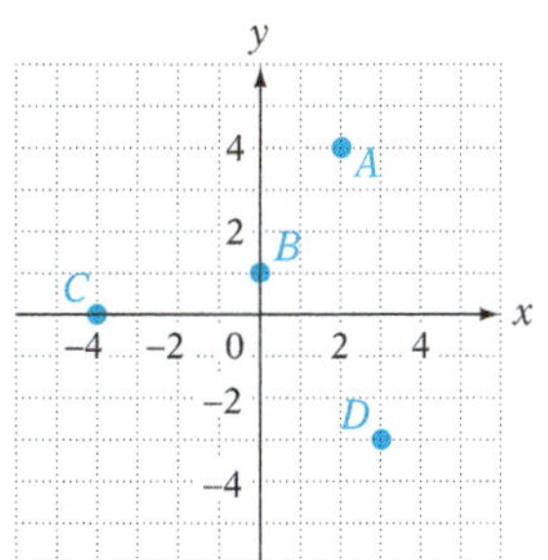

26. a. Name the abscissas of points A and C.

b. Name the ordinates of points B and D.

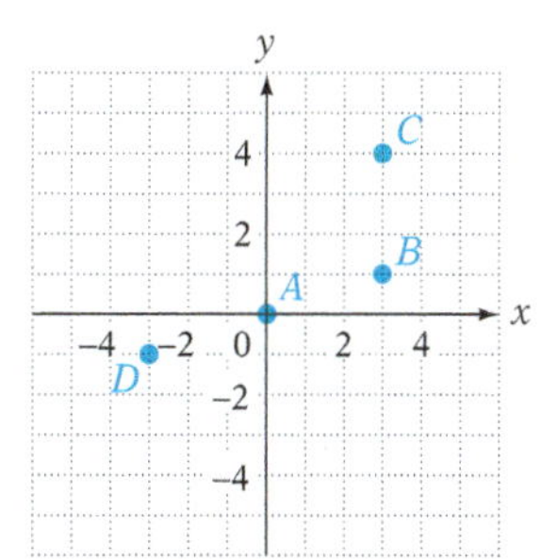

27. Let a and b be positive numbers such that $a < b$. In which quadrant is each point located?

a. (a, b) **b.** $(-a, b)$ **c.** $(b - a, -b)$ **d.** $(a - b, -b - a)$

28. Let a and b be positive numbers. State whether the two given points lie on the x-axis, the y-axis, a horizontal line other than the x-axis, or a vertical line other than the y-axis.

a. $(-a, b)$ and $(-a, 0)$ **b.** $(a, 0)$ and $(-b, 0)$

OBJECTIVE B *To determine ordered-pair solutions of an equation in two variables*

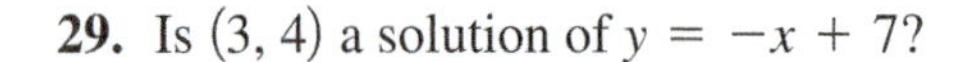

29. Is (3, 4) a solution of $y = -x + 7$?

30. Is (2, −3) a solution of $y = x + 5$?

31. Is (−1, 2) a solution of $y = \frac{1}{2}x - 1$?

32. Is (1, −3) a solution of $y = -2x - 1$?

33. Is (4, 1) a solution of $2x - 5y = 4$?

34. Is (−5, 3) a solution of $3x - 2y = 9$?

35. Suppose (x, y) is a solution of the equation $y = -3x + 6$, where $x > 2$. Is y positive or negative?

36. Suppose (x, y) is a solution of the equation $y = 4x - 8$, where $y > 0$. Is x less than or greater than 2?

For Exercises 37 to 42, graph the ordered-pair solutions of the equation for the given values of x.

37. $y = 2x$; $x = -2, -1, 0, 2$

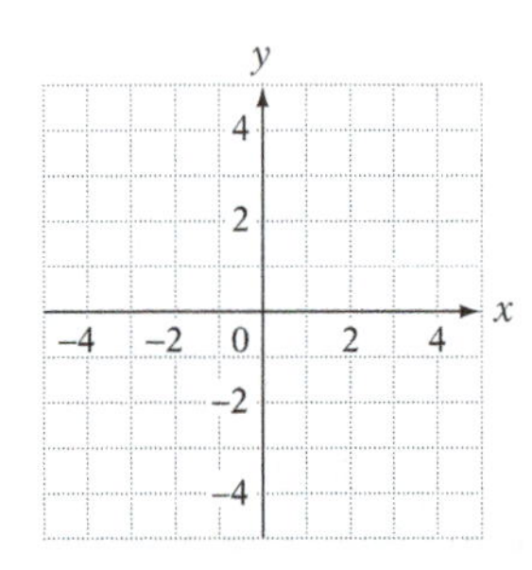

38. $y = -2x$; $x = -2, -1, 0, 2$

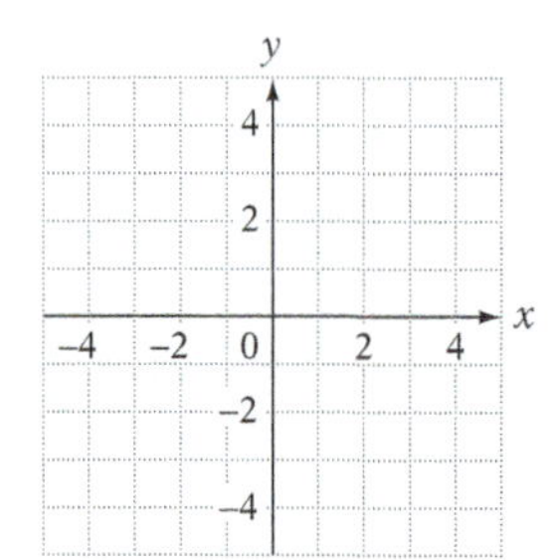

39. $y = \frac{2}{3}x + 1$; $x = -3, 0, 3$

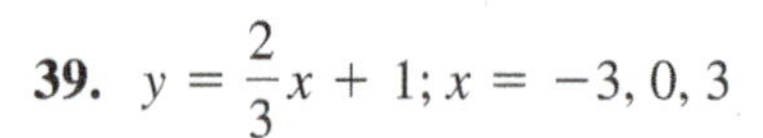

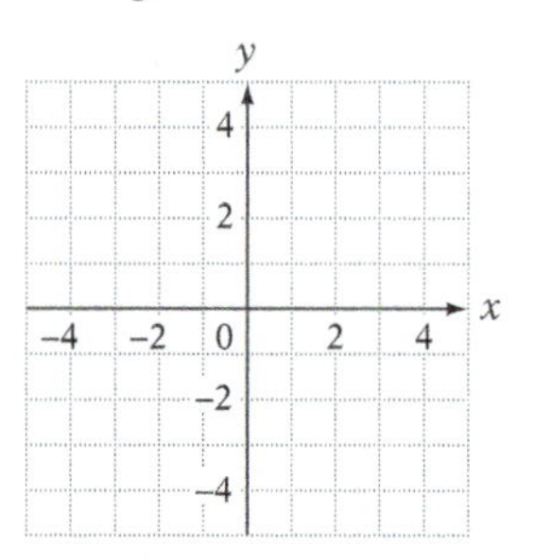

40. $y = -\frac{1}{3}x - 2$; $x = -3, 0, 3$

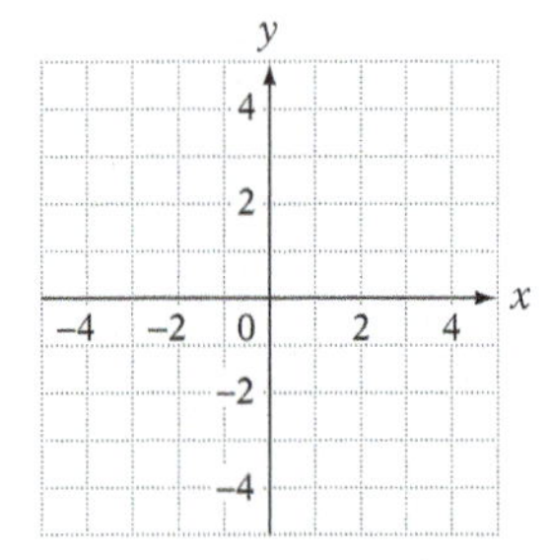

41. $2x + 3y = 6$; $x = -3, 0, 3$

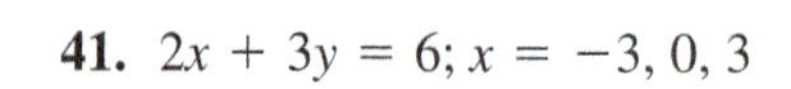

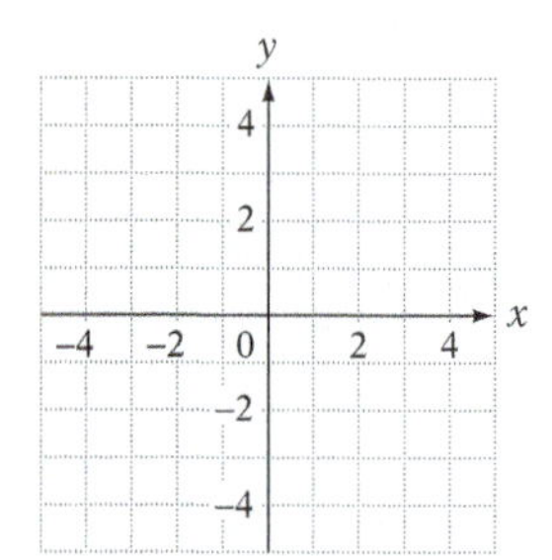

42. $x - 2y = 4$; $x = -2, 0, 2$

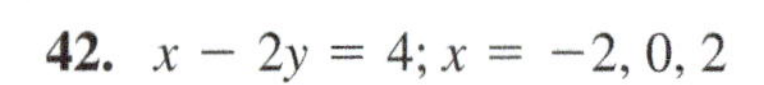

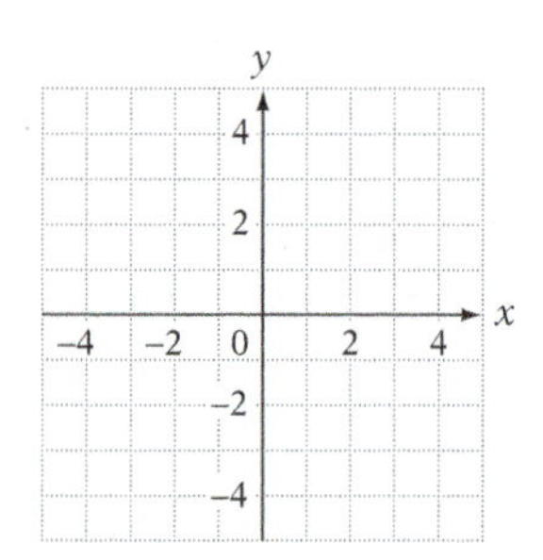

OBJECTIVE C *To determine whether a set of ordered pairs is a function*

For Exercises 43 and 44, use the following sets. Set A is the set of all dates of the year ({January 1, January 2, January 3, ...}). Set B is the set of all the people in the world.

43. A relation has domain A and range B. Each ordered pair in the relation is of the form (date, person born on that date). Is this relation a function?

44. A relation has domain B and range A. Each ordered pair in the relation is of the form (person, birth date of that person). Is this relation a function?

45. **Marathons** See the news clipping at the right. The table below shows the ages and finishing times of the top eight finishers in the Manhattan Island Swim. Write a relation in which the first coordinate is the age of a swimmer and the second coordinate is the swimmer's finishing time. Is the relation a function?

Ages (in years)	35	45	38	24	47	51	35	48
Time (in hours)	7.50	7.58	7.63	7.78	7.80	7.86	7.89	7.92

In the NEWS!

Swimmers Go the Distance

Twenty-three swimmers completed NYC Swim's annual Manhattan Island Swim. Swimmers begin at Battery Park City–South Cove and swim a 28.5-mile course around Manhattan Island. The 35-year-old first-place finisher swam the distance in 7 h, 30 min, and 15 s.

Source: www.nycswim.org

46. **Jogging** The table below shows the number of Calories a 150-pound person burns in 1 h while running at various speeds, in miles per hour. Write a relation in which the first coordinate is the speed of the runner and the second coordinate is the number of Calories burned. Is the relation a function?

Speed (in mph)	*Calories*
4	411
5	514
6	618
7	720
8	823

47. **Health** The table at the right shows the U.S. Department of Agriculture's recommended limits on saturated fat intake, in grams. Write a relation in which the first coordinate is a person's daily Calorie intake and the second coordinate is the recommended limit on saturated fat intake. Is the relation a function?

Daily Calories	*Saturated Fat (in grams)*
1600	18
2000	20
2200	24
2500	25
2800	31

48. **Health** The table at the right shows the birth rates, in births per thousand people per year, and life expectancies, in years, for various countries. (*Source:* www.cia.gov) Write a relation in which the first coordinate is the birth rate and the second coordinate is the life expectancy. Is the relation a function?

Country	*Birth Rate*	*Life Expectancy*
Belgium	10.48	78.6
Brazil	16.8	71.7
Martinique	14.14	79.0
Mexico	21.0	75.2
Sweden	10.36	80.4
United States	14.14	77.7

For Exercises 49 to 52, find the domain and range of the relation. State whether or not the relation is a function.

49. $\{(0, 0), (2, 0), (4, 0), (6, 0)\}$

50. $\{(-2, 2), (0, 2), (1, 2), (2, 2)\}$

51. $\{(2, 2), (2, 4), (2, 6), (2, 8)\}$

52. $\{(-4, 4), (-2, 2), (0, 0), (-2, -2)\}$

53. Does $y = 2x + 3$, where $x \in \{-2, -1, 1, 4\}$, define y as a function of x?

54. Does $|y| = x - 1$, where $x \in \{1, 2, 3, 4\}$, define y as a function of x?

55. Does $y = x^2$, where $x \in \{-2, -1, 0, 1, 2\}$, define y as a function of x?

OBJECTIVE D *To evaluate a function*

56. Given $f(x) = 3x - 4$, find $f(4)$.

57. Given $f(x) = 5x + 1$, find $f(2)$.

58. Given $f(x) = x^2$, find $f(3)$.

59. Given $f(x) = x^2 - 1$, find $f(1)$.

60. Given $G(x) = x^2 + x$, find $G(-2)$.

61. Given $H(x) = x^2 - x$, find $H(-2)$.

62. Given $s(t) = \frac{3}{t - 1}$, find $s(-2)$.

63. Given $P(x) = \frac{4}{2x + 1}$, find $P(-2)$.

64. Given $h(x) = 3x^2 - 2x + 1$, find $h(3)$.

65. Given $Q(r) = 4r^2 - r - 3$, find $Q(2)$.

66. Given $f(x) = \frac{x}{x + 5}$, find $f(-3)$.

67. Given $v(t) = \frac{2t}{2t + 1}$, find $v(3)$.

For Exercises 68 to 71, use the function $f(x) = x^2 - 4$. For the given condition on a, determine whether $f(a)$ *must be positive, must be negative,* or *could be either positive or negative.*

68. $a > 2$

69. $a < 0$

70. $a > -2$

71. $a < -2$

Critical Thinking

For Exercises 72 to 74, find the distance from the given point to the horizontal axis.

72. $(-5, 1)$

73. $(3, -4)$

74. $(-6, 0)$

For Exercises 75 to 77, find the distance from the given point to the vertical axis.

75. $(-2, 4)$

76. $(1, -3)$

77. $(5, 0)$

78. Name the coordinates of a point plotted at the origin of the rectangular coordinate system.

79. Write a paragraph explaining how to plot points in a rectangular coordinate system.

Projects or Group Activities

80. Functions are a part of our everyday lives. For example, the cost to mail a package via first-class mail is a function of the weight of the package. The tuition paid by a part-time student is a function of the number of credit hours the student registers for. Provide other examples of functions.

81. Define three situations that describe relations that are not functions. One example is the set of ordered pairs in which the first coordinates are the runs scored by a baseball team and the second coordinates are either W for a win or L for a loss.

82. There is an imaginary coordinate system on Earth that consists of *longitude* and *latitude.* Write a report on how location is determined on the surface of Earth.

SECTION

7.2 Linear Equations in Two Variables

OBJECTIVE A *To graph an equation of the form $y = mx + b$*

The **graph of an equation in two variables** is a graph of the ordered-pair solutions of the equation.

Consider $y = 2x + 1$. Choosing $x = -2, -1, 0, 1$, and 2 and determining the corresponding values of y produces some of the ordered pairs of the equation. These are recorded in the table at the right. See the graph of the ordered pairs in Figure 1.

x	$y = 2x + 1$	y	(x, y)
-2	$2(-2) + 1$	-3	$(-2, -3)$
-1	$2(-1) + 1$	-1	$(-1, -1)$
0	$2(0) + 1$	1	$(0, 1)$
1	$2(1) + 1$	3	$(1, 3)$
2	$2(2) + 1$	5	$(2, 5)$

Choosing values of x that are not integers produces more ordered pairs to graph, such as $\left(-\frac{5}{2}, -4\right)$ and $\left(\frac{3}{2}, 4\right)$, as shown in Figure 2. Choosing still other values of x would result in more and more ordered pairs being graphed. The result would be so many dots that the graph would appear as the straight line shown in Figure 3, which is the graph of $y = 2x + 1$.

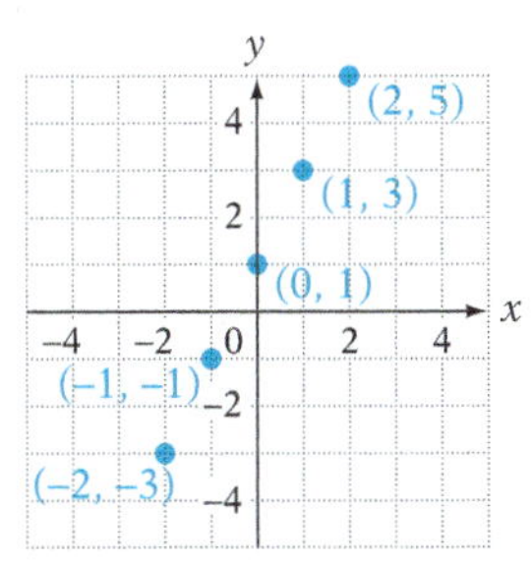

Figure 1

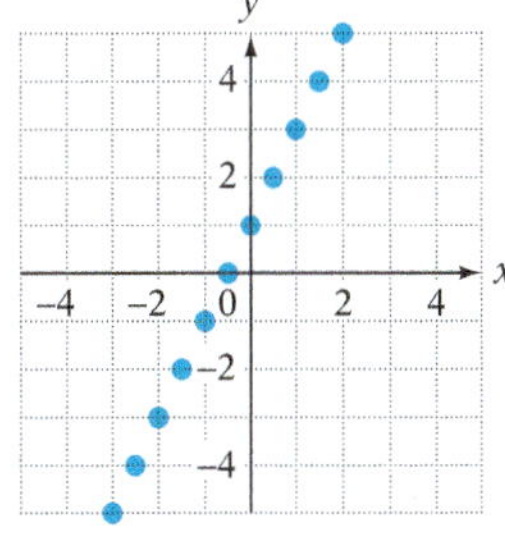

Figure 2

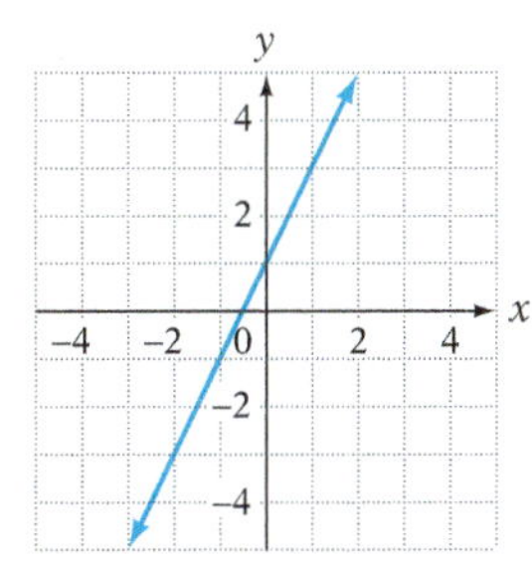

Figure 3

Equations in two variables have characteristic graphs. The equation $y = 2x + 1$ is an example of a *linear equation,* or *linear function,* because its graph is a straight line. It is also called a *first-degree equation* in two variables because the exponent on each variable is 1.

Linear Equation in Two Variables

Any equation of the form $y = mx + b$, where m is the coefficient of x and b is a constant, is a **linear equation in two variables,** or a **first-degree equation in two variables,** or a **linear function.** The graph of a linear equation in two variables is a straight line.

EXAMPLES OF LINEAR EQUATIONS IN TWO VARIABLES

1. $y = 2x + 1$ $(m = 2, b = 1)$ **2.** $y = x - 4$ $(m = 1, b = -4)$

3. $y = -\frac{3}{4}x$ $\left(m = -\frac{3}{4}, b = 0\right)$ **4.** $y = 3 - 2x$ $(m = -2, b = 3)$

The equation $y = x^2 + 4x + 3$ is not a linear equation in two variables because it has a term with a variable squared. The equation $y = \frac{3}{x-4}$ is not a linear equation in two variables because there is a variable in the denominator.

Integrating Technology

The Projects and Group Activities feature at the end of Section 7.3 contains information on using a calculator to graph an equation.

To graph a linear equation, choose some values of x and then find the corresponding values of y. Because a straight line is determined by two points, it is sufficient to find only two ordered-pair solutions. However, it is recommended that at least three ordered-pair solutions be found to ensure accuracy.

HOW TO 1 Graph $y = -\frac{3}{2}x + 2$.

This is a linear equation with $m = -\frac{3}{2}$ and $b = 2$. Find at least three solutions. Because m is a fraction, choose values of x that will simplify the calculations. We have chosen -2, 0, and 4 for x. (Any values of x could have been selected.)

x	$y = -\frac{3}{2}x + 2$	y	(x, y)
-2	$-\frac{3}{2}(-2) + 2$	5	$(-2, 5)$
0	$-\frac{3}{2}(0) + 2$	2	$(0, 2)$
4	$-\frac{3}{2}(4) + 2$	-4	$(4, -4)$

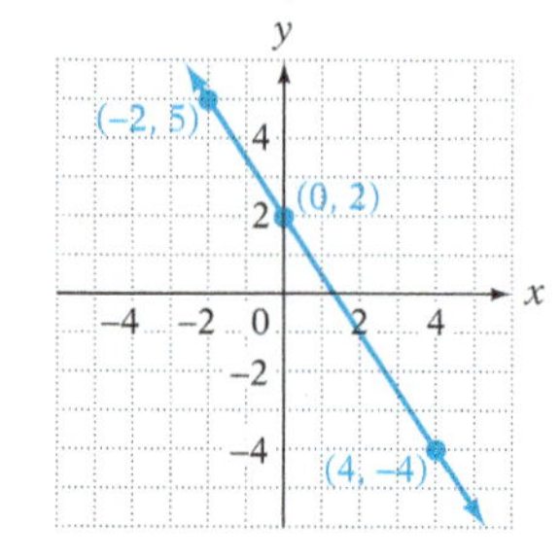

The graph of $y = -\frac{3}{2}x + 2$ is shown at the right.

Remember that a graph is a drawing of the ordered-pair solutions of an equation. Therefore, every point on the graph is a solution of the equation, and every solution of the equation is a point on the graph.

The graph at the right is the graph of $y = x + 2$. Note that $(-4, -2)$ and $(1, 3)$ are points on the graph, and these points are solutions of $y = x + 2$. The point whose coordinates are $(4, 1)$ is not a point on the graph and therefore is not a solution of the equation.

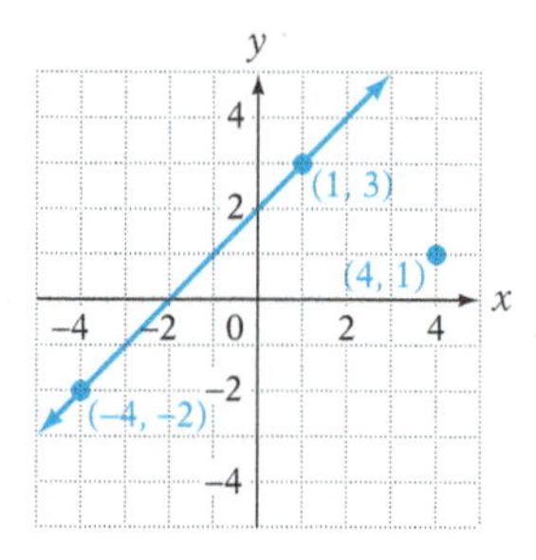

EXAMPLE 1

Graph $y = 3x - 2$.

Solution

x	y
0	-2
-1	-5
2	4

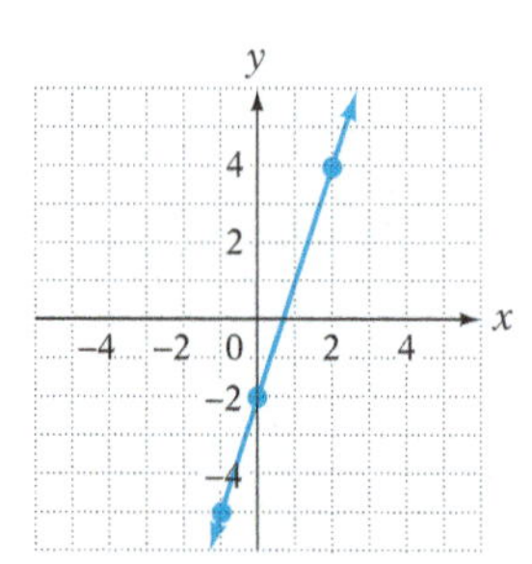

YOU TRY IT 1

Graph $y = 3x + 1$.

Your solution

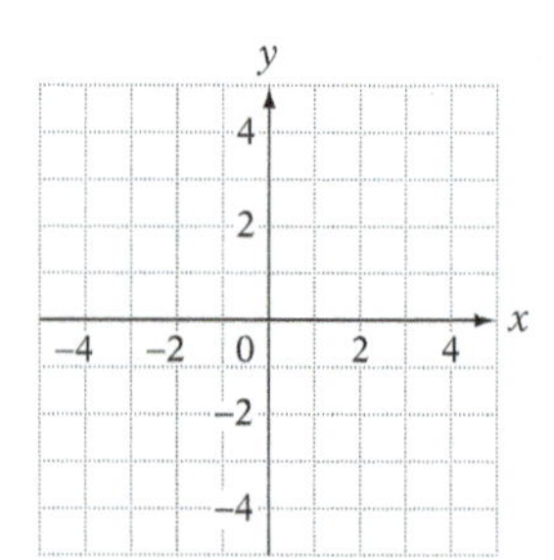

Solution on p. S18

EXAMPLE 2

Graph $y = 2x$.

Solution

x	y
0	0
2	4
−2	−4

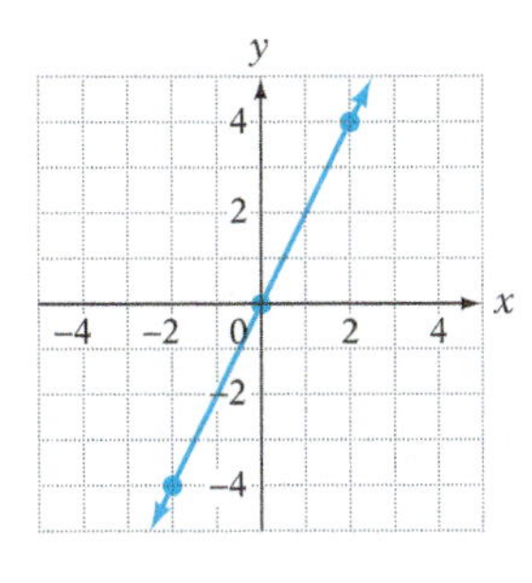

YOU TRY IT 2

Graph $y = -2x$.

Your solution

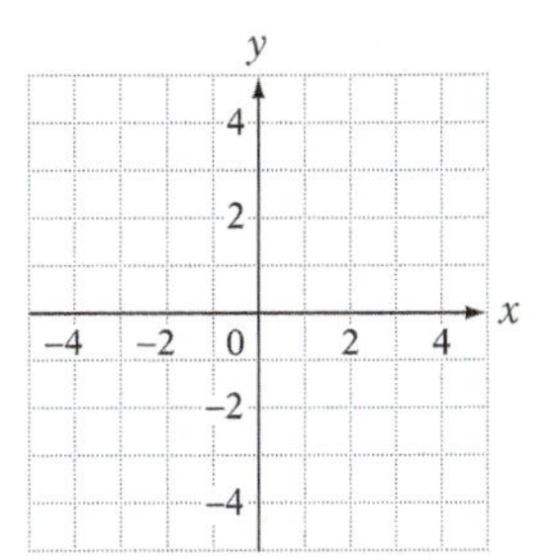

EXAMPLE 3

Graph $y = \frac{1}{2}x - 1$.

Solution

x	y
0	−1
2	0
−2	−2

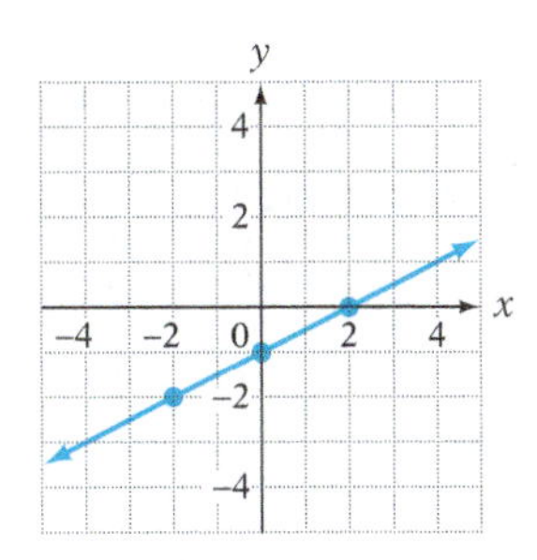

YOU TRY IT 3

Graph $y = \frac{1}{3}x - 3$.

Your solution

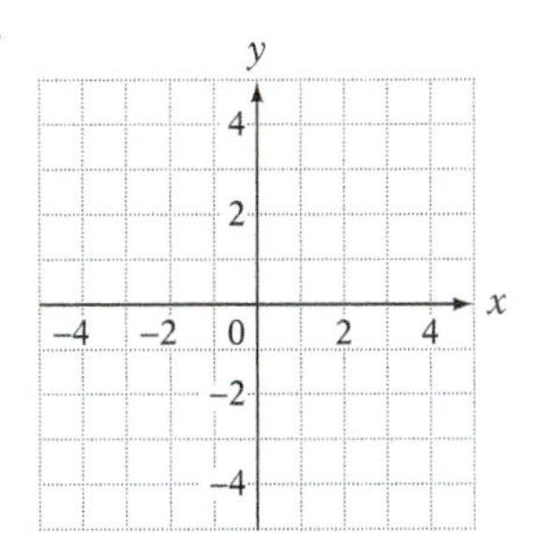

Solutions on p. S18

OBJECTIVE B *To graph an equation of the form $Ax + By = C$*

The equation $Ax + By = C$, where A and B are coefficients and C is a constant, is called the **standard form of a linear equation in two variables.** Examples are shown at the right.

$2x + 3y = 6$ ($A = 2, B = 3, C = 6$)
$x - 2y = -4$ ($A = 1, B = -2, C = -4$)
$2x + y = 0$ ($A = 2, B = 1, C = 0$)
$4x - 5y = 2$ ($A = 4, B = -5, C = 2$)

To graph an equation of the form $Ax + By = C$, first solve the equation for y. Then follow the same procedure used for graphing $y = mx + b$.

HOW TO 2 Graph $3x + 4y = 12$.

$$3x + 4y = 12$$
$$4y = -3x + 12$$
$$y = -\frac{3}{4}x + 3$$

- Solve for y.
- Subtract $3x$ from each side of the equation.
- Divide each side of the equation by 4.
- Find three ordered-pair solutions of the equation.

x	y
0	3
4	0
−4	6

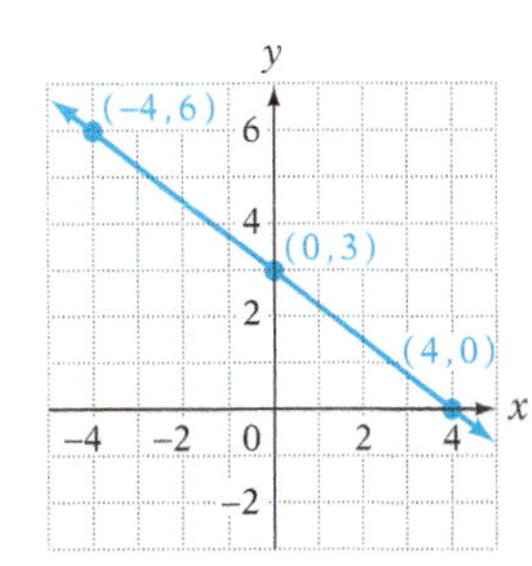

- Graph the ordered pairs and then draw a line through the points.

Tips for Success

Remember that a HOW TO example indicates a worked-out example. Using paper and pencil, work through the example. See *AIM for Success* at the front of the book.

The graph of a linear equation with one of the variables missing is either a horizontal or a vertical line.

The equation $y = 2$ could be written $0 \cdot x + y = 2$. Because $0 \cdot x = 0$ for any value of x, the value of y is always 2 no matter what value of x is chosen. For instance, replace x by -4, -1, 0, and 3. In each case, $y = 2$.

$0x + y = 2$

$0(-4) + y = 2$ $\quad (-4, 2)$ is a solution.

$0(-1) + y = 2$ $\quad (-1, 2)$ is a solution.

$0(0) + y = 2$ $\quad (0, 2)$ is a solution.

$0(3) + y = 2$ $\quad (3, 2)$ is a solution.

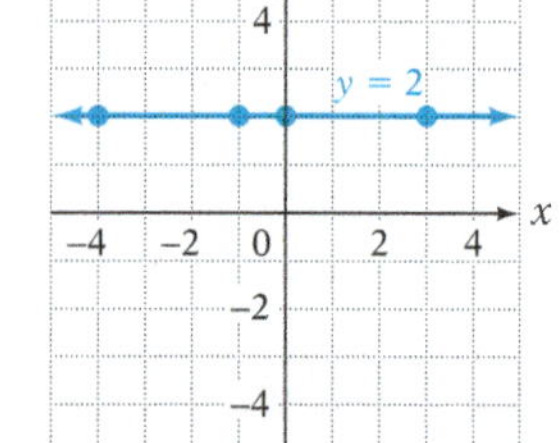

The solutions are plotted in the graph at the right, and a line is drawn through the plotted points. Note that the line is horizontal.

Graph of a Horizontal Line

The graph of $y = b$ is a horizontal line passing through $(0, b)$.

EXAMPLE

The graph of $y = 3$ is a horizontal line passing through (0, 3).

The equation $x = -2$ could be written $x + 0 \cdot y = -2$. Because $0 \cdot y = 0$ for any value of y, the value of x is always -2 no matter what value of y is chosen. For instance, replace y by -2, 0, 2, and 3. In each case, $x = -2$.

$x + 0y = -2$

$x + 0(-2) = -2$ $\quad (-2, -2)$ is a solution.

$x + 0(0) = -2$ $\quad (-2, 0)$ is a solution.

$x + 0(2) = -2$ $\quad (-2, 2)$ is a solution.

$x + 0(3) = -2$ $\quad (-2, 3)$ is a solution.

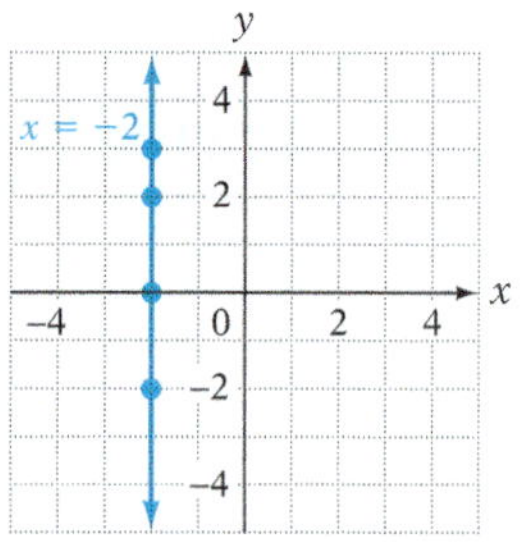

The solutions are plotted in the graph at the right, and a line is drawn through the plotted points. Note that the line is vertical.

Graph of a Vertical Line

The graph of $x = a$ is a vertical line passing through $(a, 0)$.

EXAMPLE

The graph of $x = 2$ is a vertical line passing through (2, 0).

HOW TO 3 Graph $x = -3$ and $y = 1$ on the same coordinate grid.

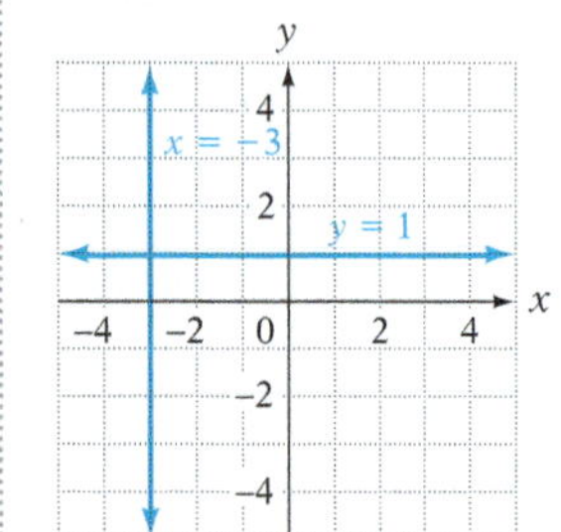

- **The graph of $x = -3$ is a vertical line passing through $(-3, 0)$.**
- **The graph of $y = 1$ is a horizontal line passing through $(0, 1)$.**

EXAMPLE 4

Graph $2x - 5y = 10$.

Solution Solve $2x - 5y = 10$ for y.

$$2x - 5y = 10$$
$$-5y = -2x + 10$$
$$y = \frac{2}{5}x - 2$$

x	y
0	−2
5	0
−5	−4

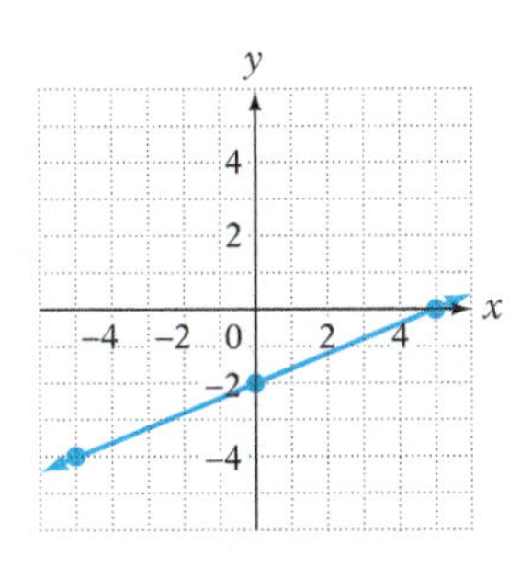

YOU TRY IT 4

Graph $5x - 2y = 10$.

Your solution

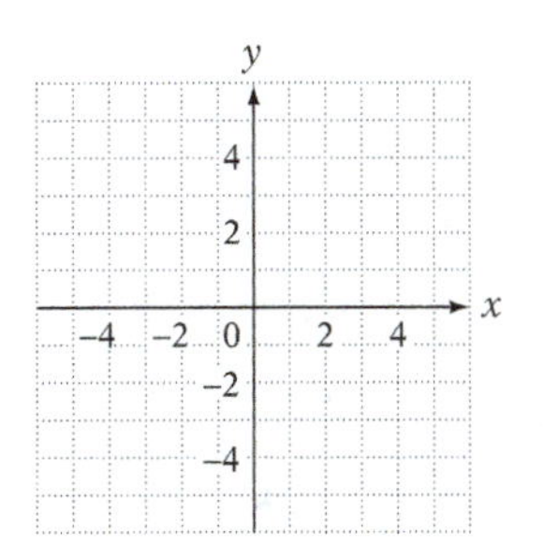

EXAMPLE 5

Graph $x + 2y = 6$.

Solution Solve $x + 2y = 6$ for y.

$$x + 2y = 6$$
$$2y = -x + 6$$
$$y = -\frac{1}{2}x + 3$$

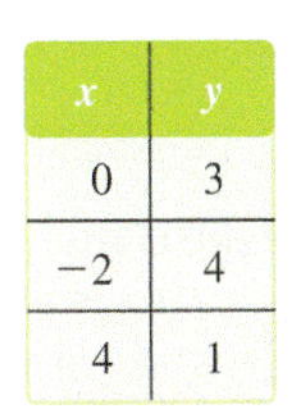

x	y
0	3
−2	4
4	1

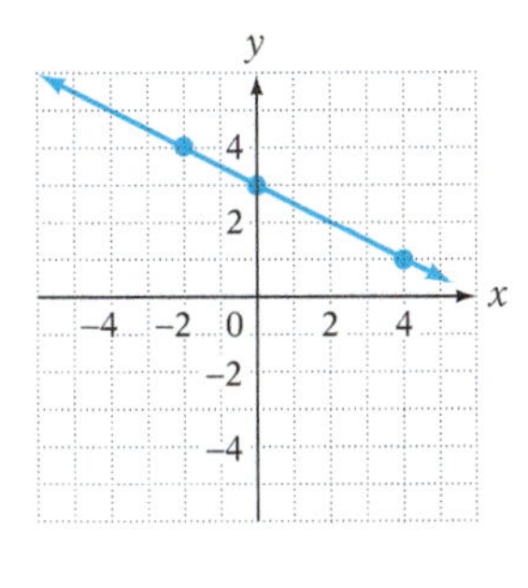

YOU TRY IT 5

Graph $x - 3y = 9$.

Your solution

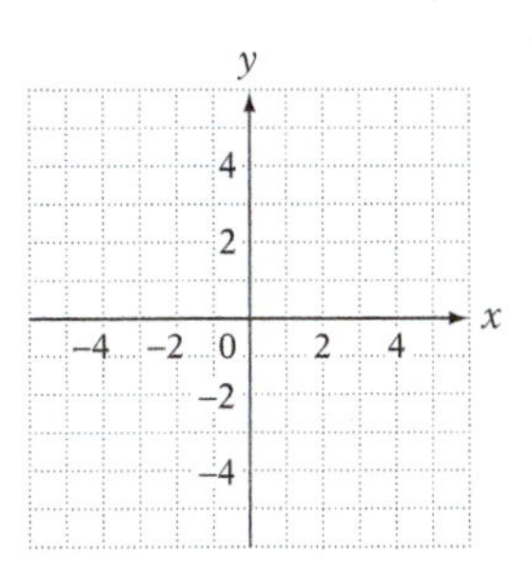

EXAMPLE 6

Graph $y = -2$.

Solution

The graph of an equation of the form $y = b$ is a horizontal line passing through the point $(0, b)$.

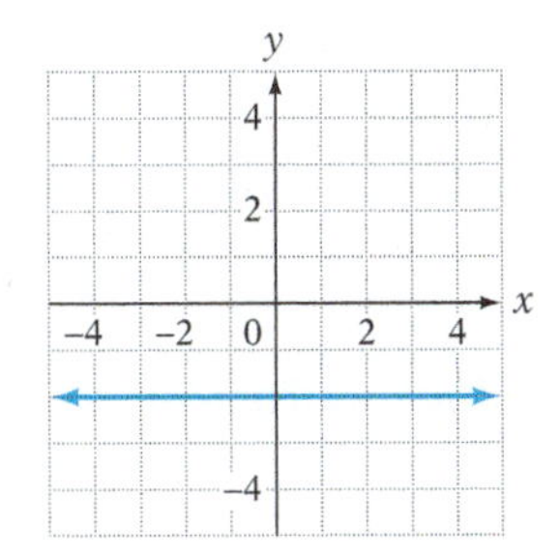

YOU TRY IT 6

Graph $y = 3$.

Your solution

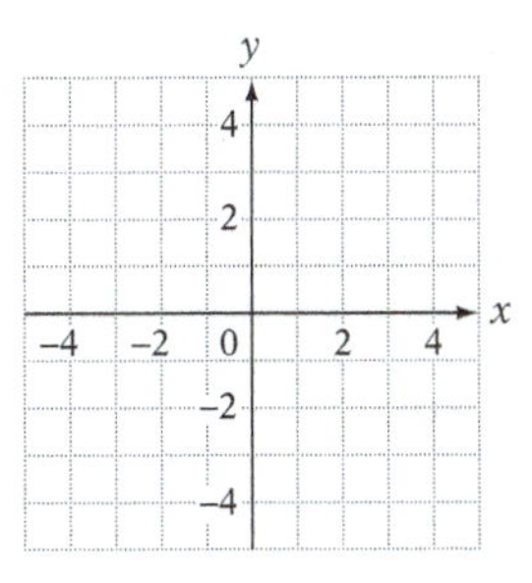

EXAMPLE 7

Graph $x = 3$.

Solution

The graph of an equation of the form $x = a$ is a vertical line passing through the point $(a, 0)$.

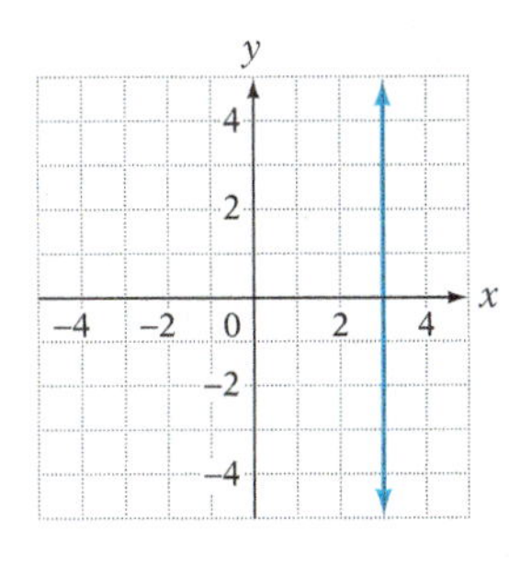

YOU TRY IT 7

Graph $x = -4$.

Your solution

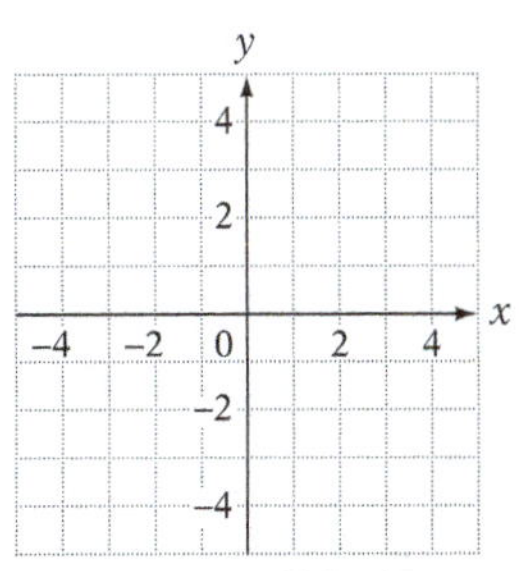

Solutions on p. S18

OBJECTIVE C *To solve application problems*

There are a variety of applications of linear functions.

HOW TO 4 The temperature of a cup of water that has been placed in a microwave oven to be heated can be approximated by the equation $T = 0.7s + 65$, where T is the temperature (in degrees Fahrenheit) of the water s seconds after the microwave oven is turned on.

a. Graph this equation for values of s from 0 to 200. (*Note:* In many applications, the domain of the variable is given so that the application makes sense. For instance, it would not be sensible to have values of s that are less than 0. This would correspond to negative time. The choice of 200 is somewhat arbitrary and was chosen so that the water would not boil over.)

b. The point whose coordinates are (120, 149) is on the graph of this equation. Write a sentence that describes the meaning of this ordered pair.

Solution

a.

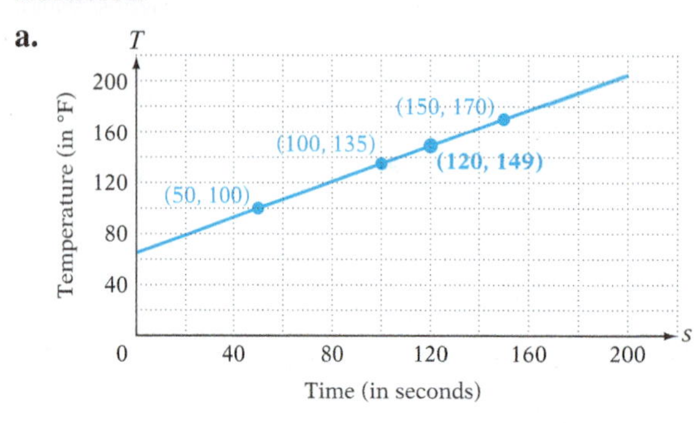

• By choosing $s = 50$, 100, and 150, you can find the corresponding ordered pairs (50, 100), (100, 135), and (150, 170). Plot these points and draw a line through the points.

b. The ordered pair (120, 149) means that 120 s (2 min) after the oven is turned on, the water temperature is 149°F.

EXAMPLE 8

The number of kilobytes K of an MP3 file that remain to be downloaded t seconds after starting the download is given by $K = 935 - 5.5t$. Graph this equation for values of t from 0 to 170. The point whose coordinates are (50, 660) is on this graph. Write a sentence that describes the meaning of this ordered pair.

Solution

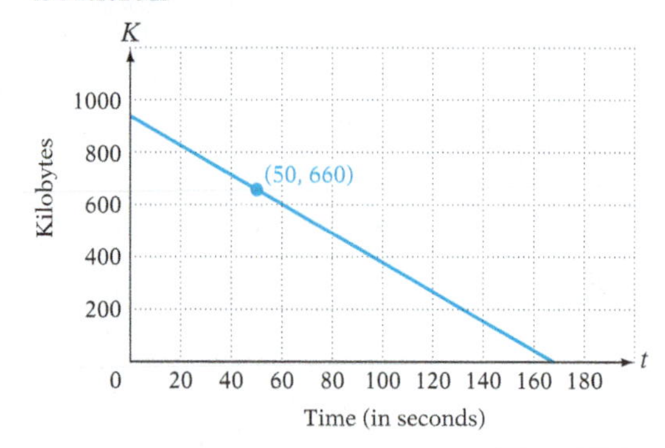

The ordered pair (50, 660) means that after 50 s, there are 660 K remaining to be downloaded.

YOU TRY IT 8

A car is traveling at a uniform speed of 40 mph. The distance d the car travels in t hours is given by $d = 40t$. Graph this equation for values of t from 0 to 5. The point whose coordinates are (3, 120) is on the graph. Write a sentence that describes the meaning of this ordered pair.

Your solution

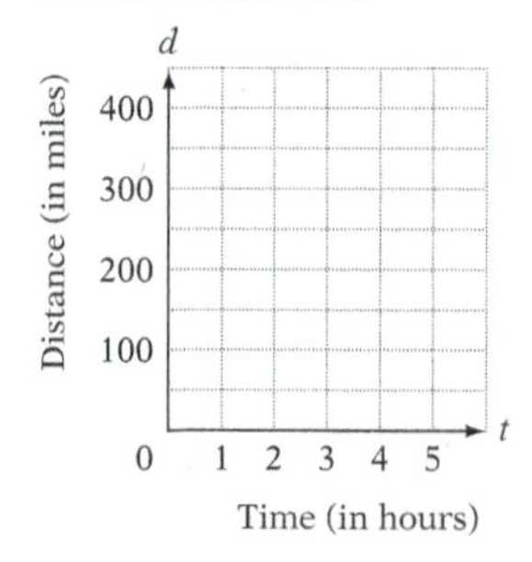

Solution on p. S18

7.2 EXERCISES

Concept Check

1. Which of the following equations are linear equations in two variables?

   (i) $y = -2x + 7$ (ii) $x - 3y = 5$ (iii) $y = -x^2 + 4$ (iv) $y^2 = x - 6$

2. Give the value of m and the value of b in each equation.

   a. $y = 5x + 3$ b. $y = -\frac{1}{2}x - 8$ c. $y = x + 1$ d. $y = -x$

3. State whether the graph of the equation is a straight line.

   a. $y = x^2 + 1$ b. $y = -x$ c. $y = \frac{1}{x}$ d. $y = 2 - \frac{1}{2}x$ e. $y = \sqrt{x} - 1$

For Exercises 4 and 5, name values of x that you would choose to find integer solutions of the equation.

4. $y = \frac{3}{2}x + 2$

5. $y = -\frac{2}{3}x - 1$

6. Is the equation in the form $y = mx + b$, the form $Ax + By = C$, or neither?

   a. $6x - 3y = 6$ b. $y = x - 1$ c. $8 - 4y = x$ d. $5x + 4y = 4$

OBJECTIVE A *To graph an equation of the form $y = mx + b$*

For Exercises 7 to 24, graph.

7. $y = 2x - 3$

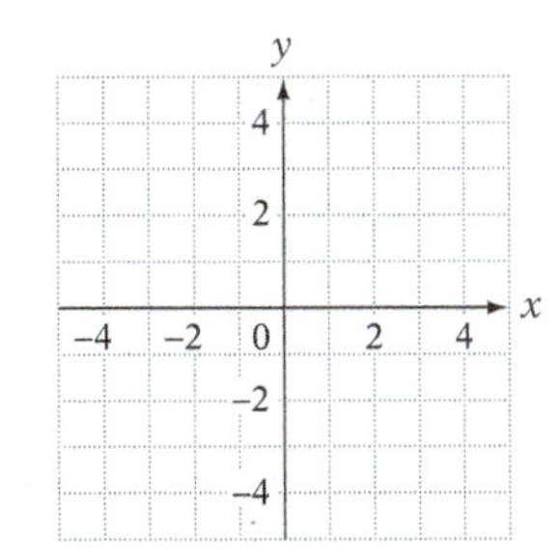

8. $y = -2x + 2$

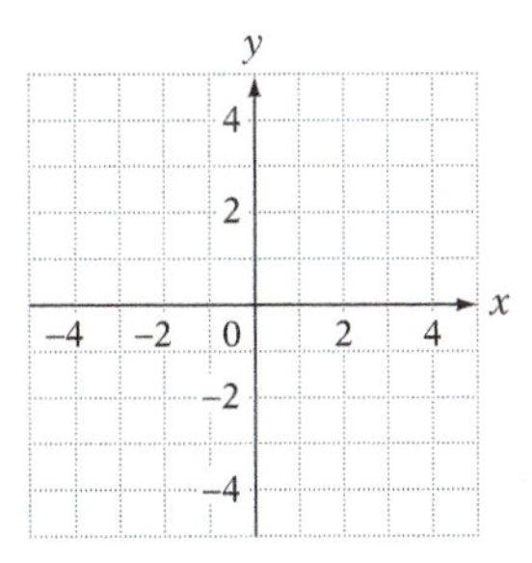

9. $y = \frac{1}{3}x$

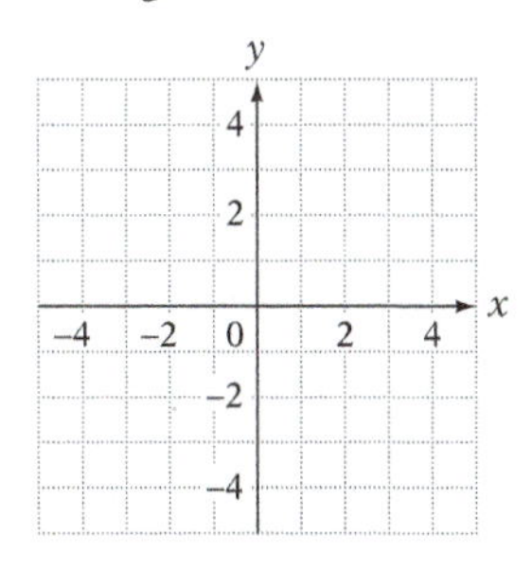

10. $y = -3x$

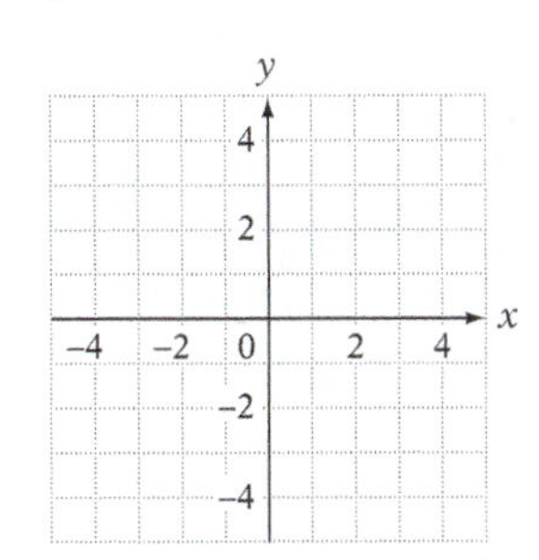

11. $y = \frac{2}{3}x - 1$

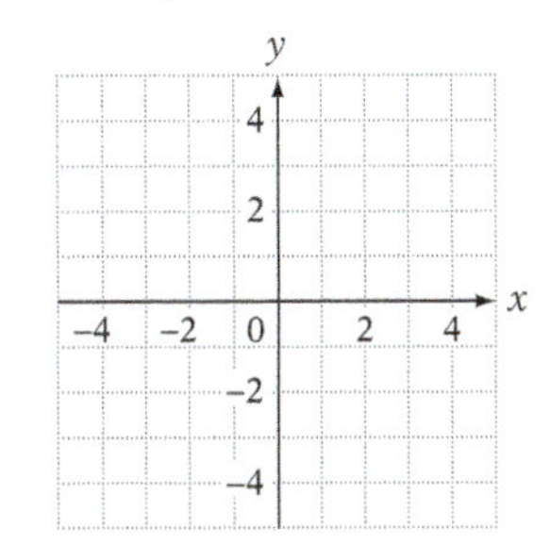

12. $y = \frac{3}{4}x + 2$

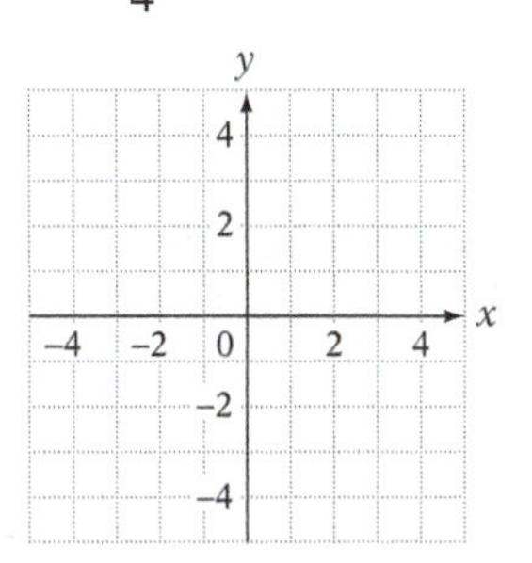

13. $y = -\frac{1}{4}x + 2$

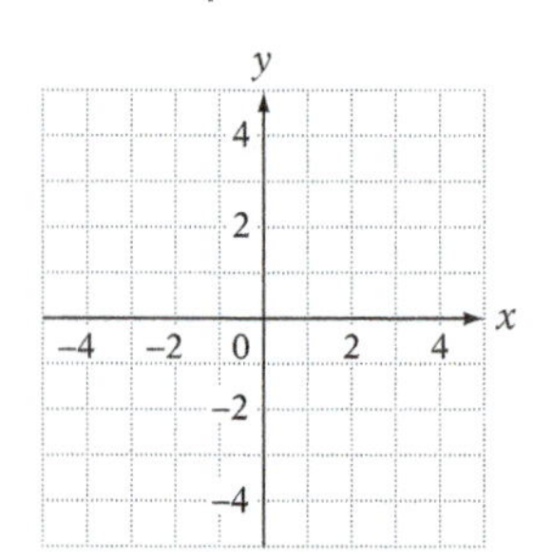

14. $y = -\frac{1}{3}x + 1$

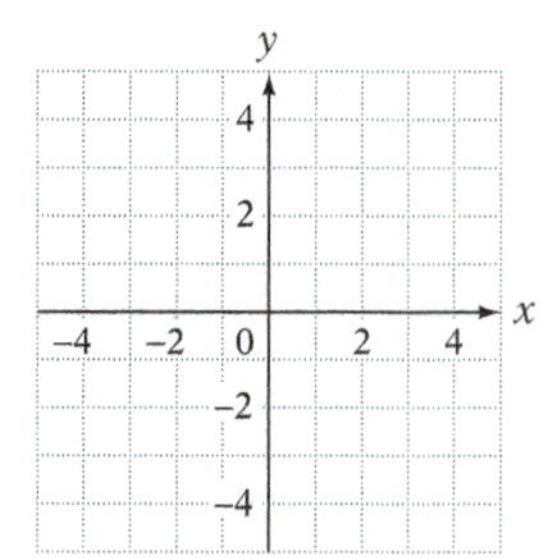

15. $y = -\frac{2}{5}x + 1$

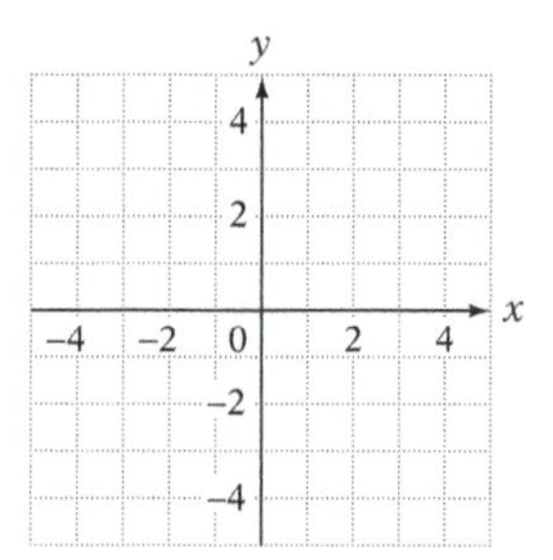

16. $y = -\frac{1}{2}x + 3$

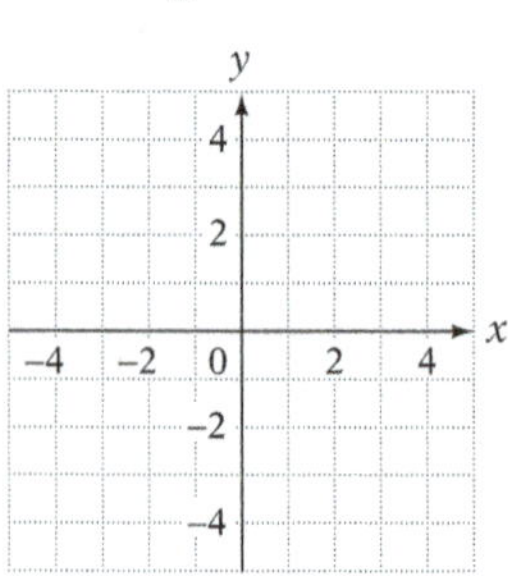

17. $y = 2x - 4$

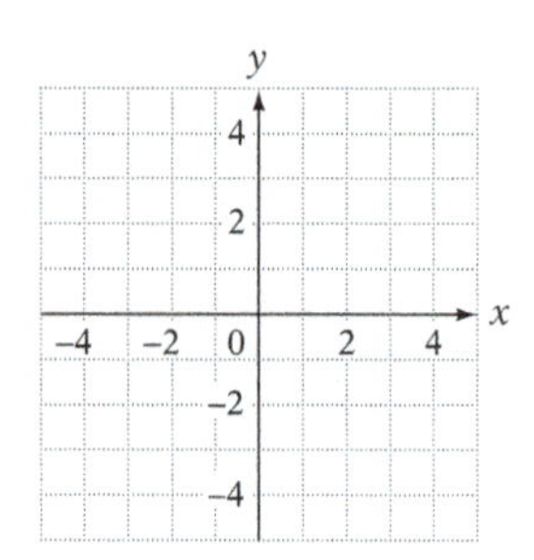

18. $y = 3x - 4$

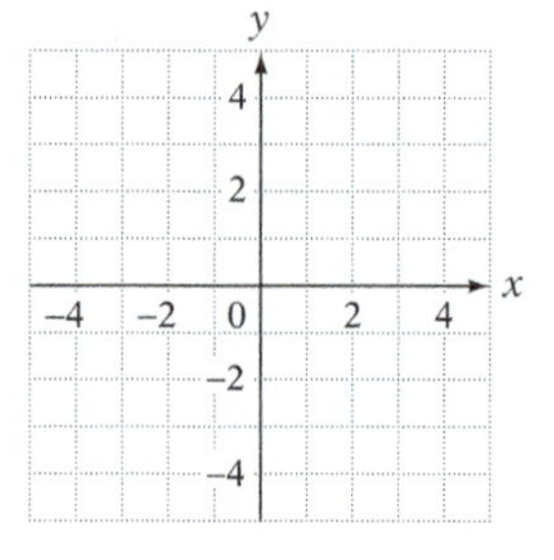

19. $y = x - 3$

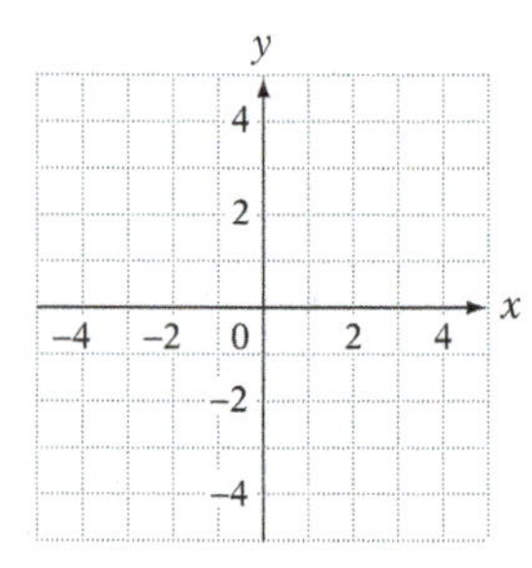

20. $y = x + 2$

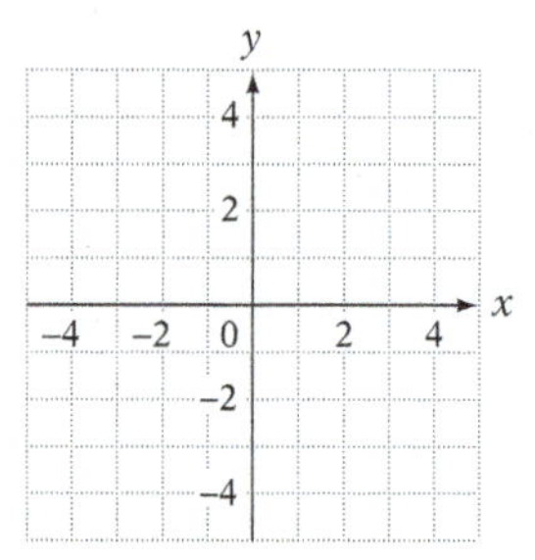

21. $y = -x + 2$

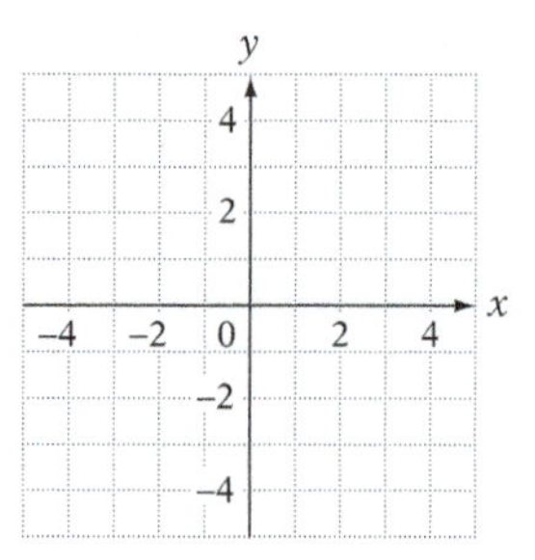

22. $y = -x - 1$

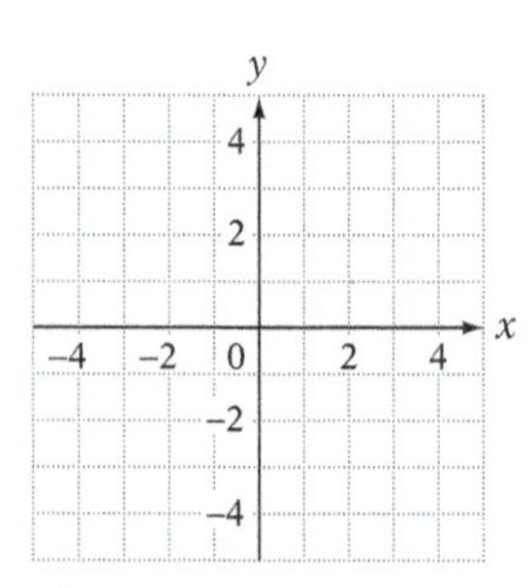

23. $y = -\frac{2}{3}x + 1$

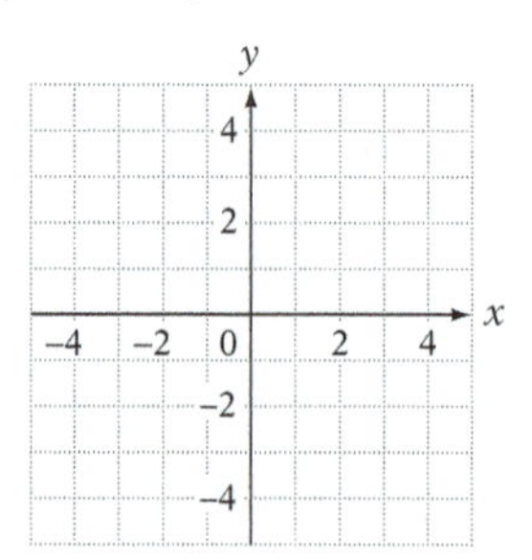

24. $y = 5x - 4$

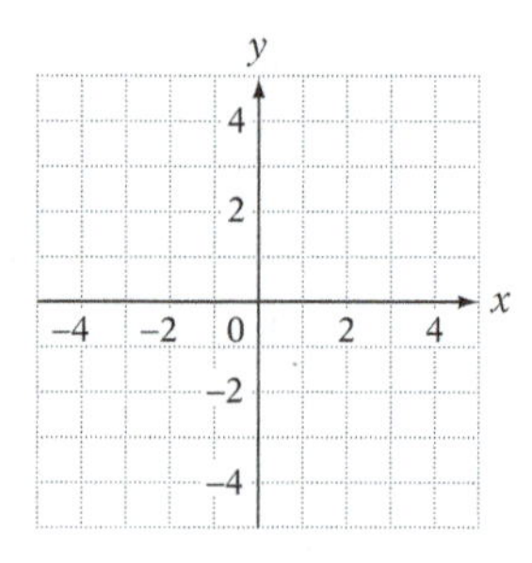

25. If the graph of $y = mx + b$ passes through the origin, (0, 0), what is the value of b?

OBJECTIVE B *To graph an equation of the form $Ax + By = C$*

For Exercises 26 to 37, write the equation in the form $y = mx + b$.

26. $3x + y = 10$ **27.** $2x + y = 5$ **28.** $4x - y = 3$ **29.** $5x - y = 7$

30. $3x + 2y = 6$ **31.** $2x + 3y = 9$ **32.** $2x - 5y = 10$ **33.** $5x - 2y = 4$

34. $2x + 7y = 14$ **35.** $6x - 5y = 10$ **36.** $x + 3y = 6$ **37.** $x - 4y = 12$

For Exercises 38 to 52, graph.

38. $3x + y = 3$

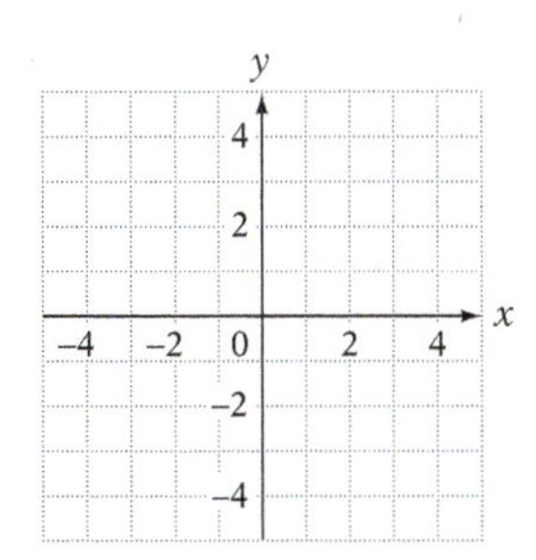

39. $2x + y = 4$

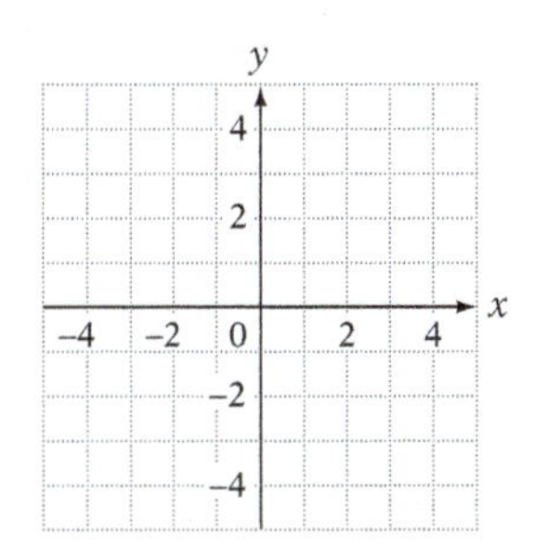

40. $2x + 3y = 6$

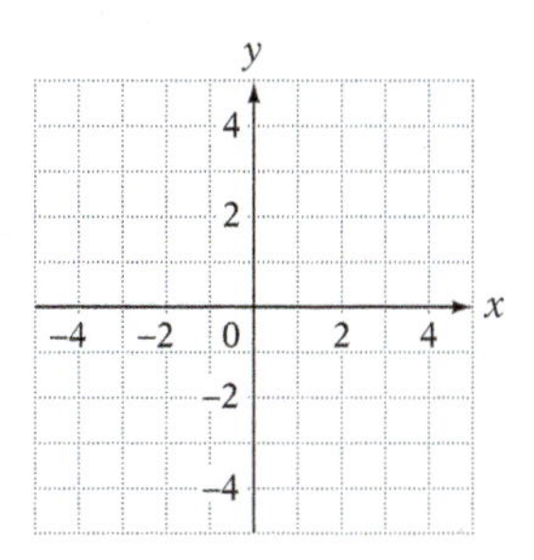

41. $3x + 2y = 4$

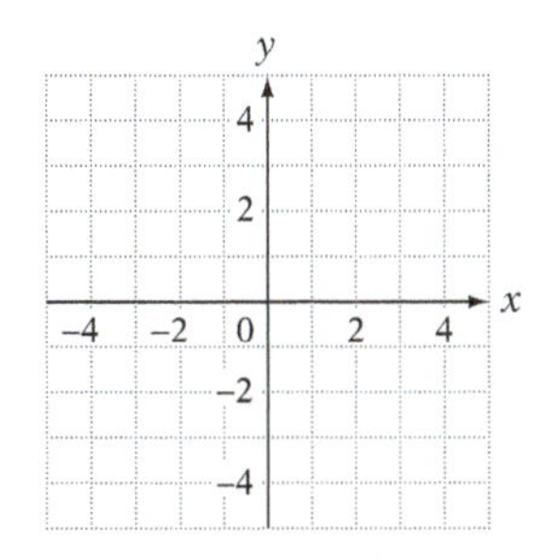

42. $x - 2y = 4$

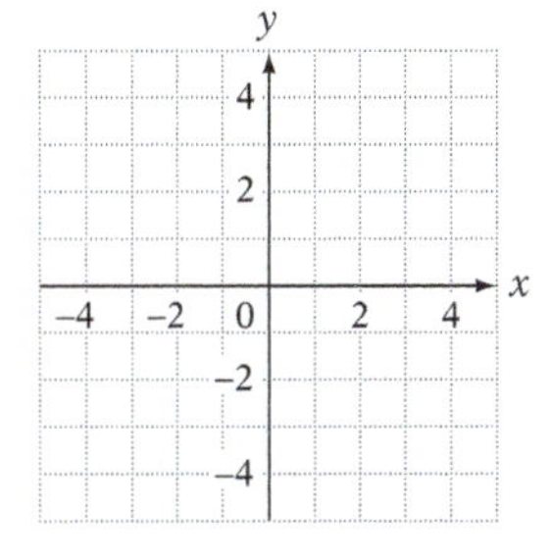

43. $x - 3y = 6$

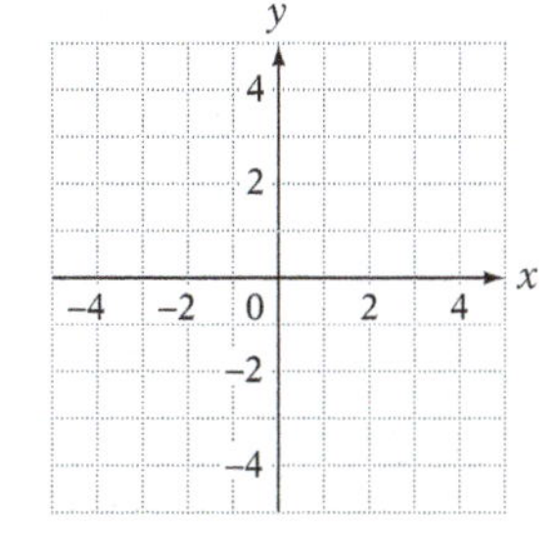

44. $2x - 3y = 6$

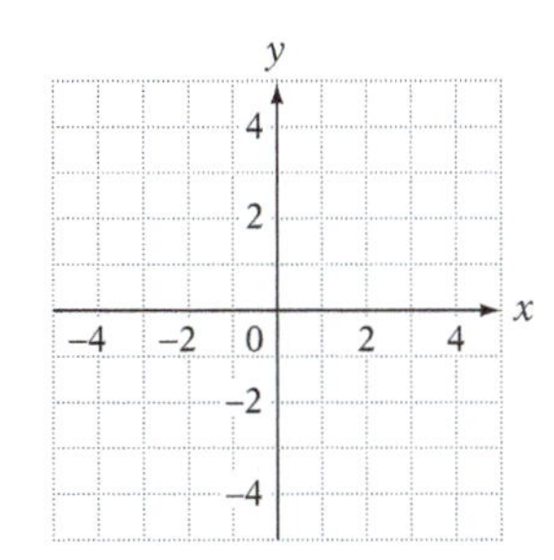

45. $3x - 2y = 8$

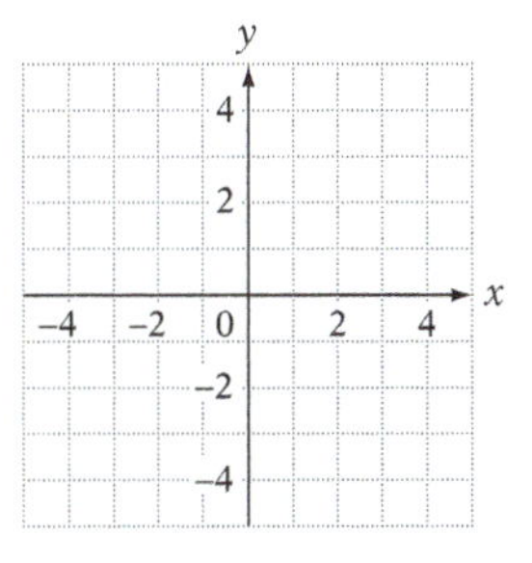

46. $2x + 5y = 10$

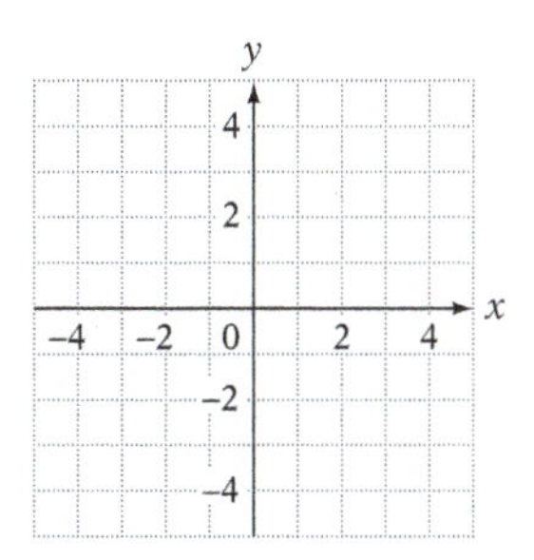

47. $3x + 4y = 12$

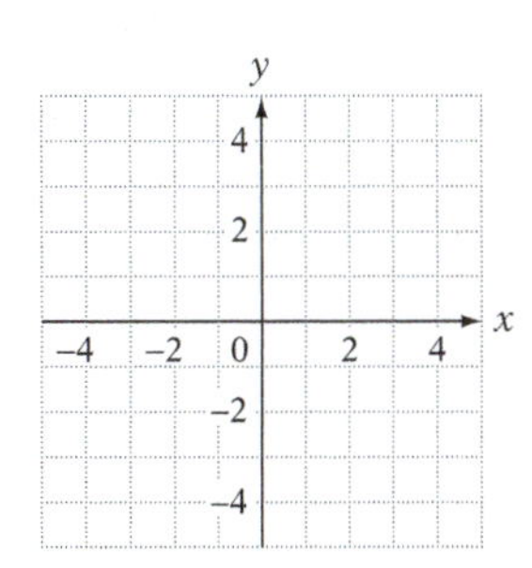

48. $x = 3$

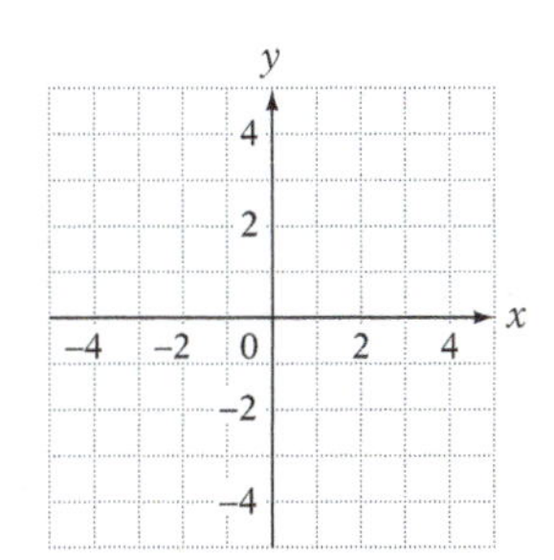

49. $y = -4$

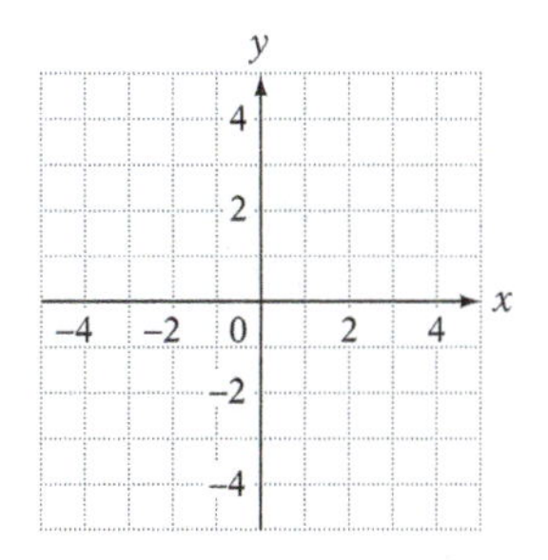

50. $x + 4y = 4$

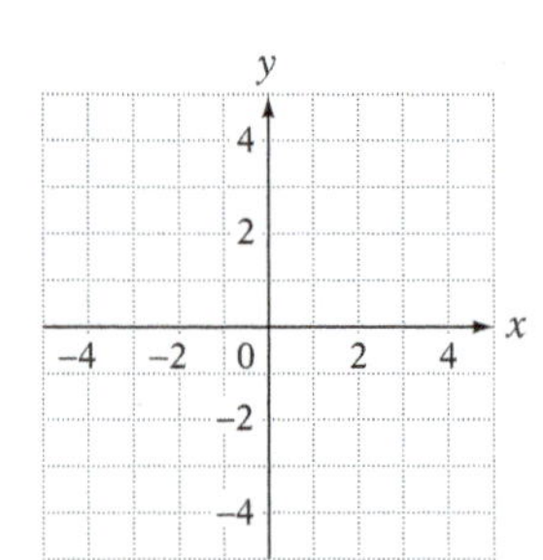

51. $4x - 3y = 12$

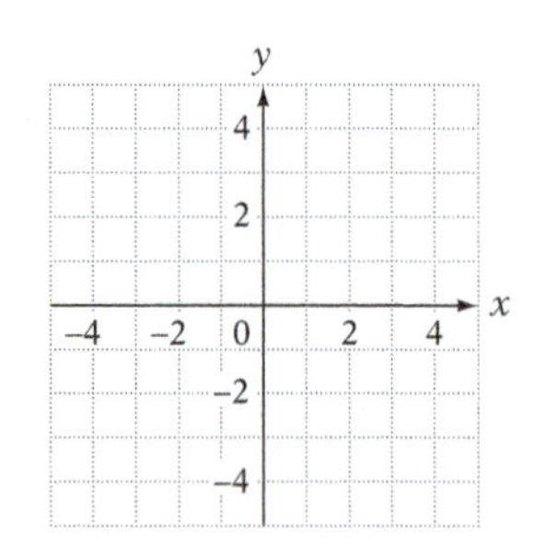

52. $y = 4$

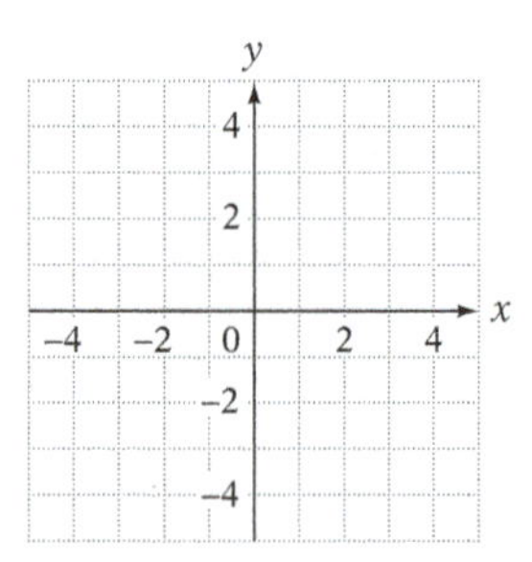

53. Which number, A, B, or C, must be zero if the graph of $Ax + By = C$ is a horizontal line?

54. Suppose A and B are positive and C is negative. Is the y-intercept of the graph of $Ax + By = C$ above or below the x-axis?

55. Suppose A and C are negative and B is positive. Is the x-intercept of the graph of $Ax + By = C$ to the left or to the right of the y-axis?

OBJECTIVE C *To solve application problems*

56. Use the oven temperature graph on page 368 to determine whether the statement is true or false.

Sixty seconds after the oven is turned on, the temperature is still below 100°F.

57. **Business** A custom-illustrated sign or banner can be commissioned for a cost of \$25 for the material and \$10.50 per square foot for the artwork. The equation that represents this cost is given by $y = 10.50x + 25$, where y is the cost and x is the number of square feet in the sign. Graph this equation for values of x from 0 to 20. The point $(15, 182.5)$ is on the graph. Write a sentence that describes the meaning of this ordered pair.

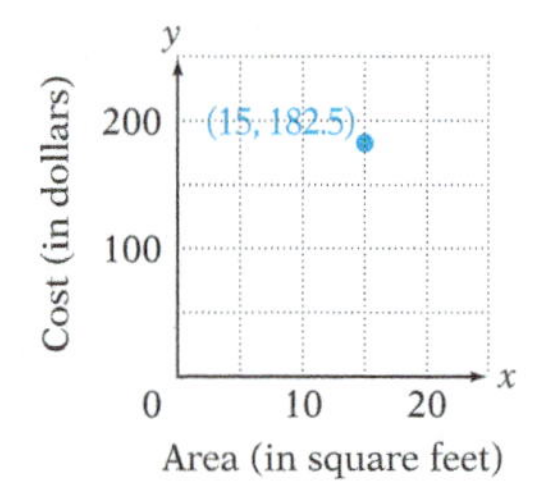

58. **Emergency Response** A rescue helicopter is rushing at a constant speed of 150 mph to reach several people stranded in the ocean 11 mi away after their boat sank. The rescuers can determine how far from the victims they are by using the equation $D = 11 - 2.5t$, where D is the distance in miles and t is the time elapsed in minutes. Graph this equation for values of t from 0 to 4. The point $(3, 3.5)$ is on the graph. Write a sentence that describes the meaning of this ordered pair.

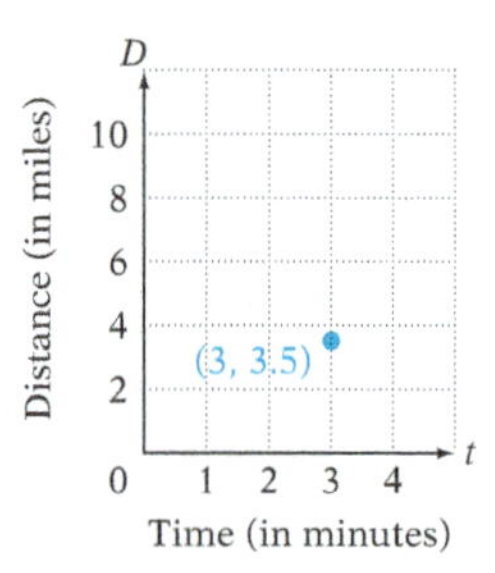

59. **Veterinary Science** According to some veterinarians, the age x of a dog can be translated to "human years" by using the equation $H = 4x + 16$, where H is the human equivalent age for the dog. Graph this equation for values of x from 2 to 21. The point whose coordinates are $(6, 40)$ is on the graph. Write a sentence that explains the meaning of this ordered pair.

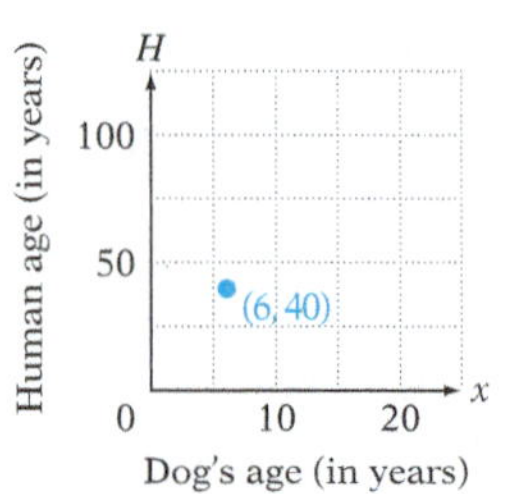

60. **Taxi Fares** See the news clipping at the right. The equation $F = 2.80M + 2.20$ can be used to calculate the fare F, in dollars, for a ride of M miles. Graph this equation for values of M from 1 to 5. The point (3, 10.6) is on the graph. Write a sentence that describes the meaning of this ordered pair.

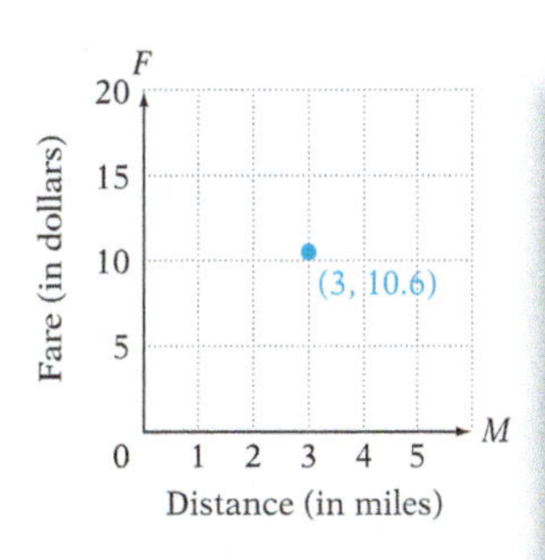

In the NEWS!

Rate Hike for Boston Cab Rides

Taxi drivers soon will be raising their rates, perhaps in an effort to help pay for their required switch to hybrid vehicles by 2015. In the near future, a passenger will have to pay \$5.00 for the first mile of a taxi ride and \$2.80 for each additional mile.

Source: The Boston Globe

Critical Thinking

61. Write the equation of a line that has (0, 0) as both the x-intercept and the y-intercept.

62. Write the equation of a line that has (0, 1) as the y-intercept.

Projects or Group Activities

63. Graph $y = 2x - 2$, $y = 2x$, and $y = 2x + 3$. What observation can you make about the graphs?

64. Graph $y = x + 3$, $y = 2x + 3$, and $y = -\frac{1}{2}x + 3$. What observation can you make about the graphs?

CHECK YOUR PROGRESS: CHAPTER 7

1. Graph (−4, 3), (−2, −1), (2, −1), and (0, 3).

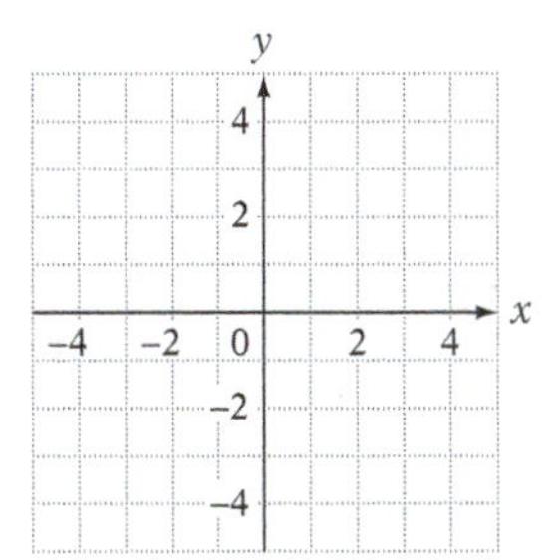

2. Graph $y = -\frac{4}{5}x + 4$.

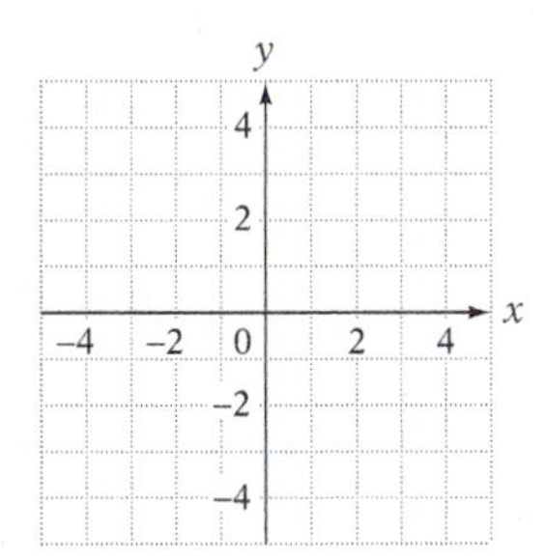

3. Graph $3x - 4y = 12$.

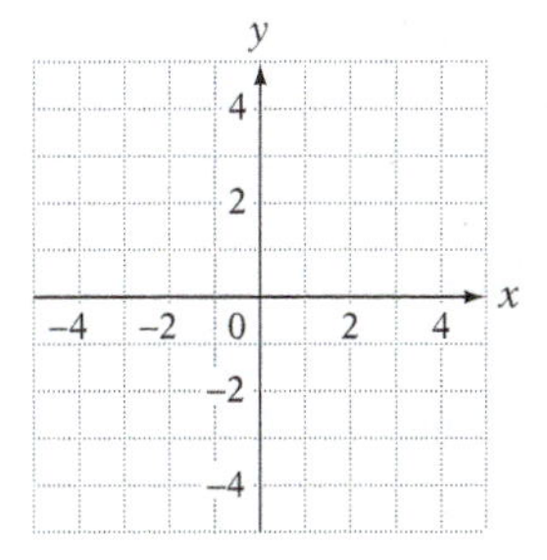

4. Find the ordered-pair solutions of $y = -3x + 2$ when $x = -1, 0, 1,$ and 2.

5. Describe the graph of $x = -5$.

6. Find the domain and range of the relation {(−3, −2), (−2, −1), (−1, 0)}. Is the relation a function?

7. Given $h(s) = s^2 + 3s$, find $h(-3)$.

8. Is (3, 0) a solution of $y = -\frac{1}{3}x - 1$?

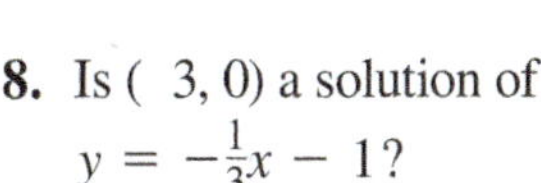

9. Does $y = x^2 - 4$, where $x \in \{-3, -1, 0, 1, 3\}$, define y as a function of x?

SECTION

7.3 Intercepts and Slopes of Straight Lines

OBJECTIVE A *To find the x- and y-intercepts of a straight line*

The graph of the equation $2x + 3y = 6$ is shown at the right. The graph crosses the x-axis at the point (3, 0) and crosses the y-axis at the point (0, 2). The point at which a graph crosses the x-axis is called the **x-intercept.** At the x-intercept, the y-coordinate is 0. The point at which a graph crosses the y-axis is called the **y-intercept.** At the y-intercept, the x-coordinate is 0.

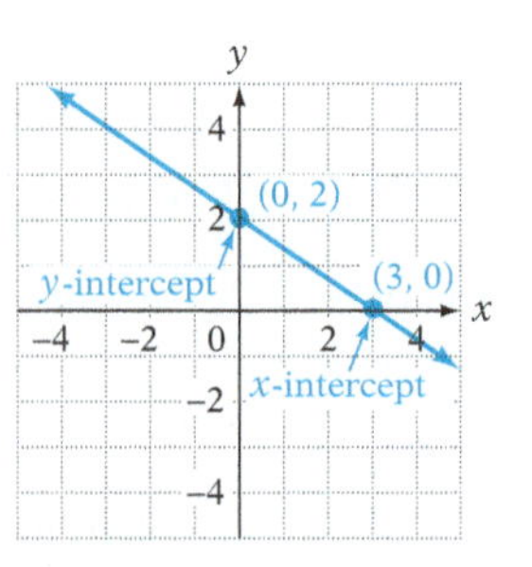

HOW TO 1 Find the x- and y-intercepts of the graph of the equation $2x - 3y = 12$.

To find the x-intercept, let $y = 0$. (Any point on the x-axis has y-coordinate 0.)

$$\begin{aligned} 2x - 3y &= 12 \\ 2x - 3(0) &= 12 \\ 2x &= 12 \\ x &= 6 \end{aligned}$$

The x-intercept is (6, 0).

To find the y-intercept, let $x = 0$. (Any point on the y-axis has x-coordinate 0.)

$$\begin{aligned} 2x - 3y &= 12 \\ 2(0) - 3y &= 12 \\ -3y &= 12 \\ y &= -4 \end{aligned}$$

The y-intercept is (0, −4).

Take Note
To find the x-intercept, let $y = 0$ and solve for x. To find the y-intercept, let $x = 0$ and solve for y.

Some linear equations can be graphed by finding the x- and y-intercepts and then drawing a line through these two points.

EXAMPLE 1

Find the x- and y-intercepts of $x - 2y = 4$. Graph the line.

Solution

To find the x-intercept, let $y = 0$ and solve for x.

$$\begin{aligned} x - 2y &= 4 \\ x - 2(0) &= 4 \\ x &= 4 \quad (4, 0) \end{aligned}$$

To find the y-intercept, let $x = 0$ and solve for y.

$$\begin{aligned} x - 2y &= 4 \\ 0 - 2y &= 4 \\ -2y &= 4 \\ y &= -2 \quad (0, -2) \end{aligned}$$

Plot the two intercepts. Draw a line through the two points.

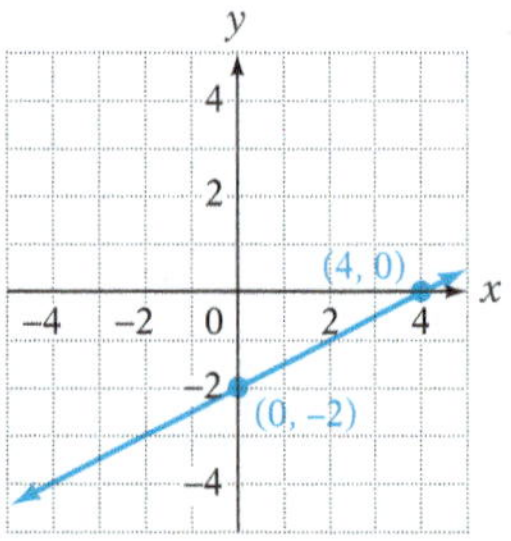

YOU TRY IT 1

Find the x- and y-intercepts of $2x - y = 4$. Graph the line.

Your solution

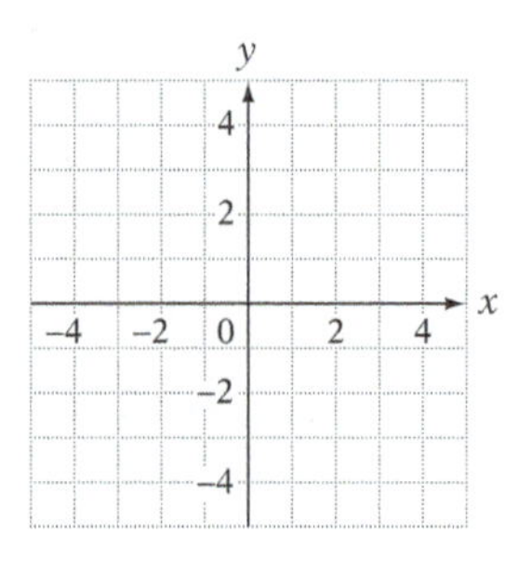

Solution on p. S18

OBJECTIVE B *To find the slope of a straight line*

The graphs of $y = \frac{2}{3}x + 1$ and $y = 2x + 1$ are shown in Figure 1. Each graph crosses the y-axis at the point (0, 1), but the graphs have different slants. The **slope** of a line is a measure of the slant of the line. The symbol for slope is m.

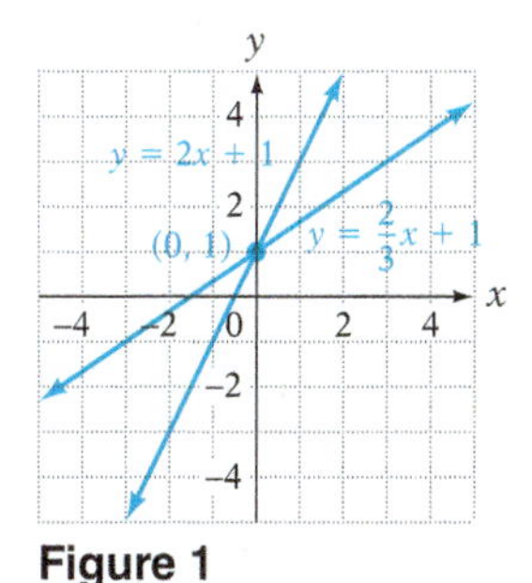

Figure 1

Take Note

The change in the y values can be thought of as the *rise* of the line, and the change in the x values can be thought of as the *run*. Then

$$\text{Slope} = m = \frac{\text{rise}}{\text{run}}$$

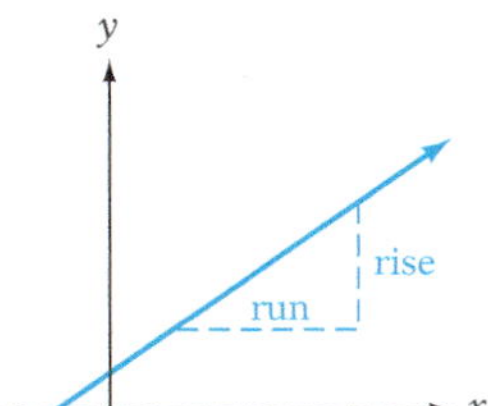
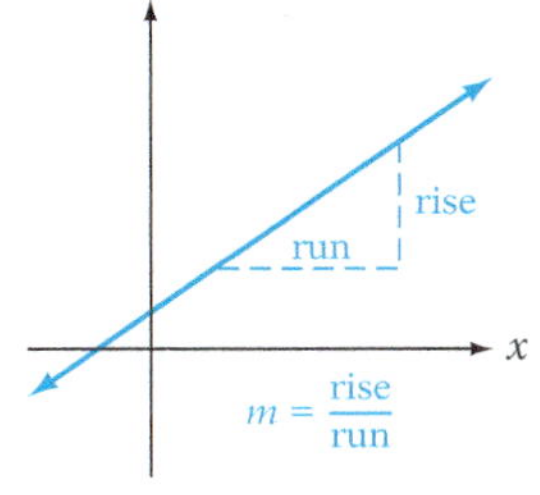

The slope of a line containing two points is the ratio of the change in the y values of the two points to the change in the x values. The line containing the points $(-2, -3)$ and $(6, 1)$ is graphed in Figure 2. The change in the y values is the difference between the two ordinates.

Figure 2

$$\text{Change in } y = 1 - (-3) = 4$$

The change in the x values is the difference between the two abscissas (Figure 3).

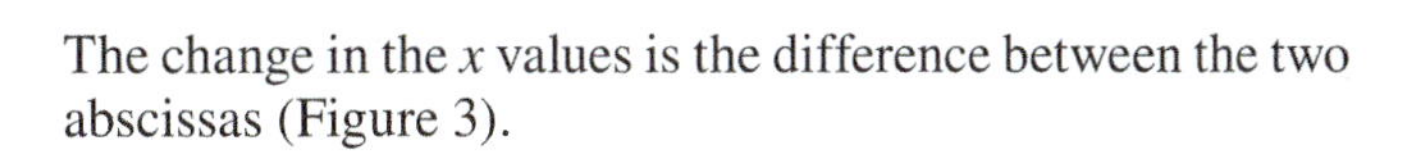

Figure 3

$$\text{Change in } x = 6 - (-2) = 8$$

$$\text{Slope} = m = \frac{\text{change in } y}{\text{change in } x} = \frac{4}{8} = \frac{1}{2}$$

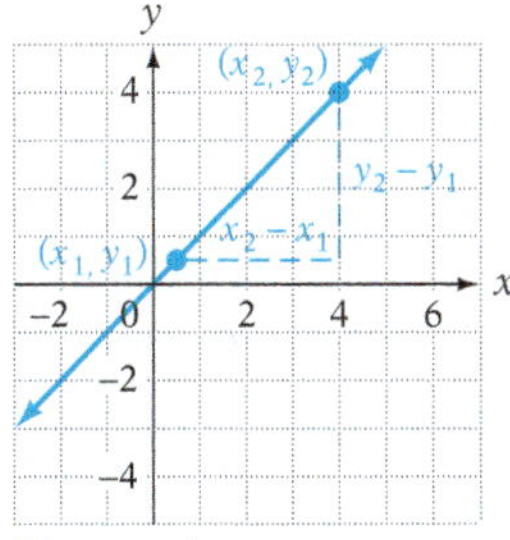

Figure 4

Slope Formula

If $P_1(x_1, y_1)$ and $P_2(x_2, y_2)$ are two points on a line and $x_1 \neq x_2$, then $m = \frac{y_2 - y_1}{x_2 - x_1}$ (Figure 4). If $x_1 = x_2$, the slope is undefined.

HOW TO 2 Find the slope of the line containing the points $(-1, 1)$ and $(2, 3)$.

Let P_1 be $(-1, 1)$ and P_2 be $(2, 3)$. Then $x_1 = -1$, $y_1 = 1$, $x_2 = 2$, and $y_2 = 3$.

$$m = \frac{y_2 - y_1}{x_2 - x_1} = \frac{3 - 1}{2 - (-1)} = \frac{2}{3}$$

The slope is $\frac{2}{3}$.

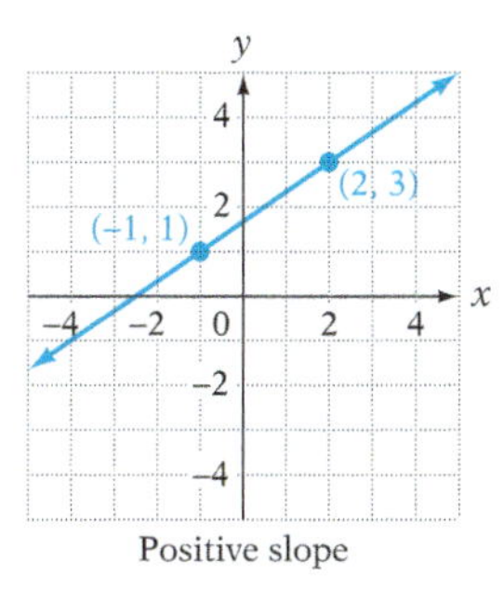

Positive slope

Take Note

Positive slope means that the value of y increases as the value of x increases.

A line that slants upward to the right always has a **positive slope.**

You obtain the same results if the points are named oppositely. Let P_1 be $(2, 3)$ and P_2 be $(-1, 1)$. The slope is $\frac{2}{3}$. Therefore, it does not matter which point is named P_1 and which is named P_2; the slope remains the same.

Take Note

Negative slope means that the value of *y* decreases as the value of *x* increases. Compare this to positive slope.

HOW TO 3 Find the slope of the line containing the points $(-3, 4)$ and $(2, -2)$.

Let P_1 be $(-3, 4)$ and P_2 be $(2, -2)$.

$$m = \frac{y_2 - y_1}{x_2 - x_1} = \frac{-2 - 4}{2 - (-3)} = \frac{-6}{5} = -\frac{6}{5}$$

The slope is $-\frac{6}{5}$.

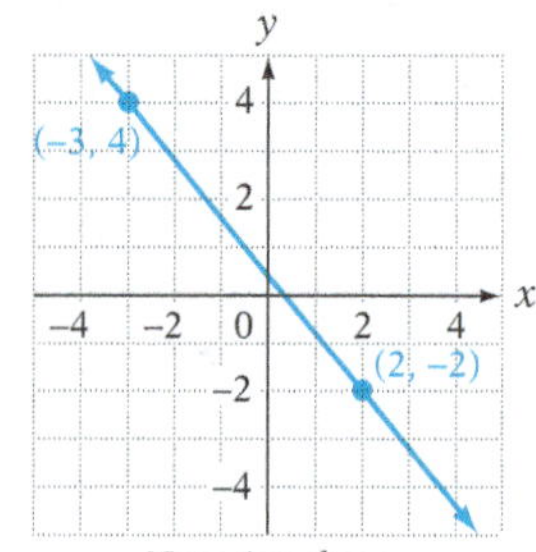

Negative slope

A line that slants downward to the right always has a **negative slope.**

HOW TO 4 Find the slope of the line containing the points $(-1, 3)$ and $(4, 3)$.

Let P_1 be $(-1, 3)$ and P_2 be $(4, 3)$.

$$m = \frac{y_2 - y_1}{x_2 - x_1} = \frac{3 - 3}{4 - (-1)} = \frac{0}{5} = 0$$

The slope is 0.

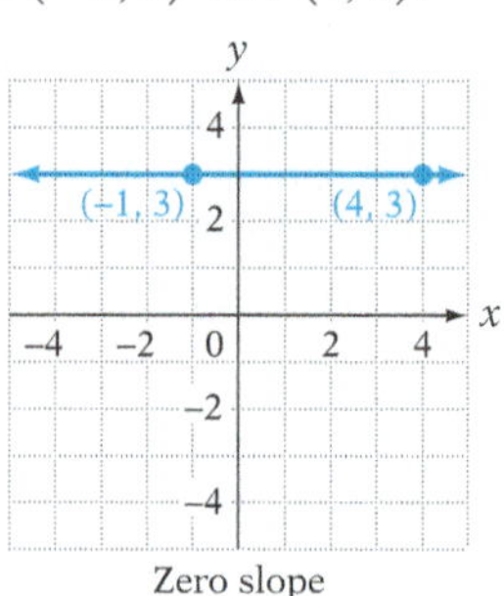

Zero slope

A horizontal line has **zero slope.**

HOW TO 5 Find the slope of the line containing the points $(2, -2)$ and $(2, 4)$.

Let P_1 be $(2, -2)$ and P_2 be $(2, 4)$.

$$m = \frac{y_2 - y_1}{x_2 - x_1} = \frac{4 - (-2)}{2 - 2} = \frac{6}{0}$$ Division by zero is not defined.

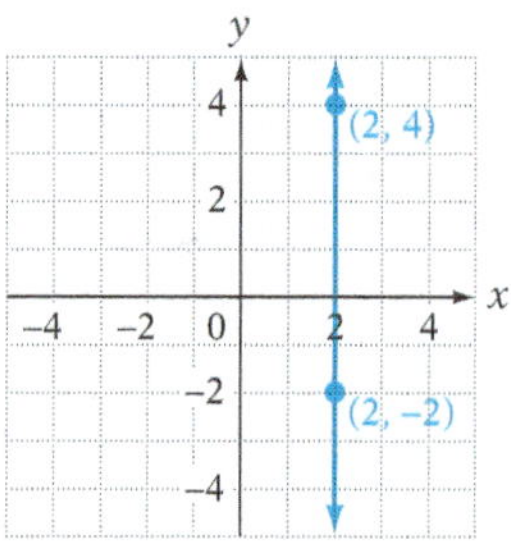

Undefined slope

A vertical line has **undefined slope.**

APPLY THE CONCEPT

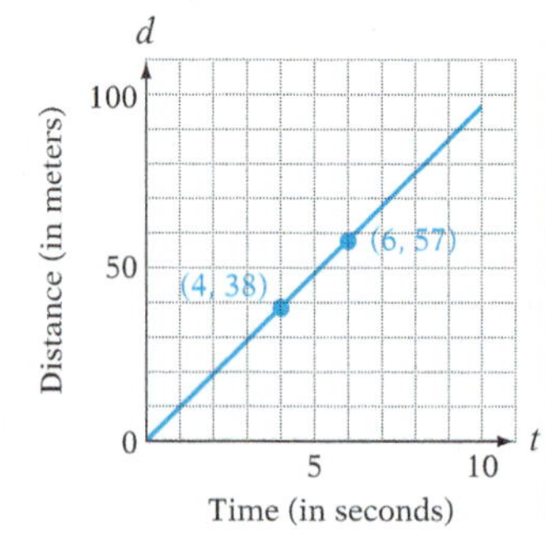

Florence Griffith-Joyner set the world record time for the 100-meter dash in 1988. The graph at the left is a distance-time graph of her record-setting run. From the graph, we can see that after 4 s, she had run 38 m, and after 6 s, she had traveled 57 m. Find her average rate of speed for the race.

To find the average rate of speed, find the slope of the line between the two points.

$$m = \frac{57 - 38}{6 - 4} = \frac{19}{2} = 9.5$$

Florence Griffith-Joyner's average rate of speed was 9.5 m/s.

Recall that two lines in the plane that never intersect are called parallel lines. The lines l_1 and l_2 in the figure at the right are parallel. Calculating the slope of each line, we have

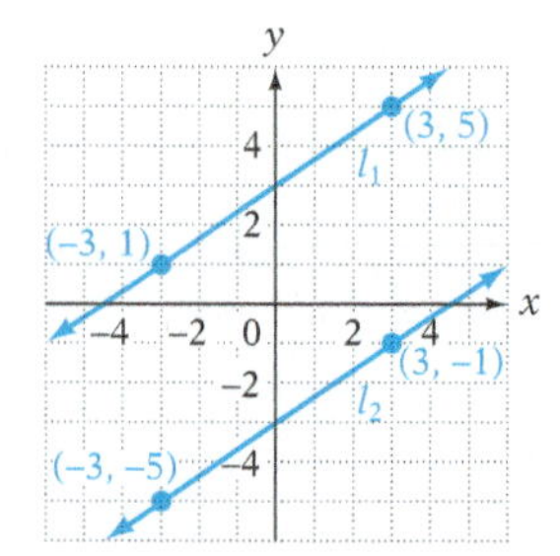

Slope of l_1: $m_1 = \frac{y_2 - y_1}{x_2 - x_1} = \frac{5 - 1}{3 - (-3)} = \frac{4}{6} = \frac{2}{3}$

Slope of l_2: $m_2 = \frac{y_2 - y_1}{x_2 - x_1} = \frac{-1 - (-5)}{3 - (-3)} = \frac{4}{6} = \frac{2}{3}$

Note that these parallel lines have the same slope. This is always true for parallel lines.

Take Note
We must separate the description of parallel lines at the right into two parts because vertical lines in the plane are parallel, but their slopes are undefined.

Parallel Lines

Two nonvertical lines in the plane are parallel if and only if they have the same slope. Vertical lines in the plane are parallel.

EXAMPLE

The slope of the line $y = 3x + 5$ is 3. The slope of the line $y = 3x - 4$ is 3. The lines have the same slope and different y-intercepts. The lines are parallel.

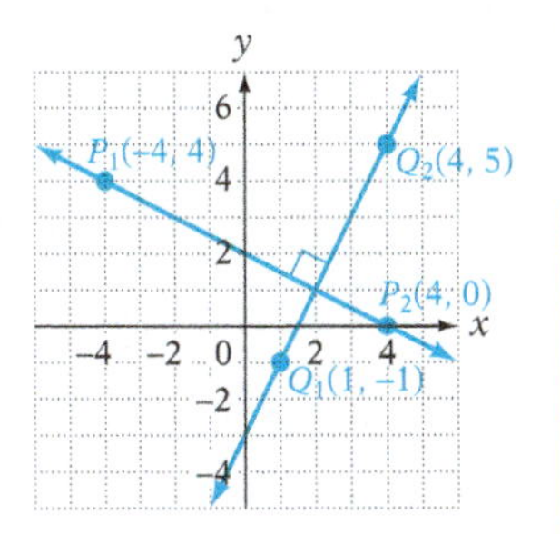

Two lines that intersect at a 90° angle (right angle) are called perpendicular lines. The lines at the left are perpendicular.

Perpendicular Lines

Two nonvertical lines in the plane are perpendicular if and only if the product of their slopes is -1. A vertical and a horizontal line are perpendicular.

EXAMPLE

The slope of the line between P_1 and P_2 in the graph at the left is $\frac{0-4}{4-(-4)} = -\frac{4}{8} = -\frac{1}{2}$.

The slope of the line between Q_1 and Q_2 is $\frac{5-(-1)}{4-1} = \frac{6}{3} = 2$. The product of the slopes is $\left(-\frac{1}{2}\right)2 = -1$. Therefore, the graphs are perpendicular.

EXAMPLE 2

Find the slope of the line containing the points $(-2, -3)$ and $(3, 4)$.

Solution

Let $P_1 = (-2, -3)$ and $P_2 = (3, 4)$.

$$m = \frac{y_2 - y_1}{x_2 - x_1} = \frac{4-(-3)}{3-(-2)}$$

- $y_2 = 4, y_1 = -3$
- $x_2 = 3, x_1 = -2$

$$= \frac{7}{5}$$

The slope is $\frac{7}{5}$.

YOU TRY IT 2

Find the slope of the line containing the points $(1, 4)$ and $(-3, 8)$.

Your solution

EXAMPLE 3

Find the slope of the line containing the points $(-1, 4)$ and $(-1, 0)$.

Solution

Let $P_1 = (-1, 4)$ and $P_2 = (-1, 0)$.

$$m = \frac{y_2 - y_1}{x_2 - x_1} = \frac{0-4}{-1-(-1)}$$

- $y_2 = 0, y_1 = 4$
- $x_2 = -1, x_1 = -1$

$$= \frac{-4}{0}$$

The slope is undefined.

YOU TRY IT 3

Find the slope of the line containing the points $(-1, 2)$ and $(4, 2)$.

Your solution

Solutions on p. S18

EXAMPLE 4

The graph below shows the altitude of a plane above an airport during its 30-minute descent from cruising altitude to landing. Find the slope of the line. Write a sentence that explains the meaning of the slope.

Solution

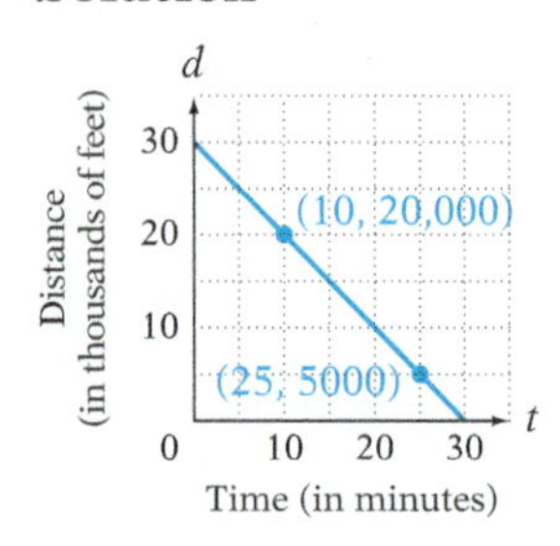

$$m = \frac{5000 - 20{,}000}{25 - 10} = \frac{-15{,}000}{15} = -1000$$

A slope of -1000 means that the altitude of the plane is *decreasing* at the rate of 1000 ft/min.

YOU TRY IT 4

The graph below shows the approximate decline in the value of a used car over a 5-year period. Find the slope of the line. Write a sentence that states the meaning of the slope.

Your solution

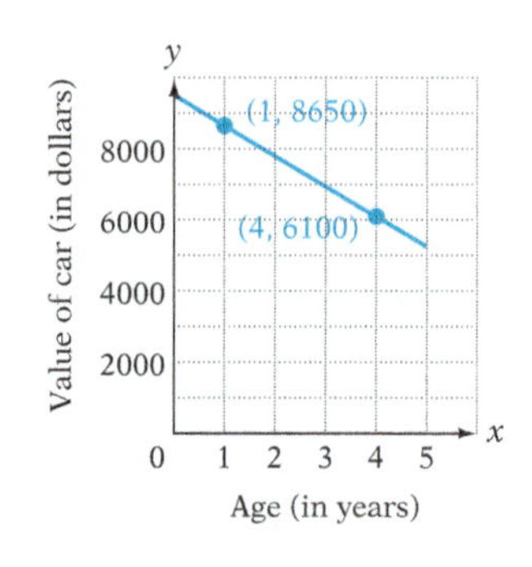

Solution on p. S18

OBJECTIVE C *To graph a line using the slope and the y-intercept*

HOW TO 6 Find the y-intercept of $y = 3x + 4$.

$y = 3x + 4 = 3(0) + 4 = 4$ • Let $x = 0$.

The y-intercept is $(0, 4)$.

For any equation of the form $y = mx + b$, the y-intercept is $(0, b)$.

The graph of the equation $y = \frac{2}{3}x + 1$ is shown at the right. The points $(-3, -1)$ and $(3, 3)$ are on the graph. The slope of the line between the two points is

$$m = \frac{3 - (-1)}{3 - (-3)} = \frac{4}{6} = \frac{2}{3}$$

Observe that the slope of the line is the coefficient of x in the equation $y = \frac{2}{3}x + 1$. The y-intercept is $(0, 1)$, where 1 is the constant term of the equation.

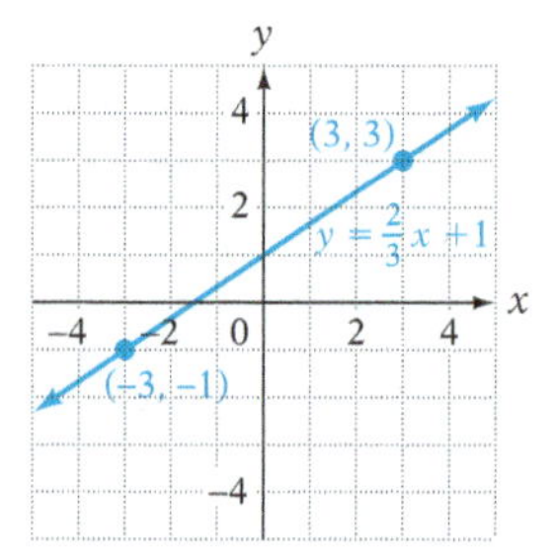

Take Note

Here are some equations in slope-intercept form.

$y = 2x - 3$: Slope is 2; y-intercept is $(0, -3)$.

$y = -x + 2$: Slope is -1 (recall that $-x = -1x$); y-intercept is $(0, 2)$.

$y = \frac{x}{2}$: Because $\frac{x}{2} = \frac{1}{2}x$, slope is $\frac{1}{2}$; y-intercept is $(0, 0)$.

Slope-Intercept Form of a Linear Equation

An equation of the form $y = mx + b$ is called the **slope-intercept form** of the equation of a straight line. The slope of the line is m, the coefficient of x. The y-intercept is $(0, b)$, where b is the constant term of the equation.

EXAMPLE

The graph of the equation $y = -4x + 3$ is a straight line.
The slope of the line is -4. The y-intercept is $(0, 3)$.

When the equation of a line is in slope-intercept form, the graph can be drawn using the slope and the y-intercept. First locate the y-intercept. Use the slope to find a second point on the line. Then draw a line through the two points.

HOW TO 7 Graph $y = 2x - 3$.

y-intercept $= (0, b) = (0, -3)$

$m = 2 = \frac{2}{1} = \frac{\text{change in } y}{\text{change in } x}$

Beginning at the y-intercept, move up 2 units (change in y) and then right 1 unit (change in x).

$(1, -1)$ is a second point on the graph.

Draw a line through the two points $(0, -3)$ and $(1, -1)$.

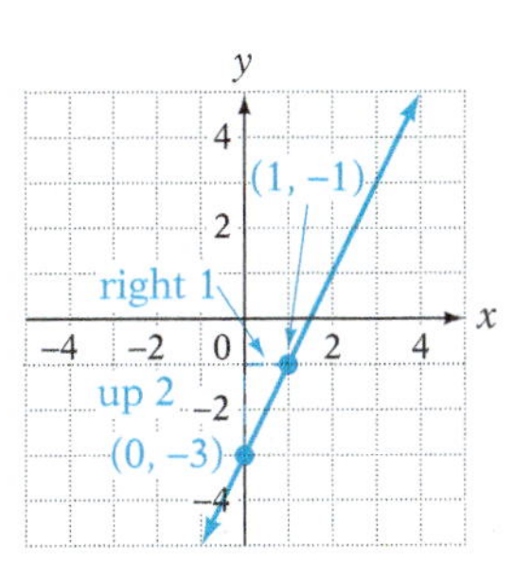

EXAMPLE 5

Graph $y = -\frac{2}{3}x + 1$ by using the slope and y-intercept.

Solution

y-intercept $= (0, b)$
$= (0, 1)$

$m = -\frac{2}{3} = \frac{-2}{3}$

$= \frac{\text{change in } y}{\text{change in } x}$

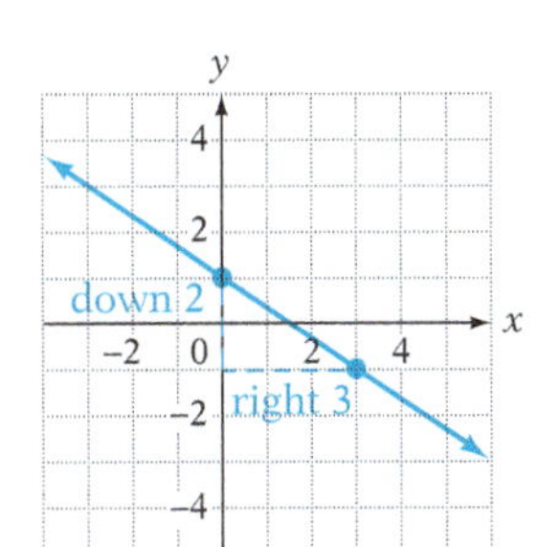

YOU TRY IT 5

Graph $y = -\frac{1}{4}x - 1$ by using the slope and y-intercept.

Your solution

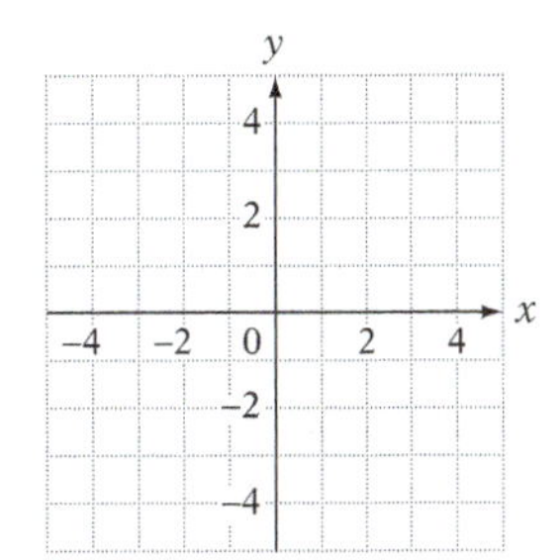

EXAMPLE 6

Graph $2x - 3y = 6$ by using the slope and y-intercept.

Solution

The equation is in the form $Ax + By = C$. Rewrite it in slope-intercept form by solving for y.

$$2x - 3y = 6$$
$$-3y = -2x + 6$$
$$y = \frac{2}{3}x - 2$$

y-intercept $= (0, -2)$

$m = \frac{2}{3} = \frac{\text{change in } y}{\text{change in } x}$

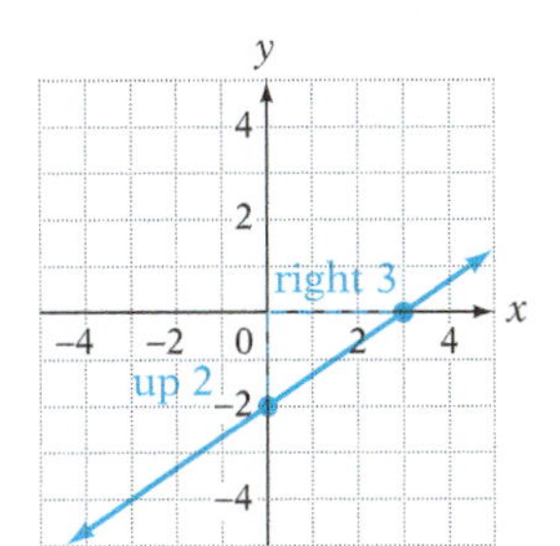

YOU TRY IT 6

Graph $x - 2y = 4$ by using the slope and y-intercept.

Your solution

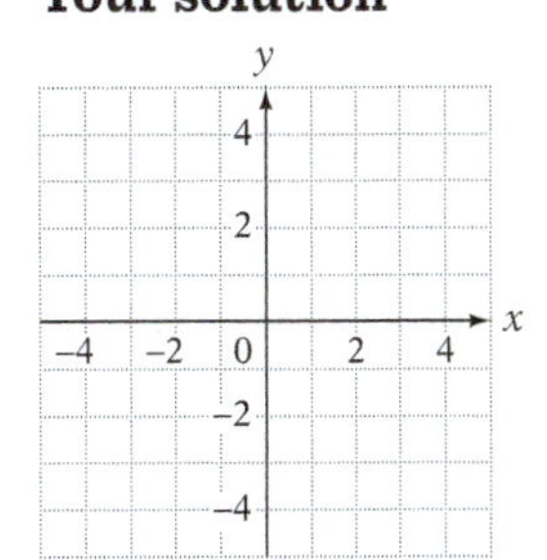

Solutions on p. S19

7.3 EXERCISES

Concept Check

1. What is the symbol for slope in the equation $y = mx + b$?

2. What is the symbol for the y-coordinate of the y-intercept in the equation $y = mx + b$?

3. **a.** A line that slants upward to the right has ____________ slope.
b. A line that slants downward to the right has ____________ slope.
c. A horizontal line has ____________ slope.
d. The slope of a vertical line is ____________.

4. Which coordinate of an x-intercept is 0?

5. Which coordinate of a y-intercept is 0?

6. Name the y-intercept of the graph shown at the right.

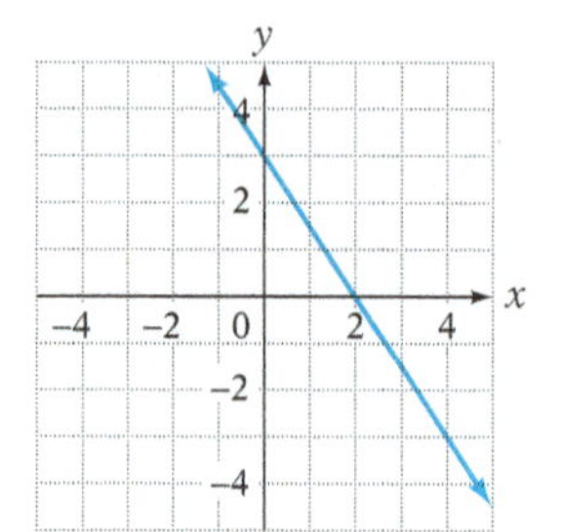

7. Identify each x value and each y value to be inserted into the slope formula $m = \frac{y_2 - y_1}{x_2 - x_1}$ to find the slope of the line containing $P_1(1, -4)$ and $P_2(3, 2)$.

$y_2 =$ ________; $y_1 =$ ________; $x_2 =$ ________; $x_1 =$ ________

8. The slope of the line with equation $y = 5x - 3$ is ________, and its y-intercept is ________.

9. Describe the graph of a line that has an x-intercept but no y-intercept.

10. Describe the graph of a line that has a y-intercept but no x-intercept.

11. The slope of a line is $\frac{6}{5}$. What is the slope of any line parallel to this line?

12. The slope of a line is $\frac{3}{2}$. What is the slope of any line perpendicular to this line?

OBJECTIVE A *To find the x- and y-intercepts of a straight line*

For Exercises 13 to 24, find the x- and y-intercepts.

13. $x - y = 3$

14. $3x + 4y = 12$

15. $3x - y = 6$

16. $2x - y = -10$

17. $x - 5y = 10$

18. $3x + 2y = 12$

19. $3x - y = -12$

20. $5x - y = -10$

21. $2x - 3y = 0$

22. $3x + 4y = 0$

23. $x + 2y = 6$

24. $2x - 3y = 12$

For Exercises 25 to 30, find the x- and y-intercepts, and then graph.

25. $5x + 2y = 10$

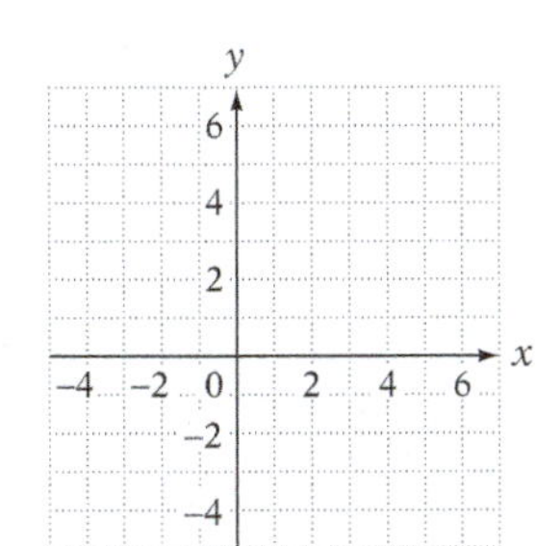

26. $x - 3y = 6$

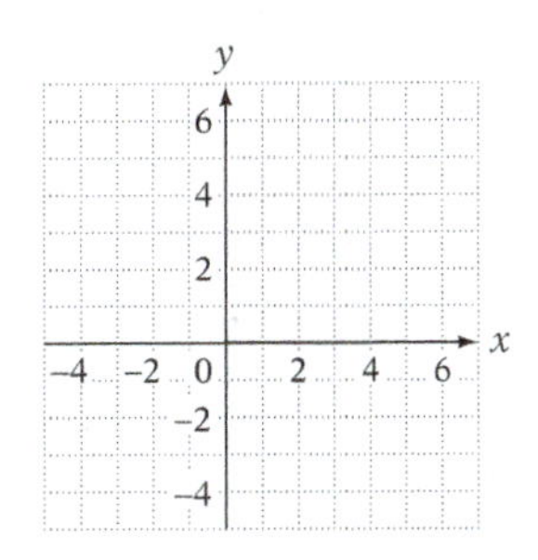

27. $3x - 4y = 12$

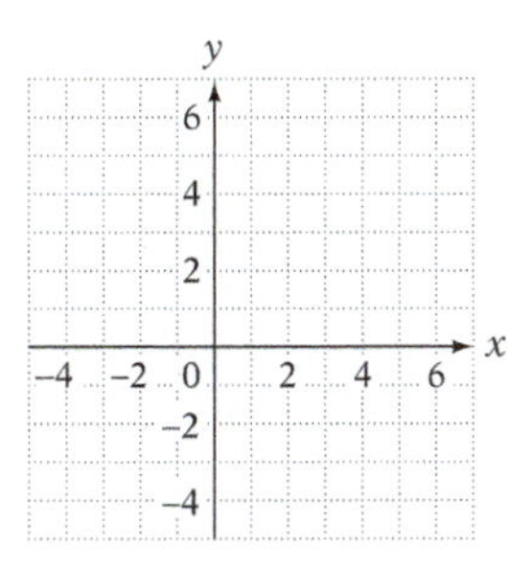

28. $2x - 5y = 10$

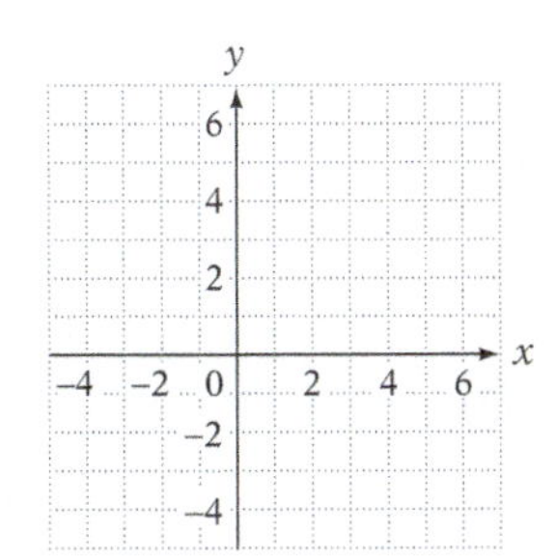

29. $5y - 3x = 15$

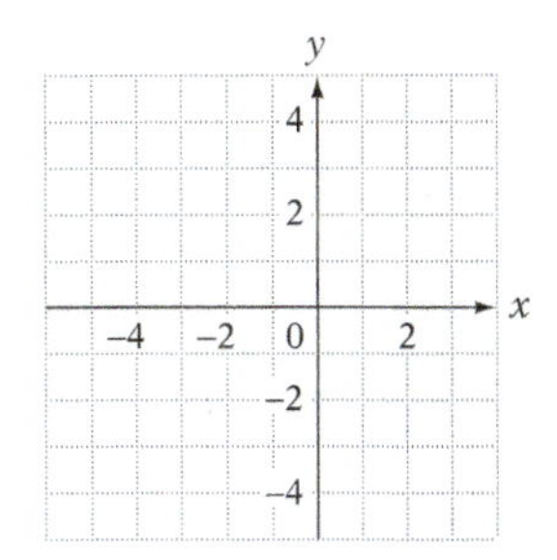

30. $9y - 4x = 18$

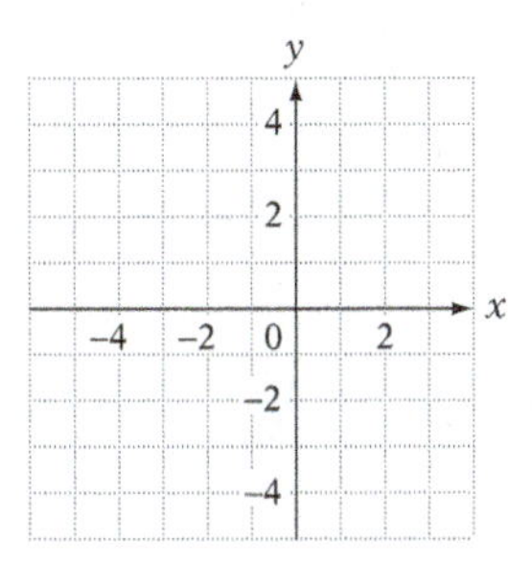

31. If $A > 0$, $B > 0$, and $C > 0$, is the y-intercept of the graph of $Ax + By = C$ above or below the x-axis?

32. If $A > 0$, $B > 0$, and $C > 0$, is the x-intercept of the graph of $Ax + By = C$ to the left or to the right of the y-axis?

OBJECTIVE B *To find the slope of a straight line*

For Exercises 33 to 44, find the slope of the line containing the given points.

33. $P_1(4, 2), P_2(3, 4)$

34. $P_1(2, 1), P_2(3, 4)$

35. $P_1(-1, 3), P_2(2, 4)$

36. $P_1(-2, 1), P_2(2, 2)$

37. $P_1(2, 4), P_2(4, -1)$

38. $P_1(1, 3), P_2(5, -3)$

39. $P_1(3, -4), P_2(3, 5)$

40. $P_1(-1, 2), P_2(-1, 3)$

41. $P_1(4, -2), P_2(3, -2)$

42. $P_1(5, 1), P_2(-2, 1)$

43. $P_1(0, -1), P_2(3, -2)$

44. $P_1(3, 0), P_2(2, -1)$

45. What is the difference between a line that has zero slope and one that has undefined slope?

For Exercises 46 and 47, l is a line passing through two distinct points (a, b) and (c, d).

46. Describe any relationships that must exist among a, b, c, and d in order for the slope of l to be undefined.

47. Describe any relationships that must exist among a, b, c, and d in order for the slope of l to be zero.

48. Are the graphs of $y = \frac{3}{8}x - 5$ and $y = \frac{3}{8}x + 2$ parallel?

49. Are the graphs of $y = -4x + 1$ and $y = 4x - 3$ parallel?

50. Are the graphs of $y = \frac{7}{2}x$ and $y = -\frac{2}{7}x + 2$ perpendicular?

51. Are the graphs of $y = 3x - 8$ and $y = -3x + 8$ perpendicular?

For Exercises 52 to 59, determine whether the line through P_1 and P_2 is parallel, perpendicular, or neither parallel nor perpendicular to the line through Q_1 and Q_2.

52. $P_1(-3, 4), P_2(2, -5); Q_1(3, 6), Q_2(-2, -3)$

53. $P_1(4, -5), P_2(6, -9); Q_1(5, -4), Q_2(1, 4)$

54. $P_1(0, 1), P_2(2, 4); Q_1(-4, -7), Q_2(2, 5)$

55. $P_1(5, 1), P_2(3, -2); Q_1(0, -2), Q_2(3, -4)$

56. $P_1(-2, 4), P_2(2, 4); Q_1(-3, 6), Q_2(4, 6)$

57. $P_1(1, -1), P_2(3, -2); Q_1(-4, 1), Q_2(2, -5)$

58. $P_1(7, -1), P_2(-4, 6); Q_1(3, 0), Q_2(-5, 3)$

59. $P_1(5, -2), P_2(-1, 3); Q_1(3, 4), Q_2(-2, -2)$

60. **Deep-Sea Diving** The pressure, in pounds per square inch, on a descending diver is shown in the graph at the right. Find the slope of the line. Write a sentence that explains the meaning of the slope.

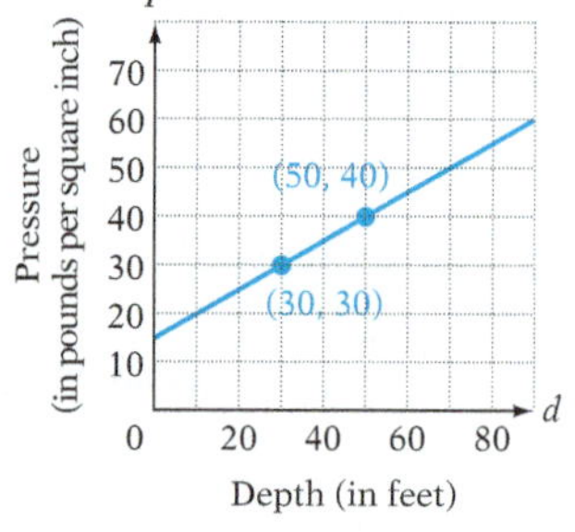

61. **Panama Canal** Ships in the Panama Canal are lowered through a series of locks. A ship is lowered as the water in a lock is discharged. The graph at the right shows the number of gallons of water N, in millions, remaining in a lock t minutes after the valves are opened to discharge the water. Find the slope of the line. Write a sentence that explains the meaning of the slope.

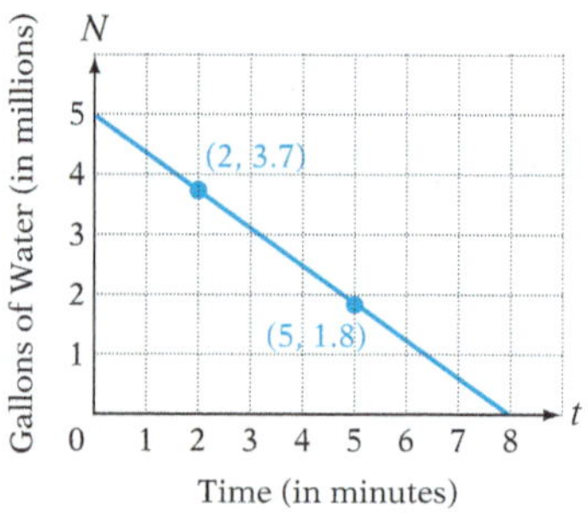

62. **Postal Service** The graph at the right shows the work accomplished by an electronic mail sorter. Find the slope of the line. Write a sentence that explains the meaning of the slope.

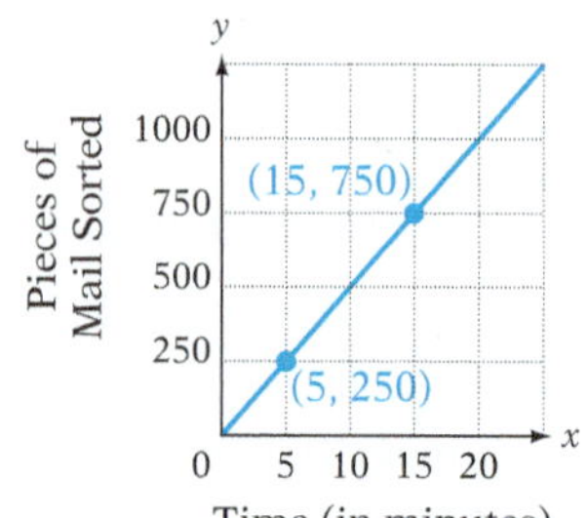

63. **Health** The graph at the right shows the relationship between distance walked and calories burned. Find the slope of the line. Write a sentence that explains the meaning of the slope.

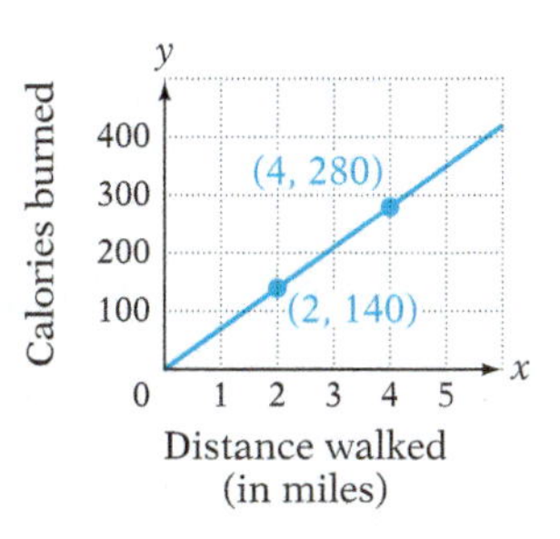

64. **Fuel Consumption** The graph at the right shows how the amount of gasoline in the tank of a car decreases as the car is driven at a constant speed of 60 mph. Find the slope of the line. Write a sentence that states the meaning of the slope.

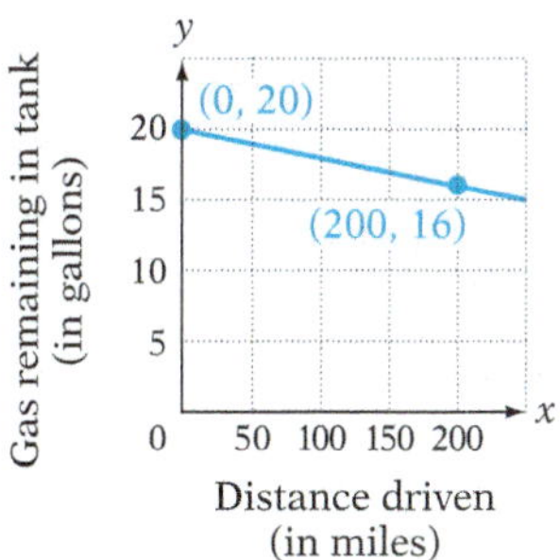

Traffic Safety See the news clipping below. Use the information in the clipping for Exercises 65 and 66.

In the NEWS!

Buckling Up Saves Lives

Annual surveys conducted by the National Highway Safety Administration show that Americans' steady increase in seat belt use has been accompanied by a steady decrease in deaths due to motor vehicle accidents.

Source: National Highway Traffic Safety Association

Seat Belt Use

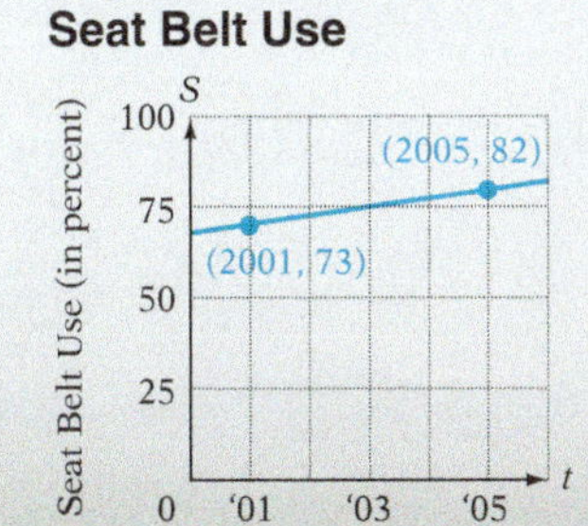

Passenger Deaths

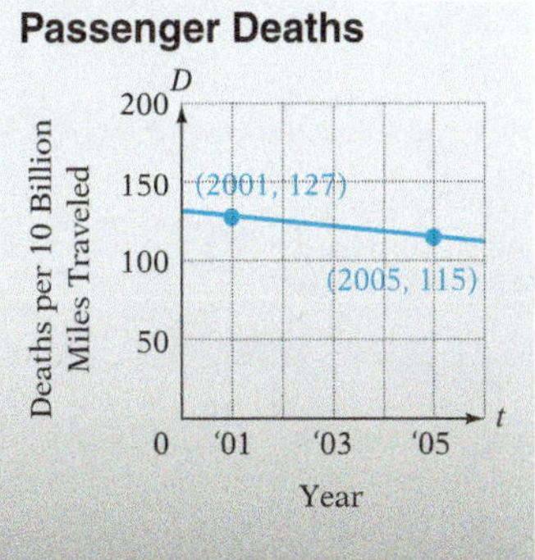

65. Find the slope of the line in the Seat Belt Use graph. Write a sentence that states the meaning of the slope in the context of the article.

66. Find the slope of the line in the Passenger Deaths graph. Write a sentence that states the meaning of the slope in the context of the article.

OBJECTIVE C *To graph a line using the slope and the y-intercept*

For Exercises 67 to 74, find the slope and y-intercept of the graph of the equation.

67. $y = -\frac{3}{8}x + 5$ **68.** $y = -x + 7$ **69.** $2x - 3y = 6$ **70.** $4x + 3y = 12$

71. $2x + 5y = 10$ **72.** $2x + y = 0$ **73.** $x - 4y = 0$ **74.** $2x + 3y = 8$

For Exercises 75 to 89, graph by using the slope and y-intercept.

75. $y = 3x + 1$

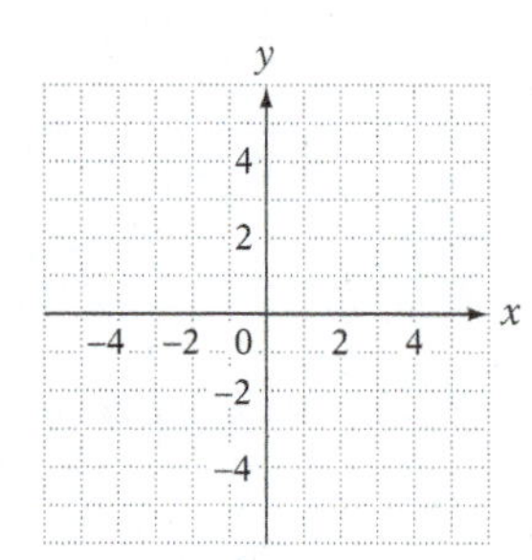

76. $y = -2x - 1$

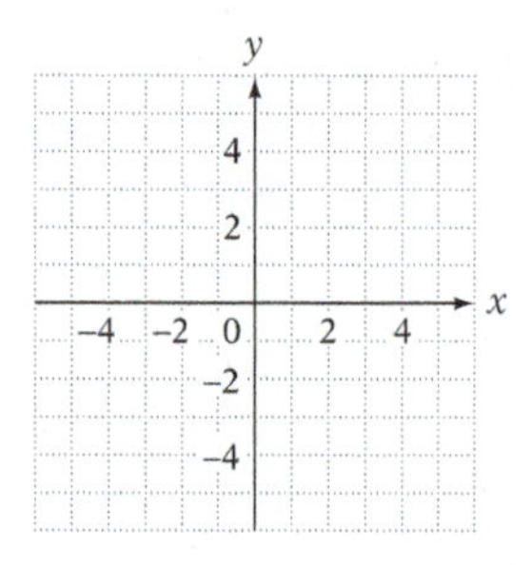

77. $y = \frac{2}{5}x - 2$

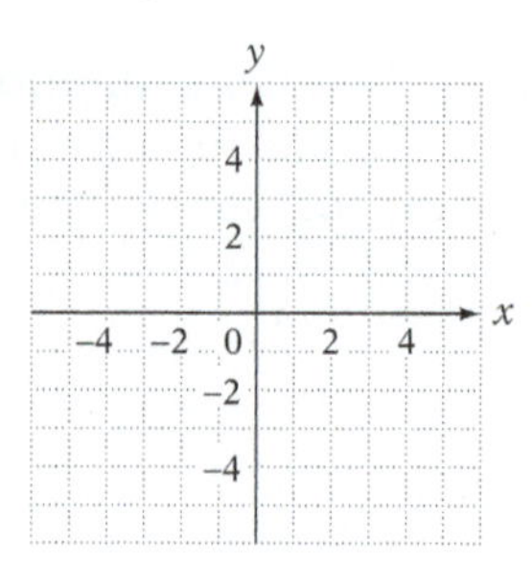

78. $y = \frac{3}{4}x + 1$

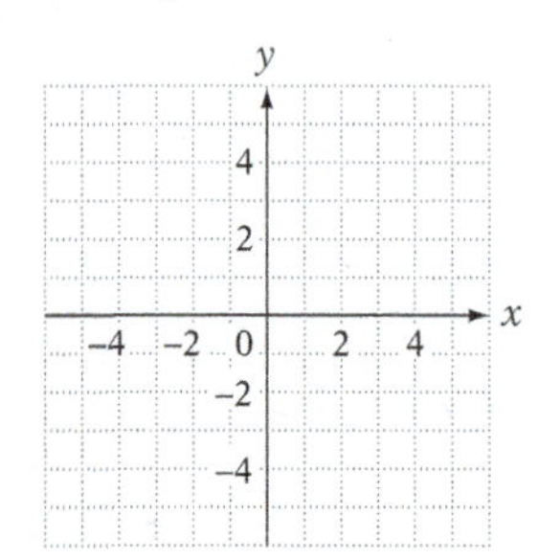

79. $2x + y = 3$

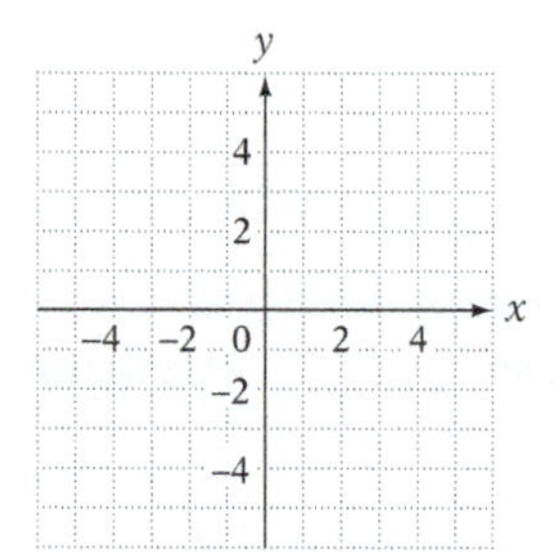

80. $3x - y = 1$

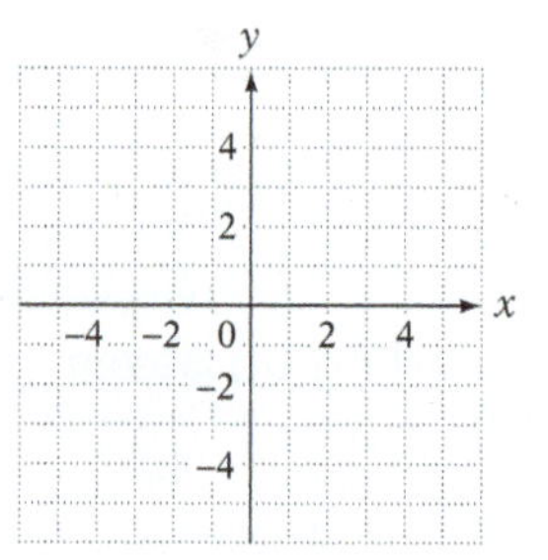

81. $x - 2y = 4$

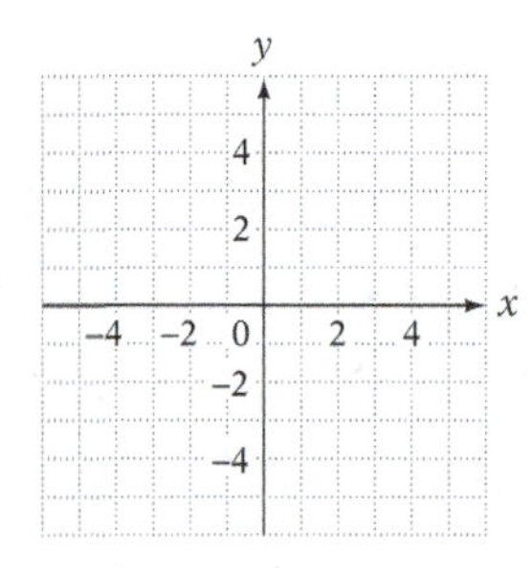

82. $x + 3y = 6$

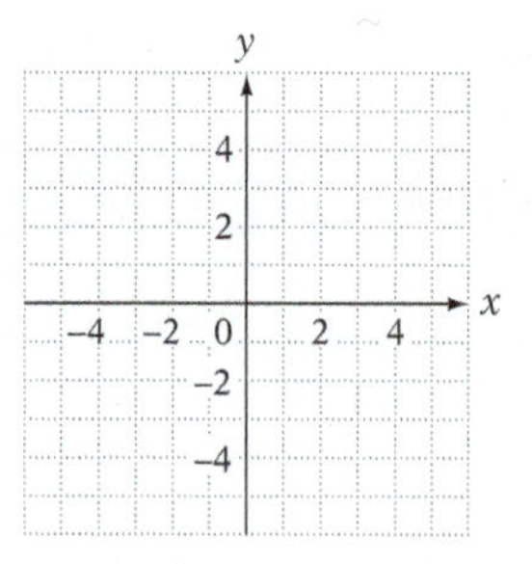

83. $y = \frac{2}{3}x$

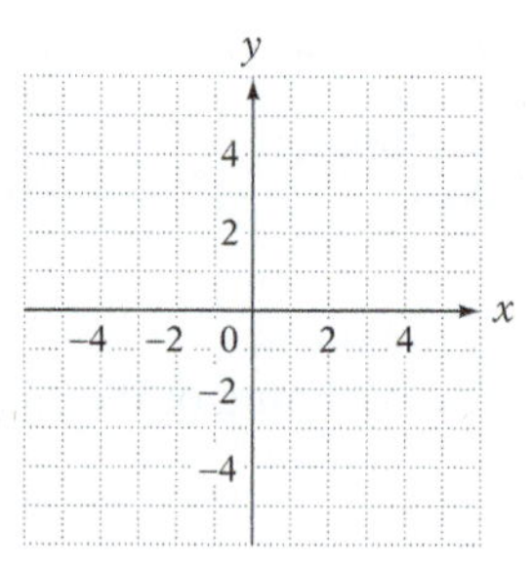

84. $y = \frac{1}{2}x$

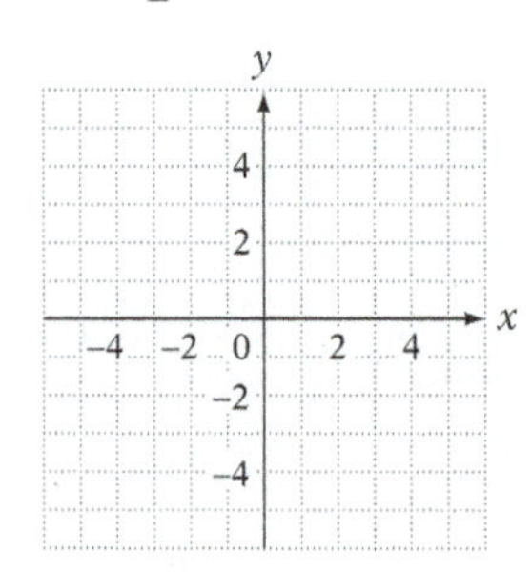

85. $y = -x + 1$

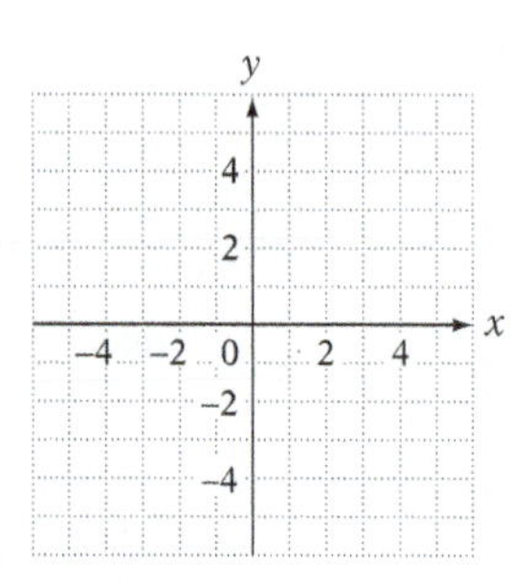

86. $y = -x - 3$

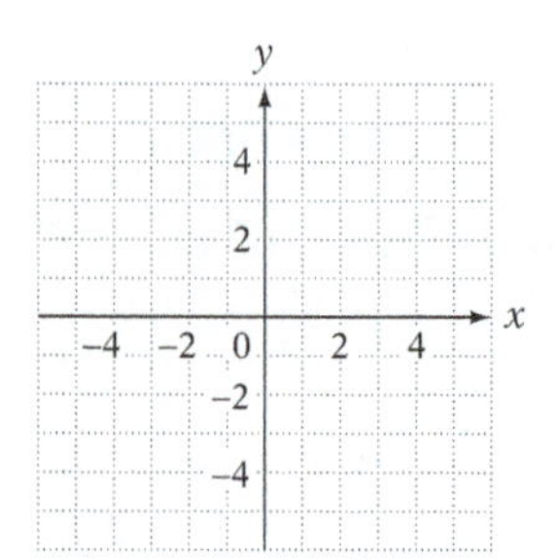

87. $3x - 4y = 12$

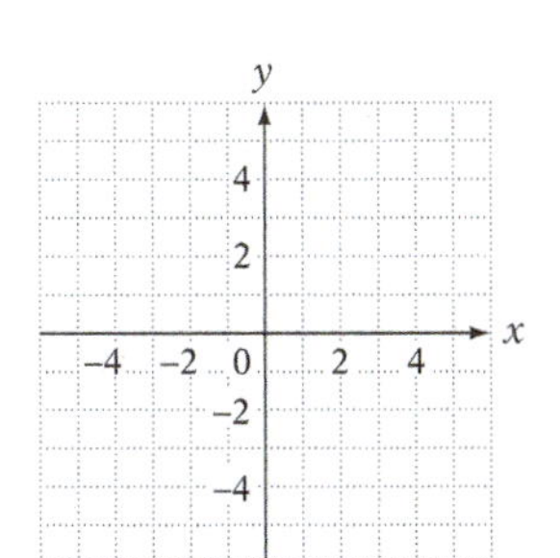

88. $5x - 2y = 10$

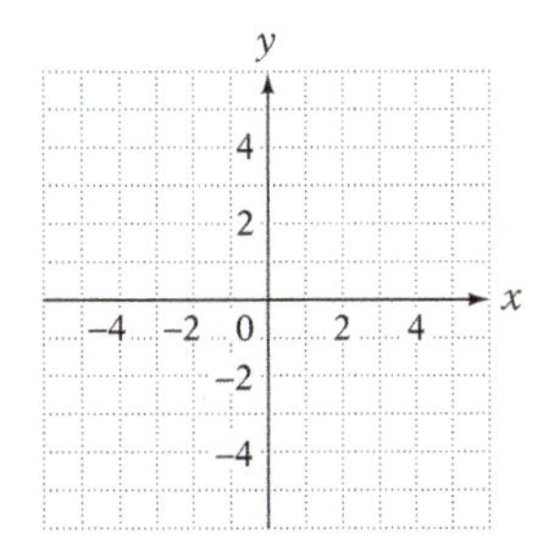

89. $y = -4x + 2$

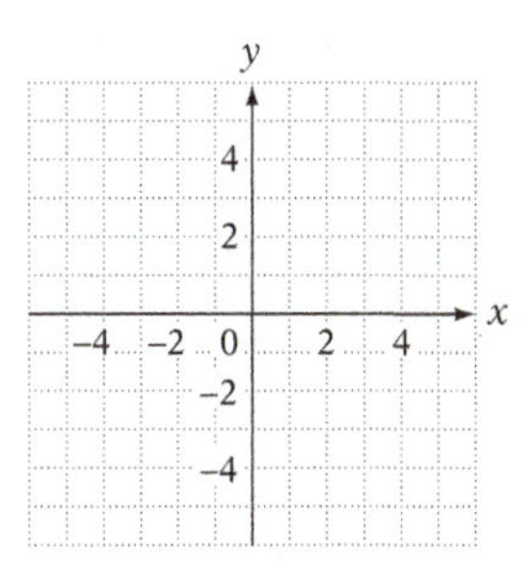

90. Suppose A, B, and C are all positive numbers. Does the y-intercept of the graph of $Ax + By = C$ lie above or below the x-axis? Does the graph slant upward to the right or downward to the right?

91. Suppose A is a negative number, and B and C are positive numbers. Does the y-intercept of the graph of $Ax + By = C$ lie above or below the x-axis? Does the graph slant upward to the right or downward to the right?

Critical Thinking

92. What effect does increasing the coefficient of x have on the graph of $y = mx + b$, $m > 0$?

93. What effect does decreasing the coefficient of x have on the graph of $y = mx + b$, $m > 0$?

94. What effect does increasing the constant term have on the graph of $y = mx + b$?

95. What effect does decreasing the constant term have on the graph of $y = mx + b$?

96. Match each equation with its graph.

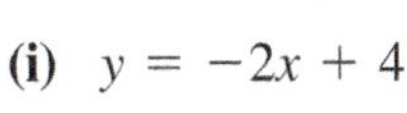

(i) $y = -2x + 4$

(ii) $y = 2x - 4$

(iii) $y = 2$

(iv) $2x + 4y = 0$

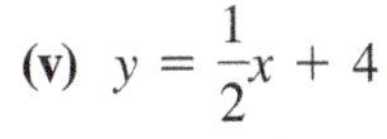

(v) $y = \frac{1}{2}x + 4$

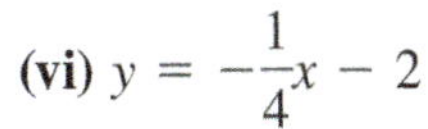

(vi) $y = -\frac{1}{4}x - 2$

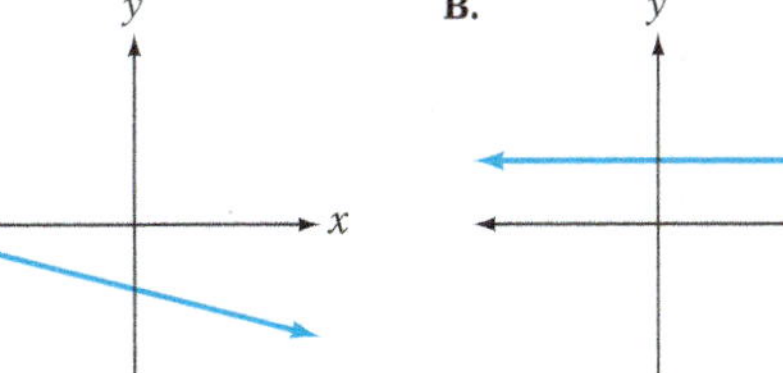

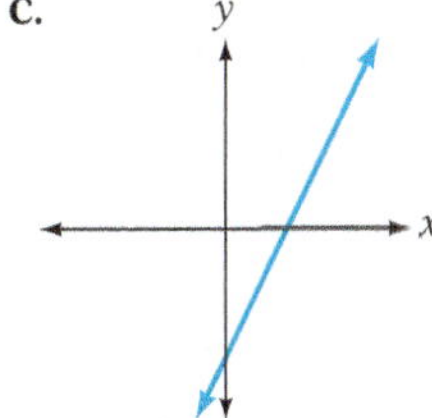

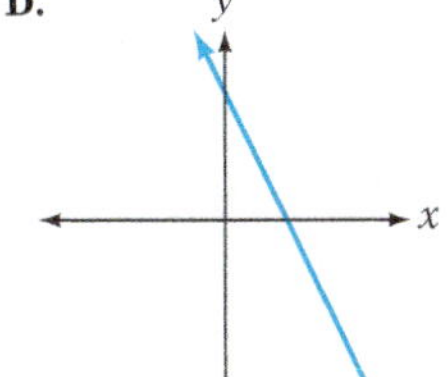

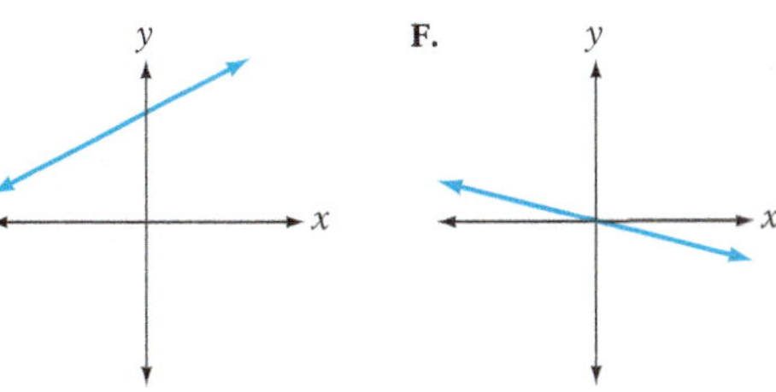

97. Do the graphs of all straight lines have a y-intercept? If not, give an example of one that does not.

98. If two lines have the same slope and the same y-intercept, must the graphs of the lines be the same? If not, give an example.

Projects or Group Activities

For Exercises 99 to 104, explain how you would distinguish between the graphs of the two equations.

99. **a.** $y = \frac{3}{5}x - 2$ **b.** $y = -\frac{3}{5}x - 2$

100. **a.** $y = x + 1$ **b.** $y = -x + 1$

101. **a.** $y = \frac{3}{4}x + 5$ **b.** $y = \frac{3}{4}x - 5$

102. **a.** $y = 2x - 4$ **b.** $y = 2x + 4$

103. **a.** $y = 6$ **b.** $x = 6$

104. **a.** $y = 1$ **b.** $y = -1$

A graphing calculator can be used to graph a linear equation. Here are the keystrokes to graph $y = \frac{2}{3}x + 1$. First the equation is entered. Then the domain (Xmin to Xmax) and the range (Ymin to Ymax) are entered. This is called the **viewing window.** Xmin and Xmax are the smallest and largest values of x that will be shown on the screen. Ymin and Ymax are the smallest and largest values of y that will be shown on the screen.

By changing the keystrokes 2 X,T,θ,n ÷ 3 + 1, you can graph different equations.

For Exercises 105 to 108, use a graphing calculator to graph the equation.

105. $y = 2x + 1$ For $2x$, you may enter $2 \times x$ or just $2x$. Entering the times sign $\times$ is not necessary on many graphing calculators.

106. $y = -\frac{1}{2}x - 2$ Use the (-) key to enter a negative sign.

107. $3x + 2y = 6$ Solve for y. Then enter the equation.

108. $4x + 3y = 75$ You must adjust the viewing window. *Suggestion:* Xmin $= -25$, Xmax $= 25$, Xscl $= 5$; Ymin $= -35$, Ymax $= 35$, Yscl $= 5$. See the Appendix for assistance.

SECTION

7.4 Equations of Straight Lines

OBJECTIVE A *To find the equation of a line using the equation $y = mx + b$*

When the slope of a line and a point on the line are known, the equation of the line can be written using the slope-intercept form, $y = mx + b$. In HOW TO 1 below, the known point is the y-intercept. In HOW TO 2, the known point is a point other than the y-intercept.

HOW TO 1 Find the equation of the line that has slope 3 and y-intercept $(0, 2)$.

$$y = mx + b$$

The given slope, 3, is m. Replace m with 3. $\quad y = 3x + b$

The given point, $(0, 2)$, is the y-intercept. Replace b with 2. $\quad y = 3x + 2$

The equation of the line that has slope 3 and y-intercept $(0, 2)$ is $y = 3x + 2$.

HOW TO 2 Find the equation of the line that has slope $\frac{1}{2}$ and contains the point whose coordinates are $(-2, 4)$.

$$y = mx + b$$

The given slope, $\frac{1}{2}$, is m. Replace m with $\frac{1}{2}$. $\quad y = \frac{1}{2}x + b$

The given point, $(-2, 4)$, is a solution of the equation of the line. Replace x and y in the equation with the coordinates of the point. $\quad 4 = \frac{1}{2}(-2) + b$

Solve for b, the y-intercept. $\quad 4 = -1 + b$
$\quad 5 = b$

Write the equation of the line by replacing m and b in the equation $y = mx + b$ by their values. $\quad y = mx + b$
$\quad y = \frac{1}{2}x + 5$

The equation of the line that has slope $\frac{1}{2}$ and contains the point whose coordinates are $(-2, 4)$ is $y = \frac{1}{2}x + 5$.

Take Note
Every ordered pair is of the form (x, y). For the point $(-2, 4)$, -2 is the x value and 4 is the y value. Substitute -2 for x and 4 for y.

EXAMPLE 1

Find the equation of the line that contains the point $(0, -1)$ and has slope $-\frac{2}{3}$.

Solution

Use the slope-intercept form, $y = mx + b$.

$y = -\frac{2}{3}x - 1 \quad$ • $m = -\frac{2}{3}; b = -1$

The equation of the line is $y = -\frac{2}{3}x - 1$.

YOU TRY IT 1

Find the equation of the line that contains the point $(0, 2)$ and has slope $\frac{5}{3}$.

Your solution

Solution on p. S19

EXAMPLE 2

Find the equation of the line that contains the point whose coordinates are $(3, -3)$ and has slope $\frac{2}{3}$.

Solution

$y = mx + b$ • Use the slope-intercept form.

$y = \frac{2}{3}x + b$ • $m = \frac{2}{3}$

$-3 = \frac{2}{3}(3) + b$ • Replace x and y in the equation with the coordinates of the given point, $(3, -3)$

$-3 = 2 + b$ • Solve for b.

$-5 = b$

$y = \frac{2}{3}x - 5$ • Replace m by $\frac{2}{3}$ and b by -5 in $y = mx + b$.

The equation of the line is $y = \frac{2}{3}x - 5$.

YOU TRY IT 2

Find the equation of the line that contains the point whose coordinates are $(4, -2)$ and has slope $\frac{3}{2}$.

Your solution

Solution on p. S19

OBJECTIVE B *To find the equation of a line using the point-slope formula*

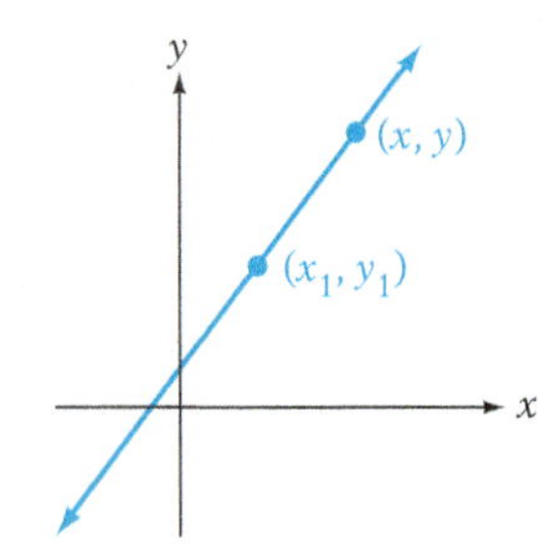

An alternative method for finding the equation of a line, given the slope and the coordinates of a point on the line, involves use of the point-slope formula. The point-slope formula is derived from the formula for slope.

Let (x_1, y_1) be the coordinates of the given point on the line, and let (x, y) be the coordinates of any other point on the line. Use the formula for slope.

$$\frac{y - y_1}{x - x_1} = m$$

Multiply both sides of the equation by $(x - x_1)$.

$$\frac{y - y_1}{x - x_1}(x - x_1) = m(x - x_1)$$

Simplify.

$$y - y_1 = m(x - x_1)$$

Point-Slope Formula

The equation of the line that has slope m and contains the point whose coordinates are (x_1, y_1) can be found by using the point-slope formula:

$$y - y_1 = m(x - x_1)$$

EXAMPLE

Find the equation of the line that passes through the point $(2, 3)$ and has slope -2.

$y - y_1 = m(x - x_1)$ • Use the point-slope formula.

$y - 3 = -2(x - 2)$ • $m = -2$; $(x_1, y_1) = (2, 3)$

$y - 3 = -2x + 4$ • Solve for y.

$y = -2x + 7$

The equation of the line is $y = -2x + 7$.

EXAMPLE 3

Use the point-slope formula to find the equation of the line that passes through the point $(-2, -1)$ and has slope $\frac{3}{2}$.

Solution

$$y - y_1 = m(x - x_1)$$

$$y - (-1) = \frac{3}{2}[x - (-2)] \quad \bullet\ m = \frac{3}{2};\ (x_1, y_1) = (-2, -1)$$

$$y + 1 = \frac{3}{2}(x + 2)$$

$$y + 1 = \frac{3}{2}x + 3$$

$$y = \frac{3}{2}x + 2$$

The equation of the line is $y = \frac{3}{2}x + 2$.

YOU TRY IT 3

Use the point-slope formula to find the equation of the line that passes through the point $(4, -2)$ and has slope $\frac{3}{4}$.

Your solution

Solutions on p. S19

OBJECTIVE C *To find the equation of a line given two points*

The point-slope formula is used to find the equation of a line when a point on the line and the slope of the line are known. But this formula can also be used to find the equation of a line given two points on the line. In this case,

1. Use the slope formula to determine the slope of the line between the points.
2. Use the point-slope formula, the slope you just calculated, and one of the given points to find the equation of the line.

HOW TO 3 Find the equation of the line that passes through the points $(-3, -1)$ and $(3, 3)$.

Use the slope formula to determine the slope of the line between the points.

$$m = \frac{y_2 - y_1}{x_2 - x_1} = \frac{3 - (-1)}{3 - (-3)} = \frac{4}{6} = \frac{2}{3} \quad \bullet\ (x_1, y_1) = (-3, -1);\ (x_2, y_2) = (3, 3)$$

Use the point-slope formula, the slope you just calculated, and one of the given points to find the equation of the line.

$$y - y_1 = m(x - x_1) \quad \bullet\ \text{Point-slope formula}$$

$$y - (-1) = \frac{2}{3}[x - (-3)] \quad \bullet\ m = \frac{2}{3};\ (x_1, y_1) = (-3, -1)$$

$$y + 1 = \frac{2}{3}(x + 3)$$

$$y + 1 = \frac{2}{3}x + 2$$

$$y = \frac{2}{3}x + 1$$

Take Note

You can verify that the equation $y = \frac{2}{3}x + 1$ passes through the points $(-3, -1)$ and $(3, 3)$ by substituting the coordinates of these points into the equation.

Check:

$$\begin{array}{c|c} y & \frac{2}{3}x + 1 \\ \hline -1 & \frac{2}{3}(-3) + 1 \\ -1 & -2 + 1 \\ -1 = -1 & \end{array}$$

• $(x, y) = (-3, -1)$

$$\begin{array}{c|c} y & \frac{2}{3}x + 1 \\ \hline 3 & \frac{2}{3}(3) + 1 \\ 3 & 2 + 1 \\ 3 = 3 & \end{array}$$

• $(x, y) = (3, 3)$

The equation of the line that passes through the two points is $y = \frac{2}{3}x + 1$.

If the two given points lie on a horizontal line, the procedure used in HOW TO 3 can be used to find the equation of the line. However, it is quicker to just remember that the equation of a horizontal line is $y = b$, where b is the y-intercept of the graph of the line. b is also the y-coordinate of each of the two given points.

HOW TO 4 Find the equation of the line that passes through the points whose coordinates are $(-4, -2)$ and $(2, -2)$.

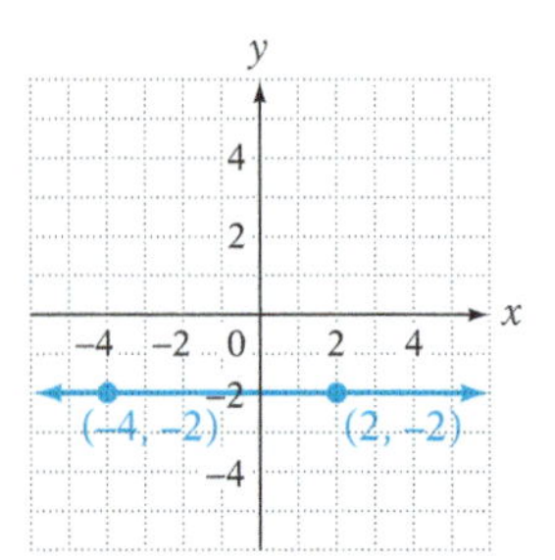

The y-coordinates of the two points are the same. The points lie on a horizontal line. The equation of the line is $y = b$, where b is the y-intercept of the graph of the line. The equation of the line is $y = -2$.

The equation of a vertical line is $x = a$, where a is the x-intercept of the graph of the line. a is also the x-coordinate of each of the two given points. For example, the equation of the line that passes through the points $(3, 4)$ and $(3, -5)$ is $x = 3$.

EXAMPLE 4

Find the equation of the line that passes through the points $(-4, 0)$ and $(2, -3)$.

Solution

Find the slope of the line between the two points.

$$m = \frac{y_2 - y_1}{x_2 - x_1} = \frac{-3 - 0}{2 - (-4)} = \frac{-3}{6} = -\frac{1}{2}$$

Use the point-slope formula.

$y - y_1 = m(x - x_1)$ • Point-slope formula

$y - 0 = -\frac{1}{2}[x - (-4)]$ • $m = -\frac{1}{2}$; $(x_1, y_1) = (-4, 0)$

$y = -\frac{1}{2}(x + 4)$

$y = -\frac{1}{2}x - 2$

The equation of the line is $y = -\frac{1}{2}x - 2$.

YOU TRY IT 4

Find the equation of the line that passes through the points $(-6, -2)$ and $(3, 1)$.

Your solution

Solution on p. S19

7.4 EXERCISES

Concept Check

1. The graph of the equation $y = 5x + 7$ has slope ______ and y-intercept (0, ______).

2. If the equation of a line has y-intercept $(0, 4)$, then 4 can be substituted for ______ in the equation $y = mx + b$.

3. Suppose a classmate says, "The y-intercept is 2." The classmate means that the y-intercept is the point (______, ______).

4. The equation of a line contains the point $(-3, 1)$. This means that when y is ______, x is ______.

5. In the equation of the line that has slope 3 and y-intercept $(0, 1)$, $m =$ ______ and $b =$ ______. The equation is $y =$ ______.

6. After you find the equation of a line given its slope and the coordinates of a point on the line, how can you determine whether you have the correct equation?

OBJECTIVE A *To find the equation of a line using the equation $y = mx + b$*

For Exercises 7 to 20, use the slope-intercept form.

7. Find the equation of the line that contains the point whose coordinates are $(0, 2)$ and has slope 2.

8. Find the equation of the line that contains the point whose coordinates are $(0, -1)$ and has slope -2.

9. Find the equation of the line that contains the point whose coordinates are $(-1, 2)$ and has slope -3.

10. Find the equation of the line that contains the point whose coordinates are $(2, -3)$ and has slope 3.

11. Find the equation of the line that contains the point whose coordinates are $(3, 1)$ and has slope $\frac{1}{3}$.

12. Find the equation of the line that contains the point whose coordinates are $(-2, 3)$ and has slope $\frac{1}{2}$.

13. Find the equation of the line that contains the point whose coordinates are $(4, -2)$ and has slope $\frac{3}{4}$.

14. Find the equation of the line that contains the point whose coordinates are $(2, 3)$ and has slope $-\frac{1}{2}$.

15. Find the equation of the line that contains the point whose coordinates are $(5, -3)$ and has slope $-\frac{3}{5}$.

16. Find the equation of the line that contains the point whose coordinates are $(5, -1)$ and has slope $\frac{1}{5}$.

17. Find the equation of the line that contains the point whose coordinates are $(2, 3)$ and has slope $\frac{1}{4}$.

18. Find the equation of the line that contains the point whose coordinates are $(-1, 2)$ and has slope $-\frac{1}{2}$.

19. Find the equation of the line that contains the point whose coordinates are $(-3, -5)$ and has slope $-\frac{2}{3}$.

20. Find the equation of the line that contains the point whose coordinates are $(-4, 0)$ and has slope $\frac{5}{2}$.

OBJECTIVE B *To find the equation of a line using the point-slope formula*

For Exercises 21 to 34, use the point-slope formula.

21. Find the equation of the line that passes through the point whose coordinates are $(1, -1)$ and has slope 2.

22. Find the equation of the line that passes through the point whose coordinates are $(2, 3)$ and has slope -1.

23. Find the equation of the line that passes through the point whose coordinates are $(-2, 1)$ and has slope -2.

24. Find the equation of the line that passes through the point whose coordinates are $(-1, -3)$ and has slope -3.

25. Find the equation of the line that passes through the point whose coordinates are $(0, 0)$ and has slope $\frac{2}{3}$.

26. Find the equation of the line that passes through the point whose coordinates are $(0, 0)$ and has slope $-\frac{1}{5}$.

27. Find the equation of the line that passes through the point whose coordinates are $(2, 3)$ and has slope $\frac{1}{2}$.

28. Find the equation of the line that passes through the point whose coordinates are $(3, -1)$ and has slope $\frac{2}{3}$.

29. Find the equation of the line that passes through the point whose coordinates are $(-4, 1)$ and has slope $-\frac{3}{4}$.

30. Find the equation of the line that passes through the point whose coordinates are $(-5, 0)$ and has slope $-\frac{1}{5}$.

31. Find the equation of the line that passes through the point whose coordinates are $(-2, 1)$ and has slope $\frac{3}{4}$.

32. Find the equation of the line that passes through the point whose coordinates are $(3, -2)$ and has slope $\frac{1}{6}$.

33. Find the equation of the line that passes through the point whose coordinates are $(-3, -5)$ and has slope $-\frac{4}{3}$.

34. Find the equation of the line that passes through the point whose coordinates are $(3, -1)$ and has slope $\frac{3}{5}$.

35. Use the point-slope formula to find the equation of the line with slope m and y-intercept $(0, b)$.

36. Use the point-slope formula to find the equation of the line that goes through the point $(5, 3)$ and has slope 0.

OBJECTIVE C *To find the equation of a line given two points*

For Exercises 37 to 60, find the equation of the line through the given points.

37. $(-2, -2)$ and $(1, 7)$
38. $(1, 5)$ and $(3, 9)$
39. $(-5, 1)$ and $(2, -6)$
40. $(-3, 9)$ and $(1, 1)$

41. $(5, -1)$ and $(-5, 11)$
42. $(-6, 12)$ and $(-4, 9)$
43. $(-10, -3)$ and $(5, -9)$
44. $(-6, -13)$ and $(6, -1)$

45. $(1, 5)$ and $(-6, 5)$
46. $(-3, -4)$ and $(5, -4)$
47. $(5, -1)$ and $(5, -7)$
48. $(-3, 6)$ and $(-3, 0)$

49. $(-20, -8)$ and $(5, 12)$
50. $(-6, 19)$ and $(2, 7)$
51. $(0, -2)$ and $(-6, 1)$
52. $(15, -9)$ and $(-20, 5)$

53. $(6, -11)$ and $(-3, 1)$
54. $(14, -1)$ and $(-7, -7)$
55. $(3, 6)$ and $(0, -3)$
56. $(5, 9)$ and $(-5, 3)$

57. $(-1, -3)$ and $(2, 6)$
58. $(-3, 6)$ and $(4, -8)$
59. $(3, -5)$ and $(3, 1)$
60. $(2, -1)$ and $(5, -1)$

61. If $y = 2x - 3$ and (x_1, y_1) and (x_2, y_2) are the coordinates of two points on the graph of the line, what is the value of $\frac{y_2 - y_1}{x_2 - x_1}$?

Critical Thinking

For Exercises 62 to 65, determine whether there is a linear equation that contains all of the given ordered pairs. If so, find the equation.

62. $(5, 1), (4, 2), (0, 6)$
63. $(-2, -4), (0, -3), (4, -1)$
64. $(-1, -5), (2, 4), (0, 2)$
65. $(3, -1), (12, -4), (-6, 2)$

For Exercises 66 to 69, the given ordered pairs are solutions of the same linear equation. Find n.

66. $(0, 1), (4, 9), (3, n)$
67. $(2, 2), (-1, 5), (3, n)$
68. $(2, -2), (-2, -4), (4, n)$
69. $(1, -2), (-2, 4), (4, n)$

Projects or Group Activities

For Exercises 70 to 73, (a) name the x-intercept of the graph, (b) name the y-intercept of the graph, (c) determine the slope of the line, and (d) write the equation of the line in slope-intercept form.

70.

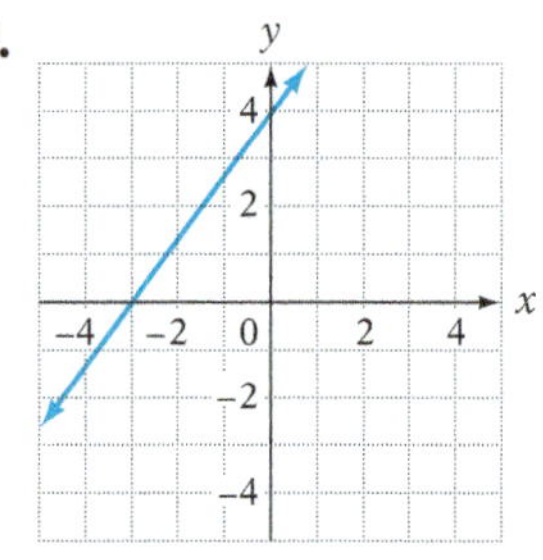

71.

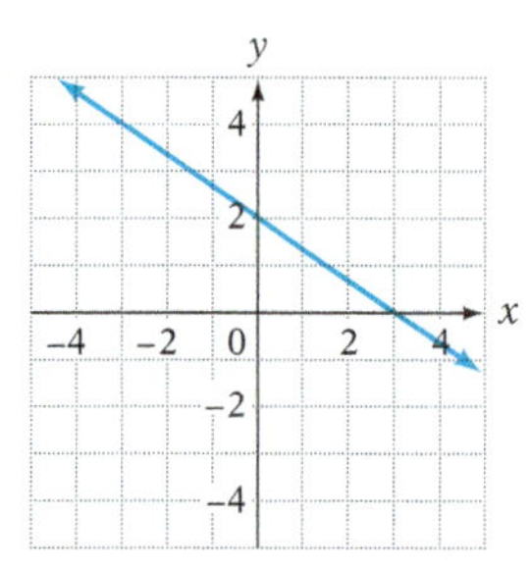

72.

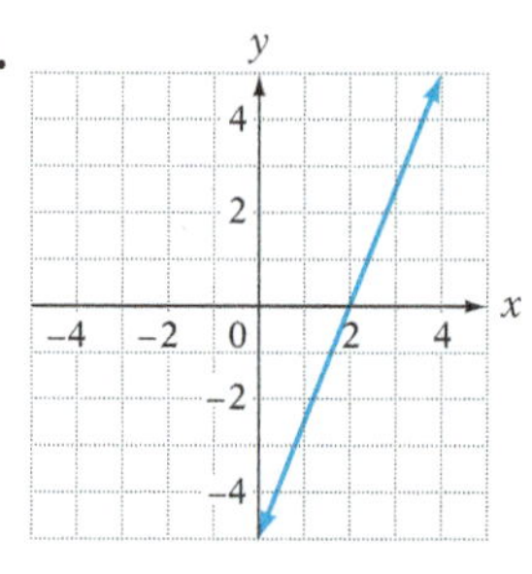

73.

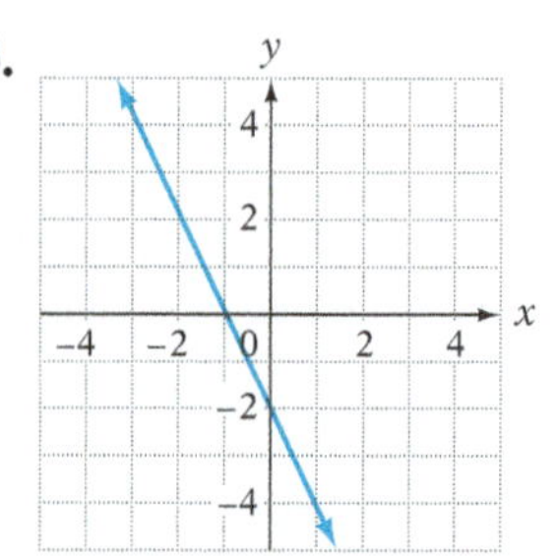

CHAPTER

7 Summary

Key Words

A **rectangular coordinate system** is formed by two number lines, one horizontal and one vertical, that intersect at the zero point of each line. The number lines that make up a rectangular coordinate system are called the **coordinate axes,** or simply **axes.** The **origin** is the point of intersection of the two coordinate axes. Generally, the horizontal axis is labeled the x-axis and the vertical axis is labeled the y-axis. The coordinate system divides the plane into four regions called **quadrants.** The **coordinates of a point** in the plane are given by an **ordered pair (x, y).** The first number in the ordered pair is called the **abscissa** or **x-coordinate.** The second number in the ordered pair is called the **ordinate** or **y-coordinate.** The **graph of an ordered pair (x, y)** is the dot drawn at the coordinates of the point in the plane. [7.1A, p. 350]

Examples

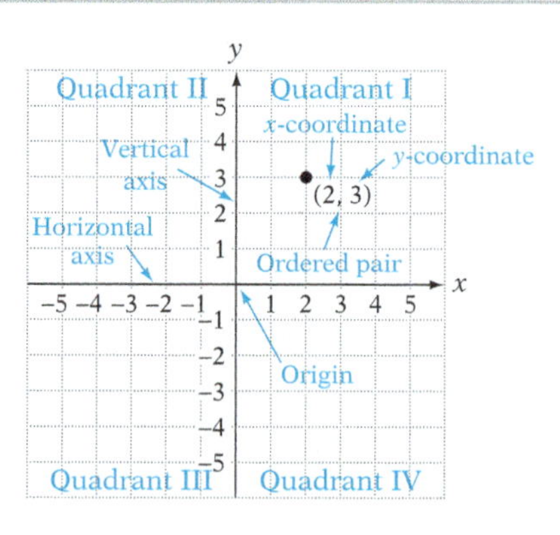

A **solution of an equation in two variables** is an ordered pair (x, y) that makes the equation a true statement. [7.1B, p. 352]

The ordered pair $(-1, 1)$ is a solution of the equation $y = 2x + 3$ because when -1 is substituted for x and 1 is substituted for y, the result is a true equation.

A **relation** is any set of ordered pairs. The **domain** of a relation is the set of first coordinates of the ordered pairs. The **range** is the set of second coordinates of the ordered pairs. [7.1C, p. 354]

For the relation $\{(-1, 2), (2, 4), (3, 5), (3, 7)\}$, the domain is $\{-1, 2, 3\}$; the range is $\{2, 4, 5, 7\}$.

A **function** is a relation in which no two ordered pairs have the same first coordinate. [7.1C, p. 354]

The relation $\{(-2, -3), (0, 4), (1, 5)\}$ is a function. No two ordered pairs have the same first coordinate.

The **graph of an equation in two variables** is a graph of the ordered-pair solutions of the equation. An equation of the form $y = mx + b$ is a **linear equation in two variables.** [7.2A, p. 363]

$y = 2x + 3$ is a linear equation in two variables. Its graph is shown at the right.

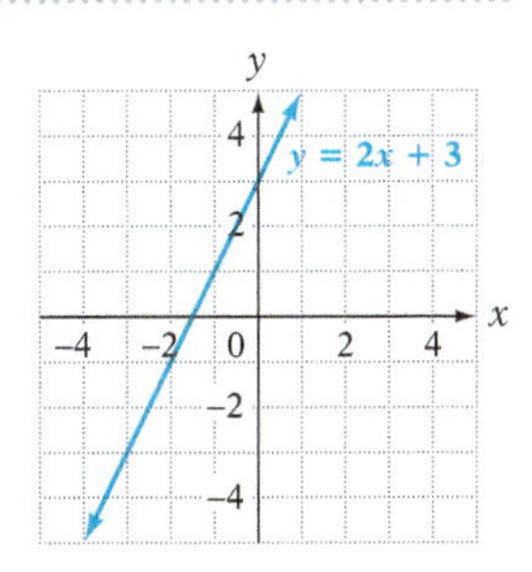

An equation written in the form $Ax + By = C$ is the **standard form of a linear equation in two variables.** [7.2B, p. 365]

$2x + 7y = 10$ is an example of a linear equation in two variables written in standard form.

The point at which a graph crosses the x-axis is called the **x-intercept.** At the x-intercept, the y-coordinate is 0. The point at which a graph crosses the y-axis is called the **y-intercept.** At the y-intercept, the x-coordinate is 0. [7.3A, p. 374]

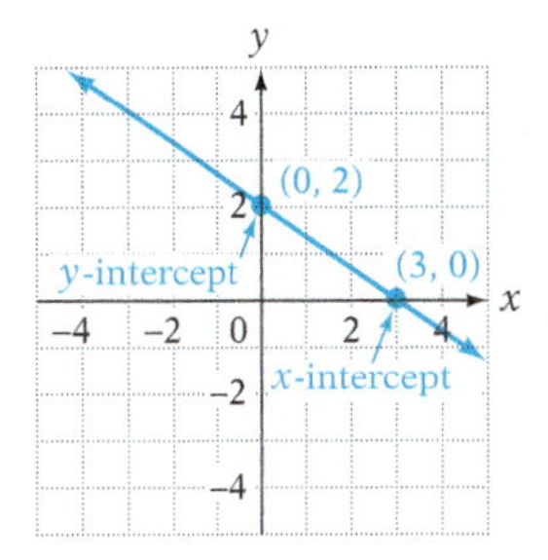

The **slope** of a line is a measure of the slant of the line. The symbol for slope is m. A line with **positive slope** slants upward to the right. A line with **negative slope** slants downward to the right. A horizontal line has **zero slope.** A vertical line has an **undefined slope.** [7.3B, pp. 375–376]

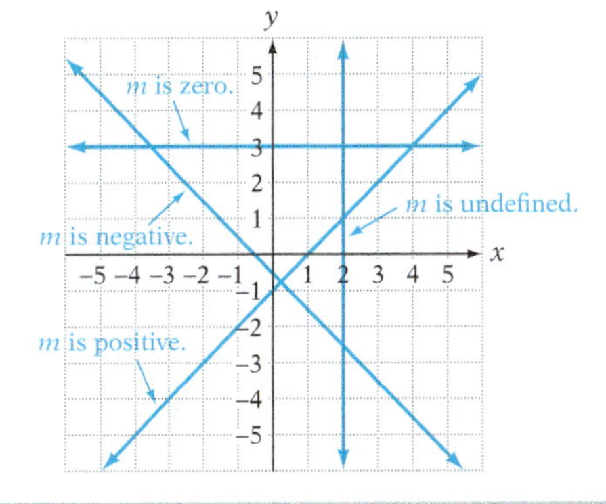

Essential Rules and Procedures

Examples

Function Notation [7.1D, p. 357]
The equation of a function is written in function notation when y is replaced by the symbol $f(x)$, where $f(x)$ is read "f of x" or "the value of f at x." To evaluate a function at a given value of x, replace x by the given value and then simplify the resulting numerical expression. This gives the value of $f(x)$.

$y = x^2 + 2x - 1$ is written in function notation as $f(x) = x^2 + 2x - 1$. To evaluate $f(x) = x^2 + 2x - 1$ at $x = -3$, find $f(-3)$.

$$\begin{aligned} f(-3) &= (-3)^2 + 2(-3) - 1 \\ &= 9 - 6 - 1 = 2 \end{aligned}$$

Horizontal and Vertical Lines [7.2B, p. 366]
The graph of $y = b$ is a horizontal line passing through $(0, b)$. The graph of $x = a$ is a vertical line passing through $(a, 0)$.

The graph of $y = -2$ is a horizontal line passing through $(0, -2)$. The graph of $x = 3$ is a vertical line passing through $(3, 0)$.

To find the x-intercept, let $y = 0$ and solve for x.
To find the y-intercept, let $x = 0$ and solve for y. [7.3A, p. 374]

To find the x-intercept of $4x - 5y = 20$, let $y = 0$ and solve for x. To find the y-intercept, let $x = 0$ and solve for y.

$$\begin{aligned} 4x - 5y &= 20 \\ 4x - 5(0) &= 20 \\ 4x &= 20 \\ x &= 5 \end{aligned} \qquad \begin{aligned} 4x - 5y &= 20 \\ 4(0) - 5y &= 20 \\ -5y &= 20 \\ y &= -4 \end{aligned}$$

The x-intercept is $(5, 0)$. The y-intercept is $(0, -4)$.

Slope Formula [7.3B, p. 375]
If $P_1(x_1, y_1)$ and $P_2(x_2, y_2)$ are two points on a line and $x_1 \neq x_2$, then

$$m = \frac{y_2 - y_1}{x_2 - x_1}$$

To find the slope of the line between the points $(1, -2)$ and $(-3, -1)$, let $P_1 = (1, -2)$ and $P_2 = (-3, -1)$. Then

$$m = \frac{y_2 - y_1}{x_2 - x_1} = \frac{-1 - (-2)}{-3 - 1} = \frac{1}{-4} = -\frac{1}{4}.$$

Parallel Lines [7.3B, p. 376]
Two nonvertical lines in the plane are parallel if and only if they have the same slope. Vertical lines in the plane are parallel.

The slope of the line through $P_1(3, -6)$ and $P_2(5, -10)$ is $m_1 = \frac{-10 - (-6)}{5 - 3} = -2$.
The slope of the line through $Q_1(4, -5)$ and $Q_2(0, 3)$ is $m_2 = \frac{3 - (-5)}{0 - 4} = -2$.
Because $m_1 = m_2$, the lines are parallel.

Perpendicular Lines [7.3B, p. 377]
Two nonvertical lines in the plane are perpendicular if and only if the product of their slopes is -1. A vertical and a horizontal line are perpendicular.

The slope of the line through $P_1(5, -3)$ and $P_2(2, -1)$ is $m_1 = \frac{-1 - (-3)}{2 - 5} = -\frac{2}{3}$.
The slope of the line through $Q_1(1, -4)$ and $Q_2(3, -1)$ is $m_2 = \frac{-1 - (-4)}{3 - 1} = \frac{3}{2}$.
Because $m_1 m_2 = \left(-\frac{2}{3}\right)\left(\frac{3}{2}\right) = -1$, the lines are perpendicular.

Slope-Intercept Form of a Linear Equation [7.3C, p. 378; 7.4A, p. 387]
An equation of the form $y = mx + b$ is called the slope-intercept form of a straight line. The slope of the line is m, the coefficient of x. The y-intercept is $(0, b)$, where b is the constant term of the equation.

For the line with equation $y = -3x + 2$, the slope is -3 and the y-intercept is $(0, 2)$.

Point-Slope Formula [7.4B, p. 388]
If (x_1, y_1) is a point on a line with slope m, then

$$y - y_1 = m(x - x_1)$$

The equation of the line that passes through the point $(5, -3)$ and has slope -2 is:

$$\begin{aligned} y - y_1 &= m(x - x_1) \\ y - (-3) &= -2(x - 5) \\ y + 3 &= -2x + 10 \\ y &= -2x + 7 \end{aligned}$$

CHAPTER 7 Review Exercises

1. a. Graph the ordered pairs $(-2, 4)$ and $(3, -2)$.
b. Name the abscissa of point A.
c. Name the ordinate of point B.

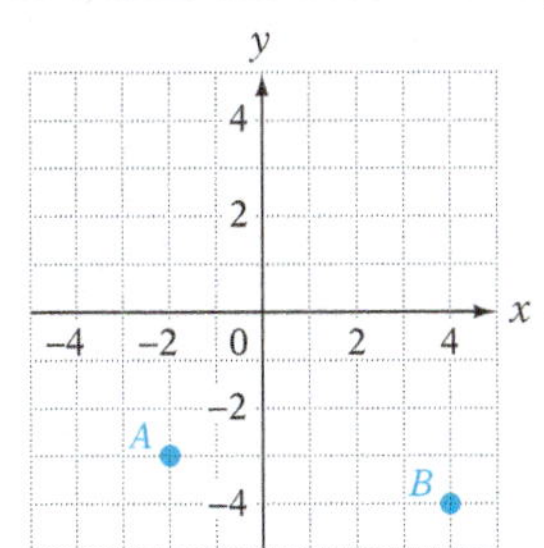

2. Graph the ordered-pair solutions of $y = -\frac{1}{2}x - 2$ when $x \in \{-4, -2, 0, 2\}$.

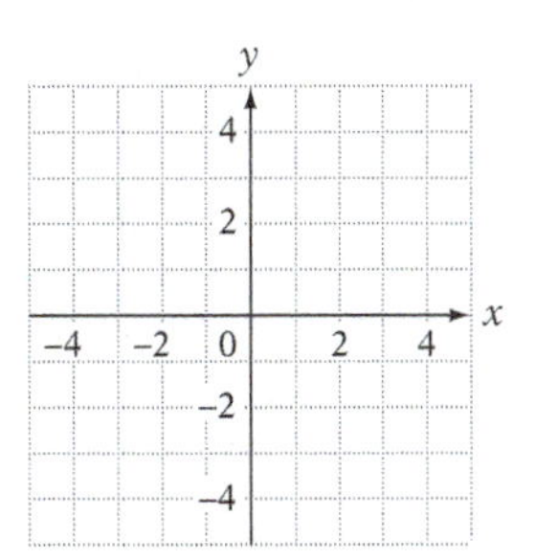

3. Determine the equation of the line that passes through the points $(-1, 3)$ and $(2, -5)$.

4. Determine the equation of the line that passes through the point $(6, 1)$ and has slope $-\frac{5}{2}$.

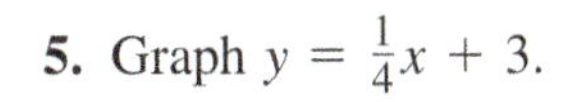

5. Graph $y = \frac{1}{4}x + 3$.

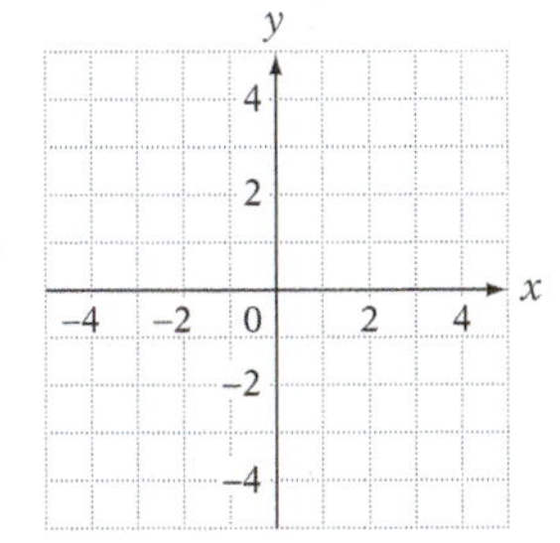

6. Graph $5x + 3y = 15$.

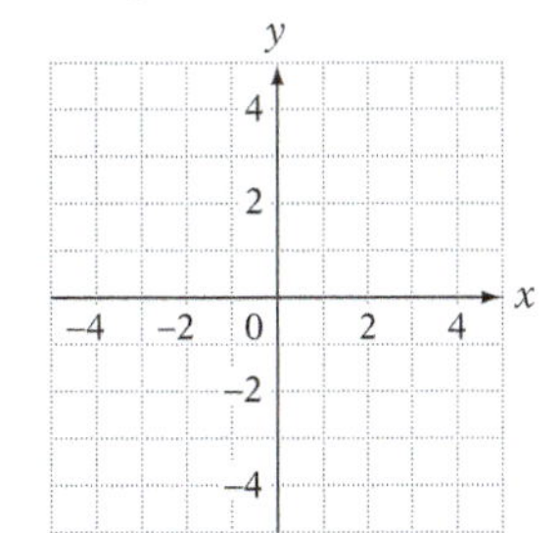

7. Is the line that passes through $(7, -5)$ and $(6, -1)$ parallel, perpendicular, or neither parallel nor perpendicular to the line that passes through $(4, 5)$ and $(2, -3)$?

8. Given $f(x) = x^2 - 2$, find $f(-1)$.

9. Does $y = -x + 3$, where $x \in \{-2, 0, 3, 5\}$, define y as a function of x?

10. Find the slope of the line containing the points $(9, 8)$ and $(-2, 1)$.

11. Find the x- and y-intercepts of $3x - 2y = 24$.

12. Find the slope of the line containing the points $(-2, -3)$ and $(4, -3)$.

13. Graph the line that has slope $\frac{1}{2}$ and y-intercept $(0, -1)$.

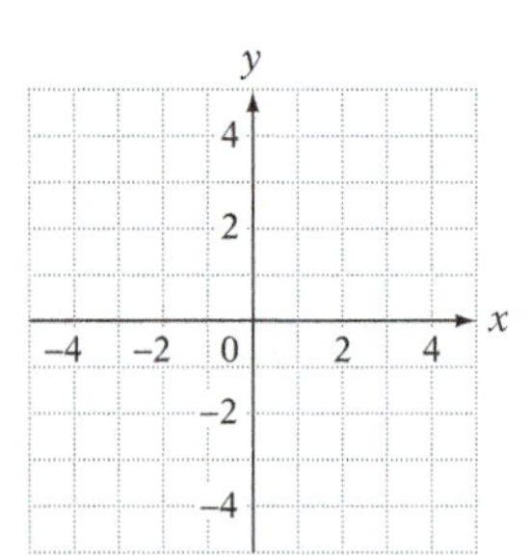

14. Graph $x = -3$.

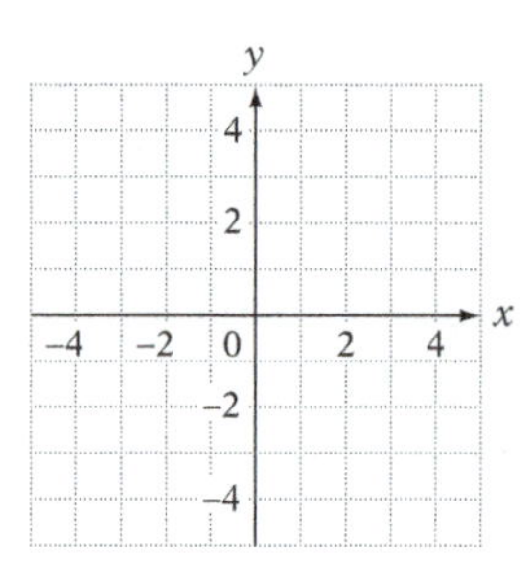

15. Graph the line that has slope $-\frac{2}{3}$ and y-intercept $(0, 2)$.

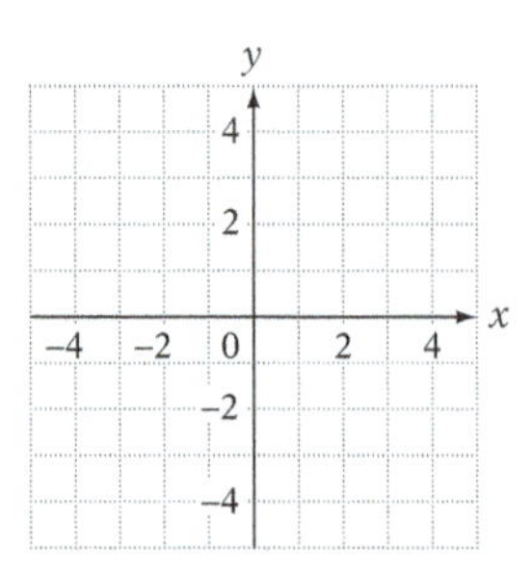

16. Graph $y = -2x - 1$.

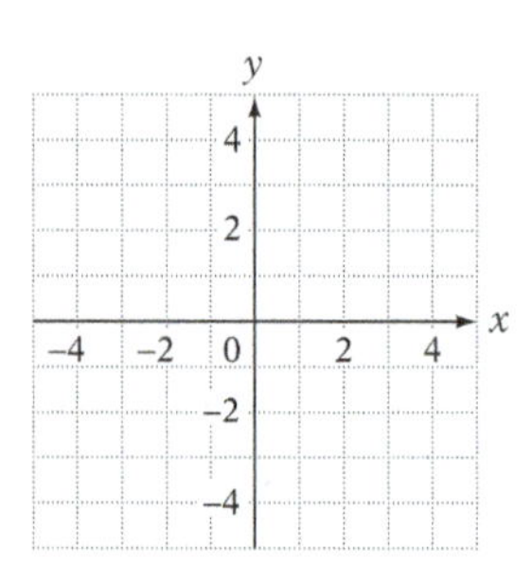

17. Graph the line that has slope 2 and y-intercept $(0, -4)$.

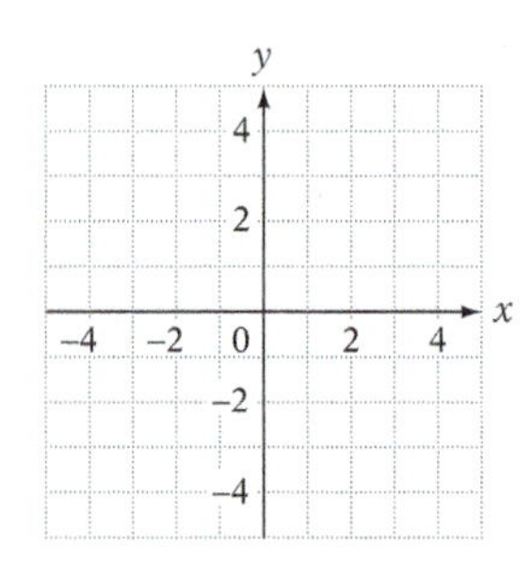

18. Graph $3x - 2y = -6$.

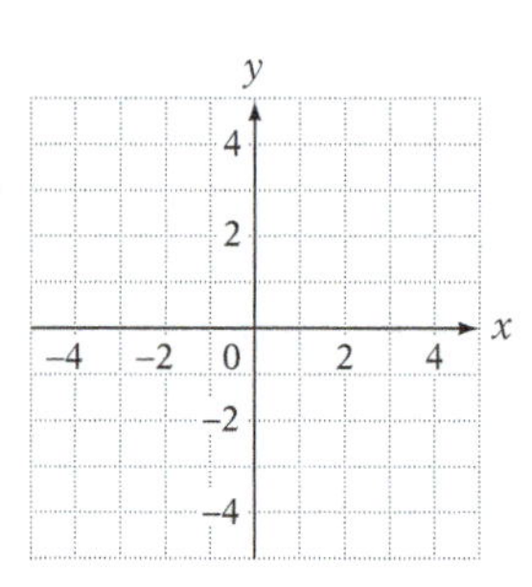

19. Health The heights and weights of eight seventh-grade students are shown in the following table. Write a relation in which the first coordinate is height in inches and the second coordinate is weight in pounds. Is the relation a function?

Height (in inches)	55	57	53	57	60	61	58	54
Weight (in pounds)	95	101	94	98	100	105	97	95

20. Business An online research service charges a monthly access fee of \$75 plus \$.45 per minute to use the service. An equation that represents the monthly cost to use this service is $C = 0.45x + 75$, where C is the monthly cost and x is the number of minutes of access used. Graph this equation for values of x from 0 to 100. The point $(50, 97.5)$ is on the graph. Write a sentence that describes the meaning of this ordered pair.

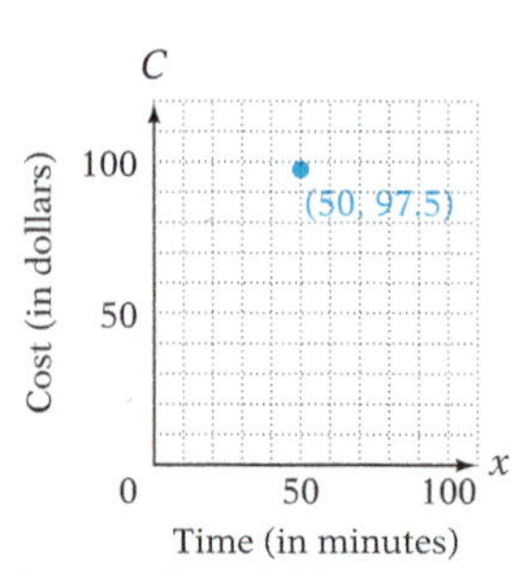

CHAPTER 7 TEST

1. Find the ordered-pair solution of $2x - 3y = 15$ corresponding to $x = 3$.

2. Graph the ordered-pair solutions of $y = -\frac{3}{2}x + 1$ when $x = -2, 0$, and 4.

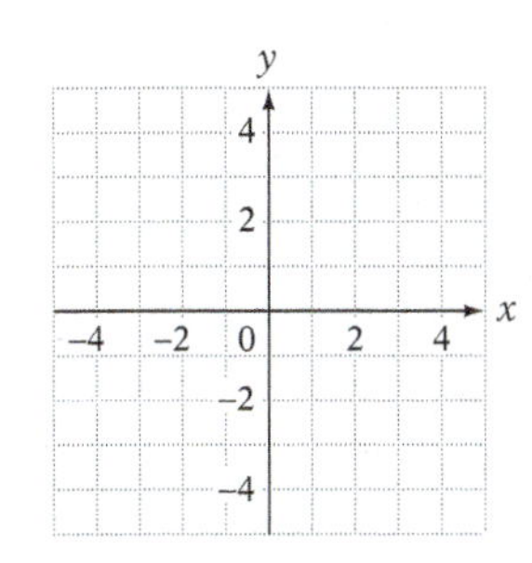

3. Does $y = \frac{1}{2}x - 3$ define y as a function of x for $x \in \{-2, 0, 4\}$?

4. Given $f(t) = t^2 + t$, find $f(2)$.

5. Given $f(x) = x^2 - 2x$, find $f(-1)$.

6. **Emergency Response** For seven homes, the distance of the house from a fire station and the amount of damage the house sustained in a fire are given in the following table. Write a relation in which the first coordinate of the ordered pair is the distance, in miles, from the fire station and the second coordinate is the amount of damage in thousands of dollars. Is the relation a function?

Distance (in miles)	3.5	4.0	5.2	5.0	4.0	6.3	5.4
Damage (in thousands of dollars)	25	30	45	38	42	12	34

7. Graph $y = 3x + 1$.

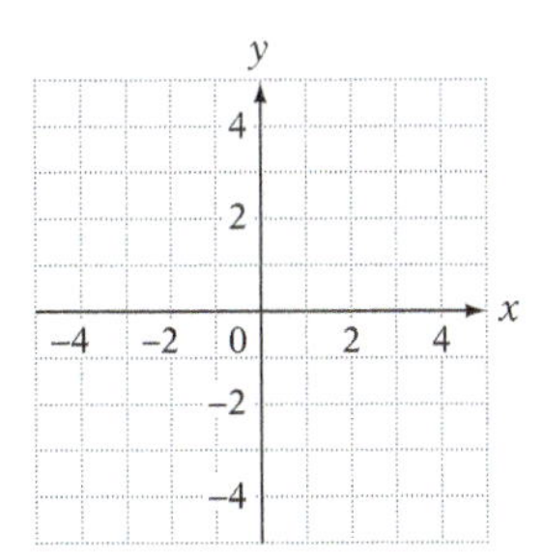

8. Graph $y = -\frac{3}{4}x + 3$.

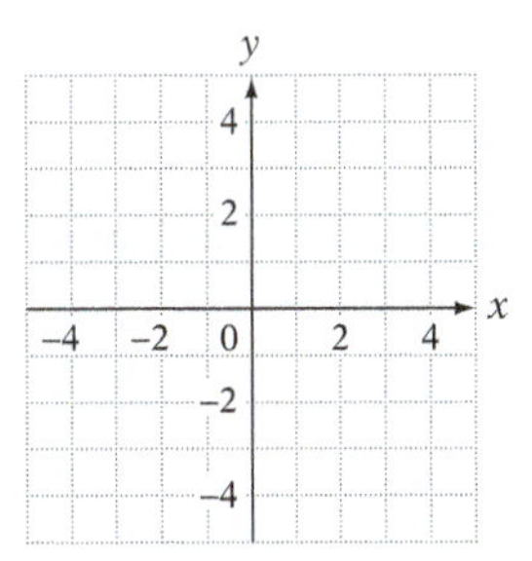

9. Graph $3x - 2y = 6$.

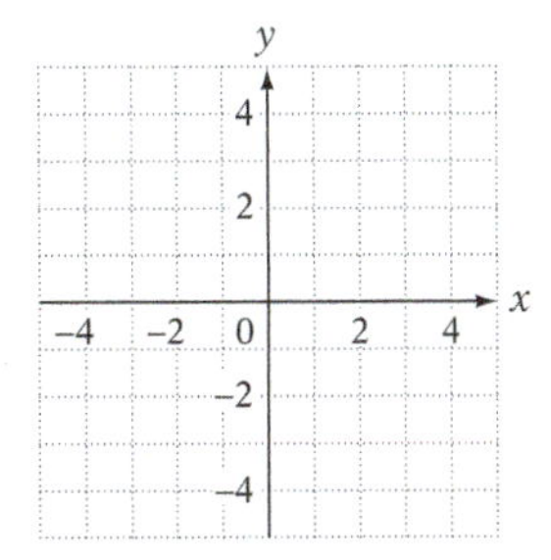

10. Graph $x + 3 = 0$.

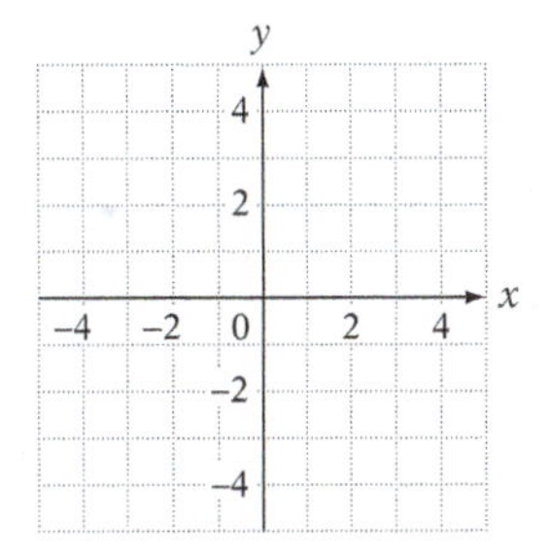

11. Graph the line that has slope $-\frac{2}{3}$ and y-intercept $(0, 4)$.

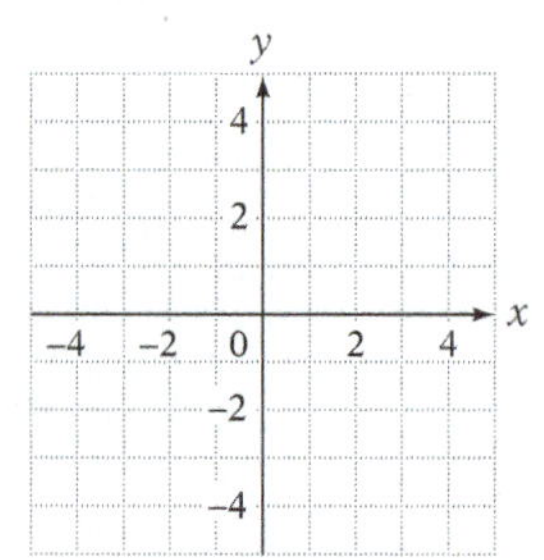

12. Graph the line that has slope 2 and y-intercept -2.

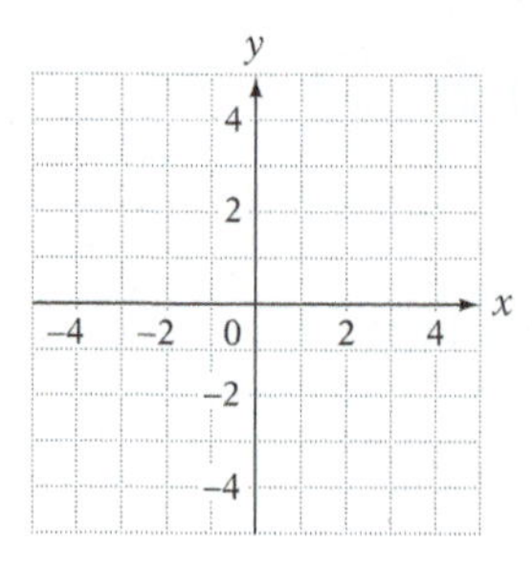

13. **Sports** The equation for the speed of a ball that is thrown straight up with an initial speed of 128 ft/s is $v = 128 - 32t$, where v is the speed of the ball after t seconds. Graph this equation for values of t from 0 to 4. The point whose coordinates are $(1, 96)$ is on the graph. Write a sentence that describes the meaning of this ordered pair.

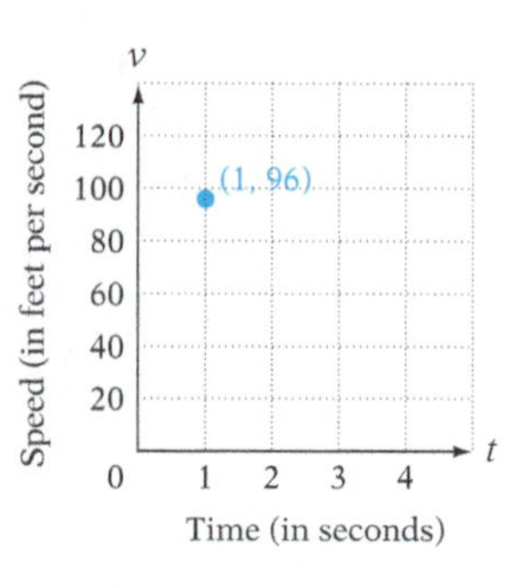

14. Find the x- and y-intercepts of $6x - 4y = 12$.

15. Find the x- and y-intercepts of $y = \frac{1}{2}x + 1$.

16. Find the slope of the line containing the points $(2, -3)$ and $(4, 1)$.

17. Is the line that passes through $(2, 5)$ and $(-1, 1)$ parallel, perpendicular, or neither parallel nor perpendicular to the line that passes through $(-2, 3)$ and $(4, 11)$?

18. Find the slope of the line containing the points $(-5, 2)$ and $(-5, 7)$.

19. Find the slope of the line whose equation is $2x + 3y = 6$.

20. Find the equation of the line that contains the point $(0, -1)$ and has slope 3.

21. Use the point-slope formula to find the equation of the line that contains the point $(-3, 1)$ and has slope $\frac{2}{3}$.

22. Find the equation of the line that passes through the points $(5, -4)$ and $(-3, 1)$.

23. Find the equation of the line that passes through the points $(-2, 0)$ and $(5, -2)$.

Cumulative Review Exercises

1. Simplify: $12 - 18 \div 3 \cdot (-2)^2$

2. Evaluate $\frac{a-b}{a^2-c}$ when $a = -2$, $b = 3$, and $c = -4$.

3. Given $f(x) = \frac{2}{x-1}$, find $f(-2)$.

4. Solve: $2x - \frac{2}{3} = \frac{7}{3}$

5. Solve: $3x - 2[x - 3(2 - 3x)] = x - 7$

6. Write $6\frac{2}{3}\%$ as a fraction.

7. Simplify: $(-2x^2y)^3(2xy^2)^2$

8. Simplify: $\frac{-15x^7}{5x^5}$

9. Divide: $(x^2 - 4x - 21) \div (x - 7)$

10. Factor: $5x^2 + 15x + 10$

11. Factor: $x(a + 2) + y(a + 2)$

12. Solve: $x(x - 2) = 8$

13. Multiply: $\frac{x^5y^3}{x^2 - x - 6} \cdot \frac{x^2 - 9}{x^2y^4}$

14. Subtract: $\frac{3x}{x^2 + 5x - 24} - \frac{9}{x^2 + 5x - 24}$

15. Solve: $3 - \frac{1}{x} = \frac{5}{x}$

16. Solve $4x - 5y = 15$ for y.

17. Find the ordered-pair solution of $y = 2x - 1$ corresponding to $x = -2$.

18. Find the slope of the line that contains the points $(2, 3)$ and $(-2, 3)$.

19. Find the equation of the line that contains the point $(2, -1)$ and has slope $\frac{1}{2}$.

20. Find the equation of the line that contains the point $(0, 2)$ and has slope -3.

21. Use the point-slope formula to find the equation of the line that contains the point $(-1, 0)$ and has slope 2.

22. Use the point-slope formula to find the equation of the line that contains the point $(6, 1)$ and has slope $\frac{2}{3}$.

23. Business A suit that regularly sells for $89 is on sale for 30% off the regular price. Find the sale price.

24. Geometry The measure of the first angle of a triangle is 3° more than the measure of the second angle. The measure of the third angle is 5° more than twice the measure of the second angle. Find the measure of each angle.

25. Taxes The real estate tax on a home that costs $500,000 is $6250. At this rate, what is the value of a home for which the real estate tax is $13,750?

26. Business An electrician requires 6 h to wire a garage. An apprentice can do the same job in 10 h. How long would it take to wire the garage if both the electrician and the apprentice worked together?

27. Graph $y = \frac{1}{2}x - 1$.

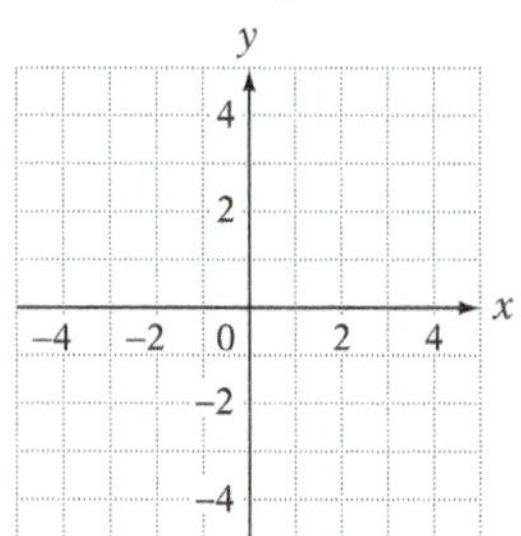

28. Graph the line that has slope $-\frac{2}{3}$ and y-intercept 2.

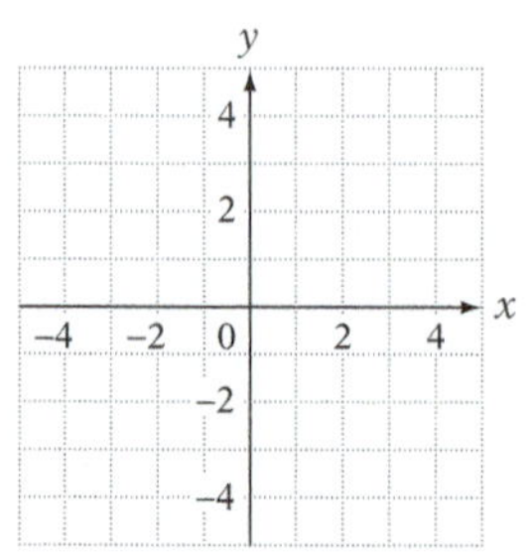

Systems of Linear Equations

8

OBJECTIVES

SECTION 8.1

A To solve a system of linear equations by graphing

SECTION 8.2

A To solve a system of linear equations by the substitution method

B To solve investment problems

SECTION 8.3

A To solve a system of linear equations by the addition method

SECTION 8.4

A To solve rate-of-wind or rate-of-current problems

B To solve application problems using two variables

Focus on Success

What resources do you use when you need help in this course? You know to read and reread the text when you are having difficulty understanding a concept. Instructors are available to help you during their office hours. Most schools have a math center where students can get help. Some schools have a tutoring program. You might also ask a student who has been successful in this class for assistance. (See Habits of Successful Students, page AIM-6.)

Monkey Business Images/Shutterstock.com

Prep Test

Are you ready to succeed in this chapter? Take the Prep Test below to find out if you are ready to learn the new material.

1. Solve $3x - 4y = 24$ for y.

2. Solve: $50 + 0.07x = 0.05(x + 1400)$

3. Simplify: $-3(2x - 7y) + 3(2x + 4y)$

4. Simplify: $4x + 2(3x - 5)$

5. Is $(-4, 2)$ a solution of $3x - 5y = -22$?

6. Find the x- and y-intercepts of $3x - 4y = 12$.

7. Are the graphs of $3x + y = 6$ and $y = -3x - 4$ parallel?

8. Graph: $y = \frac{5}{4}x - 2$

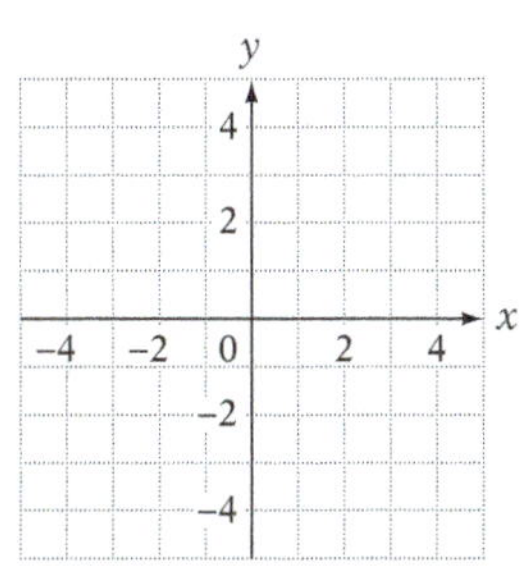

9. **Pharmacology** A pharmacist has 20 ml of an 80% acetic acid solution. How many milliliters of a 55% acetic acid solution should be mixed with the 20-milliliter solution to produce a solution that is 75% acetic acid?

10. **Hiking** One hiker starts along a trail walking at 3 mph. One-half hour later, another hiker starts on the same walking trail at a speed of 4 mph. How long after the second hiker starts will the two hikers be side-by-side?

SECTION

8.1 Solving Systems of Linear Equations by Graphing

OBJECTIVE A *To solve a system of linear equations by graphing*

Two or more equations considered together are called a **system of equations.** Three examples of *linear* systems of equations in *two* variables are shown below, along with the graphs of the equations of each system.

System I	System II	System III
$x - 2y = -8$	$4x + 2y = 6$	$4x + 6y = 12$
$2x + 5y = 11$	$y = -2x + 3$	$6x + 9y = -9$

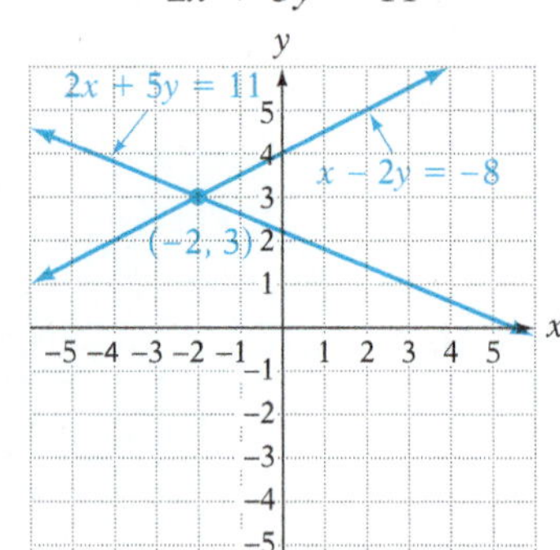

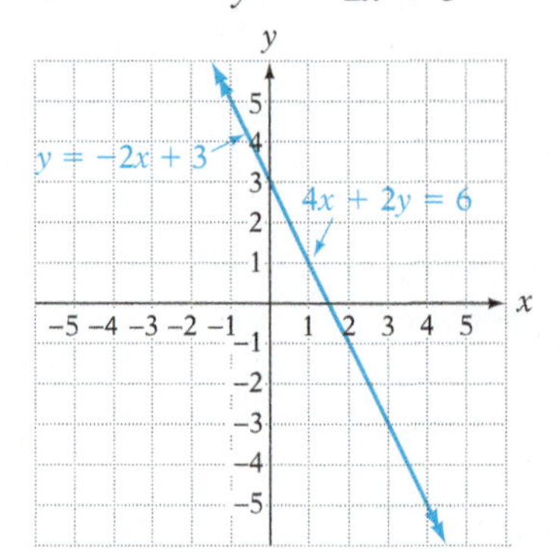

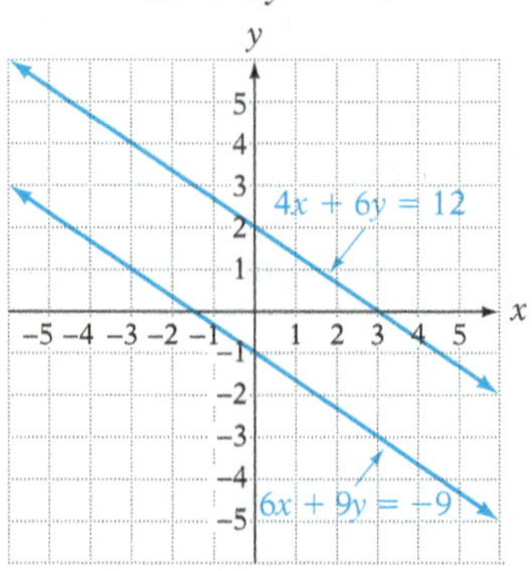

Take Note

The systems of equations above are called *linear systems of equations* because each of the equations in the system has a graph that is a line. Also, each equation has two variables. In future math courses, you will study equations that contain more than two variables.

For system I, the two lines intersect at a single point, $(-2, 3)$. Because this point lies on both lines, it is a solution of each equation of the system of equations. We can check this by replacing x by -2 and y by 3. The check is shown below.

$$\begin{array}{r|l} \multicolumn{2}{c}{x - 2y = -8} \\ \hline -2 - 2(3) & -8 \\ -2 - 6 & -8 \\ -8 = & -8 \checkmark \end{array} \qquad \begin{array}{r|l} \multicolumn{2}{c}{2x + 5y = 11} \\ \hline 2(-2) + 5(3) & 11 \\ -4 + 15 & 11 \\ 11 = & 11 \checkmark \end{array}$$

• Replace x by -2 and replace y by 3.

A **solution of a system of equations in two variables** is an ordered pair that is a solution of each equation of the system. The ordered pair $(-2, 3)$ is a solution of system I.

HOW TO 1 Is $(-1, 4)$ a solution of the system of equations? $\begin{array}{l} 7x + 3y = 5 \\ 3x - 2y = 12 \end{array}$

$$\begin{array}{r|l} \multicolumn{2}{c}{7x + 3y = 5} \\ \hline 7(-1) + 3(4) & 5 \\ -7 + 12 & 5 \\ 5 = & 5 \checkmark \end{array} \qquad \begin{array}{r|l} \multicolumn{2}{c}{3x - 2y = 12} \\ \hline 3(-1) - 2(4) & 12 \\ -3 - 8 & 12 \\ -11 \neq & 12 \end{array}$$

• Replace x by -1 and replace y by 4.

• Does not check

Because $(-1, 4)$ is not a solution of both equations, $(-1, 4)$ is not a solution of the system of equations.

Using the system of equations above and the graph at the right, note that the graph of the ordered pair $(-1, 4)$ lies on the graph of $7x + 3y = 5$ but not on *both* lines. The ordered pair $(-1, 4)$ is *not* a solution of the system of equations. The graph of the ordered pair $(2, -3)$ does lie on both lines, and therefore the ordered pair $(2, -3)$ is a solution of the system of equations.

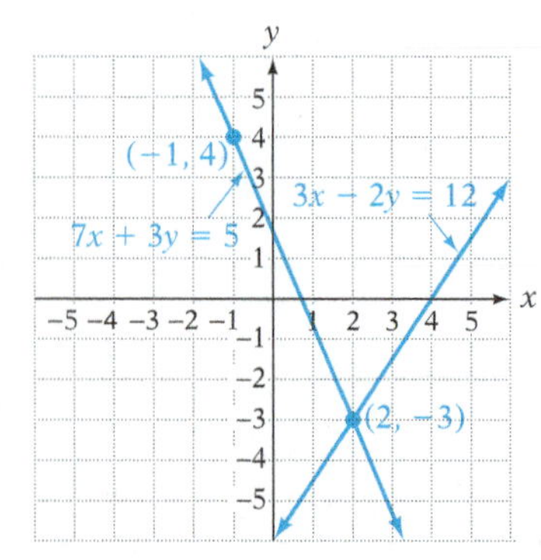

Take Note

The fact that there are an infinite number of ordered pairs that are solutions of the system at the right does not mean that *every* ordered pair is a solution. For instance, (0, 3), (−2, 7), and (2, −1) are solutions. However, (3, 1), (−1, 4), and (1, 6) are not solutions. You should verify these statements.

System II from the preceding page and the graph of the equations of that system are shown again at the right. Note that the graph of $y = -2x + 3$ lies directly on top of the graph of $4x + 2y = 6$. Thus the two lines intersect at an infinite number of points. Because the graphs intersect at an infinite number of points, there are an infinite number of solutions of this system of equations. Because each equation represents the same set of points, the solutions of the system of equations can be stated by using the ordered-pair solutions of either one of the equations. Therefore, we can say, "The solutions are the ordered pairs that satisfy $4x + 2y = 6$," or we can say "The solutions are the ordered pairs that satisfy $y = -2x + 3$."

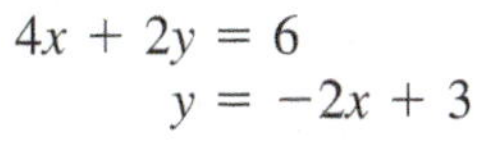

$$4x + 2y = 6$$
$$y = -2x + 3$$

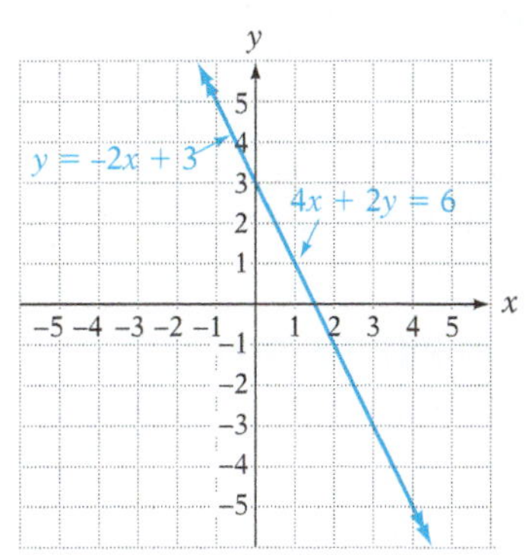

System III from the preceding page and the graph of the equations of that system are shown again at the right. Note that in this case, the graphs of the lines are parallel and do not intersect. Because the graphs do not intersect, there is no point that is on both lines. Therefore, the system of equations has no solution.

$$4x + 6y = 12$$
$$6x + 9y = -9$$

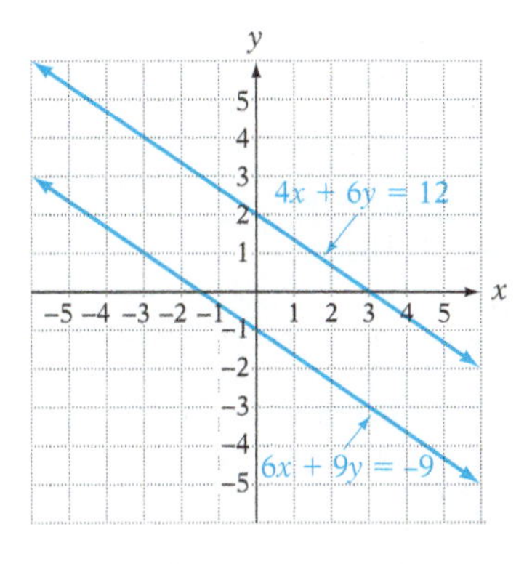

The preceding examples illustrate three types of systems of linear equations. An **independent system** has exactly one solution—the graphs intersect at one point. A **dependent system** has an infinite number of solutions—the graphs are the same line. An **inconsistent system** has no solution—the graphs are parallel lines.

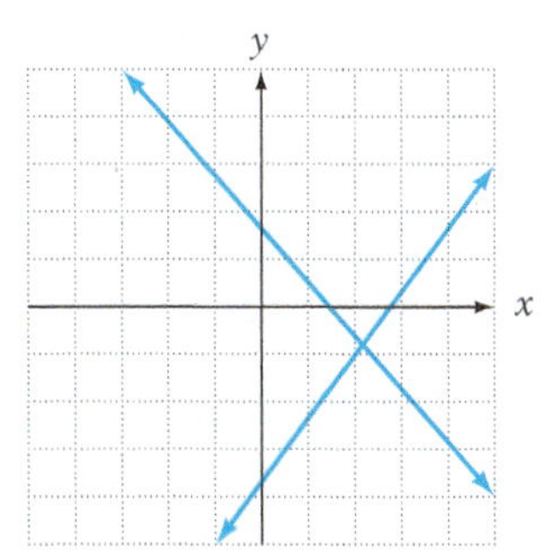

Independent system: one solution

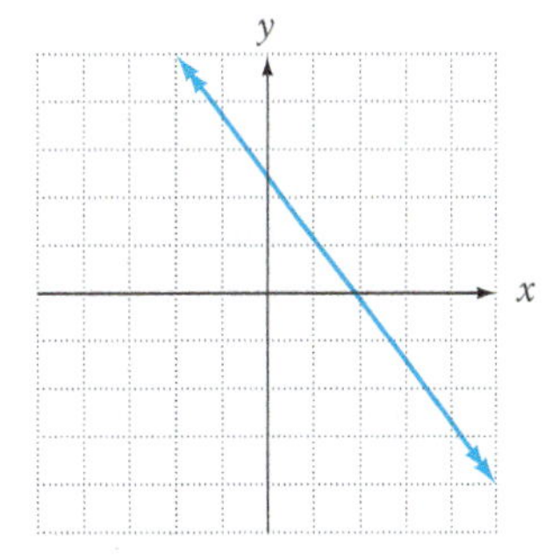

Dependent system: infinitely many solutions

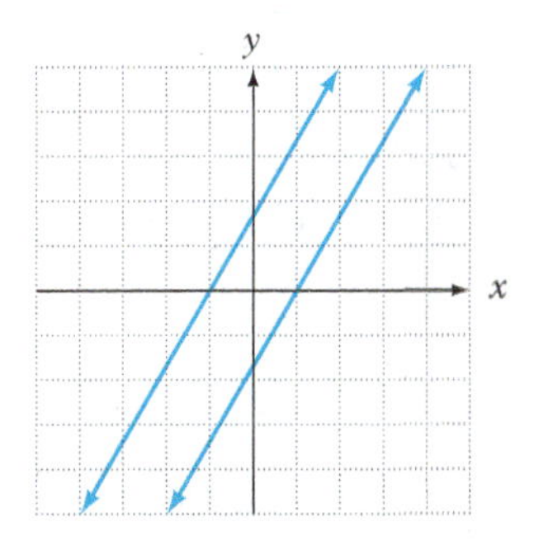

Inconsistent system: no solution

HOW TO 2 The graphs of the equations in the system of equations below are shown at the right. What is the solution of the system of equations?

$$2x + 3y = 6$$
$$2x + y = -2$$

The graphs intersect at $(-3, 4)$. This is an *independent* system of equations. The solution of the system of equations is $(-3, 4)$.

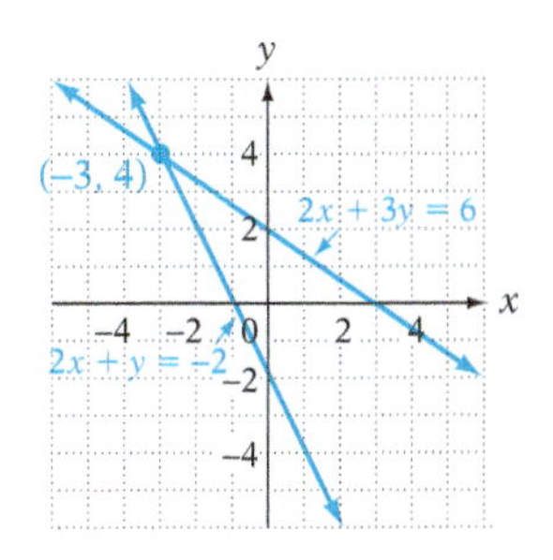

Take Note

Because both equations represent the same set of ordered pairs, we can also say that the solutions of the system of equations are the ordered pairs that satisfy $x = \frac{1}{2}y + 1$.

Either answer is correct.

HOW TO 3 The graphs of the equations in the system of equations at the right are shown below. What is the solution of the system of equations?

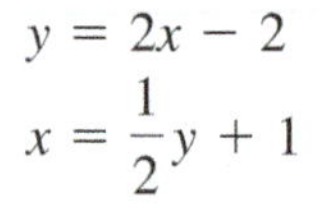

$$y = 2x - 2$$
$$x = \frac{1}{2}y + 1$$

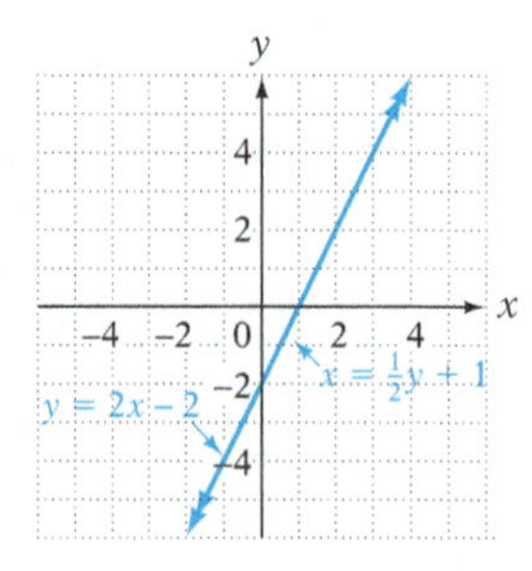

The two graphs lie directly on top of one another. Thus the two lines intersect at an infinite number of points, and the system of equations has an infinite number of solutions. This is a *dependent* system of equations. The solutions of the system of equations are the ordered pairs that satisfy $y = 2x - 2$.

Integrating Technology

The Projects or Group Activities feature at the end of Section 8.4 discusses how to use a calculator to approximate the solution of an independent system of equations. Also see the Keystroke Guide: *Intersect*.

Solving a system of equations means finding the ordered-pair solutions of the system. One way to do this is to draw the graphs of the equations in the system of equations and then determine where the graphs intersect.

To solve a system of linear equations in two variables by graphing, graph each equation on the same coordinate system, and then determine the point of intersection.

HOW TO 4 Solve by graphing: $2x - y = -1$
$x + 2y = 7$

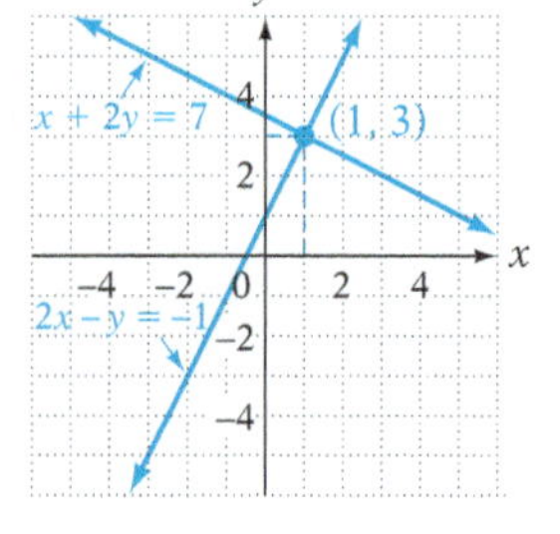

Graph each line.

The point of intersection of the two graphs lies on both lines and is therefore the solution of the system of equations.

The system of equations is independent. The ordered pair $(1, 3)$ is a solution of each equation.

The solution is $(1, 3)$.

HOW TO 5 Solve by graphing: $y = 2x + 2$
$4x - 2y = 4$

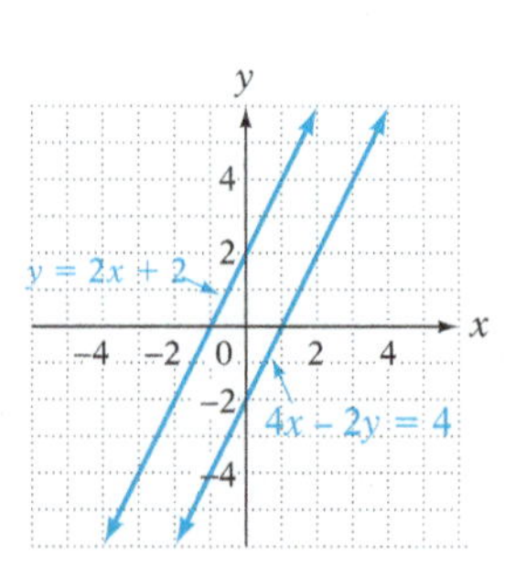

Graph each line.

The graphs do not intersect. The system of equations is inconsistent.

The system of equations has no solution.

EXAMPLE 1

Is $(1, -3)$ a solution of the following system?

$$3x + 2y = -3$$
$$x - 3y = 6$$

Solution

Replace x by 1 and y by -3.

$3x + 2y = -3$	
$3 \cdot 1 + 2(-3)$	-3
$3 + (-6)$	-3
$-3 = -3$	

$x - 3y = 6$	
$1 - 3(-3)$	6
$1 - (-9)$	6
$10 \neq 6$	

No, $(1, -3)$ is not a solution of the system of equations.

YOU TRY IT 1

Is $(-1, -2)$ a solution of the following system?

$$2x - 5y = 8$$
$$-x + 3y = -5$$

Your solution

EXAMPLE 2

Solve by graphing:

$$x - 2y = 2$$
$$x + y = 5$$

Solution

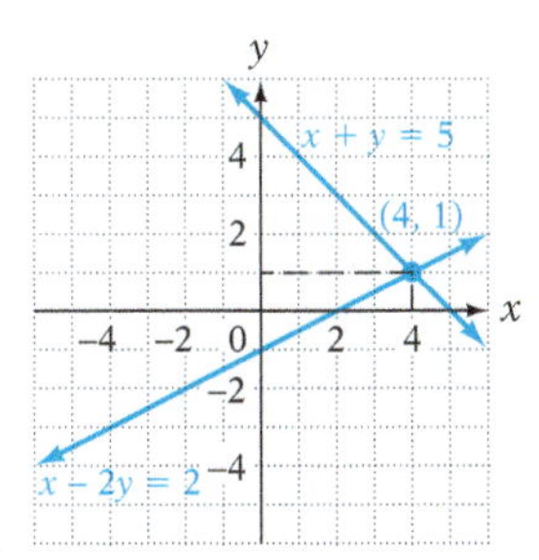

The solution is $(4, 1)$.

YOU TRY IT 2

Solve by graphing:

$$x + 3y = 3$$
$$-x + y = 5$$

Your solution

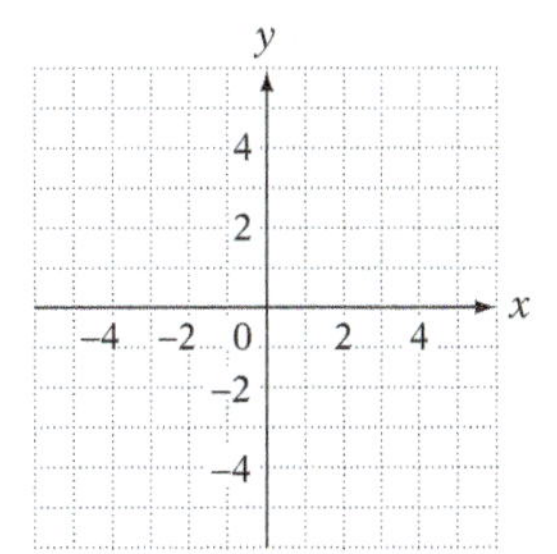

EXAMPLE 3

Solve by graphing:

$$4x - 2y = 6$$
$$y = 2x - 3$$

Solution

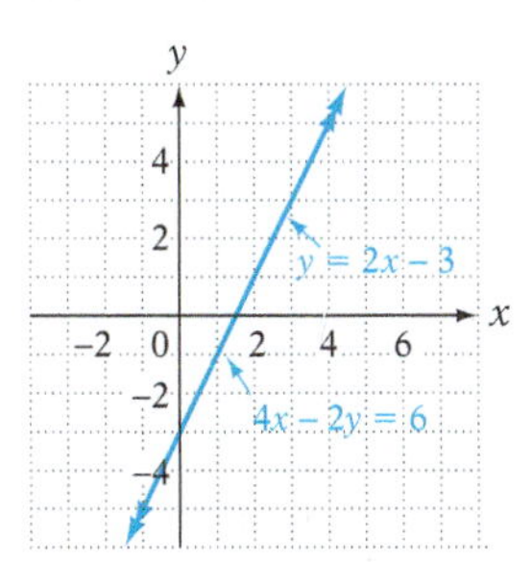

The solutions are the ordered pairs that satisfy the equation $y = 2x - 3$.

YOU TRY IT 3

Solve by graphing:

$$y = 3x - 1$$
$$6x - 2y = -6$$

Your solution

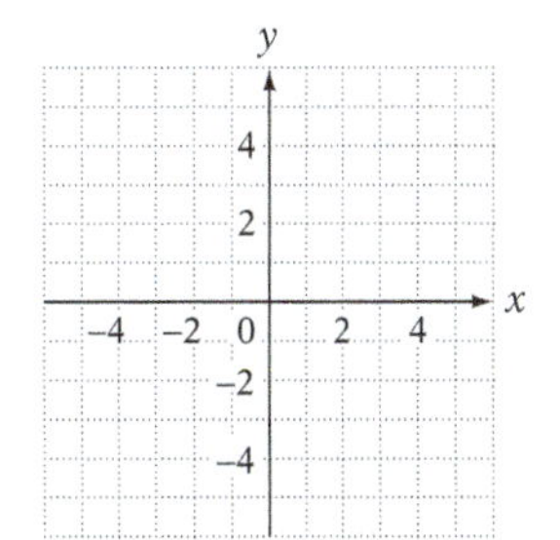

Solutions on pp. S19–S20

8.1 EXERCISES

Concept Check

Determine whether the statement is always true, sometimes true, or never true.

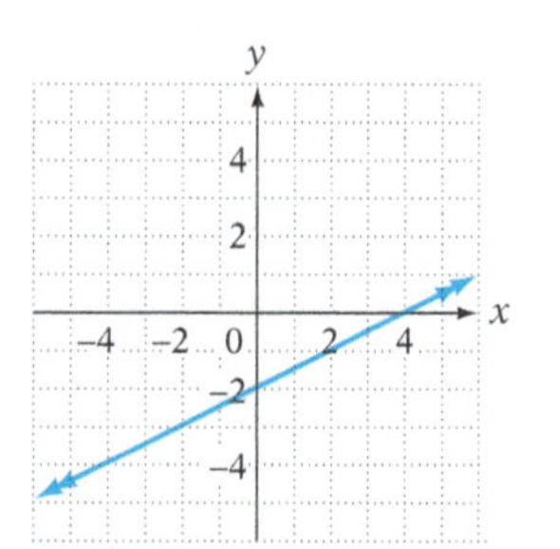

1. A solution of a system of linear equations in two variables is an ordered pair (x, y).
2. Graphically, the solution of an independent system of linear equations in two variables is the point of intersection of the graphs of the two equations.
3. The system of two linear equations graphed at the right has no solution.
4. An independent system of equations has no solution.

OBJECTIVE A *To solve a system of linear equations by graphing*

5. Is (2, 3) a solution of $\begin{aligned} 3x + 4y &= 18 \\ 2x - y &= 1 \end{aligned}$?

6. Is (2, −1) a solution of $\begin{aligned} x - 2y &= 4 \\ 2x + y &= 3 \end{aligned}$?

7. Is (4, 3) a solution of $\begin{aligned} 5x - 2y &= 14 \\ x + y &= 8 \end{aligned}$?

8. Is (2, 5) a solution of $\begin{aligned} 3x + 2y &= 16 \\ 2x - 3y &= 4 \end{aligned}$?

9. Is (2, −3) a solution of $\begin{aligned} y &= 2x - 7 \\ 3x - y &= 9 \end{aligned}$?

10. Is (−1, −2) a solution of $\begin{aligned} 3x - 4y &= 5 \\ y &= x - 1 \end{aligned}$?

11. Is (0, 0) a solution of $\begin{aligned} 3x + 4y &= 0 \\ y &= x \end{aligned}$?

12. Is (3, −4) a solution of $\begin{aligned} 5x - 2y &= 23 \\ 2x - 5y &= 25 \end{aligned}$?

For Exercises 13 to 16, identify the system of equations represented by the graph as **(i)** independent, **(ii)** dependent, or **(iii)** inconsistent.

13.

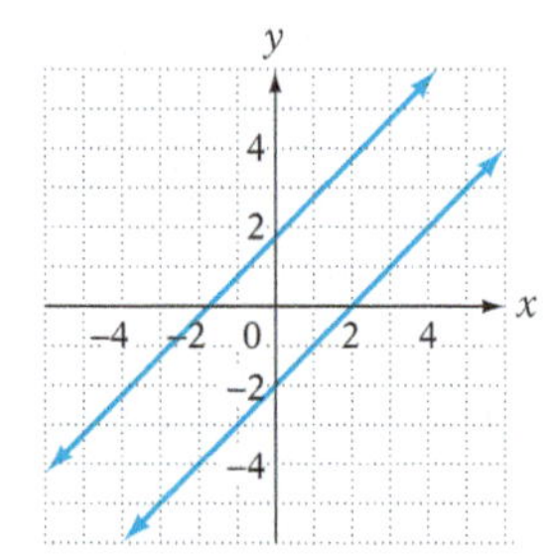

14.

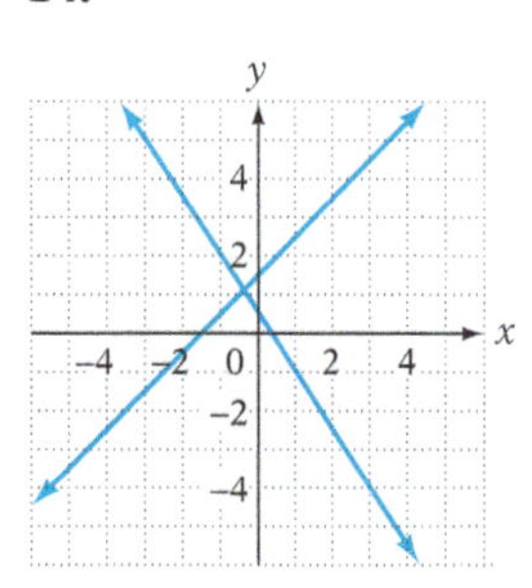

15.

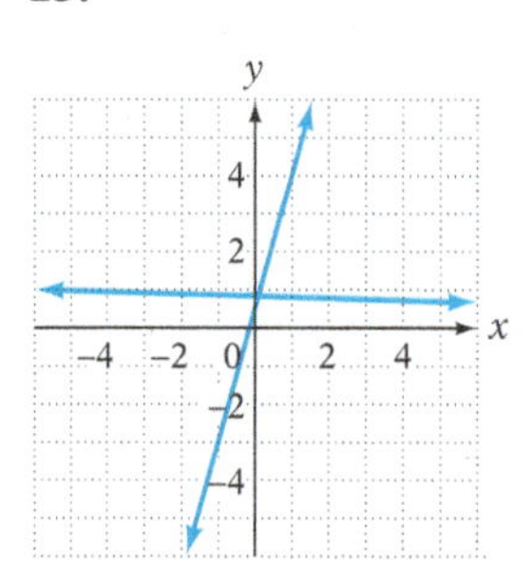

16.

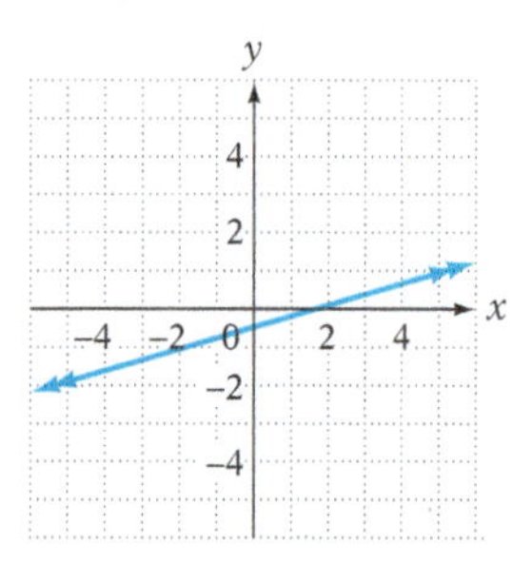

For Exercises 17 to 22, use the graphs of the equations of the system of equations to find the solution of the system of equations.

17.

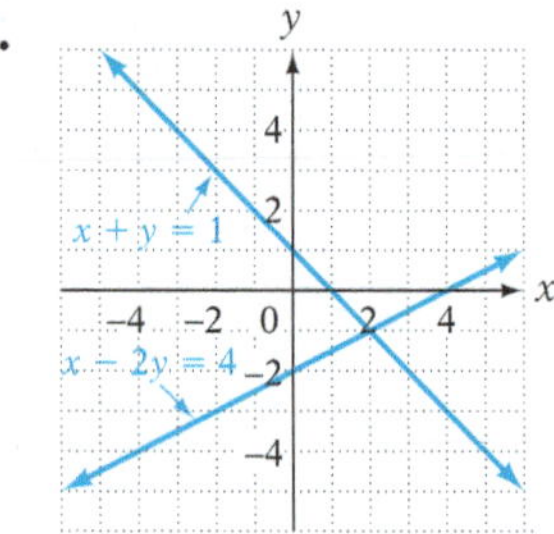

18.

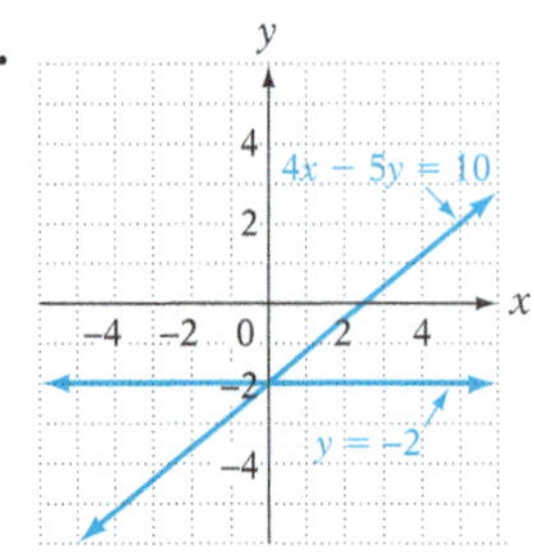

19.

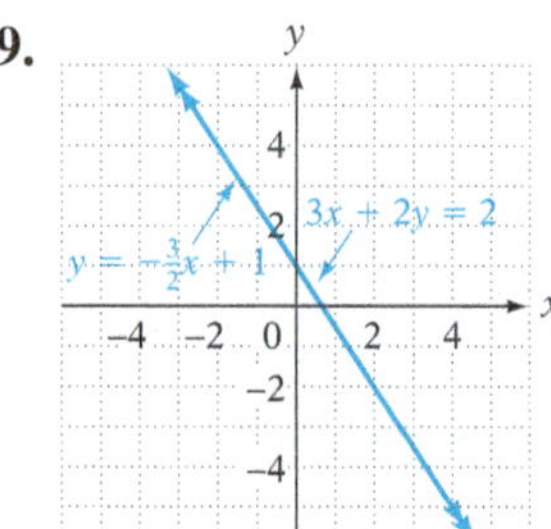

20.

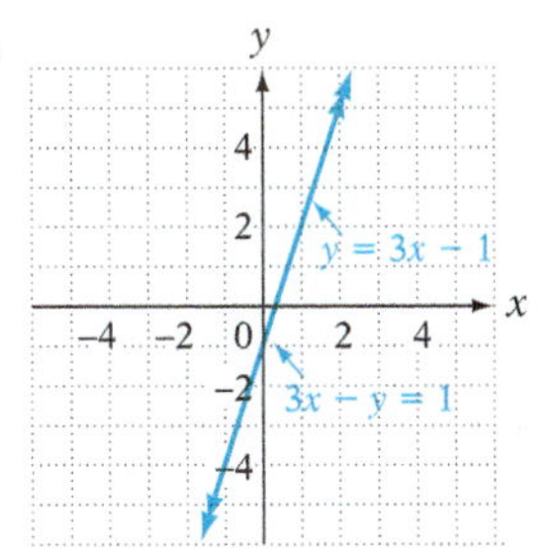

21.

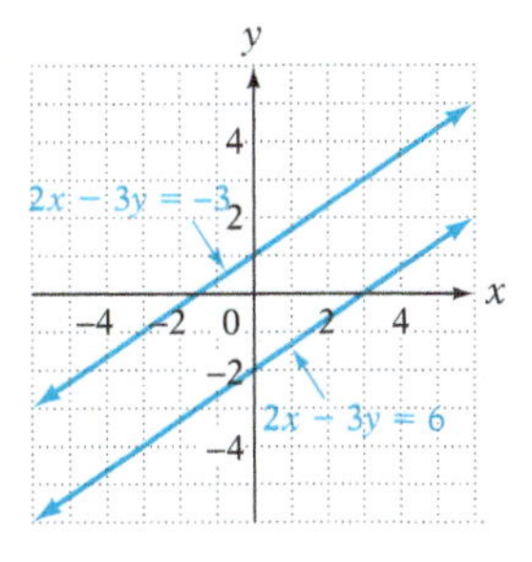

22.

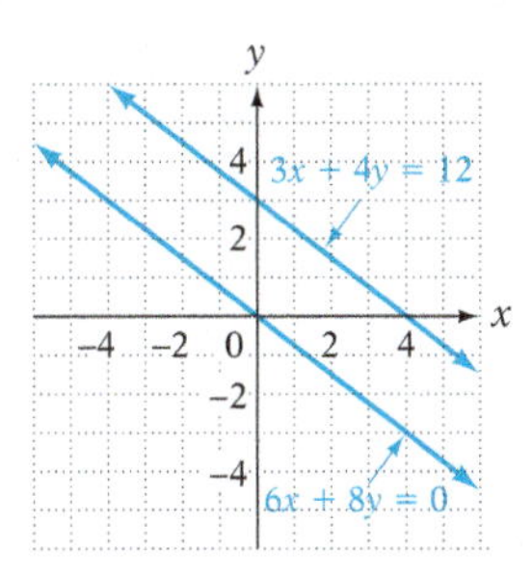

For Exercises 23 to 41, solve by graphing.

23. $2x - y = 4$
$x + y = 5$

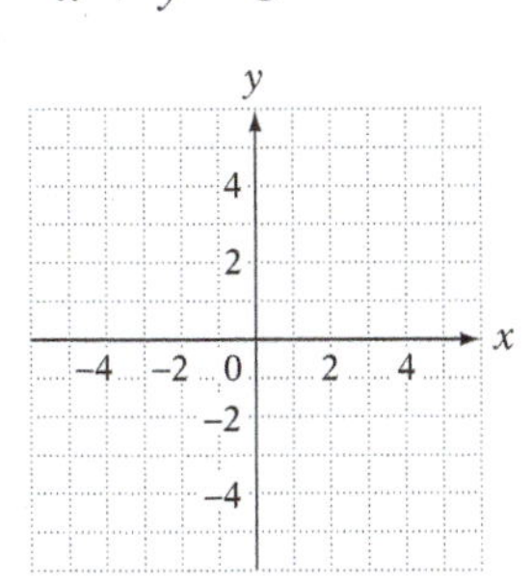

24. $x + 2y = 6$
$x - y = 3$

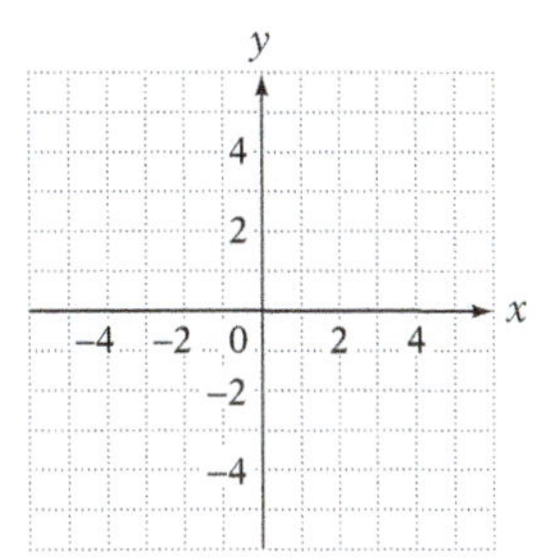

25. $3x - y = 3$
$2x + y = 2$

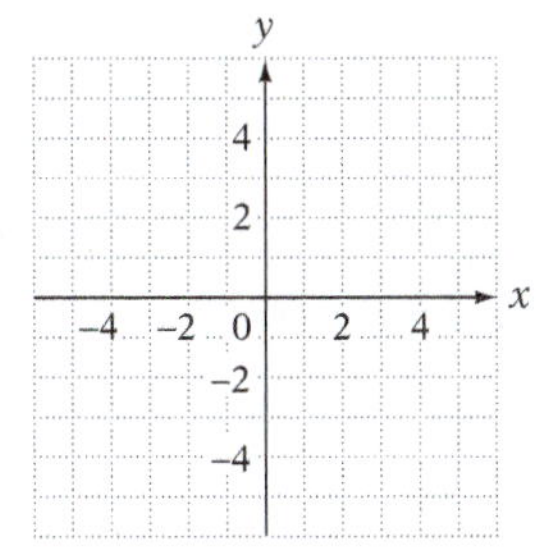

26. $3x - 2y = 6$
$y = 3$

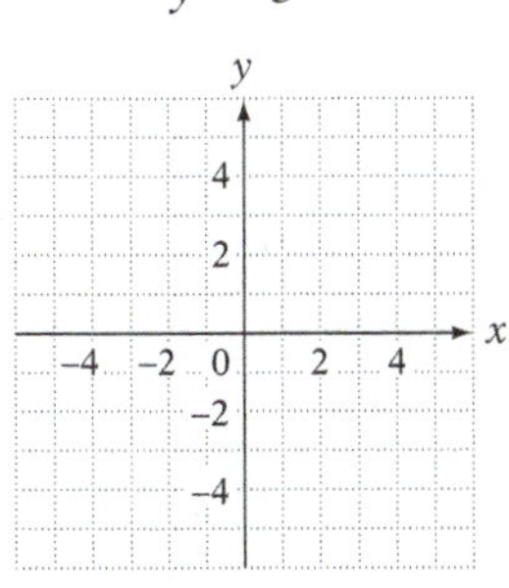

27. $x = 2$
$3x + 2y = 4$

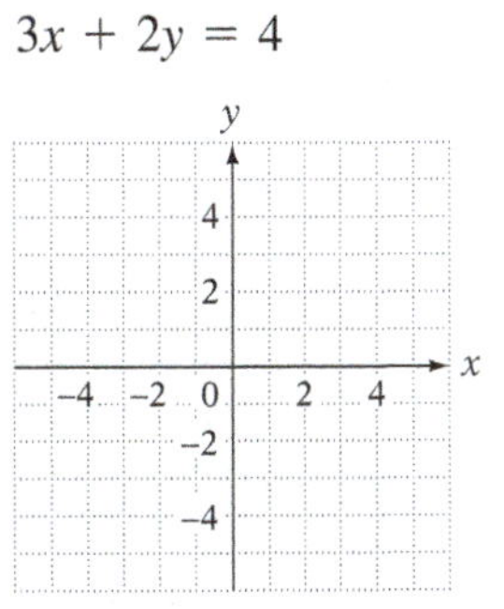

28. $x = 3$
$y = -2$

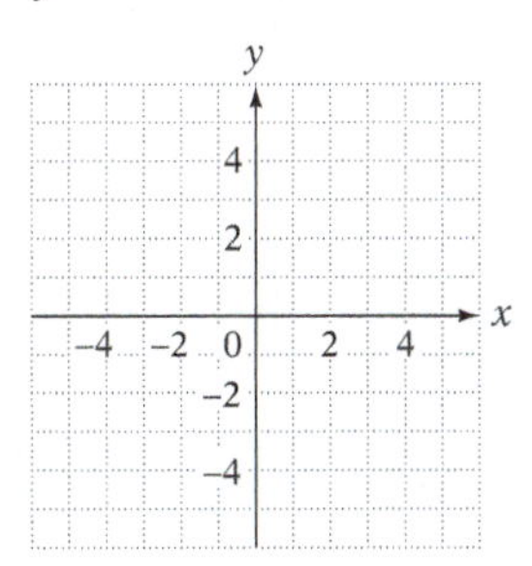

29. $x + 1 = 0$
$y - 3 = 0$

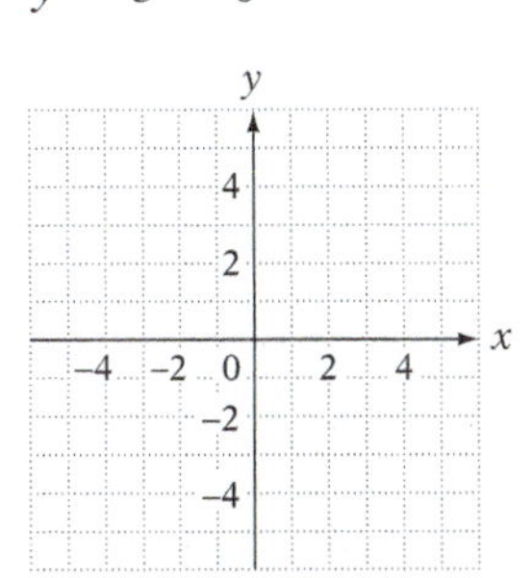

30. $y = 2x - 6$
$x + y = 0$

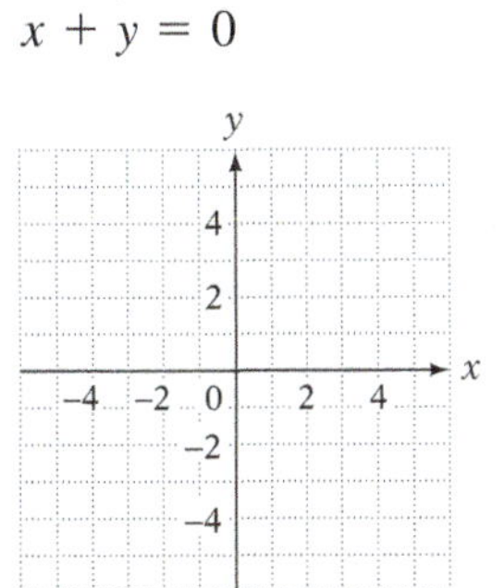

31. $5x - 2y = 11$
$y = 2x - 5$

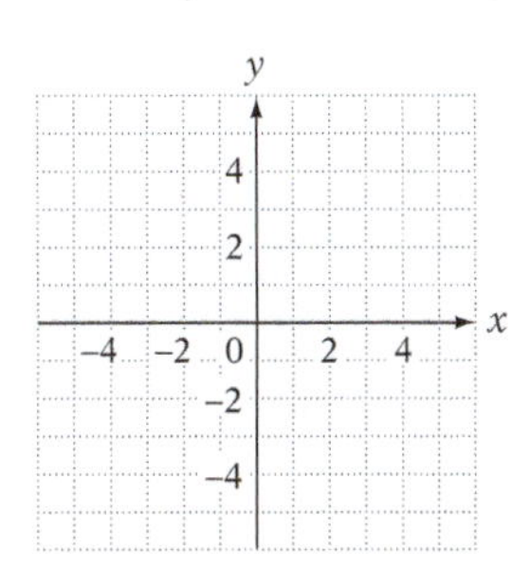

32. $2x + y = -2$
$6x + 3y = 6$

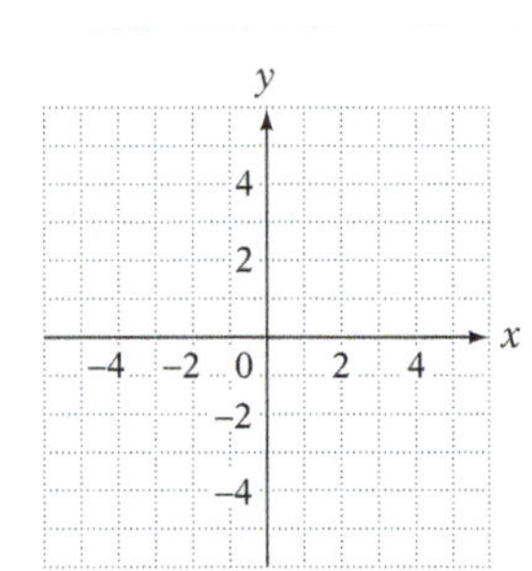

33. $x + y = 5$
$3x + 3y = 6$

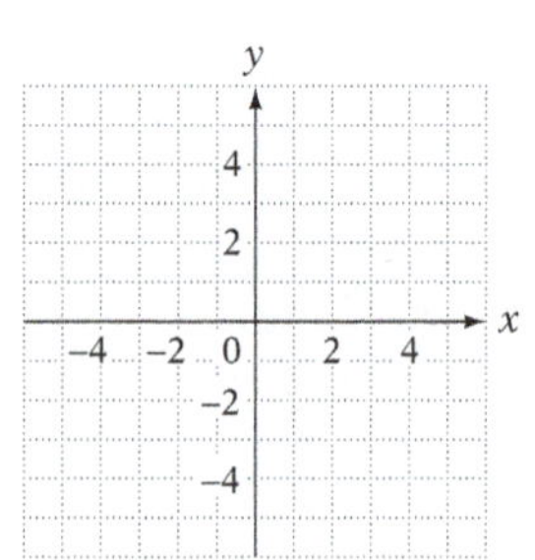

34. $y = 2x - 2$
$4x - 2y = 4$

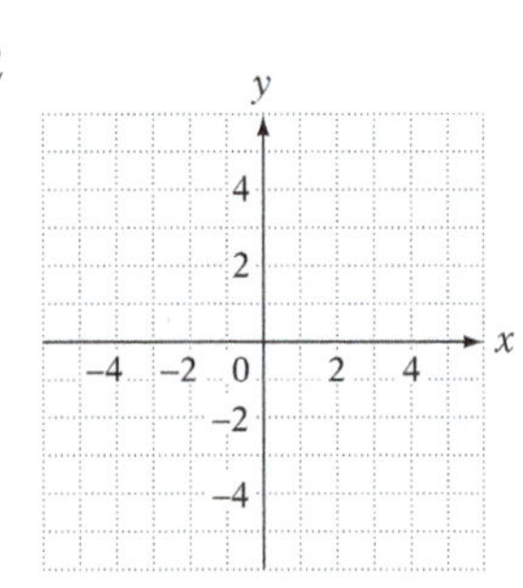

35. $y = -\frac{1}{3}x + 1$
$2x + 6y = 6$

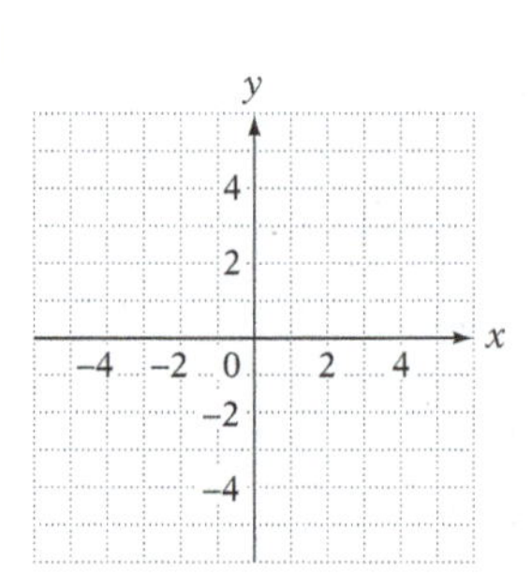

36. $x - y = 5$
$2x - y = 6$

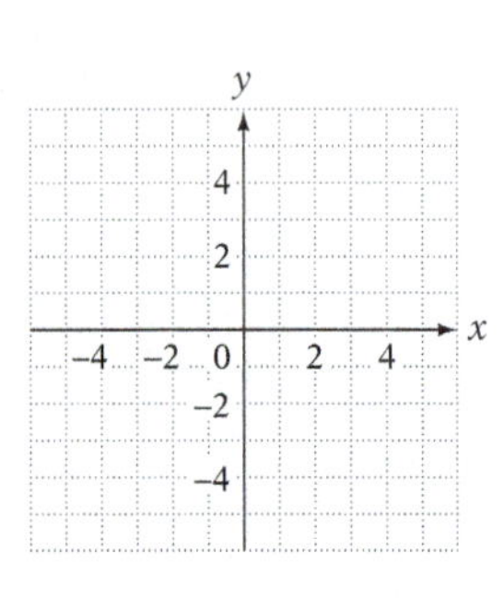

37. $5x - 2y = 10$
$3x + 2y = 6$

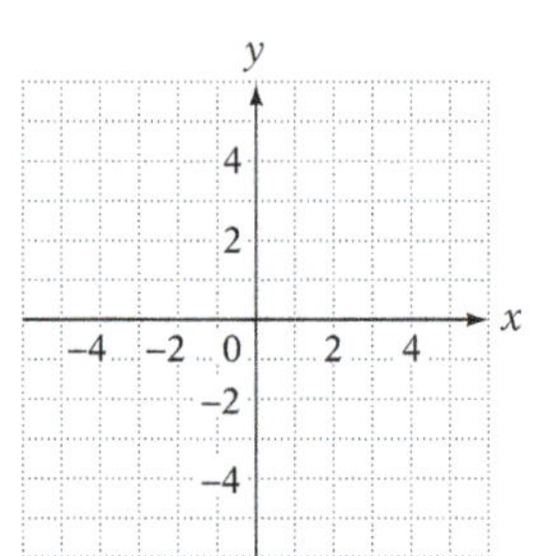

38. $3x + 4y = 0$
$2x - 5y = 0$

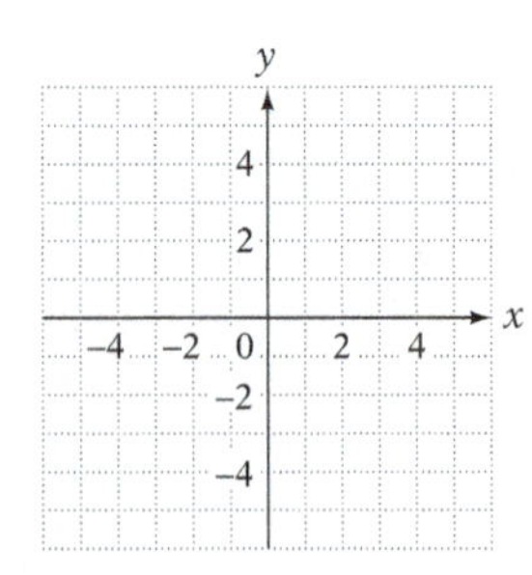

39. $2x - 3y = 0$
$y = -\frac{1}{3}x$

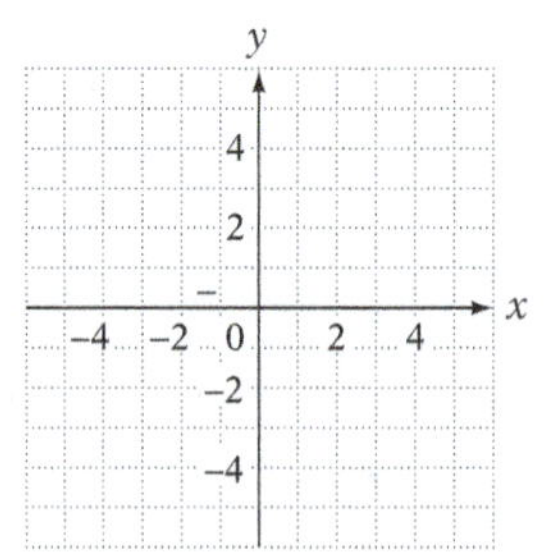

40. $x - 3y = 3$
$2x - 6y = 12$

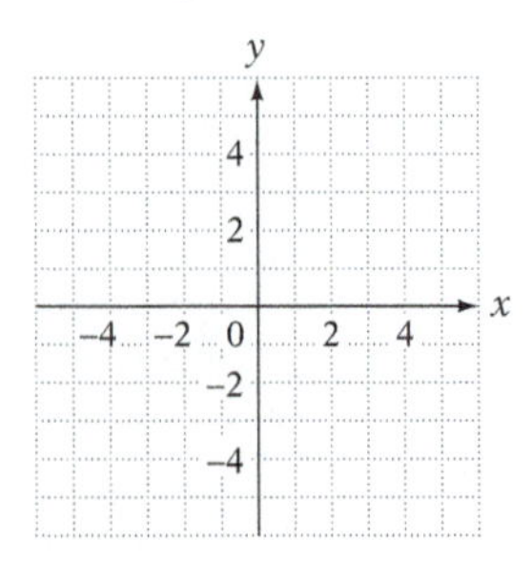

41. $4x + 6y = 12$
$6x + 9y = 18$

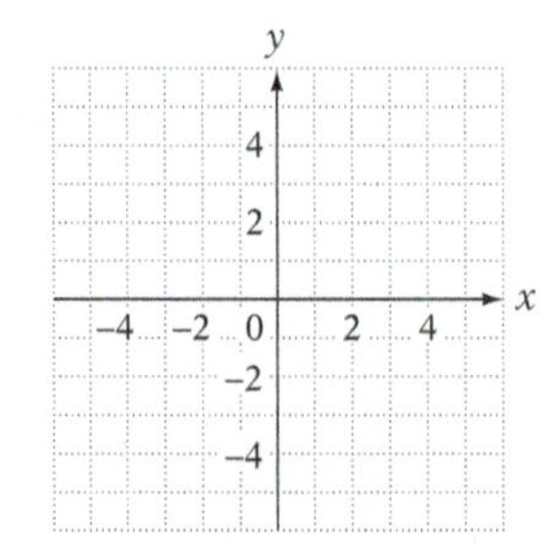

For Exercises 42 and 43, A, B, C, and D are nonzero real numbers. State whether the system of equations is independent, inconsistent, or dependent.

42. $y = Ax + B$
$y = Ax + C, B \neq C$

43. $x = C$
$y = D$

Critical Thinking

For Exercises 44 to 47, write a system of equations given the graph.

44.

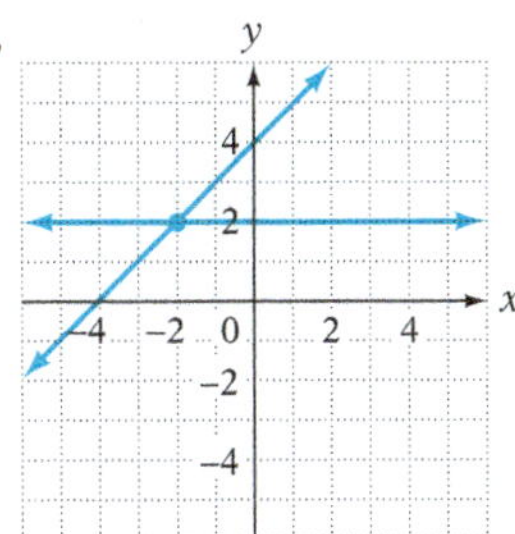

45.

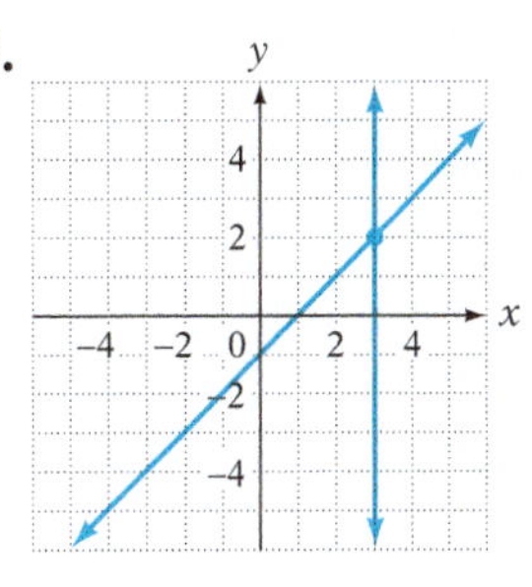

46.

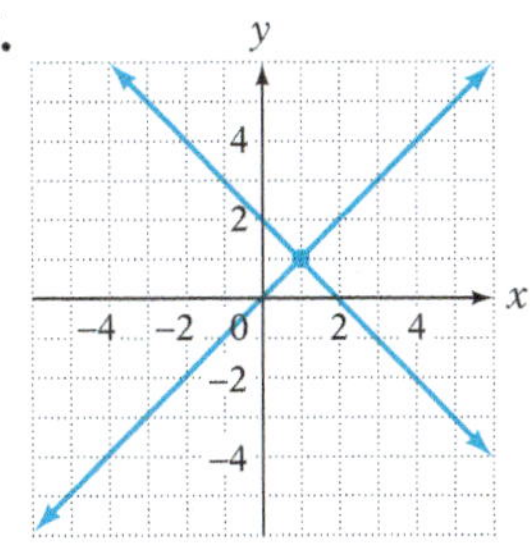

47.

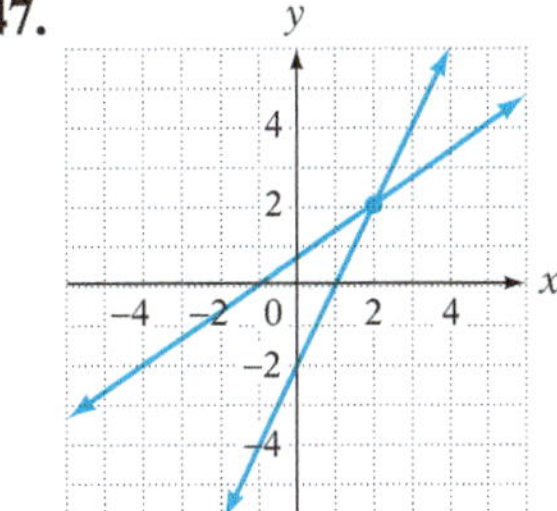

Projects or Group Activities

48. Match each system of equations with its graph.

a. $2x - 3y = 6$
$2x - 5y = 10$

b. $3x - y = -5$
$x + y = 1$

c. $x + 2y = 10$
$y = x + 2$

d. $y = -3x + 5$
$y = 2x - 5$

i.

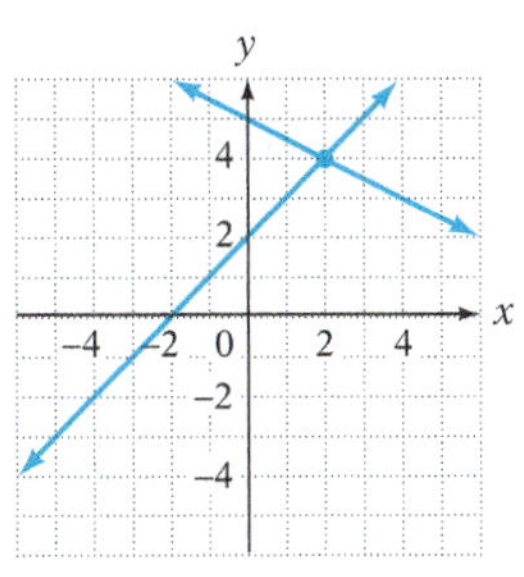

ii.

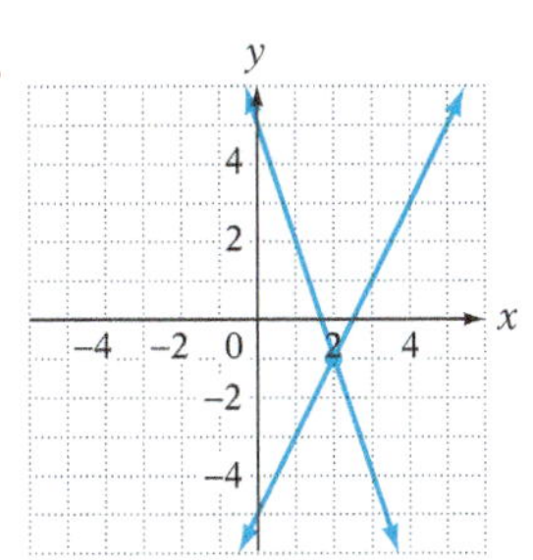

iii.

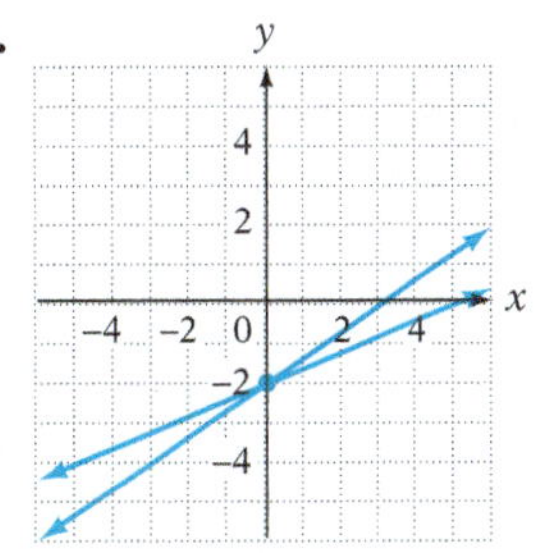

iv.

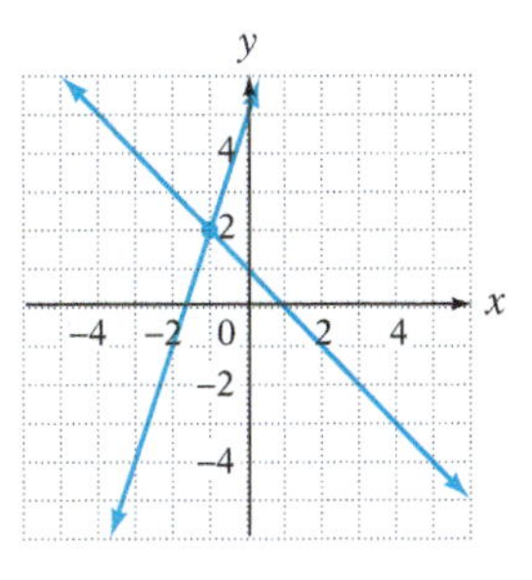

49. Write three different systems of equations: **a.** one that has $(-3, 5)$ as its only solution, **b.** one for which there is no solution, and **c.** one that is a dependent system of equations.

SECTION

8.2 Solving Systems of Linear Equations by the Substitution Method

OBJECTIVE A *To solve a system of linear equations by the substitution method*

A graphical solution of a system of equations is found by approximating the coordinates of a point of intersection. Algebraic methods can be used to find an exact solution of a system of equations. The **substitution method** can be used to eliminate one of the variables in one of the equations so that we have one equation in one unknown.

HOW TO 1 Solve by the substitution method:

$$(1)\quad 2x + 5y = -11$$
$$(2)\quad y = 3x - 9$$

Equation (2) states that $y = 3x - 9$. Substitute $3x - 9$ for y in Equation (1). Then solve for x.

$$2x + 5y = -11 \quad \text{• This is Equation (1).}$$
$$2x + 5(3x - 9) = -11 \quad \text{• From Equation (2), substitute } 3x - 9 \text{ for } y.$$
$$2x + 15x - 45 = -11 \quad \text{• Solve for } x.$$
$$17x - 45 = -11$$
$$17x = 34$$
$$x = 2$$

Now substitute the value of x into Equation (2) and solve for y.

$$y = 3x - 9 \quad \text{• This is Equation (2).}$$
$$y = 3(2) - 9 \quad \text{• Substitute 2 for } x.$$
$$y = 6 - 9 = -3$$

The solution is the ordered pair $(2, -3)$.

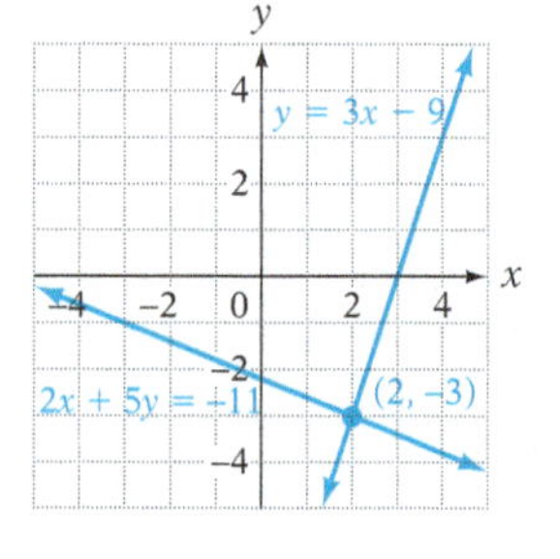

The graph of the system of equations given in HOW TO 1 is shown at the right. Note that the lines intersect at the point whose coordinates are $(2, -3)$, which is the algebraic solution we determined by the substitution method.

When solving a system of equations by the substitution method, we may first need to solve one of the equations in the system for one of its variables. For instance, the first step in solving the system of equations

$$(1)\quad x + 2y = -3$$
$$(2)\quad 2x - 3y = 5$$

is to solve one equation of the system for one of its variables. Either equation can be used.

Solving Equation (1) for x:

$$x + 2y = -3$$
$$x = -2y - 3$$

Solving Equation (2) for x:

$$2x - 3y = 5$$
$$2x = 3y + 5$$
$$x = \frac{3y + 5}{2} = \frac{3}{2}y + \frac{5}{2}$$

Because solving Equation (1) for x does not result in fractions, it is the easier of the two equations to use.

Here is the solution of the system of equations given on the preceding page.

HOW TO 2 Solve by the substitution method: (1) $x + 2y = -3$
(2) $2x - 3y = 5$

To use the substitution method, we must solve one equation of the system for one of its variables. We will use Equation (1) because solving it for x does not result in fractions.

$$x + 2y = -3$$

(3) $x = -2y - 3$ • **Solve Equation (1) for x. This is Equation (3).**

Now substitute $-2y - 3$ for x in Equation (2) and solve for y.

$$2x - 3y = 5$$ • **This is Equation (2).**

$$2(-2y - 3) - 3y = 5$$ • **From Equation (3), substitute $-2y - 3$ for x.**

$$-4y - 6 - 3y = 5$$ • **Solve for y.**

$$-7y - 6 = 5$$

$$-7y = 11$$

$$y = -\frac{11}{7}$$

Substitute the value of y into Equation (3) and solve for x.

$$x = -2y - 3$$ • **This is Equation (3).**

$$= -2\left(-\frac{11}{7}\right) - 3$$ • **Substitute $-\frac{11}{7}$ for y.**

$$= \frac{22}{7} - 3 = \frac{22}{7} - \frac{21}{7} = \frac{1}{7}$$

The solution is $\left(\frac{1}{7}, -\frac{11}{7}\right)$.

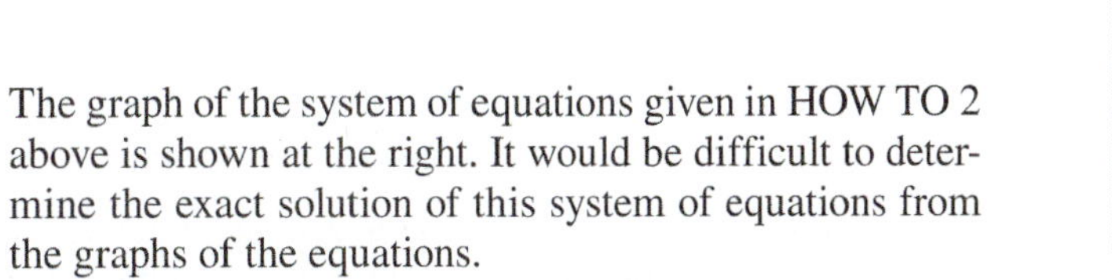

The graph of the system of equations given in HOW TO 2 above is shown at the right. It would be difficult to determine the exact solution of this system of equations from the graphs of the equations.

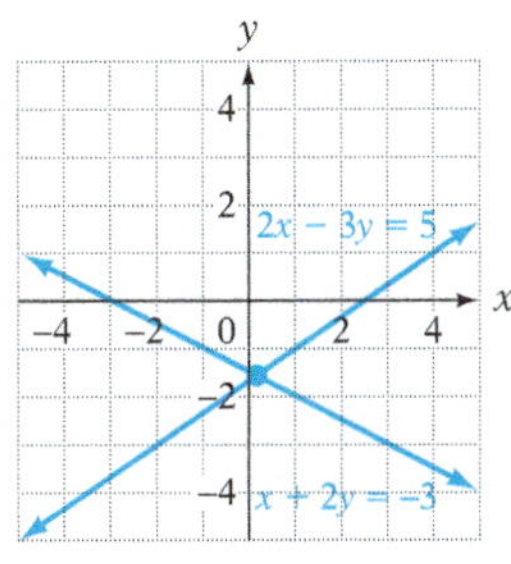

HOW TO 3 Solve by the substitution method: (1) $y = 3x - 1$
(2) $y = -2x - 6$

$$y = -2x - 6$$

$$3x - 1 = -2x - 6$$ • **Substitute $3x - 1$ for y in Equation (2).**

$$5x = -5$$ • **Solve for x.**

$$x = -1$$

Substitute this value of x into Equation (1) or Equation (2) and solve for y. Equation (1) is used here.

$$y = 3x - 1$$

$$y = 3(-1) - 1 = -4$$ • **Substitute -1 for x.**

The solution is $(-1, -4)$.

The substitution method can be used to analyze inconsistent and dependent systems of equations. If, when solving a system of equations algebraically, the variable is eliminated and the result is a false equation, such as $0 = 4$, the system of equations is inconsistent. If the variable is eliminated and the result is a true equation, such as $12 = 12$, the system of equations is dependent.

HOW TO 4 Solve by the substitution method: (1) $2x + 3y = 3$
(2) $y = -\frac{2}{3}x + 3$

$2x + 3y = 3$ • This is Equation (1).

$2x + 3\left(-\frac{2}{3}x + 3\right) = 3$ • From Equation (2), replace y with $-\frac{2}{3}x + 3$.

$2x - 2x + 9 = 3$ • Solve for x.

$9 = 3$ • This is a false equation.

Because $9 = 3$ is a false equation, the system of equations has no solution. The system is inconsistent.

Solving Equation (1) above for y, we have $y = -\frac{2}{3}x + 1$.

Comparing this equation with Equation (2) reveals that the slopes are equal and the y-intercepts are different. The graphs of the equations that make up this system of equations are parallel and thus never intersect. Because the graphs do not intersect, there are no solutions of the system of equations. The system of equations is inconsistent.

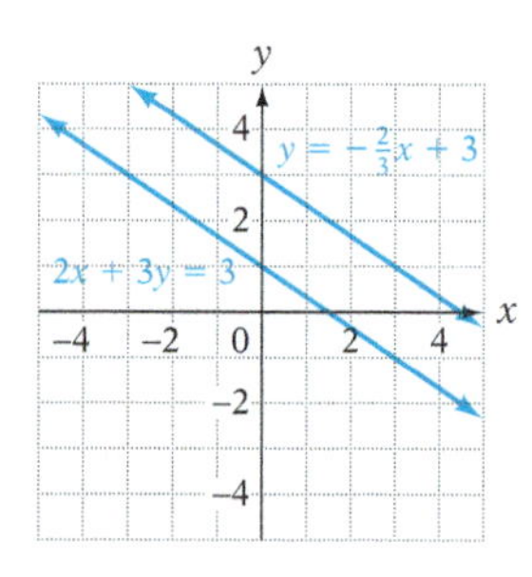

HOW TO 5 Solve by the substitution method: (1) $x = 2y + 3$
(2) $4x - 8y = 12$

$4x - 8y = 12$ • This is Equation (2).

$4(2y + 3) - 8y = 12$ • From Equation (1), replace x by $2y + 3$.

$8y + 12 - 8y = 12$ • Solve for y.

$12 = 12$ • This is a true equation.

The true equation $12 = 12$ indicates that any ordered pair (x, y) that satisfies one equation of the system satisfies the other equation. Therefore, the system of equations has an infinite number of solutions. The system is dependent. The solutions are the ordered pairs (x, y) that are solutions of $x = 2y + 3$.

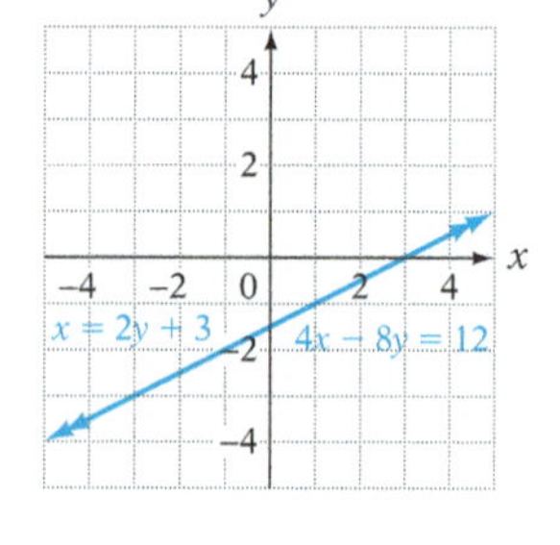

Take Note
As we mentioned in the previous section, when a system of equations is dependent, either equation can be used to write the ordered-pair solutions. Thus we could have said, "The solutions are the ordered pairs (x, y) that are solutions of $4x - 8y = 12$." Also note that, as we show at the right, if we solve each equation for y, the equations have the same slope-intercept form. This means that we could also say, "The solutions are the ordered pairs (x, y) that are solutions of $y = \frac{1}{2}x - \frac{3}{2}$." When a system of equations is dependent, there are several ways in which the solutions can be stated.

If we write Equation (1) and Equation (2) from HOW TO 5 in slope-intercept form, we have

$$x = 2y + 3 \qquad 4x - 8y = 12$$
$$-2y = -x + 3 \qquad -8y = -4x + 12$$
$$y = \frac{1}{2}x - \frac{3}{2} \qquad y = \frac{1}{2}x - \frac{3}{2}$$

The slope-intercept forms of the equations are the same, and therefore the graphs are the same. If we graph these two equations, we essentially graph one over the other, so the graphs intersect at an infinite number of points.

EXAMPLE 1

Solve by substitution:

(1) $3x + 4y = -2$

(2) $-x + 2y = 4$

Solution

$-x + 2y = 4$ • Solve Equation (2) for x.

$-x = -2y + 4$

$x = 2y - 4$

Substitute in Equation (1).

(1) $3x + 4y = -2$

$3(2y - 4) + 4y = -2$ • $x = 2y - 4$

$6y - 12 + 4y = -2$ • Solve for y.

$10y - 12 = -2$

$10y = 10$

$y = 1$

Substitute in $x = 2y - 4$.

$x = 2y - 4$

$x = 2(1) - 4$ • $y = 1$

$x = 2 - 4$

$x = -2$

The solution is $(-2, 1)$.

YOU TRY IT 1

Solve by substitution:

(1) $7x - y = 4$

(2) $3x + 2y = 9$

Your solution

EXAMPLE 2

Solve by substitution:

$4x + 2y = 5$

$y = -2x + 1$

Solution

$4x + 2y = 5$

$4x + 2(-2x + 1) = 5$ • $y = -2x + 1$

$4x - 4x + 2 = 5$ • Solve for x.

$2 = 5$ • A false equation

The system of equations is inconsistent and therefore has no solution.

YOU TRY IT 2

Solve by substitution:

$3x - y = 4$

$y = 3x + 2$

Your solution

EXAMPLE 3

Solve by substitution:

$y = 3x - 2$

$6x - 2y = 4$

Solution

$6x - 2y = 4$

$6x - 2(3x - 2) = 4$ • $y = 3x - 2$

$6x - 6x + 4 = 4$ • Solve for x.

$4 = 4$ • A true equation

The system of equations is dependent. The solutions are the ordered pairs that satisfy the equation $y = 3x - 2$.

YOU TRY IT 3

Solve by substitution:

$y = -2x + 1$

$6x + 3y = 3$

Your solution

Solutions on p. S20

OBJECTIVE B *To solve investment problems*

Recall from Section 3.2 that the annual simple interest earned by an investment is given by the equation $Pr = I$, where P is the principal, or the amount invested, r is the simple interest rate, and I is the simple interest.

For instance, if you invest \$750 at a simple interest rate of 6%, then the interest earned after one year is calculated as follows:

$$Pr = I$$
$$750(0.06) = I$$ • Replace P by 750 and r by 0.06 (6%).
$$45 = I$$ • Simplify.

The amount of interest earned is \$45.

Tips for Success

Word problems are challenging because we must read the problem, determine the quantity we must find, think of a method to find it, actually solve the problem, and then check the answer. In short, we must devise a *strategy* and then use that strategy to find the *solution*. See *AIM for Success* at the front of the book.

HOW TO 6 A medical lab technician decides to open an Individual Retirement Account (IRA) by placing \$2000 in two simple interest accounts. On one account, a corporate bond fund, the annual simple interest rate is 7.5%. On the second account, a real estate investment trust, the annual simple interest rate is 9%. If the technician wants annual earnings of \$168 from the two investments, how much must be invested in each account?

Strategy for Solving Simple-Interest Investment Problems

1. For each amount invested, use the equation $Pr = I$. Write a numerical or variable expression for the principal, the interest rate, and the interest earned.

Amount invested at 7.5%: x
Amount invested at 9%: y

	Principal, P	·	Interest rate, r	=	Interest earned, I
Amount at 7.5%	x	·	0.075	=	$0.075x$
Amount at 9%	y	·	0.09	=	$0.09y$

2. Write a system of equations. One equation will express the relationship between the amounts invested. The second equation will express the relationship between the amounts of interest earned by the investments.

The total amount invested is \$2000: $x + y = 2000$
The total annual interest earned is \$168: $0.075x + 0.09y = 168$

Solve the system of equations.

(1) $x + y = 2000$
(2) $0.075x + 0.09y = 168$

Solve Equation (1) for y and substitute into Equation (2).

(3) $y = -x + 2000$

$$0.075x + 0.09(-x + 2000) = 168$$ • Substitute $-x + 2000$ for y.
$$0.075x - 0.09x + 180 = 168$$
$$-0.015x = -12$$
$$x = 800$$

Substitute the value of x into Equation (3) and solve for y.

$$y = -x + 2000$$
$$y = -800 + 2000 = 1200$$ • Substitute 800 for x.

The amount invested at 7.5% is \$800. The amount invested at 9% is \$1200.

EXAMPLE 4

A hair stylist invested some money at an annual simple interest rate of 5.2%. A second investment, \$1000 more than the first, was invested at an annual simple interest rate of 7.2%. The total annual interest earned was \$320. How much was invested in each account?

Strategy

- Amount invested at 5.2%: x
  Amount invested at 7.2%: y

	Principal	*Rate*	*Interest*
Amount at 5.2%	x	0.052	$0.052x$
Amount at 7.2%	y	0.072	$0.072y$

- The second investment is \$1000 more than the first investment:

  $y = x + 1000$

  The sum of the interest earned at 5.2% and the interest earned at 7.2% equals \$320.

  $0.052x + 0.072y = 320$

Solution

(1) $y = x + 1000$
(2) $0.052x + 0.072y = 320$

Replace y in Equation (2) by $x + 1000$ from Equation (1). Then solve for x.

$$
\begin{aligned}
0.052x + 0.072y &= 320 \\
0.052x + 0.072(x + 1000) &= 320 && \bullet\ y = x + 1000 \\
0.052x + 0.072x + 72 &= 320 && \bullet\ \text{Solve for } x. \\
0.124x + 72 &= 320 \\
0.124x &= 248 \\
x &= 2000
\end{aligned}
$$

$$
\begin{aligned}
y &= x + 1000 \\
&= 2000 + 1000 && \bullet\ x = 2000 \\
&= 3000
\end{aligned}
$$

\$2000 was invested at an annual simple interest rate of 5.2%; \$3000 was invested at 7.2%.

YOU TRY IT 4

The manager of a city's investment income wishes to place \$330,000 in two simple interest accounts. The first account earns 6.5% annual interest, and the second account earns 4.5%. How much should be invested in each account so that both accounts earn the same annual interest?

Your strategy

Your solution

Solution on p. S20

8.2 EXERCISES

Concept Check

1. When you solve a system of equations by the substitution method, how do you determine whether the system of equations is dependent? How do you determine whether the system of equations is inconsistent?

2. Use this system of equations: (1) $y = 3x - 5$
   (2) $x = 2$

   To solve the system by substitution, substitute ______ for x in equation (1):
   $y = 3(2) - 5 =$ ______.

   The solution of the system of equations is (______, ______).

For Exercises 3 to 6, determine whether the statement is true or false.

3. For one year, you have x dollars deposited in an account that pays 7% annual simple interest. You will earn $0.07x$ in simple interest on this account.

4. If you have a total of $8000 deposited in two accounts and you represent the amount you have in the first account as x, then the amount in the second account is represented as $8000 - x$.

5. The amount of interest earned on one account is $0.05x$, and the amount of interest earned on a second account is $0.08(9000 - x)$. If the two accounts earn the same amount of interest, then we can write the equation $0.05x + 0.08(9000 - x)$.

6. If the amount of interest earned on one account is $0.06x$ and the amount of interest earned on a second account is $0.09(4000 - x)$, then the total interest earned on the two accounts can be represented as $0.06x + 0.09(4000 - x)$.

OBJECTIVE A *To solve a system of linear equations by the substitution method*

For Exercises 7 to 36, solve by substitution.

7. $2x + 3y = 7$
   $x = 2$

8. $y = 3$
   $3x - 2y = 6$

9. $y = x - 3$
   $x + y = 5$

10. $y = x + 2$
    $x + y = 6$

11. $x = y - 2$
    $x + 3y = 2$

12. $x = y + 1$
    $x + 2y = 7$

13. $y = 4 - 3x$
    $3x + y = 5$

14. $y = 2 - 3x$
    $6x + 2y = 7$

15. $x = 3y + 3$
    $2x - 6y = 12$

16. $x = 2 - y$
    $3x + 3y = 6$

17. $3x + 5y = -6$
    $x = 5y + 3$

18. $y = 2x + 3$
    $4x - 3y = 1$

19. $3x + y = 4$
$4x - 3y = 1$

20. $x - 4y = 9$
$2x - 3y = 11$

21. $3x - y = 6$
$x + 3y = 2$

22. $4x - y = -5$
$2x + 5y = 13$

23. $3x - y = 5$
$2x + 5y = -8$

24. $3x + 4y = 18$
$2x - y = 1$

25. $4x + 3y = 0$
$2x - y = 0$

26. $5x + 2y = 0$
$x - 3y = 0$

27. $2x - y = 2$
$6x - 3y = 6$

28. $3x + y = 4$
$9x + 3y = 12$

29. $x = 3y + 2$
$y = 2x + 6$

30. $x = 4 - 2y$
$y = 2x - 13$

31. $y = 2x + 11$
$y = 5x - 19$

32. $y = 2x - 8$
$y = 3x - 13$

33. $y = -4x + 2$
$y = -3x - 1$

34. $x = 3y + 7$
$x = 2y - 1$

35. $x = 4y - 2$
$x = 6y + 8$

36. $x = 3 - 2y$
$x = 5y - 10$

For Exercises 37 and 38, assume that A, B, and C are nonzero real numbers. State whether the system of equations is independent, inconsistent, or dependent.

37. $x + y = A$
$x = A - y$

38. $x + y = B$
$y = -x + C, C \neq B$

OBJECTIVE B *To solve investment problems*

For Exercises 39 and 40, use the system of equations at the right, which represents the following situation. Owen Marshall divides an investment of $10,000 between two simple interest accounts. One account earns 8% annual simple interest, and the second account earns 6.5% annual simple interest.

$$x + y = 10{,}000$$
$$0.08x + 0.065y = 710$$

39. What do the variables x and y represent? Explain the meaning of each equation in terms of the problem situation.

40. Write a question that could be answered by solving the system of equations.

41. An investment of \$3500 is divided between two simple interest accounts. On one account, the annual simple interest rate is 5%, and on the second account, the annual simple interest rate is 7.5%. How much should be invested in each account so that the total interest earned from the two accounts is \$215?

42. A mortgage broker purchased two trust deeds for a total of \$250,000. One trust deed earns 7% simple annual interest, and the second earns 8% simple annual interest. If the total annual interest earned from the two trust deeds is \$18,500, what was the purchase price of each trust deed?

43. When Sara Whitehorse changed jobs, she rolled over the \$6000 in her retirement account into two simple interest accounts. On one account, the annual simple interest rate is 9%; on the second account, the annual simple interest rate is 6%. How much was invested in each account if the accounts earned the same amount of annual interest?

44. An animal trainer decided to take the \$15,000 won on a game show and deposit it in two simple interest accounts. Part of the winnings were placed in an account paying 7% annual simple interest, and the remainder was used to purchase a government bond that earns 6.5% annual simple interest. The amount of interest earned for one year was \$1020. How much was invested in each account?

© iStockphoto.com/Richard Cano

45. A police officer has chosen a high-yield stock fund that earns 8% annual simple interest for part of a \$6000 investment. The remaining portion is used to purchase a preferred stock that earns 11% annual simple interest. How much should be invested in each account so that the amount earned on the 8% account is twice the amount earned on the 11% account?

46. To save for the purchase of a new car, a deposit was made into an account that earns 7% annual simple interest. Another deposit, \$1500 less than the first deposit, was placed in a certificate of deposit (CD) earning 9% annual simple interest. The total interest earned on both accounts for one year was \$505. How much money was deposited in the CD?

47. The Pacific Investment Group invested some money in a certificate of deposit (CD) that earns 6.5% annual simple interest. Twice the amount invested at 6.5% was invested in a second CD that earns 8.5% annual simple interest. If the total annual interest earned from the two investments was \$4935, how much was invested at 6.5%?

48. A corporation gave a university \$300,000 to support product safety research. The university deposited some of the money in a 10% annual simple interest account and the remainder in an 8.5% annual simple interest account. How much should be deposited in each account so that the annual interest earned is \$28,500?

49. Ten coworkers formed an investment club, and each member deposited $2000 in the club's account. The club decided to take the total amount and invest some of it in preferred stock that pays 8% annual simple interest and the remainder in a municipal bond that pays 7% annual simple interest. The amount of interest earned each year from the investments was $1520. How much was invested in each?

50. A financial consultant advises a client to invest part of $30,000 in municipal bonds that earn 6.5% annual simple interest and the remainder of the money in 8.5% corporate bonds. How much should be invested in each so that the total interest earned each year is $2190?

51. Alisa Rhodes placed some money in a real estate investment trust that earns 7.5% annual simple interest. A second investment, which was one-half the amount placed in the real estate investment trust, was used to purchase a trust deed that earns 9% annual simple interest. If the total annual interest earned from the two investments was $900, how much was invested in the trust deed?

Critical Thinking

For Exercises 52 to 57, rewrite each equation so that the coefficients are integers. Then solve the system of equations by the substitution method.

52. $0.1x - 0.6y = 0.5$
$-0.7x + 0.2y = 0.5$

53. $0.8x - 0.1y = 0.3$
$0.5x - 0.2y = -0.5$

54. $0.4x + 0.5y = 0.2$
$0.3x - 0.1y = 1.1$

55. $-0.1x + 0.3y = 1.1$
$0.4x - 0.1y = -2.2$

56. $1.2x + 0.1y = 1.9$
$0.1x + 0.3y = 2.2$

57. $1.25x - 0.01y = 1.5$
$0.24x - 0.02y = -1.52$

58. The following was offered as a solution of the system of equations.

(1) $y = \frac{1}{2}x + 2$

(2) $2x + 5y = 10$

$2x + 5y = 10$ • Equation (2)

$2x + 5\left(\frac{1}{2}x + 2\right) = 10$ • Substitute $\frac{1}{2}x + 2$ for y.

$2x + \frac{5}{2}x + 10 = 10$ • Solve for x.

$\frac{9}{2}x = 0$

$x = 0$

At this point the student stated that because $x = 0$, the system of equations has no solution. If this assertion is correct, is the system of equations independent, dependent, or inconsistent? If the assertion is not correct, what is the correct solution?

59. A financial manager invested 20% of a client's money in bonds paying 9% annual simple interest, 35% in an 8% simple interest account, and the remainder in 9.5% corporate bonds. Find the amount invested in each if the total annual interest earned is \$5325.

60. A plant manager invested \$3000 more in stocks than in bonds. The stocks paid 8% annual simple interest, and the bonds paid 9.5% annual simple interest. Both investments yielded the same income. Find the total annual interest received on both investments.

Projects or Group Activities

For Exercises 61 to 63, find the value of k for which the system of equations has no solution.

61. $2x - 3y = 7$
$kx - 3y = 4$

62. $8x - 4y = 1$
$2x - ky = 3$

63. $x = 4y + 4$
$kx - 8y = 4$

64. A bank offers a customer a 4-year certificate of deposit (CD) that earns 6.5% compound annual interest. This means that the interest earned each year is added to the principal before the interest for the next year is calculated. Find the value in 4 years of a nurse's investment of \$3000 in this CD.

65. A bank offers a customer a 5-year certificate of deposit (CD) that earns 7.5% compound annual interest. This means that the interest earned each year is added to the principal before the interest for the next year is calculated. Find the value in 5 years of an accountant's investment of \$2500 in this CD.

CHECK YOUR PROGRESS: CHAPTER 4

For Exercises 1 to 3, solve by graphing.

1. $x - y = 3$
$x + y = 5$

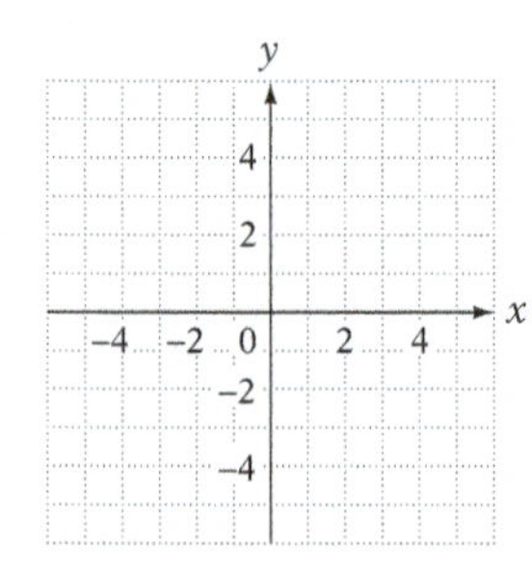

2. $4x + 3y = 12$
$y = -\frac{4}{3}x + 4$

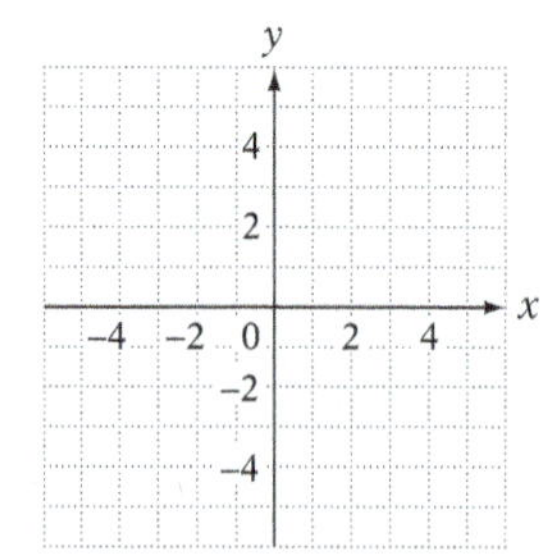

3.
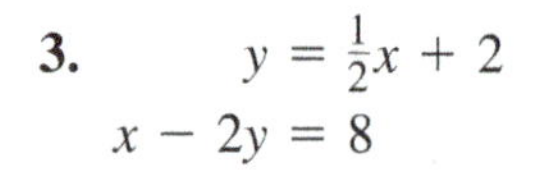
$y = \frac{1}{2}x + 2$
$x - 2y = 8$

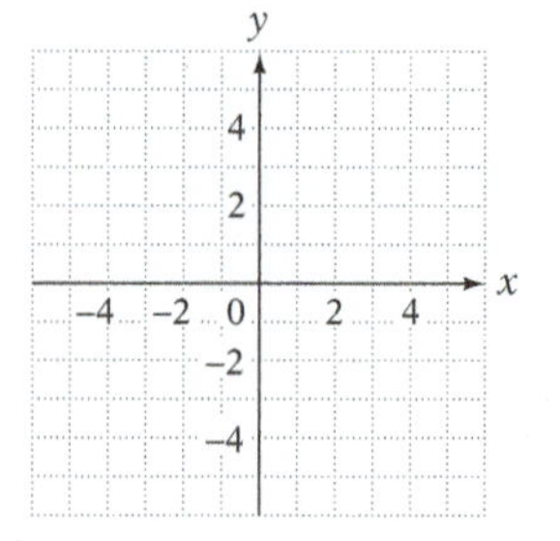

4. Is $(2, -3)$ a solution of the system $y = 2x - 7$
$y = 3x - 9$?

5. Solve by substitution:
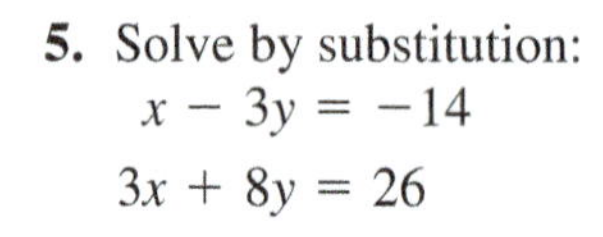
$x - 3y = -14$
$3x + 8y = 26$

6. Solve by substitution:
$x - 3y = -12$
$y = \frac{1}{3}x + 4$

7. Virak Ly invested part of \$30,000 in municipal bonds that earn 6.5% annual simple interest and the remainder of the money in 8.5% corporate bonds. How much is invested in each account if the total annual interest earned is \$2190?

SECTION

8.3 Solving Systems of Linear Equations by the Addition Method

OBJECTIVE A *To solve a system of linear equations by the addition method*

Another method of solving a system of equations is called the **addition method.** This method is based on the Addition Property of Equations.

Note, for the system of equations at the right, the effect of adding Equation (2) to Equation (1). Because $2y$ and $-2y$ are opposites, adding the equations results in an equation with only one variable.

$$\begin{aligned} (1)\quad 5x + 2y &= 11 \\ (2)\quad 3x - 2y &= 13 \\ \hline 8x + 0y &= 24 \\ 8x &= 24 \end{aligned}$$

Solving $8x = 24$ for x gives the first coordinate of the ordered-pair solution of the system of equations.

$$\frac{8x}{8} = \frac{24}{8}$$
$$x = 3$$

The second coordinate is found by substituting the value of x into Equation (1) or Equation (2) and then solving for y. Equation (1) is used here.

$$\begin{aligned} (1)\quad 5x + 2y &= 11 \\ 5(3) + 2y &= 11 \\ 15 + 2y &= 11 \\ 2y &= -4 \\ y &= -2 \end{aligned}$$

The solution is $(3, -2)$.

Sometimes, adding the two equations of a system does not eliminate one of the variables. In this case, use the Multiplication Property of Equations to rewrite one or both of the equations so that the coefficients of one variable are opposites. Then add the equations and solve for the variables.

HOW TO 1 Solve by the addition method: (1) $4x + y = 5$
(2) $2x - 5y = 19$

Multiply Equation (2) by -2. The coefficients of x will then be opposites.

$-2(2x - 5y) = -2 \cdot 19$ • Multiply Equation (2) by -2.

(3) $-4x + 10y = -38$ • Simplify. This is Equation (3).

Add Equation (3) to Equation (1). Then solve for y.

(1) $4x + y = 5$

(3) $-4x + 10y = -38$ • Note that the coefficients of x are opposites.

$11y = -33$ • Add the two equations.

$y = -3$ • Solve for y.

Substitute the value of y into Equation (1) or Equation (2) and solve for x. Equation (1) is used here.

(1) $4x + y = 5$

$4x + (-3) = 5$ • Substitute -3 for y.

$4x - 3 = 5$ • Solve for x.

$4x = 8$

$x = 2$

The solution is $(2, -3)$.

Sometimes each equation of a system of equations must be multiplied by a constant so that the coefficients of one variable are opposites.

HOW TO 2 Solve by the addition method:

$$(1) \quad 3x + 7y = 2$$
$$(2) \quad 5x - 3y = -26$$

To eliminate x, multiply Equation (1) by 5 and Equation (2) by -3. Note at the right how the constants are chosen.

$$5(3x + 7y) = 5 \cdot 2$$
$$-3(5x - 3y) = -3(-26)$$

- The negative is used so that the coefficients of x will be opposites.

$$15x + 35y = 10 \quad \text{• 5 times Equation (1)}$$
$$-15x + 9y = 78 \quad \text{• −3 times Equation (2)}$$
$$44y = 88 \quad \text{• Add the equations.}$$
$$y = 2 \quad \text{• Solve for } y.$$

Substitute the value of y into Equation (1) or Equation (2) and solve for x. Equation (1) is used here.

$$(1) \quad 3x + 7y = 2$$
$$3x + 7(2) = 2 \quad \text{• Substitute 2 for } y.$$
$$3x + 14 = 2 \quad \text{• Solve for } x.$$
$$3x = -12$$
$$x = -4$$

The solution is $(-4, 2)$.

For the system of equations in HOW TO 2, the system was solved for y, and the value of x was determined by substitution. The value of x could have been determined by eliminating y from the system.

$$9x + 21y = 6 \quad \text{• 3 times Equation (1)}$$
$$35x - 21y = -182 \quad \text{• 7 times Equation (2)}$$
$$44x = -176 \quad \text{• Add the equations.}$$
$$x = -4 \quad \text{• Solve for } x.$$

Note that this is the same value of x that we obtained by using substitution.

Take Note

When you use the addition method to solve a system of equations and the result is an equation that is always true (like the one in HOW TO 3), the system of equations is dependent. Compare this result with the result obtained in HOW TO 4.

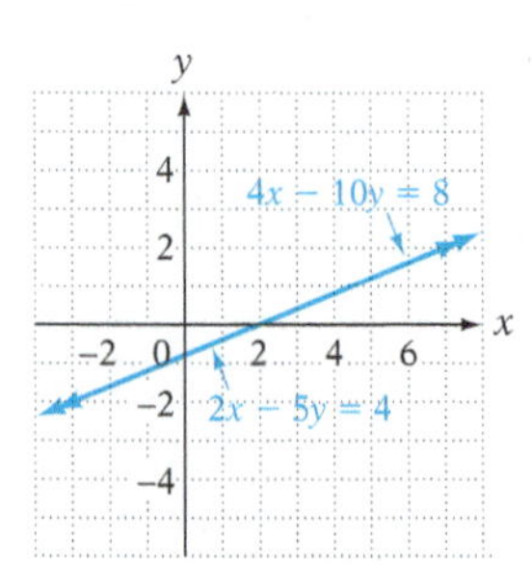

HOW TO 3 Solve by the addition method:

$$(1) \quad 2x - 5y = 4$$
$$(2) \quad 4x - 10y = 8$$

Eliminate x. Multiply Equation (1) by -2.

$$-2(2x - 5y) = -2(4) \quad \text{• −2 times Equation (1)}$$
$$(3) \quad -4x + 10y = -8 \quad \text{• This is Equation (3).}$$

Add Equation (3) to Equation (2) and solve for y.

$$(2) \quad 4x - 10y = 8$$
$$(3) \quad -4x + 10y = -8$$
$$0x + 0y = 0$$
$$0 = 0$$

The equation $0 = 0$ means that the system of equations is dependent. Therefore, the solutions of the system of equations are the ordered pairs that satisfy $2x - 5y = 4$.

The graphs of the two equations of the system in HOW TO 3 are shown at the left. One line is on top of the other; therefore, the lines intersect at an infinite number of points.

HOW TO 4 Solve by the addition method: (1) $2x + y = 2$
(2) $4x + 2y = -5$

Eliminate y. Multiply Equation (1) by -2.

$$-2(2x + y) = -2 \cdot 2$$ • -2 times Equation (1)

(3) $$-4x - 2y = -4$$ • This is Equation (3).

Add Equation (2) to Equation (3) and solve for x.

(3) $-4x - 2y = -4$
(2) $4x + 2y = -5$

$$0x + 0y = -9$$ • Add Equation (2) to Equation (3).

$$0 = -9$$ • This is a false equation.

The system of equations is inconsistent and therefore has no solution.

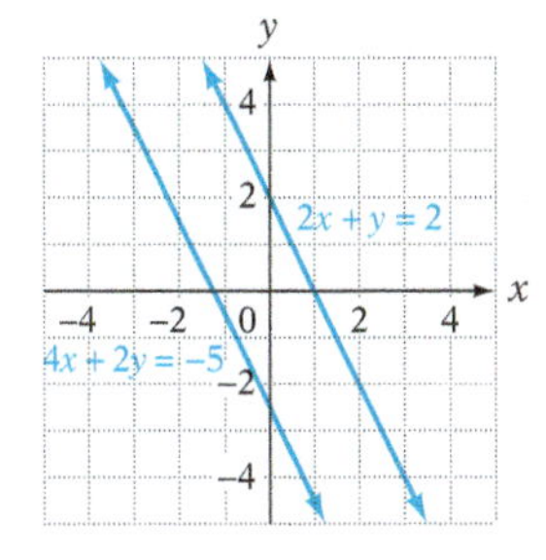

The graphs of the two equations of the system of equations in HOW TO 4 are shown at the left. Note that the graphs are parallel and therefore do not intersect. Thus the system of equations has no solution.

EXAMPLE 1

Solve by the addition method:
(1) $2x + 4y = 7$
(2) $5x - 3y = -2$

Solution

Eliminate x.

$$5(2x + 4y) = 5 \cdot 7$$ • 5 times Equation (1)

$$-2(5x - 3y) = -2(-2)$$ • -2 times Equation (2)

$$10x + 20y = 35$$
$$-10x + 6y = 4$$

$$26y = 39$$ • Add the equations.

$$y = \frac{39}{26} = \frac{3}{2}$$ • Solve for y.

Substitute $\frac{3}{2}$ for y in Equation (1).

(1) $$2x + 4y = 7$$

$$2x + 4\left(\frac{3}{2}\right) = 7$$ • Replace y by $\frac{3}{2}$.

$$2x + 6 = 7$$ • Solve for x.

$$2x = 1$$

$$x = \frac{1}{2}$$

The solution is $\left(\frac{1}{2}, \frac{3}{2}\right)$.

YOU TRY IT 1

Solve by the addition method:
(1) $2x - 3y = 1$
(2) $-3x + 4y = 6$

Your solution

Solution on p. S20

EXAMPLE 2

Solve by the addition method:

(1) $6x + 9y = 15$

(2) $4x + 6y = 10$

Solution

Eliminate x.

$$4(6x + 9y) = 4 \cdot 15$$ • 4 times Equation (1)

$$-6(4x + 6y) = -6 \cdot 10$$ • −6 times Equation (2)

$$24x + 36y = 60$$
$$-24x - 36y = -60$$

$$0x + 0y = 0$$ • Add the equations.

$$0 = 0$$

The system of equations is dependent. The solutions are the ordered pairs that satisfy the equation $6x + 9y = 15$.

YOU TRY IT 2

Solve by the addition method:

$2x - 3y = 4$

$-4x + 6y = -8$

Your solution

EXAMPLE 3

Solve by the addition method:

(1) $2x = y + 8$

(2) $3x + 2y = 5$

Solution

Write Equation (1) in the form $Ax + By = C$.

$$2x = y + 8$$

(3) $2x - y = 8$ • This is Equation (3).

Eliminate y.

$$2(2x - y) = 2 \cdot 8$$ • 2 times Equation (3)

$$3x + 2y = 5$$ • This is Equation (2).

$$4x - 2y = 16$$
$$3x + 2y = 5$$

$$7x = 21$$ • Add the equations.

$$x = 3$$

Replace x in Equation (1).

(1) $2x = y + 8$

$$2 \cdot 3 = y + 8$$ • Replace x by 3.

$$6 = y + 8$$

$$-2 = y$$

The solution is $(3, -2)$.

YOU TRY IT 3

Solve by the addition method:

$4x + 5y = 11$

$3y = x + 10$

Your solution

Solutions on p. S21

8.3 EXERCISES

Concept Check

1. Use this system of equations: (1) $-3x - y = 5$
(2) $x - 4y = 7$

a. To eliminate x from the system of equations by using the addition method, multiply each side of equation (2) by ______.

b. To eliminate y from the system of equations by using the addition method, multiply each side of equation (1) by ______.

2. Use this system of equations: (1) $2x - 3y = 3$
(2) $x + 6y = 9$

a. To eliminate x from the system of equations by using the addition method, multiply each side of equation (______) by (______).

b. To eliminate y from the system of equations by using the addition method, multiply each side of equation (______) by (______).

OBJECTIVE A *To solve a system of linear equations by the addition method*

For Exercises 3 to 38, solve by the addition method.

3. $x + y = 4$
$x - y = 6$

4. $2x + y = 3$
$x - y = 3$

5. $x + y = 4$
$2x + y = 5$

6. $x - 3y = 2$
$x + 2y = -3$

7. $2x - y = 1$
$x + 3y = 4$

8. $x - 2y = 4$
$3x + 4y = 2$

9. $4x - 5y = 22$
$x + 2y = -1$

10. $3x - y = 11$
$2x + 5y = 13$

11. $2x - y = 1$
$4x - 2y = 2$

12. $x + 3y = 2$
$3x + 9y = 6$

13. $4x + 3y = 15$
$2x - 5y = 1$

14. $3x - 7y = 13$
$6x + 5y = 7$

15. $2x - 3y = 1$
$4x - 6y = 2$

16. $2x + 4y = 6$
$3x + 6y = 9$

17. $3x - 6y = -1$
$6x - 4y = 2$

18. $5x + 2y = 3$
$3x - 10y = -1$

19. $5x + 7y = 10$
$3x - 14y = 6$

20. $7x + 10y = 13$
$4x + 5y = 6$

21. $3x - 2y = 0$
$6x + 5y = 0$

22. $5x + 2y = 0$
$3x + 5y = 0$

23. $2x - 3y = 16$
$3x + 4y = 7$

24. $3x + 4y = 10$
$4x + 3y = 11$

25. $5x + 3y = 7$
$2x + 5y = 1$

26. $-2x + 7y = 9$
$3x + 2y = -1$

27. $3x + 4y = 4$
$5x + 12y = 5$

28. $2x + 5y = 2$
$3x + 3y = 1$

29. $8x - 3y = 11$
$6x - 5y = 11$

30. $4x - 8y = 36$
$3x - 6y = 15$

31. $5x + 15y = 20$
$2x + 6y = 12$

32. $y = 2x - 3$
$3x + 4y = -1$

33. $3x = 2y + 7$
$5x - 2y = 13$

34. $2y = 4 - 9x$
$9x - y = 25$

35. $2x + 9y = 16$
$5x = 1 - 3y$

36. $3x - 4 = y + 18$
$4x + 5y = -21$

37. $2x + 3y = 7 - 2x$
$7x + 2y = 9$

38. $5x - 3y = 3y + 4$
$4x + 3y = 11$

For Exercises 39 to 41, assume that A, B, and C are nonzero real numbers, where $A \neq B \neq C$. State whether the system of equations is independent, inconsistent, or dependent.

39. $Ax + By = C$
$2Ax + 2By = 2C$

40. $x - Ay = B$
$3x - 3Ay = 3C$

41. $Ax + By = C$
$Bx + Ay = 2C$

Critical Thinking

42. The point of intersection of the graphs of the equations $Ax + 2y = 2$ and $2x + By = 10$ is $(2, -2)$. Find A and B.

43. The point of intersection of the graphs of the equations $Ax - 4y = 9$ and $4x + By = -1$ is $(-1, -3)$. Find A and B.

Projects or Group Activities

44. Find an equation such that the system of equations formed by your equation and the equation $3x - 4y = 10$ has $(2, -1)$ as a solution.

SECTION

8.4 Application Problems in Two Variables

OBJECTIVE A *To solve rate-of-wind or rate-of-current problems*

Take Note
See Section 3.2 for a discussion of how the rate of a current affects the speed of a boat traveling on a river.

We normally need two variables to solve motion problems that involve an object moving with or against a wind or current.

HOW TO 1 Flying with the wind, a small plane can fly 600 mi in 3 h. Flying against the wind, the plane can fly the same distance in 4 h. Find the rate of the plane in calm air and the rate of the wind.

Strategy for Solving Rate-of-Wind or Rate-of-Current Problems

1. Choose one variable to represent the rate of the object in calm conditions and a second variable to represent the rate of the wind or current. Using these variables, express the rate of the object traveling with and against the wind or current. Use the equation $rt = d$ to write expressions for the distance traveled by the object. The results can be recorded in a table.

Rate of plane in calm air: p
Rate of wind: w

	Rate	·	Time	=	Distance
With the wind	$p + w$	·	3	=	$3(p + w)$
Against the wind	$p - w$	·	4	=	$4(p - w)$

2. Determine how the expressions for distance are related.

The distance traveled with the wind is 600 mi.
The distance traveled against the wind is 600 mi.
Solve the system of equations.

$$3(p + w) = 600$$
$$4(p - w) = 600$$

$$3(p + w) = 600 \longrightarrow \frac{1}{3} \cdot 3(p + w) = \frac{1}{3} \cdot 600 \longrightarrow p + w = 200$$

$$4(p - w) = 600 \longrightarrow \frac{1}{4} \cdot 4(p - w) = \frac{1}{4} \cdot 600 \longrightarrow p - w = 150$$

$$2p = 350$$
$$p = 175$$

$$p + w = 200$$
$$175 + w = 200 \quad \bullet\ p = 175$$
$$w = 25$$

The rate of the plane in calm air is 175 mph.
The rate of the wind is 25 mph.

EXAMPLE 1

A 450-mile trip from one city to another takes 3 h when a plane is flying with the wind. The return trip, against the wind, takes 5 h. Find the rate of the plane in still air and the rate of the wind.

Strategy

- Rate of the plane in still air: p
  Rate of the wind: w

	Rate	*Time*	*Distance*
With wind	$p + w$	3	$3(p + w)$
Against wind	$p - w$	5	$5(p - w)$

- The distance traveled with the wind is 450 mi. The distance traveled against the wind is 450 mi.

Solution

$3(p + w) = 450 \qquad \frac{1}{3} \cdot 3(p + w) = \frac{1}{3} \cdot 450$

$5(p - w) = 450 \qquad \frac{1}{5} \cdot 5(p - w) = \frac{1}{5} \cdot 450$

$$p + w = 150$$
$$p - w = 90$$
$$2p = 240$$
$$p = 120$$

$p + w = 150$
$120 + w = 150$ • $p = 120$
$w = 30$

The rate of the plane in still air is 120 mph.
The rate of the wind is 30 mph.

YOU TRY IT 1

A canoeist paddling with the current can travel 15 mi in 3 h. Rowing against the current, it takes the canoeist 5 h to travel the same distance. Find the rate of the current and the rate of the canoeist in calm water.

Your strategy

Your solution

Solution on p. S21

OBJECTIVE B *To solve application problems using two variables*

The application problems in this section are varieties of the types of problems solved earlier in the text. Each of the strategies for the problems in this section will result in a system of equations.

Yuri Arcurs/Shutterstock.com

Point of Interest

The Babylonians had a method for solving a system of equations. Here is an adaptation of a problem from an ancient Babylonian text (around 1500 B.C.). "There are two silver blocks. The sum of $\frac{1}{7}$ of the first block and $\frac{1}{11}$ of the second block is one sheqel (a weight). The first block diminished by $\frac{1}{7}$ of its weight equals the second diminished by $\frac{1}{11}$ of its weight. What are the weights of the two blocks?"

HOW TO 2 A jeweler purchased 5 oz of a gold alloy and 20 oz of a silver alloy for a total cost of \$540. The next day, at the same prices per ounce, the jeweler purchased 4 oz of the gold alloy and 25 oz of the silver alloy for a total cost of \$450. Find the cost per ounce of the gold and silver alloys.

Strategy for Solving an Application Problem in Two Variables

1. Choose one variable to represent one of the unknown quantities and a second variable to represent the other unknown quantity. Write numerical or variable expressions for all of the remaining quantities. The results can be recorded in two tables, one for each of the conditions.

Cost per ounce of gold alloy: g
Cost per ounce of silver alloy: s

First day:

	Amount	·	Unit Cost	=	Value
Gold	5	·	g	=	$5g$
Silver	20	·	s	=	$20s$

Second day:

	Amount	·	Unit Cost	=	Value
Gold	4	·	g	=	$4g$
Silver	25	·	s	=	$25s$

2. Determine a system of equations. Each table will give one equation of the system.

The total value of the purchase on the first day was \$540. $5g + 20s = 540$

The total value of the purchase on the second day was \$450. $4g + 25s = 450$

Solve the system of equations.

$$5g + 20s = 540 \qquad 4(5g + 20s) = 4 \cdot 540 \qquad 20g + 80s = 2160$$
$$4g + 25s = 450 \qquad -5(4g + 25s) = -5 \cdot 450 \qquad -20g - 125s = -2250$$
$$-45s = -90$$
$$s = 2$$

$$5g + 20s = 540$$
$$5g + 20(2) = 540 \qquad \bullet\ s = 2$$
$$5g + 40 = 540$$
$$5g = 500$$
$$g = 100$$

The cost per ounce of the gold alloy was \$100.
The cost per ounce of the silver alloy was \$2.

EXAMPLE 2

A store owner purchased 20 halogen light bulbs and 30 fluorescent bulbs for a total cost of $630. A second purchase, at the same prices, included 30 halogen bulbs and 10 fluorescent bulbs for a total cost of $560. Find the cost of a halogen bulb and of a fluorescent bulb.

Strategy

Cost of a halogen bulb: h
Cost of a fluorescent bulb: f

First purchase:

	Amount	*Unit Cost*	*Value*
Halogen	20	h	$20h$
Fluorescent	30	f	$30f$

Second purchase:

	Amount	*Unit Cost*	*Value*
Halogen	30	h	$30h$
Fluorescent	10	f	$10f$

The total cost of the first purchase was $630.
The total cost of the second purchase was $560.

Solution

$$20h + 30f = 630$$
$$30h + 10f = 560$$

$$20h + 30f = 630$$
$$-3(30h + 10f) = -3(560)$$

$$20h + 30f = 630$$
$$-90h - 30f = -1680$$
$$-70h = -1050$$
$$h = 15$$

$$20h + 30f = 630$$
$$20(15) + 30f = 630 \quad \bullet\ h = 15$$
$$300 + 30f = 630$$
$$30f = 330$$
$$f = 11$$

The cost of a halogen light bulb is $15.
The cost of a fluorescent light bulb is $11.

YOU TRY IT 2

A citrus grower purchased 25 orange trees and 20 grapefruit trees for $2900. The next week, at the same prices, the grower bought 20 orange trees and 30 grapefruit trees for $3300. Find the cost of an orange tree and the cost of a grapefruit tree.

Your strategy

Your solution

Solution on p. S21

8.4 EXERCISES

Concept Check

For Exercises 1 to 4, determine whether the statement is true or false.

1. A plane flying with the wind is traveling faster than it would be traveling without the wind.

2. The uniform motion equation $r = dt$ is used to solve rate-of-wind and rate-of-current problems.

3. If b represents the rate of a boat in calm water and c represents the rate of the current, then $b + c$ represents the rate of the boat traveling against the current.

4. If, in a system of equations, p represents the rate of a plane in calm air and w represents the rate of the wind, and $p = 100$, this means that the rate of the wind is 100.

5. A contractor bought 100 yd of nylon carpet for x dollars per yard and 50 yd of wool carpet for y dollars per yard. How can you represent the total cost of the carpet?

6. A boat travels down a river for 2 h (traveling with the current), then turns around and takes 3 h to return (traveling against the current). Let b be the rate of the boat, in miles per hour, in calm water, and let c be the rate of the current in miles per hour. Complete the following table.

	Rate, r	·	*Time, t*	=	*Distance, d*
With current	______	·	______	=	______
Against current	______	·	______	=	______

OBJECTIVE A *To solve rate-of-wind or rate-of-current problems*

7. Traveling with the wind, a plane flies m miles in h hours. Traveling against the wind, the plane flies n miles in h hours. Is m less than, equal to, or greater than n?

8. Traveling against the current, it takes a boat h hours to go m miles. Traveling with the current, the boat takes k hours to go m miles. Is k less than, equal to, or greater than h?

9. A rowing team rowing with the current traveled 40 km in 2 h. Rowing against the current, the team could travel only 16 km in 2 h. Find the rowing rate in calm water and the rate of the current.

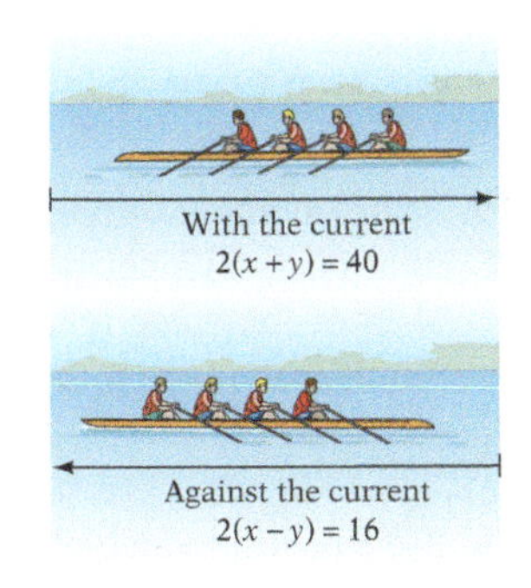

10. A plane flying with the jet stream flew from Los Angeles to Chicago, a distance of 2250 mi, in 5 h. Flying against the jet stream, the plane could fly only 1750 mi in the same amount of time. Find the rate of the plane in calm air and the rate of the wind.

11. A whale swimming against an ocean current traveled 60 mi in 2 h. Swimming in the opposite direction, with the current, the whale was able to travel the same distance in 1.5 h. Find the speed of the whale in calm water and the rate of the ocean current.

Sokolov Alexey/Shutterstock.com

12. The bird capable of the fastest flying speed is the swift. A swift flying with the wind to a favorite feeding spot traveled 26 mi in 0.2 h. On returning, now flying against the wind, the swift was able to travel only 16 mi in the same amount of time. What is the rate of the swift in calm air, and what was the rate of the wind?

13. A private Learjet 31A was flying with a tailwind and traveled 1120 mi in 2 h. Flying against the wind on the return trip, the jet was able to travel only 980 mi in 2 h. Find the speed of the jet in calm air and the rate of the wind.

14. A plane flying with a tailwind flew 300 mi in 2 h. Flying against the wind, the plane took 3 h to travel the same distance. Find the rate of the plane in calm air and the rate of the wind.

15. A Boeing Apache Longbow military helicopter traveling directly into a strong headwind was able to travel 450 mi in 2.5 h. The return trip, now with a tailwind, took 1 h 40 min. Find the speed of the helicopter in calm air and the rate of the wind.

Karl R. Martin/Shutterstock.com

16. Rowing with the current, a canoeist paddled 14 mi in 2 h. Rowing against the current, the canoeist could paddle only 10 mi in the same amount of time. Find the rate of the canoeist in calm water and the rate of the current.

17. A motorboat traveling with the current went 35 mi in 3.5 h. Traveling against the current, the boat went 12 mi in 3 h. Find the rate of the boat in calm water and the rate of the current.

Richard Paul Kane/Shutterstock.com

18. Throwing with the wind, a quarterback passes a football 140 ft in 2 s. Against the wind, the same pass would have traveled 80 ft in 2 s. Find the rate of the pass and the rate of the wind.

OBJECTIVE B *To solve application problems using two variables*

19. A merchant mixes 4 lb of cinnamon tea with 1 lb of spice tea to create a mixture that costs \$12 per pound. When the merchant mixes 1 lb of the cinnamon tea with 4 lb of the spice tea, the mixture costs \$15 per pound. Is the cost per pound of the cinnamon tea less than, equal to, or greater than the cost per pound of the spice tea?

20. The total value of nickels and dimes in a bank is \$2. If the nickels were dimes and the dimes were nickels, the total value would be \$2.95. Is the number of nickels in the bank less than, equal to, or greater than the number of dimes in the bank?

For Exercises 21 and 22, use the system of equations at the right, which represents the following situation. You spent $320 on theater tickets for 4 adults and 2 children. For the same performance, your neighbor spent $240 on tickets for 2 adults and 3 children.

$$4x + 2y = 320$$
$$2x + 3y = 240$$

Roberto Herrett/age fotostock

21. What do the variables x and y represent? Explain the meaning of each equation in terms of the problem situation.

22. Write a question that could be answered by solving the system of equations.

23. Flour Mixtures A baker purchased 12 lb of wheat flour and 15 lb of rye flour for a total cost of $18.30. A second purchase, at the same prices, included 15 lb of wheat flour and 10 lb of rye flour. The cost of the second purchase was $16.75. Find the cost per pound of the wheat flour and of the rye flour.

24. Consumerism For using a computerized financial news network for 50 min during prime time and 70 min during non-prime time, a customer was charged $10.75. A second customer was charged $13.35 for using the network for 60 min of prime time and 90 min of non-prime time. Find the cost per minute for using the financial news network during prime time.

25. Consumerism The employees of a hardware store ordered lunch from a local delicatessen. The lunch consisted of 4 turkey sandwiches and 7 orders of french fries, for a total cost of $38.30. The next day, the employees ordered 5 turkey sandwiches and 5 orders of french fries totaling $40.75. What does the delicatessen charge for a turkey sandwich? What is the charge for an order of french fries?

26. Fuel Mixtures An octane number of 87 on gasoline means that it will fight engine "knock" as effectively as a reference fuel that is 87% isooctane, a type of gas. Suppose you want to fill an empty 18-gallon tank with some 87-octane gasoline and some 93-octane fuel to produce a mixture that is 89-octane. How much of each type of gasoline must you use?

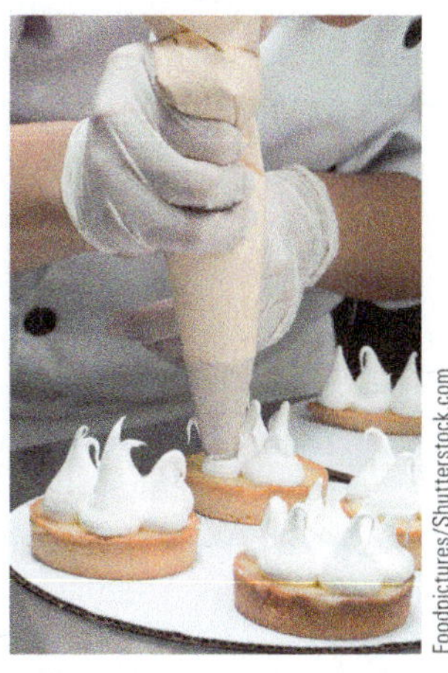
Foodpictures/Shutterstock.com

27. Food Mixtures A pastry chef created a 50-ounce sugar solution that was 34% sugar from a 20% sugar solution and a 40% sugar solution. How much of the 20% sugar solution and how much of the 40% sugar solution were used?

Ideal Body Weight There are various formulas for calculating ideal body weight. In each of the formulas in Exercises 28 and 29, W is ideal body weight in kilograms, and x is height in inches above 60 in.

28. J. D. Robinson gave the following formula for men: $W = 52 + 1.9x$. D. R. Miller published a slightly different formula for men: $W = 56.2 + 1.41x$. At what height do both formulas give the same ideal body weight? Round to the nearest whole number.

29. J. D. Robinson gave the following formula for women: $W = 49 + 1.7x$. D. R. Miller published a slightly different formula for women: $W = 53.1 + 1.36x$. At what height do both formulas give the same ideal body weight? Round to the nearest whole number.

30. **Fuel Economy** Read the article at the right. Suppose you use 10 gal of gas to drive a 2007 Ford Taurus 208 mi. Using the new miles-per-gallon estimates given in the article, find the number of city miles and the number of highway miles you drove.

In the NEWS!

New Miles-per-Gallon Estimates

Beginning with model year 2008, the Environmental Protection Agency is using a new method to estimate miles-per-gallon ratings for motor vehicles. In general, estimates will be lower than before. For example, under the new method, ratings for a 2007 Ford Taurus would be lowered to 18 mpg in the city and 25 mpg on the highway.

Source: www.fueleconomy.gov

31. **Stamps** Stolen in 1967, the famous "Ice House" envelope (named for the address shown on the envelope) was recovered in 2006. The envelope displays a Lincoln stamp, a Thomas Jefferson stamp, and a Henry Clay stamp.

a. The original postage value of three Lincoln stamps and five Jefferson stamps was \$3.20. The original postage value of two Lincoln stamps and three Jefferson stamps was \$2.10. Find the original value of the Lincoln stamp and of the Jefferson stamp.

b. The total postage on the Ice House envelope was \$1.12. What was the original postage value of the Henry Clay stamp?

Critical Thinking

32. **Geometry** Two angles are supplementary. The measure of the larger angle is 15° more than twice the measure of the smaller angle. Find the measures of the two angles. (Supplementary angles are two angles whose sum is 180°.)

33. **Geometry** Two angles are complementary. The measure of the larger angle is four times the measure of the smaller angle. Find the measures of the two angles. (Complementary angles are two angles whose sum is 90°.)

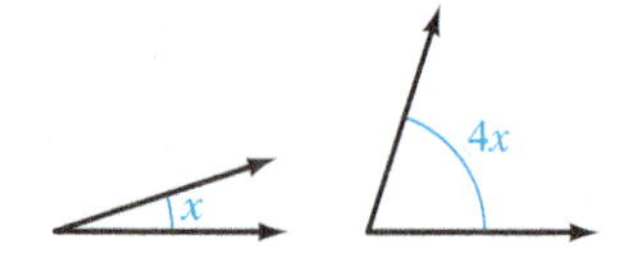

34. **Investments** An investor has \$5000 to invest in two accounts. The first account earns 8% annual simple interest, and the second account earns 10% annual simple interest. How much money should be invested in each account so that the total annual simple interest earned is \$600?

Projects or Group Activities

35. Find the time t between successive alignments of the hour and minute hands on a clock. [*Hint:* Begin with the hands aligned at 12:00. Let $d°$ be the angle, measured from 12:00, at which the hands next align. The time t it takes for the hour hand to rotate $d°$ equals the time it takes for the minute hand to rotate $(d + 360)°$. The hour hand rotates at 30° per hour, and the minute hand rotates at 360° per hour.]

A graphing calculator can be used to approximate the solution of a system of equations in two variables. First graph each equation of the system of equations, and then approximate the coordinates of the point of intersection. The process by which you approximate the solution depends on what model of calculator you have. In all cases, however, you must first solve each equation of the system of equations for y.

Solve: $2x - 5y = 9$
$4x + 3y = 2$

$$2x - 5y = 9 \qquad 4x + 3y = 2$$
$$-5y = -2x + 9 \qquad 3y = -4x + 2$$
$$y = \frac{2}{5}x - \frac{9}{5} \qquad y = -\frac{4}{3}x + \frac{2}{3}$$

• Solve each equation for y.

For the TI-84 Plus, press Y=. Enter one equation as Y1 and the other as Y2. The result should be similar to the screen at the left below. Press GRAPH. The graphs of the two equations should appear on the screen, as shown at the right below. If the point of intersection is not visible on the screen, adjust the viewing window by pressing the WINDOW key.

Take Note

The graphing calculator screens shown here are taken from a TI-84 Plus. Similar screens would display if we used a different model of graphing calculator.

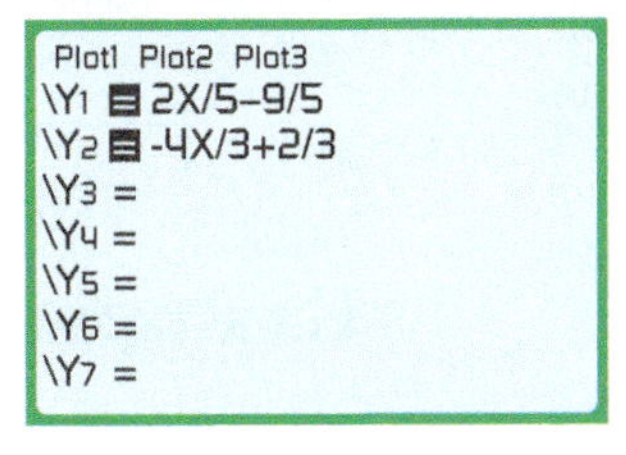

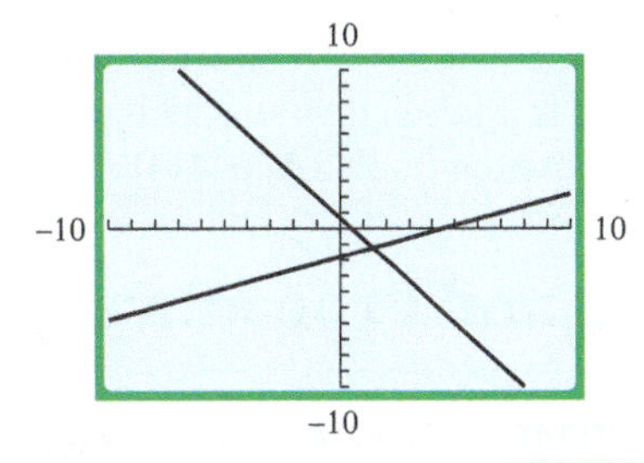

Integrating Technology

See the Keystroke Guide: *Intersect* for instructions on using a graphing calculator to solve systems of equations.

Press 2ND CALC 5 ENTER ENTER ENTER.
After a few seconds, the point of intersection will display at the bottom of the screen as X = 1.4230769, Y = −1.230769.

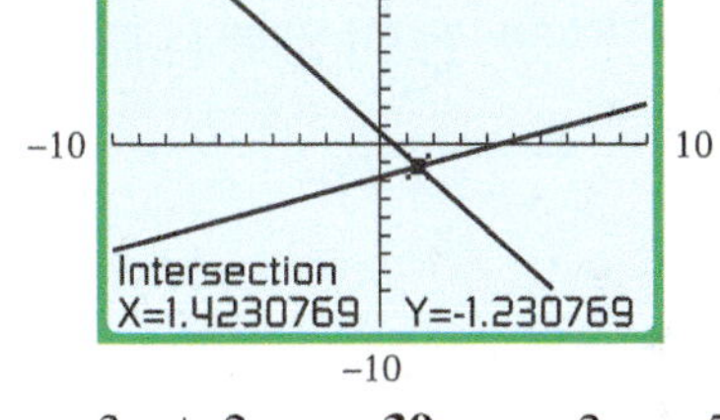

For Exercises 36 to 39, solve by using a graphing calculator.

36. $4x - 5y = 8$
$5x + 7y = 7$

37. $3x + 2y = 11$
$7x - 6y = 13$

38. $x = 3y + 2$
$y = 4x - 2$

39. $x = 2y - 5$
$x = 3y + 2$

CHAPTER

8 Summary

Key Words | Examples

Two or more equations considered together are called a **system of equations.** [8.1A, p. 404]

An example of a system of equations is

$$2x - 3y = 9$$
$$3x + 4y = 5$$

A **solution of a system of equations in two variables** is an ordered pair that is a solution of each equation of the system. [8.1A, p. 404]

The solution of the system of equations shown above is the ordered pair (3, −1) because it is a solution of each equation of the system of equations.

An **independent system** of linear equations has exactly one solution. The graphs of the equations in an independent system of linear equations intersect at one point. [8.1A, p. 405]

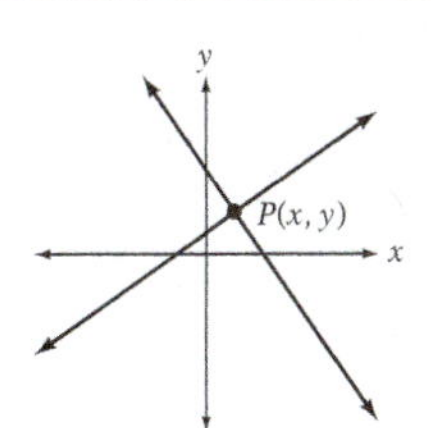

A **dependent system** of linear equations has an infinite number of solutions. The graphs of the equations in a dependent system of linear equations are the same line. [8.1A, p. 405]

If, when solving a system of equations algebraically, the variable is eliminated and the result is a true equation, such as $5 = 5$, the system of equations is dependent. [8.2A, p. 414]

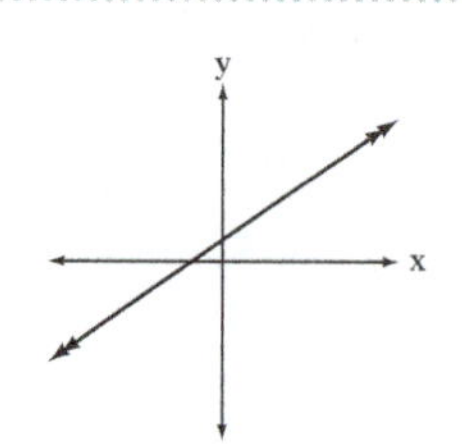

An **inconsistent system** of linear equations has no solution. The graphs of the equations of an inconsistent system of linear equations are parallel lines. [8.1A, p. 405]

If, when solving a system of equations algebraically, the variable is eliminated and the result is a false equation, such as $0 = 4$, the system of equations is inconsistent. [8.2A, p. 414]

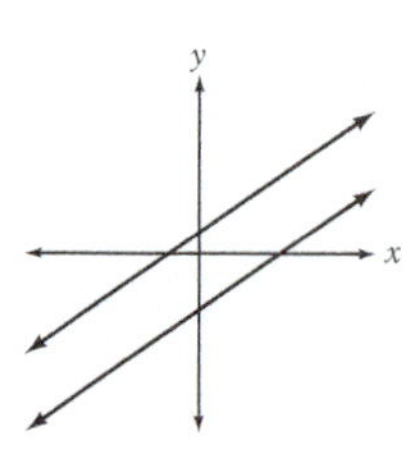

Essential Rules and Procedures

Examples

To solve a system of linear equations in two variables by graphing, graph each equation on the same coordinate system, and then determine the point of intersection. [8.1A, p. 406]

Solve by graphing:

$x + 2y = 4$
$2x + y = -1$

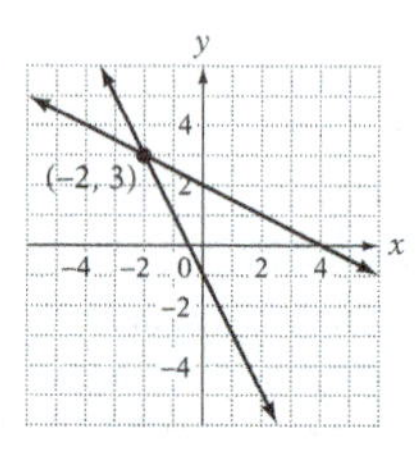

The solution is $(-2, 3)$.

To solve a system of linear equations by the substitution method, write one variable in terms of the other variable. [8.2A, p. 412]

Solve by substitution: (1) $2x + y = 5$
(2) $3x - 2y = 11$

$2x + y = 5$
$y = -2x + 5$ • Solve Equation (1) for y.

$3x - 2y = 11$
$3x - 2(-2x + 5) = 11$ • Substitute for y in Equation (2).
$3x + 4x - 10 = 11$
$7x = 21$
$x = 3$

$y = -2x + 5$
$y = -2(3) + 5$
$y = -1$ The solution is $(3, -1)$.

To solve a system of linear equations by the addition method, use the Multiplication Property of Equations to rewrite one or both of the equations so that the coefficients of one variable are opposites. Then add the equations and solve for the variables. [8.3A, p. 423]

Solve by the addition method:
(1) $2x + 5y = 8$
(2) $3x - 4y = -11$

$6x + 15y = 24$ • 3 times Equation (1)
$-6x + 8y = 22$ • −2 times Equation (2)

$23y = 46$ • Add the equations.
$y = 2$ • Solve for y.
$2x + 5y = 8$
$2x + 5(2) = 8$ • Replace y by 2 in Equation (1).
$2x + 10 = 8$ • Solve for x.
$2x = -2$
$x = -1$

The solution is $(-1, 2)$.

CHAPTER 8 Review Exercises

1. Is $(-1, -3)$ a solution of the system of equations?
$$5x + 4y = -17$$
$$2x - y = 1$$

2. Is $(-2, 0)$ a solution of the system of equations?
$$-x + 9y = 2$$
$$6x - 4y = 12$$

3. Solve by graphing:
$$3x - y = 6$$
$$y = -3$$

4. Solve by graphing:
$$4x - 2y = 8$$
$$y = 2x - 4$$

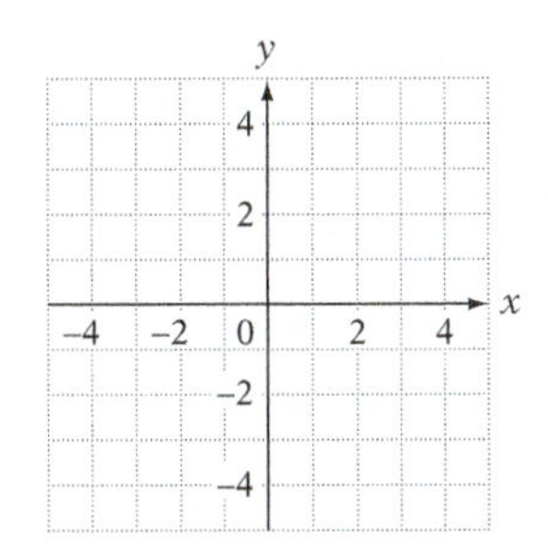

5. Solve by graphing:
$$x + 2y = 3$$
$$y = -\frac{1}{2}x + 1$$

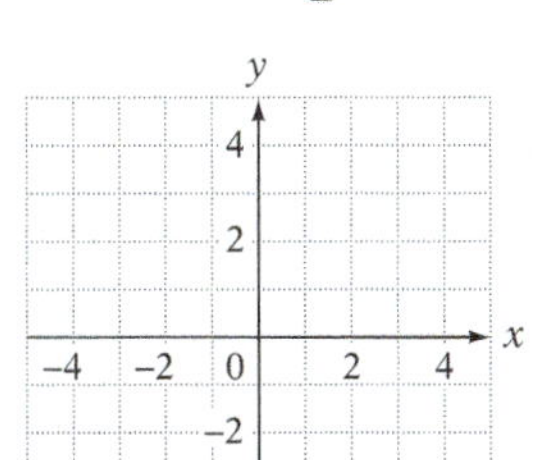

6. Solve by substitution:
$$4x + 7y = 3$$
$$x = y - 2$$

7. Solve by substitution:
$$6x - y = 0$$
$$7x - y = 1$$

8. Solve by the addition method:
$$3x + 8y = -1$$
$$x - 2y = -5$$

9. Solve by the addition method:
$$6x + 4y = -3$$
$$12x - 10y = -15$$

10. Solve by substitution:
$$12x - 9y = 18$$
$$y = \frac{4}{3}x - 3$$

11. Solve by substitution:
$$8x - y = 2$$
$$y = 5x + 1$$

12. Solve by the addition method:
$$4x - y = 9$$
$$2x + 3y = -13$$

13. Solve by the addition method:
$$5x + 7y = 21$$
$$20x + 28y = 63$$

14. Solve by substitution:
$$4x + 3y = 12$$
$$y = -\frac{4}{3}x + 4$$

15. Solve by substitution:
$$7x + 3y = -16$$
$$x - 2y = 5$$

16. Solve by the addition method:
$$3x + y = -2$$
$$-9x - 3y = 6$$

17. Solve by the addition method:
$$6x - 18y = 7$$
$$9x + 24y = 2$$

18. Sculling A sculling team rowing with the current went 24 mi in 2 h. Rowing against the current, the sculling team went 18 mi in 3 h. Find the rate of the sculling team in calm water and the rate of the current.

John Kropewnicki/Shutterstock.com

19. Investments An investor bought 1500 shares of stock, some at \$6 per share and the rest at \$25 per share. If \$12,800 worth of stock was purchased, how many shares of each kind did the investor buy?

20. Travel A flight crew flew 420 km in 3 h with a tailwind. Flying against the wind, the flight crew flew 440 km in 4 h. Find the rate of the flight crew in calm air and the rate of the wind.

21. Travel A small plane flying with the wind flew 360 mi in 3 h. Flying against a headwind, the plane took 4 h to fly the same distance. Find the rate of the plane in calm air and the rate of the wind.

22. Consumerism An online computer service charges one hourly rate for regular use and a higher hourly rate for designated "premium" services. A customer was charged \$14.00 for 9 h of basic use and 2 h of premium use. Another customer was charged \$13.50 for 6 h of regular use and 3 h of premium use. What is the service charge per hour for regular and premium services?

23. Investments Terra Cotta Art Center receives an annual income of \$915 from two simple interest investments. One investment, in a corporate bond fund, earns 8.5% annual simple interest. The second investment, in a real estate investment trust, earns 7% annual simple interest. If the total amount invested in the two accounts is \$12,000, how much is invested in each account?

24. Grain Mixtures A silo contains a mixture of lentils and corn. If 50 bushels of lentils were added, there would be twice as many bushels of lentils as of corn. If 150 bushels of corn were added instead, there would be the same amount of corn as of lentils. How many bushels of each type of grain were originally in the silo?

25. Investments Mosher Children's Hospital received a \$300,000 donation that it invested in two simple interest accounts, one earning 5.4% and the other earning 6.6%. If each account earned the same amount of annual interest, how much was invested in each account?

CHAPTER 8 TEST

1. Is $(-2, 3)$ a solution of the system?
$2x + 5y = 11$
$x + 3y = 7$

2. Is $(1, -3)$ a solution of the system?
$3x - 2y = 9$
$4x + y = 1$

3. Solve by graphing: $3x + 2y = 6$
$5x + 2y = 2$

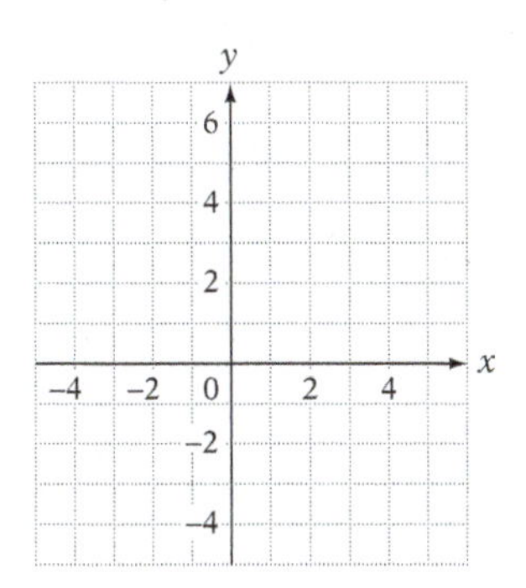

4. Solve by substitution:
$4x - y = 11$
$y = 2x - 5$

5. Solve by substitution:
$x = 2y + 3$
$3x - 2y = 5$

6. Solve by substitution:
$3x + 5y = 1$
$2x - y = 5$

7. Solve by substitution:
$3x - 5y = 13$
$x + 3y = 1$

8. Solve by substitution:
$2x - 4y = 1$
$y = \frac{1}{2}x + 3$

9. Solve by the addition method:
$4x + 3y = 11$
$5x - 3y = 7$

10. Solve by the addition method:
$2x - 5y = 6$
$4x + 3y = -1$

11. Solve by the addition method:
$x + 2y = 8$
$3x + 6y = 24$

12. Solve by the addition method:
$7x + 3y = 11$
$2x - 5y = 9$

13. Solve by the addition method:
$5x + 6y = -7$
$3x + 4y = -5$

14. Travel Flying with the wind, a plane flies 240 mi in 2 h. Flying against the wind, the plane requires 3 h to travel the same distance. Find the rate of the plane in calm air and the rate of the wind.

15. Entertainment For the first performance of a play in a community theater, 50 reserved-seat tickets and 80 general-admission tickets were sold. The total receipts were $980. For the second performance, 60 reserved-seat tickets and 90 general-admission tickets were sold. The total receipts were $1140. Find the price of a reserved-seat ticket and the price of a general-admission ticket.

16. Investments Bernardo Community Library received a $28,000 donation that it invested in two accounts, one earning 7.6% annual simple interest and the other earning 6.4% annual simple interest. If both accounts earned the same amount of annual interest, how much was invested in each account?

Cumulative Review Exercises

1. Evaluate $\dfrac{a^2 - b^2}{2a}$ when $a = 4$ and $b = -2$.

2. Solve: $-\dfrac{3}{4}x = \dfrac{9}{8}$

3. Given $f(x) = x^2 + 2x - 1$, find $f(2)$.

4. Multiply: $(2a^2 - 3a + 1)(2 - 3a)$

5. Simplify: $\dfrac{(-2x^2y)^4}{-8x^3y^2}$

6. Divide: $(4b^2 - 8b + 4) \div (2b - 3)$

7. Simplify: $\dfrac{8x^{-2}y^5}{-2xy^4}$

8. Factor: $4x^2y^4 - 64y^2$

9. Solve: $(x - 5)(x + 2) = -6$

10. Divide: $\dfrac{x^2 - 6x + 8}{2x^3 + 6x^2} \div \dfrac{2x - 8}{4x^3 + 12x^2}$

11. Add: $\dfrac{x - 1}{x + 2} + \dfrac{2x + 1}{x^2 + x - 2}$

12. Simplify: $\dfrac{x + 4 - \dfrac{7}{x - 2}}{x + 8 + \dfrac{21}{x - 2}}$

13. Solve: $\dfrac{x}{2x - 3} + 2 = \dfrac{-7}{2x - 3}$

14. Solve $A = P + Prt$ for r.

15. Find the x- and y-intercepts of $2x - 3y = 12$.

16. Find the slope of the line that passes through the points $(2, -3)$ and $(-3, 4)$.

17. Find the equation of the line that passes through the point $(-2, 3)$ and has slope $-\frac{3}{2}$.

18. Is $(2, 0)$ a solution of the system?
$5x - 3y = 10$
$4x + 7y = 8$

19. Solve by substitution:
$$3x - 5y = -23$$
$$x + 2y = -4$$

20. Solve by the addition method:
$$5x - 3y = 29$$
$$4x + 7y = -5$$

21. Graph: $2x - 3y = 6$.

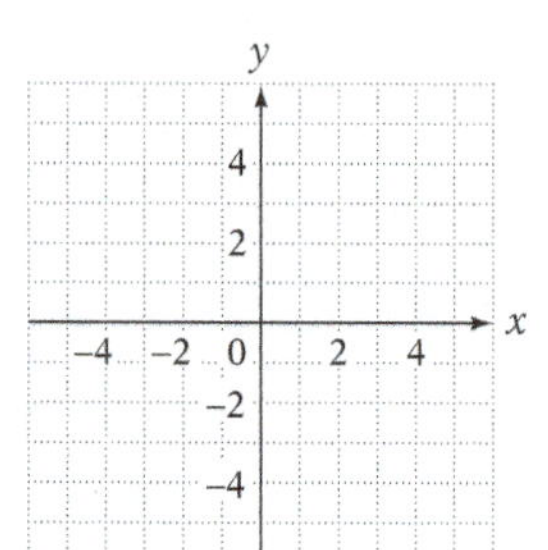

22. Solve by graphing: $3x + 2y = 6$
$3x - 2y = 6$

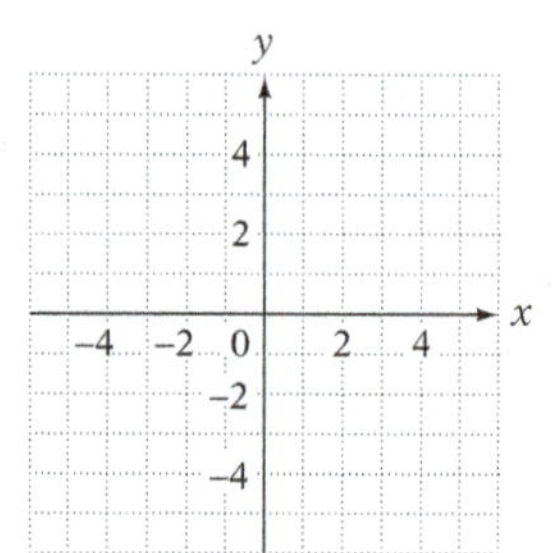

23. Investments A total of \$8750 is invested in two accounts. On one account, the annual simple interest rate is 9.6%; on the second account, the annual simple interest rate is 7.2%. How much should be invested in each account so that both accounts earn the same interest?

24. Travel A passenger train leaves a train depot $\frac{1}{2}$ h after a freight train leaves the same depot. The freight train is traveling 8 mph slower than the passenger train. Find the rate of each train if the passenger train overtakes the freight train in 3 h.

25. Geometry The length of each side of a square is extended 4 in. The area of the resulting square is 144 in^2. Find the length of a side of the original square.

26. Travel A plane can travel 160 mph in calm air. Flying with the wind, the plane can fly 570 mi in the same amount of time it takes to fly 390 mi against the wind. Find the rate of the wind.

27. Travel Traveling with the current, a motorboat can travel 48 mi in 3 h. Traveling against the current, the boat requires 4 h to cover the same distance. Find the rate of the boat in calm water.

28. Food Mixtures A child adds 8 g of sugar to a 50-gram serving of a breakfast cereal that is 25% sugar. What is the percent concentration of sugar in the resulting mixture? Round to the nearest tenth of a percent.

Inequalities

9

OBJECTIVES

SECTION 9.1

A To write a set using the roster method

B To write and graph sets of real numbers

SECTION 9.2

A To solve an inequality using the Addition Property of Inequalities

B To solve an inequality using the Multiplication Property of Inequalities

C To solve application problems

SECTION 9.3

A To solve general inequalities

B To solve application problems

SECTION 9.4

A To graph an inequality in two variables

Focus on Success

Did you make a time management plan when you started this course? If not, you can still benefit from doing so. Create a schedule that gives you enough time to do everything you need to do. We want you to schedule enough time to study math each week so that you successfully complete this course. Once you have determined the hours during which you will study, consider your study time a commitment that you cannot break. (See Time Management page AIM-4.)

Caroline Eibl/Shutterstock.com

Prep Test

Are you ready to succeed in this chapter? Take the Prep Test below to find out if you are ready to learn the new material.

1. Place the correct symbol, $<$ or $>$, between the two numbers.

$-45 \quad -27$

2. Simplify: $3x - 5(2x - 3)$

3. State the Addition Property of Equations.

4. State the Multiplication Property of Equations.

5. **Nutrition** A certain grade of hamburger contains 15% fat. How many pounds of fat are in 3 lb of this hamburger?

6. Solve:
$7 - 2(2x - 3) = 3x - 1$

7. Graph: $y = \frac{2}{3}x - 3$

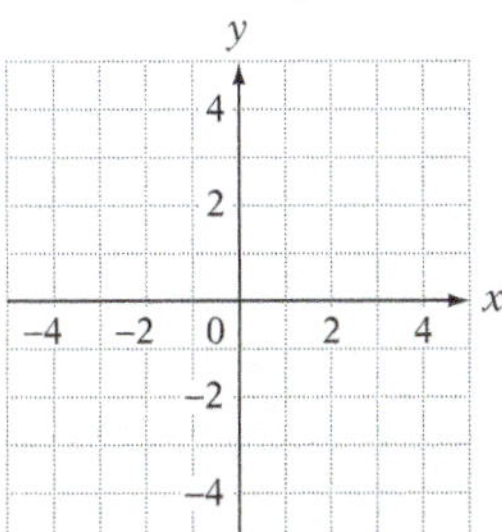

SECTION

9.1 Sets

OBJECTIVE A To write a set using the roster method

Recall that a *set* is a collection of objects, which are called the *elements* of the set. The roster method of writing a set encloses a list of the elements in braces.

The set of the positive integers less than 5 is written $\{1, 2, 3, 4\}$.

HOW TO 1 Use the roster method to write the set of integers between 0 and 10.

$A = \{1, 2, 3, 4, 5, 6, 7, 8, 9\}$ • **A set can be designated by a capital letter. Note that 0 and 10 are not elements of the set.**

HOW TO 2 Use the roster method to write the set of natural numbers.

$A = \{1, 2, 3, 4, \ldots\}$ • **The three dots mean that the pattern of numbers continues without end.**

The **empty set,** or **null set,** is the set that contains no elements. The symbol $\varnothing$ or $\{\ \}$ is used to represent the empty set.

The set of people who have run a 2-minute mile is the empty set.

Union and Intersection of Two Sets

The **union** of two sets, written $A \cup B$, is the set of all elements that belong to either set A *or* set B.

The **intersection** of two sets, written $A \cap B$, is the set that contains the elements that are common to both A and B.

EXAMPLES

Find $A \cup B$ and $A \cap B$, given $A = \{1, 2, 3, 4\}$ and $B = \{3, 4, 5, 6\}$.

$A \cup B = \{1, 2, 3, 4, 5, 6\}$ • **The union of A and B contains all the elements of A and all the elements of B. Elements in both sets are listed only once.**

$A \cap B = \{3, 4\}$ • **The intersection of A and B contains the elements common to A and B.**

EXAMPLE 1

Use the roster method to write the set of the odd positive integers less than 12.

Solution

$A = \{1, 3, 5, 7, 9, 11\}$

YOU TRY IT 1

Use the roster method to write the set of the odd negative integers greater than -10.

Your solution

Solution on p. S22

EXAMPLE 2

Use the roster method to write the set of the even positive integers.

Solution

$A = \{2, 4, 6, \ldots\}$

YOU TRY IT 2

Use the roster method to write the set of the odd positive integers.

Your solution

EXAMPLE 3

Find $D \cup E$, given $D = \{6, 8, 10, 12\}$ and $E = \{-8, -6, 10, 12\}$.

Solution

$D \cup E = \{-8, -6, 6, 8, 10, 12\}$

YOU TRY IT 3

Find $A \cup B$, given $A = \{-2, -1, 0, 1, 2\}$ and $B = \{0, 1, 2, 3, 4\}$.

Your solution

EXAMPLE 4

Find $A \cap B$, given $A = \{5, 6, 9, 11\}$ and $B = \{5, 9, 13, 15\}$.

Solution

$A \cap B = \{5, 9\}$

YOU TRY IT 4

Find $C \cap D$, given $C = \{10, 12, 14, 16\}$ and $D = \{10, 16, 20, 26\}$.

Your solution

EXAMPLE 5

Find $A \cap B$, given $A = \{1, 2, 3, 4\}$ and $B = \{8, 9, 10, 11\}$.

Solution

$A \cap B = \varnothing$

YOU TRY IT 5

Find $A \cap B$, given $A = \{-5, -4, -3, -2\}$ and $B = \{2, 3, 4, 5\}$.

Your solution

Solutions on p. S22

OBJECTIVE B *To write and graph sets of real numbers*

Point of Interest

The symbol $\in$ was first used in the book *Arithmeticae Principia*, published in 1889. It is the first letter of the Greek word $\varepsilon\sigma\tau\iota$, which means "is." The symbols for union and intersection were also introduced around the same time.

Another method of representing sets is called **set-builder notation.** This method of writing sets uses a rule to describe the elements of the set. Using set-builder notation, we represent the set of all positive integers less than 10 as

$\{x \mid x < 10, x \in \text{positive integers}\}$, which is read "the set of all positive integers x that are less than 10."

HOW TO 3 Use set-builder notation to write the set of integers less than or equal to 12.

$\{x \mid x \leq 12, x \in \text{integers}\}$ • **This is read "the set of all integers x that are less than or equal to 12."**

HOW TO 4 Use set-builder notation to write the set of real numbers greater than 4.

$\{x \mid x > 4, x \in \text{real numbers}\}$ • **This is read "the set of all real numbers x that are greater than 4."**

Take Note

Set-builder notation is mainly used to represent sets that have an infinite number of elements. The set $\{x|x > 4\}$ has an infinite number of elements and cannot be represented using the roster method.

For the remainder of this section, all variables will represent real numbers. Given this convention, $\{x|x > 4, x \in \text{real numbers}\}$ is written $\{x|x > 4\}$.

Some sets of real numbers that are written in set-builder notation can be written in **interval notation.** For instance, the interval notation $[-3, 2)$ represents the set of real numbers between -3 and 2. The bracket means that -3 is included in the set, and the parenthesis means that 2 is *not* included in the set. Using set-builder notation, the interval $[-3, 2)$ is written

$\{x|-3 \leq x < 2\}$ • **This is read "the set of all real numbers x between -3 and 2, including -3 but excluding 2."**

To indicate an interval that extends forever in the positive direction, we use the **infinity symbol, ∞;** to indicate an interval that extends forever in the negative direction, we use the **negative infinity symbol, $-\infty$.**

HOW TO 5 Write $\{x|x > 1\}$ in interval notation.

$\{x|x > 1\}$ is the set of real numbers greater than 1. This set extends forever in the positive direction. In interval notation, this set is written $(1, \infty)$.

HOW TO 6 Write $\{x|x \leq -2\}$ in interval notation.

$\{x|x \leq -2\}$ is the set of real numbers less than or equal to -2. This set extends forever in the negative direction. In interval notation, this set is written $(-\infty, -2]$.

When writing a set in interval notation, we always use a parenthesis to the right of ∞ and to the left of $-\infty$. Infinity is not a real number, so it cannot be represented as belonging to the set of real numbers by using a bracket.

HOW TO 7 Write $[1, 3]$ in set-builder notation.

This is the set of real numbers between 1 and 3, including 1 and 3. In set-builder notation, this set is written $\{x|1 \leq x \leq 3\}$.

We can graph sets of real numbers given in set-builder notation or in interval notation.

HOW TO 8 Graph: $(-\infty, -1)$

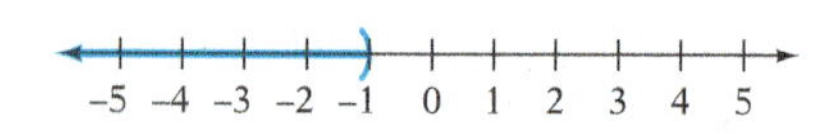

This is the set of real numbers less than -1, excluding -1. The parenthesis at -1 on the number line indicates that -1 is excluded from the set.

HOW TO 9 Graph: $\{x|x \geq 1\}$

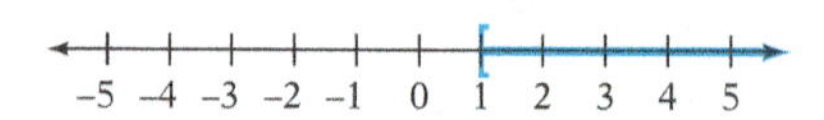

This is the set of real numbers greater than or equal to 1. The bracket at 1 indicates that 1 is included in the set.

EXAMPLE 6

Write in interval notation.
a. $\{x|x \geq 2\}$ **b.** $\{x|0 \leq x \leq 1\}$

Solution

a. $\{x|x \geq 2\}$ is the set of real numbers greater than or equal to 2. This set extends forever in the positive direction. In interval notation, this set is written $[2, \infty)$.

b. $\{x|0 \leq x \leq 1\}$ is the set of real numbers between 0 and 1, including 0 and 1. In interval notation, this set is written $[0, 1]$.

YOU TRY IT 6

Write in interval notation.
a. $\{x|x \leq 3\}$ **b.** $\{x|-5 \leq x \leq -3\}$

Your solution

EXAMPLE 7

Write in set-builder notation.
a. $(-\infty, 0]$ **b.** $(-3, 3)$

Solution

a. The interval $(-\infty, 0]$ is the set of real numbers less than or equal to 0. In set-builder notation, this set is written $\{x|x \leq 0\}$.

b. The interval $(-3, 3)$ is the set of real numbers between -3 and 3, excluding -3 and 3. In set-builder notation, this set is written $\{x|-3 < x < 3\}$.

YOU TRY IT 7

Write in set-builder notation.
a. $(-3, \infty)$ **b.** $[0, 4)$

Your solution

EXAMPLE 8

Graph.
a. $\{x|-2 < x < 1\}$ **b.** $\{x|x < 4\}$

Solution

a. The graph is the set of real numbers between -2 and 1, excluding -2 and 1. Use parentheses at -2 and 1.

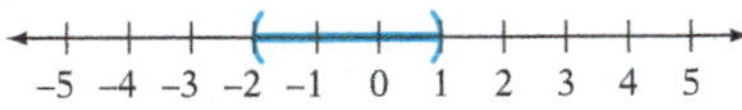

b. The graph is the set of real numbers less than 4. Use a parenthesis at 4.

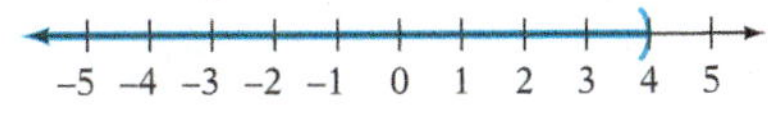

YOU TRY IT 8

Graph.
a. $\{x|-4 \leq x \leq 4\}$ **b.** $\{x|x > -3\}$

Your solution

a. –5 –4 –3 –2 –1 0 1 2 3 4 5

b. –5 –4 –3 –2 –1 0 1 2 3 4 5

EXAMPLE 9

Graph: $(-\infty, 5)$

Solution

The graph is the set of real numbers less than 5. Use a parenthesis at 5.

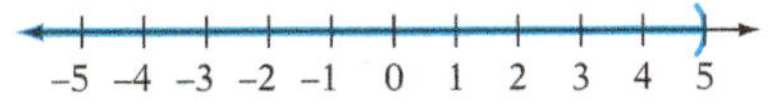

YOU TRY IT 9

Graph: $[2, 5]$

Your solution

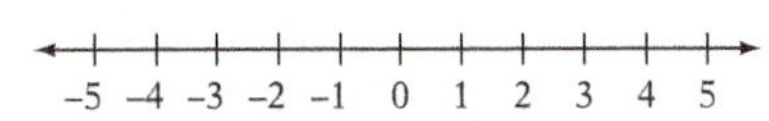

Solutions on p. S22

9.1 EXERCISES

Concept Check

1. The set $\{1, 2, 3\}$ is written using the ____________ method. The set $\{x | x < 4, x \in \text{positive integers}\}$ is written using ____________ notation. The set $[-3, 2]$ is written in ____________ notation.

2. Explain how to find **a.** the union of two sets and **b.** the intersection of two sets.

OBJECTIVE A *To write a set using the roster method*

For Exercises 3 to 6, use the roster method to write the set.

3. The integers between 15 and 22

4. The integers between -10 and -4

5. The odd integers between 8 and 18

6. The even integers between -11 and -1

For Exercises 7 to 12, find $A \cup B$.

7. $A = \{3, 4, 5\}$; $B = \{4, 5, 6\}$

8. $A = \{-3, -2, -1\}$; $B = \{-2, -1, 0\}$

9. $A = \{-10, -9, -8\}$; $B = \{8, 9, 10\}$

10. $A = \{\text{m, n, p, q}\}$; $B = \{\text{m, n, o}\}$

11. $A = \{1, 3, 7, 9\}$; $B = \{7, 9, 11, 13\}$

12. $A = \{-3, -2, -1\}$; $B = \{-1, 1, 2\}$

For Exercises 13 to 18, find $A \cap B$.

13. $A = \{3, 4, 5\}$; $B = \{4, 5, 6\}$

14. $A = \{-4, -3, -2\}$; $B = \{-6, -5, -4\}$

15. $A = \{-4, -3, -2\}$; $B = \{2, 3, 4\}$

16. $A = \{1, 2, 3, 4\}$; $B = \{1, 2, 3, 4\}$

17. $A = \{\text{a, b, c, d, e}\}$; $B = \{\text{c, d, e, f, g}\}$

18. $A = \{\text{m, n, o, p}\}$; $B = \{\text{k, l, m, n}\}$

OBJECTIVE B *To write and graph sets of real numbers*

For Exercises 19 to 24, use set-builder notation to write the set.

19. The negative integers greater than -5

20. The positive integers less than 5

21. The integers greater than 30

22. The integers less than -70

23. The real numbers greater than 8

24. The real numbers less than 57

For Exercises 25 to 33, write the set in interval notation.

25. $\{x|1 < x < 2\}$

26. $\{x|-2 < x \leq 4\}$

27. $\{x|x > 3\}$

28. $\{x|x \leq 0\}$

29. $\{x|-4 \leq x < 5\}$

30. $\{x|-3 \leq x \leq 0\}$

31. $\{x|x \leq 2\}$

32. $\{x|x \geq -3\}$

33. $\{x|-3 \leq x \leq 1\}$

For Exercises 34 to 42, write the interval in set-builder notation.

34. $[-4, 5]$

35. $(-5, -3)$

36. $(4, \infty)$

37. $(-\infty, -2]$

38. $(4, 9]$

39. $[-3, -2]$

40. $[0, \infty)$

41. $(-\infty, 6]$

42. $(-\infty, \infty)$

For Exercises 43 to 58, graph the set.

43. $[-5, 4]$

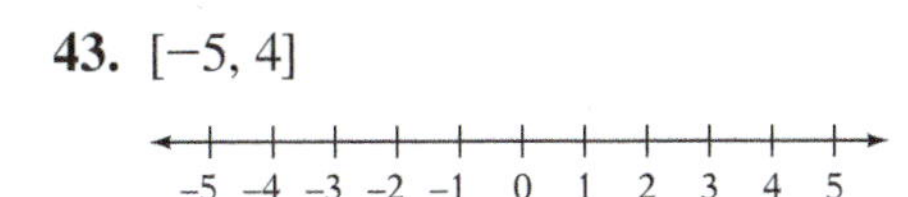

44. $(-3, 5]$

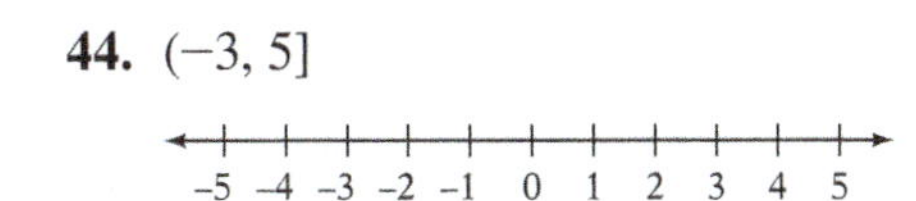

45. $\{x|x < 4\}$

–5 –4 –3 –2 –1 0 1 2 3 4 5

46. $\{x|x \geq -3\}$

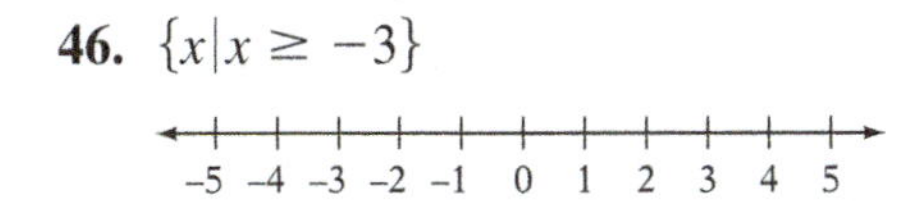

47. $\{x|x \leq -4\}$

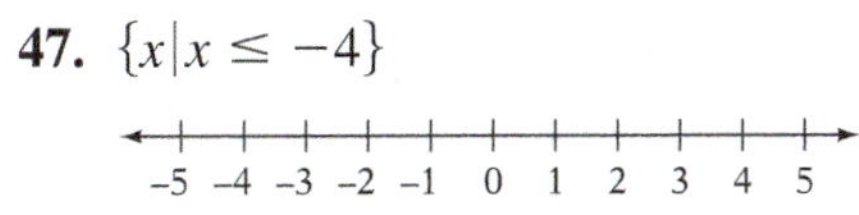

48. $\{x|x > 0\}$

–5 –4 –3 –2 –1 0 1 2 3 4 5

49. $(-\infty, 3]$

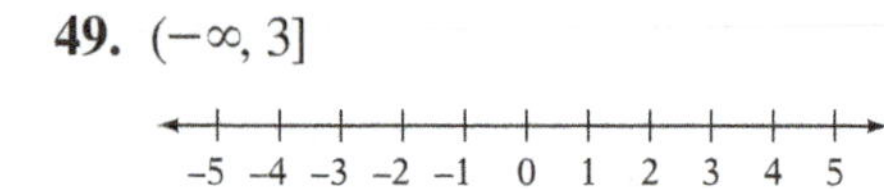

50. $(4, \infty)$

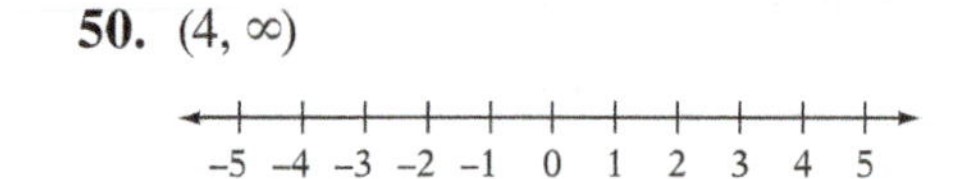

51. $[-1, 3)$

−5 −4 −3 −2 −1 0 1 2 3 4 5

52. $(-3, 0]$

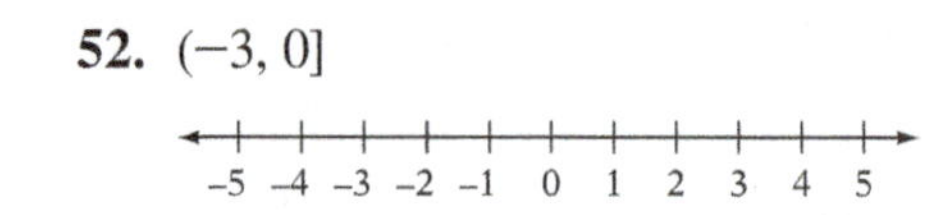

53. $\{x|-3 < x < 3\}$

−5 −4 −3 −2 −1 0 1 2 3 4 5

54. $\{x|0 \le x < 4\}$

−5 −4 −3 −2 −1 0 1 2 3 4 5

55. $\{x|2 \le x \le 4\}$

−5 −4 −3 −2 −1 0 1 2 3 4 5

56. $\{x|-4 < x < 1\}$

−5 −4 −3 −2 −1 0 1 2 3 4 5

57. $\{x|-\infty < x < \infty\}$

−5 −4 −3 −2 −1 0 1 2 3 4 5

58. $(-\infty, \infty)$

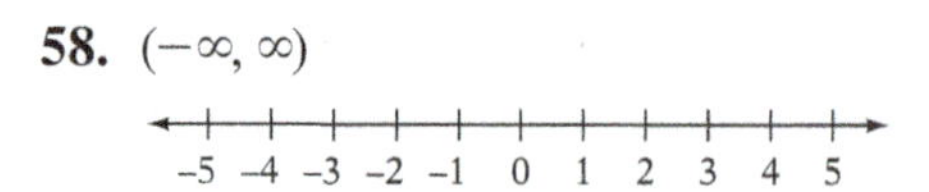

59. How many elements are in the set given in interval notation as $(4, 4)$?

60. How many elements are in the set given by $\{x|4 \le x \le 4\}$?

Critical Thinking

For Exercises 61 and 62, write an inequality that describes the situation.

61. To avoid shipping charges, one must spend a minimum m of \$250.

62. The temperature t never got above freezing (32°F).

63. True or false? If $A \cup B = A$, then $A \cap B = B$.

Projects or Group Activities

64. Make up sets A and B such that $A \cup B$ has three elements and $A \cap B$ has no elements. Write your sets using the roster method.

65. Make up sets A and B such that $A \cup B$ has four elements and $A \cap B$ has four elements. Write your sets using the roster method.

66. Make up sets A and B such that $A \cup B$ has five elements and $A \cap B$ has two elements. Write your sets using the roster method.

SECTION

9.2 The Addition and Multiplication Properties of Inequalities

OBJECTIVE A To solve an inequality using the Addition Property of Inequalities

The inequality at the right is true if the variable is replaced by 7 or 9.3.

$$x + 5 > 8$$
$$\left.\begin{array}{r} 7 + 5 > 8 \\ 9.3 + 5 > 8 \end{array}\right\} \text{True inequalities}$$

The inequality $x + 5 > 8$ is false if the variable is replaced by 2 or $-\frac{1}{2}$.

$$\left.\begin{array}{r} 2 + 5 > 8 \\ -\frac{1}{2} + 5 > 8 \end{array}\right\} \text{False inequalities}$$

The **solution set of an inequality** is the set of numbers each element of which, when substituted for the variable, results in a true inequality. The values of x that will make the inequality $x + 5 > 8$ true are the numbers greater than 3. The solution set of $x + 5 > 8$ is $\{x \mid x > 3\}$. This set can also be written in interval notation as $(3, \infty)$.

At the right is the graph of the solution set of $x + 5 > 8$.

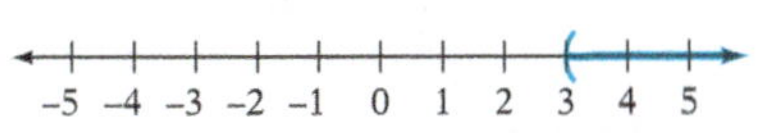

In solving an inequality, the goal is to rewrite the given inequality in the form *variable* > *constant* or *variable* < *constant*. The Addition Property of Inequalities is used to rewrite an inequality in this form.

Addition Property of Inequalities

The same term can be added to each side of an inequality without changing the solution set of the inequality.

If $a > b$, then $a + c > b + c$. If $a < b$, then $a + c < b + c$.

EXAMPLE

The inequality $x - 2 > 5$ has the same solution set as the inequality $x - 2 + 2 > 5 + 2$.

The Addition Property of Inequalities also holds true for an inequality containing the symbol $\geq$ or $\leq$. The Addition Property of Inequalities is used when, in order to rewrite an inequality in the form *variable* > *constant* or *variable* < *constant*, we must remove a term from one side of the inequality. Add the opposite of that term to each side of the inequality.

HOW TO 1 Solve and write the answer in set-builder notation: $x - 4 < -3$

$x - 4 < -3$

$x - 4 + 4 < -3 + 4$ • Add 4 to each side of the inequality.

$x < 1$ • Simplify.

$\{x \mid x < 1\}$ • Write in set-builder notation.

At the right is the graph of the solution set of $x - 4 < -3$.

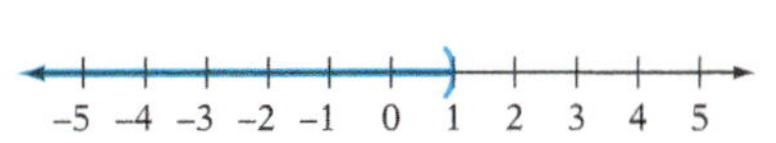

Because subtraction is defined in terms of addition, the Addition Property of Inequalities allows the same term to be subtracted from each side of an inequality.

HOW TO 2 Solve and write the answer in set-builder notation: $5x - 6 \le 4x - 4$

$5x - 6 \le 4x - 4$

$5x - 4x - 6 \le 4x - 4x - 4$ • Subtract $4x$ from each side of the inequality.

$x - 6 \le -4$ • Simplify.

$x - 6 + 6 \le -4 + 6$ • Add 6 to each side of the inequality.

$x \le 2$ • Simplify.

$\{x \mid x \le 2\}$ • Write in set-builder notation.

EXAMPLE 1

Solve. Write the solution set in set-builder notation and in interval notation.

$7x - 14 \le 6x - 16$

Solution

$7x - 14 \le 6x - 16$

$7x - 6x - 14 \le 6x - 6x - 16$ • Subtract $6x$ from each side.

$x - 14 \le -16$

$x - 14 + 14 \le -16 + 14$ • Add 14 to each side.

$x \le -2$

$\{x \mid x \le -2\}$ • Set-builder notation

$(-\infty, -2]$ • Interval notation

YOU TRY IT 1

Solve. Write the solution set in set-builder notation and in interval notation.

$5x + 3 > 4x + 5$

Your solution

Solution on p. S22

OBJECTIVE B *To solve an inequality using the Multiplication Property of Inequalities*

Consider the two inequalities below and the effect of multiplying each inequality by 2, a *positive* number.

$$-3 < 7 \qquad 6 > 4$$
$$2(-3) < 2(7) \qquad 2(6) > 2(4)$$
$$-6 < 14 \qquad 12 > 8$$

In each case, the inequality symbol remains the same. Multiplying each side of an inequality by a **positive** number does not change the inequality.

Now consider the same inequalities and the effect of multiplying by -2, a *negative* number.

$$-3 < 7 \qquad 6 > 4$$
$$-2(-3) > -2(7) \qquad -2(6) < -2(4)$$
$$6 > -14 \qquad -12 < -8$$

In order for the inequality to be true, the inequality symbol must be reversed. If each side of an inequality is multiplied by a **negative** number, the inequality symbol must be reversed in order for the inequality to remain a true inequality.

Take Note

Any time an inequality is multiplied or divided by a negative number, the inequality symbol must be reversed. Compare the next two examples.

$2x < -4$ Divide each side by *positive* 2.

$\frac{2x}{2} < \frac{-4}{2}$

$x < -2$ Inequality *is not* reversed.

$-2x < 4$ Divide each side by *negative* 2.

$\frac{-2x}{-2} > \frac{4}{-2}$

$x > -2$ Inequality *is* reversed.

Multiplication Property of Inequalities—Part 1

Each side of an inequality can be multiplied by the same **positive** number without changing the solution set of the inequality. In symbols, this is stated as follows.

If $a < b$ and $c > 0$, then $ac < bc$. If $a > b$ and $c > 0$, then $ac > bc$.

Multiplication Property of Inequalities—Part 2

Multiplying each side of an inequality by the same **negative** number and reversing the inequality symbol does not change the solution set of the inequality. In symbols, this is stated as follows.

If $a < b$ and $c < 0$, then $ac > bc$. If $a > b$ and $c < 0$, then $ac < bc$.

EXAMPLES

The inequality $3x < 6$ has the same solution set as the inequality $\frac{3x}{3} < \frac{6}{3}$.

The inequality $-4x > 8$ has the same solution set as the inequality $\frac{-4x}{-4} < \frac{8}{-4}$.

In solving an inequality, the goal is to rewrite the given inequality in the form *variable* > *constant* or *variable* < *constant*. The Multiplication Property of Inequalities is used when, in order to rewrite an inequality in this form, we must remove a coefficient from one side of the inequality.

The Multiplication Property of Inequalities also holds true for an inequality containing the symbol $\geq$ or $\leq$.

HOW TO 3 Solve $-\frac{3}{2}x \leq 6$ and write the answer in set-builder notation. Graph the solution set.

$$-\frac{3}{2}x \leq 6$$

$$-\frac{2}{3}\left(-\frac{3}{2}x\right) \geq -\frac{2}{3}(6)$$

- Multiply each side of the inequality by $-\frac{2}{3}$. Because $-\frac{2}{3}$ is a negative number, the inequality symbol must be reversed.

$$x \geq -4$$

$$\{x \mid x \geq -4\}$$

- Write in set-builder notation.

−5 −4 −3 −2 −1 0 1 2 3 4 5

- Graph $\{x \mid x \geq -4\}$.

Because division is defined in terms of multiplication, the Multiplication Property of Inequalities allows us to divide each side of an inequality by a nonzero constant.

Take Note

As shown in HOW TO 4 at the right, the goal in solving an inequality can be *constant* < *variable* or *constant* > *variable*. We could have written the third line of HOW TO 4 as $x > -\frac{2}{3}$.

HOW TO 4 Solve $-4 < 6x$ and write the answer in set-builder notation.

$$-4 < 6x$$

$$\frac{-4}{6} < \frac{6x}{6}$$

- Divide each side of the inequality by 6.

$$-\frac{2}{3} < x$$

- Simplify: $\frac{-4}{6} = -\frac{2}{3}$.

$$\left\{x \mid x > -\frac{2}{3}\right\}$$

- Write in set-builder notation.

EXAMPLE 2

Solve $-7x > 14$ and write the answer in interval notation. Graph the solution set.

Solution

$-7x > 14$

$\frac{-7x}{-7} < \frac{14}{-7}$ • Divide by -7. Reverse the inequality symbol.

$x < -2$

$(-\infty, -2)$

YOU TRY IT 2

Solve $-3x > -9$ and write the answer in interval notation. Graph the solution set.

Your solution

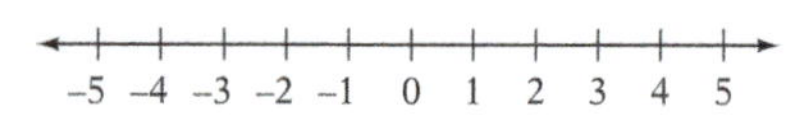

EXAMPLE 3

Solve $-\frac{5}{8}x \le \frac{5}{12}$ and write the answer in set-builder notation.

Solution

$$-\frac{5}{8}x \le \frac{5}{12}$$

$$-\frac{8}{5}\left(-\frac{5}{8}x\right) \ge -\frac{8}{5}\left(\frac{5}{12}\right)$$ • Multiply by $-\frac{8}{5}$. Reverse the inequality symbol.

$$x \ge -\frac{2}{3}$$

$$\left\{x \mid x \ge -\frac{2}{3}\right\}$$

YOU TRY IT 3

Solve $-\frac{3}{4}x \ge 18$ and write the answer in set-builder notation.

Your solution

Solutions on p. S22

OBJECTIVE C *To solve application problems*

EXAMPLE 4

A student must have at least 450 points out of 500 points on five tests to receive an A in a course. One student's results on the first four tests were 94, 87, 77, and 95. What scores on the last test will enable this student to receive an A in the course?

Strategy

To find the scores, write and solve an inequality using N to represent the possible scores on the last test.

Solution

Total number of points on the five tests	is greater than or equal to	450

$$94 + 87 + 77 + 95 + N \ge 450$$
$$353 + N \ge 450$$ • Simplify.
$$353 - 353 + N \ge 450 - 353$$ • Subtract 353.
$$N \ge 97$$

The student's score on the last test must be greater than or equal to 97.

YOU TRY IT 4

A consumer electronics dealer will make a profit on the sale of an LCD HDTV if the cost of the TV is less than 70% of the selling price. What selling prices will enable the dealer to make a profit on a TV that costs the dealer $942?

Your strategy

Your solution

Solution on p. S22

9.2 EXERCISES

Concept Check

1. State whether or not you would need to reverse the inequality symbol when solving the inequality.
   a. $x - 3 > 6$ b. $3x < 6$ c. $-3x > 6$
   d. $3x \le -6$ e. $3 + x \ge -6$ f. $-\frac{x}{3} < 6$

2. Which numbers are solutions of the inequality $x - 5 < -6$?
   (i) 1 (ii) -1 (iii) 12 (iv) -5

3. Which numbers are solutions of the inequality $-4x \le 12$?
   (i) 0 (ii) 3 (iii) -3 (iv) -4

Complete Exercises 4 and 5 by filling in the blank in the first statement with "includes" or "does not include." Fill in the blank in the second statement with the correct inequality symbol: $>$, $<$, $\ge$, or $\le$.

4. The graph of the solution set shown at the right ____________ the number -2. The graph is of the solution set of the inequality x ____________ -2.

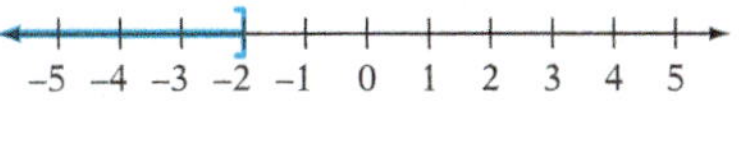

5. The graph of the solution set shown at the right ____________ the number -3. The graph is of the solution set of the inequality x ____________ -3.

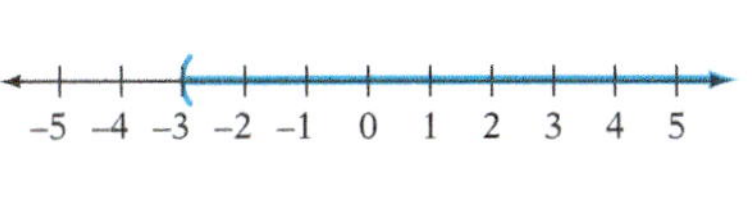

6. In your own words, state the Addition Property of Inequalities and the Multiplication Property of Inequalities.

OBJECTIVE A *To solve an inequality using the Addition Property of Inequalities*

For Exercises 7 to 14, solve the inequality and write the answer in set-builder notation. Graph the solution set.

7. $x + 1 < 3$

8. $y + 2 < 2$

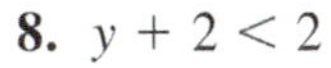

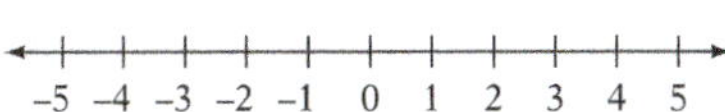

9. $x - 5 > -2$

10. $x - 3 > -2$

11. $7 \le n + 4$

12. $3 \le 5 + x$

13. $x - 6 \le -10$

14. $y - 8 \le -11$

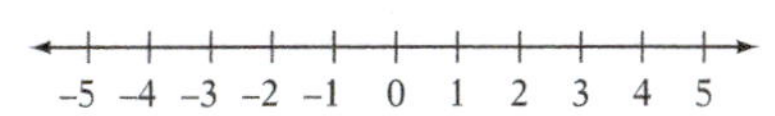

For Exercises 15 to 26, solve and write the answer in interval notation.

15. $y - 3 \ge -12$

16. $x + 8 \ge -14$

17. $3x - 5 < 2x + 7$

18. $5x + 4 < 4x - 10$

19. $8x - 7 \ge 7x - 2$

20. $3n - 9 \ge 2n - 8$

21. $2x + 4 < x - 7$

22. $9x + 7 < 8x - 7$

23. $4x - 8 \le 2 + 3x$

24. $5b - 9 < 3 + 4b$

25. $6x + 4 \ge 5x - 2$

26. $7x - 3 \ge 6x - 2$

For Exercises 27 to 38, solve and write the answer in set-builder notation.

27. $2x - 12 > x - 10$

28. $3x + 9 > 2x + 7$

29. $d + \frac{1}{2} < \frac{1}{3}$

30. $x - \frac{3}{8} < \frac{5}{6}$

31. $x + \frac{5}{8} \ge -\frac{2}{3}$

32. $y + \frac{5}{12} \ge -\frac{3}{4}$

33. $x - \frac{3}{8} < \frac{1}{4}$

34. $y + \frac{5}{9} \le \frac{5}{6}$

35. $2x - \frac{1}{2} < x + \frac{3}{4}$

36. $x + 5.8 \le 4.6$

37. $x - 3.5 < 2.1$

38. $x - 0.23 \le 0.47$

For Exercises 39 to 42, assume that n and a are both positive numbers. State whether the solution set of an inequality of the given form contains only negative numbers, only positive numbers, or both negative and positive numbers.

39. $x + n < a$, where $n > a$

40. $x + n > a$, where $n < a$

41. $x + n < a$, where $n < a$

42. $x + n > a$, where $n > a$

OBJECTIVE B *To solve an inequality using the Multiplication Property of Inequalities*

For Exercises 43 to 52, solve and write the answer in set-builder notation. Graph the solution set.

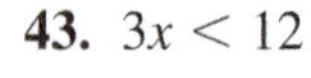

43. $3x < 12$

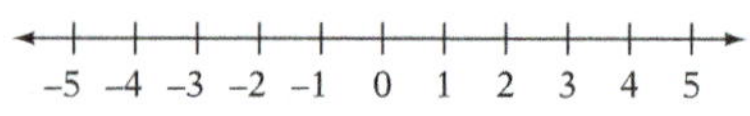

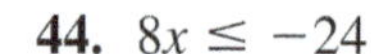

44. $8x \le -24$

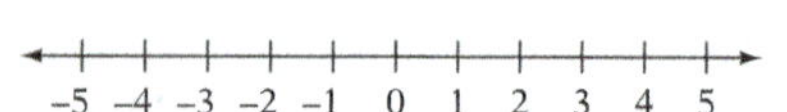

45. $15 \le 5y$

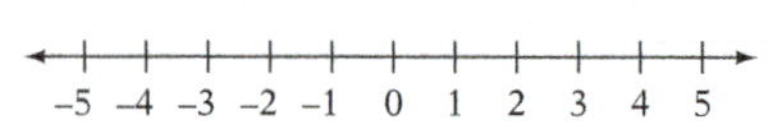

46. $-48 < 24x$

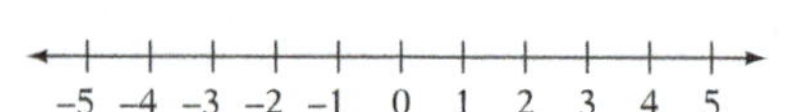

47. $16x \le 16$

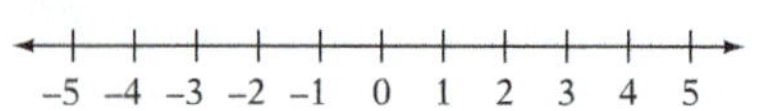

48. $3x > 0$

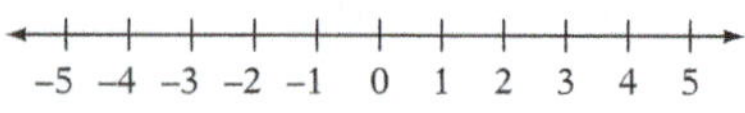

49. $-8x > 8$

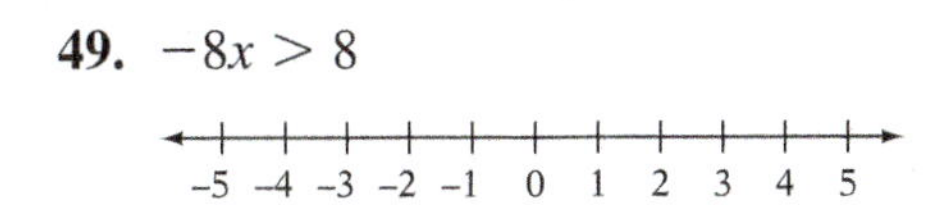

50. $-2n \leq -8$

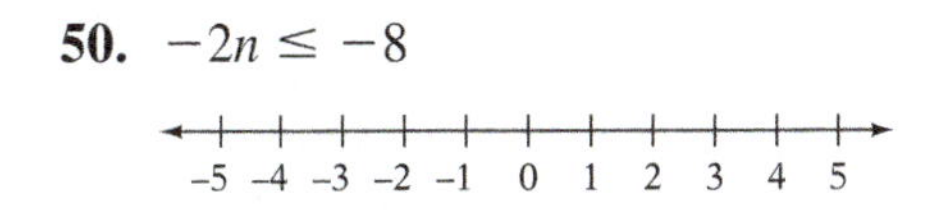

51. $-6b > 24$

–5 –4 –3 –2 –1 0 1 2 3 4 5

52. $-4x < 8$

–5 –4 –3 –2 –1 0 1 2 3 4 5

For Exercises 53 to 64, solve and write the answer in interval notation.

53. $-5y \geq 0$

54. $-3z < 0$

55. $7x > 2$

56. $6x \leq -1$

57. $-x \geq 3$

58. $-y < 4$

59. $2 > -y$

60. $-5 \leq -x$

61. $\frac{5}{6}n < 15$

62. $\frac{3}{4}x < 12$

63. $10 \leq \frac{5}{8}x$

64. $4 \geq \frac{2}{3}x$

For Exercises 65 to 76, solve and write the answer in set-builder notation.

65. $-\frac{2}{11}b \geq -6$

66. $-\frac{4}{7}x \geq -12$

67. $-\frac{3}{5}x < 0$

68. $-\frac{2}{3}x \geq 0$

69. $-\frac{3}{8}x \geq \frac{9}{14}$

70. $-\frac{3}{5}x < -\frac{6}{7}$

71. $-\frac{4}{5}x < -\frac{8}{15}$

72. $-\frac{8}{9}x \geq -\frac{16}{27}$

73. $1.5x \leq 6.30$

74. $2.3x \leq 5.29$

75. $4.25m > -34$

76. $-3.9x \geq -19.5$

For Exercises 77 to 79, without actually solving the inequality or using a calculator, determine which of the following statements is true.

(i) n must be positive. **(ii)** n must be negative. **(iii)** n can be positive, negative, or zero.

77. $-0.8157n > 7.304$

78. $3.978n \leq 0.615$

79. $-917n \geq -10{,}512$

OBJECTIVE C *To solve application problems*

80. Consider the following statement: Today's high temperature will be at least 10 degrees lower than yesterday's high temperature. If the inequality $T \leq t - 10$ correctly represents this statement, what does the variable t represent?

81. **Mortgages** See the news clipping at the right. Suppose a couple's mortgage application is approved. Their monthly mortgage payment is $2050. What is the couple's monthly household income? Round to the nearest dollar.

In the NEWS!

New Federal Standard for Mortgages

A new federal regulation states that the purchaser of a house is not to be approved for a monthly mortgage payment that is more than 38% of the purchaser's monthly household income.

Source: US News & World Report

82. **Sports** To be eligible for a basketball tournament, a basketball team must win at least 60% of its remaining games. If the team has 17 games remaining, how many games must the team win to qualify for the tournament?

83. **Health** A health official recommends a maximum cholesterol level of 200 units. By how many units must a patient with a cholesterol level of 275 units reduce her cholesterol level to satisfy the recommended maximum level?

84. **Recycling** A service organization will receive a bonus of $200 for collecting more than 1850 lb of aluminum cans during its four collection drives. On the first three drives, the organization collected 505 lb, 493 lb, and 412 lb. How many pounds of cans must the organization collect on the fourth drive to receive the bonus?

85. **Grading** To pass a course with a B grade, a student must have an average of 80 points on five tests. The student's grades on the first four tests were 75, 83, 86, and 78. What scores can the student receive on the fifth test to earn a B grade?

Alternative Energy For Exercises 86 to 88, use the information in the article at the right.

86. **a.** A couple living in a town that has not changed the set-back requirement wants to install an 80-foot wind turbine on their property. How far back from the property line must the turbine be set?

b. Suppose the town lowers the 150% requirement to 125%. How far back from the property line must the turbine be set?

87. You live in a town that has not changed the set-back requirement. You want to install a wind turbine 68 ft from your property line. To the nearest foot, what is the height of the tallest wind turbine you can install?

88. You live in a town that has changed the set-back requirement to 115%. A good spot for a wind turbine on your property is 75 ft from the property line. To the nearest foot, what is the height of the tallest wind turbine you can install?

In the NEWS!

New Law Eases Restrictions on Small Wind Systems

A research project created by students in the University of New Hampshire's Environmental Politics class has led to a change in New Hampshire state law. Under the new law, a small wind turbine installed on a residential property must be set back from the property line by a distance greater than 150% of the turbine height. Individual towns may lower the 150% requirement, but they may not increase it.

Source: www.gencourt.state.nh.us

Critical Thinking

89. How does the solution set of $x \leq 4$ differ from the solution set of $x < 4$?

90. True or false: The solution set of $x \geq 4$ is the set $\{4, 5, 6, 7, 8, 9, \ldots\}$

For Exercises 91 and 92, write an inequality that describes the graph.

91. –5 –4 –3 –2 –1 0 1 2 3 4 5

92. 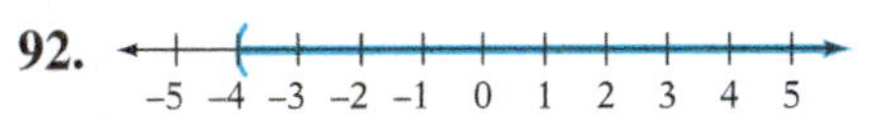

Projects or Group Activities

For Exercises 93 to 96, graph the solution set.

93. $|x| < 3$

94. $|x| < 4$

95. $|x| > 2$

96. $|x| > 1$

CHECK YOUR PROGRESS: CHAPTER 9

1. Use the roster method to write the set of integers between -12 and -9.

2. Find $A \cup B$, given $A = \{4, 8, 16, 20\}$ and $B = \{8, 16, 24\}$.

3. Find $A \cap B$, given $A = \{10, 20, 30, 40\}$ and $B = \{20, 40, 60, 80\}$.

4. Find $A \cap B$, given $A = \{-3, -2, -1, 0\}$ and $B = \{1, 2, 3\}$.

5. Write $\{x | -1 \leq x \leq 3\}$ in interval notation.

6. Write $\{x | x > 8\}$ in interval notation.

7. Write $[-9, \infty)$ in set-builder notation.

8. Write $(-4, 7]$ in set-builder notation.

9. Graph: $(-5, \infty)$

–5 –4 –3 –2 –1 0 1 2 3 4 5

10. Graph: $\{x | -3 \leq x < 5\}$

–5 –4 –3 –2 –1 0 1 2 3 4 5

11. Solve $x - 5 \geq -3$ and write the answer in set-builder notation. Graph the solution set.

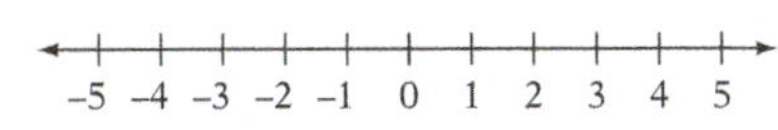

12. Solve $4 < x + 7$ and write the answer in interval notation. Graph the solution set.

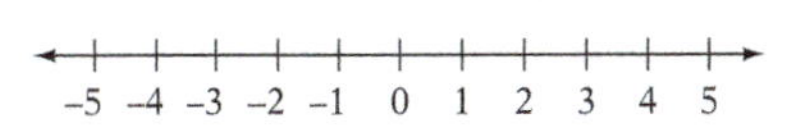

13. Solve $10x - 15 \leq 9x - 20$ and write the answer in set-builder notation.

14. Solve $-12 \leq -3x$ and write the answer in interval notation.

15. **Grading** A student must have at least 400 points out of 500 points on five tests to receive an A in a course. One student's results on the first four tests were 88, 91, 83, and 76. What scores on the last test will enable the student to receive an A in the course?

SECTION

9.3 General Inequalities

OBJECTIVE A *To solve general inequalities*

Solving an inequality frequently requires application of both the Addition and Multiplication Properties of Inequalities.

HOW TO 1 Solve and write the answer in interval notation: $4y - 3 \geq 6y + 5$

$$4y - 3 \geq 6y + 5$$

$$4y - 6y - 3 \geq 6y - 6y + 5$$
• Subtract $6y$ from each side of the inequality.

$$-2y - 3 \geq 5$$
• Simplify.

$$-2y - 3 + 3 \geq 5 + 3$$
• Add 3 to each side of the inequality.

$$-2y \geq 8$$
• Simplify.

$$\frac{-2y}{-2} \leq \frac{8}{-2}$$
• Divide each side of the inequality by -2. Because -2 is a negative number, the inequality symbol must be reversed.

$$y \leq -4$$

$(-\infty, -4]$
• Write in interval notation.

Take Note

When an inequality contains parentheses, one of the steps in solving the inequality is to use the Distributive Property.

HOW TO 2 Solve and write the answer in set-builder notation: $-2(x - 7) > 8 - 4(2x - 3)$

$$-2(x - 7) > 8 - 4(2x - 3)$$

$$-2x + 14 > 8 - 8x + 12$$
• Use the Distributive Property.

$$-2x + 14 > -8x + 20$$
• Simplify.

$$-2x + 8x + 14 > -8x + 8x + 20$$
• Add $8x$ to each side of the inequality.

$$6x + 14 > 20$$
• Simplify.

$$6x + 14 - 14 > 20 - 14$$
• Subtract 14 from each side of the inequality.

$$6x > 6$$
• Simplify.

$$\frac{6x}{6} > \frac{6}{6}$$
• Divide each side of the inequality by 6.

$$x > 1$$

$\{x \mid x > 1\}$
• Write in set-builder notation.

EXAMPLE 1

Solve and write the answer in interval notation: $7x - 3 \leq 3x + 17$

Solution

$$7x - 3 \leq 3x + 17$$

$$7x - 3x - 3 \leq 3x - 3x + 17$$
• Subtract $3x$ from each side.

$$4x - 3 \leq 17$$

$$4x - 3 + 3 \leq 17 + 3$$
• Add 3 to each side.

$$4x \leq 20$$

$$\frac{4x}{4} \leq \frac{20}{4}$$
• Divide each side by 4.

$$x \leq 5$$

$(-\infty, 5]$

YOU TRY IT 1

Solve and write the answer in interval notation: $5 - 4x > 9 - 8x$

Your solution

Solution on p. S22

EXAMPLE 2

Solve and write the answer in set-builder notation: $3(3 - 2x) \geq -5x - 2(3 - x)$

Solution

$$3(3 - 2x) \geq -5x - 2(3 - x)$$
$$9 - 6x \geq -5x - 6 + 2x \quad \text{• Distributive Property}$$
$$9 - 6x \geq -3x - 6$$
$$9 - 6x + 3x \geq -3x + 3x - 6 \quad \text{• Add } 3x \text{ to each side.}$$
$$9 - 3x \geq -6$$
$$9 - 9 - 3x \geq -6 - 9 \quad \text{• Subtract 9 from each side.}$$
$$-3x \geq -15$$
$$\frac{-3x}{-3} \leq \frac{-15}{-3} \quad \text{• Divide each side by } -3.$$
$$x \leq 5$$
$$\{x|x \leq 5\}$$

YOU TRY IT 2

Solve and write the answer in set-builder notation: $8 - 4(3x + 5) \leq 6(x - 8)$

Your solution

Solution on pp. S22–S23

OBJECTIVE B *To solve application problems*

EXAMPLE 3

A rectangle is 10 ft wide and $(2x + 4)$ ft long. Express as an integer the maximum length of the rectangle when the area is less than 200 ft^2. (The area of a rectangle is equal to its length times its width.)

Strategy

To find the maximum length:
- Replace the variables in the area formula by the given values and solve for x.
- Replace the variable in the expression $2x + 4$ with the value found for x.

Solution

Length times width	is less than	200 ft^2

$$10(2x + 4) < 200$$
$$20x + 40 < 200 \quad \text{• Distributive Property}$$
$$20x + 40 - 40 < 200 - 40 \quad \text{• Subtract 40 from each side.}$$
$$20x < 160$$
$$\frac{20x}{20} < \frac{160}{20} \quad \text{• Divide each side by 20.}$$
$$x < 8$$

The length is $(2x + 4)$ ft. Because $x < 8$, $2x + 4 < 2(8) + 4 = 20$. Therefore, the length is less than 20 ft. The maximum length is 19 ft.

YOU TRY IT 3

Company A rents cars for \$8 a day and \$.10 for every mile driven. Company B rents cars for \$10 a day and \$.08 per mile driven. You want to rent a car for one week. What is the maximum number of miles you can drive a Company A car if it is to cost you less than a Company B car?

Your strategy

Your solution

Solution on p. S23

9.3 EXERCISES

Concept Check

Determine whether the statement is true or false.

1. Both "is greater than" and "is more than" are represented by the inequality symbol $\geq$.
2. A minimum refers to a lower limit, whereas a maximum refers to an upper limit.
3. Given that $x > \frac{32}{6}$, the minimum integer that satisfies the inequality is 6.
4. Given that $x < \frac{25}{4}$, the maximum integer that satisfies the inequality is 7.

OBJECTIVE A *To solve general inequalities*

For Exercises 5 to 13, solve and write the answer in interval notation.

5. $4x - 8 < 2x$
6. $7x - 4 < 3x$
7. $2x - 8 > 4x$
8. $3y + 2 > 7y$
9. $8 - 3x \leq 5x$
10. $10 - 3x \leq 7x$
11. $3x + 2 > 5x - 8$
12. $2n - 9 \geq 5n + 4$
13. $5x - 2 < 3x - 2$

For Exercises 14 to 24, solve and write the answer in set-builder notation.

14. $8x - 9 > 3x - 9$
15. $0.1(180 + x) > x$
16. $x > 0.2(50 + x)$
17. $2(2y - 5) \leq 3(5 - 2y)$
18. $2(5x - 8) \leq 7(x - 3)$
19. $5(2 - x) > 3(2x - 5)$
20. $4(3d - 1) > 3(2 - 5d)$
21. $4 - 3(3 - n) \leq 3(2 - 5n)$
22. $15 - 5(3 - 2x) \leq 4(x - 3)$
23. $2x - 3(x - 4) \geq 4 - 2(x - 7)$
24. $4 + 2(3 - 2y) \leq 4(3y - 5) - 6y$
25. Which of the following inequalities are equivalent to the inequality $-7x - 2 > -4x + 1$?
(i) $-3 > -11x$ (ii) $3x > 3$ (iii) $-3 > 3x$ (iv) $3x < -3$

OBJECTIVE B *To solve application problems*

26. An automatic garage door opener costs $325 plus an installation labor charge of $30 per hour, with a minimum of 1 h and a maximum of 3 h of labor. Which of the following are *not* possible amounts for the total cost of the door and installation?
(i) $355 (ii) $450 (iii) $325 (iv) $415 (v) $350

27. Compensation A sales agent for a jewelry company is offered a flat monthly salary of \$3200 or a base salary of \$1000 plus an 11% commission on the selling price of each item sold by the agent. If the agent chooses the \$3200 flat salary, what dollar amount does the agent expect to sell in one month?

28. Compensation A baseball player is offered an annual salary of \$200,000 or a base salary of \$100,000 plus a bonus of \$1000 for each hit over 100 hits. How many hits must the baseball player make to earn more than \$200,000?

29. Comparing Services A site licensing fee for a computer program is \$1500. Paying this fee allows the company to use the program at any computer terminal within the company. Alternatively, the company can choose to pay \$200 for each individual computer it owns. How many individual computers must a company own for the site license to be the more economical choice for the company?

30. Transportation A shuttle service taking skiers to a ski area charges \$8 per person each way. Four skiers are debating whether to take the shuttle bus or rent a car for \$45 plus \$.25 per mile. Assuming that the skiers will share the cost of the car and that they want the least expensive method of transportation, how far away is the ski area if they choose the shuttle service?

Photobac/Shutterstock.com

31. Nutrition For a product to be labeled orange juice, a state agency requires that at least 80% of the drink be real orange juice. How many ounces of artificial flavors can be added to 32 oz of real orange juice if the product is to be legally labeled orange juice?

32. Nutrition Grade A hamburger cannot contain more than 20% fat. How much fat can a butcher mix with 300 lb of lean meat to meet the 20% requirement?

Critical Thinking

33. What number is a solution of $3x - 4 \geq 5$ but not a solution of $3x - 4 > 5$?

34. What number is a solution of $8 - 2(x + 6) \leq 4$ but not a solution of $8 - 2(x + 6) < 4$?

35. A theorem from geometry called the Triangle Inequality Theorem states that the sum of the lengths of two sides of a triangle must be greater than the length of the third side. Suppose two sides of a triangle measure 10 in. and 18 in. Let x be the length of the third side. What are the possible values for x?

Projects or Group Activities

36. Determine whether the statement is always true, sometimes true, or never true, given that a, b, and c are real numbers.

a. If $a > b$, then $-a > -b$.

b. If $a < b$, then $ac < bc$.

c. If $a > b$, then $a + c > b + c$.

d. If $a \neq 0$, $b \neq 0$, and $a > b$, then $\frac{1}{a} > \frac{1}{b}$.

SECTION

9.4 Graphing Linear Inequalities

OBJECTIVE A *To graph an inequality in two variables*

Point of Interest

Linear inequalities play an important role in applied mathematics. They are used in a branch of mathematics called *linear programming,* which was developed during World War II to help with the logistics of supplying the Air Force with the machine parts necessary to keep planes flying. Today, linear programming applications extend to many other disciplines.

Tips for Success

Be sure to do all you need to do in order to be successful at graphing linear inequalities: Read through the introductory material, work through the How To example, study the paired examples, do the You Try Its, and check your solutions against those in the back of the book. See *AIM for Success* at the front of the book.

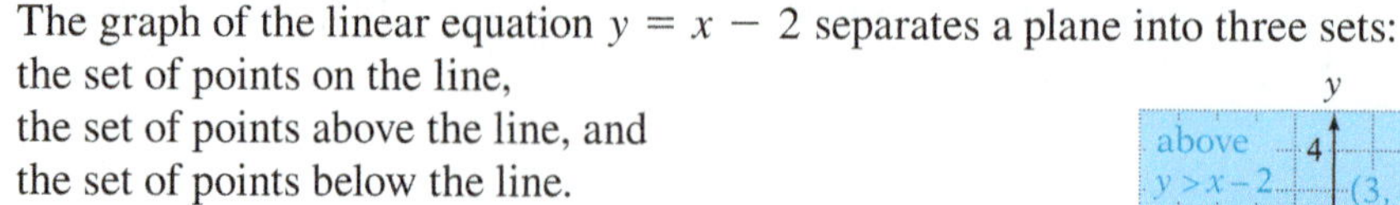

The graph of the linear equation $y = x - 2$ separates a plane into three sets:
the set of points on the line,
the set of points above the line, and
the set of points below the line.

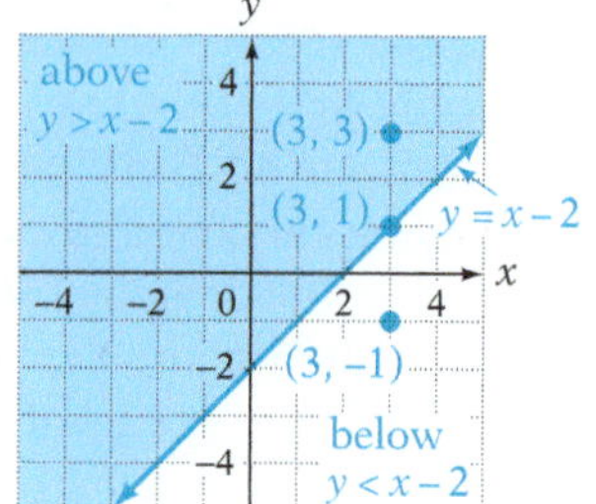

The point (3, 1) is a solution of $y = x - 2$.

$$\begin{array}{c|c} y & x - 2 \\ \hline 1 & 3 - 2 \\ 1 = 1 & \end{array}$$

The point (3, 3) is a solution of $y > x - 2$.

$$\begin{array}{c|c} y > & x - 2 \\ \hline 3 & 3 - 2 \\ 3 > 1 & \end{array}$$

Any point above the line is a solution of $y > x - 2$.

The point $(3, -1)$ is a solution of $y < x - 2$.

$$\begin{array}{c|c} y < & x - 2 \\ \hline -1 & 3 - 2 \\ -1 < 1 & \end{array}$$

Any point below the line is a solution of $y < x - 2$.

The solution set of $y = x - 2$ is all points on the line. The solution set of $y > x - 2$ is all points above the line. The solution set of $y < x - 2$ is all points below the line. The solution set of an inequality in two variables is a **half-plane.**

HOW TO 1 illustrates the procedure for graphing a linear inequality.

HOW TO 1 Graph the solution set of $2x + 3y \le 6$.

Solve the inequality for y.

$$2x + 3y \le 6$$

$$2x - 2x + 3y \le -2x + 6 \quad \text{• Subtract } 2x \text{ from each side.}$$

$$3y \le -2x + 6 \quad \text{• Simplify.}$$

$$\frac{3y}{3} \le \frac{-2x + 6}{3} \quad \text{• Divide each side by 3.}$$

$$y \le -\frac{2}{3}x + 2 \quad \text{• Simplify.}$$

Change the inequality to an equality and graph $y = -\frac{2}{3}x + 2$. If the inequality is $\ge$ or $\le$, the line is part of the solution set and is shown by a solid line. If the inequality is $>$ or $<$, the line is not part of the solution set and is shown by a dashed line.

If the inequality is $>$ or $\ge$, shade the upper half-plane. If the inequality is $<$ or $\le$, shade the lower half-plane.

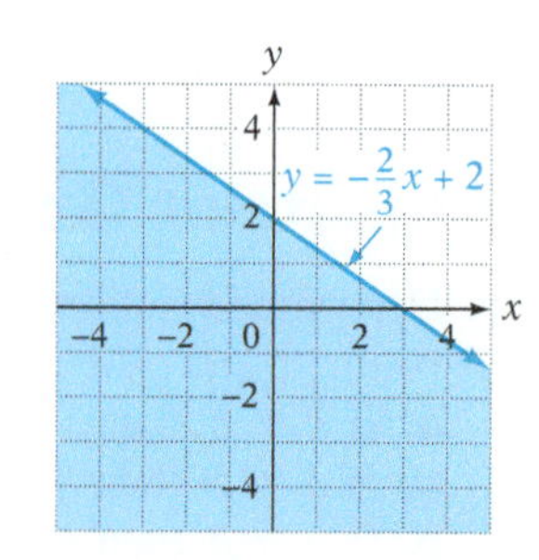

EXAMPLE 1

Graph the solution set of $3x + y > -2$.

Solution

$$3x + y > -2$$
$$3x - 3x + y > -3x - 2$$
$$y > -3x - 2$$

• Subtract $3x$ from each side.

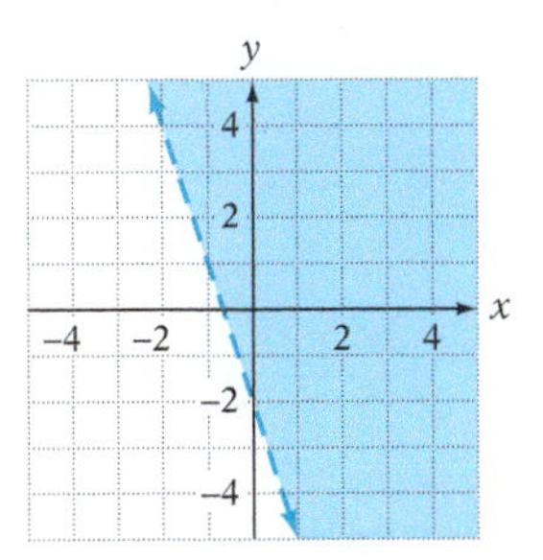

• Graph $y = -3x - 2$ as a dashed line. Shade the upper half-plane.

YOU TRY IT 1

Graph the solution set of $x - 3y < 2$.

Your solution

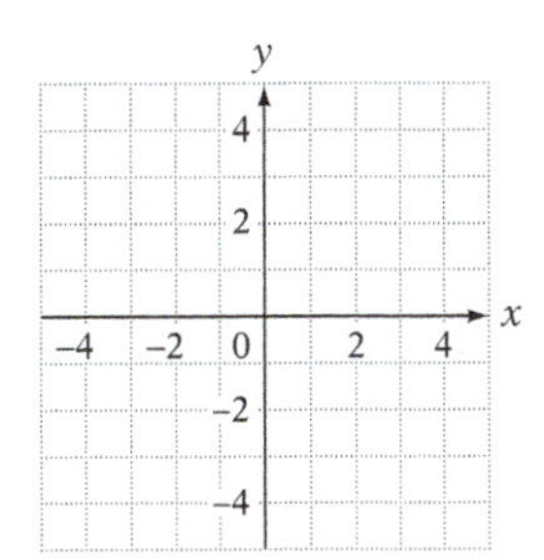

EXAMPLE 2

Graph the solution set of $2x - y \geq 2$.

Solution

$$2x - y \geq 2$$
$$2x - 2x - y \geq -2x + 2$$
$$-y \geq -2x + 2$$
$$-1(-y) \leq -1(-2x + 2)$$
$$y \leq 2x - 2$$

• Subtract $2x$ from each side.

• Multiply each side by -1.

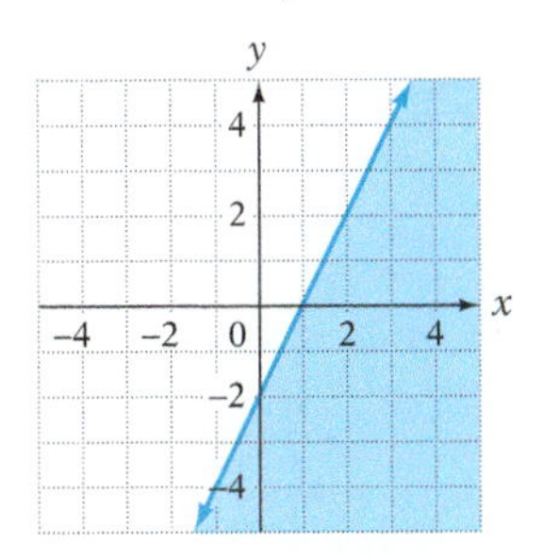

• Graph $y = 2x - 2$ as a solid line. Shade the lower half-plane.

YOU TRY IT 2

Graph the solution set of $2x - 4y \leq 8$.

Your solution

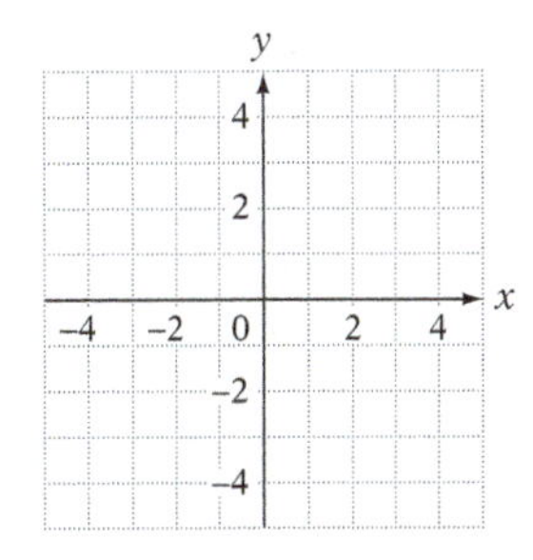

EXAMPLE 3

Graph the solution set of $y > -1$.

Solution

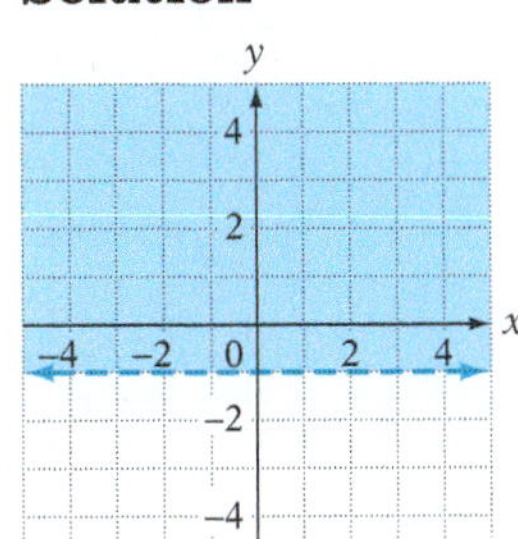

• Graph $y = -1$ as a dashed line. Shade the upper half-plane.

YOU TRY IT 3

Graph the solution set of $x < 3$.

Your solution

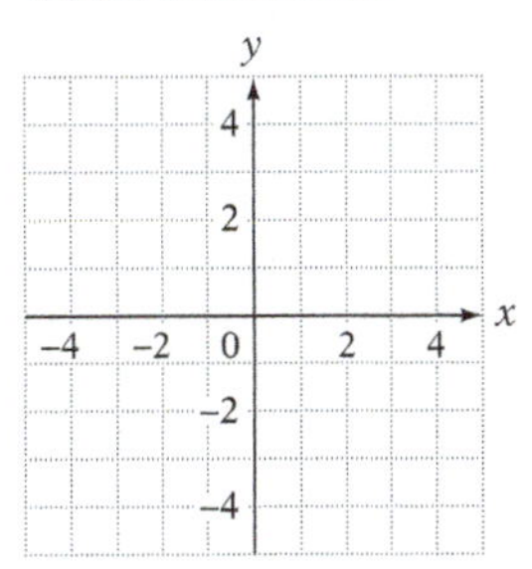

Solutions on p. S23

9.4 EXERCISES

Concept Check

For Exercises 1 to 4, determine whether (0, 0) is a solution of the inequality.

1. $y < -5x + 2$

2. $y > x + 1$

3. $y \le \frac{1}{4}x - 5$

4. $y \ge -\frac{2}{3}x - 6$

OBJECTIVE A *To graph an inequality in two variables*

For Exercises 5 to 22, graph the solution set of the inequality.

5. $y > -x + 4$

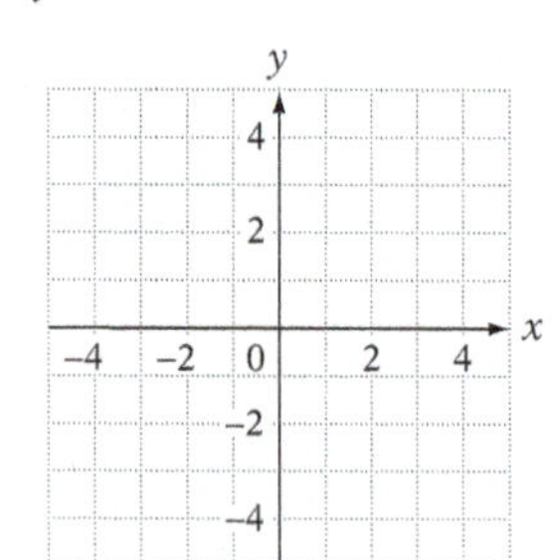

6. $y < x + 3$

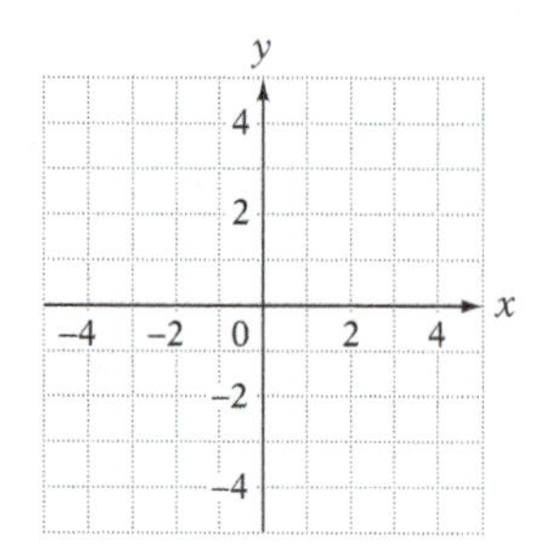

7. $y > 2x + 3$

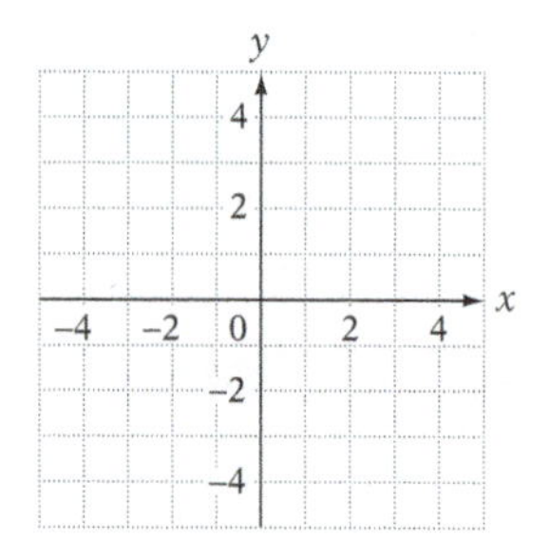

8. $y > 3x - 9$

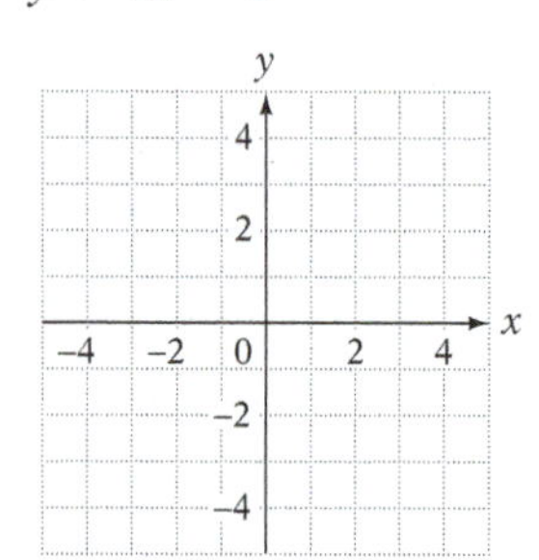

9. $2x + y \ge 4$

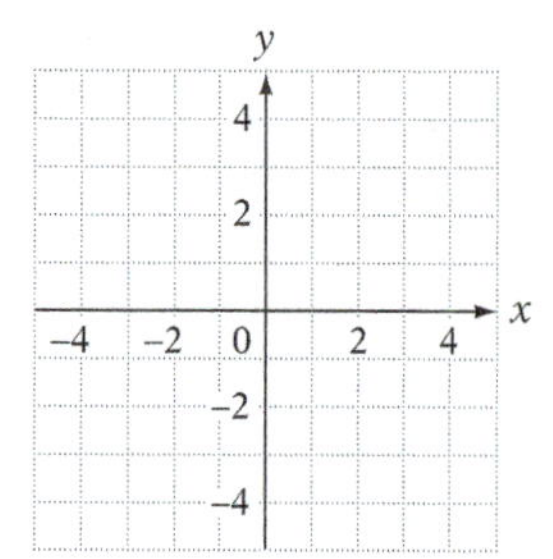

10. $3x + y \ge 6$

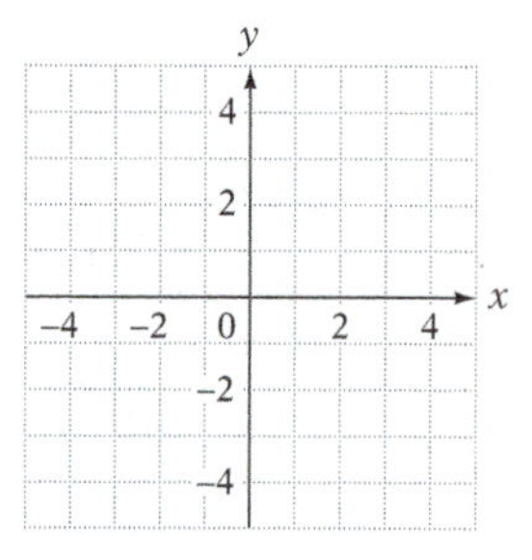

11. $y \le -2$

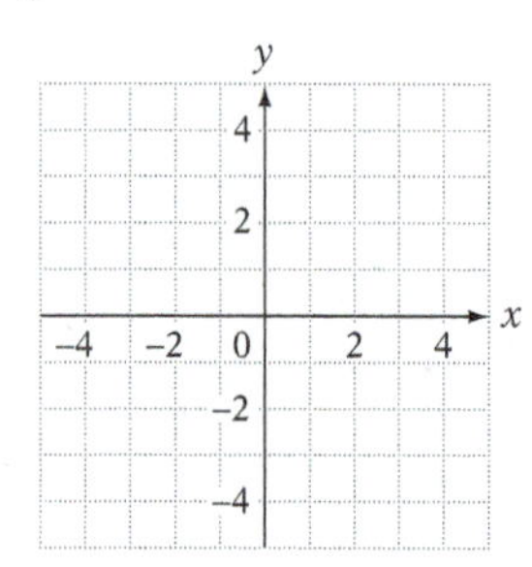

12. $y > 3$

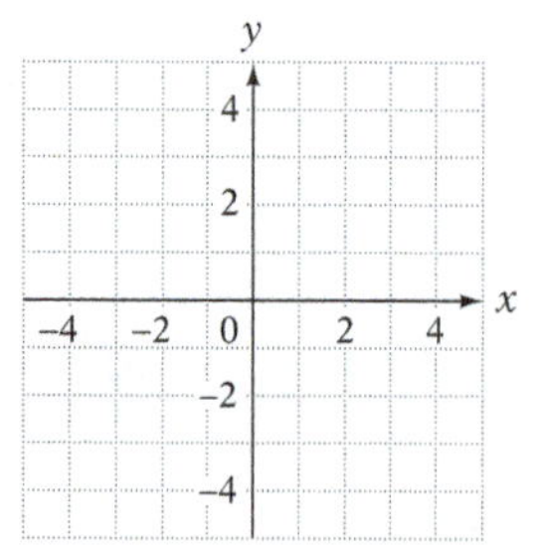

13. $3x - 2y < 8$

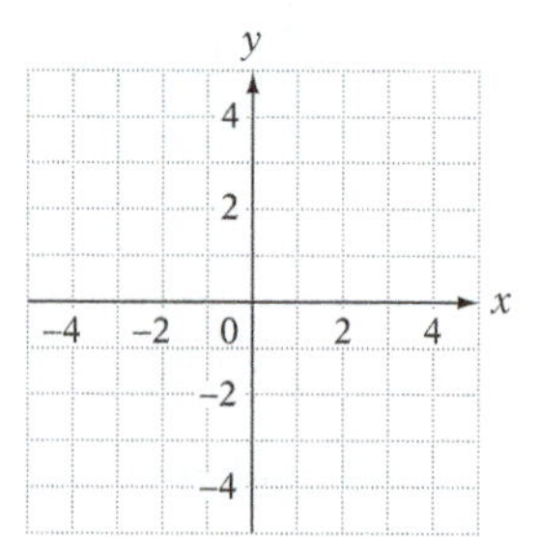

14. $5x + 4y > 4$

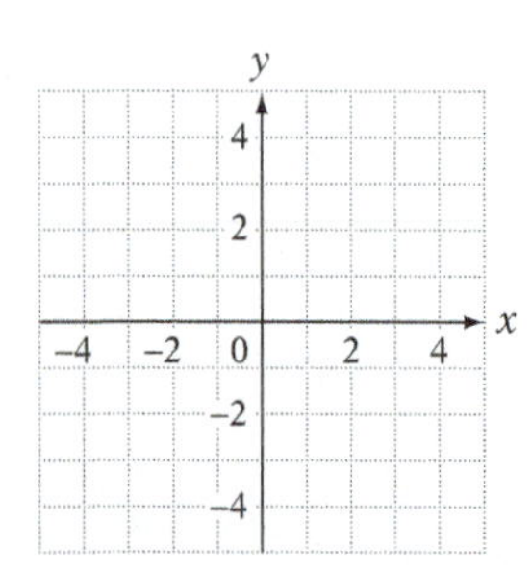

15. $-3x - 4y \ge 4$

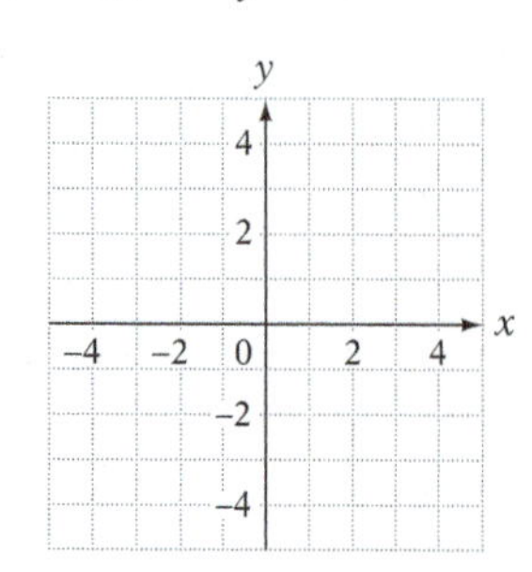

16. $-5x - 2y \ge 8$

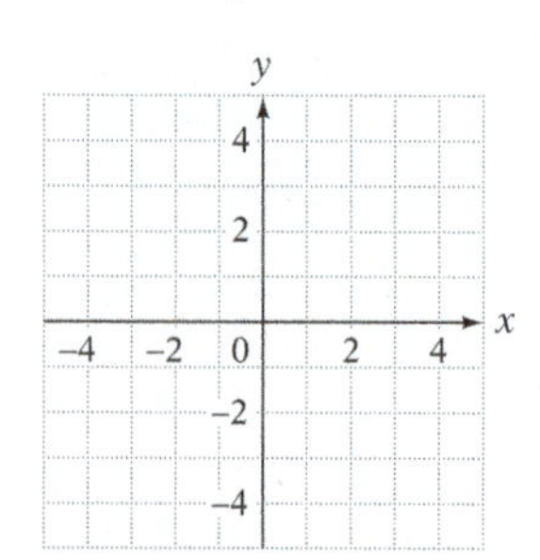

17. $6x + 5y \leq -10$

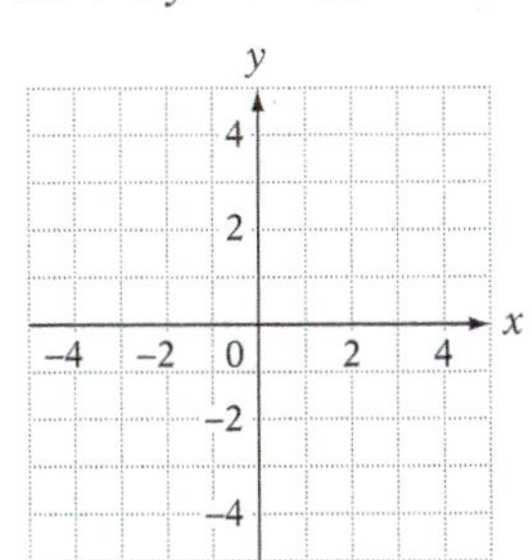

18. $2x + 2y \leq -4$

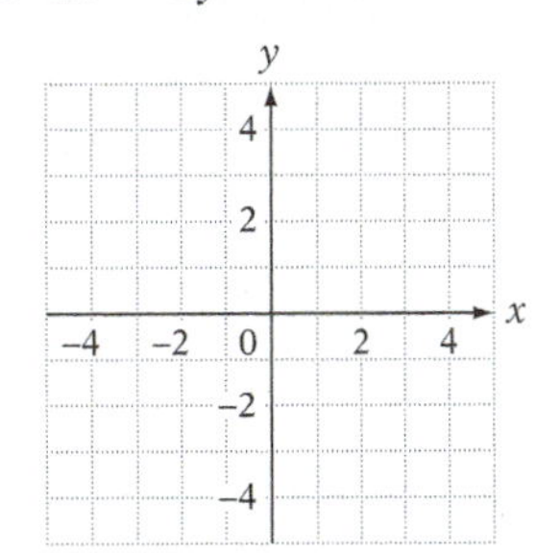

19. $-4x + 3y < -12$

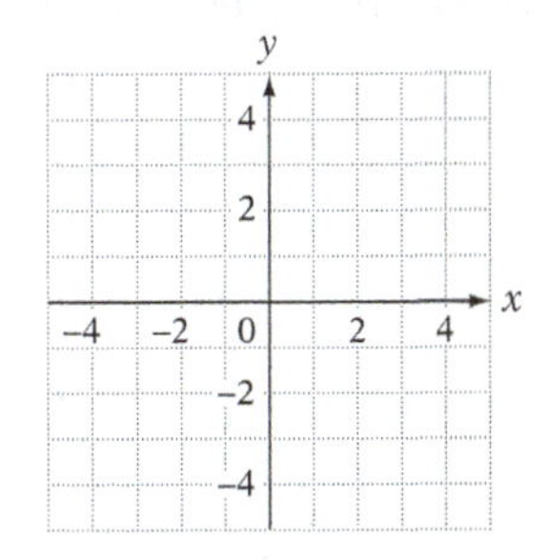

20. $-4x + 5y < 15$

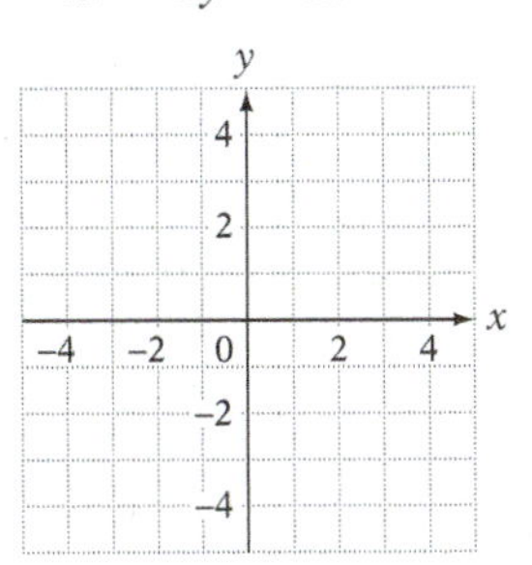

21. $-2x + 3y \leq 6$

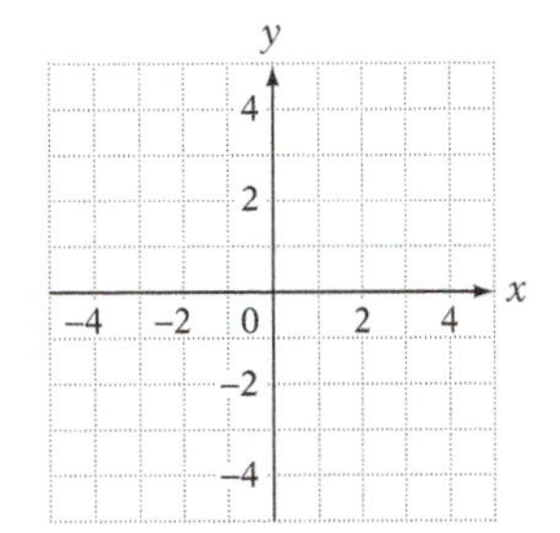

22. $3x - 4y > 12$

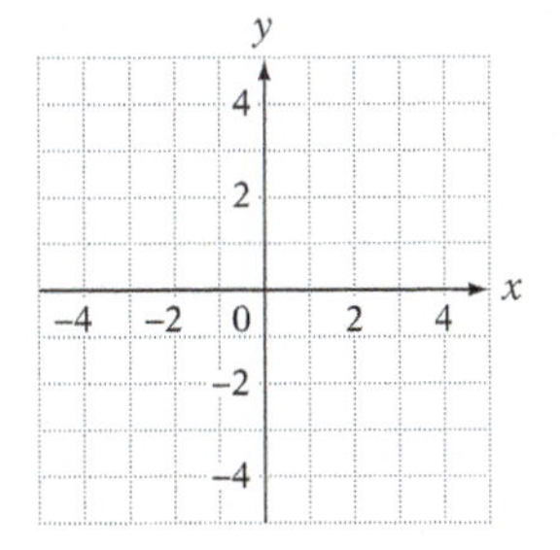

23. Suppose (0, 0) is a point on the graph of the linear inequality $Ax + By > C$, where C is not zero. Is C positive or negative?

24. Suppose $Ax + By < C$, where C is a negative number. Is (0, 0) a point on the graph of $Ax + By < C$?

Critical Thinking

For Exercises 25 to 27, write the inequality given its graph.

25.

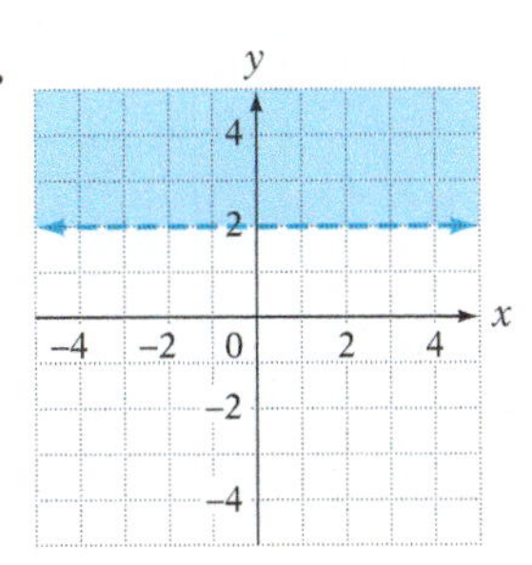

26.

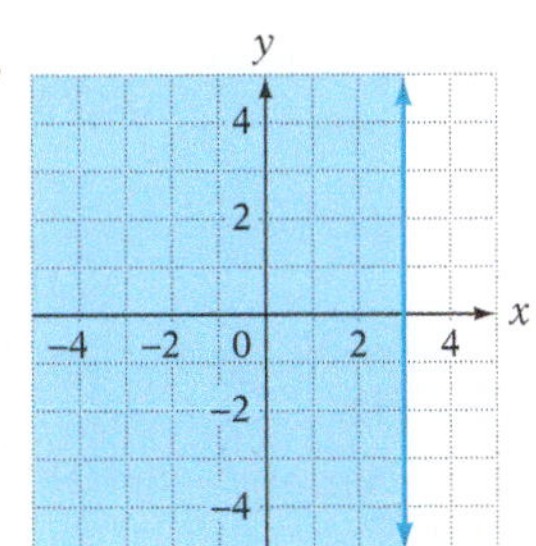

27.

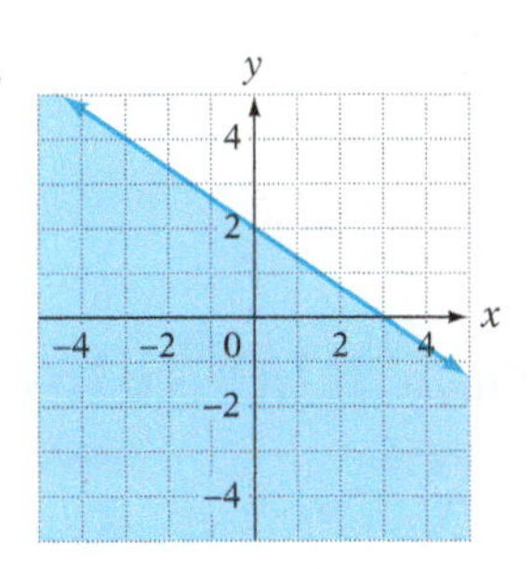

Projects or Group Activities

28. Does an inequality in two variables define a relation? Why or why not? Does an inequality in two variables define a function? Why or why not?

29. Are there any points whose coordinates satisfy both $y < 2x - 3$ and $y > -\frac{1}{4}x + 1$? If so, give the coordinates of three such points. If not, explain why not.

30. Are there any points whose coordinates satisfy both $y > 3x + 1$ and $y < 3x - 4$? If so, give the coordinates of three such points. If not, explain why not.

CHAPTER 9 Summary

Key Words

The **empty set** or **null set,** written $\emptyset$, is the set that contains no elements. [9.1A, p. 446]

Example: The set of cars that can travel faster than 1000 mph is the empty set.

The **union** of two sets, written $A \cup B$, is the set that contains the elements of A and the elements of B. [9.1A, p. 446]

Example: Let $A = \{2, 4, 6, 8\}$ and $B = \{0, 1, 2, 3, 4\}$. Then $A \cup B = \{0, 1, 2, 3, 4, 6, 8\}$.

The **intersection** of two sets, written $A \cap B$, is the set that contains the elements that are common to both A and B. [9.1A, p. 446]

Example: Let $A = \{2, 4, 6, 8\}$ and $B = \{0, 1, 2, 3, 4\}$. Then $A \cap B = \{2, 4\}$.

Set-builder notation and **interval notation** are used to describe the elements of a set. [9.1B, p. 447–448]

Example: The set of real numbers greater than 2 is written in set-builder notation as $\{x \mid x > 2\}$ and in interval notation as $(2, \infty)$.

The **solution set of an inequality** is a set of numbers each element of which, when substituted for the variable, results in a true inequality. The solution set of an inequality can be graphed on a number line. [9.2A, p. 453]

Example: The solution set of $3x - 1 < 5$ is $\{x \mid x < 2\}$. The graph of the solution set is

−5 −4 −3 −2 −1 0 1 2 3 4 5

The solution set of a linear inequality in two variables is a **half-plane.** [9.4A, p. 466]

Example: The solution set of $3x + 4y \geq 12$ is the half-plane shown at the right.

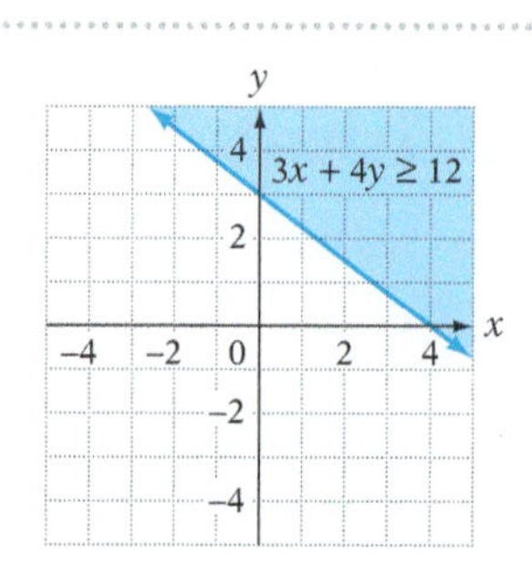

Essential Rules and Procedures

Addition Property of Inequalities [9.2A, p. 453]
The same term can be added to each side of an inequality without changing the solution set of the inequality.

If $a > b$, then $a + c > b + c$.
If $a < b$, then $a + c < b + c$.

Example:

$$x - 3 < -7$$
$$x - 3 + 3 < -7 + 3$$
$$x < -4$$

Multiplication Property of Inequalities [9.2B, p. 455]
Each side of an inequality can be multiplied by the same positive number without changing the solution set of the inequality.

If each side of an inequality is multiplied by the same negative number and the inequality symbol is reversed, then the solution set of the inequality is not changed.

Examples:

$$4x > -8 \qquad \frac{4x}{4} > \frac{-8}{4} \qquad x > -2$$

$$-2x < 6 \qquad \frac{-2x}{-2} > \frac{6}{-2} \qquad x > -3$$

CHAPTER

9 Review Exercises

1. Solve and write the solution in set-builder notation: $2x - 3 > x + 15$

2. Find $A \cap B$, given $A = \{0, 2, 4, 6, 8\}$ and $B = \{-2, -4\}$.

3. Use set-builder notation to write the set of odd integers greater than -8.

4. Find $A \cup B$, given $A = \{6, 8, 10\}$ and $B = \{2, 4, 6\}$.

5. Use the roster method to write the set of odd positive integers less than 8.

6. Solve and write the solution set in interval notation: $12 - 4(x - 1) \le 5(x - 4)$

7. Graph: $\{x \mid x > 3\}$

–5 –4 –3 –2 –1 0 1 2 3 4 5

8. Solve and write the solution set in set-builder notation: $3x + 4 \ge -8$

9. Graph: $3x + 2y \le 12$

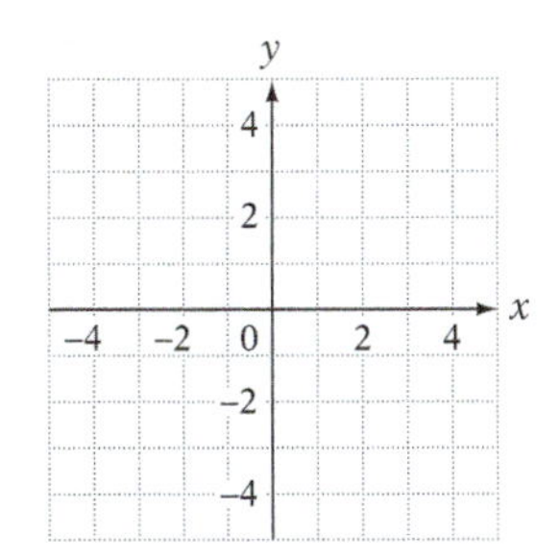

10. Graph: $5x + 2y < 6$

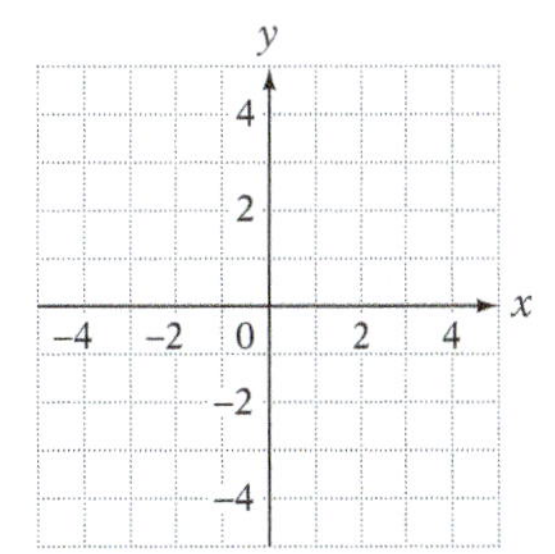

11. Write the set $\{x \mid x > -4\}$ in interval notation.

12. Solve $x - 3 > -1$ and write the solution set in interval notation. Graph the solution set.

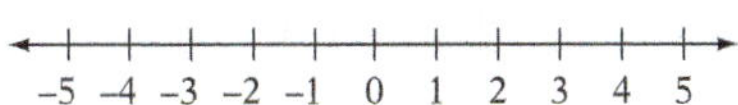

13. Find $A \cap B$, given $A = \{1, 5, 9, 13\}$ and $B = \{1, 3, 5, 7, 9\}$.

14. Graph the interval [1, 4].

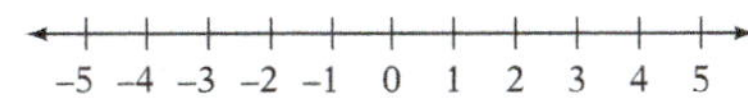

15. Graph: $\{x | -1 < x \leq 2\}$

-5 -4 -3 -2 -1 0 1 2 3 4 5

16. Solve and write the solution set in set-builder notation: $-15x \leq 45$

17. Solve and write the solution set in interval notation: $6x - 9 < 4x + 3(x + 3)$

18. Solve and write the solution set in set-builder notation: $5 - 4(x + 9) > 11(12x - 9)$

19. Solve and write the solution set in set-builder notation: $-\frac{3}{4}x > \frac{2}{3}$

20. Solve and write the solution set in interval notation: $7x - 2(x + 3) \geq x + 10$

21. Graph: $2x - 3y < 9$

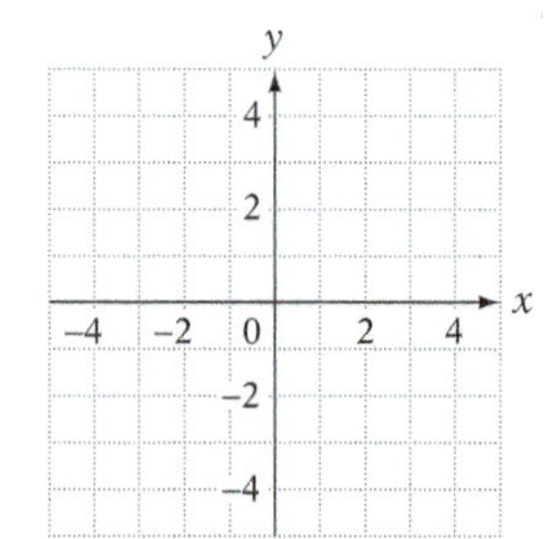

22. Floral Delivery Florist A charges a \$6 delivery fee plus \$70 per bouquet delivered. Florist B charges a \$18 delivery fee plus \$64 per bouquet delivered. A church wants to supply each resident of a small nursing home with a bouquet for Grandparents Day. Find the number of residents in the nursing home if using florist B is more economical than using florist A.

ElenaGaak/Shutterstock.com

23. Gardens The width of a rectangular garden is 12 ft. The length of the garden is $(3x + 5)$ ft. Express as an integer the minimum length of the garden when the area is greater than 276 ft^2. (The area of a rectangle is equal to its length times its width.)

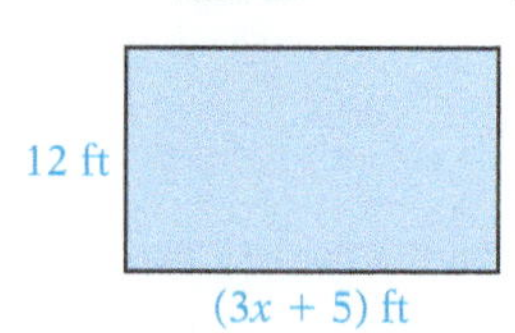

24. Integer Problem Six less than a number is greater than twenty-five. Find the smallest integer that will satisfy the inequality.

25. Grading A student's grades on five sociology tests were 68, 82, 90, 73, and 95. What is the lowest score the student can receive on the next test and still be able to attain a minimum of 480 points?

CHAPTER 9 TEST

1. Graph the interval (0, 5).

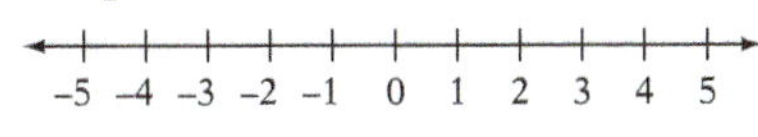

2. Use set-builder notation to write the set of positive integers less than 50.

3. Use the roster method to write the set of the even positive integers between 3 and 9.

4. Solve and write the solution set in interval notation: $3(2x - 5) \geq 8x - 9$

5. Solve and write the solution set in set-builder notation: $x + \frac{1}{2} > \frac{5}{8}$

6. Graph: $\{x \mid x > -2\}$

−5 −4 −3 −2 −1 0 1 2 3 4 5

7. Solve and write the solution set in interval notation: $5 - 3x > 8$

8. Use set-builder notation to write the set of real numbers greater than -23.

9. Graph the solution set of $3x + y > 4$.

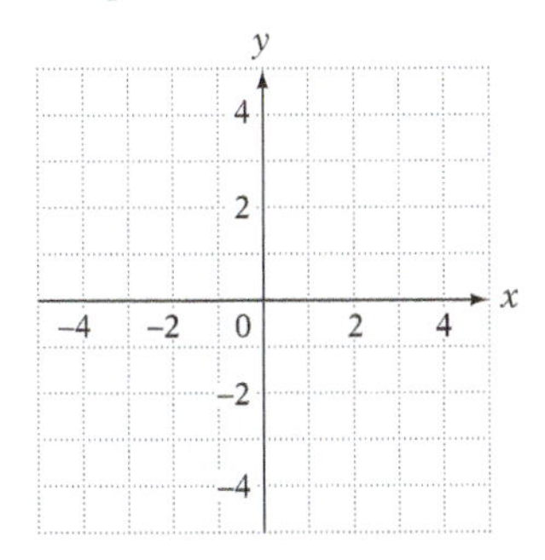

10. Graph the solution set of $4x - 5y \geq 15$.

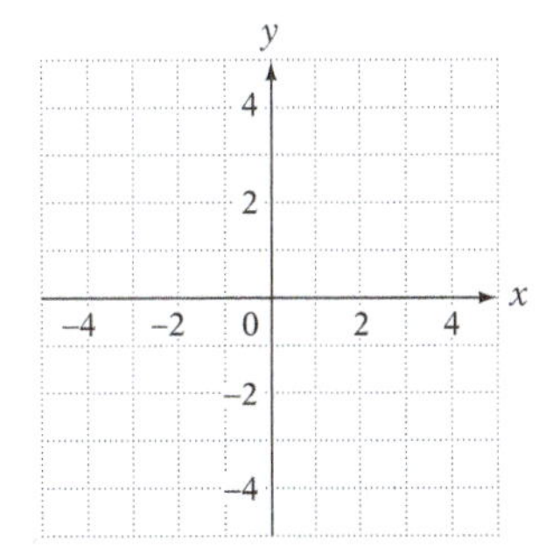

11. Find $A \cap B$, given $A = \{6, 8, 10, 12\}$ and $B = \{12, 14, 16\}$.

12. Solve $4 + x < 1$ and write the solution set in set-builder notation. Graph the solution set.

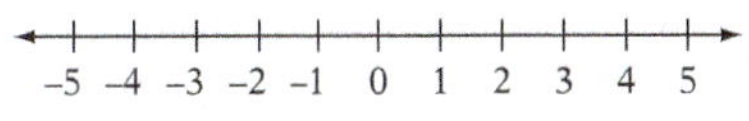

13. Solve and write the solution set in set-builder notation: $-\frac{3}{8}x \leq 5$

14. Solve and write the solution set in interval notation: $6x - 3(2 - 3x) < 4(2x - 7)$

15. Solve $\frac{2}{3}x \geq 2$ and write the solution set in interval notation. Graph the solution set.

–5 –4 –3 –2 –1 0 1 2 3 4 5

16. Solve and write the solution set in set-builder notation: $2x - 7 \leq 6x + 9$

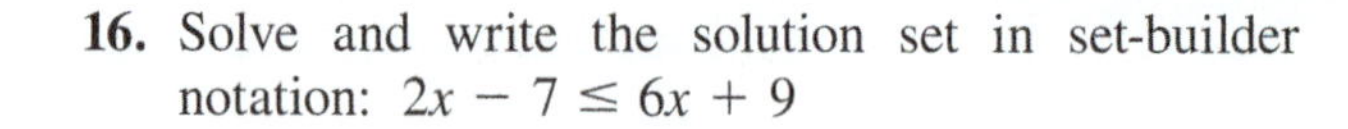

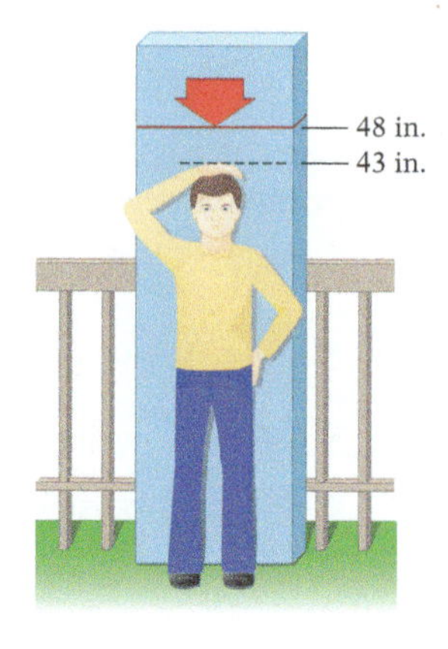

17. Safety To ride a certain roller coaster at an amusement park, a person must be at least 48 in. tall. How many inches must a child who is 43 in. tall grow to be eligible to ride the roller coaster?

18. Geometry A rectangle is 15 ft long and $(2x - 4)$ ft wide. Express as an integer the maximum width of the rectangle if the area is less than 180 ft^2. (The area of a rectangle is equal to its length times its width.)

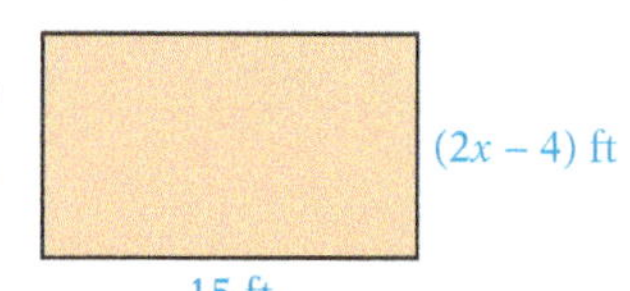

19. Machining A ball bearing for a rotary engine must have a circumference between 0.1220 in. and 0.1240 in. What are the allowable diameters for the bearing? Round to the nearest ten-thousandth. Recall that $C = \pi d$. Use 3.14 for π.

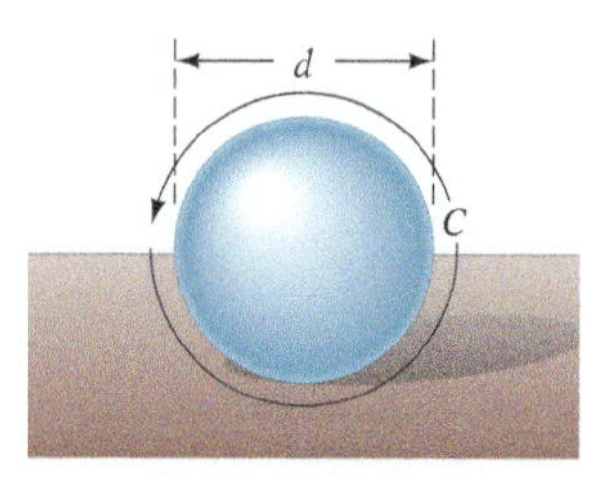

20. Compensation A stockbroker receives a monthly salary that is the greater of \$5000 or \$1000 plus 2% of the total value of all stock transactions the broker processes during the month. What dollar amounts of transactions did the broker process in a month for which the broker's salary was \$5000?

Cumulative Review Exercises

1. Simplify: $2[5a - 3(2 - 5a) - 8]$

2. Solve: $\frac{5}{8} - 4x = \frac{1}{8}$

3. Solve: $2x - 3[x - 2(x - 3)] = 2$

4. Simplify: $(-3a)(-2a^3b^2)^2$

5. Simplify: $\frac{27a^3b^2}{(-3ab^2)^3}$

6. Divide: $(16x^2 - 12x - 2) \div (4x - 1)$

7. Given $f(x) = x^2 - 4x - 5$, find $f(-1)$.

8. Factor: $27a^2x^2 - 3a^2$

9. Divide: $\frac{x^2 - 2x}{x^2 - 2x - 8} \div \frac{x^3 - 5x^2 + 6x}{x^2 - 7x + 12}$

10. Subtract: $\frac{4a}{2a - 3} - \frac{2a}{a + 3}$

11. Solve: $\frac{5y}{6} - \frac{5}{9} = \frac{y}{3} - \frac{5}{6}$

12. Solve $R = \frac{C - S}{t}$ for C.

13. Find the slope of the line that passes through the points $(2, -3)$ and $(-1, 4)$.

14. Find the equation of the line that passes through the point $(1, -3)$ and has slope $-\frac{3}{2}$.

15. Solve by substitution.

$$x = 3y + 1$$
$$2x + 5y = 13$$

16. Solve by the addition method.

$$9x - 2y = 17$$
$$5x + 3y = -7$$

17. Find $A \cup B$, given $A = \{0, 1, 2\}$ and $B = \{-10, -2\}$.

18. Use set-builder notation to write the set of real numbers less than 48.

19. Write $\{x \mid x < 4\}$ in interval notation.

20. Graph the solution set of $\frac{3}{8}x > -\frac{3}{4}$.

−5 −4 −3 −2 −1 0 1 2 3 4 5

21. Solve: $-\frac{4}{5}x > 12$

22. Solve: $15 - 3(5x - 7) < 2(7 - 2x)$

23. Graph: $y = 2x - 1$

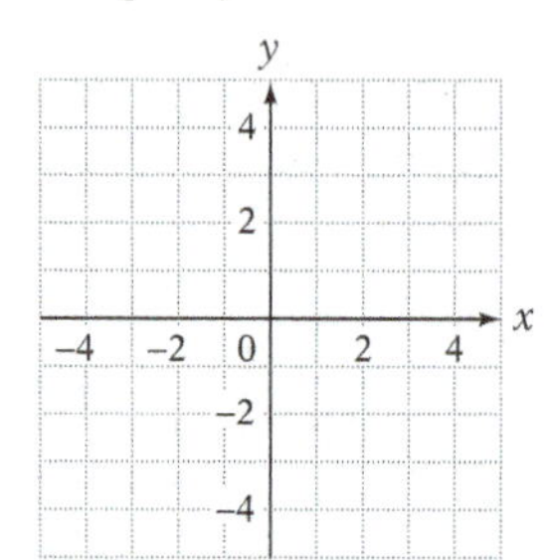

24. Graph the solution set of $6x - 3y \geq 6$.

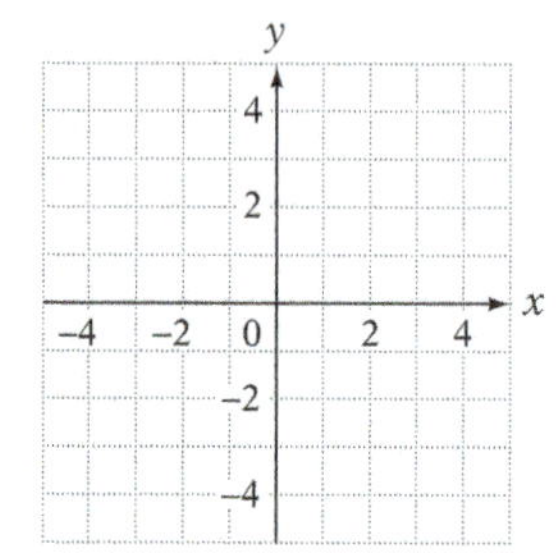

25. Integer Problem Three-fifths of a number is less than negative fifteen. What integers satisfy this inequality? Write the answer in set-builder notation.

26. Rental Agencies Company A rents cars for \$6 a day and \$.25 for every mile driven. Company B rents cars for \$15 a day and \$.10 per mile driven. You want to rent a car for 6 days. What is the maximum number of miles you can drive a Company A car if it is to cost you less than a Company B car?

27. Conservation In a lake, 100 fish are caught, tagged, and then released. Later, 150 fish are caught. Three of these 150 fish are found to have tags. Estimate the number of fish in the lake.

Dmitrijs Bindemanis/Shutterstock.com

28. Geometry The measure of the first angle of a triangle is 30° more than the measure of the second angle. The measure of the third angle is 10° more than twice the measure of the second angle. Find the measure of each angle.

Radical Expressions

10

OBJECTIVES

SECTION 10.1

A To simplify numerical radical expressions

B To simplify variable radical expressions

SECTION 10.2

A To add and subtract radical expressions

SECTION 10.3

A To multiply radical expressions

B To divide radical expressions

SECTION 10.4

A To solve an equation containing a radical expression

B To solve application problems

Focus on Success

Do you get nervous before taking a math test? The more prepared you are, the less nervous you will be. We suggest you study the Chapter Summary. Then do the Chapter Review Exercises to test your understanding of the material in the chapter. If you have trouble with any of the questions, restudy the objectives the questions are taken from. Take the Chapter Test in a quiet place, working on it as if it were the actual exam. (See Ace the Test, page AIM-11.)

Prep Test

Are you ready to succeed in this chapter? Take the Prep Test below to find out if you are ready to learn the new material.

1. Evaluate: $-|-14|$

2. Simplify: $3x^2y - 4xy^2 - 5x^2y$

3. Solve: $1.5h = 21$

4. Solve: $3x - 2 = 5 - 2x$

5. Simplify: $x^3 \cdot x^3$

6. Expand: $(x + y)^2$

7. Expand: $(2x - 3)^2$

8. Multiply: $(2 - 3v)(2 + 3v)$

9. Multiply: $(a - 5)(a + 5)$

10. Simplify: $\dfrac{2x^4y^3}{18x^2y}$

SECTION

10.1 Introduction to Radical Expressions

OBJECTIVE A *To simplify numerical radical expressions*

Point of Interest

The radical symbol was first used in 1525, when it was written as √. Some historians suggest that the radical symbol also developed into the symbols for "less than" and "greater than." Because typesetters of that time did not want to make additional symbols, the radical was rotated to the position ⋟ and used as a "greater than" symbol and rotated to ⋞ and used as the "less than" symbol. Other evidence, however, suggests that the "less than" and "greater than" symbols were developed independently of the radical symbol.

Take Note

Recall that a factor of a number divides the number evenly. For instance, 6 is a factor of 18. The perfect square 9 is also a factor of 18. It is a *perfect-square factor* of 18. The number 6 is not a perfect-square factor of 18 because 6 is not a perfect square.

A **square root** of a positive number a is a number whose square is a.

A square root of 16 is 4 because $4^2 = 16$.

A square root of 16 is -4 because $(-4)^2 = 16$.

Every positive number has two square roots, one positive and one negative. The symbol $\sqrt{\ }$, called a **radical sign,** is used to indicate the positive or **principal square root** of a number. For example, $\sqrt{16} = 4$ (the principal square root of 16 is 4) and $\sqrt{25} = 5$ (the principal square root of 25 is 5). The number under the radical sign is called the **radicand.**

When the negative square root of a number is to be found, a negative sign is placed in front of the radical. For example, $-\sqrt{16} = -4$ and $-\sqrt{25} = -5$.

The square of an integer is a **perfect square.** For instance, 49, 81, and 144 are perfect squares. The principal square root of a perfect-square integer is a positive integer.

$7^2 = 49 \qquad \sqrt{49} = 7$

$9^2 = 81 \qquad \sqrt{81} = 9$

$12^2 = 144 \qquad \sqrt{144} = 12$

If a number is not a perfect square, its square root can only be approximated. For example, 2 and 7 are not perfect squares. The square roots of these numbers are *irrational numbers.* Their decimal approximations never terminate or repeat.

$\sqrt{2} \approx 1.4142135\ldots$

$\sqrt{7} \approx 2.6457513\ldots$

A radical expression is in *simplest form* when the radicand contains no factor greater than 1 that is a perfect square. For instance, $\sqrt{50}$ is not in simplest form because 25 is a perfect-square factor of 50. The radical expression $\sqrt{15}$ is in simplest form because there are no perfect-square factors of 15 that are greater than 1.

A knowledge of perfect squares and the Product Property of Square Roots are used to simplify radicands that are not perfect squares. The chart below shows the square roots of some perfect squares.

Square Roots of Perfect Squares			
$\sqrt{1} = 1$	$\sqrt{16} = 4$	$\sqrt{49} = 7$	$\sqrt{100} = 10$
$\sqrt{4} = 2$	$\sqrt{25} = 5$	$\sqrt{64} = 8$	$\sqrt{121} = 11$
$\sqrt{9} = 3$	$\sqrt{36} = 6$	$\sqrt{81} = 9$	$\sqrt{144} = 12$

The Product Property of Square Roots

If a and b are positive real numbers, then $\sqrt{ab} = \sqrt{a} \cdot \sqrt{b}$.

EXAMPLE

Simplify: $\sqrt{72}$

$\sqrt{72} = \sqrt{36 \cdot 2}$ • Write the radicand as the product of a perfect square and a factor that does not contain a perfect square.

$= \sqrt{36}\sqrt{2}$ • Use the Product Property of Square Roots to write the expression as a product. Then simplify.

$= 6\sqrt{2}$

Note in the example above that 72 must be written as the product of a perfect square and *a factor that does not contain a perfect square.* Therefore, it would not be correct to simplify $\sqrt{72}$ as $\sqrt{9 \cdot 8}$. Although 9 is a perfect-square factor of 72, 8 also contains a perfect-square factor $(8 = 4 \cdot 2)$. Therefore, $\sqrt{8}$ is not in simplest form. Remember to find the largest perfect-square factor of the radicand.

$$\sqrt{72} = \sqrt{9 \cdot 8} = \sqrt{9} \cdot \sqrt{8} = 3\sqrt{8}$$

Not in simplest form

HOW TO 1 Simplify: $\sqrt{360}$

$\sqrt{360} = \sqrt{36 \cdot 10}$ • Write the radicand as the product of a perfect square and a factor that does not contain a perfect square.

$= \sqrt{36}\sqrt{10}$ • Use the Product Property of Square Roots to write the expression as a product.

$= 6\sqrt{10}$ • Simplify.

From HOW TO 1, note that $\sqrt{360} = 6\sqrt{10}$. The two expressions are different representations of the same number. Using a calculator, we find that $\sqrt{360} \approx 18.973666$ and $6\sqrt{10} \approx 18.973666$.

HOW TO 2 Simplify: $\sqrt{-16}$

Because the square of any real number is positive, there is no real number whose square is -16. $\sqrt{-16}$ is not a real number.

EXAMPLE 1

Simplify: $3\sqrt{90}$

Solution

$3\sqrt{90} = 3\sqrt{9 \cdot 10}$ • 9 is the largest perfect-square factor.

$= 3\sqrt{9}\sqrt{10}$ • Product Property of Square Roots

$= 3 \cdot 3\sqrt{10}$

$= 9\sqrt{10}$

YOU TRY IT 1

Simplify: $\sqrt{216}$

Your solution

EXAMPLE 2

Simplify: $\sqrt{252}$

Solution

$\sqrt{252} = \sqrt{36 \cdot 7}$ • 36 is the largest perfect-square factor.

$= \sqrt{36}\sqrt{7}$ • Product Property of Square Roots

$= 6\sqrt{7}$

YOU TRY IT 2

Simplify: $-5\sqrt{32}$

Your solution

Solutions on p. S23

OBJECTIVE B *To simplify variable radical expressions*

Variable expressions that contain radicals do not always represent real numbers. For example, if $a = -4$, then

$$\sqrt{a^3} = \sqrt{(-4)^3} = \sqrt{-64}$$

and $\sqrt{-64}$ is not a real number.

Now consider the expression $\sqrt{x^2}$. Evaluate this expression for $x = -2$ and $x = 2$.

$$\sqrt{x^2} \qquad\qquad \sqrt{x^2}$$
$$\sqrt{(-2)^2} = \sqrt{4} = 2 = |-2| \qquad \sqrt{2^2} = \sqrt{4} = 2 = |2|$$

This suggests the following rule:

For any real number a, $\sqrt{a^2} = |a|$. If $a \geq 0$, then $\sqrt{a^2} = a$.

In order to avoid variable expressions that do not represent real numbers, and so that absolute value signs are not needed for certain expressions, the variables in this chapter will represent *positive* numbers unless otherwise stated.

A variable raised to a power or a product of variables written in exponential form is a perfect square when each exponent is an even number. To find the square root of a perfect square, remove the radical sign and multiply each exponent by $\frac{1}{2}$.

HOW TO 3 Simplify: $\sqrt{a^6}$

$\sqrt{a^6} = a^3$

- The exponent, 6, is an even number. Remove the radical sign and multiply 6 by $\frac{1}{2}$.

A variable radical expression is in simplest form when the radicand contains no factor greater than 1 that is a perfect square.

HOW TO 4 Simplify: $\sqrt{x^7}$

$\sqrt{x^7} = \sqrt{x^6 \cdot x}$
- Write x^7 as the product of a perfect square and x.

$= \sqrt{x^6}\sqrt{x}$
- Use the Product Property of Square Roots.

$= x^3\sqrt{x}$
- Simplify the perfect square.

HOW TO 5 Simplify: $3x\sqrt{8x^3y^{13}}$

$3x\sqrt{8x^3y^{13}} = 3x\sqrt{4x^2y^{12}(2xy)}$
- Write the radicand as the product of perfect squares and factors that do not contain a perfect square.

$= 3x\sqrt{4x^2y^{12}}\sqrt{2xy}$
- Use the Product Property of Square Roots.

$= 3x \cdot 2xy^6\sqrt{2xy}$
- Simplify.

$= 6x^2y^6\sqrt{2xy}$

HOW TO 6 Simplify: $\sqrt{25(x+2)^2}$

$\sqrt{25(x+2)^2} = 5(x+2)$ • 25 is a perfect square. $(x+2)^2$ is a perfect square

$= 5x + 10$ • Distributive Property

EXAMPLE 3

Simplify: $\sqrt{b^{15}}$

Solution

$\sqrt{b^{15}} = \sqrt{b^{14} \cdot b}$ • b^{14} is a perfect square.

$= \sqrt{b^{14}} \cdot \sqrt{b} = b^7\sqrt{b}$

YOU TRY IT 3

Simplify: $\sqrt{y^{19}}$

Your solution

EXAMPLE 4

Simplify: $\sqrt{24x^5}$

Solution

$\sqrt{24x^5} = \sqrt{4x^4(6x)}$ • 4 and x^4 are perfect squares.

$= \sqrt{4x^4}\sqrt{6x}$

$= 2x^2\sqrt{6x}$

YOU TRY IT 4

Simplify: $\sqrt{45b^7}$

Your solution

EXAMPLE 5

Simplify: $2a\sqrt{18a^3b^{10}}$

Solution

$2a\sqrt{18a^3b^{10}}$

$= 2a\sqrt{9a^2b^{10}(2a)}$ • 9, a^2, and b^{10} are perfect squares.

$= 2a\sqrt{9a^2b^{10}}\sqrt{2a}$

$= 2a \cdot 3ab^5\sqrt{2a}$

$= 6a^2b^5\sqrt{2a}$

YOU TRY IT 5

Simplify: $3a\sqrt{28a^9b^{18}}$

Your solution

EXAMPLE 6

Simplify: $\sqrt{16(x+5)^2}$

Solution

$\sqrt{16(x+5)^2} = 4(x+5) = 4x + 20$

YOU TRY IT 6

Simplify: $\sqrt{25(a+3)^2}$

Your solution

EXAMPLE 7

Simplify: $\sqrt{x^2 + 10x + 25}$

Solution

$\sqrt{x^2 + 10x + 25} = \sqrt{(x+5)^2} = x + 5$

YOU TRY IT 7

Simplify: $\sqrt{x^2 + 14x + 49}$

Your solution

Solutions on p. S23

10.1 EXERCISES

Concept Check

1. In the expression $\sqrt{a}$, the symbol $\sqrt{\ }$ is called the __________, and a is called the __________.

2. $16x^6y^8$ is a perfect square because $16 = (\_\_\_\_\_)^2$, $x^6 = (\_\_\_\_\_)^2$, and $y^8 = (\_\_\_\_\_)^2$.

3. How can you tell whether a variable exponential expression is a perfect square?

4. Explain why $2\sqrt{2}$ is in simplest form and $\sqrt{8}$ is not in simplest form.

OBJECTIVE A *To simplify numerical radical expressions*

For Exercises 5 to 28, simplify.

5. $\sqrt{16}$ **6.** $\sqrt{64}$ **7.** $\sqrt{49}$ **8.** $\sqrt{144}$ **9.** $\sqrt{32}$ **10.** $\sqrt{50}$

11. $\sqrt{8}$ **12.** $\sqrt{12}$ **13.** $-6\sqrt{18}$ **14.** $-3\sqrt{48}$ **15.** $5\sqrt{40}$ **16.** $2\sqrt{28}$

17. $\sqrt{15}$ **18.** $\sqrt{21}$ **19.** $\sqrt{29}$ **20.** $\sqrt{13}$ **21.** $-9\sqrt{72}$ **22.** $-11\sqrt{80}$

23. $\sqrt{45}$ **24.** $\sqrt{225}$ **25.** $\sqrt{0}$ **26.** $\sqrt{210}$ **27.** $6\sqrt{128}$ **28.** $9\sqrt{288}$

For Exercises 29 to 32, find consecutive integers m and n such that the given number is between m and n, or state that the given number is not a real number. Do not use a calculator.

29. $-\sqrt{115}$ **30.** $-\sqrt{-90}$ **31.** $\sqrt{\sqrt{64}}$ **32.** $\sqrt{200}$

For Exercises 33 to 38, find the decimal approximation rounded to the nearest thousandth.

33. $\sqrt{240}$ **34.** $\sqrt{300}$ **35.** $\sqrt{288}$ **36.** $\sqrt{600}$ **37.** $\sqrt{350}$ **38.** $\sqrt{500}$

OBJECTIVE B *To simplify variable radical expressions*

For Exercises 39 to 78, simplify.

39. $\sqrt{x^{14}}$ **40.** $\sqrt{x^{12}}$ **41.** $\sqrt{y^{15}}$ **42.** $\sqrt{y^{11}}$

43. $\sqrt{a^{20}}$ **44.** $\sqrt{a^{16}}$ **45.** $\sqrt{x^4y^4}$ **46.** $\sqrt{x^{12}y^8}$

47. $\sqrt{4x^4}$ **48.** $\sqrt{25y^8}$ **49.** $\sqrt{24x^2}$ **50.** $\sqrt{x^3y^{15}}$

51. $\sqrt{60x^5}$ **52.** $\sqrt{72y^7}$ **53.** $\sqrt{49a^4b^8}$ **54.** $\sqrt{144x^2y^8}$

55. $\sqrt{18x^5y^7}$ **56.** $\sqrt{32a^5b^{15}}$ **57.** $\sqrt{40x^{11}y^7}$ **58.** $\sqrt{72x^9y^3}$

59. $\sqrt{80a^9b^{10}}$ **60.** $\sqrt{96a^5b^7}$ **61.** $-2\sqrt{16a^2b^3}$ **62.** $-5\sqrt{25a^4b^7}$

63. $x\sqrt{x^4y^2}$ **64.** $y\sqrt{x^3y^6}$ **65.** $-4\sqrt{20a^4b^7}$ **66.** $-5\sqrt{12a^3b^4}$

67. $3x\sqrt{12x^2y^7}$ **68.** $4y\sqrt{18x^5y^4}$ **69.** $2x^2\sqrt{8x^2y^3}$ **70.** $3y^2\sqrt{27x^4y^3}$

71. $\sqrt{25(a+4)^2}$ **72.** $\sqrt{9(x+2)^2}$ **73.** $\sqrt{4(x+2)^4}$ **74.** $\sqrt{81(x+y)^4}$

75. $\sqrt{x^2+4x+4}$ **76.** $\sqrt{b^2+8b+16}$ **77.** $\sqrt{y^2+2y+1}$ **78.** $\sqrt{a^2+6a+9}$

For Exercises 79 to 82, assume that a is a positive integer that is not a perfect square. State whether the expression represents a rational number or an irrational number.

79. $\sqrt{100a^6}$ **80.** $\sqrt{9a^9}$ **81.** $\sqrt{\sqrt{25a^{16}}}$ **82.** $\sqrt{\sqrt{81a^8}}$

Critical Thinking

83. **Credit Cards** See the news clipping at the right. The equation $N = 2.3\sqrt{S}$, where S is a student's year in college, can be used to find the average number of credit cards N that a student has. Use this equation to find the average number of credit cards for **a.** a first-year student, **b.** a sophomore, **c.** a junior, and **d.** a senior. Round to the nearest tenth.

In the NEWS!

Student Credit Card Debt Grows

With each advancing year in college, students acquire more credit cards and accumulate more debt. The average credit card balance for a first-year student is \$1585, for a sophomore is \$1581, for a junior is \$2000, and for a senior or fifth-year student is \$2864.

Source: Nellie Mae

84. Given $f(x) = \sqrt{2x-1}$, find each of the following. Write your answer in simplest form.

a. $f(1)$ **b.** $f(5)$ **c.** $f(14)$

Projects or Group Activites

85. **Automotive Safety** Traffic accident investigators can estimate the speed S, in miles per hour, at which a car was traveling from the length of its skid mark by using the formula $S = \sqrt{30fl}$, where f is the coefficient of friction (which depends on the type of road surface) and l is the length, in feet, of the skid mark. Say the coefficient of friction is 1.2 and the length of a skid mark is 60 ft.

a. Determine the speed of the car as a radical expression in simplest form.

b. Write the answer to part (a) as a decimal rounded to the nearest integer.

SECTION

10.2 Addition and Subtraction of Radical Expressions

OBJECTIVE A *To add and subtract radical expressions*

The Distributive Property is used to simplify the sum or difference of radical expressions with like radicands.

$5\sqrt{2} + 3\sqrt{2} = (5 + 3)\sqrt{2} = 8\sqrt{2}$

$6\sqrt{2x} - 4\sqrt{2x} = (6 - 4)\sqrt{2x} = 2\sqrt{2x}$

Radical expressions that are in simplest form and have unlike radicands cannot be simplified by the Distributive Property.

$2\sqrt{3} + 4\sqrt{2}$ cannot be simplified by the Distributive Property.

To simplify the sum or difference of radical expressions, first simplify each radical expression.

HOW TO 1 Simplify: $4\sqrt{8} - 10\sqrt{2}$

$$\begin{aligned} 4\sqrt{8} - 10\sqrt{2} &= 4\sqrt{4 \cdot 2} - 10\sqrt{2} \\ &= 4\sqrt{4}\sqrt{2} - 10\sqrt{2} \\ &= 4 \cdot 2\sqrt{2} - 10\sqrt{2} \\ &= 8\sqrt{2} - 10\sqrt{2} \\ &= (8 - 10)\sqrt{2} \\ &= -2\sqrt{2} \end{aligned}$$

- **The radical expressions have unlike radicands. Use the Product Property of Square Roots to simplify $\sqrt{8}$.**
- **The radical expressions now have like radicands. Simplify the expression by using the Distributive Property.**

HOW TO 2 Simplify: $8\sqrt{18x} - 2\sqrt{32x}$

$$\begin{aligned} 8\sqrt{18x} - 2\sqrt{32x} &= 8\sqrt{9 \cdot 2x} - 2\sqrt{16 \cdot 2x} \\ &= 8\sqrt{9}\sqrt{2x} - 2\sqrt{16}\sqrt{2x} \\ &= 8 \cdot 3\sqrt{2x} - 2 \cdot 4\sqrt{2x} \\ &= 24\sqrt{2x} - 8\sqrt{2x} \\ &= (24 - 8)\sqrt{2x} \\ &= 16\sqrt{2x} \end{aligned}$$

- **The radical expressions have unlike radicands. Use the Product Property of Square Roots to simplify each radical expression.**
- **The radical expressions now have like radicands. Simplify the expression by using the Distributive Property.**

EXAMPLE 1

Simplify: $5\sqrt{2} - 3\sqrt{2} + 12\sqrt{2}$

Solution

$5\sqrt{2} - 3\sqrt{2} + 12\sqrt{2}$

- **The radical expressions have like radicands.**

$= (5 - 3 + 12)\sqrt{2}$

- **Distributive Property**

$= 14\sqrt{2}$

YOU TRY IT 1

Simplify: $9\sqrt{3} + 3\sqrt{3} - 18\sqrt{3}$

Your solution

Solutions on p. S24

EXAMPLE 2

Simplify: $3\sqrt{12} - 5\sqrt{27}$

Solution

$3\sqrt{12} - 5\sqrt{27}$

$= 3\sqrt{4 \cdot 3} - 5\sqrt{9 \cdot 3}$ • Unlike radicals

$= 3\sqrt{4}\sqrt{3} - 5\sqrt{9}\sqrt{3}$ • Simplify $\sqrt{12}$ and $\sqrt{27}$.

$= 3 \cdot 2\sqrt{3} - 5 \cdot 3\sqrt{3}$

$= 6\sqrt{3} - 15\sqrt{3}$ • Like radicands

$= (6 - 15)\sqrt{3}$ • Distributive Property

$= -9\sqrt{3}$

YOU TRY IT 2

Simplify: $2\sqrt{50} - 5\sqrt{32}$

Your solution

EXAMPLE 3

Simplify: $3\sqrt{12x^3} - 2x\sqrt{3x}$

Solution

$3\sqrt{12x^3} - 2x\sqrt{3x}$ • Unlike radicands

$= 3\sqrt{4x^2 \cdot 3x} - 2x\sqrt{3x}$ • Simplify $\sqrt{12x^3}$.

$= 3\sqrt{4x^2}\sqrt{3x} - 2x\sqrt{3x}$

$= 3 \cdot 2x\sqrt{3x} - 2x\sqrt{3x}$

$= 6x\sqrt{3x} - 2x\sqrt{3x}$ • Like radicands

$= (6x - 2x)\sqrt{3x}$ • Distributive Property

$= 4x\sqrt{3x}$

YOU TRY IT 3

Simplify: $y\sqrt{28y} + 7\sqrt{63y^3}$

Your solution

EXAMPLE 4

Simplify: $2x\sqrt{8y} - 3\sqrt{2x^2y} + 2\sqrt{32x^2y}$

Solution

$2x\sqrt{8y} - 3\sqrt{2x^2y} + 2\sqrt{32x^2y}$

$= 2x\sqrt{4 \cdot 2y} - 3\sqrt{x^2 \cdot 2y} + 2\sqrt{16x^2 \cdot 2y}$

$= 2x\sqrt{4}\sqrt{2y} - 3\sqrt{x^2}\sqrt{2y} + 2\sqrt{16x^2}\sqrt{2y}$

$= 2x \cdot 2\sqrt{2y} - 3 \cdot x\sqrt{2y} + 2 \cdot 4x\sqrt{2y}$

$= 4x\sqrt{2y} - 3x\sqrt{2y} + 8x\sqrt{2y}$

$= 9x\sqrt{2y}$

YOU TRY IT 4

Simplify: $2\sqrt{27a^5} - 4a\sqrt{12a^3} + a^2\sqrt{75a}$

Your solution

Solutions on p. S24

10.2 EXERCISES

Concept Check

1. Which of the numbers 2, 9, 20, 25, 50, 81, and 100 are *not* perfect squares?

2. Write down a number that has a perfect-square factor that is greater than 1.

For Exercises 3 to 6, determine whether the expression can be simplified.

3. $5\sqrt{3} + 6\sqrt{3}$
4. $3\sqrt{5} + 3\sqrt{6}$
5. $4\sqrt{2x} - 8\sqrt{2x}$
6. $3\sqrt{5x} + 5\sqrt{3x}$

OBJECTIVE A *To add and subtract radical expressions*

For Exercises 7 to 62, simplify.

7. $2\sqrt{2} + \sqrt{2}$
8. $3\sqrt{5} + 8\sqrt{5}$
9. $-3\sqrt{7} + 2\sqrt{7}$
10. $4\sqrt{5} - 10\sqrt{5}$
11. $-3\sqrt{11} - 8\sqrt{11}$
12. $-3\sqrt{3} - 5\sqrt{3}$
13. $2\sqrt{x} + 8\sqrt{x}$
14. $3\sqrt{y} + 2\sqrt{y}$
15. $8\sqrt{y} - 10\sqrt{y}$
16. $-5\sqrt{2a} + 2\sqrt{2a}$
17. $-2\sqrt{3b} - 9\sqrt{3b}$
18. $-7\sqrt{5a} - 5\sqrt{5a}$
19. $3x\sqrt{2} - x\sqrt{2}$
20. $2y\sqrt{3} - 9y\sqrt{3}$
21. $2a\sqrt{3a} - 5a\sqrt{3a}$
22. $-5b\sqrt{3x} - 2b\sqrt{3x}$
23. $3\sqrt{xy} - 8\sqrt{xy}$
24. $-4\sqrt{xy} + 6\sqrt{xy}$
25. $\sqrt{45} + \sqrt{125}$
26. $\sqrt{32} - \sqrt{98}$
27. $2\sqrt{2} + 3\sqrt{8}$
28. $4\sqrt{128} - 3\sqrt{32}$
29. $5\sqrt{18} - 2\sqrt{75}$
30. $5\sqrt{75} - 2\sqrt{18}$
31. $5\sqrt{4x} - 3\sqrt{9x}$
32. $-3\sqrt{25y} + 8\sqrt{49y}$
33. $3\sqrt{3x^2} - 5\sqrt{27x^2}$
34. $-2\sqrt{8y^2} + 5\sqrt{32y^2}$
35. $2x\sqrt{xy^2} - 3y\sqrt{x^2y}$
36. $4a\sqrt{b^2a} - 3b\sqrt{a^2b}$
37. $3x\sqrt{12x} - 5\sqrt{27x^3}$
38. $2a\sqrt{50a} + 7\sqrt{32a^3}$
39. $4y\sqrt{8y^3} - 7\sqrt{18y^5}$
40. $2a\sqrt{8ab^2} - 2b\sqrt{2a^3}$
41. $b^2\sqrt{a^5b} + 3a^2\sqrt{ab^5}$
42. $y^2\sqrt{x^5y} + x\sqrt{x^3y^5}$

43. $4\sqrt{2} - 5\sqrt{2} + 8\sqrt{2}$

44. $3\sqrt{3} + 8\sqrt{3} - 16\sqrt{3}$

45. $5\sqrt{x} - 8\sqrt{x} + 9\sqrt{x}$

46. $\sqrt{x} - 7\sqrt{x} + 6\sqrt{x}$

47. $8\sqrt{2} - 3\sqrt{y} - 8\sqrt{2}$

48. $8\sqrt{3} - 5\sqrt{2} - 5\sqrt{3}$

49. $8\sqrt{8} - 4\sqrt{32} - 9\sqrt{50}$

50. $2\sqrt{12} - 4\sqrt{27} + \sqrt{75}$

51. $-2\sqrt{3} + 5\sqrt{27} - 4\sqrt{45}$

52. $-2\sqrt{8} - 3\sqrt{27} + 3\sqrt{50}$

53. $4\sqrt{75} + 3\sqrt{48} - \sqrt{99}$

54. $2\sqrt{75} - 5\sqrt{20} + 2\sqrt{45}$

55. $\sqrt{25x} - \sqrt{9x} + \sqrt{16x}$

56. $\sqrt{4x} - \sqrt{100x} - \sqrt{49x}$

57. $3\sqrt{3x} + \sqrt{27x} - 8\sqrt{75x}$

58. $5\sqrt{5x} + 2\sqrt{45x} - 3\sqrt{80x}$

59. $2a\sqrt{75b} - a\sqrt{20b} + 4a\sqrt{45b}$

60. $2b\sqrt{75a} - 5b\sqrt{27a} + 2b\sqrt{20a}$

61. $x\sqrt{3y^2} - 2y\sqrt{12x^2} + xy\sqrt{3}$

62. $a\sqrt{27b^2} + 3b\sqrt{147a^2} - ab\sqrt{3}$

63. Which expression is equivalent to $\sqrt{2ab} + \sqrt{2ab}$?
(i) $2\sqrt{ab}$ **(ii)** $\sqrt{4ab}$ **(iii)** $2ab$ **(iv)** $\sqrt{8ab}$

Critical Thinking

For Exercises 64 to 66, simplify.

64. $\frac{1}{4}\sqrt{48ab^2} + \frac{1}{5}\sqrt{75ab^2}$

65. $\frac{a}{3}\sqrt{54ab^3} + \frac{b}{4}\sqrt{96a^3b}$

66. $\frac{x}{6}\sqrt{72xy^5} + \frac{y}{7}\sqrt{98x^3y^3}$

67. Geometry The length of a rectangle is $3\sqrt{2}$ cm. The width is $\sqrt{2}$ cm. Find the perimeter of the rectangle.

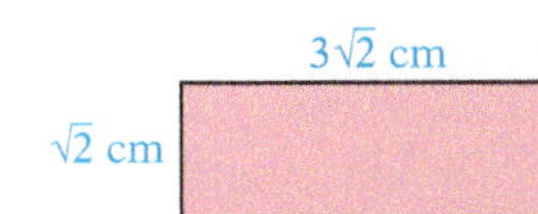

68. Given $G(x) = \sqrt{x + 5} + \sqrt{5x + 3}$, write $G(3)$ in simplest form.

Projects or Group Activites

69. Write a paragraph that compares adding two monomials to adding two radical expressions. For example, compare the addition of $5x + 3x$ to the addition of $5\sqrt{x} + 3\sqrt{x}$.

SECTION

10.3 Multiplication and Division of Radical Expressions

OBJECTIVE A *To multiply radical expressions*

The Product Property of Square Roots is used to multiply radical expressions. $\sqrt{2x}\sqrt{3y} = \sqrt{2x \cdot 3y} = \sqrt{6xy}$

HOW TO 1 Simplify: $\sqrt{2x^2}\sqrt{32x^5}$

$\sqrt{2x^2}\sqrt{32x^5} = \sqrt{2x^2 \cdot 32x^5}$ • Use the Product Property of Square Roots.

$= \sqrt{64x^7}$ • Multiply.

$= \sqrt{64x^6 \cdot x}$ • Simplify.

$= \sqrt{64x^6}\sqrt{x} = 8x^3\sqrt{x}$

HOW TO 2 Simplify: $\sqrt{2x}(x + \sqrt{2x})$

$\sqrt{2x}(x + \sqrt{2x}) = \sqrt{2x}(x) + \sqrt{2x}\sqrt{2x}$ • Use the Distributive Property to remove parentheses.

$= x\sqrt{2x} + \sqrt{4x^2}$

$= x\sqrt{2x} + 2x$ • Simplify.

Use FOIL to multiply radical expressions with two terms.

HOW TO 3 Simplify: $(\sqrt{2} - 3x)(\sqrt{2} + x)$

$(\sqrt{2} - 3x)(\sqrt{2} + x) = \sqrt{2}\sqrt{2} + x\sqrt{2} - 3x\sqrt{2} - 3x^2$ • Use the FOIL method to remove parentheses.

$= \sqrt{4} + (x - 3x)\sqrt{2} - 3x^2$

$= 2 - 2x\sqrt{2} - 3x^2$

The expressions $a + b$ and $a - b$, which differ only in the sign of one term, are called **conjugates.** Recall that $(a + b)(a - b) = a^2 - b^2$.

Take Note

For $x > 0$, $(\sqrt{x})^2 = x$ because $(\sqrt{x})^2 = \sqrt{x} \cdot \sqrt{x} = \sqrt{x^2} = x$.

HOW TO 4 Simplify: $(3 + \sqrt{y})(3 - \sqrt{y})$

$(3 + \sqrt{y})(3 - \sqrt{y}) = 3^2 - (\sqrt{y})^2$ • $(3 + \sqrt{y})(3 - \sqrt{y})$ is the product of conjugates.

$= 9 - y$

EXAMPLE 1

Simplify: $\sqrt{3x^4}\sqrt{2x^2y}\sqrt{6xy^2}$

Solution

$\sqrt{3x^4}\sqrt{2x^2y}\sqrt{6xy^2}$

$= \sqrt{36x^7y^3}$ • Product Property of Square Roots

$= \sqrt{36x^6y^2 \cdot xy}$ • Simplify.

$= \sqrt{36x^6y^2}\sqrt{xy}$

$= 6x^3y\sqrt{xy}$

YOU TRY IT 1

Simplify: $\sqrt{5a}\sqrt{15a^3b^4}\sqrt{20b^5}$

Your solution

Solution on p. S24

EXAMPLE 2

Simplify: $\sqrt{3ab}(\sqrt{3a} + \sqrt{9b})$

Solution

$\sqrt{3ab}(\sqrt{3a} + \sqrt{9b})$

$= \sqrt{9a^2b} + \sqrt{27ab^2}$ • Distributive Property

$= \sqrt{9a^2 \cdot b} + \sqrt{9b^2 \cdot 3a}$ • Simplify.

$= \sqrt{9a^2}\sqrt{b} + \sqrt{9b^2}\sqrt{3a}$

$= 3a\sqrt{b} + 3b\sqrt{3a}$

YOU TRY IT 2

Simplify: $\sqrt{5x}(\sqrt{5x} - \sqrt{25y})$

Your solution

EXAMPLE 3

Simplify: $(\sqrt{x} - 2\sqrt{y})(4\sqrt{x} + \sqrt{y})$

Solution

$(\sqrt{x} - 2\sqrt{y})(4\sqrt{x} + \sqrt{y})$

$= 4(\sqrt{x})^2 + \sqrt{xy} - 8\sqrt{xy} - 2(\sqrt{y})^2$ • FOIL

$= 4x - 7\sqrt{xy} - 2y$

YOU TRY IT 3

Simplify: $(3\sqrt{x} - \sqrt{y})(5\sqrt{x} - 2\sqrt{y})$

Your solution

EXAMPLE 4

Simplify: $(\sqrt{a} - \sqrt{b})(\sqrt{a} + \sqrt{b})$

Solution

$(\sqrt{a} - \sqrt{b})(\sqrt{a} + \sqrt{b})$ • Product of conjugates

$= (\sqrt{a})^2 - (\sqrt{b})^2$

$= a - b$

YOU TRY IT 4

Simplify: $(2\sqrt{x} + 7)(2\sqrt{x} - 7)$

Your solution

Solutions on p. S24

OBJECTIVE B *To divide radical expressions*

The Quotient Property of Square Roots, given below, states that the square root of a quotient is equal to the quotient of the square roots.

The Quotient Property of Square Roots

If a and b are positive real numbers, then $\sqrt{\frac{a}{b}} = \frac{\sqrt{a}}{\sqrt{b}}$ and $\frac{\sqrt{a}}{\sqrt{b}} = \sqrt{\frac{a}{b}}$.

EXAMPLE

Simplify: $\sqrt{\frac{4x^2}{z^6}}$

$\sqrt{\frac{4x^2}{z^6}} = \frac{\sqrt{4x^2}}{\sqrt{z^6}}$ • Rewrite the radical expression as a quotient of square roots.

$= \frac{2x}{z^3}$ • Simplify.

Point of Interest

A radical expression that occurs in Einstein's Theory of Relativity is

$$\frac{1}{\sqrt{1-\frac{v^2}{c^2}}}$$

where v is the velocity of an object and c is the speed of light.

HOW TO 5 Simplify: $\sqrt{\frac{24x^3y^7}{3x^7y^2}}$

$\sqrt{\frac{24x^3y^7}{3x^7y^2}} = \sqrt{\frac{8y^5}{x^4}}$ • Simplify the radicand.

$= \frac{\sqrt{8y^5}}{\sqrt{x^4}}$ • Rewrite the radical expression as a quotient of square roots.

$= \frac{\sqrt{4y^4 \cdot 2y}}{\sqrt{x^4}}$ • Simplify.

$= \frac{\sqrt{4y^4}\sqrt{2y}}{\sqrt{x^4}}$

$= \frac{2y^2\sqrt{2y}}{x^2}$

The Quotient Property of Square Roots is used to divide radical expressions.

HOW TO 6 Simplify: $\frac{\sqrt{4x^2y}}{\sqrt{xy}}$

$\frac{\sqrt{4x^2y}}{\sqrt{xy}} = \sqrt{\frac{4x^2y}{xy}}$ • Use the Quotient Property of Square Roots.

$= \sqrt{4x}$ • Simplify the radicand.

$= \sqrt{4}\sqrt{x}$ • Simplify the radical expression.

$= 2\sqrt{x}$

The previous examples all result in radical expressions written in simplest form.

Simplest Form of a Radical Expression

For a radical expression to be in simplest form, three conditions must be met:

1. The radicand contains no factor greater than 1 that is a perfect square.
2. There is no fraction under the radical sign.
3. There is no radical in the denominator of a fraction.

The procedure used to remove a radical from a denominator is called **rationalizing the denominator.**

HOW TO 7 Simplify: $\frac{2}{\sqrt{3}}$

$\frac{2}{\sqrt{3}} = \frac{2}{\sqrt{3}} \cdot \frac{\sqrt{3}}{\sqrt{3}}$ • To rationalize the denominator, multiply the expression by $\frac{\sqrt{3}}{\sqrt{3}}$, which equals 1.

$= \frac{2\sqrt{3}}{(\sqrt{3})^2}$

$= \frac{2\sqrt{3}}{3}$ • Simplify.

When the denominator contains a radical expression with two terms, rationalize the denominator by multiplying the numerator and denominator by the conjugate of the denominator.

HOW TO 8 Simplify: $\dfrac{\sqrt{2y}}{\sqrt{y}+3}$

$$\frac{\sqrt{2y}}{\sqrt{y}+3} = \frac{\sqrt{2y}}{\sqrt{y}+3} \cdot \frac{\sqrt{y}-3}{\sqrt{y}-3}$$

• Multiply the numerator and denominator by $\sqrt{y}-3$, the conjugate of $\sqrt{y}+3$.

$$= \frac{\sqrt{2y^2} - 3\sqrt{2y}}{(\sqrt{y})^2 - 3^2} = \frac{y\sqrt{2} - 3\sqrt{2y}}{y-9}$$

EXAMPLE 5

Simplify: $\dfrac{\sqrt{4x^2y^5}}{\sqrt{3x^4y}}$

Solution

$$\frac{\sqrt{4x^2y^5}}{\sqrt{3x^4y}} = \sqrt{\frac{4x^2y^5}{3x^4y}} = \sqrt{\frac{4y^4}{3x^2}} = \frac{\sqrt{4y^4}}{\sqrt{3x^2}}$$

$$= \frac{2y^2}{x\sqrt{3}} = \frac{2y^2}{x\sqrt{3}} \cdot \frac{\sqrt{3}}{\sqrt{3}}$$

• Rationalize the denominator.

$$= \frac{2y^2\sqrt{3}}{3x}$$

YOU TRY IT 5

Simplify: $\dfrac{\sqrt{15x^6y^7}}{\sqrt{3x^7y^9}}$

Your solution

EXAMPLE 6

Simplify: $\dfrac{\sqrt{2}}{\sqrt{2}+\sqrt{6}}$

Solution

$$\frac{\sqrt{2}}{\sqrt{2}+\sqrt{6}}$$

$$= \frac{\sqrt{2}}{\sqrt{2}+\sqrt{6}} \cdot \frac{\sqrt{2}-\sqrt{6}}{\sqrt{2}-\sqrt{6}}$$

• Multiply the numerator and denominator by the conjugate of the denominator.

$$= \frac{(\sqrt{2})^2 - \sqrt{12}}{2-6} = \frac{2-2\sqrt{3}}{-4}$$

$$= \frac{2(1-\sqrt{3})}{-4} = \frac{1-\sqrt{3}}{-2} = -\frac{1-\sqrt{3}}{2}$$

YOU TRY IT 6

Simplify: $\dfrac{\sqrt{3}}{\sqrt{3}-\sqrt{6}}$

Your solution

EXAMPLE 7

Simplify: $\dfrac{3-\sqrt{y}}{2+3\sqrt{y}}$

Solution

$$\frac{3-\sqrt{y}}{2+3\sqrt{y}} = \frac{3-\sqrt{y}}{2+3\sqrt{y}} \cdot \frac{2-3\sqrt{y}}{2-3\sqrt{y}}$$

• Rationalize the denominator.

$$= \frac{6 - 9\sqrt{y} - 2\sqrt{y} + 3(\sqrt{y})^2}{4-9y}$$

$$= \frac{6 - 11\sqrt{y} + 3y}{4-9y}$$

YOU TRY IT 7

Simplify: $\dfrac{5+\sqrt{y}}{1-2\sqrt{y}}$

Your solution

Solutions on p. S24

10.3 EXERCISES

Concept Check

For Exercises 1 to 3, determine the conjugate of the expression.

1. $3 + \sqrt{5}$

2. $6 - \sqrt{x}$

3. $\sqrt{2a} - 8$

For Exercises 4 and 5, find the product of the expression and its conjugate.

4. $4 + \sqrt{3}$

5. $5 - \sqrt{y}$

For Exercises 6 to 8, by what form of 1 should the expression be multiplied to rationalize the denominator?

6. $\frac{2}{\sqrt{6}}$

7. $\frac{3}{\sqrt{x}}$

8. $\frac{2 - \sqrt{x}}{\sqrt{y}}$

9. Why is $\frac{\sqrt{3}}{3}$ in simplest form but $\frac{1}{\sqrt{3}}$ not in simplest form?

10. Why can we multiply $\frac{2}{\sqrt{5}}$ by $\frac{\sqrt{5}}{\sqrt{5}}$ without changing the value of $\frac{2}{\sqrt{5}}$?

OBJECTIVE A *To multiply radical expressions*

For Exercises 11 to 46, simplify.

11. $\sqrt{5} \cdot \sqrt{5}$

12. $\sqrt{11} \cdot \sqrt{11}$

13. $\sqrt{3} \cdot \sqrt{12}$

14. $\sqrt{2} \cdot \sqrt{8}$

15. $\sqrt{x} \cdot \sqrt{x}$

16. $\sqrt{y} \cdot \sqrt{y}$

17. $\sqrt{xy^3} \cdot \sqrt{x^5y}$

18. $\sqrt{a^3b^5} \cdot \sqrt{ab^5}$

19. $\sqrt{3a^2b^5} \cdot \sqrt{6ab^7}$

20. $\sqrt{5x^3y} \cdot \sqrt{10x^2y}$

21. $\sqrt{6a^3b^2} \cdot \sqrt{24a^5b}$

22. $\sqrt{8ab^5} \cdot \sqrt{12a^7b}$

23. $\sqrt{2ac} \cdot \sqrt{5ab} \cdot \sqrt{10cb}$

24. $\sqrt{3xy} \cdot \sqrt{6x^3y} \cdot \sqrt{2y^2}$

25. $\sqrt{2}(\sqrt{2} - \sqrt{3})$

26. $3(\sqrt{12} - \sqrt{3})$

27. $\sqrt{x}(\sqrt{x} - \sqrt{y})$

28. $\sqrt{b}(\sqrt{a} - \sqrt{b})$

29. $\sqrt{5}(\sqrt{10} - \sqrt{x})$

30. $\sqrt{6}(\sqrt{y} - \sqrt{18})$

31. $\sqrt{3a}(\sqrt{3a} - \sqrt{3b})$

32. $\sqrt{5x}(\sqrt{10x} - \sqrt{x})$

33. $(\sqrt{x} - 3)^2$

34. $(2\sqrt{a} - y)^2$

35. $(\sqrt{5} + 3)(2\sqrt{5} - 4)$

36. $(2 - 3\sqrt{7})(5 + 2\sqrt{7})$

37. $(4 + \sqrt{8})(3 + \sqrt{2})$

38. $(6 - \sqrt{27})(2 + \sqrt{3})$

39. $(2\sqrt{x} + 4)(3\sqrt{x} - 1)$

40. $(5 + \sqrt{y})(6 - 3\sqrt{y})$

41. $(3\sqrt{x} - 2y)(5\sqrt{x} - 4y)$

42. $(5\sqrt{x} + 2\sqrt{y})(3\sqrt{x} - \sqrt{y})$

43. $(3 + \sqrt{5})(3 - \sqrt{5})$

44. $(1 + \sqrt{6})(1 - \sqrt{6})$

45. $(3\sqrt{x} - 4)(3\sqrt{x} + 4)$

46. $(\sqrt{x} - y)(\sqrt{x} + y)$

47. For $a > 0$, is $(\sqrt{a} - 1)(\sqrt{a} + 1)$ less than, equal to, or greater than a?

48. For $a > 0$, is $\sqrt{a}(\sqrt{2a} - \sqrt{a})$ less than, equal to, or greater than a?

OBJECTIVE B *To divide radical expressions*

For Exercises 49 to 78, simplify.

49. $\frac{\sqrt{32}}{\sqrt{2}}$

50. $\frac{\sqrt{45}}{\sqrt{5}}$

51. $\frac{\sqrt{98}}{\sqrt{2}}$

52. $\frac{\sqrt{48}}{\sqrt{3}}$

53. $\frac{\sqrt{27a}}{\sqrt{3a}}$

54. $\frac{\sqrt{72x^5}}{\sqrt{2x}}$

55. $\frac{\sqrt{15x^3y}}{\sqrt{3xy}}$

56. $\frac{\sqrt{40x^5y^2}}{\sqrt{5xy}}$

57. $\frac{\sqrt{2a^5b^4}}{\sqrt{98ab^4}}$

58. $\frac{\sqrt{48x^5y^2}}{\sqrt{3x^3y}}$

59. $\frac{\sqrt{9xy^2}}{\sqrt{27x}}$

60. $\frac{\sqrt{4x^2y}}{\sqrt{3xy^3}}$

61. $\frac{\sqrt{16x^3y^2}}{\sqrt{8x^3y}}$

62. $\frac{\sqrt{2}}{\sqrt{8} + 4}$

63. $\frac{1}{\sqrt{2} - 3}$

64. $\frac{5}{\sqrt{7} - 3}$

65. $\frac{3}{5 + \sqrt{5}}$

66. $\frac{\sqrt{3}}{5 - \sqrt{27}}$

67. $\frac{7}{\sqrt{2} - 7}$

68. $\frac{-6}{4 + \sqrt{2}}$

69. $\frac{-\sqrt{15}}{3 - \sqrt{12}}$

70. $\frac{-12}{\sqrt{6} - 3}$

71. $\frac{\sqrt{xy}}{\sqrt{x} - \sqrt{y}}$

72. $\frac{\sqrt{x}}{\sqrt{x} - \sqrt{y}}$

73. $\frac{3 - \sqrt{6}}{5 - 2\sqrt{6}}$

74. $\frac{6 - 2\sqrt{3}}{4 + 3\sqrt{3}}$

75. $\frac{\sqrt{2} + 2\sqrt{6}}{2\sqrt{2} - 3\sqrt{6}}$

76. $\frac{2\sqrt{3} - \sqrt{6}}{5\sqrt{3} + 2\sqrt{6}}$

77. $\frac{3 + \sqrt{x}}{2 - \sqrt{x}}$

78. $\frac{\sqrt{a} - 4}{2\sqrt{a} + 2}$

79. For $a > 0$, is $\frac{a}{\sqrt{a}}$ less than, equal to, or greater than $\sqrt{a}$?

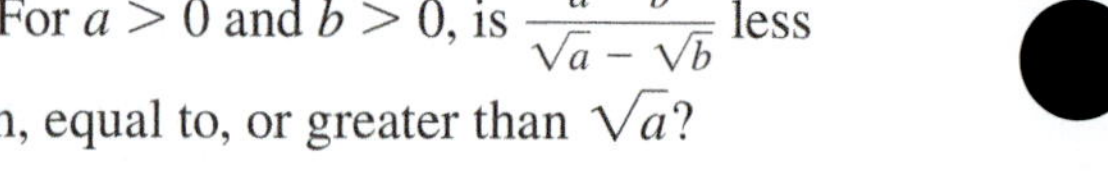

80. For $a > 0$ and $b > 0$, is $\frac{a - b}{\sqrt{a} - \sqrt{b}}$ less than, equal to, or greater than $\sqrt{a}$?

Critical Thinking

81. **Geometry** Find the area of the rectangle shown at the right. All dimensions are given in meters.

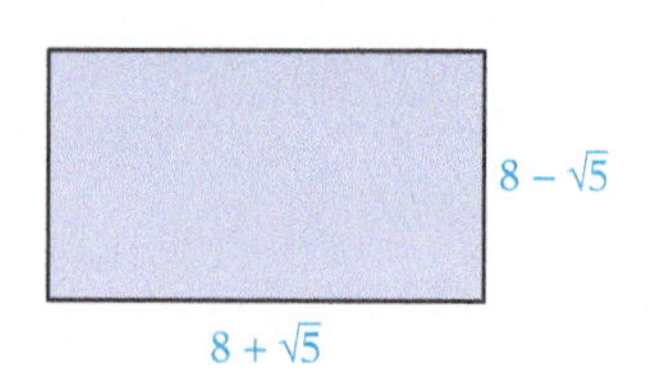

For Exercises 82 to 85, simplify.

82. $-\sqrt{1.3}\,\sqrt{1.3}$

83. $\sqrt{\frac{5}{8}}\sqrt{\frac{5}{8}}$

84. $-\sqrt{\frac{16}{81}}$

85. $\sqrt{1\frac{9}{16}}$

86. Show that 2 is a solution of the equation $\sqrt{x + 2} + \sqrt{x - 1} = 3$.

87. Show that $1 + \sqrt{6}$ and $1 - \sqrt{6}$ are solutions of the equation $x^2 - 2x - 5 = 0$.

Projects or Group Activites

88. The number $\frac{\sqrt{5} + 1}{2}$ is called the golden ratio. Research the golden ratio and write a few paragraphs about this number and its applications.

CHECK YOUR PROGRESS: CHAPTER 10

For Exercises 1 to 14, simplify.

1. $\sqrt{300}$

2. $5\sqrt{180}$

3. $\sqrt{64x^{10}}$

4. $\sqrt{18x^5y^4}$

5. $5\sqrt{5} - 8\sqrt{5}$

6. $5\sqrt{a^3b} + a\sqrt{4ab} - 3\sqrt{49a^3b}$

7. $\sqrt{2a^3b^5}\sqrt{32ab^5}$

8. $\sqrt{8}(\sqrt{2} - \sqrt{5})$

9. $(\sqrt{a} - 3)(3\sqrt{a} + 2)$

10. $(\sqrt{2y} + 5)(\sqrt{2y} - 5)$

11. $\frac{\sqrt{50}}{\sqrt{2}}$

12. $\frac{6}{\sqrt{12x}}$

13. $\frac{7}{7 - \sqrt{2}}$

14. $\frac{5 + \sqrt{2}}{3 - \sqrt{2}}$

SECTION

10.4 Solving Equations Containing Radical Expressions

OBJECTIVE A *To solve an equation containing a radical expression*

An equation that contains a variable expression in a radicand is a **radical equation.**

$\sqrt{x} = 4$
$\sqrt{x+2} = \sqrt{x-7}$ } Radical equations

The following property of equality states that if two numbers are equal, the squares of the numbers are equal. This property is used to solve radical equations.

Property of Squaring Both Sides of an Equation

If a and b are real numbers and $a = b$, then $a^2 = b^2$.

EXAMPLES

1. If $\sqrt{x} = 7$, then $(\sqrt{x})^2 = 7^2$, or $x = 49$.
2. If $\sqrt{x+1} = 5$, then $(\sqrt{x+1})^2 = 5^2$, or $x + 1 = 25$.

Procedure for Solving a Radical Equation

1. Write the equation with a radical alone on one side.
2. Square both sides of the equation (Property of Squaring Both Sides of an Equation).
3. Solve for the variable.
4. Check the solution(s) in the original equation.

Tips for Success

Always check a solution. You should substitute the solution into the *original* equation. Below is the check for the equation in HOW TO 1.

Check:

$$\begin{array}{r|l} \sqrt{x-2} - 7 & 0 \\ \sqrt{51-2} - 7 & 0 \\ \sqrt{49} - 7 & 0 \\ 7 - 7 & 0 \\ 0 & 0 \end{array}$$

A true equation

HOW TO 1 Solve: $\sqrt{x-2} - 7 = 0$

$\sqrt{x-2} - 7 = 0$ • Isolate the radical by adding 7 to both sides of the equation.

$\sqrt{x-2} = 7$

$(\sqrt{x-2})^2 = 7^2$ • Square both sides of the equation.

$x - 2 = 49$ • Solve the resulting equation.

$x = 51$

The check is shown at the left. The solution is 51.

When both sides of an equation are squared, the resulting equation may have a solution that is not a solution of the original equation. Checking a proposed solution of a radical equation, as we did at the left, is a necessary step.

HOW TO 2 Solve: $\sqrt{2x-5} + 3 = 0$

$\sqrt{2x-5} + 3 = 0$ • Isolate the radical by subtracting 3 from both sides of the equation.

$\sqrt{2x-5} = -3$

$(\sqrt{2x-5})^2 = (-3)^2$ • Square both sides of the equation.

$2x - 5 = 9$ • Solve for x.

$2x = 14$

$x = 7$

Take Note
Any time each side of an equation is squared, you *must* check the proposed solution of the equation.

Here is the check for the equation from HOW TO 2 on the preceding page.

Check:
$$\sqrt{2x-5}+3=0$$
$$\sqrt{2\cdot 7-5}+3 \;|\; 0$$
$$\sqrt{14-5}+3 \;|\; 0$$
$$\sqrt{9}+3 \;|\; 0$$
$$3+3 \;|\; 0$$
$$6 \neq 0$$

7 does not check as a solution. The equation has no solution.

EXAMPLE 1

Solve: $\sqrt{3x}+2=5$

Solution

$$\sqrt{3x}+2=5$$
$$\sqrt{3x}=3 \quad \bullet \text{ Isolate } \sqrt{3x}.$$
$$(\sqrt{3x})^2=3^2 \quad \bullet \text{ Square both sides.}$$
$$3x=9$$
$$x=3 \quad \bullet \text{ Solve for } x.$$

Check:
$$\sqrt{3x}+2=5$$
$$\sqrt{3\cdot 3}+2 \;|\; 5$$
$$\sqrt{9}+2 \;|\; 5$$
$$3+2 \;|\; 5$$
$$5=5$$

The solution checks. The solution is 3.

YOU TRY IT 1

Solve: $\sqrt{4x}+3=7$

Your solution

EXAMPLE 2

Solve: $1=\sqrt{x}-\sqrt{x-5}$

Solution

When an equation contains two radicals, isolate the radicals one at a time.

$$1=\sqrt{x}-\sqrt{x-5}$$
$$1+\sqrt{x-5}=\sqrt{x} \quad \bullet \text{ Isolate } \sqrt{x}.$$
$$(1+\sqrt{x-5})^2=(\sqrt{x})^2 \quad \bullet \text{ Square both sides.}$$
$$1+2\sqrt{x-5}+(x-5)=x \quad \bullet \text{ Expand the left side.}$$
$$2\sqrt{x-5}=4 \quad \bullet \text{ Simplify.}$$
$$\sqrt{x-5}=2 \quad \bullet \text{ Isolate } \sqrt{x-5}.$$
$$(\sqrt{x-5})^2=2^2 \quad \bullet \text{ Square both sides.}$$
$$x-5=4$$
$$x=9 \quad \bullet \text{ Solve for } x.$$

Check:
$$1=\sqrt{x}-\sqrt{x-5}$$
$$1 \;|\; \sqrt{9}-\sqrt{9-5}$$
$$1 \;|\; \sqrt{9}-\sqrt{4}$$
$$1 \;|\; 3-2$$
$$1=1$$

The solution is 9.

YOU TRY IT 2

Solve: $\sqrt{x}+\sqrt{x+9}=9$

Your solution

Solutions on pp. S24–S25

OBJECTIVE B *To solve application problems*

Pythagoras (c. 580 B.C.–520 B.C.)

A **right triangle** is a triangle that contains a 90° angle. The side opposite the 90° angle is called the **hypotenuse.** The other two sides are called **legs.**

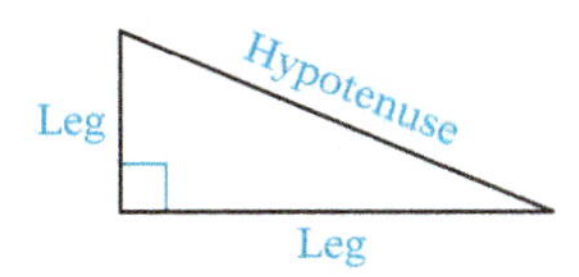

Pythagoras, a Greek mathematician who lived around 550 B.C., is given credit for the Pythagorean Theorem. It states that the square of the hypotenuse of a right triangle is equal to the sum of the squares of the two legs. Actually, this theorem was known to the Babylonians around 1200 B.C.

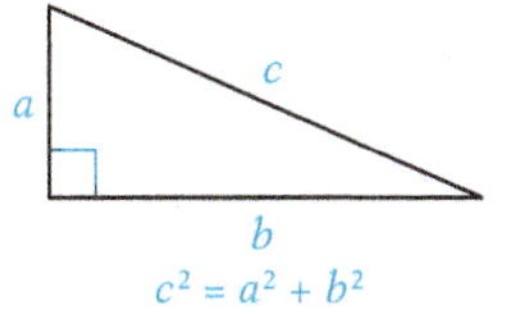

Point of Interest

The first known proof of the Pythagorean Theorem occurs in a Chinese text, *Arithmetic Classic,* which was first written around 600 B.C. (there are no existing copies) and revised over a period of 500 years. The earliest known copy of this text dates from approximately 100 B.C.

Pythagorean Theorem

If a and b are the lengths of the legs of a right triangle and c is the length of the hypotenuse, then $c^2 = a^2 + b^2$.

Using this theorem, we can find the hypotenuse of a right triangle when we know the two legs. Use the formula

$$\text{Hypotenuse} = \sqrt{(\text{leg})^2 + (\text{leg})^2}$$

$$c = \sqrt{a^2 + b^2}$$

$$= \sqrt{(5)^2 + (12)^2}$$

$$= \sqrt{25 + 144}$$

$$= \sqrt{169}$$

$$= 13$$

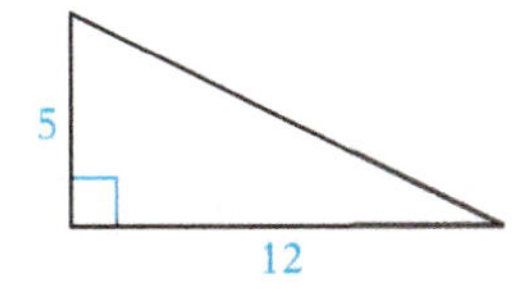

The leg of a right triangle can be found when one leg and the hypotenuse are known. Use the formula

$$\text{Leg} = \sqrt{(\text{hypotenuse})^2 - (\text{leg})^2}$$

$$a = \sqrt{c^2 - b^2}$$

$$= \sqrt{(25)^2 - (20)^2}$$

$$= \sqrt{625 - 400}$$

$$= \sqrt{225}$$

$$= 15$$

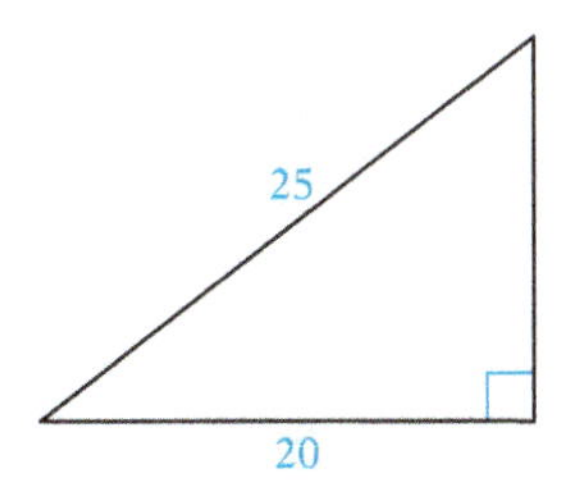

Example 3 and You Try It 3 on the following page illustrate the use of the Pythagorean Theorem. Example 4 and You Try It 4 illustrate other applications of radical equations.

EXAMPLE 3

A guy wire is attached to a point 20 m above the ground on a telephone pole. The wire is anchored to the ground at a point 8 m from the base of the pole. Find the length of the guy wire. Round to the nearest tenth.

Strategy

To find the length of the guy wire, use the Pythagorean Theorem. One leg is 20 m. The other leg is 8 m. The guy wire is the hypotenuse. Solve the Pythagorean Theorem for the hypotenuse.

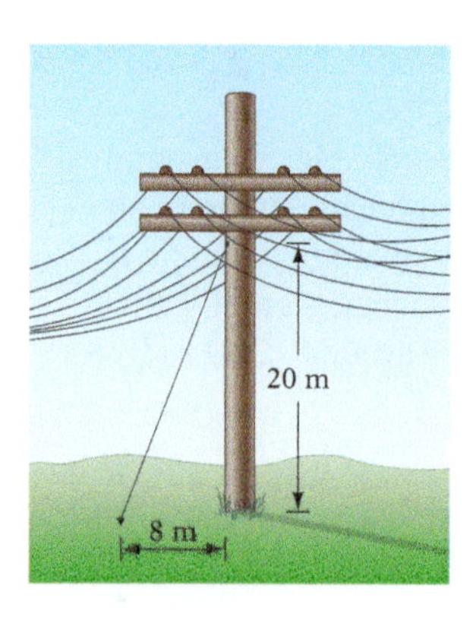

Solution

$c = \sqrt{a^2 + b^2}$

$= \sqrt{(20)^2 + (8)^2}$ • $a = 20, b = 8$

$= \sqrt{400 + 64} = \sqrt{464} \approx 21.5$

The guy wire has a length of approximately 21.5 m.

YOU TRY IT 3

A ladder 8 ft long is resting against a building. How high on the building will the ladder reach when the bottom of the ladder is 3 ft from the building? Round to the nearest hundredth.

Your strategy

Your solution

EXAMPLE 4

How far above the water must a submarine's periscope be for a lookout to see a ship 4 mi away? The equation for the distance in miles that the lookout can see is $d = \sqrt{1.5h}$, where h is the periscope's height in feet above the surface of the water. Round to the nearest hundredth.

Strategy

To find the height above the water, replace d in the equation with the given value and solve for h.

Solution

$d = \sqrt{1.5h}$

$4 = \sqrt{1.5h}$ • $d = 4$

$4^2 = (\sqrt{1.5h})^2$

$16 = 1.5h$

$10.67 \approx h$

The periscope must be approximately 10.67 ft above the water.

YOU TRY IT 4

Find the length of a pendulum that makes one swing in 2.5 s. The equation for the time of one swing is $T = 2\pi\sqrt{\frac{L}{32}}$, where T is the time in seconds and L is the length in feet. Use 3.14 for π. Round to the nearest hundredth.

Your strategy

Your solution

Solutions on p. S25

10.4 EXERCISES

Concept Check

For Exercises 1 to 4, determine whether the equation is a radical equation.

1. $8 = \sqrt{5}x$ **2.** $\sqrt{x - 7} = 9$ **3.** $\sqrt{x} + 4 = 6$ **4.** $12 = \sqrt{3}x$

For Exercises 5 to 8, determine whether the statement is always true, sometimes true, or never true.

5. A radical equation is an equation that contains a radical.

6. We can square both sides of an equation without changing the solution(s) of the equation.

7. We use the Property of Squaring Both Sides of an Equation to eliminate a radical expression from an equation.

8. The first step in solving a radical equation is to square both sides of the equation.

9. In a right triangle, the hypotenuse is the side opposite the ______ angle. The other two sides are called ______.

10. Label the right triangle shown at the right. Include the right angle symbol, the three angles, the two legs, and the hypotenuse.

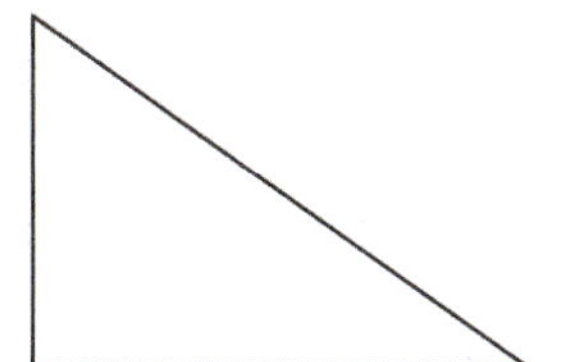

OBJECTIVE A *To solve an equation containing a radical expression*

For Exercises 11 to 46, solve and check.

11. $\sqrt{x} = 5$ **12.** $\sqrt{y} = 7$ **13.** $\sqrt{a} = 12$ **14.** $\sqrt{a} = 9$

15. $\sqrt{5x} = 5$ **16.** $\sqrt{3x} = 4$ **17.** $\sqrt{4x} = 8$ **18.** $\sqrt{6x} = 3$

19. $\sqrt{2x} - 4 = 0$ **20.** $3 - \sqrt{5x} = 0$ **21.** $\sqrt{4x} + 5 = 2$ **22.** $\sqrt{3x} + 9 = 4$

23. $\sqrt{3x - 2} = 4$ **24.** $\sqrt{5x + 6} = 1$ **25.** $\sqrt{2x + 1} = 7$ **26.** $\sqrt{5x + 4} = 3$

27. $\sqrt{5x + 2} = 0$ **28.** $\sqrt{3x - 7} = 0$ **29.** $\sqrt{3x} - 6 = -4$ **30.** $\sqrt{5x} + 8 = 23$

31. $0 = 2 - \sqrt{3 - x}$ **32.** $0 = 5 - \sqrt{10 + x}$ **33.** $0 = \sqrt{3x - 9} - 6$ **34.** $0 = \sqrt{2x + 7} - 3$

35. $\sqrt{5x - 1} = \sqrt{3x + 9}$ **36.** $\sqrt{3x + 4} = \sqrt{12x - 14}$

37. $\sqrt{5x - 3} = \sqrt{4x - 2}$

38. $\sqrt{5x - 9} = \sqrt{2x - 3}$

39. $\sqrt{x^2 - 5x + 6} = \sqrt{x^2 - 8x + 9}$

40. $\sqrt{x^2 - 2x + 4} = \sqrt{x^2 + 5x - 12}$

41. $\sqrt{x} = \sqrt{x + 3} - 1$

42. $\sqrt{x + 5} = \sqrt{x} + 1$

43. $\sqrt{2x + 5} = 5 - \sqrt{2x}$

44. $\sqrt{2x} + \sqrt{2x + 9} = 9$

45. $\sqrt{3x} - \sqrt{3x + 7} = 1$

46. $\sqrt{x} - \sqrt{x + 9} = 1$

47. Without solving the equations, identify which equation has no solution.
(i) $-\sqrt{2x - 5} = -3$ **(ii)** $\sqrt{2x} - 5 = -3$ **(iii)** $\sqrt{2x - 5} = -3$

OBJECTIVE B *To solve application problems*

48. **Integer Problem** Five added to the square root of the product of four and a number is equal to seven. Find the number.

49. **Integer Problem** Two added to the square root of the sum of a number and five is equal to six. Find the number.

50. A 20-foot ladder leans against the side of a building with its bottom d feet from the building. The ladder reaches a height of h feet. Which of the following distances is not possible as a value for h?
(i) 4 ft **(ii)** 10 ft **(iii)** 16 ft **(iv)** 22 ft

Geometry For Exercises 51 to 53, solve. Round to the nearest hundredth.

51. The two legs of a right triangle measure 5 cm and 9 cm. Find the length of the hypotenuse.

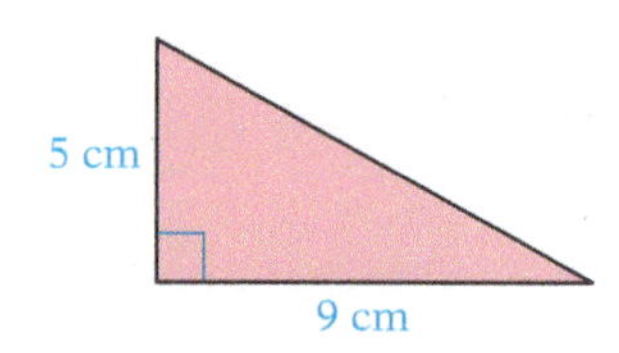

52. The two legs of a right triangle measure 8 in. and 4 in. Find the length of the hypotenuse.

53. The hypotenuse of a right triangle measures 12 ft. One leg of the triangle measures 7 ft. Find the length of the other leg of the triangle.

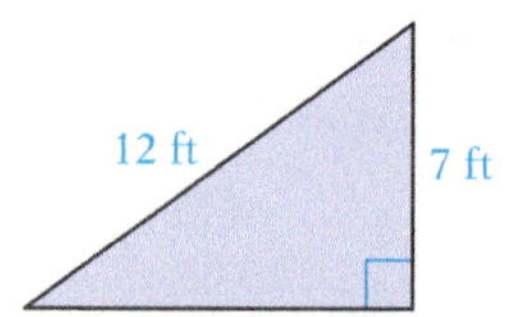

54. The hypotenuse of a right triangle measures 20 cm. One leg of the triangle measures 16 cm. Find the length of the other leg of the triangle.

55. A diagonal of a rectangle is a line drawn from one vertex to the opposite vertex. Find the length of the diagonal in the rectangle shown at the right. Round to the nearest tenth.

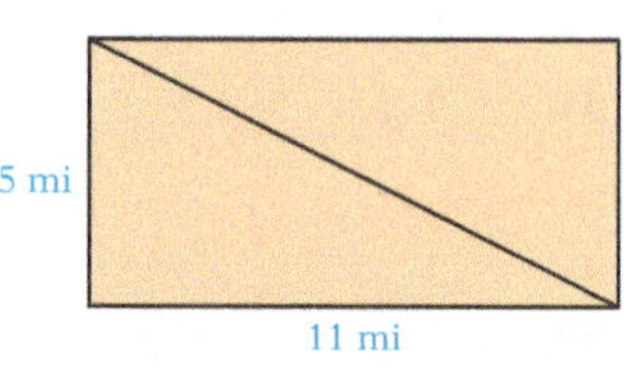

56. Education One method used to "curve" the grades on an exam is to use the formula $R = 10\sqrt{O}$, where R is the revised score and O is the original score. Use this formula to find the original score on an exam that has a revised score of 75. Round to the nearest whole number.

57. Physics A formula used in the study of shallow-water wave motion is $C = \sqrt{32H}$, where C is the wave velocity in feet per second and H is the depth in feet. Use this formula to find the depth of the water when the wave velocity is 20 ft/s.

58. Physics See the news clipping at the right. The time it takes an object to fall a certain distance is given by the equation $t = \sqrt{\frac{d}{16}}$, where t is the time in seconds and d is the distance in feet. Use this equation to find the height from which the hay was dropped.

In the NEWS!

Hay Drop for Stranded Cattle

The Wyoming and Colorado National Guards have come to the aid of thousands of cattle stranded by the blizzard that has paralyzed southeastern Colorado. Flying low over the cattle, the guardsmen drop bales of hay that 6 s later smash into the ground, break apart, and provide food for the animals, which would otherwise starve.

Sources: The Denver Post; www.af.mil

59. Sports The infield of a softball diamond is a square. The distance between successive bases is 60 ft. The pitcher's mound is on the diagonal between home plate and second base at a distance of 46 ft from home plate. Is the pitcher's mound more or less than halfway between home plate and second base?

60. Sports The infield of a baseball diamond is a square. The distance between successive bases is 90 ft. The pitcher's mound is on the diagonal between home plate and second base at a distance of 60.5 ft from home plate. Is the pitcher's mound more or less than halfway between home plate and second base?

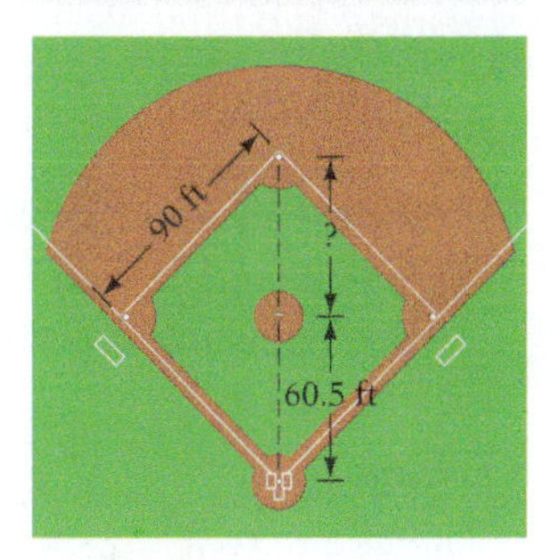

61. Communications Marta Lightfoot leaves a dock in her sailboat and sails 2.5 mi due east. She then tacks and sails 4 mi due north. The walkie-talkie Marta has on board has a range of 5 mi. Will she be able to call a friend on the dock from her location using the walkie-talkie?

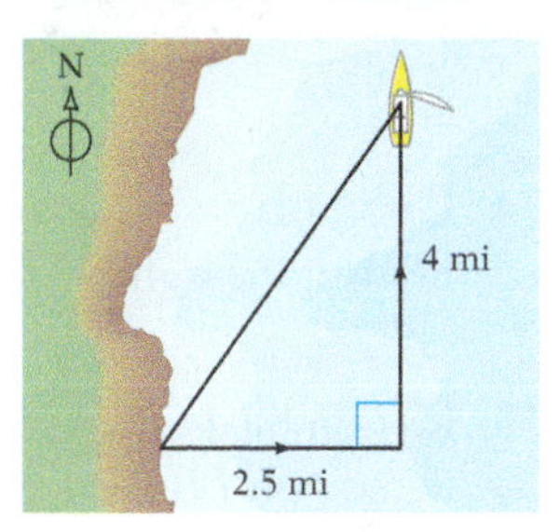

62. Navigation How far above the water would a submarine's periscope have to be for the lookout to locate a ship 5 mi away? The equation for the distance in miles that the lookout can see is $d = \sqrt{1.5h}$, where h is the periscope's height in feet above the surface of the water. Round to the nearest hundredth.

63. Home Maintenance Rick Wyman needs to clean the gutters of his home. The gutters are 24 ft above the ground. For safety, the distance a ladder reaches up a wall should be four times the distance from the bottom of the ladder to the base of the side of the house. Therefore, the bottom of the ladder must be 6 ft from the base of the house. Will a 25-foot ladder be long enough to reach the gutters?

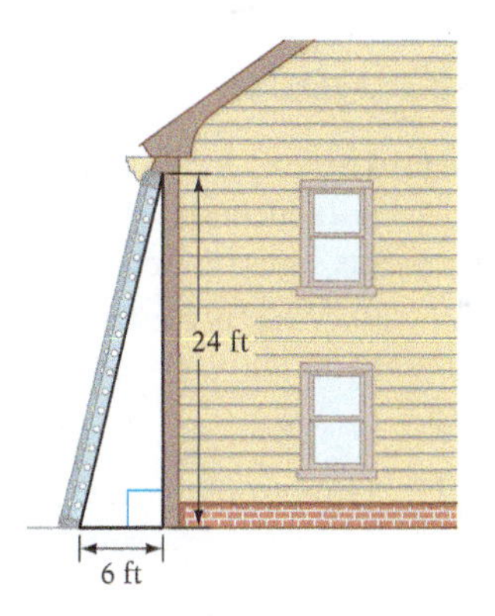

64. Physics The speed of a child riding a merry-go-round at a carnival is given by the equation $v = \sqrt{12r}$, where v is the speed in feet per second and r is the distance in feet from the center of the merry-go-round to the rider. If a child is moving at 15 ft/s, how far is the child from the center of the merry-go-round?

65. Physics Find the length of a pendulum that makes one swing in 1.5 s. The equation for the time of one swing is $T = 2\pi\sqrt{\frac{L}{32}}$, where T is the time in seconds and L is the length in feet. Use 3.14 for π. Round to the nearest hundredth.

66. Aviation A commuter plane leaves an airport and travels due south at 400 mph. Another plane leaves at the same time and travels due east at 300 mph. Find the distance between the two planes after 2 h.

67. Physics A stone is dropped from a bridge and hits the water 2 s later. How high is the bridge? The equation for the distance an object falls in T seconds is $T = \sqrt{\frac{d}{16}}$, where d is the distance in feet.

68. Physics A stone is dropped into a mine shaft and hits the bottom 3.5 s later. How deep is the mine shaft? The equation for the distance an object falls in T seconds is $T = \sqrt{\frac{d}{16}}$, where d is the distance in feet.

Critical Thinking

For Exercises 69 to 71, solve.

69. $\sqrt{\frac{5y + 2}{3}} = 3$

70. $\sqrt{\frac{3y}{5}} - 1 = 2$

71. $\sqrt{9x^2 + 49} + 1 = 3x + 2$

72. Geometry In the coordinate plane, a triangle is formed by drawing lines between the points (0, 0) and (5, 0), (5, 0) and (5, 12), and (5, 12) and (0, 0). Find the number of units in the perimeter of the triangle.

73. Geometry The hypotenuse of a right triangle is $5\sqrt{2}$ cm, and the length of one leg is $4\sqrt{2}$ cm.

a. Find the perimeter of the triangle. **b.** Find the area of the triangle.

74. Geometry Write an expression in factored form for the shaded region in the diagram at the right.

75. Can the Pythagorean Theorem be used to find the length of side c of the triangle at the right? If so, determine c. If not, explain why the theorem cannot be used.

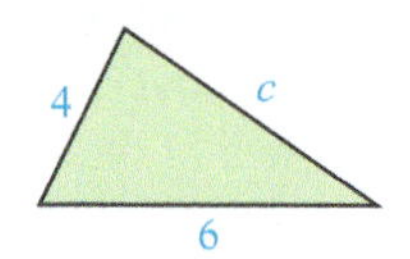

Projects or Group Activities

76. The length of a side of the outer square in the diagram at the right is $2x$ inches. The corners of the inner square are the midpoints of the sides of the outer square.

a. What is the length of a side of the inner square?

b. What is the area of the inner square?

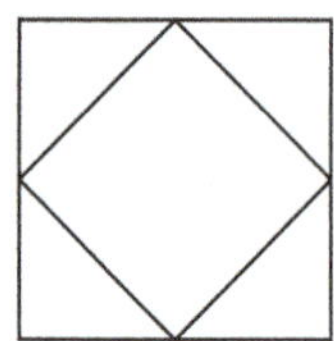

77. Three squares are lined up along the x-axis as shown at the right. Find AB. Round to the nearest tenth.

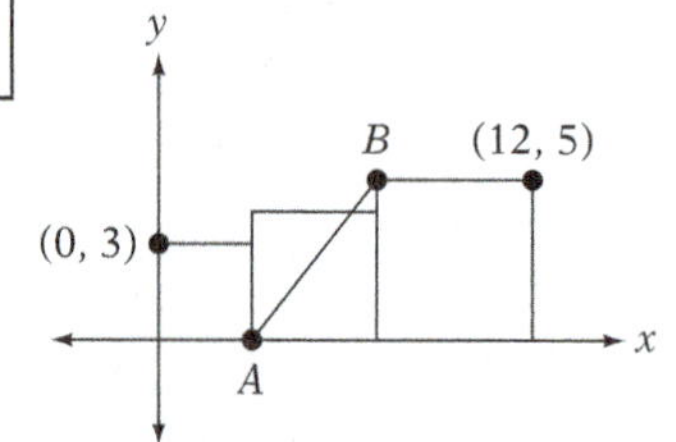

CHAPTER 10 Summary

Key Words

A **square root** of a positive number a is a number whose square is a. Every positive number has two square roots, one positive and one negative. The square root of a negative number is not a real number. [10.1A, p. 478]

Examples

A square root of 49 is 7 because $7^2 = 49$.

A square root of 49 is -7 because $(-7)^2 = 49$.

$\sqrt{-9}$ is not a real number.

The symbol $\sqrt{\ }$ is called a **radical sign** and is used to indicate the positive or **principal square root** of a number. The negative square root of a number is indicated by placing a negative sign in front of the radical. The **radicand** is the expression under the radical sign. [10.1A, p. 478]

$\sqrt{49} = 7$

$-\sqrt{49} = -7$

In the expression $\sqrt{49xy}$, $49xy$ is the radicand.

The square of an integer is a **perfect square.** If a number is not a perfect square, its square root can only be approximated. Such square roots are **irrational numbers.** Their decimal representations never terminate or repeat. [10.1A, p. 478]

1, 4, 9, 16, 25, 36, 49, 64, . . . are examples of perfect squares.

7 is not a perfect square. $\sqrt{7}$ is an irrational number.

Conjugates are expressions with two terms that differ only in the sign of one term. The expressions $a + b$ and $a - b$ are conjugates. [10.3A, p. 488]

$-5 + \sqrt{11}$ and $-5 - \sqrt{11}$ are conjugates.

$\sqrt{x} - 3$ and $\sqrt{x} + 3$ are conjugates.

A **radical equation** is an equation that contains a variable expression in a radicand. [10.4A, p. 495]

$\sqrt{2x} + 5 = 9$ is a radical equation.

$2x + \sqrt{5} = 9$ is not a radical equation.

A **right triangle** is a triangle that contains a 90° angle. The side opposite the 90° angle is called the **hypotenuse.** The other two sides are called **legs.** [10.4B, p. 497]

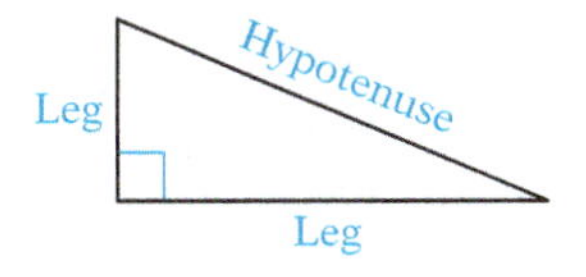

Essential Rules and Procedures

Examples

The Product Property of Square Roots [10.1A, p. 478]
If a and b are positive real numbers, then $\sqrt{ab} = \sqrt{a} \cdot \sqrt{b}$.
Use the Product Property of Square Roots and a knowledge of perfect squares to simplify radicands that are not perfect squares.

$\sqrt{28} = \sqrt{4 \cdot 7} = \sqrt{4} \cdot \sqrt{7} = 2\sqrt{7}$

$\sqrt{9x^7} = \sqrt{9x^6 \cdot x} = \sqrt{9x^6}\sqrt{x} = 3x^3\sqrt{x}$

Adding or Subtracting Radical Expressions [10.2A, p. 484]
The Distributive Property is used to simplify the sum or difference of radical expressions with like radicands.

$8\sqrt{2x} - 3\sqrt{2x} = (8 - 3)\sqrt{2x} = 5\sqrt{2x}$

Multiplying Radical Expressions [10.3A, p. 488]
The Product Property of Square Roots is used to multiply radical expressions.
Use FOIL to multiply radical expressions with two terms.

$\sqrt{2y}(\sqrt{3} - \sqrt{x}) = \sqrt{6y} - \sqrt{2xy}$

$$\begin{aligned}(3 - \sqrt{x})(5 + \sqrt{x}) &\\ &= 15 + 3\sqrt{x} - 5\sqrt{x} - (\sqrt{x})^2\\ &= 15 - 2\sqrt{x} - x\end{aligned}$$

The Quotient Property of Square Roots [10.3B, p. 489]
If a and b are positive real numbers, then $\sqrt{\frac{a}{b}} = \frac{\sqrt{a}}{\sqrt{b}}$ and $\frac{\sqrt{a}}{\sqrt{b}} = \sqrt{\frac{a}{b}}$.

The Quotient Property of Square Roots is used to divide radical expressions.

$$\frac{\sqrt{27}}{\sqrt{3}} = \sqrt{\frac{27}{3}} = \sqrt{9} = 3$$

$$\frac{\sqrt{3x^5y}}{\sqrt{75xy^3}} = \sqrt{\frac{3x^5y}{75xy^3}} = \sqrt{\frac{x^4}{25y^2}} = \frac{x^2}{5y}$$

Simplest Form of a Radical Expression [10.3B, p. 490]
For a radical expression to be in simplest form, three conditions must be met:

1. The radicand contains no factor greater than 1 that is a perfect square.
2. There is no fraction under the radical sign.
3. There is no radical in the denominator of a fraction.

$\sqrt{12}$, $\sqrt{\frac{3}{4}}$, and $\frac{1}{\sqrt{3}}$ are not in simplest form.

$5\sqrt{3}$ and $\frac{\sqrt{3}}{3}$ are in simplest form.

Rationalizing the Denominator [10.3B, p. 490]
The procedure used to remove a radical from a denominator is called **rationalizing the denominator.**

$$\frac{5}{\sqrt{7}} = \frac{5}{\sqrt{7}} \cdot \frac{\sqrt{7}}{\sqrt{7}} = \frac{5\sqrt{7}}{7}$$

Property of Squaring Both Sides of an Equation [10.4A, p. 495]
If a and b are real numbers and $a = b$, then $a^2 = b^2$.

$$\begin{aligned}\sqrt{x} &= 5\\ (\sqrt{x})^2 &= 5^2\\ x &= 25\end{aligned}$$

Solving a Radical Equation Containing One Radical [10.4A, p. 495]

1. Write the equation with the radical alone on one side.
2. Square both sides of the equation.
3. Solve for the variable.
4. Check the solution(s) in the original equation.

$$\begin{aligned}\sqrt{2x} - 1 &= 5\\ \sqrt{2x} &= 6 && \bullet \text{ Isolate the radical.}\\ (\sqrt{2x})^2 &= 6^2 && \bullet \text{ Square both sides.}\\ 2x &= 36\\ x &= 18 && \bullet \text{ Solve for } x.\end{aligned}$$

The solution checks.

Pythagorean Theorem [10.4B, p. 497]
If a and b are the lengths of the legs of a right triangle and c is the length of the hypotenuse, then $c^2 = a^2 + b^2$.

Two legs of a right triangle measure 4 cm and 7 cm. Find the length of the hypotenuse.

$$\begin{aligned}c &= \sqrt{a^2 + b^2}\\ c &= \sqrt{4^2 + 7^2} && \bullet\ a = 4, b = 7\\ c &= \sqrt{16 + 49}\\ c &= \sqrt{65}\end{aligned}$$

The length of the hypotenuse is $\sqrt{65}$ cm.

CHAPTER

10 Review Exercises

1. Simplify: $\sqrt{3}(\sqrt{12} - \sqrt{3})$

2. Simplify: $3\sqrt{18a^5b}$

3. Simplify: $2\sqrt{36}$

4. Simplify: $\sqrt{6a}(\sqrt{3a} + \sqrt{2a})$

5. Simplify: $\dfrac{12}{\sqrt{6}}$

6. Simplify: $2\sqrt{8} - 3\sqrt{32}$

7. Simplify: $(3 - \sqrt{7})(3 + \sqrt{7})$

8. Solve: $\sqrt{x + 3} - \sqrt{x} = 1$

9. Simplify: $\dfrac{2x}{\sqrt{3} - \sqrt{5}}$

10. Simplify: $-3\sqrt{120}$

11. Solve: $\sqrt{5x} = 10$

12. Simplify: $5\sqrt{48}$

13. Simplify: $\dfrac{\sqrt{98x^7y^9}}{\sqrt{2x^3y}}$

14. Solve: $3 - \sqrt{7x} = 5$

15. Simplify: $6a\sqrt{80b} - \sqrt{180a^2b} + 5a\sqrt{b}$

16. Simplify: $4\sqrt{250}$

17. Simplify: $2x\sqrt{60x^3y^3} + 3x^2y\sqrt{15xy}$

18. Simplify: $(4\sqrt{y} - \sqrt{5})(2\sqrt{y} + 3\sqrt{5})$

19. Simplify: $3\sqrt{12x} + 5\sqrt{48x}$

20. Solve: $\sqrt{2x - 3} + 4 = 0$

21. Simplify: $\dfrac{8}{\sqrt{x} - 3}$

22. Simplify: $4y\sqrt{243x^{17}y^9}$

23. Simplify: $y\sqrt{24y^6}$

24. Solve: $2x + 4 = \sqrt{x^2 + 3}$

25. Simplify:
$2x^2\sqrt{18x^2y^5} + 6y\sqrt{2x^6y^3} - 9xy^2\sqrt{8x^4y}$

26. Simplify: $\dfrac{16}{\sqrt{a}}$

27. Surveying To find the distance across a pond, a surveyor constructs a right triangle as shown at the right. Find the distance d across the pond. Round to the nearest foot.

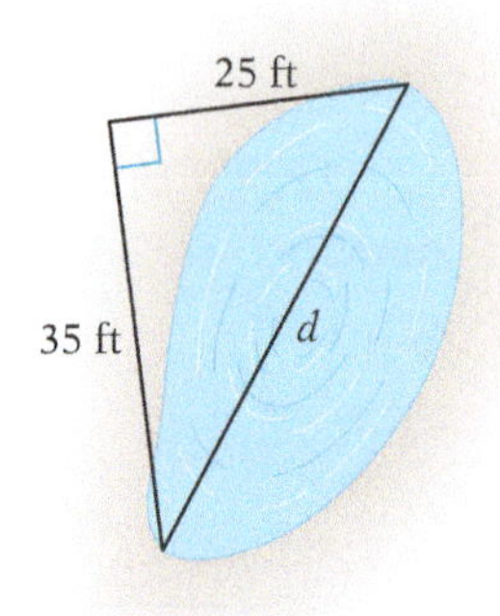

28. Space Exploration The weight of an object is related to the object's distance above the surface of Earth. An equation for this relationship is $d = 4000\sqrt{\dfrac{W_0}{W_d}} - 4000$, where W_0 is an object's weight on the surface of Earth and W_d is the object's weight at a distance of d miles above Earth's surface. If a space explorer weighs 36 lb at a distance of 4000 mi above the surface of Earth, how much does the explorer weigh on the surface of Earth?

29. Tsunamis A tsunami is a great sea wave produced by underwater earthquakes or volcanic eruption. The velocity of a tsunami as it approaches land depends on the depth of the water and can be approximated by the equation $v = 3\sqrt{d}$, where d is the depth of the water in feet and v is the velocity of the tsunami in feet per second. Find the depth of the water if the velocity of a tsunami is 30 ft/s.

30. Bicycle Safety A bicycle will overturn if it rounds a corner too sharply or too fast. An equation for the maximum velocity at which a cyclist can turn a corner without tipping over is $v = 4\sqrt{r}$, where v is the velocity of the bicycle in miles per hour and r is the radius of the corner in feet. What is the radius of the sharpest corner that a cyclist can safely turn while riding at 20 mph?

mypokcik/Shutterstock.com

CHAPTER 10 TEST

1. Simplify: $\sqrt{121x^8y^2}$

2. Simplify: $\sqrt{3x^2y}\sqrt{6xy^2}\sqrt{2x}$

3. Simplify: $5\sqrt{8} - 3\sqrt{50}$

4. Simplify: $\sqrt{45}$

5. Simplify: $\dfrac{\sqrt{162}}{\sqrt{2}}$

6. Solve: $\sqrt{9x} + 3 = 18$

7. Simplify: $\sqrt{32a^5b^{11}}$

8. Simplify: $\dfrac{\sqrt{98a^6b^4}}{\sqrt{2a^3b^2}}$

9. Simplify: $\dfrac{2}{\sqrt{3} - 1}$

10. Simplify: $\sqrt{8x^3y}\sqrt{10xy^4}$

11. Solve: $\sqrt{x-5} + \sqrt{x} = 5$

12. Simplify: $3\sqrt{8y} - 2\sqrt{72x} + 5\sqrt{18y}$

13. Simplify: $\sqrt{72x^7y^2}$

14. Simplify: $(\sqrt{y} - 3)(\sqrt{y} + 5)$

15. Simplify: $2x\sqrt{3xy^3} - 2y\sqrt{12x^3y} - 3xy\sqrt{xy}$

16. Simplify: $\dfrac{2 - \sqrt{5}}{6 + \sqrt{5}}$

17. Simplify: $\sqrt{a}(\sqrt{a} - \sqrt{b})$

18. Simplify: $\sqrt{75}$

19. Physics Find the length of a pendulum that makes one swing in 3 s. The equation for the time of one swing of a pendulum is $T = 2\pi\sqrt{\frac{L}{32}}$, where T is the time in seconds and L is the length in feet. Use 3.14 for π. Round to the nearest hundredth.

20. Camping A support rope for a tent is attached to the top of a pole and then secured to the ground as shown in the figure at the right. If the rope is 8 ft long and the pole is 4 ft high, how far x from the base of the pole should the rope be secured? Round to the nearest foot.

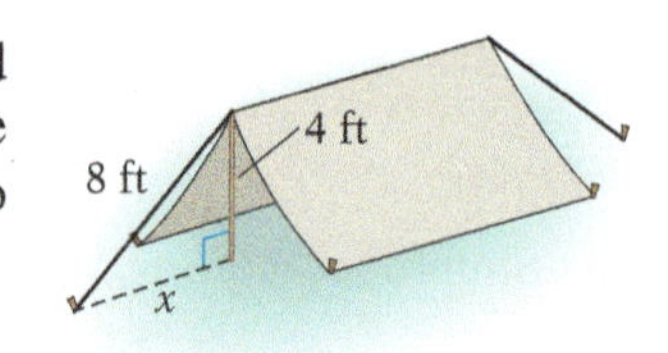

Cumulative Review Exercises

1. Simplify:
$\left(\frac{2}{3}\right)^2 \cdot \left(\frac{3}{4} - \frac{3}{2}\right) + \left(\frac{1}{2}\right)^2$

2. Simplify:
$-3[x - 2(3 - 2x) - 5x] + 2x$

3. Solve:
$2x - 4[3x - 2(1 - 3x)] = 2(3 - 4x)$

4. Simplify: $(-3x^2y)(-2x^3y^4)$

5. Simplify: $\dfrac{12b^4 - 6b^2 + 2}{-6b^2}$

6. Given $f(x) = \dfrac{2x}{x - 3}$, find $f(-3)$.

7. Factor: $2a^3 - 16a^2 + 30a$

8. Multiply: $\dfrac{3x^3 - 6x^2}{4x^2 + 4x} \cdot \dfrac{3x - 9}{9x^3 - 45x^2 + 54x}$

9. Subtract: $\dfrac{x + 2}{x - 4} - \dfrac{6}{(x - 4)(x - 3)}$

10. Solve: $\dfrac{x}{2x - 5} - 2 = \dfrac{3x}{2x - 5}$

11. Find the equation of the line that contains the point $(-2, -3)$ and has slope $\frac{1}{2}$.

12. Solve by substitution:
$4x - 3y = 1$
$2x + y = 3$

13. Solve by the addition method:
$5x + 4y = 7$
$3x - 2y = 13$

14. Solve: $3(x - 7) \geq 5x - 12$

15. Simplify: $\sqrt{108}$

16. Simplify: $3\sqrt{32} - 2\sqrt{128}$

17. Simplify: $2a\sqrt{2ab^3} + b\sqrt{8a^3b} - 5ab\sqrt{ab}$

18. Simplify: $\sqrt{2a^9b}\sqrt{98ab^3}\sqrt{2a}$

19. Simplify: $\sqrt{3}(\sqrt{6} - x)$

20. Simplify: $\dfrac{\sqrt{320}}{\sqrt{5}}$

21. Simplify: $\dfrac{3}{2 - \sqrt{5}}$

22. Solve: $\sqrt{3x - 2} - 4 = 0$

23. Markup The selling price of a book is \$59.40. The markup rate used by the bookstore is 20%. Find the cost of the book. Use the formula $S = C + rC$, where S is the selling price, C is the cost, and r is the markup rate.

24. Mixtures How many ounces of pure water must be added to 40 oz of a 12% salt solution to make a salt solution that is 5% salt?

25. Number Problems The sum of two numbers is twenty-one. The product of the two numbers is one hundred four. Find the two numbers.

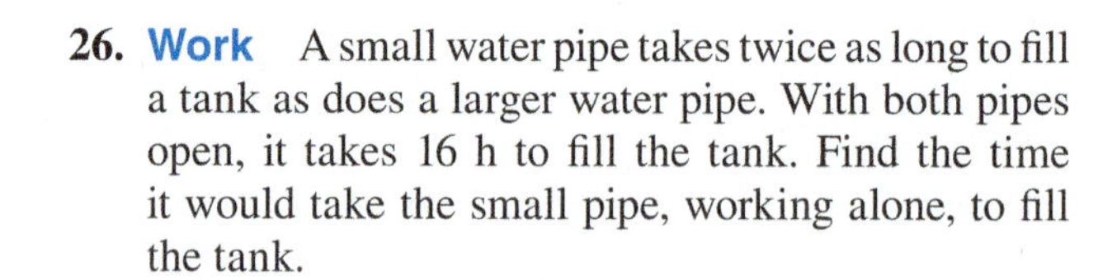

26. Work A small water pipe takes twice as long to fill a tank as does a larger water pipe. With both pipes open, it takes 16 h to fill the tank. Find the time it would take the small pipe, working alone, to fill the tank.

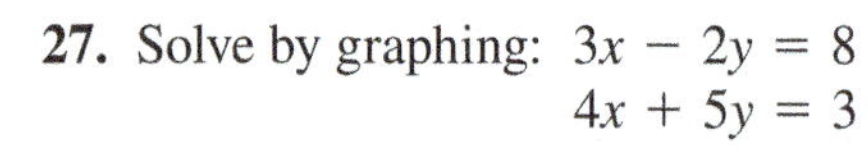

27. Solve by graphing: $3x - 2y = 8$
$4x + 5y = 3$

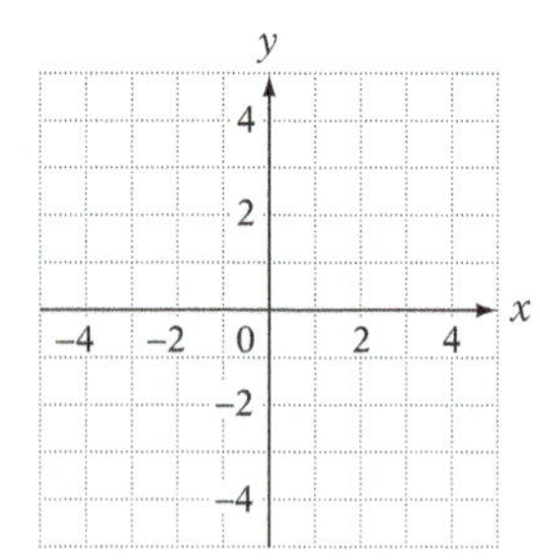

28. Graph the solution set of $3x + y \leq 2$.

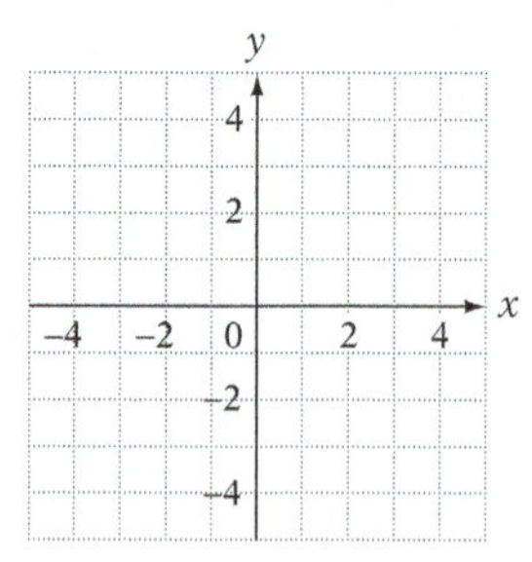

29. Integer Problem The square root of the sum of two consecutive integers is equal to 9. Find the smaller integer.

30. Physics A stone is dropped from a building and hits the ground 5 s later. How tall is the building? The equation for the distance an object falls in T seconds is $T = \sqrt{\dfrac{d}{16}}$, where d is the distance in feet.

Quadratic Equations

OBJECTIVES

SECTION 11.1

A To solve a quadratic equation by factoring

B To solve a quadratic equation by taking square roots

SECTION 11.2

A To solve a quadratic equation by completing the square

SECTION 11.3

A To solve a quadratic equation by using the quadratic formula

SECTION 11.4

A To graph a quadratic equation of the form $y = ax^2 + bx + c$

SECTION 11.5

A To solve application problems

Focus on Success

The end of the semester is generally a very busy and stressful time. You may be dealing with the anxiety of taking final exams. You have covered a great deal of material in this course, and reviewing all of it may be daunting. You might begin by reviewing the Chapter Summary for each chapter that you were assigned during the term. Then take the Final Exam on page 551. The answer to each exercise is given at the back of the book. (See Ace the Test, page AIM-11.)

F.C.G./Shutterstock.com

Prep Test

Are you ready to succeed in this chapter? Take the Prep Test below to find out if you are ready to learn the new material.

1. Evaluate $b^2 - 4ac$ when $a = 2$, $b = -3$, and $c = -4$.

2. Solve: $5x + 4 = 3$

3. Factor: $x^2 + x - 12$

4. Factor: $4x^2 - 12x + 9$

5. Is $x^2 - 10x + 25$ a perfect square trinomial?

6. Solve: $\dfrac{5}{x-2} = \dfrac{15}{x}$

7. Graph: $y = -2x + 3$

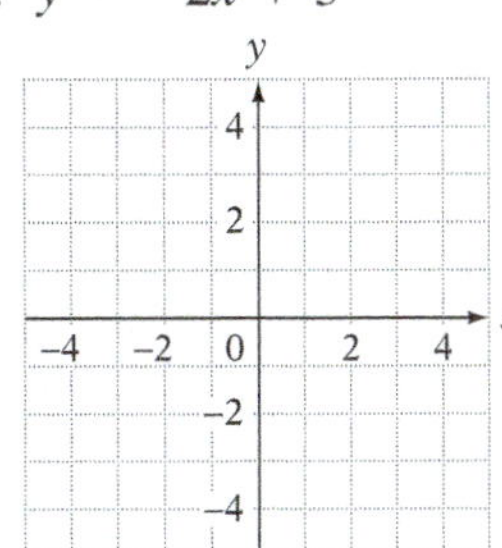

8. Simplify: $\sqrt{28}$

9. If a is *any* real number, simplify $\sqrt{a^2}$.

10. **Exercising** Walking at a constant speed of 4.5 mph, Lucy and Sam walked from the beginning to the end of a hiking trail. When they reached the end, they immediately started back along the same path at a constant speed of 3 mph. If the round-trip took 2 h, what is the length of the hiking trail?

SECTION

11.1 Solving Quadratic Equations by Factoring or by Taking Square Roots

OBJECTIVE A *To solve a quadratic equation by factoring*

An equation of the form $ax^2 + bx + c = 0$, where a, b, and c are real numbers and $a \neq 0$, is a **quadratic equation.**

$4x^2 - 3x + 1 = 0$, $\quad a = 4, b = -3, c = 1$

$3x^2 - 4 = 0$, $\quad a = 3, b = 0, c = -4$

$\frac{x^2}{2} - 2x + 4 = 0$, $\quad a = \frac{1}{2}, b = -2, c = 4$

A quadratic equation is also called a **second-degree equation.**

A quadratic equation is in **standard form** when the polynomial is in descending order and equal to zero. $3x^2 + 5x - 2 = 0$ is a quadratic equation in standard form.

Recall that the Principle of Zero Products states that if the product of two factors is zero, then at least one of the factors must be zero.

If $a \cdot b = 0$,
then $a = 0$ or $b = 0$.

The Principle of Zero Products can be used to solve quadratic equations by factoring. Write the equation in standard form, factor the polynomial, apply the Principle of Zero Products, and solve for the variable.

HOW TO 1 Solve by factoring: $2x^2 - x = 1$

$$2x^2 - x = 1$$

$$2x^2 - x - 1 = 0 \qquad \text{• Write the equation in standard form.}$$

$$(2x + 1)(x - 1) = 0 \qquad \text{• Factor.}$$

$$2x + 1 = 0 \qquad x - 1 = 0 \qquad \text{• Use the Principle of Zero Products to set each factor equal to zero.}$$

$$2x = -1 \qquad x = 1 \qquad \text{• Solve each equation for } x.$$

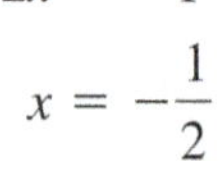

$$x = -\frac{1}{2}$$

Take Note

You should always check your proposed solutions by substituting them back into the *original* equation.

Check:

$2x^2 - x = 1$	
$2\left(-\frac{1}{2}\right)^2 - \left(-\frac{1}{2}\right)$	1
$2 \cdot \frac{1}{4} + \frac{1}{2}$	1
$\frac{1}{2} + \frac{1}{2}$	1
$1 = 1$	

$2x^2 - x = 1$	
$2(1)^2 - 1$	1
$2 \cdot 1 - 1$	1
$2 - 1$	1
$1 = 1$	

The solutions are $-\frac{1}{2}$ and 1.

HOW TO 2 Solve by factoring: $3x^2 - 4x + 8 = (4x + 1)(x - 2)$

$3x^2 - 4x + 8 = (4x + 1)(x - 2)$

$3x^2 - 4x + 8 = 4x^2 - 7x - 2$ • Multiply the factors on the right side of the equation.

$0 = x^2 - 3x - 10$ • Write the equation in standard form.

$0 = (x - 5)(x + 2)$ • Factor.

$x - 5 = 0 \quad x + 2 = 0$ • Use the Principle of Zero Products to set each factor equal to zero.

$x = 5 \quad x = -2$ • Solve each equation for x.

Check:

$3x^2 - 4x + 8$	$(4x + 1)(x - 2)$
$3(5)^2 - 4(5) + 8$	$(4[5] + 1)(5 - 2)$
$3(25) - 4(5) + 8$	$(20 + 1)(3)$
$75 - 20 + 8$	$(21)(3)$
$63 =$	63

$3x^2 - 4x + 8$	$(4x + 1)(x - 2)$
$3(-2)^2 - 4(-2) + 8$	$(4[-2] + 1)(-2 - 2)$
$3(4) - 4(-2) + 8$	$(-8 + 1)(-4)$
$12 + 8 + 8$	$(-7)(-4)$
$28 =$	28

The solutions are 5 and -2.

HOW TO 3 Solve by factoring: $x^2 - 10x + 25 = 0$

$x^2 - 10x + 25 = 0$

$(x - 5)(x - 5) = 0$ • Factor.

$x - 5 = 0 \quad x - 5 = 0$ • Use the Principle of Zero Products.

$x = 5 \quad x = 5$ • Solve each equation for x.

The solution is 5.

In HOW TO 3, 5 is called a **double root** of the quadratic equation.

EXAMPLE 1

Solve by factoring: $\frac{z^2}{2} - \frac{z}{4} - \frac{1}{4} = 0$

Solution

$\frac{z^2}{2} - \frac{z}{4} - \frac{1}{4} = 0$ • The equation is in standard form.

$4\left(\frac{z^2}{2} - \frac{z}{4} - \frac{1}{4}\right) = 4(0)$ • Multiply each side by 4 to clear fractions.

$2z^2 - z - 1 = 0$

$(2z + 1)(z - 1) = 0$ • Factor.

$2z + 1 = 0 \quad z - 1 = 0$ • Principle of Zero Products

$2z = -1 \quad z = 1$

$z = -\frac{1}{2}$

The solutions are $-\frac{1}{2}$ and 1.

YOU TRY IT 1

Solve by factoring: $\frac{3y^2}{2} + y - \frac{1}{2} = 0$

Your solution

Solution on p. S25

OBJECTIVE B *To solve a quadratic equation by taking square roots*

Consider a quadratic equation of the form $x^2 = a$. This equation can be solved by factoring.

$$x^2 = 25$$
$$x^2 - 25 = 0$$
$$(x-5)(x+5) = 0$$
$$x - 5 = 0 \qquad x + 5 = 0$$
$$x = 5 \qquad x = -5$$

The solutions are 5 and -5. The solutions are plus or minus the same number, which is frequently written by using $\pm$; for example, "the solutions are ± 5." An alternative method of solving this equation is suggested by the fact that ± 5 can be written as $\pm\sqrt{25}$.

Take Note

Recall that the solution of the equation $|x| = 5$ is ± 5. This principle is used when solving an equation by taking square roots. Remember that $\sqrt{x^2} = |x|$. Therefore,

$$x^2 = 25$$
$$\sqrt{x^2} = \sqrt{25}$$
$$|x| = 5 \quad \bullet\ \sqrt{x^2} = |x|$$
$$x = \pm 5 \quad \bullet\ \text{If } |x| = 5, \text{ then } x = \pm 5.$$

Principle of Taking the Square Root of Each Side of an Equation

If $x^2 = a$, then $x = \pm\sqrt{a}$.

EXAMPLE

Solve by taking square roots: $x^2 = 25$

$$x^2 = 25$$
$$\sqrt{x^2} = \sqrt{25} \quad \bullet \text{ Take the square root of each side of the equation. Then simplify.}$$
$$x = \pm\sqrt{25}$$
$$x = \pm 5$$

The solutions are 5 and -5.

Take Note

Here is a check for HOW TO 4 at the right.

Check:

$3x^2 = 36$	
$3(2\sqrt{3})^2$	36
$3(12)$	36
$36 = 36$	

$3x^2 = 36$	
$3(-2\sqrt{3})^2$	36
$3(12)$	36
$36 = 36$	

HOW TO 4 Solve by taking square roots: $3x^2 = 36$

$$3x^2 = 36$$
$$x^2 = 12 \quad \bullet \text{ Solve for } x^2. \text{ Divide each side by 3.}$$
$$\sqrt{x^2} = \sqrt{12} \quad \bullet \text{ Take the square root of each side.}$$
$$x = \pm\sqrt{12} \quad \bullet \text{ Simplify.}$$
$$x = \pm 2\sqrt{3}$$

The solutions are $2\sqrt{3}$ and $-2\sqrt{3}$.

HOW TO 5 Solve by taking square roots: $49y^2 - 25 = 0$

$$49y^2 - 25 = 0$$
$$49y^2 = 25 \quad \bullet \text{ Solve for } y^2. \text{ Add 25 to each side.}$$
$$y^2 = \frac{25}{49} \quad \bullet \text{ Divide each side by 49.}$$
$$\sqrt{y^2} = \sqrt{\frac{25}{49}} \quad \bullet \text{ Take the square root of each side.}$$
$$y = \pm\frac{5}{7} \quad \bullet \text{ Simplify.}$$

The solutions are $\frac{5}{7}$ and $-\frac{5}{7}$.

An equation that contains the square of a binomial can be solved by taking square roots.

Take Note

Here is a check for one of the solutions in HOW TO 6 at the right. You should check all solutions.

Check:

$2(x-1)^2 - 36 = 0$	
$2(1+3\sqrt{2}-1)^2 - 36$	0
$2(3\sqrt{2})^2 - 36$	0
$2(18) - 36$	0
$36 - 36$	0
$0 = 0$	

HOW TO 6 Solve by taking square roots: $2(x-1)^2 - 36 = 0$

$2(x-1)^2 - 36 = 0$

$2(x-1)^2 = 36$ • Solve for $(x-1)^2$. Add 36 to each side.

$(x-1)^2 = 18$ • Divide each side by 2.

$\sqrt{(x-1)^2} = \sqrt{18}$ • Take the square root of each side.

$x - 1 = \pm\sqrt{18}$

$x - 1 = \pm 3\sqrt{2}$ • Simplify.

$x = 1 \pm 3\sqrt{2}$ • Solve for x.

The solutions are $1 + 3\sqrt{2}$ and $1 - 3\sqrt{2}$.

EXAMPLE 2

Solve by taking square roots:
$x^2 + 16 = 0$

Solution

$x^2 + 16 = 0$

$x^2 = -16$ • Solve for x^2.

$\sqrt{x^2} = \sqrt{-16}$ • Take square roots.

$\sqrt{-16}$ is not a real number.

The equation has no real number solution.

YOU TRY IT 2

Solve by taking square roots:
$x^2 + 81 = 0$

Your solution

EXAMPLE 3

Solve by taking square roots:
$5(y-4)^2 = 25$

Solution

$5(y-4)^2 = 25$

$(y-4)^2 = 5$ • Solve for $(y-4)^2$.

$\sqrt{(y-4)^2} = \sqrt{5}$ • Take square roots.

$y - 4 = \pm\sqrt{5}$ • Simplify.

$y = 4 \pm \sqrt{5}$ • Solve for y.

The solutions are $4 + \sqrt{5}$ and $4 - \sqrt{5}$.

YOU TRY IT 3

Solve by taking square roots:
$7(z+2)^2 = 21$

Your solution

Solutions on pp. S25–S26

11.1 EXERCISES

Concept Check

1. By the Principle of Zero Products, if $(3x + 4)(x - 7) = 0$, then ______ $= 0$ or ______ $= 0$.

2. The solutions of an equation are $x = \pm 6$. This means that $x =$ ______ or $x =$ ______.

For Exercises 3 to 5, write the quadratic equation in standard form.

3. $x^2 - 8 = 3x$
4. $2x^2 = 4x - 1$
5. $x + 5 = x(x - 3)$

OBJECTIVE A *To solve a quadratic equation by factoring*

For Exercises 6 to 8, solve for x.

6. $x(x - 7) = 0$
7. $(2x + 5)(3x - 1) = 0$
8. $(x - 4)(2x - 7) = 0$

For Exercises 9 to 38, solve by factoring.

9. $x^2 + 2x - 15 = 0$
10. $t^2 + 3t - 10 = 0$
11. $z^2 - 4z + 3 = 0$
12. $s^2 - 5s + 4 = 0$
13. $p^2 + 3p + 2 = 0$
14. $v^2 + 6v + 5 = 0$
15. $x^2 - 6x + 9 = 0$
16. $y^2 - 8y + 16 = 0$
17. $12y^2 + 8y = 0$
18. $6x^2 - 9x = 0$
19. $r^2 - 10 = 3r$
20. $t^2 - 12 = 4t$
21. $3v^2 - 5v + 2 = 0$
22. $2p^2 - 3p - 2 = 0$
23. $3s^2 + 8s = 3$
24. $3x^2 + 5x = 12$
25. $\frac{3}{4}z^2 - z = -\frac{1}{3}$
26. $\frac{r^2}{2} = 1 - \frac{r}{12}$
27. $4t^2 = 4t + 3$
28. $5y^2 + 11y = 12$
29. $4v^2 - 4v + 1 = 0$
30. $9s^2 - 6s + 1 = 0$
31. $x^2 - 9 = 0$
32. $t^2 - 16 = 0$
33. $4y^2 - 1 = 0$
34. $9z^2 - 4 = 0$
35. $x + 15 = x(x - 1)$
36. $p + 18 = p(p - 2)$
37. $r^2 - r - 2 = (2r - 1)(r - 3)$
38. $s^2 + 5s - 4 = (2s + 1)(s - 4)$

39. Let a be a positive integer. Which equation has a positive double root?
(i) $x^2 - a^2 = 0$ **(ii)** $x^2 + 2ax + a^2 = 0$ **(iii)** $x^2 - 2ax + a^2 = 0$

OBJECTIVE B *To solve a quadratic equation by taking square roots*

For Exercises 40 to 66, solve by taking square roots.

40. $x^2 = 36$

41. $y^2 = 49$

42. $v^2 - 1 = 0$

43. $z^2 - 64 = 0$

44. $4x^2 - 49 = 0$

45. $9w^2 - 64 = 0$

46. $9y^2 = 4$

47. $4z^2 = 25$

48. $16v^2 - 9 = 0$

49. $25x^2 - 64 = 0$

50. $y^2 + 81 = 0$

51. $z^2 + 49 = 0$

52. $w^2 - 24 = 0$

53. $v^2 - 48 = 0$

54. $(x - 1)^2 = 36$

55. $(y + 2)^2 = 49$

56. $2(x + 5)^2 = 8$

57. $4(z - 3)^2 = 100$

58. $9(x - 1)^2 - 16 = 0$

59. $4(y + 3)^2 - 81 = 0$

60. $49(v + 1)^2 - 25 = 0$

61. $81(y - 2)^2 - 64 = 0$

62. $(x - 4)^2 - 20 = 0$

63. $(y + 5)^2 - 50 = 0$

64. $(x + 1)^2 + 36 = 0$

65. $2\left(z - \frac{1}{2}\right)^2 = 12$

66. $3\left(v + \frac{3}{4}\right)^2 = 36$

For Exercises 67 to 70, assume that a and b are both positive numbers. For each equation, state the number of real number solutions.

67. $(x + a)^2 = 0$

68. $ax^2 - b = 0$

69. $(x + a)^2 = b$

70. $ax^2 + b = 0$

Critical Thinking

71. Evaluate $2n^2 - 7n - 4$, given $n(n - 2) = 15$.

72. Evaluate $3y^2 + 5y - 2$, given $y(y + 3) = 28$.

Projects or Group Activities

73. Investments The value A of an initial investment of P dollars after 2 years is given by $A = P(1 + r)^2$, where r is the annual interest rate earned by the investment. If an initial investment of \$1500 grew to a value of \$1782.15 in 2 years, what was the annual interest rate?

SECTION

11.2 Solving Quadratic Equations by Completing the Square

OBJECTIVE A *To solve a quadratic equation by completing the square*

Recall that a perfect-square trinomial is the square of a binomial.

Perfect-Square Trinomial		Square of a Binomial
$x^2 + 6x + 9$	$=$	$(x + 3)^2$
$x^2 - 10x + 25$	$=$	$(x - 5)^2$
$x^2 + 8x + 16$	$=$	$(x + 4)^2$

For each perfect-square trinomial, the square of $\frac{1}{2}$ of the coefficient of x equals the constant term.

$x^2 + 6x + 9$, $\quad \left(\frac{1}{2} \cdot 6\right)^2 = 9$

$x^2 - 10x + 25$, $\quad \left[\frac{1}{2}(-10)\right]^2 = 25$

$x^2 + 8x + 16$, $\quad \left(\frac{1}{2} \cdot 8\right)^2 = 16$

Adding to a binomial the constant term that makes it a perfect-square trinomial is called **completing the square.**

HOW TO 1 Complete the square on $x^2 - 8x$. Write the resulting perfect-square trinomial as the square of a binomial.

$\left[\frac{1}{2}(-8)\right]^2 = 16$ • **Find the constant term.**

$x^2 - 8x + 16$ • **Complete the square on $x^2 - 8x$ by adding the constant term.**

$x^2 - 8x + 16 = (x - 4)^2$ • **Write the resulting perfect-square trinomial as the square of a binomial.**

HOW TO 2 Complete the square on $y^2 + 5y$. Write the resulting perfect-square trinomial as the square of a binomial.

$\left(\frac{1}{2} \cdot 5\right)^2 = \left(\frac{5}{2}\right)^2 = \frac{25}{4}$ • **Find the constant term.**

$y^2 + 5y + \frac{25}{4}$ • **Complete the square on $y^2 + 5y$ by adding the constant term.**

$y^2 + 5y + \frac{25}{4} = \left(y + \frac{5}{2}\right)^2$ • **Write the resulting perfect-square trinomial as the square of a binomial.**

A quadratic equation that cannot be solved by factoring can be solved by completing the square. When the quadratic equation is in the form $x^2 + bx = c$, add to each side of the equation the term that completes the square on $x^2 + bx$. Factor the perfect-square trinomial, and write it as the square of a binomial. Take the square root of each side of the equation, and then solve for x.

Tips for Success

This is a new skill and one that is difficult for many students. Be sure to do all you need to do in order to be successful at solving quadratic equations by completing the square: Read through the introductory material, work through the How To examples, study the paired examples, do the You Try Its, and check your solutions against the ones given in the back of the book. See *AIM for Success* at the front of the book.

HOW TO 3 Solve by completing the square: $x^2 + 8x - 2 = 0$

$$x^2 + 8x - 2 = 0$$

$$x^2 + 8x = 2$$
- Add 2 to each side of the equation.

$$x^2 + 8x + \left(\frac{1}{2}\cdot 8\right)^2 = 2 + \left(\frac{1}{2}\cdot 8\right)^2$$
- Complete the square on $x^2 + 8x$. Add $\left(\frac{1}{2}\cdot 8\right)^2$ to each side of the equation.

$$x^2 + 8x + 16 = 2 + 16$$
- Simplify.

$$(x + 4)^2 = 18$$
- Factor the perfect-square trinomial.

$$\sqrt{(x + 4)^2} = \sqrt{18}$$
- Take the square root of each side of the equation.

$$x + 4 = \pm\sqrt{18}$$
- Solve for x.

$$x + 4 = \pm 3\sqrt{2}$$

$$x = -4 \pm 3\sqrt{2}$$

Check:

$x^2 + 8x - 2 = 0$	
$(-4 + 3\sqrt{2})^2 + 8(-4 + 3\sqrt{2}) - 2$	0
$16 - 24\sqrt{2} + 18 - 32 + 24\sqrt{2} - 2$	0
$0 = 0$	

$x^2 + 8x - 2 = 0$	
$(-4 - 3\sqrt{2})^2 + 8(-4 - 3\sqrt{2}) - 2$	0
$16 + 24\sqrt{2} + 18 - 32 - 24\sqrt{2} - 2$	0
$0 = 0$	

The solutions are $-4 + 3\sqrt{2}$ and $-4 - 3\sqrt{2}$.

If the coefficient of the second-degree term is not 1, a necessary step in completing the square is to multiply each side of the equation by the reciprocal of that coefficient.

HOW TO 4 Solve by completing the square: $2x^2 - 3x + 1 = 0$

$$2x^2 - 3x + 1 = 0$$

$$2x^2 - 3x = -1$$
- Subtract 1 from each side of the equation.

$$\frac{1}{2}(2x^2 - 3x) = \frac{1}{2}\cdot(-1)$$
- In order to complete the square, the coefficient of x^2 must be 1. Multiply each side of the equation by $\frac{1}{2}$.

$$x^2 - \frac{3}{2}x = -\frac{1}{2}$$

$$x^2 - \frac{3}{2}x + \left[\frac{1}{2}\left(-\frac{3}{2}\right)\right]^2 = -\frac{1}{2} + \left[\frac{1}{2}\left(-\frac{3}{2}\right)\right]^2$$
- Complete the square. Add $\left[\frac{1}{2}\left(-\frac{3}{2}\right)\right]^2$ to each side of the equation.

$$x^2 - \frac{3}{2}x + \frac{9}{16} = -\frac{1}{2} + \frac{9}{16}$$
- Simplify.

$$\left(x - \frac{3}{4}\right)^2 = \frac{1}{16}$$
- Factor the perfect-square trinomial.

$$\sqrt{\left(x - \frac{3}{4}\right)^2} = \sqrt{\frac{1}{16}}$$
- Take the square root of each side of the equation.

$$x - \frac{3}{4} = \pm\frac{1}{4}$$
- Solve for x.

$$x = \frac{3}{4} \pm \frac{1}{4}$$

$$x = \frac{3}{4} + \frac{1}{4} = 1 \qquad x = \frac{3}{4} - \frac{1}{4} = \frac{1}{2}$$

The solutions are $\frac{1}{2}$ and 1.

EXAMPLE 1

Solve by completing the square:
$2x^2 - 4x - 1 = 0$

Solution

$2x^2 - 4x - 1 = 0$

$2x^2 - 4x = 1$ • Add 1.

$\frac{1}{2}(2x^2 - 4x) = \frac{1}{2} \cdot 1$ • Multiply by $\frac{1}{2}$.

$x^2 - 2x = \frac{1}{2}$ • The coefficient of x^2 is 1.

Complete the square.

$x^2 - 2x + 1 = \frac{1}{2} + 1$ • $\left[\frac{1}{2} \cdot (-2)\right]^2 = [-1]^2 = 1$

$(x - 1)^2 = \frac{3}{2}$ • Factor.

$\sqrt{(x - 1)^2} = \sqrt{\frac{3}{2}}$ • Take square roots.

$x - 1 = \pm\frac{\sqrt{6}}{2}$ • Solve for x.

$x = 1 \pm \frac{\sqrt{6}}{2}$

$x = 1 + \frac{\sqrt{6}}{2} = \frac{2 + \sqrt{6}}{2}$ $\qquad$ $x = 1 - \frac{\sqrt{6}}{2} = \frac{2 - \sqrt{6}}{2}$

Check:

$2x^2 - 4x - 1 = 0$	
$2\left(\frac{2 + \sqrt{6}}{2}\right)^2 - 4\left(\frac{2 + \sqrt{6}}{2}\right) - 1$	0
$2\left(\frac{4 + 4\sqrt{6} + 6}{4}\right) - 2(2 + \sqrt{6}) - 1$	0
$2 + 2\sqrt{6} + 3 - 4 - 2\sqrt{6} - 1$	0

$0 = 0$

$2x^2 - 4x - 1 = 0$	
$2\left(\frac{2 - \sqrt{6}}{2}\right)^2 - 4\left(\frac{2 - \sqrt{6}}{2}\right) - 1$	0
$2\left(\frac{4 - 4\sqrt{6} + 6}{4}\right) - 2(2 - \sqrt{6}) - 1$	0
$2 - 2\sqrt{6} + 3 - 4 + 2\sqrt{6} - 1$	0

$0 = 0$

The solutions are $\frac{2 + \sqrt{6}}{2}$ and $\frac{2 - \sqrt{6}}{2}$.

YOU TRY IT 1

Solve by completing the square:
$3x^2 - 6x - 2 = 0$

Your solution

Solution on p. S26

EXAMPLE 2

Solve by completing the square:
$x^2 + 4x + 5 = 0$

Solution

$x^2 + 4x + 5 = 0$

$x^2 + 4x = -5$ • **Subtract 5.**

Complete the square.

$x^2 + 4x + 4 = -5 + 4$ • $\left(\frac{1}{2} \cdot 4\right)^2 = 2^2 = 4$

$(x + 2)^2 = -1$ • **Factor.**

$\sqrt{(x + 2)^2} = \sqrt{-1}$ • **Take square roots.**

$\sqrt{-1}$ is not a real number.

The quadratic equation has no real number solution.

YOU TRY IT 2

Solve by completing the square:
$x^2 + 6x + 12 = 0$

Your solution

EXAMPLE 3

Solve $x^2 = -6x - 4$ by completing the square. Approximate the solutions to the nearest thousandth.

Solution

$x^2 = -6x - 4$

$x^2 + 6x = -4$ • **Add $6x$.**

Complete the square.

$x^2 + 6x + 9 = -4 + 9$ • $\left(\frac{1}{2} \cdot 6\right)^2 = 3^2 = 9$

$(x + 3)^2 = 5$ • **Factor.**

$\sqrt{(x + 3)^2} = \sqrt{5}$ • **Take square roots.**

$x + 3 = \pm\sqrt{5}$

$x + 3 = \sqrt{5}$ $\qquad$ $x + 3 = -\sqrt{5}$

$x = -3 + \sqrt{5}$ $\qquad$ $x = -3 - \sqrt{5}$

$\approx -3 + 2.236$ $\qquad$ $\approx -3 - 2.236$

≈ -0.764 $\qquad$ ≈ -5.236

The solutions are approximately -0.764 and -5.236.

YOU TRY IT 3

Solve $x^2 + 8x + 8 = 0$ by completing the square. Approximate the solutions to the nearest thousandth.

Your solution

Solutions on p. S26

11.2 EXERCISES

Concept Check

1. When we square a binomial, the result is a ____________.
2. When solving the equation $x^2 - 8x + 16 = 18$ by completing the square, the next step after writing the equation in the form $(x - 4)^2 = 18$ is to ____________.

For Exercises 3 to 6, complete the square on the binomial. Write the resulting trinomial as the square of a binomial.

3. $x^2 - 6x$
4. $x^2 + 6x$
5. $x^2 - 5x$
6. $x^2 - 3x$

OBJECTIVE A *To solve a quadratic equation by completing the square*

For Exercises 7 to 47, solve by completing the square.

7. $x^2 + 2x - 3 = 0$
8. $y^2 + 4y - 5 = 0$
9. $z^2 - 6z - 16 = 0$
10. $w^2 + 8w - 9 = 0$
11. $x^2 = 4x - 4$
12. $z^2 = 8z - 16$
13. $v^2 - 6v + 13 = 0$
14. $x^2 + 4x + 13 = 0$
15. $y^2 + 5y + 4 = 0$
16. $v^2 - 5v - 6 = 0$
17. $w^2 + 7w = 8$
18. $y^2 + 5y = -4$
19. $v^2 + 4v + 1 = 0$
20. $y^2 - 2y - 5 = 0$
21. $x^2 + 6x = 5$
22. $w^2 - 8w = 3$
23. $\frac{z^2}{2} = z + \frac{1}{2}$
24. $\frac{y^2}{10} = y - 2$
25. $p^2 + 3p = 1$
26. $r^2 + 5r = 2$
27. $t^2 - 3t = -2$
28. $z^2 - 5z = -3$
29. $v^2 + v - 3 = 0$
30. $x^2 - x = 1$
31. $y^2 = 7 - 10y$
32. $v^2 = 14 + 16v$
33. $r^2 - 3r = 5$

34. $s^2 + 3s = -1$

35. $t^2 - t = 4$

36. $y^2 + y - 4 = 0$

37. $x^2 - 3x + 5 = 0$

38. $z^2 + 5z + 7 = 0$

39. $2t^2 - 3t + 1 = 0$

40. $2x^2 - 7x + 3 = 0$

41. $2r^2 + 5r = 3$

42. $2y^2 - 3y = 4$

43. $2s^2 = 7s - 1$

44. $4v^2 + 4v - 1 = 0$

45. $6s^2 + s = 3$

46. $6z^2 = z + 2$

47. $6p^2 = 5p + 4$

For Exercises 48 and 49, without using a calculator, determine if both of the given solutions are negative, both are positive, or one is negative and one is positive.

48. A quadratic equation has solutions $-3 \pm \sqrt{5}$.

49. A quadratic equation has solutions $2 \pm \sqrt{7}$.

For Exercises 50 to 53, solve by completing the square. Approximate the solutions to the nearest thousandth.

50. $y^2 + 3y = 5$

51. $w^2 + 5w = 2$

52. $2z^2 - 3z = 7$

53. $2x^2 + 3x = 11$

Critical Thinking

54. If $(x + 6)^2 = 9$, then $x + 6$ is equal to what number(s)?

55. Find the solutions of the quadratic equation $ax^2 + bx + c = 0$ in which $a = 1$, $b = 8$, and $c = -14$.

For Exercises 56 to 58, solve.

56. $\sqrt{2x + 7} - 4 = x$

57. $\dfrac{x + 1}{2} + \dfrac{3}{x - 1} = 4$

58. $\dfrac{x - 2}{3} + \dfrac{2}{x + 2} = 4$

Projects or Group Activities

59. Explain why the equation $(x - 2)^2 = -4$ does not have a real number solution.

60. What number is equal to three less than its square?

61. Baseball A ball player hits a ball. The height of the ball above the ground after t seconds can be approximated by the equation $h = -16t^2 + 76t + 5$. When will the ball hit the ground? *Hint:* The ball strikes the ground when $h = 0$ ft.

SECTION

11.3 Solving Quadratic Equations by Using the Quadratic Formula

OBJECTIVE A *To solve a quadratic equation by using the quadratic formula*

Any quadratic equation can be solved by completing the square. Applying this method to the standard form of a quadratic equation produces a formula that can be used to solve any quadratic equation.

Solve $ax^2 + bx + c = 0$ by completing the square.

$$ax^2 + bx + c = 0$$

Add the opposite of the constant term to each side of the equation.

$$ax^2 + bx + c + (-c) = 0 + (-c)$$
$$ax^2 + bx = -c$$

Multiply each side of the equation by the reciprocal of a, the coefficient of x^2.

$$\frac{1}{a}(ax^2 + bx) = \frac{1}{a}(-c)$$
$$x^2 + \frac{b}{a}x = -\frac{c}{a}$$

Complete the square by adding $\left(\frac{1}{2} \cdot \frac{b}{a}\right)^2$ to each side of the equation.

$$x^2 + \frac{b}{a}x + \left(\frac{1}{2} \cdot \frac{b}{a}\right)^2 = \left(\frac{1}{2} \cdot \frac{b}{a}\right)^2 - \frac{c}{a}$$
$$x^2 + \frac{b}{a}x + \frac{b^2}{4a^2} = \frac{b^2}{4a^2} - \frac{c}{a}$$

Simplify the right side of the equation.

$$x^2 + \frac{b}{a}x + \frac{b^2}{4a^2} = \frac{b^2}{4a^2} - \left(\frac{c}{a} \cdot \frac{4a}{4a}\right)$$
$$x^2 + \frac{b}{a}x + \frac{b^2}{4a^2} = \frac{b^2}{4a^2} - \frac{4ac}{4a^2}$$
$$x^2 + \frac{b}{a}x + \frac{b^2}{4a^2} = \frac{b^2 - 4ac}{4a^2}$$

Factor the perfect-square trinomial on the left side of the equation.

$$\left(x + \frac{b}{2a}\right)^2 = \frac{b^2 - 4ac}{4a^2}$$

Take the square root of each side of the equation.

$$\sqrt{\left(x + \frac{b}{2a}\right)^2} = \sqrt{\frac{b^2 - 4ac}{4a^2}}$$
$$x + \frac{b}{2a} = \pm\frac{\sqrt{b^2 - 4ac}}{2a}$$

Solve for x.

$$x + \frac{b}{2a} = \frac{\sqrt{b^2 - 4ac}}{2a} \qquad x + \frac{b}{2a} = -\frac{\sqrt{b^2 - 4ac}}{2a}$$
$$x = -\frac{b}{2a} + \frac{\sqrt{b^2 - 4ac}}{2a} \qquad x = -\frac{b}{2a} - \frac{\sqrt{b^2 - 4ac}}{2a}$$
$$= \frac{-b + \sqrt{b^2 - 4ac}}{2a} \qquad = \frac{-b - \sqrt{b^2 - 4ac}}{2a}$$

The Quadratic Formula

The solutions of the quadratic equation $ax^2 + bx + c = 0$, $a \neq 0$, are

$$x = \frac{-b \pm \sqrt{b^2 - 4ac}}{2a}$$

HOW TO 1 Solve by using the quadratic formula: $2x^2 = 4x - 1$

$$2x^2 = 4x - 1$$
$$2x^2 - 4x + 1 = 0$$

• Write the equation in standard form. Subtract $4x$ from each side and add 1 to each side.

$$x = \frac{-b \pm \sqrt{b^2 - 4ac}}{2a}$$

• The quadratic formula

$$= \frac{-(-4) \pm \sqrt{(-4)^2 - (4 \cdot 2 \cdot 1)}}{2 \cdot 2}$$

• $a = 2, b = -4, c = 1$. Replace a, b, and c by their values.

$$= \frac{4 \pm \sqrt{16 - 8}}{4} = \frac{4 \pm \sqrt{8}}{4}$$

• Simplify.

$$= \frac{4 \pm 2\sqrt{2}}{4} = \frac{2 \pm \sqrt{2}}{2}$$

The solutions are $\frac{2 + \sqrt{2}}{2}$ and $\frac{2 - \sqrt{2}}{2}$.

Take Note

$$\frac{4 \pm 2\sqrt{2}}{4} = \frac{2(2 \pm \sqrt{2})}{2 \cdot 2} = \frac{2 \pm \sqrt{2}}{2}$$

EXAMPLE 1

Solve by using the quadratic formula:
$2x^2 - 3x + 1 = 0$

Solution

$$2x^2 - 3x + 1 = 0$$

• Standard form

$$x = \frac{-(-3) \pm \sqrt{(-3)^2 - 4(2)(1)}}{2 \cdot 2}$$

• $a = 2, b = -3, c = 1$

$$= \frac{3 \pm \sqrt{9 - 8}}{4} = \frac{3 \pm \sqrt{1}}{4} = \frac{3 \pm 1}{4}$$

$$x = \frac{3 + 1}{4} = 1 \qquad x = \frac{3 - 1}{4} = \frac{1}{2}$$

The solutions are 1 and $\frac{1}{2}$.

YOU TRY IT 1

Solve by using the quadratic formula:
$3x^2 + 4x - 4 = 0$

Your solution

EXAMPLE 2

Solve by using the quadratic formula: $\frac{x^2}{2} = 2x - \frac{5}{4}$

Solution

$$\frac{x^2}{2} = 2x - \frac{5}{4}$$

$$4\left(\frac{x^2}{2}\right) = 4\left(2x - \frac{5}{4}\right)$$

• Multiply by 4.

$$2x^2 = 8x - 5$$
$$2x^2 - 8x + 5 = 0$$

• Standard form

$$x = \frac{-(-8) \pm \sqrt{(-8)^2 - 4(2)(5)}}{2 \cdot 2}$$

• $a = 2, b = -8, c = 5$

$$= \frac{8 \pm \sqrt{64 - 40}}{4} = \frac{8 \pm \sqrt{24}}{4}$$

$$= \frac{8 \pm 2\sqrt{6}}{4} = \frac{4 \pm \sqrt{6}}{2}$$

The solutions are $\frac{4 + \sqrt{6}}{2}$ and $\frac{4 - \sqrt{6}}{2}$.

YOU TRY IT 2

Solve by using the quadratic formula: $\frac{x^2}{4} + \frac{x}{2} = \frac{1}{4}$

Your solution

Solutions on p. S26

11.3 EXERCISES

Concept Check

1. If a quadratic equation is solved by using the quadratic formula and the result is $x = \frac{1 \pm \sqrt{13}}{2}$, what are the solutions of the equation?

2. If a quadratic equation is solved by using the quadratic formula and the result is $x = \frac{2 \pm 6}{4}$, what are the solutions of the equation?

3. Explain what the quadratic formula is used for.

4. Write the quadratic formula. Explain what each letter in the formula represents.

OBJECTIVE A *To solve a quadratic equation by using the quadratic formula*

For Exercises 5 to 34, solve by using the quadratic formula.

5. $x^2 - 4x - 5 = 0$

6. $y^2 + 3y + 2 = 0$

7. $y^2 = 2y + 3$

8. $w^2 = 3w + 18$

9. $2y^2 - y - 1 = 0$

10. $2t^2 - 5t + 3 = 0$

11. $w^2 + 3w + 5 = 0$

12. $x^2 - 2x + 6 = 0$

13. $4y^2 + 4y = 15$

14. $6y^2 + 5y - 4 = 0$

15. $2x^2 + x + 1 = 0$

16. $3r^2 - r + 2 = 0$

17. $\frac{1}{2}t^2 - t = \frac{5}{2}$

18. $y^2 - 4y = 6$

19. $\frac{1}{3}t^2 + 2t - \frac{1}{3} = 0$

20. $z^2 + 4z + 1 = 0$

21. $w^2 = 4w + 9$

22. $y^2 = 8y + 3$

23. $9y^2 + 6y - 1 = 0$

24. $9s^2 - 6s - 2 = 0$

25. $4p^2 + 4p + 1 = 0$

26. $9z^2 + 12z + 4 = 0$

27. $\frac{x^2}{2} = x - \frac{5}{4}$

28. $r^2 = \frac{5}{3}r - 2$

29. $4p^2 + 16p = -11$

30. $4y^2 - 12y = -1$

31. $4x^2 = 4x + 11$

32. $4s^2 + 12s = 3$

33. $9v^2 = -30v - 23$

34. $9t^2 = 30t + 17$

35. True or false? If you use the quadratic formula to solve $ax^2 + bx + c = 0$ and get rational solutions, then you could have solved the equation by factoring.

36. True or false? If the value of $b^2 - 4ac$ in the quadratic formula is 0, then $ax^2 + bx + c = 0$ has only one solution, a double root.

For Exercises 37 to 45, solve by using the quadratic formula. Approximate the solutions to the nearest thousandth.

37. $x^2 - 2x - 21 = 0$

38. $y^2 + 4y - 11 = 0$

39. $s^2 - 6s - 13 = 0$

40. $w^2 + 8w - 15 = 0$

41. $2p^2 - 7p - 10 = 0$

42. $3t^2 - 8t - 1 = 0$

43. $4z^2 + 8z - 1 = 0$

44. $4x^2 + 7x + 1 = 0$

45. $5v^2 - v - 5 = 0$

Critical Thinking

46. Find the solutions of the quadratic equation in which $a = 4$, $b = -8$, and $c = 1$.

47. Find the difference between the larger root and the smaller root of $x^2 - 6x = 14$.

For Exercises 48 to 50, solve.

48. $\sqrt{x^2 + 2x + 1} = x - 1$

49. $\frac{x + 2}{3} - \frac{4}{x - 2} = 2$

50. $\frac{x + 1}{5} - \frac{3}{x - 1} = 2$

51. Explain why the equation $0x^2 + 3x + 4 = 0$ cannot be solved by using the quadratic formula.

52. **Basketball** A basketball player shoots at a basket 25 ft away. The height of the ball above the ground at time t is given by $h = -16t^2 + 32t + 6.5$. How many seconds after the ball is released does it hit the basket? *Hint:* When the ball hits the basket, $h = 10$ ft. Round to the nearest hundredth.

Projects or Group Activities

For a quadratic equation of the form $x^2 + bx + c = 0$, the sum of the solutions is equal to the opposite of b, and the product of the solutions is equal to c. For example, the solutions of the equation $x^2 + 5x + 6 = 0$ are -2 and -3. The sum of the solutions is -5, the opposite of the coefficient of x. The product of the solutions is 6, the constant term. This is one way to check the solutions of a quadratic equation. For Exercises 53 to 56, use this method to determine whether the given numbers are solutions of the equation. If they are not solutions of the equation, find the solutions.

53. $x^2 - 4x - 21 = 0$; -3 and 7

54. $x^2 - 4x - 3 = 0$; $2 + \sqrt{7}$ and $2 - \sqrt{7}$

55. $x^2 - 4x + 1 = 0$; $2 + \sqrt{3}$ and $2 - \sqrt{3}$

56. $x^2 - 8x - 14 = 0$; $-4 + \sqrt{15}$ and $-4 - \sqrt{15}$

57. Factoring, completing the square, and using the quadratic formula are three methods of solving quadratic equations. Describe each method, and cite the advantages and disadvantages of each.

CHECK YOUR PROGRESS: CHAPTER 11

1. Solve for x: $(x - 9)(x + 11) = 0$

2. Solve by factoring: $6r^2 = 12 - r$

3. Solve by taking square roots: $2(x + 1)^2 = 50$

4. Solve by completing the square: $y^2 - 2y - 5 = 0$

5. Solve by using the quadratic formula: $t^2 - 2t = 6$

6. Solve for x: $(2x - 7)(3x + 4) = 0$

7. Solve by taking square roots: $(x - 4)^2 = 20$

8. Solve by completing the square: $x^2 + 6x + 4 = 0$

9. Solve by using the quadratic formula: $4t^2 - 12t - 15 = 0$

10. Solve by taking square roots: $y^2 - 12 = 0$

11. Solve by factoring: $5y^2 + 11y = 12$

12. Solve by completing the square: $2y^2 - 4y = 1$

13. Solve by using the quadratic formula: $\frac{x^2}{2} = 3x - \frac{7}{2}$

14. Solve by taking square roots: $(x + 2)^2 + 49 = 0$

15. Solve $4x^2 + 6x - 1 = 0$ by using the quadratic formula. Approximate the solutions to the nearest thousandth.

SECTION

11.4 Graphing Quadratic Equations in Two Variables

OBJECTIVE A *To graph a quadratic equation of the form $y = ax^2 + bx + c$*

Take Note

For the equation $y = 3x^2 - x + 1$, $a = 3$, $b = -1$, and $c = 1$.

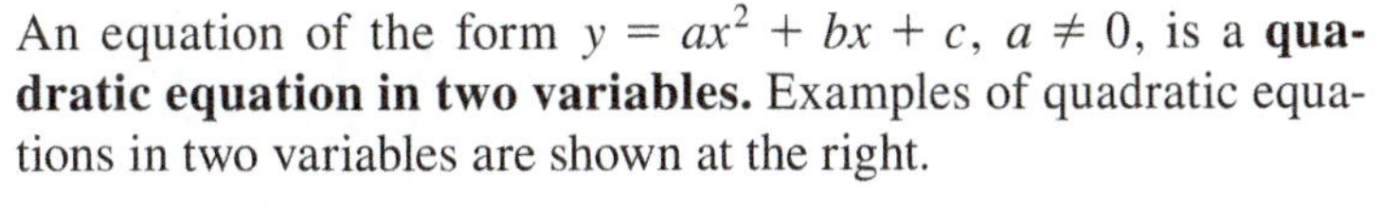

An equation of the form $y = ax^2 + bx + c$, $a \neq 0$, is a **quadratic equation in two variables.** Examples of quadratic equations in two variables are shown at the right.

$y = 3x^2 - x + 1$
$y = -x^2 - 3$
$y = 2x^2 - 5x$

For these equations, y is a function of x, and we can write $f(x) = ax^2 + bx + c$. This equation represents a **quadratic function.**

Point of Interest

Mirrors in some telescopes are ground into the shape of a parabola. The mirror at the Palomar Mountain Observatory is 2 ft thick at the ends and weighs 14.75 tons. The mirror has been ground to a true paraboloid (the three-dimensional version of a parabola) to within 0.0000015 in. A possible equation of the mirror is $y = 2640x^2$.

HOW TO 1 Evaluate $f(x) = 2x^2 - 3x + 4$ when $x = -2$.

$f(x) = 2x^2 - 3x + 4$

$f(-2) = 2(-2)^2 - 3(-2) + 4$ • Replace x by -2.

$= 2(4) + 6 + 4 = 18$ • Simplify.

The value of the function when $x = -2$ is 18.

The graph of $y = ax^2 + bx + c$ or $f(x) = ax^2 + bx + c$ is a **parabola.** The graph is ∪-shaped, and opens up when a is positive and down when a is negative. The graphs of two parabolas are shown below.

Take Note

One of the equations at the right was written as $y = 2x^2 + 3x - 2$, and the other was written using function notation as $f(x) = -x^2 + 3x + 2$. Remember that y and $f(x)$ are different symbols for the same quantity.

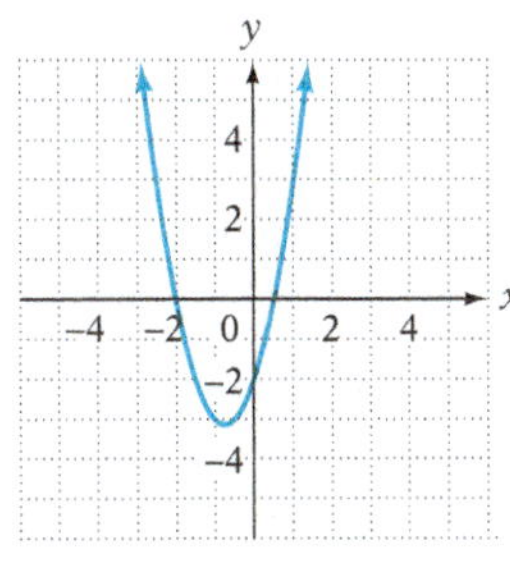

$y = 2x^2 + 3x - 2$
$a = 2$, a positive number
Parabola opens up.

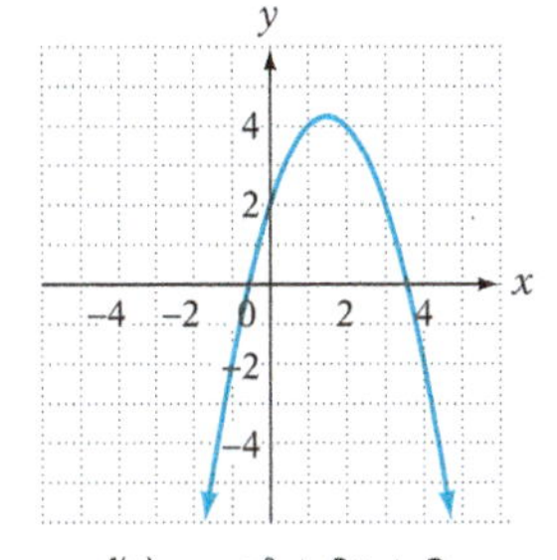

$f(x) = -x^2 + 3x + 2$
$a = -1$, a negative number
Parabola opens down.

HOW TO 2 Graph $y = x^2 - 2x - 3$.

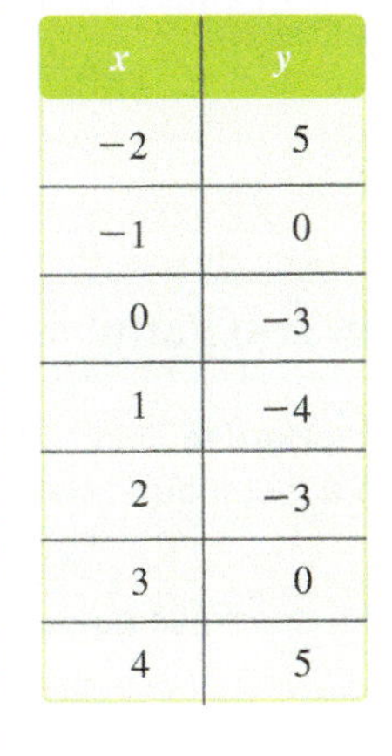

x	y
−2	5
−1	0
0	−3
1	−4
2	−3
3	0
4	5

• Find several solutions of the equation. Because the graph is not a straight line, several solutions must be found in order to determine the ∪-shape. Record the ordered pairs in a table.

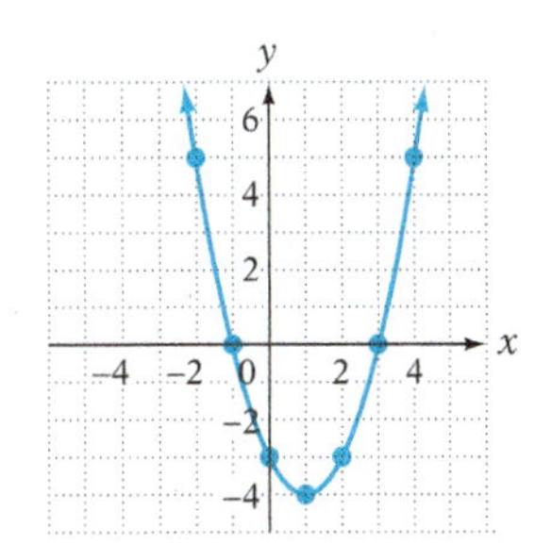

• Graph the ordered-pair solutions on a rectangular coordinate system. Draw a parabola through the points.

Note that the graph of $y = x^2 - 2x - 3$, shown again below, crosses the x-axis at $(-1, 0)$ and $(3, 0)$. This is also confirmed from the table for the graph. From the table, note that $y = 0$ when $x = -1$ and when $x = 3$. The x-intercepts of the graph are $(-1, 0)$ and $(3, 0)$.

x	y
−2	5
−1	0
0	−3
1	−4
2	−3
3	0
4	5

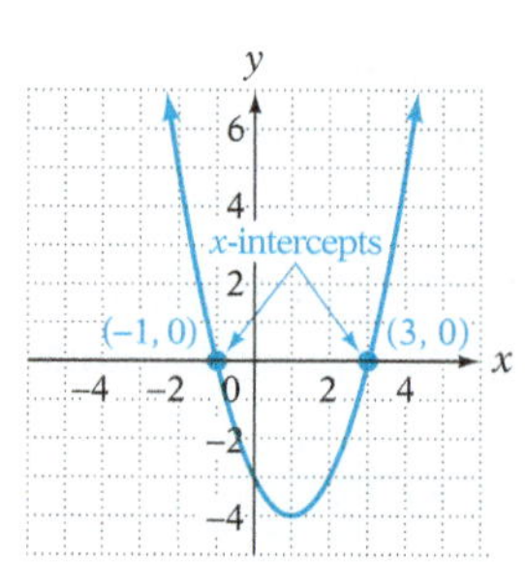

The y-intercept is the point at which the graph crosses the y-axis. At this point, $x = 0$. From the graph, we can see that the y-intercept is $(0, -3)$.

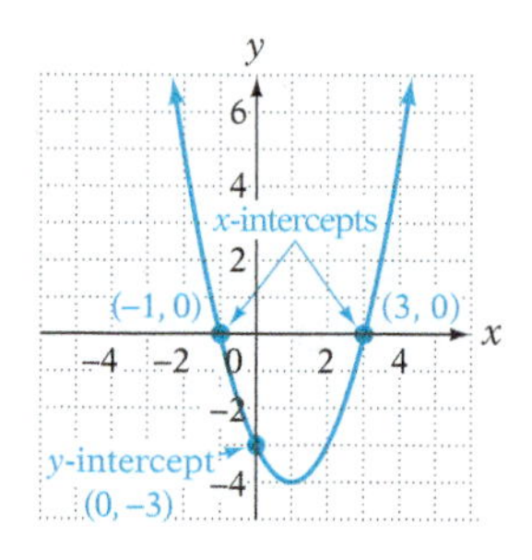

We can find the x-intercepts algebraically by letting $y = 0$ and solving for x.

$y = x^2 - 2x - 3$

$0 = x^2 - 2x - 3$ • **Replace y by 0 and solve for x.**

$0 = (x + 1)(x - 3)$ • **This equation can be solved by factoring. However, it will be necessary to use the quadratic formula to solve some quadratic equations.**

$x + 1 = 0 \qquad x - 3 = 0$

$x = -1 \qquad x = 3$

The x-intercepts are $(-1, 0)$ and $(3, 0)$.

We can find the y-intercept algebraically by letting $x = 0$ and solving for y.

$y = x^2 - 2x - 3$

$y = 0^2 - 2(0) - 3$ • **Replace x by 0 and simplify.**

$= -3$

The y-intercept is $(0, -3)$.

Integrating Technology

One of the Projects or Group Activities at the end of the exercise set for this section shows how to use a graphing calculator to draw the graph of a parabola and find the x-intercepts. You may want to verify the graphs you draw in this section by drawing them on a graphing calculator.

Graph of a Quadratic Equation in Two Variables

To graph a quadratic equation in two variables, find several solutions of the equation. Graph the ordered-pair solutions on a rectangular coordinate system. Draw a parabola through the points.

To find the x-intercepts of the graph of a quadratic equation in two variables, let $y = 0$ and solve for x.

To find the y-intercept, let $x = 0$ and solve for y.

EXAMPLE 1

Graph $y = x^2 - 2x$.

Solution

x	y
-1	3
0	0
1	-1
2	0
3	3

• **Find several solutions of the equation.**

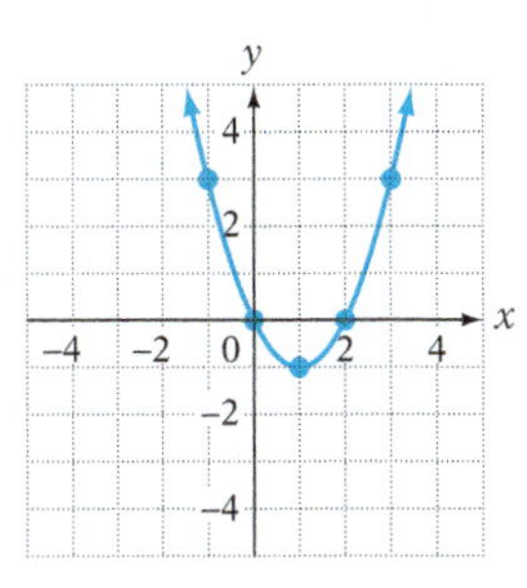

• **Graph the ordered-pair solutions. Draw a parabola through the points.**

YOU TRY IT 1

Graph $y = x^2 + 2$.

Your solution

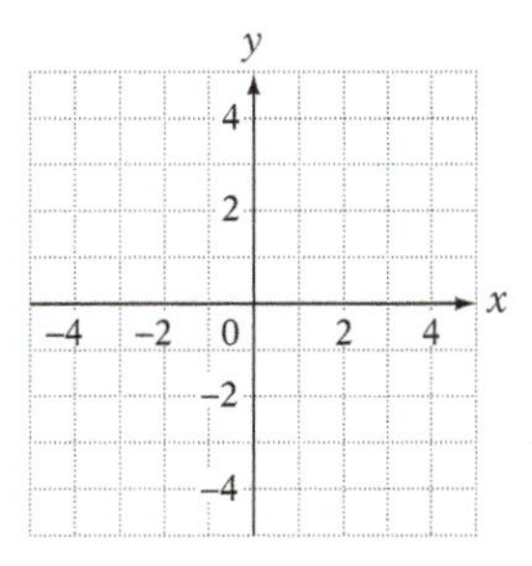

EXAMPLE 2

Find the x- and y-intercepts of the graph of $y = x^2 - 2x - 5$.

Solution

To find the x-intercepts, let $y = 0$ and solve for x. This gives the equation $0 = x^2 - 2x - 5$, which is not factorable over the integers. Use the quadratic formula.

$$x = \frac{-b \pm \sqrt{b^2 - 4ac}}{2a}$$

$$= \frac{-(-2) \pm \sqrt{(-2)^2 - 4(1)(-5)}}{2(1)}$$

• **$a = 1, b = -2, c = -5$**

$$= \frac{2 \pm \sqrt{24}}{2} = \frac{2 \pm 2\sqrt{6}}{2}$$

$$= 1 \pm \sqrt{6}$$

The x-intercepts are $(1 - \sqrt{6}, 0)$ and $(1 + \sqrt{6}, 0)$.

To find the y-intercept, let $x = 0$ and solve for y.

$$y = x^2 - 2x - 5$$
$$= 0^2 - 2(0) - 5$$

• **Replace x by 0.**

$$= -5$$

The y-intercept is $(0, -5)$.

YOU TRY IT 2

Find the x- and y-intercepts of the graph of $f(x) = x^2 - 6x + 9$.

Your solution

Solutions on p. S27

11.4 EXERCISES

Concept Check

1. What is the name of the graph of a quadratic equation in two variables?
2. What is the clue in the equation $y = x^2 - 4x + 3$ that the graph will be a parabola and not a straight line?
3. Explain how to find the x-intercepts of the graph of $y = x^2 - 4x + 3$.
4. Explain how to find the y-intercept of the graph of $y = x^2 - 5x + 4$.

For Exercises 5 to 8, determine whether the graph of the equation opens up or down.

5. $y = -\frac{1}{3}x^2$
6. $y = x^2 - 2x - 3$
7. $f(x) = 2x^2 - 4$
8. $f(x) = 3 - 2x - x^2$

OBJECTIVE A *To graph a quadratic equation of the form $y = ax^2 + bx + c$*

For Exercises 9 to 14, evaluate the function for the given value of x.

9. $f(x) = x^2 - 2x + 1; x = 3$
10. $f(x) = 2x^2 + x - 1; x = -2$
11. $f(x) = 4 - x^2; x = -3$
12. $f(x) = x^2 + 6x + 9; x = -3$
13. $f(x) = -x^2 + 5x - 6; x = -4$
14. $f(x) = -2x^2 + 2x - 1; x = -3$

For Exercises 15 to 29, graph.

15. $y = x^2$

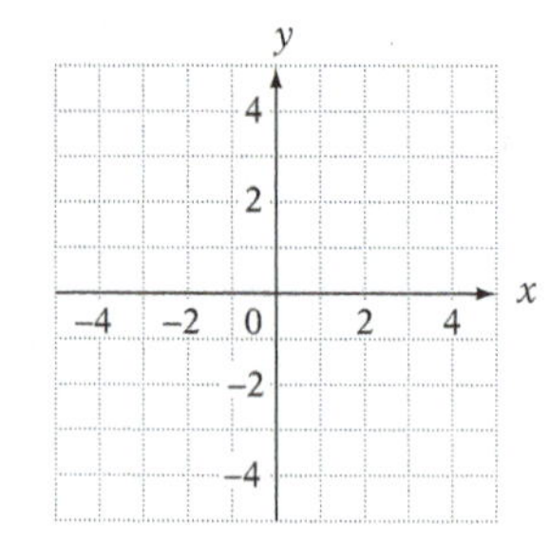

16. $y = -x^2$

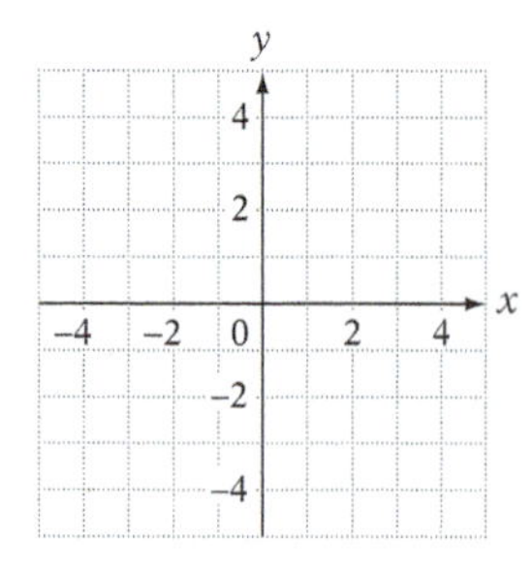

17. $y = -x^2 + 1$

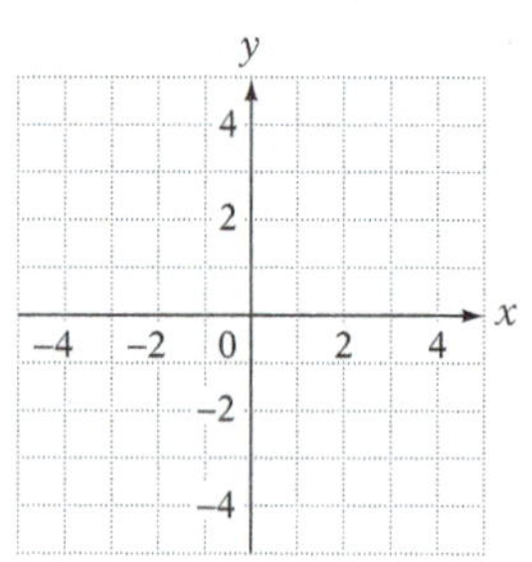

18. $y = x^2 - 1$

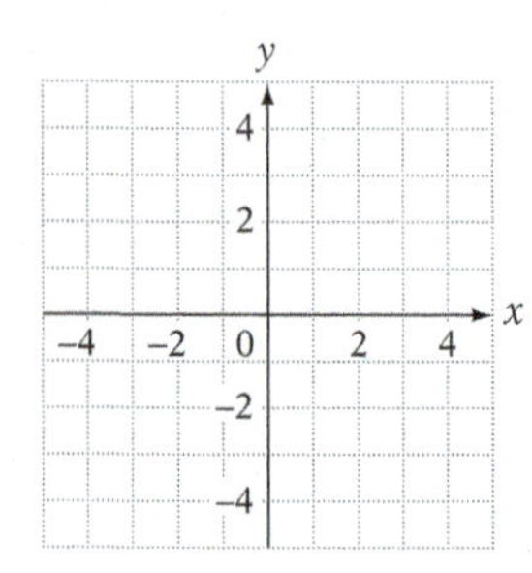

19. $f(x) = 2x^2$

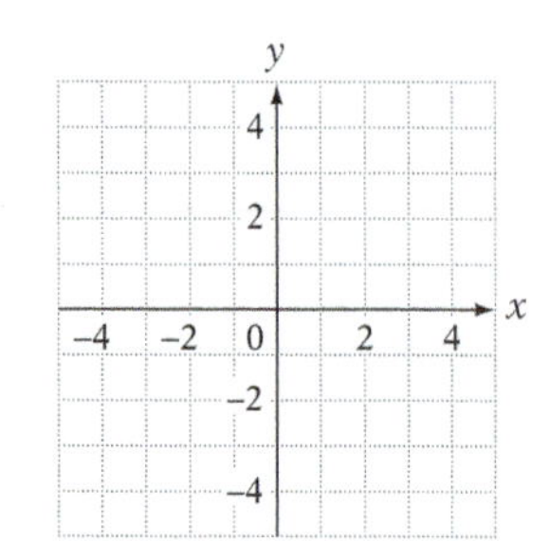

20. $f(x) = \frac{1}{2}x^2$

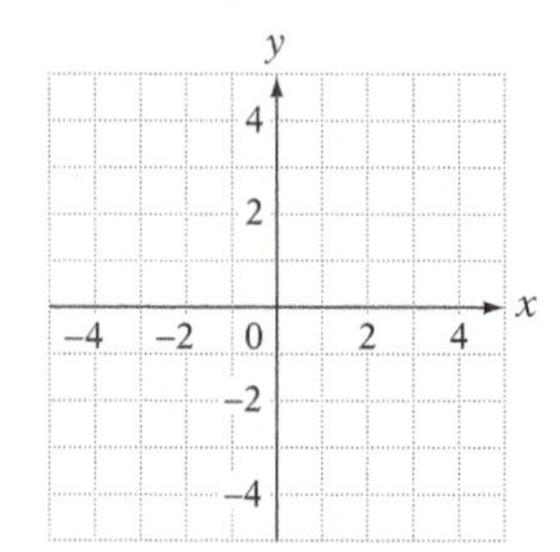

21. $f(x) = -\frac{1}{2}x^2 + 1$ 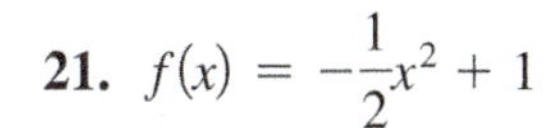

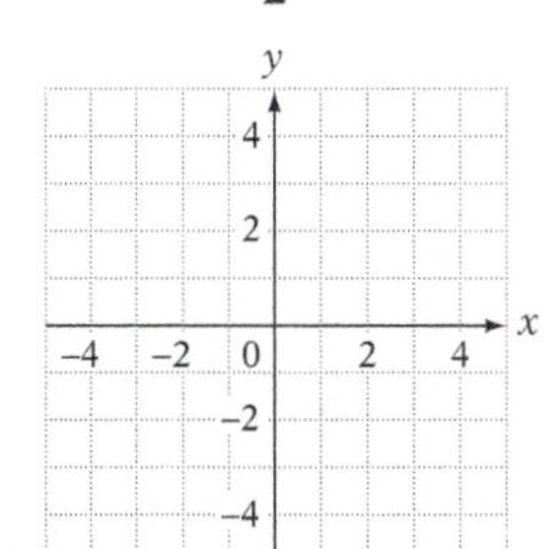

22. $f(x) = 2x^2 - 1$

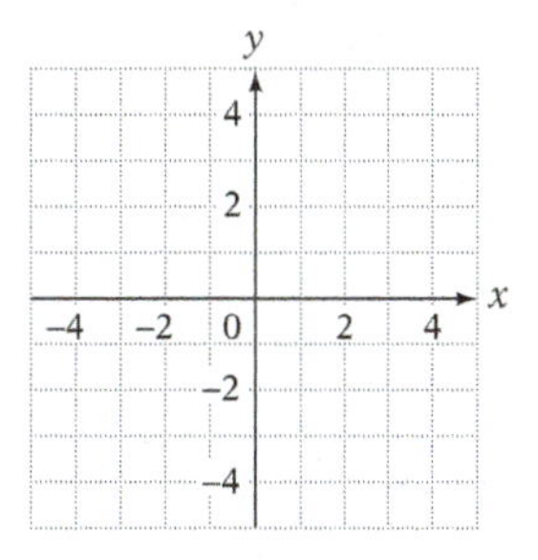

23. $y = x^2 - 4x$

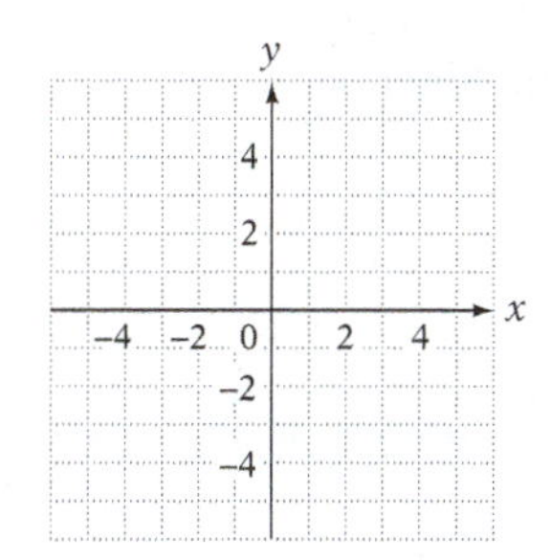

24. $y = x^2 + 4x$

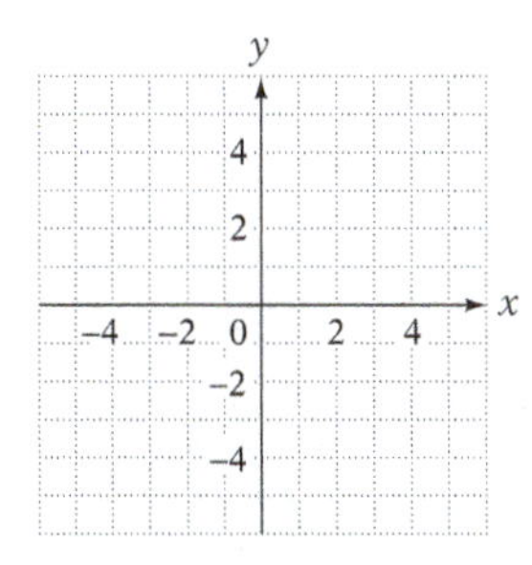

25. $y = x^2 - 2x + 3$

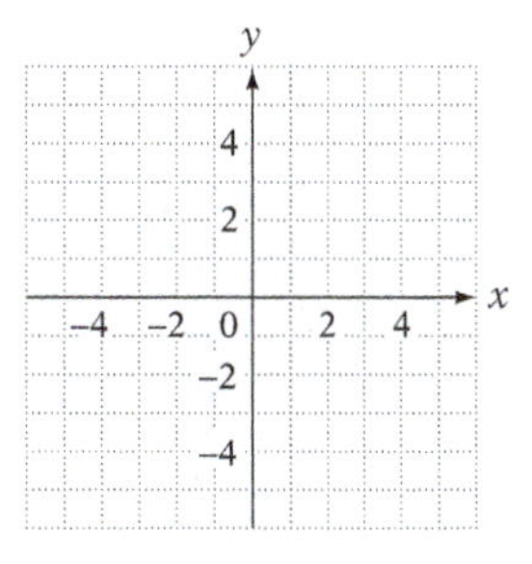

26. $y = x^2 - 4x + 2$

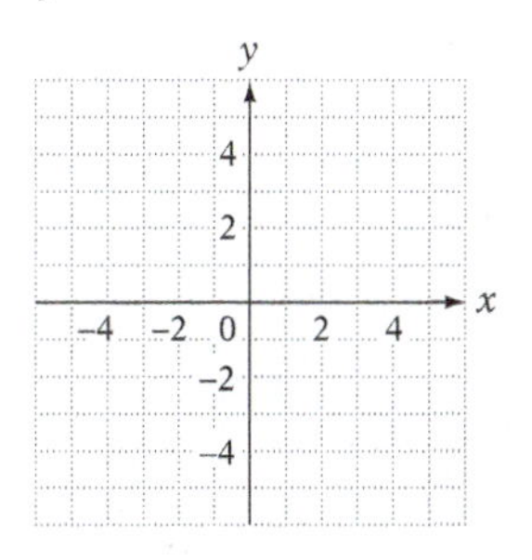

27. $y = -x^2 + 2x + 3$

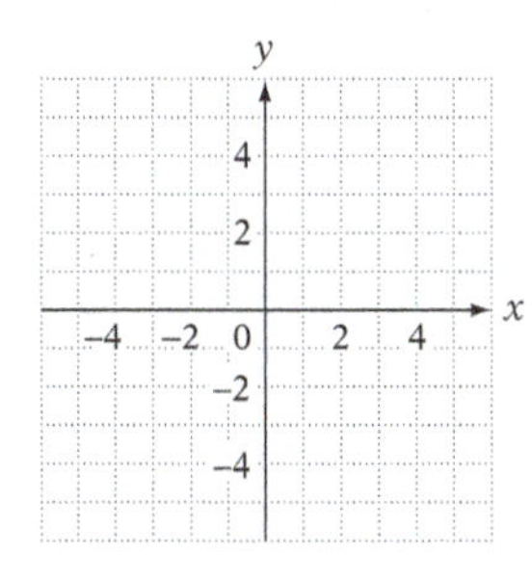

28. $y = -x^2 - 2x + 3$

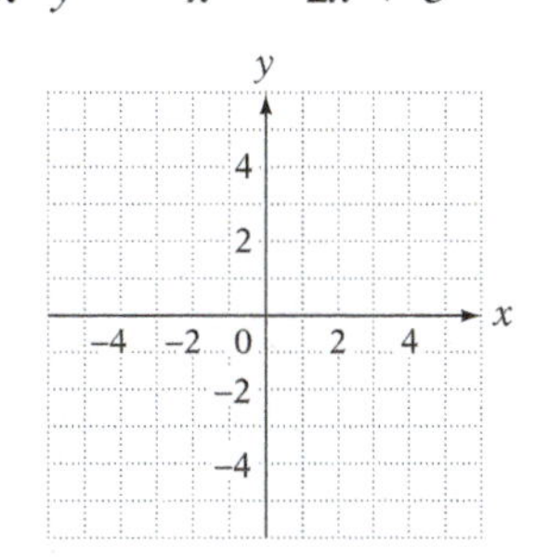

29. $y = -x^2 + 4x - 4$

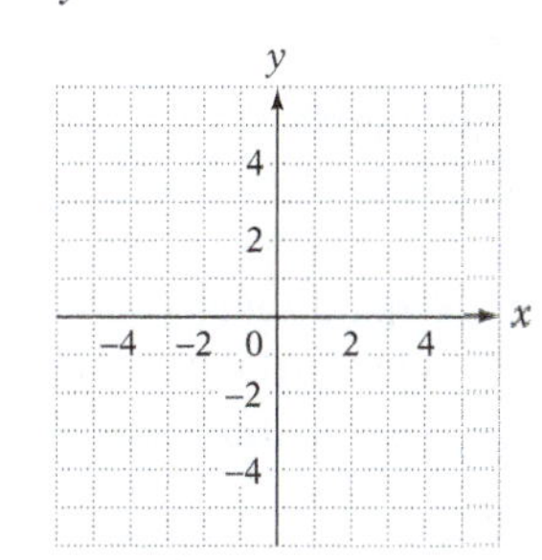

For Exercises 30 to 41, determine the x- and y-intercepts.

30. $y = x^2 - 5x + 6$

31. $y = x^2 + 5x - 6$

32. $f(x) = 9 - x^2$

33. $f(x) = x^2 + 12x + 36$

34. $y = x^2 + 2x - 6$

35. $f(x) = x^2 + 4x - 2$

36. $y = x^2 + 2x + 3$

37. $y = x^2 - x + 1$

38. $f(x) = 2x^2 - x - 3$

39. $f(x) = 2x^2 - 13x + 15$

40. $y = 4 - x - x^2$

41. $y = 2 - 3x - 3x^2$

42. What is the y-intercept of the parabola with equation $y = ax^2 + bx + c$?

43. Suppose the graph of $y = ax^2 + bx + c$, $c \neq 0$, is a parabola with only one x-intercept, and a is negative. Is c positive or negative?

Critical Thinking

For Exercises 44 to 49, state whether the graph is the graph of a linear function, a quadratic function, or neither.

44.

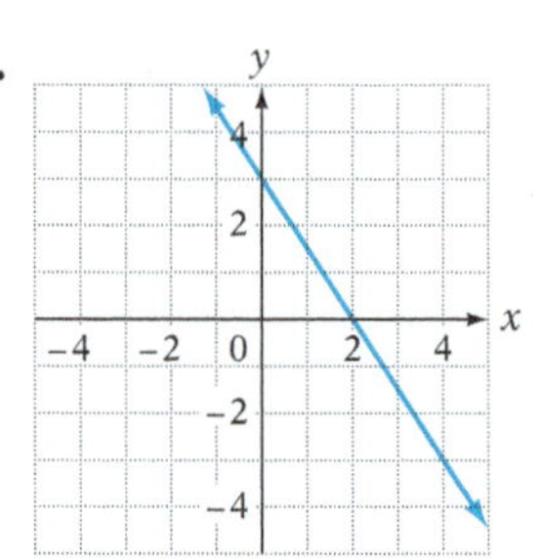

45.

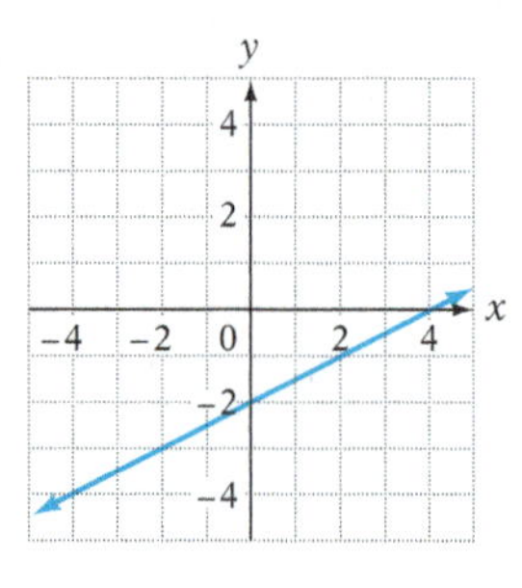

46.

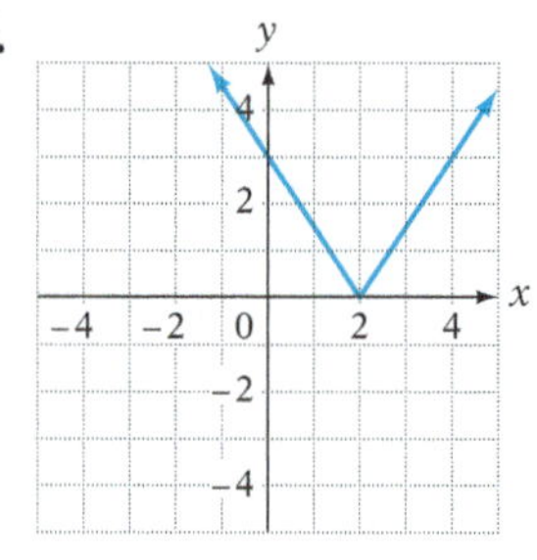

47.

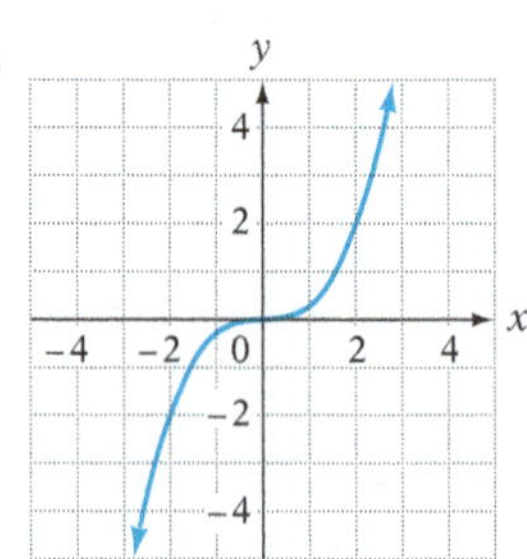

48.

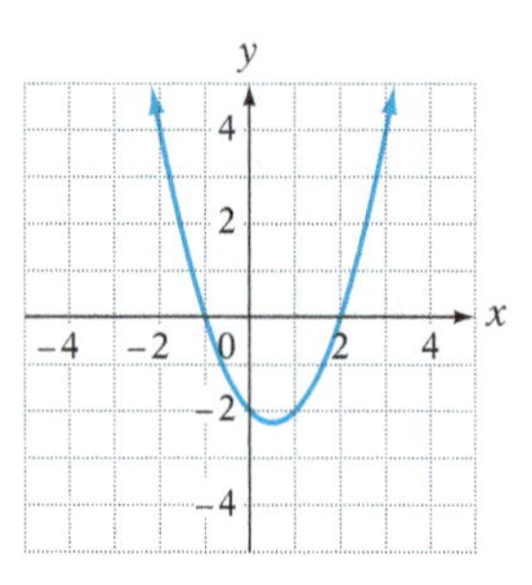

49.

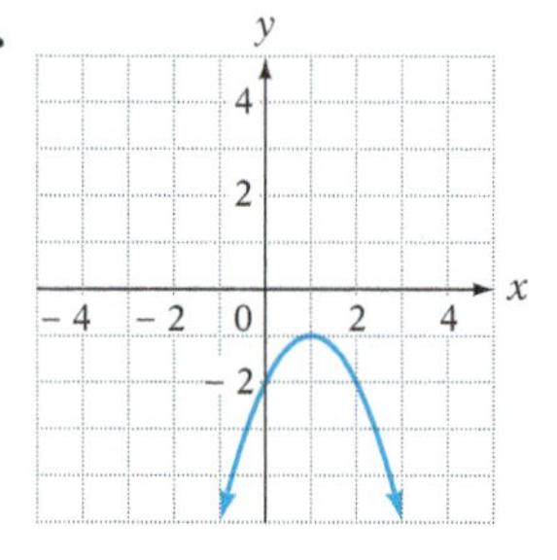

50. Consider the graph shown at the right.
  a. What are the x-intercepts?
  b. What is the y-intercept?
  c. What do you know about the value of a?
  d. What is the value of x when $y = 2$?
  e. What is the value of y when $x = 1$?

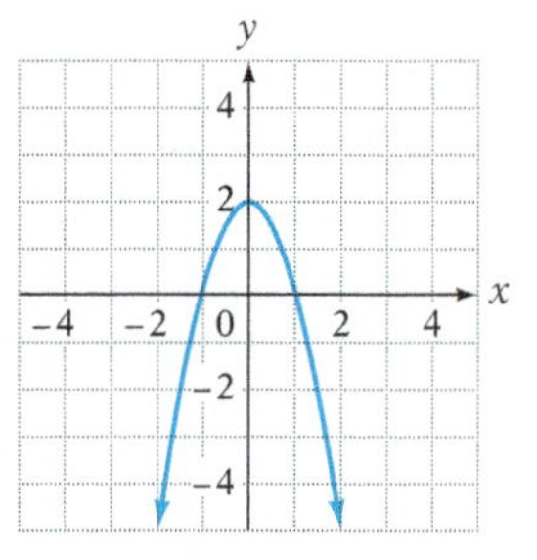

51. Consider the graph shown at the right.
  a. What are the x-intercepts?
  b. What is the y-intercept?
  c. What do you know about the value of a?
  d. What is the value of x when $y = -4$?
  e. What is the value of y when $x = -1$?

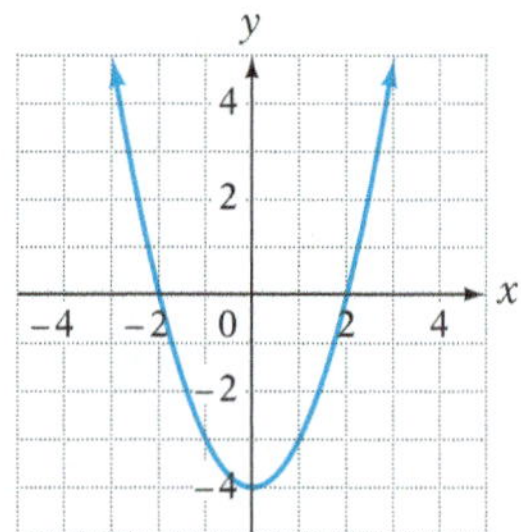

Projects or Group Activities

52. Draw a parabola that opens up and has $(-2, -4)$ as its vertex.

53. Draw a parabola that opens down and has $(3, 1)$ as its vertex.

54. The point whose coordinates are (x_1, y_1) lies in quadrant I and is a point on the graph of the equation $y = 2x^2 - 2x + 1$. Given $y_1 = 13$, find x_1.

55. The point whose coordinates are (x_1, y_1) lies in quadrant II and is a point on the graph of the equation $y = 2x^2 - 3x - 2$. Given $y_1 = 12$, find x_1.

Graphical Solutions of Quadratic Equations A real number x is called a **zero of a function** if the function evaluated at x is equal to zero. That is, if $f(x) = 0$, then x is called a zero of the function. For instance, evaluating $f(x) = x^2 + x - 6$ when $x = -3$, we have

$$f(x) = x^2 + x - 6$$
$$f(-3) = (-3)^2 + (-3) - 6 \qquad \text{• Replace } x \text{ by } -3.$$
$$f(-3) = 9 - 3 - 6 = 0$$

For this function, $f(-3) = 0$, so -3 is a zero of the function.

Verify that 2 is a zero of $f(x) = x^2 + x - 6$ by showing that $f(2) = 0$.

The graph of $f(x) = x^2 + x - 6$ is shown at the right. Note that the graph crosses the x-axis at -3 and 2, the two zeros of the function. The points $(-3, 0)$ and $(2, 0)$ are x-intercepts of the graph.

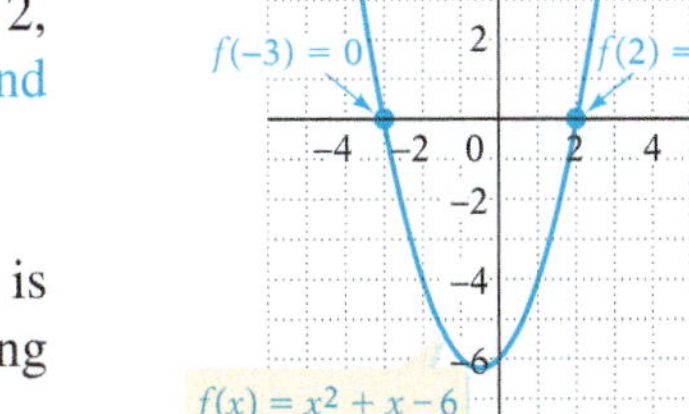

Consider the equation $0 = x^2 + x - 6$, which is $f(x) = x^2 + x - 6$ with $f(x)$ replaced by 0. Solving $0 = x^2 + x - 6$, we have

$$0 = x^2 + x - 6$$
$$0 = (x + 3)(x - 2) \qquad \text{• Solve by factoring and using the Principle of Zero Products.}$$
$$x + 3 = 0 \qquad x - 2 = 0$$
$$x = -3 \qquad x = 2$$

Observe that the solutions of the equation are the zeros of the function. This important connection among the real zeros of a function, the x-intercepts of its graph, and the solutions of the equation is the basis for using a graphing calculator to solve an equation.

The following method of solving a quadratic equation by using a graphing calculator is based on a TI-84 Plus calculator. Other calculators will require a slightly different approach.

HOW TO Approximate the solutions of $x^2 + 4x = 6$ by using a graphing calculator.

1. Write the equation in standard form: $x^2 + 4x - 6 = 0$.
2. Press Y= and enter $x^2 + 4x - 6$ for Y1.
3. Press GRAPH. If the graph does not appear on the screen, press ZOOM 6.
4. Press 2ND CALC 2. Note that the selection for 2 says **zero**. This will begin the calculation of the zeros of the function, which are the solutions of the equation.

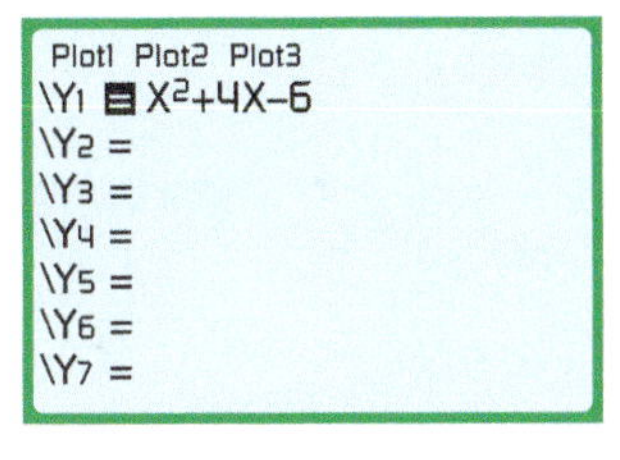

Step 2

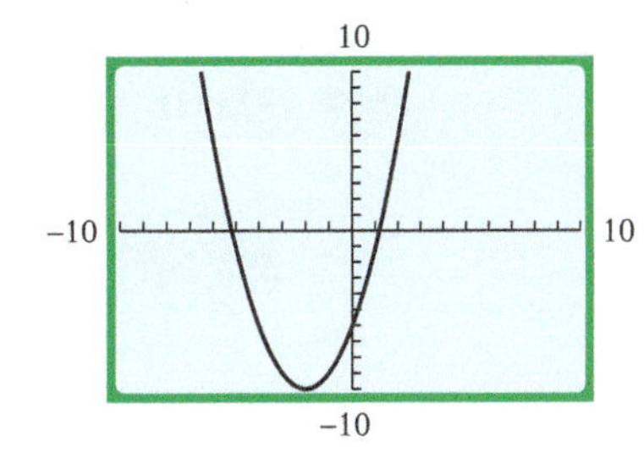

Step 3

CALCULATE
1: value
2: zero
3: minimum
4: maximum
5: intersect
6: dy/dx
7: ∫f(x)dx

Step 4

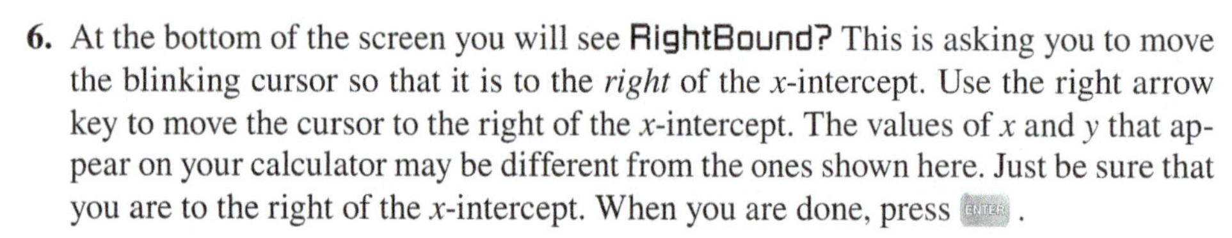

5. At the bottom of the screen you will see **LeftBound?** This is asking you to move the blinking cursor so that it is to the *left* of the first x-intercept. Use the left arrow key to move the cursor to the left of the first x-intercept. The values of x and y that appear on your calculator may be different from the ones shown here. Just be sure that you are to the left of the x-intercept. When you are done, press ENTER.

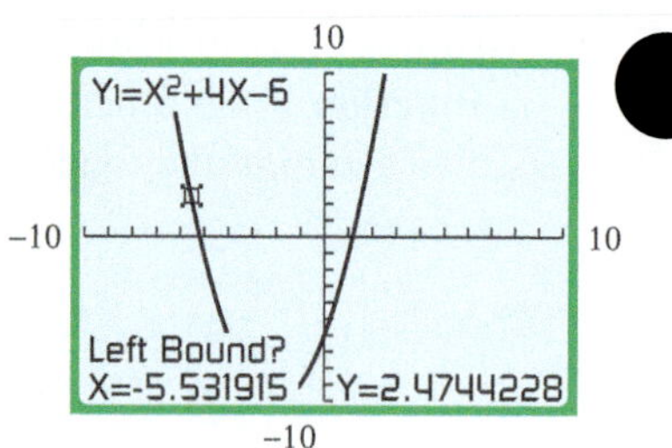

Step 5

6. At the bottom of the screen you will see **RightBound?** This is asking you to move the blinking cursor so that it is to the *right* of the x-intercept. Use the right arrow key to move the cursor to the right of the x-intercept. The values of x and y that appear on your calculator may be different from the ones shown here. Just be sure that you are to the right of the x-intercept. When you are done, press ENTER.

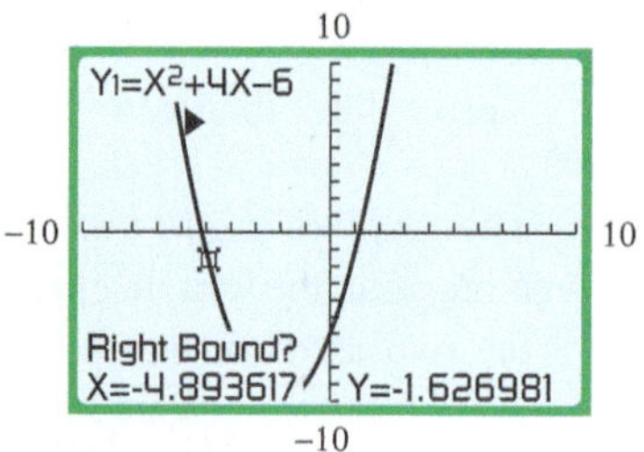

Step 6

7. At the bottom of the screen you will see **Guess?** Press ENTER.

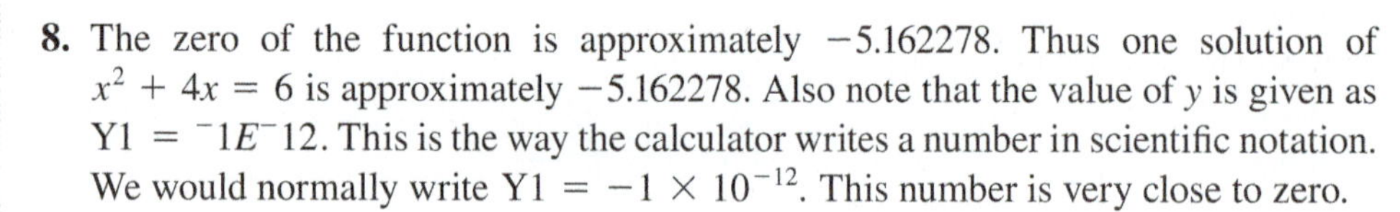

8. The zero of the function is approximately -5.162278. Thus one solution of $x^2 + 4x = 6$ is approximately -5.162278. Also note that the value of y is given as $\text{Y1} = {}^-1E^-12$. This is the way the calculator writes a number in scientific notation. We would normally write $\text{Y1} = -1 \times 10^{-12}$. This number is very close to zero.

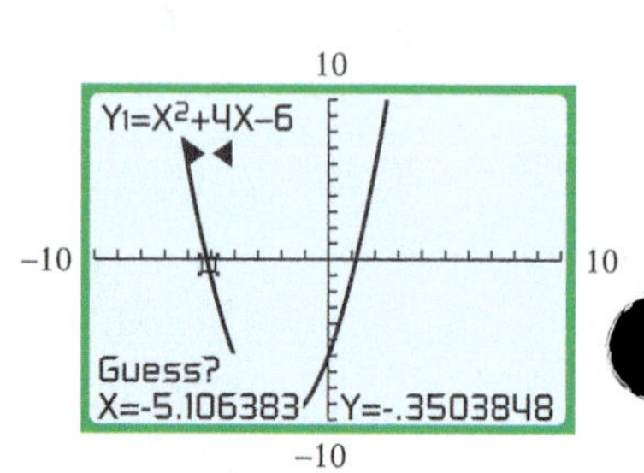

Step 7

To find the other solution of $x^2 + 4x = 6$, we repeat Steps 4 through 8. The screens for Steps 5 through 8 are shown below.

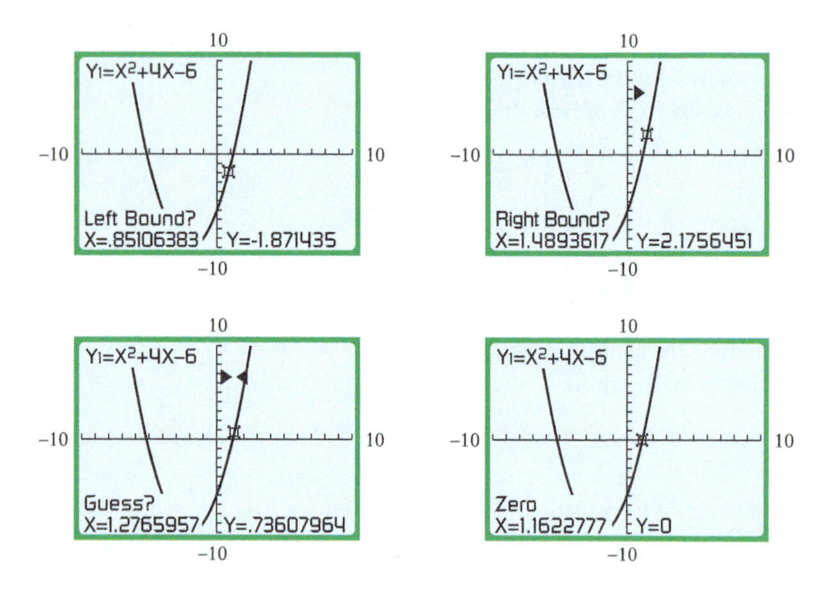

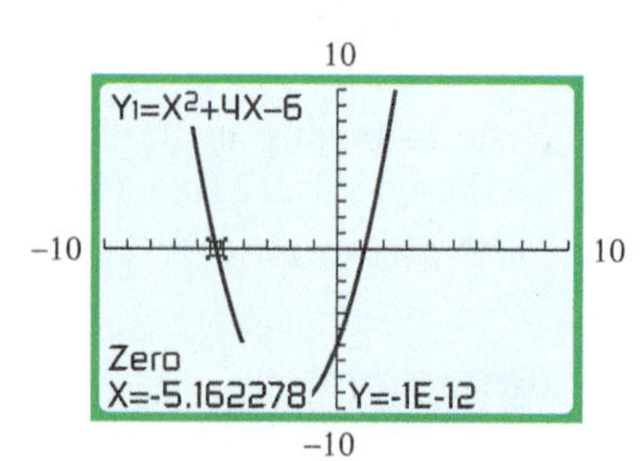

Step 8

A second zero of the function is approximately 1.1622777. Thus the two solutions of $x^2 + 4x = 6$ are $x \approx -5.162278$ and $x \approx 1.1622777$.

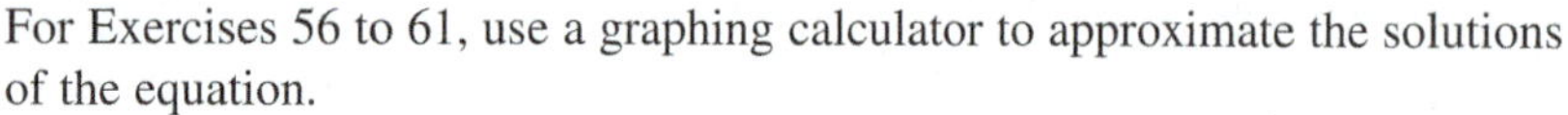

For Exercises 56 to 61, use a graphing calculator to approximate the solutions of the equation.

56. $x^2 + 3x - 4 = 0$

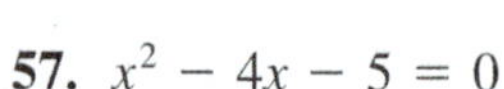

57. $x^2 - 4x - 5 = 0$

58. $x^2 + 3.4x = 4.15$

59. $2x^2 - \frac{5}{9}x = \frac{3}{8}$

60. $\pi x^2 - \sqrt{17}x - 2 = 0$

61. $\sqrt{2}x^2 + x - \sqrt{7} = 0$

SECTION

11.5 Application Problems

OBJECTIVE A *To solve application problems*

The application problems in this section are varieties of the types of problems solved earlier in the text. Each of the strategies for the problems in this section will result in a quadratic equation.

© iStockphoto.com/AVAVA

HOW TO 1 In 5 h, two campers paddled 12 mi down a stream and then paddled back to their campsite. The rate of the stream's current was 1 mph. Find the rate at which the campers paddled.

Strategy for Solving an Application Problem

1. Determine the type of problem. For example, is it a uniform motion problem, a geometry problem, or a work problem?

The problem is a uniform motion problem.

2. Choose a variable to represent the unknown quantity. Write numerical or variable expressions for all the remaining quantities. The results can be recorded in a table.

The unknown rate of the campers: r

	Distance	÷	Rate	=	Time
Downstream	12	÷	$r + 1$	=	$\frac{12}{r+1}$
Upstream	12	÷	$r - 1$	=	$\frac{12}{r-1}$

3. Determine how the quantities are related.

The time going downstream plus the time going upstream is equal to 5 h.

$$\frac{12}{r+1} + \frac{12}{r-1} = 5$$

Solve for r.

$$(r+1)(r-1)\left(\frac{12}{r+1} + \frac{12}{r-1}\right) = (r+1)(r-1)5$$

$$(r-1)12 + (r+1)12 = (r^2 - 1)5$$

$$12r - 12 + 12r + 12 = 5r^2 - 5$$

$$24r = 5r^2 - 5$$

$$0 = 5r^2 - 24r - 5$$

$$0 = (5r+1)(r-5)$$

$$5r + 1 = 0 \qquad r - 5 = 0$$

$$5r = -1 \qquad r = 5$$

$$r = -\frac{1}{5}$$

The rate cannot be a negative number; therefore, the solution $-\frac{1}{5}$ is not possible.

The paddling rate was 5 mph.

EXAMPLE 1

Working together, a painter and the painter's apprentice can paint a room in 2 h. Working alone, the apprentice requires 3 more hours to paint the room than the painter requires working alone. How long does it take the painter, working alone, to paint the room?

Strategy

- This is a work problem.
- Time for the painter to paint the room: t
  Time for the apprentice to paint the room: $t + 3$

	Rate	*Time*	*Part*
Painter	$\frac{1}{t}$	2	$\frac{2}{t}$
Apprentice	$\frac{1}{t+3}$	2	$\frac{2}{t+3}$

- The sum of the parts of the task completed must equal 1.

Solution

$$\frac{2}{t} + \frac{2}{t+3} = 1$$

• The parts completed by the painter and the apprentice must equal 1.

$$t(t+3)\left(\frac{2}{t} + \frac{2}{t+3}\right) = t(t+3) \cdot 1$$

• Multiply by $t(t + 3)$.

$$(t+3)2 + t(2) = t(t+3)$$

$$2t + 6 + 2t = t^2 + 3t$$

• Quadratic equation

$$4t + 6 = t^2 + 3t$$

$$0 = t^2 - t - 6$$

• Standard form

$$0 = (t-3)(t+2)$$

• Factor.

$$t - 3 = 0 \qquad t + 2 = 0$$

$$t = 3 \qquad t = -2$$

• Set each factor equal to zero.

The solution $t = -2$ is not possible.

The time is 3 h.

YOU TRY IT 1

The length of a rectangle is 2 m more than the width. The area is 15 m². Find the width.

Your strategy

Your solution

Solution on p. S27

11.5 EXERCISES

Concept Check

1. If the length of a rectangle is three more than twice the width and the width is represented by W, then the length is represented by ______.

2. If it takes one pipe 15 min longer to fill a tank than it does a second pipe, and the rate of work for the second pipe is represented by $\frac{1}{t}$, then the rate of work for the first pipe can be represented by ______.

3. If a plane's rate of speed is r and the rate of the wind is 30 mph, then the plane's rate of speed flying with the wind is $r + 30$, and the plane's rate of speed flying against the wind is ______.

4. When using the quadratic formula to solve the equation $2 = -16t^2 + 24t + 4$ for t, substitute ______ for a in the quadratic formula, ______ for b, and ______ for c.

OBJECTIVE A *To solve application problems*

5. **Geometry** The height of a triangle is 2 m more than twice the length of the base. The area of the triangle is 20 m^2. Find the height of the triangle and the length of the base.

6. **Geometry** The length of a rectangle is 4 ft more than twice the width. The area of the rectangle is 160 ft^2. Find the length and width of the rectangle.

7. **Sports** The area of the batter's box on a major-league baseball field is 24 ft^2. The length of the batter's box is 2 ft more than the width. Find the length and width of the rectangular batter's box.

Mike Liu/Shutterstock.com

8. **Sports** The length of the batter's box on a softball field is 1 ft more than twice the width. The area of the batter's box is 21 ft^2. Find the length and width of the rectangular batter's box.

9. **Work Problem** A tank has two drains. One drain takes 16 min longer to empty the tank than does the second drain. With both drains open, the tank is emptied in 6 min. How long would it take each drain, working alone, to empty the tank?

10. Work Problem One computer takes 21 min longer than a second computer to calculate the value of a complex expression. Working together, the computers can complete the calculation in 10 min. How long would it take each computer, working alone, to calculate the value?

11. Sports The length of a swimming pool is twice the width. The area of the pool is 5000 ft^2. Find the length and width of the pool.

12. Sports Read the article at the right. The Longhorns' old scoreboard was a rectangle with a length 30 ft greater than its width. Find the length and width of the old scoreboard.

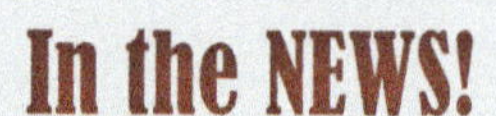

Long Board for the Longhorns

The University of Texas Longhorns have replaced their stadium's old 2800-square-foot scoreboard with a new, state-of-the-art, 7370-square-foot scoreboard designed and built by local business Daktronics, Inc.

Sources: Business Wire, www.engadget.com

13. Transportation Using one engine of a ferryboat, it takes 6 h longer to cross a channel than it does using a second engine alone. With both engines operating, the ferryboat can make the crossing in 4 h. How long would it take each engine, working alone, to power the ferryboat across the channel?

14. Work Problem An apprentice mason takes 8 h longer than an experienced mason to build a small fireplace. Working together, the masons can build the fireplace in 3 h. How long would it take the experienced mason, working alone, to build the fireplace?

15. Uniform Motion It took a small plane 2 h longer to fly 375 mi against the wind than it took to fly the same distance with the wind. The rate of the wind was 25 mph. Find the rate of the plane in calm air.

Against wind: $r - 25$

375 mi

With wind: $r + 25$

16. Uniform Motion It took a motorboat 1 h longer to travel 36 mi against the current than it took to travel 36 mi with the current. The rate of the current was 3 mph. Find the rate of the boat in calm water.

17. Uniform Motion A motorcycle traveled 150 mi at a constant rate before its speed was decreased by 15 mph. Another 35 mi was driven at the decreased speed. The total time for the 185-mile trip was 4 h. Find the cyclist's rate during the first 150 mi.

Ljupco Smokovski/Shutterstock.com

18. Uniform Motion A cruise ship sailed through a 20-mile inland passageway at a constant rate before its speed was increased by 15 mph. Another 75 mi was traveled at the increased rate. The total time for the 95-mile trip was 5 h. Find the rate of the ship during the last 75 mi.

19. **Physics** An arrow is projected into the air with an initial velocity of 48 ft/s. At what times will the arrow be 32 ft above the ground? Use the equation $h = 48t - 16t^2$, where h is the height, in feet, above the ground after t seconds.

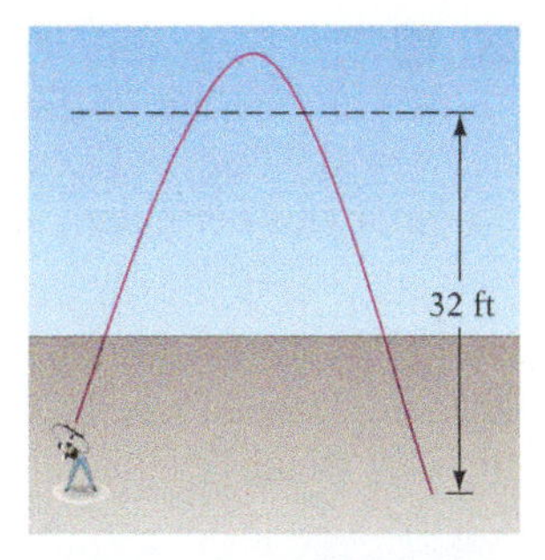

20. **Physics** A model rocket is launched with an initial velocity of 200 ft/s. The height h of the rocket t seconds after launch is given by $h = -16t^2 + 200t$. How many seconds after launch will the rocket be 300 ft above the ground? Round to the nearest hundredth.

21. **Botany** Botanists have determined that some species of weeds grow in a circular pattern. For one such weed, the area of growth A, in square meters, can be approximated by $A(t) = 0.005\pi t^2$, where t is the time in days after the growth of the weed first can be observed. How many days after the growth is first observed will this weed cover an area of 10 m^2? Round to the nearest whole number.

Malgorzata Kistryn/Shutterstock.com

22. **Physics** The kinetic energy of a moving body is given by $E = \frac{1}{2}mv^2$, where E is the kinetic energy, m is the mass, and v is the velocity in meters per second. What is the velocity of a moving body whose mass is 5 kg and whose kinetic energy is 250 newton-meters?

In the NEWS!

Boomers Turn 65

By the time the last baby boomer turns 65, the population of people aged 65 and older will have more than doubled, from 35 million to 71 million.

Source: Census Bureau

23. **Demography** See the news clipping at the right. Approximate the year in which there will be 50 million people aged 65 and older in the United States. Use the equation $y = 0.03x^2 + 0.36x + 34.6$, where y is the population, in millions, in year x, where $x = 0$ corresponds to the year 2000.

24. **Sports** A basketball player shoots at a basket 25 ft away. The height h, in feet, of the ball above the ground at time t, in seconds, is given by $h = -16t^2 + 32t + 6.5$. How many seconds after the ball is released does it hit the basket? Round to the nearest hundredth. (*Hint:* When the ball hits the basket, $h = 10$ ft.)

25. **Sports** In a slow-pitch softball game, the height of the ball thrown by a pitcher can be modeled by the equation $h = -16t^2 + 24t + 4$, where h is the height of the ball in feet and t is the time, in seconds, since it was released by the pitcher. If the batter hits the ball when it is 2 ft off the ground, for how many seconds has the ball been in the air? Round to the nearest hundredth.

In the NEWS!

Alzheimer's Diagnoses Rising

As the population of senior citizens grows, so will the number of people diagnosed with Alzheimer's, the disease that afflicted former president Ronald Reagan for the last 10 years of his life.

Source: The Alzheimer's Association

26. **Alzheimer's** See the news clipping at the right. Find the year in which 15 million Americans are expected to have Alzheimer's. Use the equation $y = 0.002x^2 + 0.05x + 2$, where y is the population with Alzheimer's, in millions, in year x, where $x = 0$ corresponds to the year 1980.

27. **Sports** The hang time of a football that is kicked on the opening kickoff is given by $s = -16t^2 + 88t + 1$, where s is the height, in feet, of the football t seconds after leaving the kicker's foot. What is the hang time of a kickoff that hits the ground without being caught? Round to the nearest tenth.

28. **The Internet** See the news clipping at the right. Find the year in which consumer Internet traffic will reach 55 million terabytes per month. Use the equation $y = 0.932x^2 - 12.6x + 49.4$, where y is consumer Internet traffic in millions of terabytes per month and x is the year, where $x = 10$ corresponds to the year 2010.

In the NEWS!

72 Million Years of Video

Transmission of video content through the Internet is increasing so quickly that before long you will need 72 million years to watch the video content that will be transmitted in one year. Total consumer Internet traffic is projected to reach 55 million terabytes per month before 2015, with over 90% of that traffic being video content.

Source: businessweek.com

Complete Exercises 29 and 30 *without* writing and solving an equation. Use this situation: A small pipe takes 12 min longer to fill a tank than does a larger pipe. Working together, the pipes can fill the tank in 4 min.

29. True or false? The amount of time it takes for the larger pipe to fill the tank is less than 4 min.

30. True or false? The amount of time it takes for the small pipe to fill the tank is greater than 16 min.

Critical Thinking

31. **Geometry** The hypotenuse of a right triangle measures $\sqrt{13}$ cm. The length of one leg is 1 cm shorter than twice the length of the other leg. Find the lengths of the legs of the right triangle.

32. **Integer Problem** The sum of the squares of four consecutive integers is 86. Find the four integers.

33. **Geometry** Find the radius of a right circular cone that has a volume of 800 cm^3 and a height of 12 cm. Round to the nearest hundredth.

12 cm

34. **Food Industry** The radius of a large pizza is 1 in. less than twice the radius of a small pizza. The difference between the areas of the two pizzas is 33π in^2. Find the radius of the large pizza.

35. **Food Industry** A square piece of cardboard is to be formed into a box to transport pizzas. The box is formed by cutting 2-inch-square corners from the cardboard and folding them up as shown in the figure at the right. If the volume of the box is 512 in^3, what are the dimensions of the cardboard?

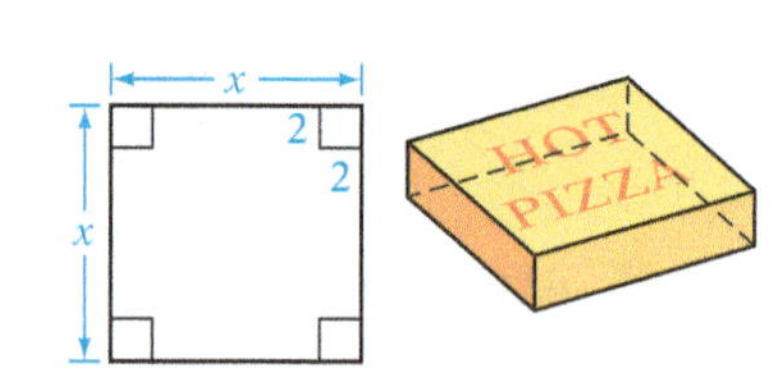

Projects or Group Activities

36. **Metalwork** A wire 8 ft long is cut into two pieces. A circle is formed from one piece and a square is formed from the other. The total area of both figures is given by $A = \frac{1}{16}(8 - x)^2 + \frac{x^2}{4\pi}$. What is the length of each piece of wire if the total area is 4.5 ft^2? Round to the nearest thousandth.

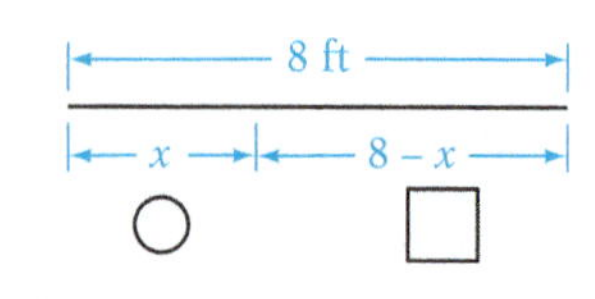

37. **Geometry** Consider the two rectangles shown below. The rectangles have the same perimeter but different areas.

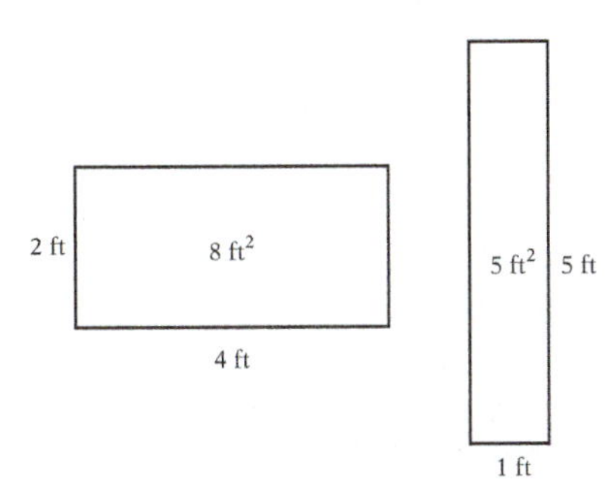

a. Using L for the length and W for the width, write the perimeter formula for a rectangle whose perimeter is 12 ft.
b. Using A for the area, L for the length, and W for the width, write the formula for the area of a rectangle.
c. Solve the formula in part (a) for L. Substitute your expression for L into the formula in part (b). Then simplify.
d. The formula you wrote in part (c) gives the area of a rectangle in terms of the width. Experiment with this formula until you find the dimensions of the rectangle of perimeter 12 ft that has the largest area.

CHAPTER 11 Summary

Key Words	Examples
A **quadratic equation** is an equation that can be written in the form $ax^2 + bx + c = 0$, where a, b, and c are real numbers and $a \neq 0$. [11.1A, p. 512]	$3x^2 - 5x - 3 = 0$ is a quadratic equation. For this equation, $a = 3$, $b = -5$, and $c = -3$.
A quadratic equation is in **standard form** when the polynomial is in descending order and equal to zero. [11.1A, p. 512]	$2x - 4 + 5x^2 = 0$ is not in standard form. The same equation in standard form is $5x^2 + 2x - 4 = 0$.
Adding to a binomial the constant term that makes it a perfect-square trinomial is called **completing the square**. [11.2A, p. 518]	Adding to $x^2 - 8x$ the constant term 16 results in a perfect square trinomial: $x^2 - 8x + 16 = (x - 4)^2$.
An equation of the form $y = ax^2 + bx + c$, $a \neq 0$, is a **quadratic equation in two variables**. [11.4A, p. 529]	$y = 2x^2 + 3x - 4$ is a quadratic equation in two variables.

The graph of an equation of the form $y = ax^2 + bx + c, a \neq 0$, is a **parabola**. The graph is U-shaped, and opens up when $a > 0$ and down when $a < 0$. [11.4A, p. 529]

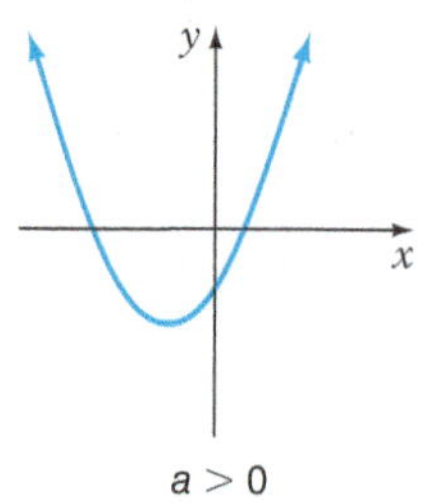

$a > 0$
Parabola opens up

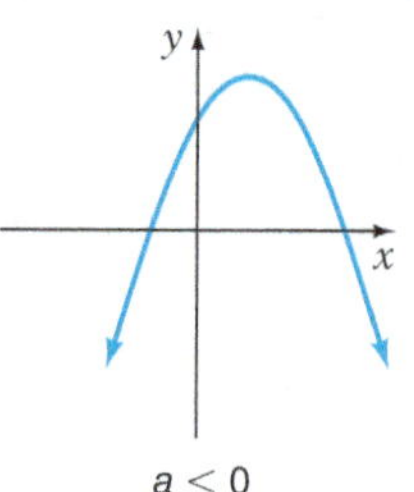

$a < 0$
Parabola opens down

Essential Rules and Procedures

Examples

Solving a Quadratic Equation by Factoring [11.1A, p. 512]
Write the equation in standard form, factor the polynomial, apply the Principle of Zero Products, and solve for the variable.

$$x^2 - 3x = 10$$
$$x^2 - 3x - 10 = 0$$
$$(x + 2)(x - 5) = 0$$
$$x + 2 = 0 \qquad x - 5 = 0$$
$$x = -2 \qquad x = 5$$

Principle of Taking the Square Root of Each Side of an Equation [11.1B, p. 514]
If $x^2 = a$, then $x = \pm\sqrt{a}$.
This principle is used to solve quadratic equations by taking square roots.

$$2x^2 - 36 = 0$$
$$2x^2 = 36$$
$$x^2 = 18$$
$$\sqrt{x^2} = \sqrt{18}$$
$$x = \pm\sqrt{18} = \pm 3\sqrt{2}$$

Solving a Quadratic Equation by Completing the Square [11.2A, p. 518]
When a quadratic equation is in the form $x^2 + bx = c$, add to each side of the equation the term that completes the square on $x^2 + bx$. Factor the perfect-square trinomial, and write it as the square of a binomial. Take the square root of each side of the equation, and solve for x.

$$x^2 + 6x = 5$$
$$x^2 + 6x + 9 = 5 + 9$$
$$(x + 3)^2 = 14$$
$$\sqrt{(x + 3)^2} = \sqrt{14}$$
$$x + 3 = \pm\sqrt{14}$$
$$x = -3 \pm \sqrt{14}$$

The Quadratic Formula [11.3A, p. 524]
The solutions of the quadratic equation $ax^2 + bx + c = 0, a \neq 0$, are $x = \dfrac{-b \pm \sqrt{b^2 - 4ac}}{2a}$.

$$2x^2 + 3x - 6 = 0$$
$$x = \frac{-b \pm \sqrt{b^2 - 4ac}}{2a}$$
$$= \frac{-3 \pm \sqrt{(3)^2 - 4(2)(-6)}}{2(2)}$$
$$= \frac{-3 \pm \sqrt{9 + 48}}{4} = \frac{-3 \pm \sqrt{57}}{4}$$

Graph of a Quadratic Equation in Two Variables [11.4A, p. 530]
To graph a quadratic equation in two variables, find several solutions of the equation. Graph the ordered-pair solutions on a rectangular coordinate system. Draw a parabola through the points.
To find the x-intercepts of the graph of a quadratic equation in two variables, let $y = 0$ and solve for x.
To find the y-intercept, let $x = 0$ and solve for y.

$y = x^2 - x - 2$

x	y
−2	4
−1	0
0	−2
1	−2
2	0
3	4

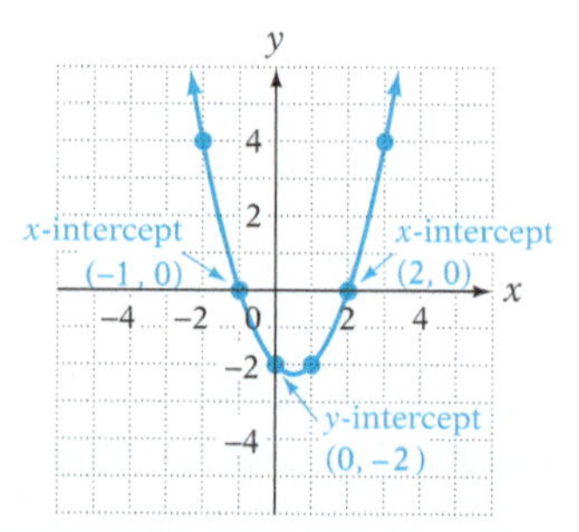

CHAPTER 11 Review Exercises

1. Solve by factoring: $6x^2 + 13x - 28 = 0$

2. Solve by taking square roots:
$49x^2 = 25$

3. Solve by completing the square:
$x^2 + 2x - 24 = 0$

4. Solve by using the quadratic formula:
$x^2 + 5x - 6 = 0$

5. Solve by completing the square:
$2x^2 + 5x = 12$

6. Solve by factoring: $12x^2 + 10 = 29x$

7. Solve by taking square roots:
$(x + 2)^2 - 24 = 0$

8. Solve by using the quadratic formula:
$2x^2 + 3 = 5x$

9. Solve by factoring: $6x(x + 1) = x - 1$

10. Solve by taking square roots:
$4y^2 + 9 = 0$

11. Solve by completing the square:
$x^2 - 4x + 1 = 0$

12. Solve by using the quadratic formula:
$x^2 - 3x - 5 = 0$

13. Solve by completing the square:
$x^2 + 6x + 12 = 0$

14. Solve by factoring: $(x + 9)^2 = x + 11$

15. Solve by taking square roots:
$\left(x - \frac{1}{2}\right)^2 = \frac{9}{4}$

16. Solve by completing the square:
$4x^2 + 16x = 7$

17. Solve by using the quadratic formula:
$x^2 - 4x + 8 = 0$

18. Solve by using the quadratic formula:
$2x^2 + 5x + 2 = 0$

19. Graph $y = -3x^2$.

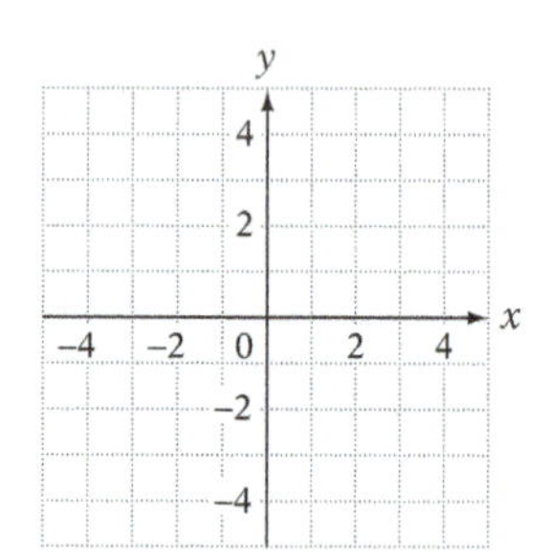

20. Graph $y = -\frac{1}{4}x^2$.

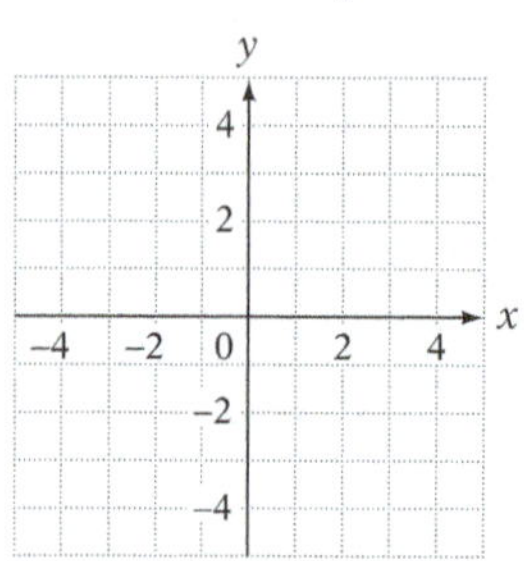

21. Graph $y = 2x^2 + 1$.

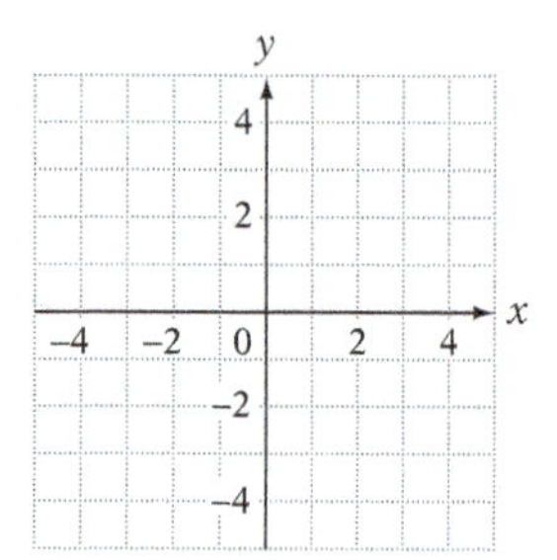

22. Graph $y = x^2 - 4x + 3$.

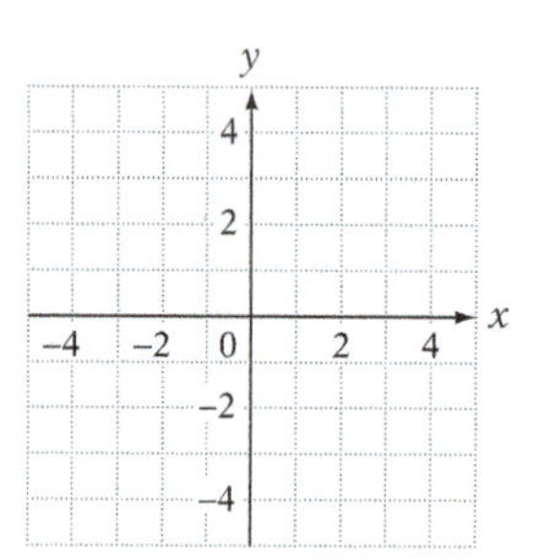

23. Graph $y = -x^2 + 4x - 5$.

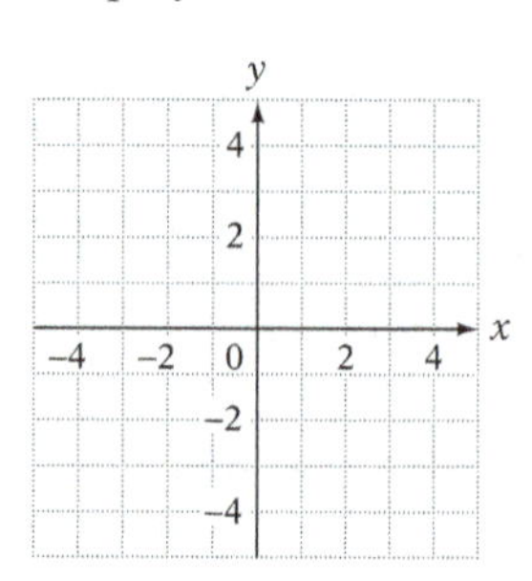

24. Find the x- and y-intercepts of the graph of $y = x^2 - 2x - 15$.

iStockphoto.com/Robert Szajkowski

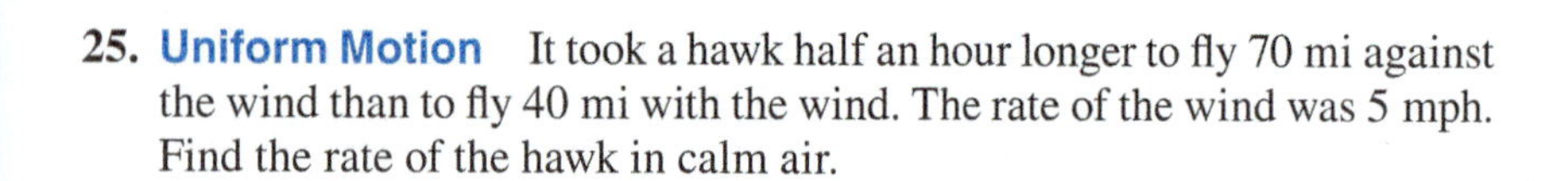
25. Uniform Motion It took a hawk half an hour longer to fly 70 mi against the wind than to fly 40 mi with the wind. The rate of the wind was 5 mph. Find the rate of the hawk in calm air.

CHAPTER 11 TEST

1. Solve by factoring: $x^2 - 5x - 6 = 0$

2. Solve by factoring: $3x^2 + 7x = 20$

3. Solve $2x^2 + x = 0$ by factoring.

4. Solve $4x^2 - 9 = 0$ by taking square roots.

5. Solve by taking square roots:
$2(x - 5)^2 - 50 = 0$

6. Solve by taking square roots:
$3(x + 4)^2 - 60 = 0$

7. Solve by completing the square:
$x^2 + 4x - 16 = 0$

8. Solve by completing the square:
$x^2 + 3x = 8$

9. Solve by completing the square:
$2x^2 - 6x + 1 = 0$

10. Solve by completing the square:
$2x^2 + 8x = 3$

11. Solve by using the quadratic formula:
$x^2 + 4x + 2 = 0$

12. Solve by using the quadratic formula:
$x^2 - 3x = 6$

13. Solve by using the quadratic formula:
$2x^2 - 5x - 3 = 0$

14. Solve by using the quadratic formula:
$3x^2 - x = 1$

15. Solve $4x^2 + 6x - 1 = 0$ by using the quadratic formula. Approximate the solutions to the nearest thousandth.

16. Solve $3x^2 + 2x - 3 = 0$ by using the quadratic formula. Approximate the solutions to the nearest thousandth.

17. Graph $y = x^2 + 2x - 4$.

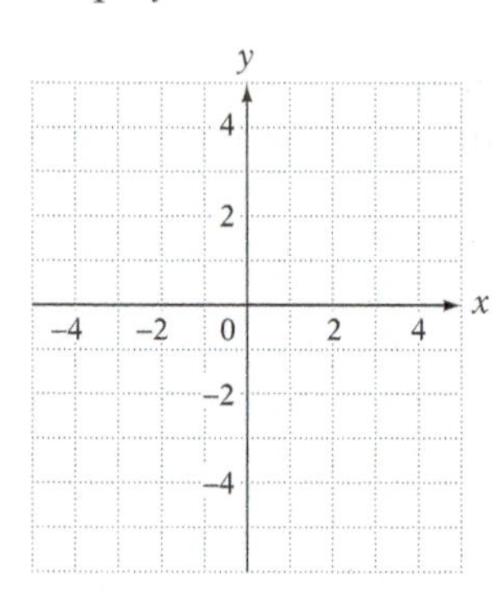

18. Find the x- and y-intercepts of the graph of $f(x) = x^2 + x - 12$.

19. Geometry The length of a rectangle is 2 ft less than twice the width. The area of the rectangle is 40 ft². Find the length and width of the rectangle.

20. Uniform Motion It took a motorboat 1 h longer to travel 60 mi against a current than it took to travel 60 mi with the current. The rate of the current was 1 mph. Find the rate of the boat in calm water.

Yuriy Chertok/Shutterstock.com

Cumulative Review Exercises

1. Simplify: $2x - 3[2x - 4(3 - 2x) + 2] - 3$

2. Solve: $-\frac{3}{5}x = -\frac{9}{10}$

3. Solve: $2x - 3(4x - 5) = -3x - 6$

4. Simplify: $(2a^2b)^2(-3a^4b^2)$

5. Divide: $(x^2 - 8) \div (x - 2)$

6. Factor: $3x^3 + 2x^2 - 8x$

7. Divide: $\frac{3x^2 - 6x}{4x - 6} \div \frac{2x^2 + x - 6}{6x^3 - 24x}$

8. Subtract: $\frac{x}{2(x - 1)} - \frac{1}{(x - 1)(x + 1)}$

9. Simplify: $\dfrac{1 - \frac{7}{x} + \frac{12}{x^2}}{2 - \frac{1}{x} - \frac{15}{x^2}}$

10. Find the x- and y-intercepts of the graph of $4x - 3y = 12$.

11. Find the equation of the line that contains the point $(-3, 2)$ and has slope $-\frac{4}{3}$.

12. Solve the system of equations by substitution:
$3x - y = 5$
$y = 2x - 3$

13. Solve the system of equations by the addition method:
$3x + 2y = 2$
$5x - 2y = 14$

14. Solve: $2x - 3(2 - 3x) > 2x - 5$

15. Simplify: $(\sqrt{a} - \sqrt{2})(\sqrt{a} + \sqrt{2})$

16. Simplify: $\frac{\sqrt{108a^7b^3}}{\sqrt{3a^4b}}$

17. Simplify: $\dfrac{\sqrt{3}}{5 + 2\sqrt{3}}$

18. Solve: $3 = 8 - \sqrt{5x}$

19. Solve by factoring: $6x^2 - 17x = -5$

20. Solve by taking square roots:
$2(x - 5)^2 = 36$

21. Solve by completing the square:
$3x^2 + 7x = -3$

22. Solve by using the quadratic formula:
$2x^2 - 3x - 2 = 0$

23. Food Mixtures Find the cost per pound of a mixture made from 20 lb of cashews that cost $4.90 per pound and 50 lb of peanuts that cost $2.10 per pound.

24. The Stock Market A stock investment of 100 shares paid a dividend of $215. At this rate, how many additional shares must the investor own to earn a dividend of $752.50?

25. Uniform Motion A 720-mile trip from one city to another takes 3 h when a plane is flying with the wind. The return trip, against the wind, takes 4.5 h. Find the rate of the plane in still air and the rate of the wind.

26. Grading A student received a 70, a 91, an 85, and a 77 on four tests in a mathematics class. What scores on the last test will enable the student to receive a minimum of 400 points?

27. Integer Problem The sum of the squares of three consecutive odd integers is 83. Find the middle odd integer.

28. Exercise A jogger ran 7 mi at a constant rate and then reduced the rate by 3 mph. An additional 8 mi was run at the reduced rate. The total time spent jogging the 15 mi was 3 h. Find the jogger's rate for the last 8 mi.

29. Graph the solution set of $2x - 3y > 6$.

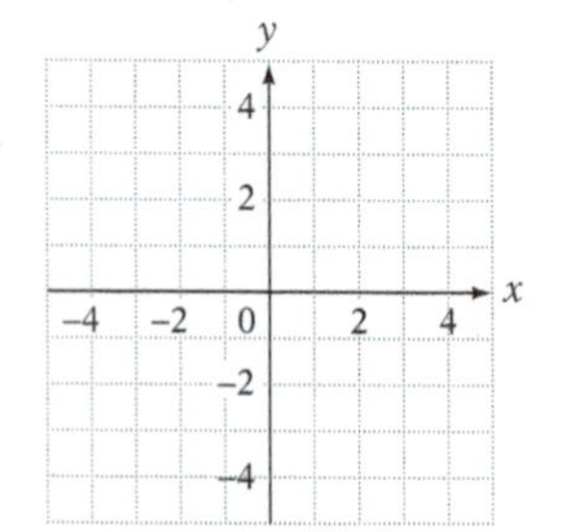

30. Graph $y = x^2 - 2x - 3$.

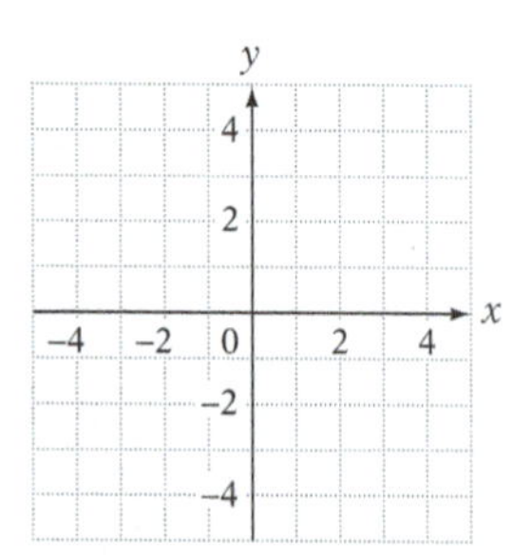

FINAL EXAM

1. Evaluate $-|-3|$.

2. Subtract: $-15 - (-12) - 3$

3. Simplify: $-2^4 \cdot (-2)^4$

4. Simplify: $-7 - \dfrac{12 - 15}{2 - (-1)} \cdot (-4)$

5. Evaluate $\dfrac{a^2 - 3b}{2a - 2b^2}$ when $a = 3$ and $b = -2$.

6. Simplify: $6x - (-4y) - (-3x) + 2y$

7. Simplify: $(-15z)\left(-\dfrac{2}{5}\right)$

8. Simplify: $-2[5 - 3(2x - 7) - 2x]$

9. Solve: $20 = -\dfrac{2}{5}x$

10. Solve: $4 - 2(3x + 1) = 3(2 - x) + 5$

11. Write $\dfrac{1}{8}$ as a percent.

12. Find 19% of 80.

13. Subtract: $(2x^2 - 5x + 1) - (5x^2 - 2x - 7)$

14. Simplify: $(-3xy^3)^4$

15. Multiply: $(3x^2 - x - 2)(2x + 3)$

16. Simplify: $\dfrac{(-2x^2y^3)^3}{(-4xy^4)^2}$

17. Divide: $\dfrac{12x^2y - 16x^3y^2 - 20y^2}{4xy^2}$

18. Divide: $(5x^2 - 2x - 1) \div (x + 2)$

19. Simplify: $(4x^{-2}y)^2(2xy^{-2})^{-2}$

20. Given $f(t) = \dfrac{t}{t + 1}$, find $f(3)$.

21. Factor: $x^2 - 5x - 6$

22. Factor: $6x^2 - 5x - 6$

23. Factor: $8x^3 - 28x^2 + 12x$

24. Factor: $25x^2 - 16$

25. Factor: $2a(4 - x) - 6(x - 4)$

26. Factor: $75y - 12x^2y$

27. Solve: $2x^2 = 7x - 3$

28. Multiply: $\dfrac{2x^2 - 3x + 1}{4x^2 - 2x} \cdot \dfrac{4x^2 + 4x}{x^2 - 2x + 1}$

29. Subtract: $\dfrac{5}{x + 3} - \dfrac{3x}{2x - 5}$

30. Simplify: $x - \dfrac{1}{1 - \dfrac{1}{x}}$

31. Solve: $\dfrac{5x}{3x - 5} - 3 = \dfrac{7}{3x - 5}$

32. Solve $a = 3a - 2b$ for a.

33. Find the slope of the line that contains the points $(-1, -3)$ and $(2, -1)$.

34. Find the equation of the line that contains the point $(3, -4)$ and has slope $-\frac{2}{3}$.

35. Solve the system of equations by substitution:
$y = 4x - 7$
$y = 2x + 5$

36. Solve the system of equations by the addition method:
$4x - 3y = 11$
$2x + 5y = -1$

37. Solve: $4 - x \geq 7$

38. Solve: $2 - 2(y - 1) \leq 2y - 6$

39. Simplify: $\sqrt{49x^6}$

40. Simplify: $2\sqrt{27a} + 8\sqrt{48a}$

41. Simplify: $\dfrac{\sqrt{3}}{\sqrt{5} - 2}$

42. Solve: $\sqrt{2x - 3} + 4 = 5$

43. Solve by factoring:
$3x^2 - x = 4$

44. Solve by using the quadratic formula:
$4x^2 - 2x - 1 = 0$

45. **Number Sense** Translate and simplify "the sum of twice a number and three times the difference between the number and two."

46. **Depreciation** Because of depreciation, the value of an office machine is now \$4800. This is 80% of its original value. Find the original value.

47. **Business** The manufacturer's cost for a photo printer is \$900. The manufacturer then sells the printer for \$1485. What is the markup rate?

48. **Investment** An investment of \$3000 is made at an annual simple interest rate of 8%. How much additional money must be invested at 11% so that the total interest earned is 10% of the total investment?

Olga Popova/Shutterstock.com

49. **Food Mixtures** A grocer mixes 4 lb of peanuts that cost \$2.50 per pound with 2 lb of walnuts that cost \$7 per pound. What is the cost per pound of the resulting mixture?

50. **Pharmacology** A pharmacist mixes 20 L of a solution that is 60% acid with 30 L of a solution that is 20% acid. What is the percent concentration of acid in the resulting mixture?

51. **Travel** At 2 P.M., a small plane had been flying for 1 h when a change of wind direction doubled its average ground speed. The complete 860-kilometer trip took 2.5 h. How far did the plane travel in the first hour?

52. **Geometry** The angles of a triangle are such that the measure of the second angle is 10° more than the measure of the first angle, and the measure of the third angle is 10° more than the measure of the second angle. Find the measure of each of the three angles.

michaeljung/Shutterstock.com

53. **Number Problem** The sum of the squares of three consecutive integers is 50. Find the middle integer.

54. **Food Preparation** It takes a chef 1 h to prepare a dinner. The chef's apprentice can prepare the dinner in 1.5 h. How long would it take the chef and the apprentice, working together, to prepare the dinner?

55. **Geometry** The length of a rectangle is 5 m more than the width. The area of the rectangle is 50 m^2. Find the dimensions of the rectangle.

56. Paint Mixtures A paint formula requires 2 oz of dye for every 15 oz of base paint. How many ounces of dye are required for 120 oz of base paint?

57. Travel Traveling with the current, a motorboat travels 50 mi in 2.5 h. Traveling against the current, the boat takes twice as long to go 50 mi. Find the rate of the boat in calm water and the rate of the current.

58. Travel Flying against the wind, it took a pilot $\frac{1}{2}$ h longer to travel 500 mi than it took flying with the wind. The rate of the plane in calm air is 225 mph. Find the rate of the wind.

59. Graph $\{x \mid x > -4\}$.

−5 −4 −3 −2 −1 0 1 2 3 4 5

60. Graph $y = -\frac{3}{2}x + 4$.

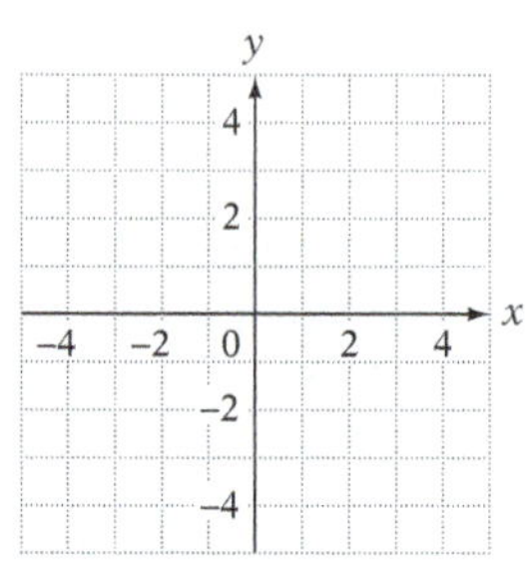

61. Graph $x - 4y = 4$.

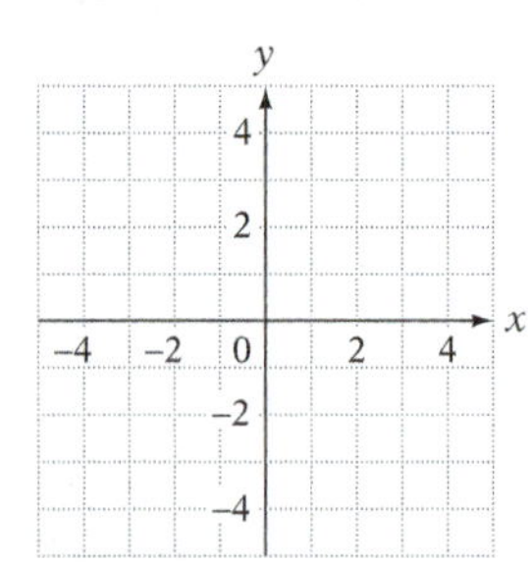

62. Graph the line that has slope $-\frac{1}{2}$ and y-intercept $(0, -3)$.

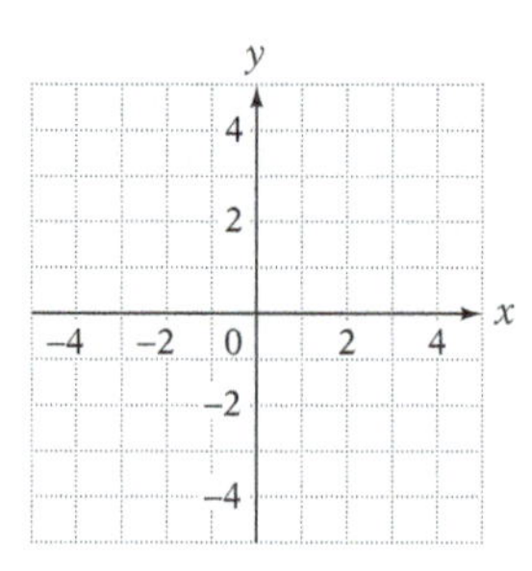

63. Graph $5x - 2y < 10$.

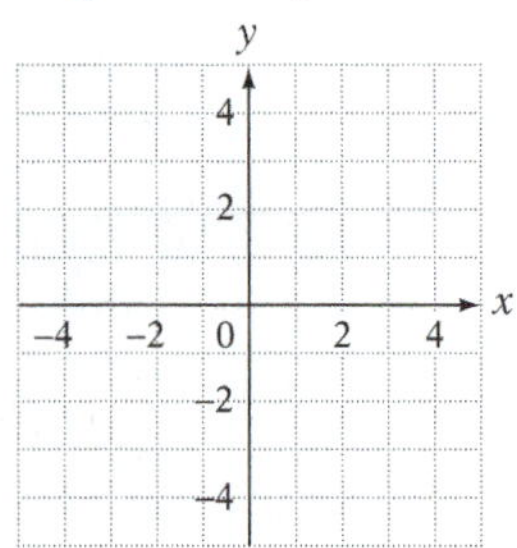

64. Graph $y = x^2 - 4x + 3$.

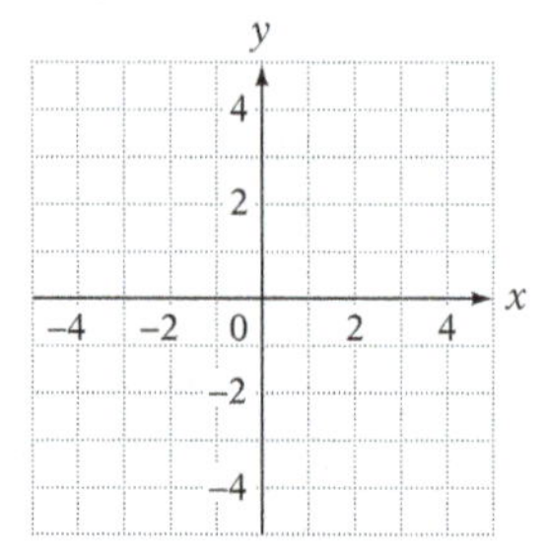

Appendix A

Keystroke Guide for the TI-84 Plus

Basic Operations

Numerical calculations are performed on the **home screen**. You can always return to the home screen by pressing 2ND QUIT. Pressing CLEAR erases the home screen.

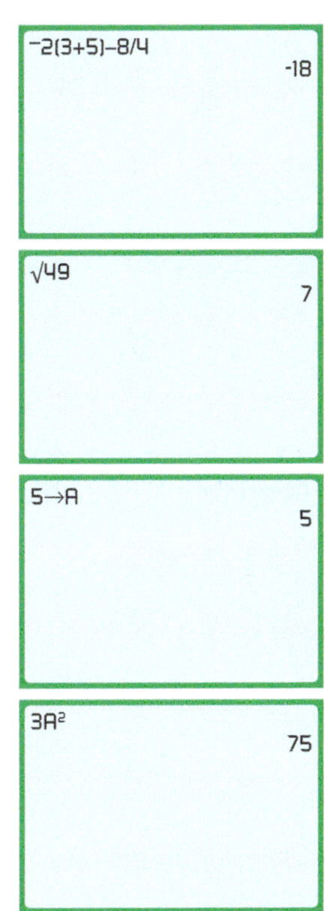

To evaluate the expression $-2(3 + 5) - 8 \div 4$, use the following keystrokes.

Note: There is a difference between the key to enter a negative number, (-), and the key for subtraction, −. You cannot use these keys interchangeably.

The 2ND key is used to access the commands in blue writing above a key. For instance, to evaluate $\sqrt{49}$, press 2ND $\sqrt{\ }$ 49) ENTER.

The ALPHA key is used to place a letter on the screen. One reason to do this is to store a value of a variable. The following keystrokes give A the value of 5.

5 STO▸ ALPHA A ENTER

This value is now available in calculations. For instance, we can find the value of $3a^2$ by using the following keystrokes: 3 ALPHA A x^2. To display the value of the variable on the screen, press 2ND RCL ALPHA A.

Note: When you use the ALPHA key, only capital letters are available on the TI-83 calculator.

Take Note

The descriptions in the margins (for example, Basic Operations and Evaluating Functions) are the same as those used in the text and are arranged alphabetically.

Evaluating Functions

There are various methods of evaluating a function, but all methods require that the expression be entered as one of the ten functions Y_1 to Y_0. To evaluate $f(x) = \frac{x^2}{x - 1}$ when $x = -3$, enter the expression into, for instance, Y_1, and then press VARS ▸ 11 ((-)

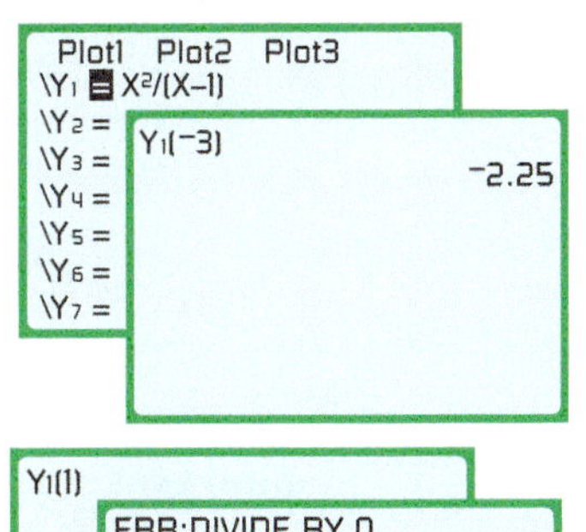

Note: If you try to evaluate a function at a number that is not in the domain of the function, you will get an error message. For instance, 1 is not in the domain of $f(x) = \frac{x^2}{x - 1}$. If we try to evaluate the function at 1, the error screen at the right appears.

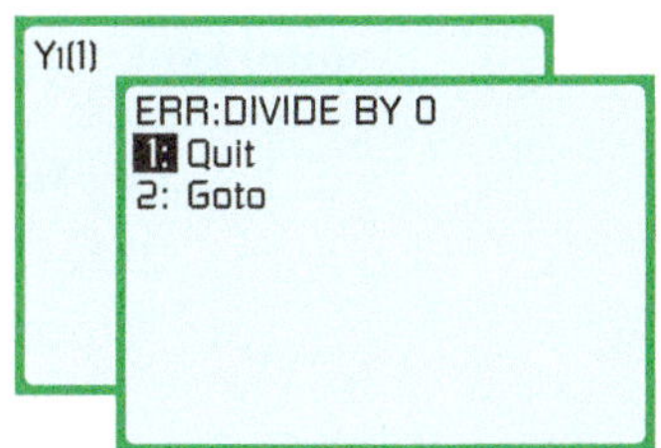

Take Note

Use the down arrow key to scroll past Y7 to see Y8, Y9, and Y0.

Evaluating Variable Expressions

To evaluate a variable expression, first store the values of each variable. Then enter the variable expression. For instance, to evaluate $s^2 + 2sl$ when $s = 4$ and $l = 5$, use the following keystrokes.

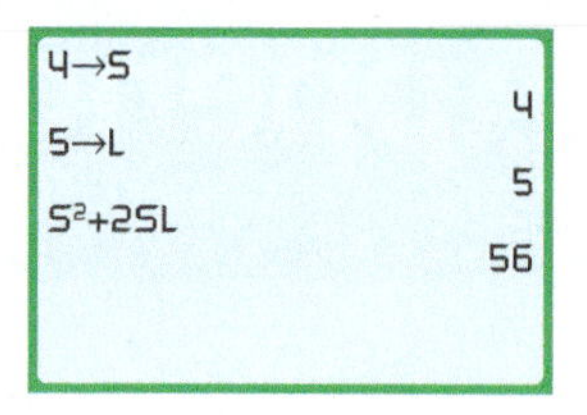

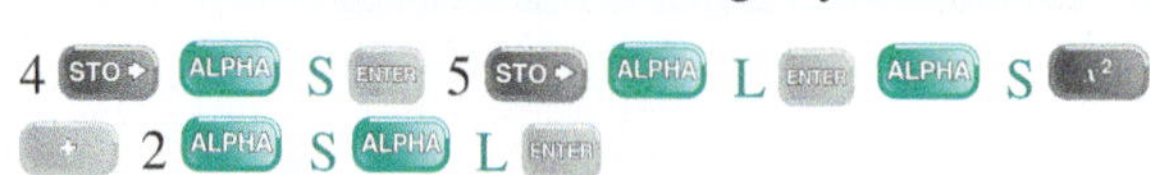

Graph

To graph a function, use the Y= key to enter the expression for the function, select a suitable viewing window, and then press GRAPH. For instance, to graph $f(x) = 0.1x^3 - 2x - 1$ in the standard viewing window, use the following keystrokes.

Y= 0.1 X,T,θ,n ^ 3 ▸ − 2 X,T,θ,n − 1 ZOOM (scroll to 6) ENTER

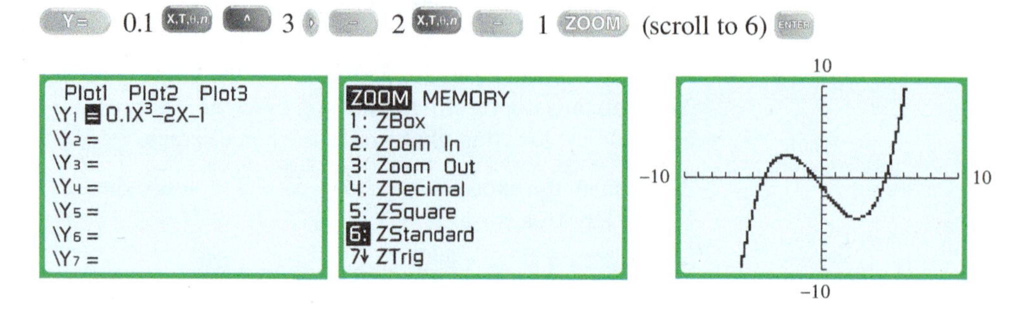

Note: For the keystrokes above, you do not have to scroll to 6. Alternatively, use ZOOM 6. This will select the standard viewing window and automatically start the graph. Use the WINDOW key to create a custom window for a graph.

Graphing Inequalities

To illustrate this feature, we will graph $y \leq 2x - 1$. Enter $2x - 1$ into Y1. Because $y \leq 2x - 1$, we want to shade below the graph. Move the cursor to the left of Y1 and press ENTER three times. Press GRAPH.

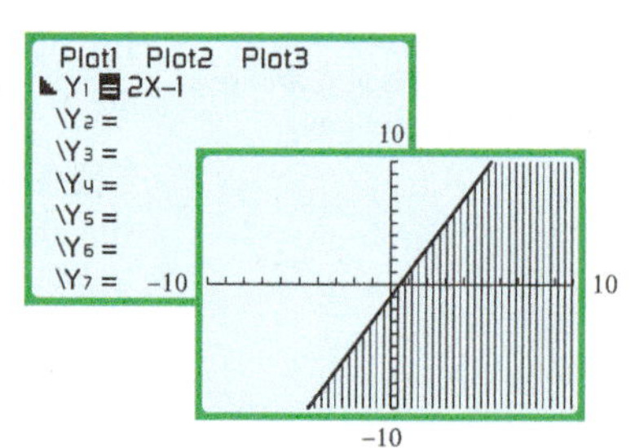

Note: To shade above the graph, move the cursor to the left of Y1 and press ENTER two times. An inequality with the symbol ≤ or ≥ should be graphed with a solid line, and an inequality with the symbol < or > should be graphed with a dashed line. However, a graphing calculator does not distinguish between a solid line and a dashed line.

To graph the solution set of a system of inequalities, solve each inequality for y and graph each inequality. The solution set is the intersection of the two inequalities. The solution set of

$$\begin{aligned} 3x + 2y &> 10 \\ 4x - 3y &\leq 5 \end{aligned}$$

is shown at the right.

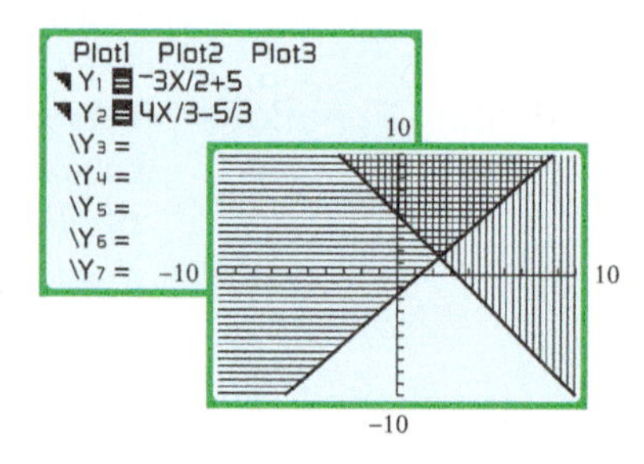

Intersect

The INTERSECT feature is used to solve a system of equations. To illustrate this feature, we will use the system of equations

$$\begin{aligned} 2x - 3y &= 13 \\ 3x + 4y &= -6 \end{aligned}.$$

Note: Some equations can be solved by this method. See the section "Solve an equation" on the next page. Also, this method is used to find a number in the domain of a function for a given number in the range. See the section "Find a domain element."

Solve each of the equations in the system of equations for y. In this case, we have $y = \frac{2}{3}x - \frac{13}{3}$ and $y = -\frac{3}{4}x - \frac{3}{2}$.

Use the Y-editor to enter $\frac{2}{3}x - \frac{13}{3}$ into Y_1 and $-\frac{3}{4}x - \frac{3}{2}$ into Y_2. Graph the two functions in the standard viewing window. (If the window does not show the point of intersection of the two graphs, adjust the window until you can see the point of intersection.)

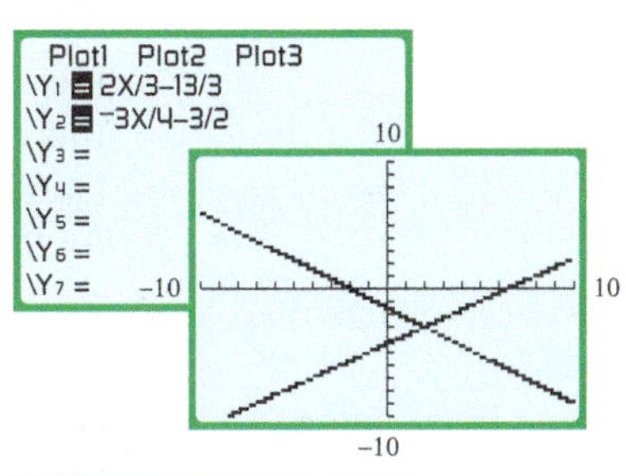

Press 2ND CALC (scroll to 5, intersect) ENTER.

Alternatively, you can just press 2ND CALC 5.

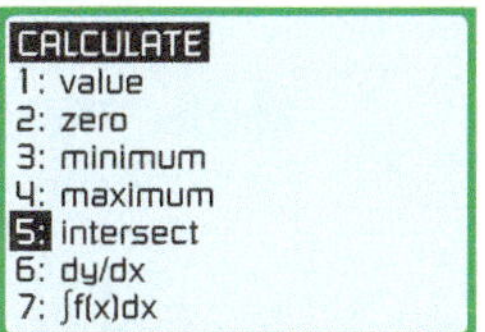

First curve? is shown at the bottom of the screen and identifies one of the two graphs on the screen. Press ENTER.

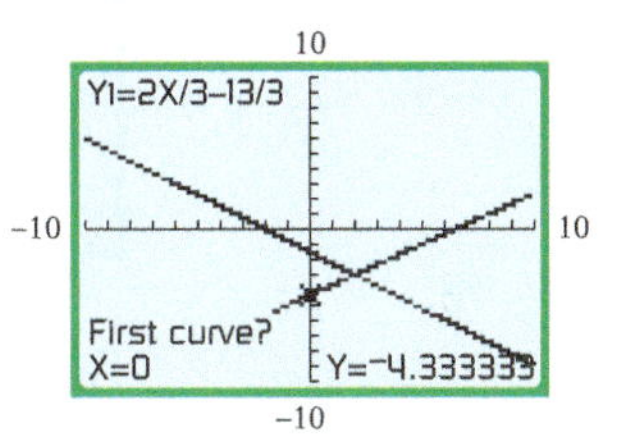

Second curve? is shown at the bottom of the screen and identifies the second of the two graphs on the screen. Press ENTER.

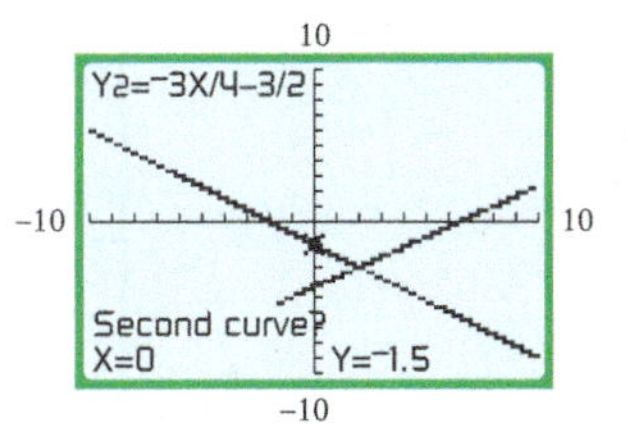

Guess? shown at the bottom of the screen asks you to use the left or right arrow key to move the cursor to the *approximate* location of the point of intersection. (If there are two or more points of intersection, it does not matter which one you choose first.) Press ENTER.

The solution of the system of equations is $(2, -3)$.

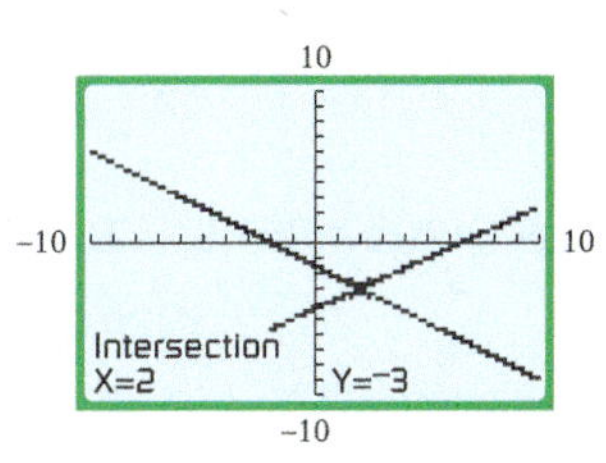

Solve an equation To illustrate the steps involved, we will solve the equation $2x + 4 = -3x - 1$. The idea is to write the equation as the system of equations $y = 2x + 4$, $y = -3x - 1$ and then use the steps for solving a system of equations.

Use the Y-editor to enter the left and right sides of the equation into Y_1 and Y_2. Graph the two functions and then follow the steps for Intersect.

The solution is -1, the x-coordinate of the point of intersection.

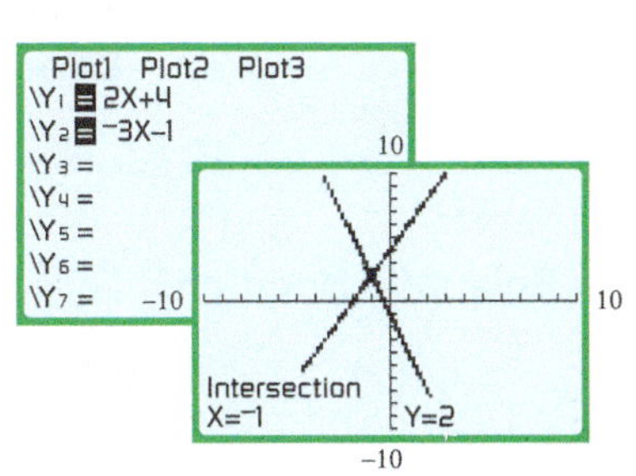

Find a domain element For this example, we will find a number in the domain of $f(x) = -\frac{2}{3}x + 2$ that corresponds to 4 in the range of the function. This is like solving the system of equations $y = -\frac{2}{3}x + 2$ and $y = 4$.

Use the Y= editor to enter the expression for the function in Y_1 and the desired output, 4, in Y_2. Graph the two functions and then follow the steps for Intersect.

The point of intersection is $(-3, 4)$. The number -3 in the domain of f produces an output of 4 in the range of f.

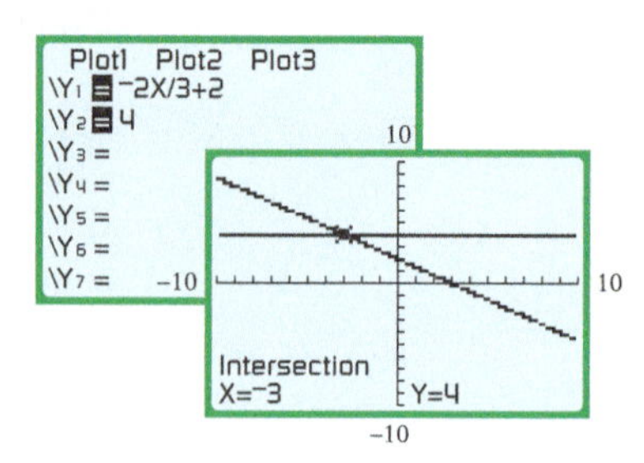

Math

Pressing MATH gives you access to many built-in functions. The following keystrokes will convert 0.125 to a fraction: .125 MATH 1 ENTER.

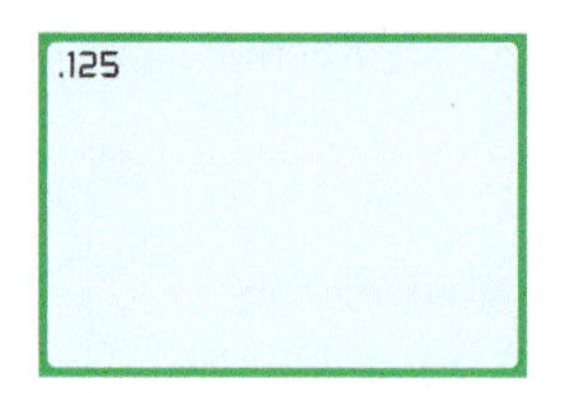

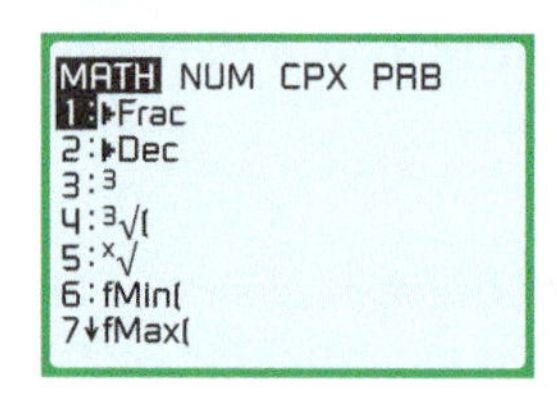

Additional built-in functions under MATH can be found by pressing MATH ▸. For instance, to evaluate $-|-25|$, press (–) MATH ▸ 1 (–) 25) ENTER.

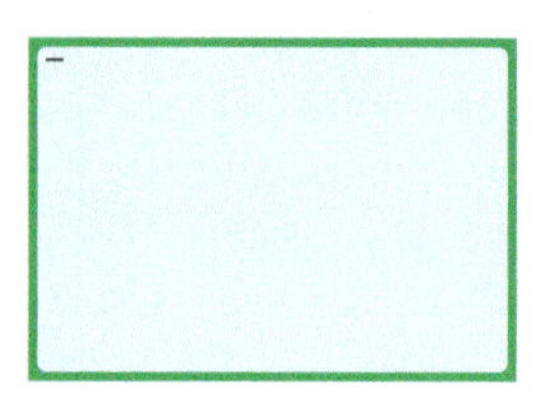

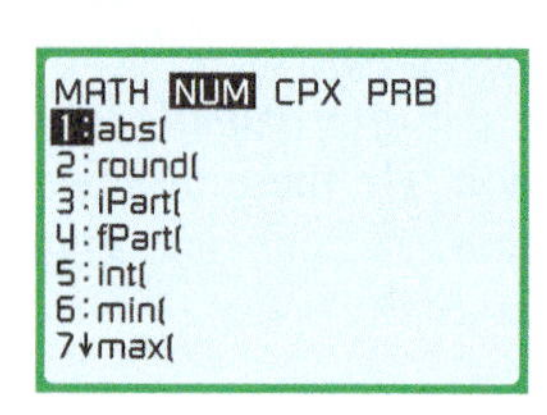

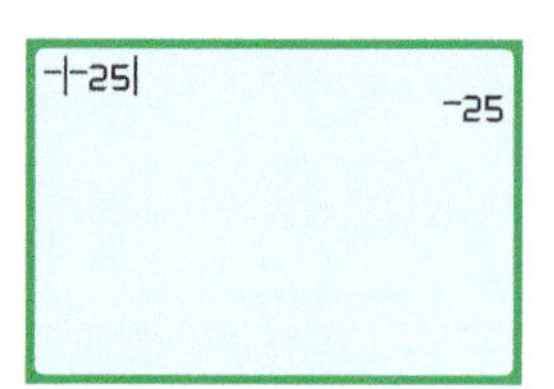

See your owner's manual for assistance with other functions under the MATH key.

Radical Expressions

To evaluate a square-root expression, press 2ND $\sqrt{\ }$.

For instance, to evaluate $0.15\sqrt{p^2 + 4p + 10}$ when $p = 100{,}000$, first store 100,000 in P. Then press 0.15 2ND $\sqrt{\ }$ ALPHA P x^2 + 4 ALPHA P + 10) ENTER.

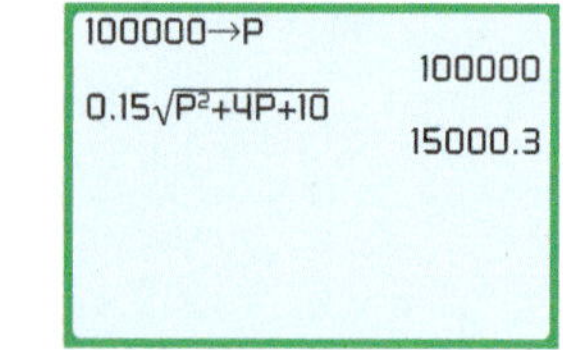

To evaluate a radical expression other than a square root, access $\sqrt[x]{\ }$ by pressing MATH. For instance, to evaluate $\sqrt[4]{67}$, press 4 (the index of the radical) MATH (scroll to 5) ENTER 67 ENTER.

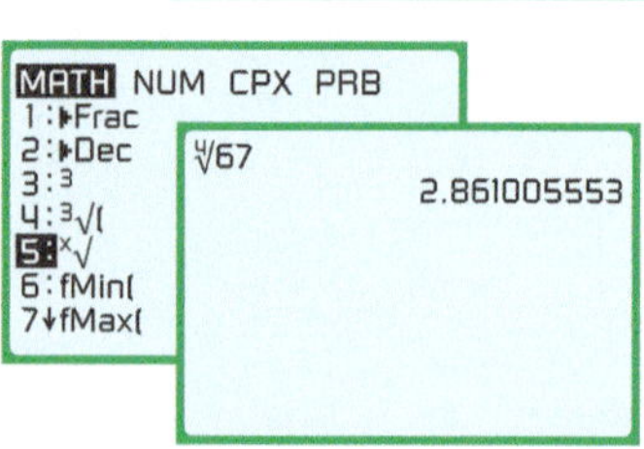

Scientific Notation

To enter a number in scientific notation, use 2ND EE. For instance, to find $\frac{3.45 \times 10^{-12}}{1.5 \times 10^{25}}$, press 3.45 2ND EE (–) 12 ÷ 1.5 2ND EE 25 ENTER. The answer is 2.3×10^{-37}.

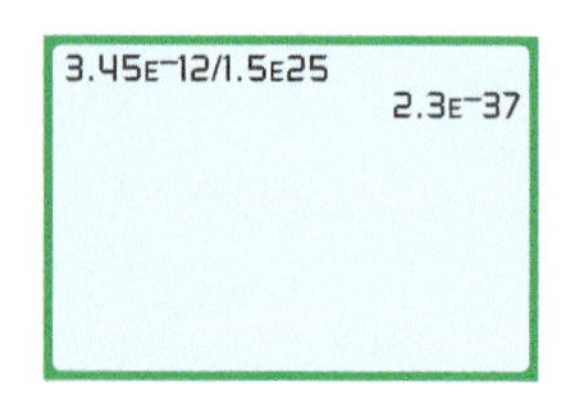

Table There are three steps in creating an input/output table for a function. First use the Y= editor to input the function. The second step is setting up the table, and the third step is displaying the table.

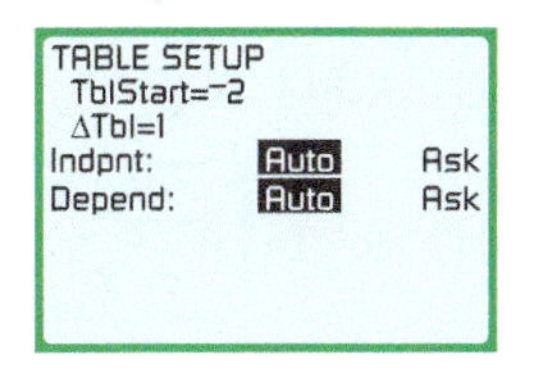

To set up the table, press 2ND TBLSET. **TblStart** is the first value of the independent variable in the input/output table. **ΔTbl** is the difference between successive values. Setting this to 1 means that, for this table, the input values are $-2, -1, 0, 1, 2, \ldots$ If $\Delta\text{Tbl} = 0.5$, then the input values are $-2, -1.5, -1, -0.5, 0, 0.5, \ldots$

Indpnt is the independent variable. When this is set to **Auto**, values of the independent variable are automatically entered into the table. **Depend** is the dependent variable. When this is set to **Auto**, values of the dependent variable are automatically entered into the table.

To display the table, press 2ND TABLE. An input/output table for $f(x) = x^2 - 1$ is shown at the right.

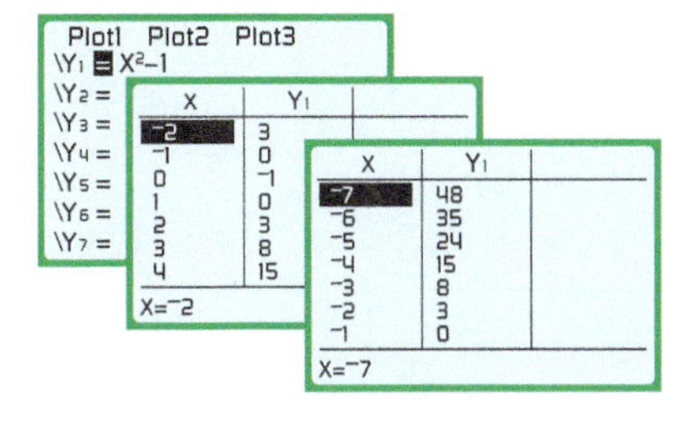

Once the table is on the screen, the up and down arrow keys can be used to display more values in the table. For the table at the right, we used the up arrow key to move to $x = -7$.

An input/output table for any given input can be created by selecting **Ask** for the independent variable. The table at the right shows an input/output table for $f(x) = \frac{4x}{x-2}$ for selected values of x. Note the word **ERROR** when 2 was entered. This occurred because f is not defined when $x = 2$.

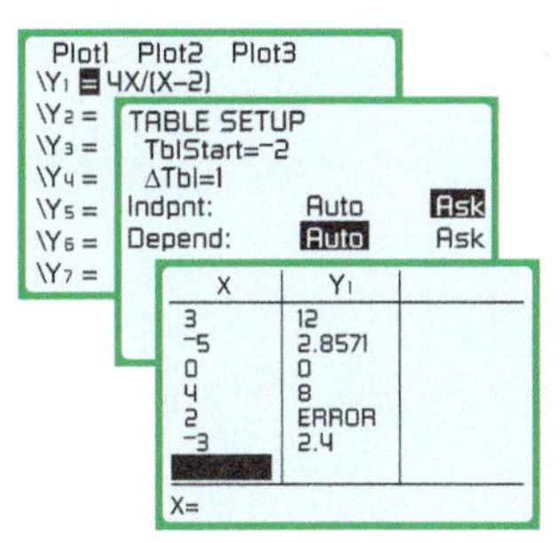

Note: Using the table feature in **Ask** mode is the same as evaluating a function for given values of the independent variable. For instance, from the table at the right, we have $f(4) = 8$.

Test The TEST feature has many uses, one of which is to graph the solution set of a linear inequality in one variable. To illustrate this feature, we will graph the solution set of $x - 1 < 4$. Press Y= X,T,θ,n − 1 2ND TEST (scroll to 5) ENTER 4 GRAPH .

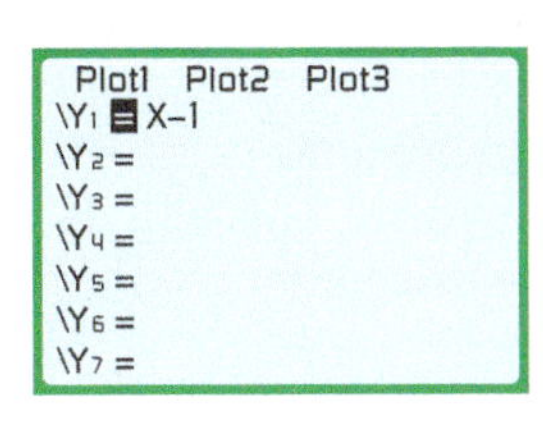

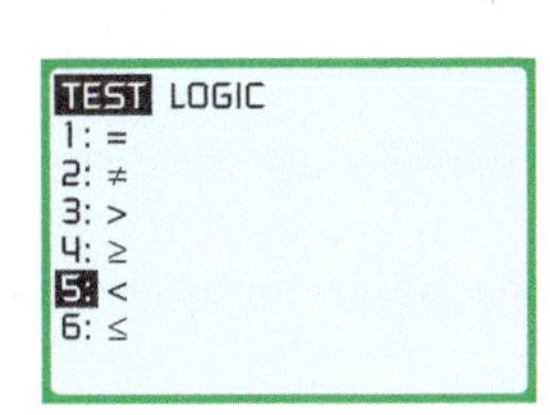

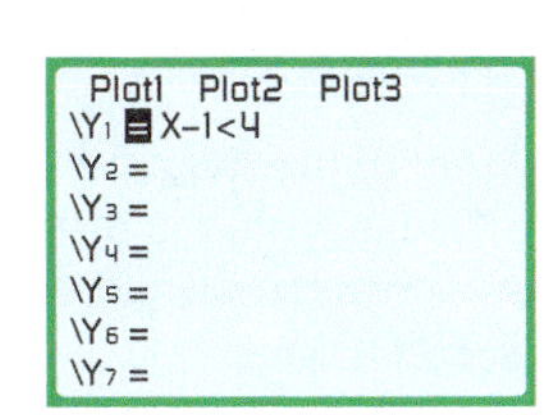

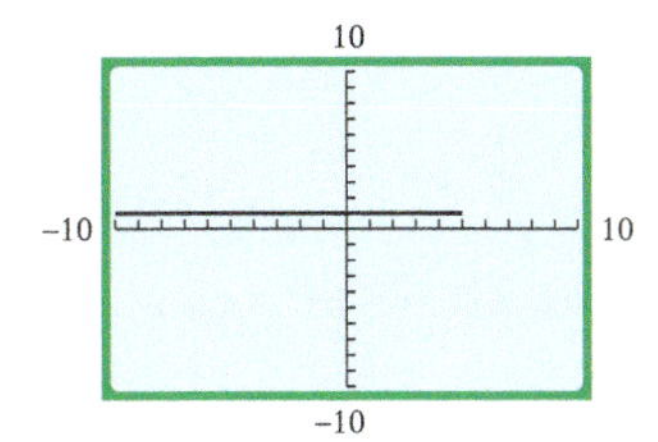

Trace Once a graph is drawn, pressing TRACE will place a cursor on the screen, and the coordinates of the point below the cursor are shown at the bottom of the screen. Use the left and right arrow keys to move the cursor along the graph. For the graph at the right, we have $f(4.8) = 3.4592$, where $f(x) = 0.1x^3 - 2x + 2$ is shown at the top left of the screen.

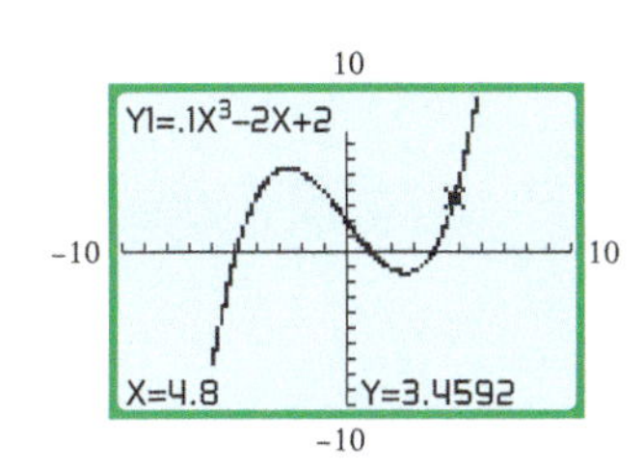

In TRACE mode, you can evaluate a function at any value of the independent variable that is within Xmin and Xmax. To do this, first graph the function. Now press TRACE (the value of x) ENTER. For the leftmost graph at the top of the next page, we used $x = -3.5$. If a value of x is chosen outside the window, an error message is displayed.

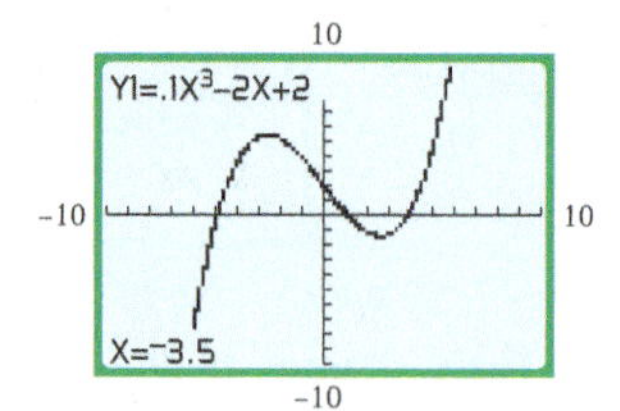

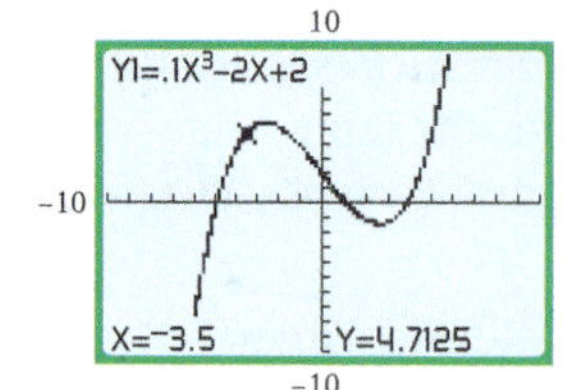

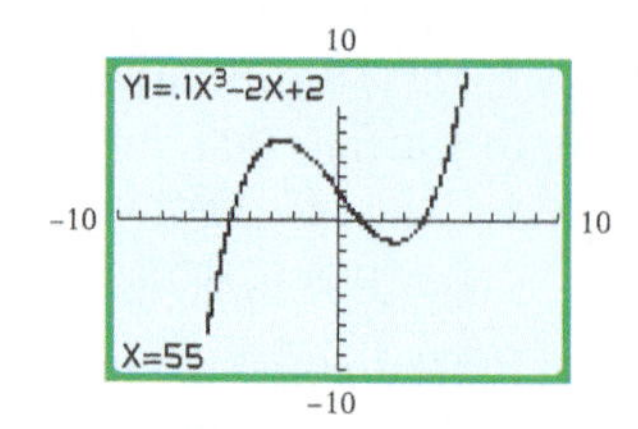

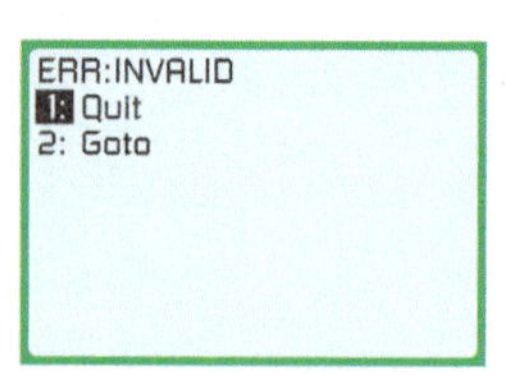

In the example above where we entered -3.5 for x, the value of the function was calculated as 4.7125. This means that $f(-3.5) = 4.7125$. The keystrokes 2ND QUIT VARS ▶ 11 MATH 1 ENTER will convert the decimal value to a fraction.

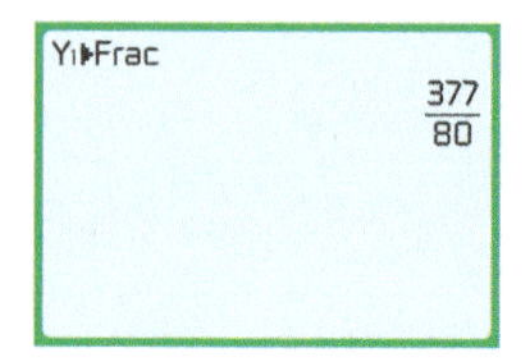

When the TRACE feature is used with two or more graphs, the up and down arrow keys are used to move between the graphs. The graphs below are for the functions $f(x) = 0.1x^3 - 2x + 2$ and $g(x) = 2x - 3$. By using the up and down arrows, we can place the cursor on either graph. The right and left arrows are used to move along the graph.

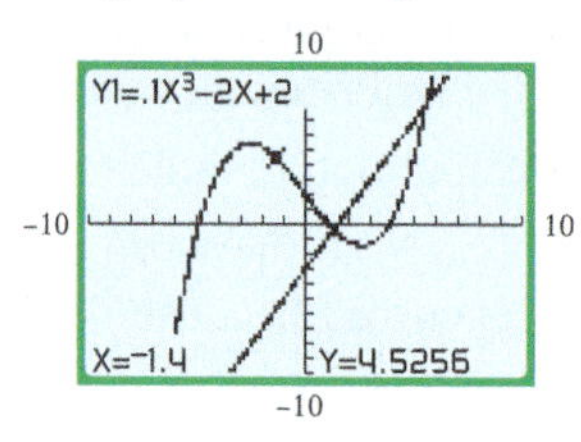

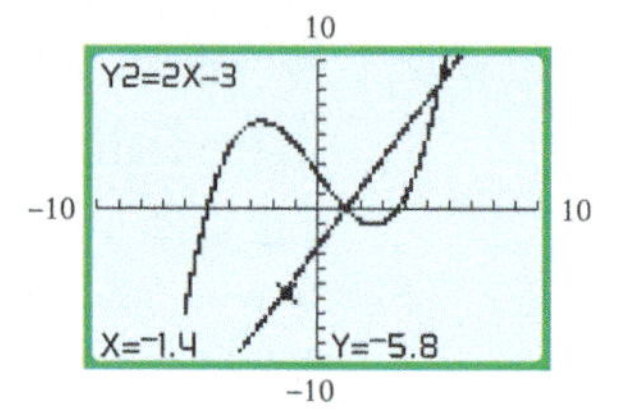

Window The viewing window for a graph is controlled by pressing WINDOW. Xmin and Xmax are the minimum value and maximum value, respectively, of the independent variable shown on the graph. Xscl is the distance between tic marks on the x-axis. Ymin and Ymax are the minimum value and maximum value, respectively, of the dependent variable shown on the graph. Yscl is the distance between tic marks on the y-axis. Leave Xres as 1.

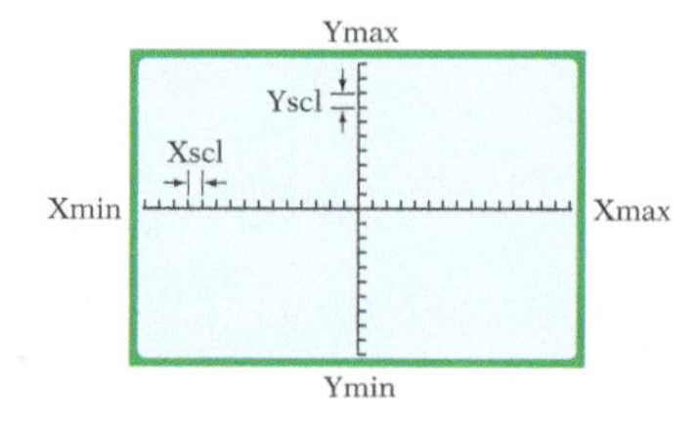

Note: In the standard viewing window, the distance between tic marks on the x-axis is different from the distance between tic marks on the y-axis. This will distort a graph. A more accurate picture of a graph can be created by using a square viewing window. See ZOOM.

The Y= editor is used to enter the expression for a function. There are ten possible functions, labeled Y_1 to Y_0, that can be active at any one time. For instance, to enter $f(x) = x^2 + 3x - 2$ as Y_1, use the following keystrokes.

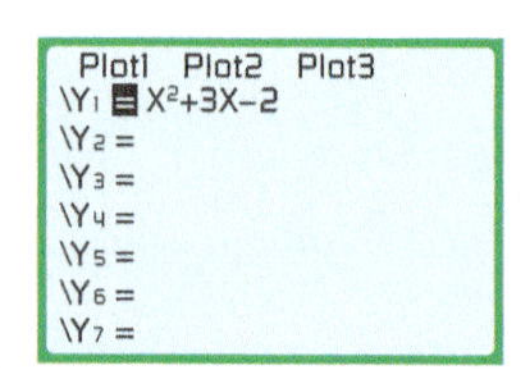

Note: If an expression is already entered for Y_1, place the cursor anywhere on that expression and press CLEAR.

To enter $s = \dfrac{2v - 1}{v^3 - 3}$ into Y_2, place the cursor to the right of the equals sign for Y_2. Then press (2 X,T,θ,n − 1) ÷ (X,T,θ,n ^ 3 ▶ − 3).

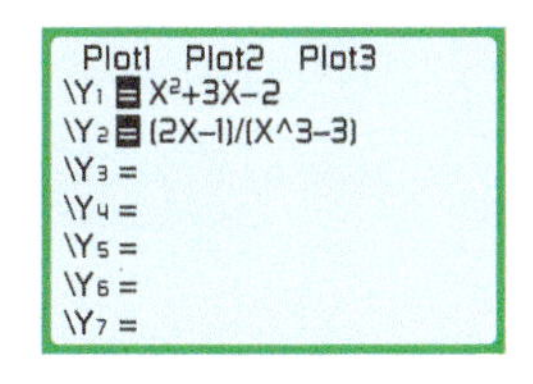

Note: When we enter an equation, the independent variable, v in the expression above, is entered using X,T,θ,n. The dependent variable, s in the expression above, is one of Y_1 to Y_0. Also note the use of parentheses to ensure the correct order of operations.

Observe the black rectangle that covers the equals sign for the two examples we have shown. This rectangle means that the function is "active." If we were to press GRAPH, then the graphs of both functions would appear. You can make a function inactive by using the arrow keys to move the cursor over the equals sign of that function and then pressing ENTER. This will remove the black rectangle. We have done that for Y_2, as shown above. Now if GRAPH is pressed, only Y_1 will be graphed.

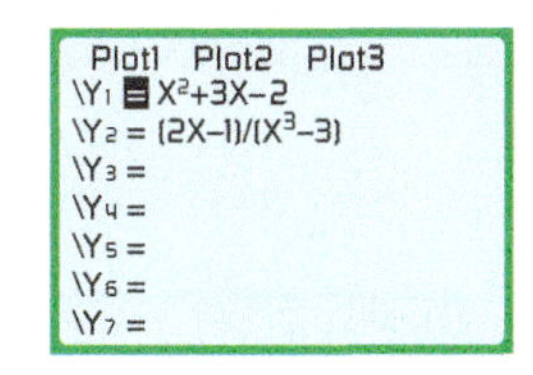

It is also possible to control the appearance of the graph by moving the cursor on the Y= screen to the left of any Y. With the cursor in this position, pressing ENTER will change the appearance of the graph. The options are shown at the right.

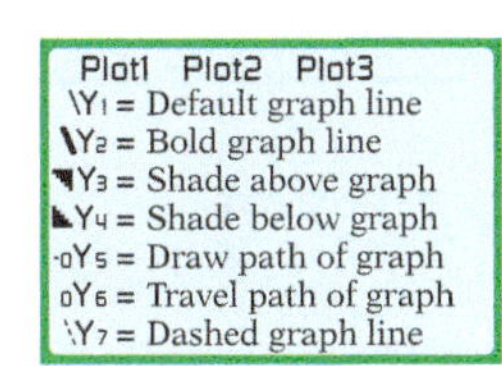

Zero The ZERO feature of a graphing calculator is used for various calculations: to find the x-intercepts of a function, to solve some equations, and to find the zeros of a function.

***x*-intercepts** To illustrate the procedure for finding x-intercepts, we will use $f(x) = x^2 + x - 2$.

First, use the Y-editor to enter the expression for the function and then graph the function in the standard viewing window. (It may be necessary to adjust this window so that the intercepts are visible.) Once the graph is displayed, use the keystrokes below to find the x-intercepts of the graph of the function.

Press 2ND CALC (scroll to 2 for **zero** of the function) ENTER.

Alternatively, you can just press 2ND CALC 2.

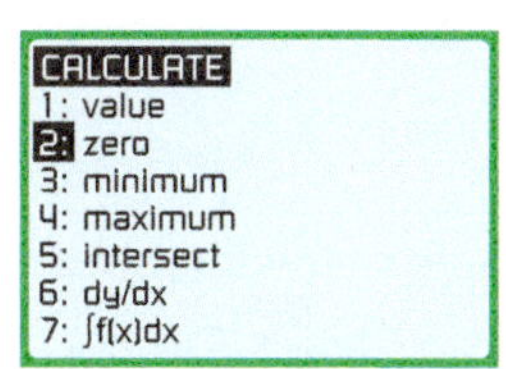

Left Bound? shown at the bottom of the screen asks you to use the left or right arrow key to move the cursor to the *left* of the desired x-intercept. Press ENTER.

Right Bound? shown at the bottom of the screen asks you to use the left or right arrow key to move the cursor to the *right* of the desired x-intercept. Press ENTER.

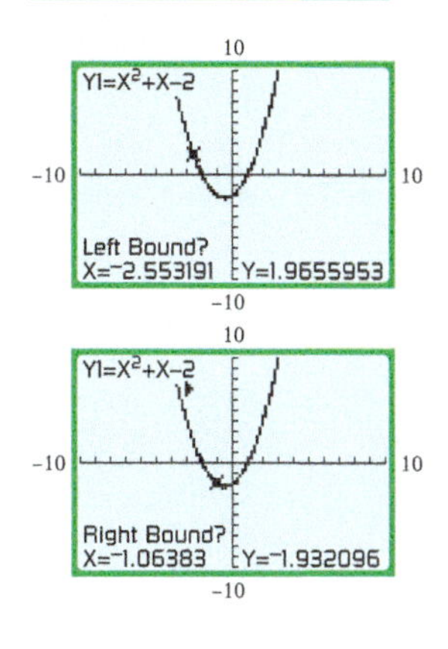

Guess? shown at the bottom of the screen asks you to use the left or right arrow key to move the cursor to the *approximate* location of the desired x-intercept. Press ENTER.

The x-coordinate of an x-intercept is -2. Therefore, an x-intercept is $(-2, 0)$.

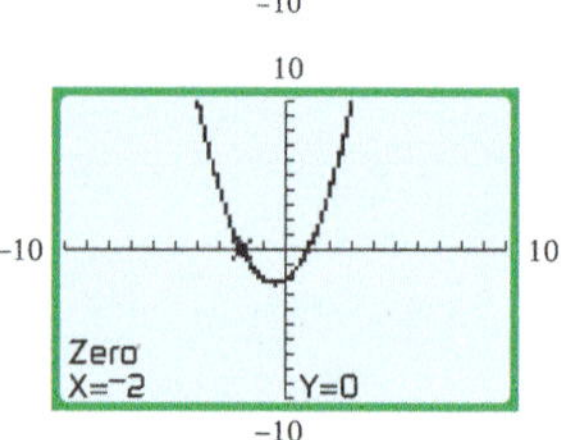

To find the other x-intercept, follow the same steps as above. The screens for this calculation are shown below.

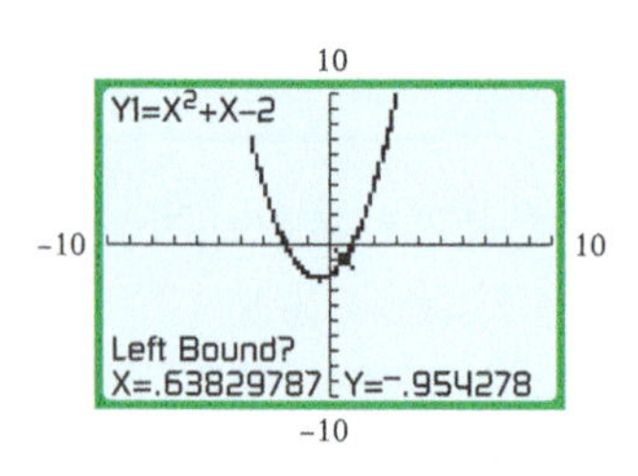

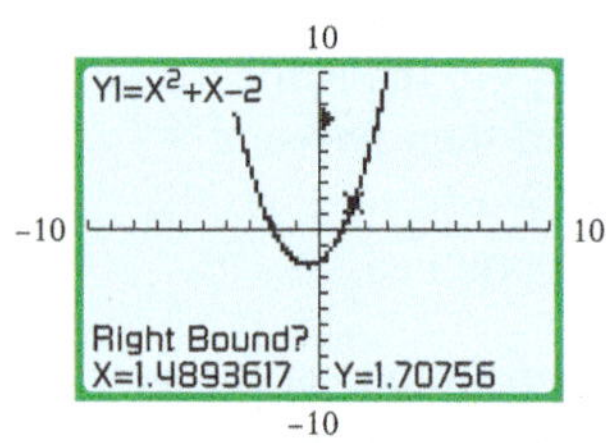

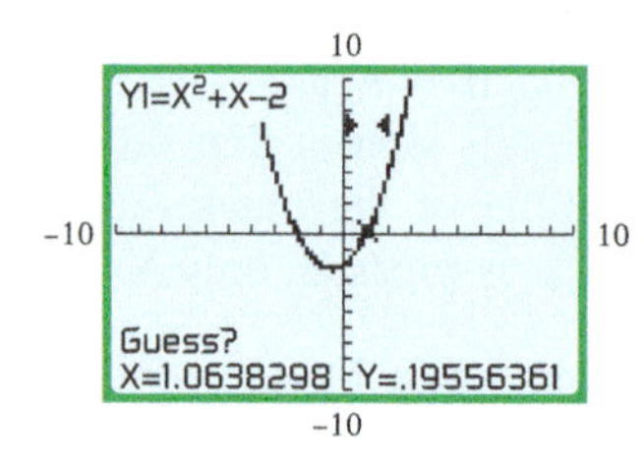

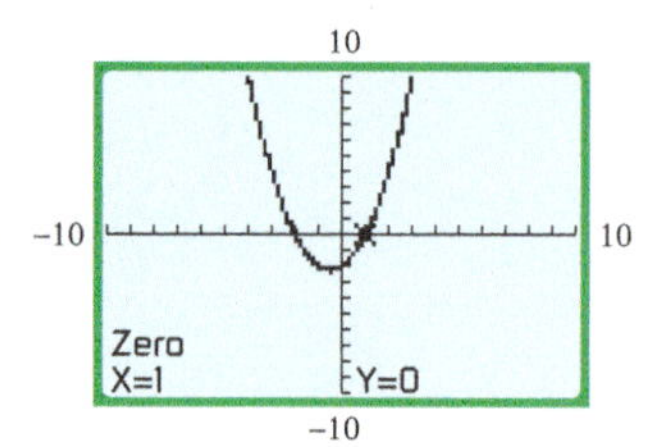

A second x-intercept is $(1, 0)$.

Solve an equation To use the ZERO feature to solve an equation, first rewrite the equation with all terms on one side. For instance, one way to solve the equation $x^3 - x + 1 = -2x + 3$ is first to rewrite it as $x^3 + x - 2 = 0$. Enter $x^3 + x - 2$ into Y1 and then follow the steps for finding x-intercepts.

Find the real zeros of a function To find the real zeros of a function, follow the steps for finding x-intercepts.

ZOOM Pressing ZOOM allows you to select some preset viewing windows. This key also gives you access to ZBox, Zoom In, and Zoom Out. These functions enable you to redraw a selected portion of a graph in a new window. Some windows used frequently in this text are shown below.

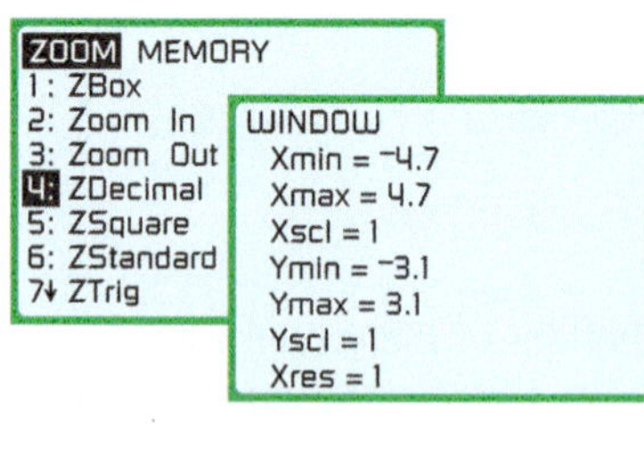

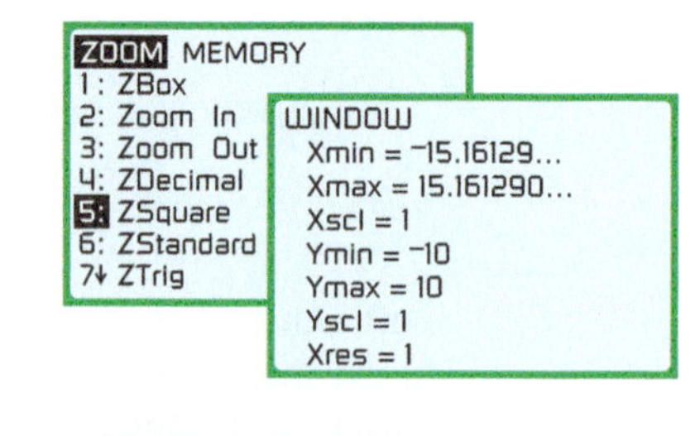

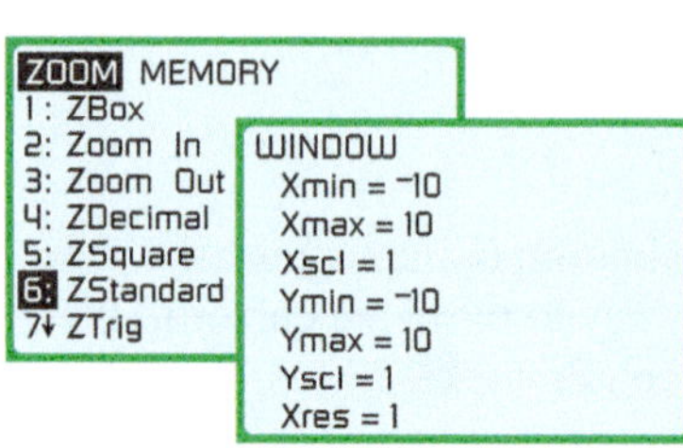

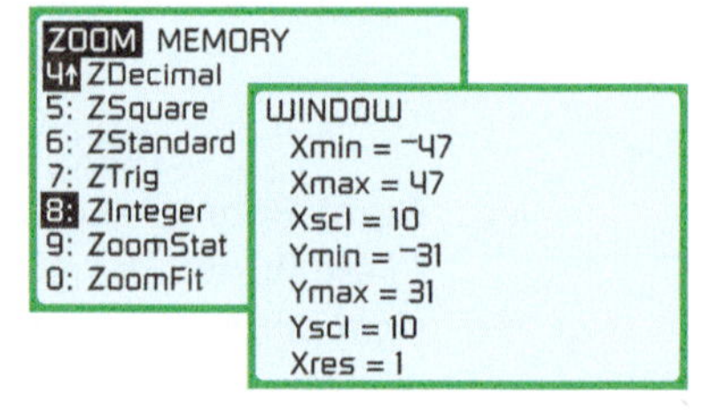

Appendix B

Tables

Table of Symbols

Symbol	Meaning	Symbol	Meaning
$+$	add	$<$	is less than
$-$	subtract	$\leq$	is less than or equal to
$\cdot$, $\times$, $(a)(b)$	multiply	$>$	is greater than
$\frac{a}{b}$, $\div$	divide	$\geq$	is greater than or equal to
( )	parentheses, a grouping symbol	(a, b)	an ordered pair whose first component is a and whose second component is b
[ ]	brackets, a grouping symbol	$^\circ$	degree (for angles)
π	pi, a number approximately equal to $\frac{22}{7}$ or 3.14	$\sqrt{a}$	the principal square root of a
$-a$	the opposite, or additive inverse, of a	$\varnothing$, { }	the empty set
$\frac{1}{a}$	the reciprocal, or multiplicative inverse, of a	$\lvert a \rvert$	the absolute value of a
$=$	is equal to	$\cup$	union of two sets
$\approx$	is approximately equal to	$\cap$	intersection of two sets
$\neq$	is not equal to	$\in$	is an element of (for sets)
		$\notin$	is not an element of (for sets)

Table of Measurement Abbreviations

U.S. Customary System

Length		Capacity		Weight		Area	
in.	inches	oz	fluid ounces	oz	ounces	in^2	square inches
ft	feet	c	cups	lb	pounds	ft^2	square feet
yd	yards	qt	quarts				
mi	miles	gal	gallons				

Metric System

Length		Capacity		Weight/Mass		Area	
mm	millimeter (0.001 m)	ml	milliliter (0.001 L)	mg	milligram (0.001 g)	cm^2	square centimeters
cm	centimeter (0.01 m)	cl	centiliter (0.01 L)	cg	centigram (0.01 g)	m^2	square meters
dm	decimeter (0.1 m)	dl	deciliter (0.1 L)	dg	decigram (0.1 g)		
m	meter	L	liter	g	gram		
dam	decameter (10 m)	dal	decaliter (10 L)	dag	decagram (10 g)		
hm	hectometer (100 m)	hl	hectoliter (100 L)	hg	hectogram (100 g)		
km	kilometer (1000 m)	kl	kiloliter (1000 L)	kg	kilogram (1000 g)		

Time

h	hours	min	minutes	s	seconds

Table of Equations and Formulas

Slope of a Line

$$m = \frac{y_2 - y_1}{x_2 - x_1},\ x_1 \neq x_2$$

Slope-intercept Form of a Straight Line

$$y = mx + b$$

Point-slope Formula for a Line

$$y - y_1 = m(x - x_1)$$

Quadratic Formula

$$x = \frac{-b \pm \sqrt{b^2 - 4ac}}{2a}$$

$$\text{discriminant} = b^2 - 4ac$$

Perimeter and Area of a Triangle, and Sum of the Measures of the Angles

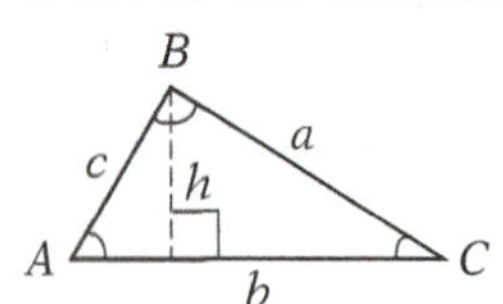

$$P = a + b + c$$

$$A = \frac{1}{2}bh$$

$$A + B + C = 180°$$

Pythagorean Theorem

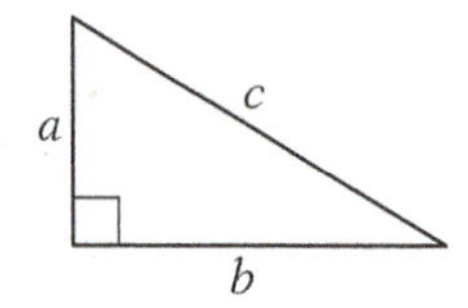

$$a^2 + b^2 = c^2$$

Perimeter and Area of a Rectangle

$$P = 2L + 2W$$

$$A = LW$$

Perimeter and Area of a Square

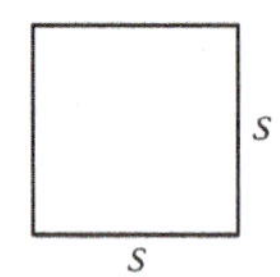

$$P = 4s$$

$$A = s^2$$

Circumference and Area of a Circle

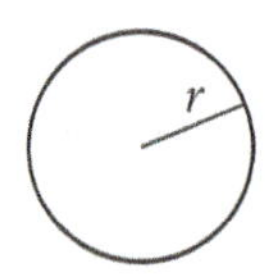

$$C = 2\pi r \text{ or } C = \pi d$$

$$A = \pi r^2$$

Volume of a Rectangular Solid

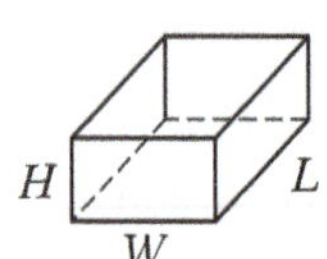

$$V = LWH$$

Volume of a Cube

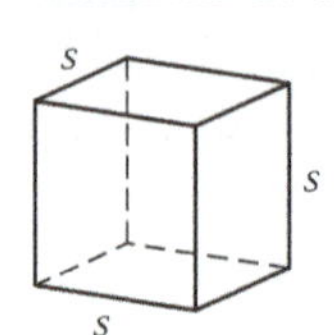

$$V = s^3$$

Volume of a Sphere

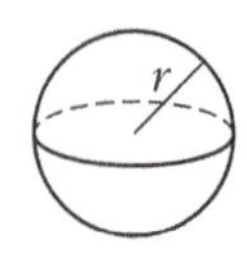

$$V = \frac{4}{3}\pi r^3$$

Volume of a Right Circular Cylinder

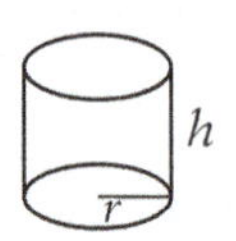

$$V = \pi r^2 h$$

Table of Properties

Properties of Real Numbers

The Associative Property of Addition
If a, b, and c are real numbers, then
$(a + b) + c = a + (b + c)$.

The Commutative Property of Addition
If a and b are real numbers, then
$a + b = b + a$.

The Addition Property of Zero
If a is a real number, then
$a + 0 = 0 + a = a$.

The Multiplication Property of Zero
If a is a real number, then
$a \cdot 0 = 0 \cdot a = 0$.

The Inverse Property of Addition
If a is a real number, then
$a + (-a) = (-a) + a = 0$.

The Associative Property of Multiplication
If a, b, and c are real numbers, then
$(a \cdot b) \cdot c = a \cdot (b \cdot c)$.

The Commutative Property of Multiplication
If a and b are real numbers, then
$a \cdot b = b \cdot a$.

The Multiplication Property of One
If a is a real number, then
$a \cdot 1 = 1 \cdot a = a$.

The Inverse Property of Multiplication
If a is a real number and $a \neq 0$, then
$a \cdot \frac{1}{a} = \frac{1}{a} \cdot a = 1$.

Distributive Property
If a, b, and c are real numbers, then
$a(b + c) = ab + ac$.

Properties of Equations

Addition Property of Equations
If $a = b$, then $a + c = b + c$.

Multiplication Property of Equations
If $a = b$ and $c \neq 0$, then $a \cdot c = b \cdot c$.

Properties of Exponents

If m and n are integers, then $x^m \cdot x^n = x^{m+n}$.
If m and n are integers, then $(x^m)^n = x^{mn}$.

If $x \neq 0$, then $x^0 = 1$.

If m and n are integers and $x \neq 0$, then $\frac{x^m}{x^n} = x^{m-n}$.

If m, n, and p are integers, then $(x^m \cdot y^n)^p = x^{mp}y^{np}$.
If n is a positive integer and $x \neq 0$, then

$x^{-n} = \frac{1}{x^n}$ and $\frac{1}{x^{-n}} = x^n$.

If m, n, and p are integers and $y \neq 0$, then $\left(\frac{x^m}{y^n}\right)^p = \frac{x^{mp}}{y^{np}}$.

Properties of Inequalities

Addition Property of Inequalities
If $a > b$, then $a + c > b + c$.
If $a < b$, then $a + c < b + c$.

Multiplication Property of Inequalities
If $a > b$ and $c > 0$, then $ac > bc$.
If $a < b$ and $c > 0$, then $ac < bc$.
If $a > b$ and $c < 0$, then $ac < bc$.
If $a < b$ and $c < 0$, then $ac > bc$.

Principle of Zero Products

If $a \cdot b = 0$, then $a = 0$ or $b = 0$.

Properties of Radical Expressions

If a and b are positive real numbers, then $\sqrt{ab} = \sqrt{a}\sqrt{b}$.

If a and b are positive real numbers, then $\sqrt{\frac{a}{b}} = \frac{\sqrt{a}}{\sqrt{b}}$.

Property of Squaring Both Sides of an Equation

If a and b are real numbers and $a = b$, then $a^2 = b^2$.

Solutions to "You Try It"

Solutions to Chapter 1 "You Try It"

SECTION 1.1

You Try It 1 $A = \{1, 2, 3, 4, 5, 6\}$

You Try It 2 $-5 < -1$

$-1 = -1$

$5 > -1$

The element 5 is greater than -1.

You Try It 3 $|-5| = 5$

$-|-23| = -23$

You Try It 4 $-(-11) = 11$

$-0 = 0$

$-(8) = -8$

You Try It 5 $|-37| = 37$

$|0| = 0$

$|29| = 29$

SECTION 1.2

You Try It 1 $100 + (-43) = 57$

You Try It 2
$$\begin{aligned} &-51 + 42 + 17 + (-102) \\ &\quad = -9 + 17 + (-102) \\ &\quad = 8 + (-102) \\ &\quad = -94 \end{aligned}$$

You Try It 3 $-8 + 7 = -1$

You Try It 4
$$\begin{aligned} &-9 - (-12) - 17 - 4 \\ &\quad = -9 + 12 + (-17) + (-4) \\ &\quad = 3 + (-17) + (-4) \\ &\quad = -14 + (-4) \\ &\quad = -18 \end{aligned}$$

You Try It 5 $-11 - (-12) = -11 + 12 = 1$

You Try It 6

Strategy To find the difference between the two average temperatures, subtract the smaller number (-130) from the larger number (-17).

Solution $-17 - (-130) = -17 + 130 = 113$

The difference is 113°F.

SECTION 1.3

You Try It 1
$$\begin{aligned} 8(-9)10 &= -72(10) \\ &= -720 \end{aligned}$$

You Try It 2
$$\begin{aligned} (-2)3(-8)7 &= -6(-8)7 \\ &= 48(7) \\ &= 336 \end{aligned}$$

You Try It 3 $-9(34) = -306$

You Try It 4 $(-135) \div (-9) = 15$

You Try It 5 $\dfrac{-72}{4} = -18$

You Try It 6
$$\begin{aligned} -\frac{36}{-12} &= -(-3) \\ &= 3 \end{aligned}$$

You Try It 7 $\dfrac{-72}{-8} = 9$

You Try It 8

Strategy

To find the average daily low temperature:

- Add the seven temperature readings.
- Divide the sum by 7.

Solution

$-6 + (-7) + 0 + (-5) + (-8) + (-1) + (-1) = -28$

$-28 \div 7 = -4$

The average daily low temperature was -4°C.

SECTION 1.4

You Try It 1 $-6^3 = -(6 \cdot 6 \cdot 6) = -216$

You Try It 2 $(-3)^4 = (-3)(-3)(-3)(-3) = 81$

You Try It 3
$$\begin{aligned} (3^3)(-2)^3 &= (3)(3)(3) \cdot (-2)(-2)(-2) \\ &= 27(-8) = -216 \end{aligned}$$

You Try It 4 The product of an odd number of negative factors is negative. Therefore, $(-1)^7 = -1$.

You Try It 5
$$\begin{aligned} &-2^2 \cdot (-1)^{12} \cdot (-3)^2 \\ &\quad = -(2 \cdot 2) \cdot 1 \cdot (-3) \cdot (-3) \\ &\quad = -4 \cdot 1 \cdot 9 = -36 \end{aligned}$$

You Try It 6

$7 - 2[2 \cdot 3 - 7 \cdot 2]^2$

$= 7 - 2[6 - 14]^2$ • Perform operations inside grouping symbols.

$= 7 - 2[-8]^2$ • Simplify exponential expressions.

$= 7 - 2[64]$ • Do multiplication and division from left to right.

$= 7 - 128$

$= -121$ • Do addition and subtraction from left to right.

You Try It 7

$18 - 5[8 - 2(2 - 5)] \div 10$

$= 18 - 5[8 - 2(-3)] \div 10$ • Perform operations inside grouping symbols.

$= 18 - 5[8 + 6] \div 10$

$= 18 - 5[14] \div 10$

$= 18 - 70 \div 10$ • Do multiplication and division from left to right.

$= 18 - 7$

$= 11$ • Do addition and subtraction from left to right.

You Try It 8

$36 \div (8 - 5)^2 - (-3)^2 \cdot 2$

$= 36 \div (3)^2 - (-3)^2 \cdot 2$ • Perform operations inside grouping symbols.

$= 36 \div 9 - 9 \cdot 2$ • Simplify exponential expressions.

$= 4 - 9 \cdot 2$ • Do multiplication and division from left to right.

$= 4 - 18$

$= -14$ • Do addition and subtraction from left to right.

SECTION 1.5

You Try It 1

$24 \div 1 = 24$

$24 \div 2 = 12$

$24 \div 3 = 8$

$24 \div 4 = 6$

$24 \div 5$ Remainder is not 0.

$24 \div 6 = 4$ The factors are repeating.

The factors of 24 are 1, 2, 3, 4, 6, 8, 12, and 24.

You Try It 2

315	
3	105
3	35
5	7
7	1

$315 = 3^2 \cdot 5 \cdot 7$

You Try It 3

326	
2	163
163	1

• For 163, try prime numbers up to 13 only, because $13^2 > 163$.

$326 = 2 \cdot 163$

You Try It 4 $20 = 2 \cdot 2 \cdot 5$ $21 = 3 \cdot 7$

$\text{LCM} = 2 \cdot 2 \cdot 3 \cdot 5 \cdot 7 = 420$

You Try It 5 $42 = 2 \cdot 3 \cdot 7$ $63 = 3 \cdot 3 \cdot 7$

$\text{GCF} = 3 \cdot 7 = 21$

SECTION 1.6

You Try It 1 $\frac{60}{140} = \frac{\overset{1}{\cancel{2}} \cdot \overset{1}{\cancel{2}} \cdot 3 \cdot \overset{1}{\cancel{5}}}{\underset{1}{\cancel{2}} \cdot \underset{1}{\cancel{2}} \cdot \underset{1}{\cancel{5}} \cdot 7} = \frac{3}{7}$

You Try It 2 $\frac{4}{9} = 4 \div 9 = 0.\overline{4}$

You Try It 3 The LCM of 9 and 12 is 36.

$\frac{5}{9} + \left(-\frac{11}{12}\right) = \frac{20}{36} + \left(-\frac{33}{36}\right) = \frac{20 + (-33)}{36}$

$= \frac{-13}{36} = -\frac{13}{36}$

You Try It 4 The LCM of 8 and 6 is 24.

$-\frac{5}{6} + \frac{7}{8} = -\frac{20}{24} + \frac{21}{24} = \frac{-20 + 21}{24}$

$= \frac{1}{24}$

You Try It 5 $-6.12 + (-12.881) = -19.001$

You Try It 6 The LCM of 8, 12, and 9 is 72.

$\frac{7}{8} - \left(-\frac{5}{12}\right) - \frac{1}{9} = \frac{63}{72} - \left(-\frac{30}{72}\right) - \frac{8}{72}$

$= \frac{63 - (-30) - 8}{72}$

$= \frac{63 + 30 - 8}{72} = \frac{85}{72}$

You Try It 7

$-12.03 - 19.117 = -12.03 + (-19.117)$

$= -31.147$

You Try It 8

Strategy

To find the fraction of her day Barbara spent on these activities, add the fractions $\frac{1}{6}$, $\frac{1}{8}$, and $\frac{1}{4}$.

Solution

The common denominator is 24.

$\frac{1}{6} + \frac{1}{8} + \frac{1}{4} = \frac{4}{24} + \frac{3}{24} + \frac{6}{24}$ • Write each fraction in terms of the common denominator.

$= \frac{4 + 3 + 6}{24} = \frac{13}{24}$ • Add the fractions.

Barbara spent $\frac{13}{24}$ of her day on these activities.

SECTION 1.7

You Try It 1

$\frac{5}{8}\left(-\frac{4}{25}\right) = -\frac{5 \cdot 4}{8 \cdot 25}$ • The signs are different. The product is negative.

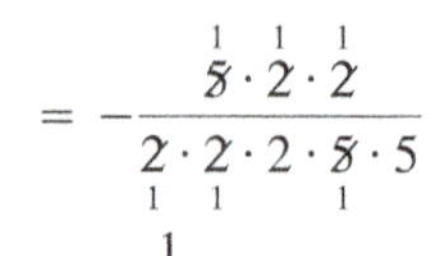

$= -\frac{\overset{1}{\cancel{5}} \cdot \overset{1}{\cancel{2}} \cdot \overset{1}{\cancel{2}}}{\underset{1}{\cancel{2}} \cdot \underset{1}{\cancel{2}} \cdot 2 \cdot \underset{1}{\cancel{5}} \cdot 5}$

$= -\frac{1}{10}$ • Write the answer in simplest form.

You Try It 2

$$-\frac{4}{5}\cdot\left(-\frac{3}{8}\right)\cdot\left(-\frac{10}{27}\right)$$

$$= -\frac{\overset{1}{\cancel{2}}\cdot\overset{1}{\cancel{2}}\cdot\overset{1}{\cancel{3}}\cdot\overset{1}{\cancel{2}}\cdot\overset{1}{\cancel{5}}}{\underset{1}{\cancel{5}}\cdot\underset{1}{\cancel{2}}\cdot\underset{1}{\cancel{2}}\cdot\underset{1}{\cancel{2}}\cdot\underset{1}{\cancel{3}}\cdot 3\cdot 3}$$

• The product is negative.

$$= -\frac{1}{9}$$

• Write the answer in simplest form.

You Try It 3 The product is negative.

$0.034(-2.14) = -0.07276$

You Try It 4 The quotient is negative.

$$\frac{5}{8}\div\left(-\frac{10}{11}\right) = -\left(\frac{5}{8}\cdot\frac{11}{10}\right)$$

• Multiply by the reciprocal of the divisor.

$$= -\frac{\overset{1}{\cancel{5}}\cdot 11}{2\cdot 2\cdot 2\cdot 2\cdot \underset{1}{\cancel{5}}}$$

$$= -\frac{11}{16}$$

• Write the answer in simplest form.

You Try It 5 The quotient is positive.

$-34 \div (-9.02) \approx 3.77$

You Try It 6 $125\% = 125\left(\frac{1}{100}\right) = \frac{125}{100} = \frac{5}{4}$

$125\% = 125(0.01) = 1.25$

You Try It 7 $\frac{9}{16} = \frac{9}{16}(100\%)$

$= \frac{900}{16}\% = 56.25\%$ or $56\frac{1}{4}\%$

You Try It 8 $0.043 = 0.043(100\%) = 4.3\%$

You Try It 9

Strategy To find the number of cushions, divide 20 by $1\frac{1}{2}$.

Solution $20 \div 1\frac{1}{2} = 20 \div \frac{3}{2} = \frac{20}{1}\cdot\frac{2}{3}$

$= \frac{40}{3} = 13\frac{1}{3}$

The number of cushions must be a whole number. Therefore, the number of cushions is 13.

SECTION 1.8

You Try It 1 To find the complement of 87°, subtract 87° from 90°.

$90° - 87° = 3°$

3° is the complement of 87°.

You Try It 2 To find the supplement of 87°, subtract 87° from 180°.

$180° - 87° = 93°$

93° is the supplement of 87°.

You Try It 3 $m\angle x$ is the sum of the measures of two angles.

$m\angle x = 34° + 95° = 129°$

You Try It 4 Perimeter $= 4\cdot$ side

$= 4\cdot 4.2$ m $= 16.8$ m

You Try It 5 Circumference $= \pi\cdot$ diameter

$\approx 3.14\cdot 5$ in.

$= 15.7$ in.

You Try It 6

Strategy To find the cost of the metal strip:

- ▶ Find the circumference of the table in inches.
- ▶ Convert inches to feet.
- ▶ Multiply the circumference by the per-foot cost of the metal strip.

Solution Circumference $= \pi\cdot$ diameter

$\approx 3.14\cdot 36$ in.

$= 113.04$ in.

$\frac{113.04}{12} = 9.42$

The circumference in feet is 9.42 ft.

Cost: $9.42(3.21) = 30.2382$

The cost is $30.24.

You Try It 7 Area $= \frac{1}{2}\cdot$ base $\cdot$ height

$= \frac{1}{2}\cdot 5$ ft $\cdot$ 3 ft $= 7.5\ \text{ft}^2$

You Try It 8 Area $= \pi\cdot(\text{radius})^2$

$\approx 3.14\cdot(6\ \text{in.})^2$

$= 113.04\ \text{in}^2$

You Try It 9 Area $=$ base $\cdot$ height

$= 28$ in. $\cdot$ 15 in. $= 420\ \text{in}^2$

You Try It 10

Strategy

To find how much more expensive the wool rug is:

- ▶ Find the area of the hallway by multiplying 4 ft by 18 ft.
- ▶ Convert the area of the hallway to square yards by dividing the square footage by 9.
- ▶ Find the cost of the nylon rug by multiplying the number of square yards by $17.50.
- ▶ Find the cost of the wool rug by multiplying the number of square yards by $24.30.
- ▶ Subtract the cost of the wool rug from the cost of the nylon rug.

Solution

Area = length × width
$= 4 \text{ ft} \times 18 \text{ ft} = 72 \text{ ft}^2$

$72 \div 9 = 8$ • The area is 8 yd^2.

$8 \times \$17.50 = \$140$

$8 \times \$19.30 = \$194.40$

$\$194.40 - \$140 = \$54.40$

The wool rug costs $54.40 more than the nylon rug.

Solutions to Chapter 2 "You Try It"

SECTION 2.1

You Try It 1 -4 is the constant term.

You Try It 2
$$\begin{aligned} &2xy + y^2 \\ &2(-4)(2) + (2)^2 \\ &\quad = 2(-4)(2) + 4 \\ &\quad = (-8)(2) + 4 \\ &\quad = (-16) + 4 \\ &\quad = -12 \end{aligned}$$

You Try It 3
$$\frac{a^2 + b^2}{a + b}$$
$$\frac{5^2 + (-3)^2}{5 + (-3)} = \frac{25 + 9}{5 + (-3)} = \frac{34}{2} = 17$$

You Try It 4
$$\begin{aligned} &x^3 - 2(x + y) + z^2 \\ &(2)^3 - 2[2 + (-4)] + (-3)^2 \\ &\quad = 8 - 2(-2) + 9 \\ &\quad = 8 + 4 + 9 \\ &\quad = 12 + 9 \\ &\quad = 21 \end{aligned}$$

SECTION 2.2

You Try It 1 $3a - 2b - 5a + 6b = -2a + 4b$

You Try It 2 $-3y^2 + 7 + 8y^2 - 14 = 5y^2 - 7$

You Try It 3 $-5(4y^2) = -20y^2$

You Try It 4 $-7(-2a) = 14a$

You Try It 5 $-\frac{3}{5}\left(-\frac{7}{9}a\right) = \frac{7}{15}a$

You Try It 6 $5(3 + 7b) = 15 + 35b$

You Try It 7 $(3a - 1)5 = 15a - 5$

You Try It 8 $-8(-2a + 7b) = 16a - 56b$

You Try It 9 $3(12x^2 - x + 8) = 36x^2 - 3x + 24$

You Try It 10 $3(-a^2 - 6a + 7) = -3a^2 - 18a + 21$

You Try It 11
$$\begin{aligned} 3y - 2(y - 7x) &= 3y - 2y + 14x \\ &= y + 14x \end{aligned}$$

You Try It 12
$$\begin{aligned} -2(x - 2y) - (-x + 3y) &= -2x + 4y + x - 3y \\ &= -x + y \end{aligned}$$

You Try It 13
$$\begin{aligned} 3y - 2[x - 4(2 - 3y)] &= 3y - 2[x - 8 + 12y] \\ &= 3y - 2x + 16 - 24y \\ &= -2x - 21y + 16 \end{aligned}$$

SECTION 2.3

You Try It 1 the difference between twice n and the *square* of n

$2n - n^2$

You Try It 2 the quotient of 7 less than b and 15

$$\frac{b - 7}{15}$$

You Try It 3 the unknown number: x

the difference between the number and sixty: $x - 60$

$5(x - 60)$
$= 5x - 300$

You Try It 4 the unknown number: n

the cube of the number: n^3

the total of ten and the cube of the number: $10 + n^3$

$-4(10 + n^3)$

You Try It 5 the speed of the older model: s

the speed of the new jet plane is twice the speed of the older model: $2s$

You Try It 6 the length of the longer piece: y

the length of the shorter piece: $6 - y$

Solutions To Chapter 3 "You Try It"

SECTION 3.1

You Try It 1

$10x - x^2$	$= 3x - 10$
$10(5) - (5)^2$	$3(5) - 10$
$50 - 25$	$15 - 10$
$25 \neq 5$	

No, 5 is not a solution.

You Try It 2
$$\begin{aligned} 26 &= y - 14 \\ 26 + 14 &= y - 14 + 14 \\ 40 &= y - 0 \\ 40 &= y \end{aligned}$$

The solution is 40.

You Try It 3

$$-\frac{2x}{5} = 6$$
$$\left(-\frac{5}{2}\right)\left(-\frac{2}{5}x\right) = \left(-\frac{5}{2}\right)(6)$$
$$x = -15$$

The solution is -15.

You Try It 4

$$4x - 8x = 16$$
$$-4x = 16$$
$$\frac{-4x}{-4} = \frac{16}{-4}$$
$$x = -4$$

The solution is -4.

SECTION 3.2

You Try It 1

$$P \cdot B = A$$
$$\frac{1}{6}B = 18 \quad \bullet\ 16\frac{2}{3}\% = \frac{1}{6}$$
$$6 \cdot \frac{1}{6}B = 6 \cdot 18$$
$$B = 108$$

18 is $16\frac{2}{3}\%$ of 108.

You Try It 2

Strategy Use the basic percent equation. $B = 310$, the U.S. population; $A = 162.9$, the number of people who watched the game; P is the unknown percent.

Solution

$$P \cdot 310 = 162.9$$
$$\frac{P \cdot 310}{310} = \frac{162.9}{310}$$
$$P \approx 0.525$$

Approximately 52.5% of the U.S. population watched Super Bowl XLV.

You Try It 3

Strategy To find how much Clarissa must deposit into the account:

- Find the amount of interest earned on the municipal bond by solving $I = Prt$ for I using $P = 1000$, $r = 6.4\% = 0.064$, and $t = 1$.
- Solve $I = Prt$ for P using the amount of interest earned on the municipal bond as I. $r = 8\% = 0.08$, and $t = 1$.

Solution

$$I = Prt$$
$$= 1000(0.064)(1) = 64$$

The interest earned on the municipal bond was \$64.

$$I = Prt$$
$$64 = P(0.08)(1) \quad \bullet\ I = 64, r = 0.08, t = 1$$
$$64 = 0.08P$$
$$\frac{64}{0.08} = \frac{0.08P}{0.08}$$
$$800 = P$$

Clarissa must invest \$800 in the account.

You Try It 4

Strategy To find the number of ounces of cereal in the bowl, solve $Q = Ar$ for A using $Q = 2$ and $r = 25\% = 0.25$.

Solution

$$Q = Ar$$
$$2 = A(0.25) \quad \bullet\ Q = 2, r = 0.25$$
$$\frac{2}{0.25} = \frac{A(0.25)}{0.25}$$
$$8 = A$$

The bowl contains 8 oz of cereal.

You Try It 5

Strategy To find the distance, solve the equation $d = rt$ for d. The time is 3 h. Therefore, $t = 3$. The plane is moving against the wind, which means the headwind is slowing the actual speed of the plane. 250 mph − 25 mph = 225 mph. Thus $r = 225$.

Solution

$$d = rt$$
$$d = 225(3) \quad \bullet\ r = 225, t = 3$$
$$= 675$$

The plane travels 675 mi in 3 h.

SECTION 3.3

You Try It 1

$$5x + 7 = 10$$
$$5x + 7 - 7 = 10 - 7 \quad \bullet\ \text{Subtract 7.}$$
$$5x = 3$$
$$\frac{5x}{5} = \frac{3}{5} \quad \bullet\ \text{Divide by 5.}$$
$$x = \frac{3}{5}$$

The solution is $\frac{3}{5}$.

You Try It 2

$$2 = 11 + 3x$$
$$2 - 11 = 11 - 11 + 3x \quad \bullet\ \text{Subtract 11.}$$
$$-9 = 3x$$
$$\frac{-9}{3} = \frac{3x}{3} \quad \bullet\ \text{Divide by 3.}$$
$$-3 = x$$

The solution is -3.

You Try It 3

$$\frac{5}{8} - \frac{2x}{3} = \frac{5}{4}$$
$$\frac{5}{8} - \frac{5}{8} - \frac{2}{3}x = \frac{5}{4} - \frac{5}{8}$$
• Recall that $\frac{2x}{3} = \frac{2}{3}x$.
$$-\frac{2}{3}x = \frac{5}{8}$$
$$-\frac{3}{2}\left(-\frac{2}{3}x\right) = -\frac{3}{2}\left(\frac{5}{8}\right)$$
• Multiply by $-\frac{3}{2}$.
$$x = -\frac{15}{16}$$

The solution is $-\frac{15}{16}$.

You Try It 4

$$\frac{2}{3}x + 3 = \frac{7}{2}$$
$$6\left(\frac{2}{3}x + 3\right) = 6\left(\frac{7}{2}\right)$$
$$6\left(\frac{2}{3}x\right) + 6(3) = 6\left(\frac{7}{2}\right)$$
• Distributive Property
$$4x + 18 = 21$$
$$4x + 18 - 18 = 21 - 18$$
• Subtract 18.
$$4x = 3$$
$$\frac{4x}{4} = \frac{3}{4}$$
• Divide by 4.
$$x = \frac{3}{4}$$

The solution is $\frac{3}{4}$.

You Try It 5

$$x - 5 + 4x = 25$$
$$5x - 5 = 25$$
$$5x - 5 + 5 = 25 + 5$$
$$5x = 30$$
$$\frac{5x}{5} = \frac{30}{5}$$
$$x = 6$$

The solution is 6.

You Try It 6

Strategy Given: $S = 986$
$r = 45\% = 0.45$
Unknown: C

Solution
$$S = C + rC$$
$$986 = C + 0.45C$$
$$986 = 1.45C$$
$$\frac{986}{1.45} = \frac{1.45C}{1.45}$$
$$680 = C$$

The cost of the outboard motor is $680.

You Try It 7

Strategy Given: $S = 159$
$r = 25\% = 0.25$
Unknown: R

Solution
$$S = R - rR$$
$$159 = R - 0.25R$$
$$159 = 0.75R$$
$$\frac{159}{0.75} = \frac{0.75R}{0.75}$$
$$212 = R$$

The regular price of the MP3 player is $212.

You Try It 8

Strategy Given: $P = 45$
Unknown: D

Solution
$$P = 15 + \frac{1}{2}D$$
$$45 = 15 + \frac{1}{2}D$$
$$45 - 15 = 15 - 15 + \frac{1}{2}D$$
$$30 = \frac{1}{2}D$$
$$2(30) = 2 \cdot \frac{1}{2}D$$
$$60 = D$$

The depth is 60 ft.

SECTION 3.4

You Try It 1

$$5x + 4 = 6 + 10x$$
$$5x - 10x + 4 = 6 + 10x - 10x$$
• Subtract $10x$.
$$-5x + 4 = 6$$
$$-5x + 4 - 4 = 6 - 4$$
• Subtract 4.
$$-5x = 2$$
$$\frac{-5x}{-5} = \frac{2}{-5}$$
• Divide by -5.
$$x = -\frac{2}{5}$$

The solution is $-\frac{2}{5}$.

You Try It 2

$$5x - 10 - 3x = 6 - 4x$$
$$2x - 10 = 6 - 4x$$
• Combine like terms.
$$2x + 4x - 10 = 6 - 4x + 4x$$
• Add $4x$.
$$6x - 10 = 6$$
$$6x - 10 + 10 = 6 + 10$$
• Add 10.
$$6x = 16$$
$$\frac{6x}{6} = \frac{16}{6}$$
• Divide by 6.
$$x = \frac{8}{3}$$

The solution is $\frac{8}{3}$.

You Try It 3

$$\begin{aligned} 5x - 4(3 - 2x) &= 2(3x - 2) + 6 \\ 5x - 12 + 8x &= 6x - 4 + 6 && \bullet \text{ Distributive Property} \\ 13x - 12 &= 6x + 2 \\ 13x - 6x - 12 &= 6x - 6x + 2 && \bullet \text{ Subtract } 6x. \\ 7x - 12 &= 2 \\ 7x - 12 + 12 &= 2 + 12 && \bullet \text{ Add 12.} \\ 7x &= 14 \\ \frac{7x}{7} &= \frac{14}{7} && \bullet \text{ Divide by 7.} \\ x &= 2 \end{aligned}$$

The solution is 2.

You Try It 4

$$\begin{aligned} -2[3x - 5(2x - 3)] &= 3x - 8 \\ -2[3x - 10x + 15] &= 3x - 8 && \bullet \text{ Distributive Property} \\ -2[-7x + 15] &= 3x - 8 \\ 14x - 30 &= 3x - 8 \\ 14x - 3x - 30 &= 3x - 3x - 8 && \bullet \text{ Subtract } 3x. \\ 11x - 30 &= -8 \\ 11x - 30 + 30 &= -8 + 30 && \bullet \text{ Add 30.} \\ 11x &= 22 \\ \frac{11x}{11} &= \frac{22}{11} && \bullet \text{ Divide by 11.} \\ x &= 2 \end{aligned}$$

The solution is 2.

You Try It 5

Strategy Given: $F_1 = 45$, $F_2 = 80$, $d = 25$

Unknown: x

Solution

$$\begin{aligned} F_1 x &= F_2(d - x) \\ 45x &= 80(25 - x) \\ 45x &= 2000 - 80x \\ 45x + 80x &= 2000 - 80x + 80x \\ 125x &= 2000 \\ \frac{125x}{125} &= \frac{2000}{125} \\ x &= 16 \end{aligned}$$

The fulcrum is 16 ft from the 45-pound force.

SECTION 3.5

You Try It 1

The total of three times the smaller number and six	amounts to	seven less than the product of four and the larger number

Strategy

The smaller number: n

The larger number: $12 - n$

Solution

$$\begin{aligned} 3n + 6 &= 4(12 - n) - 7 \\ 3n + 6 &= 48 - 4n - 7 \\ 3n + 6 &= 41 - 4n \\ 3n + 4n + 6 &= 41 - 4n + 4n \\ 7n + 6 &= 41 \\ 7n + 6 - 6 &= 41 - 6 \\ 7n &= 35 \\ \frac{7n}{7} &= \frac{35}{7} \\ n &= 5 \end{aligned}$$

$12 - n = 12 - 5 = 7$

The smaller number is 5.

The larger number is 7.

You Try It 2

Strategy

- First integer: n
  Second integer: $n + 1$
  Third integer: $n + 2$
- The sum of the three integers is -6.

Solution

$$\begin{aligned} n + (n + 1) + (n + 2) &= -6 \\ 3n + 3 &= -6 \\ 3n &= -9 \\ n &= -3 \end{aligned}$$

$n + 1 = -3 + 1 = -2$

$n + 2 = -3 + 2 = -1$

The three consecutive integers are -3, -2, and -1.

You Try It 3

Strategy

To find the number of tickets purchased, write and solve an equation using x to represent the number of tickets purchased.

\$3.50 plus \$17.50 for each ticket	is	\$161

Solution

$$\begin{aligned} 3.50 + 17.50x &= 161 \\ 3.50 - 3.50 + 17.50x &= 161 - 3.50 \\ 17.50x &= 157.50 \\ \frac{17.50x}{17.50} &= \frac{157.50}{17.50} \\ x &= 9 \end{aligned}$$

You purchased 9 tickets.

You Try It 4

Strategy

To find the length, write and solve an equation using x to represent the length of the shorter piece and $22 - x$ to represent the length of the longer piece.

The length of the longer piece	is	4 in. more than twice the length of the shorter piece

Solution

$$\begin{aligned} 22 - x &= 2x + 4 \\ 22 - x - 2x &= 2x - 2x + 4 \\ 22 - 3x &= 4 \\ 22 - 22 - 3x &= 4 - 22 \\ -3x &= -18 \\ \frac{-3x}{-3} &= \frac{-18}{-3} \\ x &= 6 \end{aligned}$$

$22 - x = 22 - 6 = 16$

The length of the shorter piece is 6 in.

The length of the longer piece is 16 in.

SECTION 3.6

You Try It 1

Strategy The angles labeled are adjacent angles of intersecting lines and are therefore supplementary angles. To find x, write an equation and solve for x.

Solution

$$\begin{aligned} x + (3x + 20°) &= 180° \\ 4x + 20° &= 180° \\ 4x &= 160° \\ x &= 40° \end{aligned}$$

You Try It 2

Strategy $2x = y$ because alternate exterior angles have the same measure. $y + (x + 15°) = 180°$ because adjacent angles of intersecting lines are supplementary angles. Substitute $2x$ for y and solve for x.

Solution

$$\begin{aligned} y + (x + 15°) &= 180° \\ 2x + (x + 15°) &= 180° \\ 3x + 15° &= 180° \\ 3x &= 165° \\ x &= 55° \end{aligned}$$

You Try It 3

Strategy

- To find the measure of angle a, use the fact that $\angle a$ and $\angle y$ are vertical angles.
- To find the measure of angle b, use the fact that the sum of the measures of the interior angles of a triangle is 180°.
- To find the measure of angle d, use the fact that the sum of an interior and an adjacent exterior angle is 180°.

Solution

$m\angle a = m\angle y = 55°$

$$\begin{aligned} m\angle a + m\angle b + 90° &= 180° \\ 55° + m\angle b + 90° &= 180° \\ m\angle b + 145° &= 180° \\ m\angle b &= 35° \end{aligned}$$

$$\begin{aligned} m\angle d + m\angle b &= 180° \\ m\angle d + 35° &= 180° \\ m\angle d &= 145° \end{aligned}$$

You Try It 4

Strategy To find the measure of the third angle, use the fact that the sum of the measures of the interior angles of a triangle is 180°. Write an equation using x to represent the measure of the third angle. Solve the equation for x.

Solution

$$\begin{aligned} x + 90° + 27° &= 180° \\ x + 117° &= 180° \\ x &= 63° \end{aligned}$$

The measure of the third angle is 63°.

SECTION 3.7

You Try It 1

Strategy

- Pounds of \$.75 fertilizer: x

	Amount	*Cost*	*Value*
\$.90 fertilizer	20	0.90	0.90(20)
\$.75 fertilizer	x	0.75	$0.75x$
\$.85 fertilizer	$20 + x$	0.85	$0.85(20 + x)$

- The sum of the values before mixing equals the value after mixing.

Solution

$$\begin{aligned} 0.90(20) + 0.75x &= 0.85(20 + x) \\ 18 + 0.75x &= 17 + 0.85x \\ 18 - 0.10x &= 17 \\ -0.10x &= -1 \\ x &= 10 \end{aligned}$$

10 lb of the \$.75 fertilizer must be added.

You Try It 2

Strategy

- Liters of 6% solution: x

	Amount	*Percent*	*Quantity*
6% solution	x	0.06	$0.06x$
12% solution	5	0.12	5(0.12)
8% solution	$x + 5$	0.08	$0.08(x +$ [illegible]

- The sum of the quantities before mixing equals the quantity after mixing.

Solution

$$\begin{aligned} 0.06x + 5(0.12) &= 0.08(x + 5) \\ 0.06x + 0.60 &= 0.08x + 0.40 \\ -0.02x + 0.60 &= 0.40 \\ -0.02x &= -0.20 \\ x &= 10 \end{aligned}$$

The pharmacist adds 10 L of the 6% solution to the 12% solution to get an 8% solution.

You Try It 3

Strategy

► Rate of the first train: r
Rate of the second train: $2r$

	Rate	Time	Distance
1st train	r	3	$3r$
2nd train	$2r$	3	$3(2r)$

► The sum of the distances traveled by the two trains equals 288 mi.

Solution

$$\begin{aligned} 3r + 3(2r) &= 288 \\ 3r + 6r &= 288 \\ 9r &= 288 \\ r &= 32 \\ 2r = 2(32) &= 64 \end{aligned}$$

The first train is traveling at 32 mph.
The second train is traveling at 64 mph.

You Try It 4

Strategy

► Time spent flying out: t
Time spent flying back: $5 - t$

	Rate	Time	Distance
Out	150	t	$150t$
Back	100	$5 - t$	$100(5 - t)$

► The distance out equals the distance back.

Solution

$$\begin{aligned} 150t &= 100(5 - t) \\ 150t &= 500 - 100t \\ 250t &= 500 \\ t &= 2 \qquad \text{(The time out was 2 h.)} \end{aligned}$$

The distance out $= 150t = 150(2)$
$= 300$

The parcel of land was 300 mi away.

Solutions to Chapter 4 "You Try It"

SECTION 4.1

You Try It 1

$(-4x^3 + 2x^2 - 8) + (4x^3 + 6x^2 - 7x + 5)$
$= (-4x^3 + 4x^3) + (2x^2 + 6x^2) + (-7x) + (-8 + 5)$
$= 8x^2 - 7x - 3$

You Try It 2

$$\begin{array}{r} 6x^3 \qquad\quad + 2x + 8 \\ -9x^3 + 2x^2 - 12x - 8 \\ \hline -3x^3 + 2x^2 - 10x \qquad \end{array}$$

You Try It 3

a. $(-4w^3 + 8w - 8) - (3w^3 - 4w^2 - 2w - 1)$
$= (-4w^3 + 8w - 8)$
$+ (-3w^3 + 4w^2 + 2w + 1)$
$= -7w^3 + 4w^2 + 10w - 7$

b.
$$\begin{array}{r} 13y^3 \qquad\quad - 6y - 7 \\ -4y^2 + 6y + 9 \\ \hline 13y^3 - 4y^2 \qquad\quad + 2 \end{array}$$

SECTION 4.2

You Try It 1

$(12p^4q^3)(-3p^5q^2)$
$= [12(-3)](p^4 \cdot p^5)(q^3 \cdot q^2)$
$= -36p^9q^5$

• Multiply coefficients. Add exponents with the same base.

You Try It 2

$(-xy^4)(-2x^3y^2)^2 = (-xy^4)[(-2)^{1\cdot 2}x^{3\cdot 2}y^{2\cdot 2}]$
$= (-xy^4)[(-2)^2x^6y^4]$
$= (-xy^4)(4x^6y^4)$
$= -4x^7y^8$

• Rule for Simplifying the Power of a Product

SECTION 4.3

You Try It 1

$(-2y + 3)(-4y) = -2y(-4y) + 3(-4y) = 8y^2 - 12y$

You Try It 2

$-a^2(3a^2 + 2a - 7) = -a^2(3a^2) + (-a^2)(2a) - (-a^2)(7)$
$= -3a^4 - 2a^3 + 7a^2$

You Try It 3

$$\begin{array}{r} 2y^3 + 2y^2 \qquad - 3 \\ 3y - 1 \\ \hline -2y^3 - 2y^2 \qquad + 3 \\ 6y^4 + 6y^3 \qquad\quad - 9y \qquad \\ \hline 6y^4 + 4y^3 - 2y^2 - 9y + 3 \end{array}$$

$= -1(2y^3 + 2y^2 - 3)$
$= 3y(2y^3 + 2y^2 - 3)$

You Try It 4

$(4y - 5)(2y - 3) = 8y^2 - 12y - 10y + 15$
$= 8y^2 - 22y + 15$

You Try It 5

$(3b + 2)(3b - 5) = 9b^2 - 15b + 6b - 10$
$= 9b^2 - 9b - 10$

You Try It 6 $(2a + 5c)(2a - 5c) = 4a^2 - 25c^2$

You Try It 7 $(3x + 2y)^2 = 9x^2 + 12xy + 4y^2$

You Try It 8

Strategy To find the area, replace the variable r in the equation $A = \pi r^2$ by $(x - 4)$ and solve for A.

Solution
$$A = \pi r^2$$
$$A = \pi(x - 4)^2$$
$$A = \pi(x^2 - 8x + 16)$$
$$A = \pi x^2 - 8\pi x + 16\pi$$

The area of the circle is $(\pi x^2 - 8\pi x + 16\pi)$ ft^2.

SECTION 4.4

You Try It 1
$$(-2x^2)(x^{-3}y^{-4})^{-2}$$
$$= (-2x^2)(x^6y^8) \quad \text{• Rule for Simplifying the Power of a Product}$$
$$= -2x^8y^8$$

You Try It 2
$$\frac{(6a^{-2}b^3)^{-1}}{(4a^3b^{-2})^{-2}}$$
$$= \frac{6^{-1}a^2b^{-3}}{4^{-2}a^{-6}b^4} \quad \text{• Rule for Simplifying the Power of a Product}$$
$$= 4^2(6^{-1}a^8b^{-7}) \quad \text{• Rule for Dividing Exponential Expressions}$$
$$= \frac{16a^8}{6b^7} = \frac{8a^8}{3b^7}$$

You Try It 3
$$\left[\frac{6r^3s^{-3}}{9r^3s^{-1}}\right]^{-2} = \left[\frac{2r^0s^{-2}}{3}\right]^{-2}$$
$$= \frac{2^{-2}s^4}{3^{-2}} = \frac{9s^4}{4}$$

You Try It 4 $290{,}000{,}000{,}000 = 2.9 \times 10^{11}$

You Try It 5 $0.000000961 = 9.61 \times 10^{-7}$

You Try It 6 $7.329 \times 10^6 = 7{,}329{,}000$

You Try It 7 $1.802 \times 10^{-12} = 0.000000000001802$

SECTION 4.5

You Try It 1
$$\frac{24x^2y^2 - 18xy + 6y}{6xy} = \frac{24x^2y^2}{6xy} - \frac{18xy}{6xy} + \frac{6y}{6xy}$$
$$= 4xy - 3 + \frac{1}{x}$$

You Try It 2
$$\begin{array}{r} x^2 + 2x - 1 \\ 2x - 3\overline{)2x^3 + x^2 - 8x - 3} \\ \underline{2x^3 - 3x^2} \\ 4x^2 - 8x \\ \underline{4x^2 - 6x} \\ -2x - 3 \\ \underline{-2x + 3} \\ -6 \end{array}$$

$$(2x^3 + x^2 - 8x - 3) \div (2x - 3)$$
$$= x^2 + 2x - 1 - \frac{6}{2x - 3}$$

You Try It 3
$$\begin{array}{r} x^2 + x - 1 \\ x - 1\overline{)x^3 + 0x^2 - 2x + 1} \\ \underline{x^3 - x^2} \\ x^2 - 2x \\ \underline{x^2 - x} \\ -x + 1 \\ \underline{-x + 1} \\ 0 \end{array}$$

$$(x^3 - 2x + 1) \div (x - 1) = x^2 + x - 1$$

Solutions to Chapter 5 "You Try It"

SECTION 5.1

You Try It 1 The GCF is $7a^2$.
$$14a^2 - 21a^4b = 7a^2(2) + 7a^2(-3a^2b)$$
$$= 7a^2(2 - 3a^2b)$$

You Try It 2 The GCF is 9.
$$27b^2 + 18b + 9$$
$$= 9(3b^2) + 9(2b) + 9(1)$$
$$= 9(3b^2 + 2b + 1)$$

You Try It 3

The GCF is $3x^2y^2$.
$$6x^4y^2 - 9x^3y^2 + 12x^2y^4$$
$$= 3x^2y^2(2x^2) + 3x^2y^2(-3x) + 3x^2y^2(4y^2)$$
$$= 3x^2y^2(2x^2 - 3x + 4y^2)$$

You Try It 4
$$2y(5x - 2) - 3(2 - 5x)$$
$$= 2y(5x - 2) + 3(5x - 2) \quad \text{• } 5x - 2 \text{ is the common factor.}$$
$$= (5x - 2)(2y + 3)$$

You Try It 5
$$a^2 - 3a + 2ab - 6b$$
$$= (a^2 - 3a) + (2ab - 6b)$$
$$= a(a - 3) + 2b(a - 3) \quad \text{• } a - 3 \text{ is the common factor.}$$
$$= (a - 3)(a + 2b)$$

You Try It 6
$$2mn^2 - n + 8mn - 4$$
$$= (2mn^2 - n) + (8mn - 4)$$
$$= n(2mn - 1) + 4(2mn - 1) \quad \text{• } 2mn - 1 \text{ is the common factor.}$$
$$= (2mn - 1)(n + 4)$$

You Try It 7
$$3xy - 9y - 12 + 4x$$
$$= (3xy - 9y) - (12 - 4x) \quad \text{• } -12 + 4x = -(12 - 4x)$$
$$= 3y(x - 3) - 4(3 - x) \quad \text{• } -(3 - x) = (x - 3)$$
$$= 3y(x - 3) + 4(x - 3) \quad \text{• } x - 3 \text{ is the common factor.}$$
$$= (x - 3)(3y + 4)$$

SECTION 5.2

You Try It 1

Find the positive factors of 20 whose sum is 9.

Factors	*Sum*
1, 20	21
2, 10	12
4, 5	**9**

$x^2 + 9x + 20 = (x + 4)(x + 5)$

You Try It 2

Find the factors of -18 whose sum is 7.

Factors	*Sum*
+1, −18	−17
−1, +18	17
+2, −9	−7
−2, +9	**7**
+3, −6	−3
−3, +6	3

$x^2 + 7x - 18 = (x + 9)(x - 2)$

You Try It 3

The GCF is $-2x$.

$-2x^3 + 14x^2 - 12x = -2x(x^2 - 7x + 6)$

Factor the trinomial $x^2 - 7x + 6$. Find two negative factors of 6 whose sum is -7.

Factors	*Sum*
−1, −6	**−7**
−2, −3	−5

$-2x^3 + 14x^2 - 12x = -2x(x - 6)(x - 1)$

You Try It 4

The GCF is 3.

$3x^2 - 9xy - 12y^2 = 3(x^2 - 3xy - 4y^2)$

Factor the trinomial.

Find the factors of -4 whose sum is -3.

Factors	*Sum*
+1, −4	**−3**
−1, +4	3
+2, −2	0

$3x^2 - 9xy - 12y^2 = 3(x + y)(x - 4y)$

SECTION 5.3

You Try It 1

Factor the trinomial $2x^2 - x - 3$.

Positive factors of 2: 1, 2

Factors of -3: $+1, -3$; $-1, +3$

Trial Factors	*Middle Term*
$(x + 1)(2x - 3)$	$-3x + 2x = \mathbf{-x}$
$(x - 3)(2x + 1)$	$x - 6x = -5x$
$(x - 1)(2x + 3)$	$3x - 2x = x$
$(x + 3)(2x - 1)$	$-x + 6x = 5x$

$2x^2 - x - 3 = (x + 1)(2x - 3)$

You Try It 2

The GCF is $-3y$.

$-45y^3 + 12y^2 + 12y = -3y(15y^2 - 4y - 4)$

Factor the trinomial $15y^2 - 4y - 4$.

Positive factors of 15: 1, 15; 3, 5

Factors of -4: $1, -4$; $-1, 4$; $2, -2$

Trial Factors	*Middle Term*
$(y + 1)(15y - 4)$	$-4y + 15y = 11y$
$(y - 4)(15y + 1)$	$y - 60y = -59y$
$(y - 1)(15y + 4)$	$4y - 15y = -11y$
$(y + 4)(15y - 1)$	$-y + 60y = 59y$
$(y + 2)(15y - 2)$	$-2y + 30y = 28y$
$(y - 2)(15y + 2)$	$2y - 30y = -28y$
$(3y + 1)(5y - 4)$	$-12y + 5y = -7y$
$(3y - 4)(5y + 1)$	$3y - 20y = -17y$
$(3y - 1)(5y + 4)$	$12y - 5y = 7y$
$(3y + 4)(5y - 1)$	$-3y + 20y = 17y$
$(3y + 2)(5y - 2)$	$-6y + 10y = 4y$
$(3y - 2)(5y + 2)$	$6y - 10y = \mathbf{-4y}$

$-45y^3 + 12y^2 + 12y = -3y(3y - 2)(5y + 2)$

You Try It 3

Factors of −14 [2(−7)]	Sum
+1, −14	−13
−1, +14	**13**
+2, −7	−5
−2, +7	5

$$\begin{aligned}2a^2 + 13a - 7 &= 2a^2 - a + 14a - 7\\ &= (2a^2 - a) + (14a - 7)\\ &= a(2a - 1) + 7(2a - 1)\\ &= (2a - 1)(a + 7)\end{aligned}$$

$2a^2 + 13a - 7 = (2a - 1)(a + 7)$

You Try It 4

The GCF is $5x$.

$15x^3 + 40x^2 - 80x = 5x(3x^2 + 8x - 16)$

Factors of −48 [3(−16)]	Sum
+1, −48	−47
−1, +48	47
+2, −24	−22
−2, +24	22
+3, −16	−13
−3, +16	13
+4, −12	−8
−4, +12	**8**

$$\begin{aligned}3x^2 + 8x - 16 &= 3x^2 - 4x + 12x - 16\\ &= (3x^2 - 4x) + (12x - 16)\\ &= x(3x - 4) + 4(3x - 4)\\ &= (3x - 4)(x + 4)\end{aligned}$$

$$\begin{aligned}15x^3 + 40x^2 - 80x &= 5x(3x^2 + 8x - 16)\\ &= 5x(3x - 4)(x + 4)\end{aligned}$$

SECTION 5.4

You Try It 1

$$\begin{aligned}25a^2 - b^2 &= (5a)^2 - b^2\\ &= (5a + b)(5a - b)\end{aligned}$$

- Difference of two squares

You Try It 2

$n^4 - 81 = (n^2)^2 - 9^2$ • Difference of two squares

$= (n^2 + 9)(n^2 - 9)$ • Difference of two squares

$= (n^2 + 9)(n + 3)(n - 3)$

You Try It 3

Because $16y^2 = (4y)^2$, $1 = 1^2$, and $8y = 2(4y)(1)$, the trinomial is a perfect-square trinomial.

$16y^2 + 8y + 1 = (4y + 1)^2$

You Try It 4

$x^2 = (x)^2$ and $36 = 6^2$

Because $2(x)(6) \neq 15x$, the trinomial is not a perfect-square trinomial. Try to factor the trinomial by another method.

$x^2 + 15x + 36 = (x + 3)(x + 12)$

SECTION 5.5

You Try It 1

The GCF is $4x$.

$4x^3 + 28x^2 - 120x$

$= 4x(x^2 + 7x - 30)$ • Factor out the GCF, $4x$.

$= 4x(x + 10)(x - 3)$ • Factor the trinomial.

SECTION 5.6

You Try It 1

$2x(x + 7) = 0$

$2x = 0 \qquad x + 7 = 0$ • Principle of Zero Products

$x = 0 \qquad x = -7$

The solutions are 0 and −7.

You Try It 2

$4x^2 - 9 = 0$ • Difference of two squares

$(2x - 3)(2x + 3) = 0$

$2x - 3 = 0 \qquad 2x + 3 = 0$ • Principle of Zero Products

$2x = 3 \qquad 2x = -3$

$x = \frac{3}{2} \qquad x = -\frac{3}{2}$

The solutions are $\frac{3}{2}$ and $-\frac{3}{2}$.

You Try It 3

$$\begin{aligned}(x + 2)(x - 7) &= 52\\ x^2 - 5x - 14 &= 52\\ x^2 - 5x - 66 &= 0\\ (x + 6)(x - 11) &= 0\end{aligned}$$

$x + 6 = 0 \qquad x - 11 = 0$ • Principle of Zero Products

$x = -6 \qquad x = 11$

The solutions are −6 and 11.

You Try It 4

Strategy First consecutive positive integer: n

Second consecutive positive integer: $n + 1$

The sum of the squares of the two consecutive positive integers is 61.

Solution

$$n^2 + (n+1)^2 = 61$$
$$n^2 + n^2 + 2n + 1 = 61$$
$$2n^2 + 2n + 1 = 61$$
$$2n^2 + 2n - 60 = 0$$
$$2(n^2 + n - 30) = 0$$
$$2(n-5)(n+6) = 0$$

$n - 5 = 0 \quad n + 6 = 0$ • Principle of Zero Products
$n = 5 \quad n = -6$

Because -6 is not a positive integer, it is not a solution.

$n = 5$
$n + 1 = 5 + 1 = 6$

The two integers are 5 and 6.

You Try It 5

Strategy

Width $= x$
Length $= 2x + 4$

The area of the rectangle is 96 in^2.
Use the equation $A = L \cdot W$.

Solution

$$A = L \cdot W$$
$$96 = (2x+4)x$$
$$96 = 2x^2 + 4x$$
$$0 = 2x^2 + 4x - 96$$
$$0 = 2(x^2 + 2x - 48)$$
$$0 = 2(x+8)(x-6)$$

$x + 8 = 0 \quad x - 6 = 0$ • Principle of Zero Products
$x = -8 \quad x = 6$

Because the width cannot be a negative number, -8 is not a solution.

$x = 6$
$2x + 4 = 2(6) + 4 = 12 + 4 = 16$

The length is 16 in. The width is 6 in.

Solutions to Chapter 6 "You Try It"

SECTION 6.1

You Try It 1

$$\frac{6x^5y}{12x^2y^3} = \frac{\overset{1}{\cancel{2}} \cdot \overset{1}{\cancel{3}} \cdot x^5y}{\underset{1}{\cancel{2}} \cdot 2 \cdot \underset{1}{\cancel{3}} \cdot x^2y^3} = \frac{x^3}{2y^2}$$

You Try It 2

$$\frac{x^2 + 4x - 12}{x^2 - 3x + 2} = \frac{\overset{1}{\cancel{(x-2)}}(x+6)}{(x-1)\underset{1}{\cancel{(x-2)}}} = \frac{x+6}{x-1}$$

You Try It 3

$$\frac{x^2 + 2x - 24}{16 - x^2} = \frac{\overset{-1}{\cancel{(x-4)}}(x+6)}{\underset{1}{\cancel{(4-x)}}(4+x)} = -\frac{x+6}{x+4}$$

• $\frac{x-4}{4-x} = \frac{x-4}{-1(x-4)} = -1$

You Try It 4

$$\frac{12x^2 + 3x}{10x - 15} \cdot \frac{8x - 12}{9x + 18} = \frac{3x(4x+1)}{5(2x-3)} \cdot \frac{4(2x-3)}{9(x+2)}$$
$$= \frac{\overset{1}{\cancel{3}}x(4x+1) \cdot 4\overset{1}{\cancel{(2x-3)}}}{5\underset{1}{\cancel{(2x-3)}} \cdot \underset{1}{\cancel{3}} \cdot 3(x+2)}$$
$$= \frac{4x(4x+1)}{15(x+2)}$$

You Try It 5

$$\frac{x^2 + 2x - 15}{9 - x^2} \cdot \frac{x^2 - 3x - 18}{x^2 - 7x + 6}$$
$$= \frac{(x-3)(x+5)}{(3-x)(3+x)} \cdot \frac{(x+3)(x-6)}{(x-1)(x-6)}$$ • Factor.
$$= \frac{\overset{-1}{\cancel{(x-3)}}(x+5) \cdot \overset{1}{\cancel{(x+3)}}\overset{1}{\cancel{(x-6)}}}{\underset{1}{\cancel{(3-x)}}\underset{1}{\cancel{(3+x)}} \cdot (x-1)\underset{1}{\cancel{(x-6)}}} = -\frac{x+5}{x-1}$$

You Try It 6

$$\frac{a^2}{4bc^2 - 2b^2c} \div \frac{a}{6bc - 3b^2}$$
$$= \frac{a^2}{4bc^2 - 2b^2c} \cdot \frac{6bc - 3b^2}{a}$$ • Multiply by the reciprocal.
$$= \frac{a^2 \cdot 3\overset{1}{\cancel{b}}\overset{1}{\cancel{(2c-b)}}}{2\underset{1}{\cancel{b}}c\underset{1}{\cancel{(2c-b)}} \cdot a} = \frac{3a}{2c}$$

You Try It 7

$$\frac{3x^2 + 26x + 16}{3x^2 - 7x - 6} \div \frac{2x^2 + 9x - 5}{x^2 + 2x - 15}$$
$$= \frac{3x^2 + 26x + 16}{3x^2 - 7x - 6} \cdot \frac{x^2 + 2x - 15}{2x^2 + 9x - 5}$$ • Multiply by the reciprocal.
$$= \frac{\overset{1}{\cancel{(3x+2)}}(x+8) \cdot \overset{1}{\cancel{(x+5)}}\overset{1}{\cancel{(x-3)}}}{\underset{1}{\cancel{(3x+2)}}\underset{1}{\cancel{(x-3)}} \cdot (2x-1)\underset{1}{\cancel{(x+5)}}} = \frac{x+8}{2x-1}$$

SECTION 6.2

You Try It 1

$8uv^2 = 2 \cdot 2 \cdot 2 \cdot u \cdot v \cdot v$
$12uw = 2 \cdot 2 \cdot 3 \cdot u \cdot w$
$\text{LCM} = 2 \cdot 2 \cdot 2 \cdot 3 \cdot u \cdot v \cdot v \cdot w = 24uv^2w$

You Try It 2

$m^2 - 6m + 9 = (m-3)(m-3)$
$m^2 - 2m - 3 = (m+1)(m-3)$
$\text{LCM} = (m-3)(m-3)(m+1)$

You Try It 3

The LCM is $36xy^2z$.

$$\frac{x-3}{4xy^2} = \frac{x-3}{4xy^2} \cdot \frac{9z}{9z} = \frac{9xz - 27z}{36xy^2z}$$

$$\frac{2x+1}{9y^2z} = \frac{2x+1}{9y^2z} \cdot \frac{4x}{4x} = \frac{8x^2 + 4x}{36xy^2z}$$

You Try It 4

The LCM is $(x + 2)(x - 5)(x + 5)$.

$$\frac{x+4}{x^2-3x-10} = \frac{x+4}{(x+2)(x-5)} \cdot \frac{x+5}{x+5}$$
$$= \frac{x^2+9x+20}{(x+2)(x-5)(x+5)}$$

$$\frac{2x}{25-x^2} = \frac{2x}{-(x^2-25)} = -\frac{2x}{(x-5)(x+5)} \cdot \frac{x+2}{x+2}$$
$$= -\frac{2x^2+4x}{(x+2)(x-5)(x+5)}$$

SECTION 6.3

You Try It 1

$$\frac{2x^2}{x^2-x-12} - \frac{7x+4}{x^2-x-12}$$
$$= \frac{2x^2-(7x+4)}{x^2-x-12} = \frac{2x^2-7x-4}{x^2-x-12}$$
$$= \frac{(2x+1)\overset{1}{\cancel{(x-4)}}}{(x+3)\underset{1}{\cancel{(x-4)}}} = \frac{2x+1}{x+3}$$

You Try It 2

$$\frac{x^2-1}{x^2-8x+12} - \frac{2x+1}{x^2-8x+12} + \frac{x}{x^2-8x+12}$$
$$= \frac{(x^2-1)-(2x+1)+x}{x^2-8x+12} = \frac{x^2-1-2x-1+x}{x^2-8x+12}$$
$$= \frac{x^2-x-2}{x^2-8x+12} = \frac{(x+1)\overset{1}{\cancel{(x-2)}}}{\underset{1}{\cancel{(x-2)}}(x-6)} = \frac{x+1}{x-6}$$

You Try It 3

The LCM of the denominators is $24y$.

$$\frac{z}{8y} - \frac{4z}{3y} + \frac{5z}{4y}$$
$$= \frac{z}{8y} \cdot \frac{3}{3} - \frac{4z}{3y} \cdot \frac{8}{8} + \frac{5z}{4y} \cdot \frac{6}{6}$$
• Write each fraction using the LCM.
$$= \frac{3z}{24y} - \frac{32z}{24y} + \frac{30z}{24y}$$
$$= \frac{3z-32z+30z}{24y} = \frac{z}{24y}$$
• Combine the numerators.

You Try It 4

The LCM is $x - 3$.

$$2 - \frac{1}{x-3} = 2 \cdot \frac{x-3}{x-3} - \frac{1}{x-3}$$
$$= \frac{2x-6}{x-3} - \frac{1}{x-3}$$
$$= \frac{2x-6-1}{x-3}$$
$$= \frac{2x-7}{x-3}$$

You Try It 5

$2 - x = -(x - 2)$; therefore, $\dfrac{3}{2-x} = \dfrac{-3}{x-2}$.

$$\frac{5x}{x-2} + \frac{3}{2-x} = \frac{5x}{x-2} + \frac{-3}{x-2}$$
• The LCM is $x - 2$.
$$= \frac{5x+(-3)}{x-2} = \frac{5x-3}{x-2}$$
• Combine the numerators.

You Try It 6

The LCM is $(3x - 1)(x + 4)$.

$$\frac{4x}{3x-1} + \frac{9}{x+4} = \frac{4x}{3x-1} \cdot \frac{x+4}{x+4} + \frac{9}{x+4} \cdot \frac{3x-1}{3x-1}$$
$$= \frac{4x^2+16x}{(3x-1)(x+4)} + \frac{27x-9}{(3x-1)(x+4)}$$
$$= \frac{(4x^2+16x)+(27x-9)}{(3x-1)(x+4)}$$
$$= \frac{4x^2+16x+27x-9}{(3x-1)(x+4)}$$
$$= \frac{4x^2+43x-9}{(3x-1)(x+4)}$$

You Try It 7

$$\frac{2}{5-x} = \frac{-2}{x-5}$$

The LCM is $(x + 5)(x - 5)$.

$$\frac{2x-1}{x^2-25} + \frac{2}{5-x} = \frac{2x-1}{(x+5)(x-5)} + \frac{-2}{x-5}$$
$$= \frac{2x-1}{(x+5)(x-5)} + \frac{-2}{x-5} \cdot \frac{x+5}{x+5}$$
$$= \frac{2x-1}{(x+5)(x-5)} + \frac{-2(x+5)}{(x+5)(x-5)}$$
$$= \frac{2x-1+(-2)(x+5)}{(x+5)(x-5)}$$
$$= \frac{2x-1-2x-10}{(x+5)(x-5)}$$
$$= \frac{-11}{(x+5)(x-5)}$$
$$= -\frac{11}{(x+5)(x-5)}$$

You Try It 8

The LCM is $(3x + 2)(x - 1)$.

$$\frac{2x-3}{3x^2-x-2}+\frac{5}{3x+2}-\frac{1}{x-1}$$

$$=\frac{2x-3}{(3x+2)(x-1)}+\frac{5}{3x+2}\cdot\frac{x-1}{x-1}-\frac{1}{x-1}\cdot\frac{3x+2}{3x+2}$$

$$=\frac{2x-3}{(3x+2)(x-1)}+\frac{5x-5}{(3x+2)(x-1)}-\frac{3x+2}{(3x+2)(x-1)}$$

$$=\frac{(2x-3)+(5x-5)-(3x+2)}{(3x+2)(x-1)}$$

$$=\frac{2x-3+5x-5-3x-2}{(3x+2)(x-1)}$$

$$=\frac{4x-10}{(3x+2)(x-1)}=\frac{2(2x-5)}{(3x+2)(x-1)}$$

SECTION 6.4

You Try It 1

The LCM of 3, x, 9, and x^2 is $9x^2$.

$$\frac{\frac{1}{3}-\frac{1}{x}}{\frac{1}{9}-\frac{1}{x^2}}=\frac{\frac{1}{3}-\frac{1}{x}}{\frac{1}{9}-\frac{1}{x^2}}\cdot\frac{9x^2}{9x^2}=\frac{\frac{1}{3}\cdot 9x^2-\frac{1}{x}\cdot 9x^2}{\frac{1}{9}\cdot 9x^2-\frac{1}{x^2}\cdot 9x^2}$$

• Multiply by the LCM.

$$=\frac{3x^2-9x}{x^2-9}=\frac{3x(x-3)}{(x-3)(x+3)}=\frac{3x}{x+3}$$

You Try It 2

The LCM of x and x^2 is x^2.

$$\frac{1+\frac{4}{x}+\frac{3}{x^2}}{1+\frac{10}{x}+\frac{21}{x^2}}=\frac{1+\frac{4}{x}+\frac{3}{x^2}}{1+\frac{10}{x}+\frac{21}{x^2}}\cdot\frac{x^2}{x^2}$$

• Multiply by the LCM.

$$=\frac{1\cdot x^2+\frac{4}{x}\cdot x^2+\frac{3}{x^2}\cdot x^2}{1\cdot x^2+\frac{10}{x}\cdot x^2+\frac{21}{x^2}\cdot x^2}$$

• Distributive Property

$$=\frac{x^2+4x+3}{x^2+10x+21}=\frac{(x+1)(x+3)}{(x+3)(x+7)}$$

$$=\frac{x+1}{x+7}$$

You Try It 3

The LCM is $x - 5$.

$$\frac{x+3-\frac{20}{x-5}}{x+8+\frac{30}{x-5}}=\frac{x+3-\frac{20}{x-5}}{x+8+\frac{30}{x-5}}\cdot\frac{x-5}{x-5}$$

$$=\frac{(x+3)(x-5)-\frac{20}{x-5}\cdot(x-5)}{(x+8)(x-5)+\frac{30}{x-5}\cdot(x-5)}$$

$$=\frac{x^2-2x-15-20}{x^2+3x-40+30}=\frac{x^2-2x-35}{x^2+3x-10}$$

$$=\frac{(x+5)(x-7)}{(x-2)(x+5)}=\frac{x-7}{x-2}$$

SECTION 6.5

You Try It 1

$$\frac{x}{x+6}=\frac{3}{x}$$ • The LCM is $x(x + 6)$.

$$\frac{x(x+6)}{1}\cdot\frac{x}{x+6}=\frac{x(x+6)}{1}\cdot\frac{3}{x}$$ • Multiply by the LCM.

$x^2 = (x + 6)3$ • Simplify.

$x^2 = 3x + 18$

$x^2 - 3x - 18 = 0$ • Standard form

$(x + 3)(x - 6) = 0$ • Factor.

$x + 3 = 0 \qquad x - 6 = 0$ • Principle of Zero Products

$x = -3 \qquad x = 6$

Both -3 and 6 check as solutions.

The solutions are -3 and 6.

You Try It 2

$$\frac{5x}{x+2}=3-\frac{10}{x+2}$$ • The LCM is $x + 2$.

$$\frac{(x+2)}{1}\cdot\frac{5x}{x+2}=\frac{(x+2)}{1}\left(3-\frac{10}{x+2}\right)$$ • Clear denominators.

$$\frac{x+2}{1}\cdot\frac{5x}{x+2}=\frac{x+2}{1}\cdot 3-\frac{x+2}{1}\cdot\frac{10}{x+2}$$

$5x = (x + 2)3 - 10$ • Solve for x.

$5x = 3x + 6 - 10$

$5x = 3x - 4$

$2x = -4$

$x = -2$

-2 does not check as a solution.

The equation has no solution.

SECTION 6.6

You Try It 1

A.

$$\frac{2}{x+3} = \frac{6}{5x+5}$$

$$\frac{(x+3)(5x+5)}{1} \cdot \frac{2}{x+3} = \frac{(x+3)(5x+5)}{1} \cdot \frac{6}{5x+5}$$

$$\frac{\overset{1}{\cancel{(x+3)}}(5x+5)}{1} \cdot \frac{2}{\underset{1}{\cancel{x+3}}} = \frac{(x+3)\overset{1}{\cancel{(5x+5)}}}{1} \cdot \frac{6}{\underset{1}{\cancel{5x+5}}}$$

$$\begin{aligned} (5x+5)2 &= (x+3)6 &&\text{• Solve for } x. \\ 10x+10 &= 6x+18 \\ 4x+10 &= 18 \\ 4x &= 8 \\ x &= 2 \end{aligned}$$

The solution is 2.

B.

$$\frac{5}{2x-3} = \frac{10}{x+3}$$

$$\frac{(2x-3)(x+3)}{1} \cdot \frac{5}{2x-3} = \frac{(2x-3)(x+3)}{1} \cdot \frac{10}{x+3}$$

$$\frac{\overset{1}{\cancel{(2x-3)}}(x+3)}{1} \cdot \frac{5}{\underset{1}{\cancel{2x-3}}} = \frac{(2x-3)\overset{1}{\cancel{(x+3)}}}{1} \cdot \frac{10}{\underset{1}{\cancel{x+3}}}$$

$$\begin{aligned} (x+3)5 &= (2x-3)10 &&\text{• Solve for } x. \\ 5x+15 &= 20x-30 \\ 15 &= 15x-30 \\ 45 &= 15x \\ 3 &= x \end{aligned}$$

The solution is 3.

You Try It 2

Strategy To find the ounces of medication required, write and solve a proportion using M to represent the ounces of medication.

Solution

$$\begin{aligned} \frac{3}{120} &= \frac{M}{180} &&\text{• Write a proportion.} \\ (180)(120)\left(\frac{3}{120}\right) &= (180)(120)\left(\frac{M}{180}\right) &&\text{• Clear denominators.} \\ 540 &= 120M \\ 4.5 &= M \end{aligned}$$

4.5 oz of medication are required for a 180-pound adult.

You Try It 3

Strategy To find DE, write and solve a proportion.

Solution

$$\begin{aligned} \frac{DE}{AB} &= \frac{DF}{AC} &&\text{• Write a proportion.} \\ \frac{DE}{9} &= \frac{9}{5} &&\text{• } AB = 9, DF = 9, AC = 5 \\ 9\left(\frac{DE}{9}\right) &= 9\left(\frac{9}{5}\right) &&\text{• Multiply by 9.} \\ DE &= \frac{81}{5} \\ DE &= 16.2 \end{aligned}$$

DE is 16.2 in.

You Try It 4

Strategy To find the area of triangle AOB:

- Solve a proportion to find AO (the height of triangle AOB).
- Use the formula for the area of a triangle. $\overline{AB}$ is the base and $\overline{AO}$ is the height.

Solution

$$\begin{aligned} \frac{CD}{AB} &= \frac{DO}{AO} &&\text{• Write a proportion.} \\ \frac{4}{10} &= \frac{3}{AO} &&\text{• Substitute.} \\ 10 \cdot AO \cdot \frac{4}{10} &= 10 \cdot AO \cdot \frac{3}{AO} \\ 4(AO) &= 30 \\ AO &= 7.5 \end{aligned}$$

$$\begin{aligned} A &= \frac{1}{2}bh &&\text{• Area of a triangle} \\ &= \frac{1}{2}(10)(7.5) &&\text{• Substitute.} \\ &= 37.5 \end{aligned}$$

The area of triangle AOB is 37.5 cm^2.

SECTION 6.7

You Try It 1

$$\begin{aligned} 5x - 2y &= 10 \\ 5x - 5x - 2y &= -5x + 10 &&\text{• Subtract } 5x. \\ -2y &= -5x + 10 \\ \frac{-2y}{-2} &= \frac{-5x+10}{-2} &&\text{• Divide by } -2. \\ y &= \frac{5}{2}x - 5 \end{aligned}$$

You Try It 2

$$\begin{aligned} s &= \frac{A+L}{2} \\ 2 \cdot s &= 2\left(\frac{A+L}{2}\right) &&\text{• Multiply by 2.} \\ 2s &= A + L \\ 2s - A &= A - A + L &&\text{• Subtract } A. \\ 2s - A &= L \end{aligned}$$

You Try It 3

$$\begin{aligned} S &= a + (n-1)d \\ S &= a + nd - d &&\text{• Distributive Property} \\ S - a &= a - a + nd - d &&\text{• Subtract } a. \\ S - a &= nd - d \\ S - a + d &= nd - d + d &&\text{• Add } d. \\ S - a + d &= nd \\ \frac{S-a+d}{d} &= \frac{nd}{d} &&\text{• Divide by } d. \\ \frac{S-a+d}{d} &= n \end{aligned}$$

You Try It 4

$$S = rS + C$$

$$S - rS = rS - rS + C \quad \text{• Subtract } rS.$$

$$S - rS = C$$

$$(1 - r)S = C \quad \text{• Factor.}$$

$$\frac{(1 - r)S}{1 - r} = \frac{C}{1 - r} \quad \text{• Divide by } 1 - r.$$

$$S = \frac{C}{1 - r}$$

SECTION 6.8

You Try It 1

Strategy

► Time for one printer to complete the job: t

	Rate	Time	Part
1st printer	$\frac{1}{t}$	2	$\frac{2}{t}$
2nd printer	$\frac{1}{t}$	5	$\frac{5}{t}$

► The sum of the parts of the task completed must equal 1.

Solution

$$\frac{2}{t} + \frac{5}{t} = 1$$

$$t\left(\frac{2}{t} + \frac{5}{t}\right) = t \cdot 1$$

$$2 + 5 = t$$

$$7 = t$$

Working alone, one printer takes 7 h to print the payroll.

You Try It 2

Strategy

► Rate sailing across the lake: r
Rate sailing back: $3r$

	Distance	Rate	Time
Across	6	r	$\frac{6}{r}$
Back	6	$3r$	$\frac{6}{3r}$

► The total time for the trip was 2 h.

Solution

$$\frac{6}{r} + \frac{6}{3r} = 2$$

$$3r\left(\frac{6}{r} + \frac{6}{3r}\right) = 3r(2) \quad \text{• Multiply by the LCM, } 3r.$$

$$3r \cdot \frac{6}{r} + 3r \cdot \frac{6}{3r} = 6r$$

$$18 + 6 = 6r \quad \text{• Solve for } r.$$

$$24 = 6r$$

$$4 = r$$

The rate sailing across the lake was 4 km/h.

Solutions to Chapter 7 "You Try It"

SECTION 7.1

You Try It 1

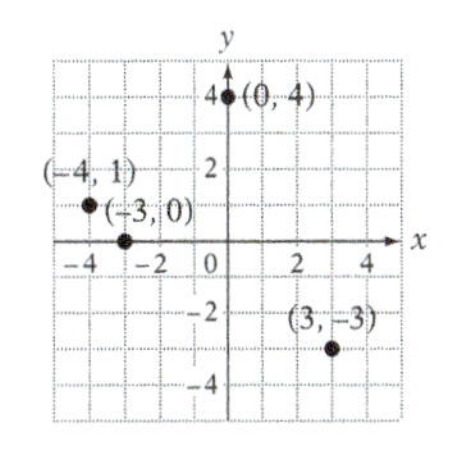

You Try It 2

$A(4, -2), B(-2, 4)$
The abscissa of D is 0.
The ordinate of C is 0.

You Try It 3

$x - 3y = -14$	
$-2 - 3(4)$	-14
$-2 - 12$	-14

$$-14 = -14$$

Yes, $(-2, 4)$ is a solution of $x - 3y = -14$.

You Try It 4

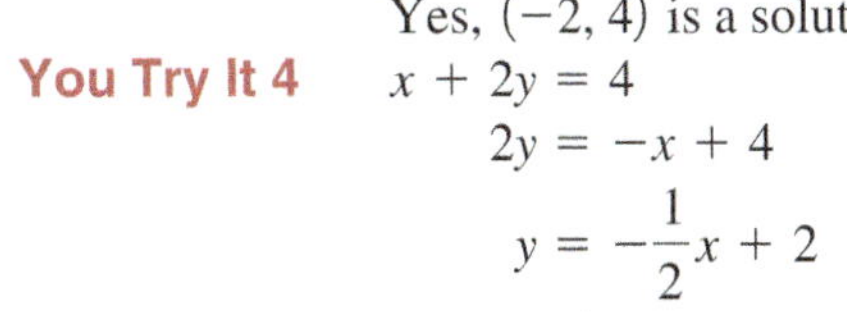

$$x + 2y = 4$$

$$2y = -x + 4$$

$$y = -\frac{1}{2}x + 2$$

x	y
−4	4
−2	3
0	2
2	1

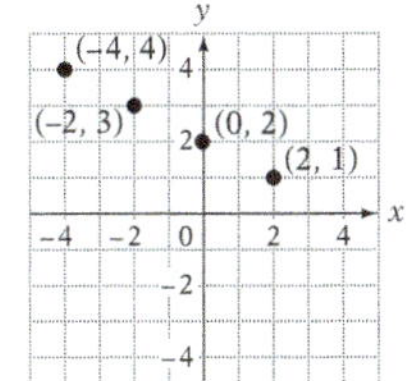

You Try It 5

$\{(145, 140), (140, 125), (150, 130), (165, 150), (140, 130)\}$
No, the relation is not a function. The two ordered pairs (140, 125) and (140, 130) have the same first coordinate but different second coordinates.

You Try It 6

Determine the ordered pairs defined by the equation. Replace x in $y = \frac{1}{2}x + 1$ by the given values and solve for y:
$\{(-4, -1), (0, 1), (2, 2)\}$.
Yes, y is a function of x.

You Try It 7

$$H(x) = \frac{x}{x - 4}$$

$$H(8) = \frac{8}{8 - 4} \quad \text{• Replace } x \text{ by 8.}$$

$$H(8) = \frac{8}{4} = 2$$

SECTION 7.2

You Try It 1

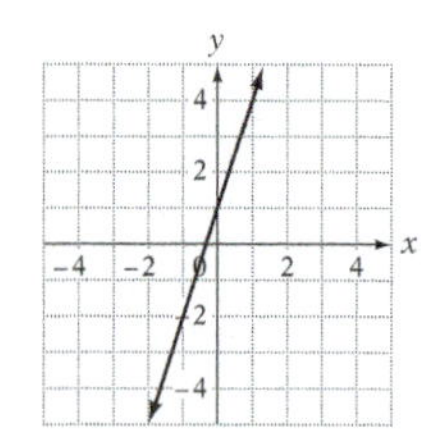

You Try It 2

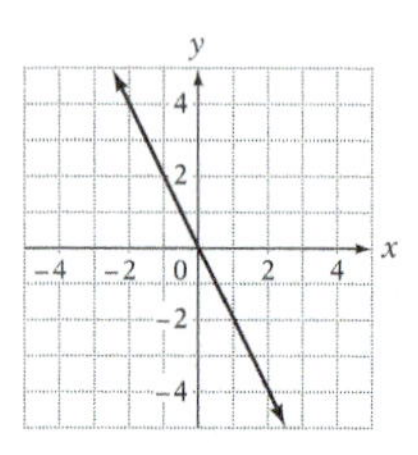

You Try It 3

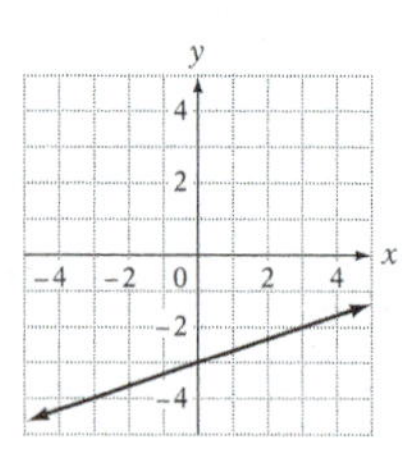

You Try It 4

$$5x - 2y = 10 \qquad \bullet \text{ Solve for } y.$$
$$-2y = -5x + 10$$
$$y = \frac{5}{2}x - 5$$

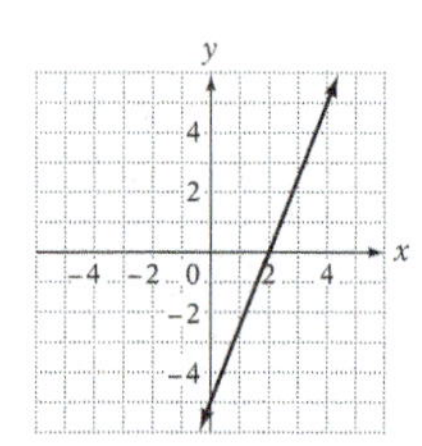

You Try It 5

$$x - 3y = 9 \qquad \bullet \text{ Solve for } y.$$
$$-3y = -x + 9$$
$$y = \frac{1}{3}x - 3$$

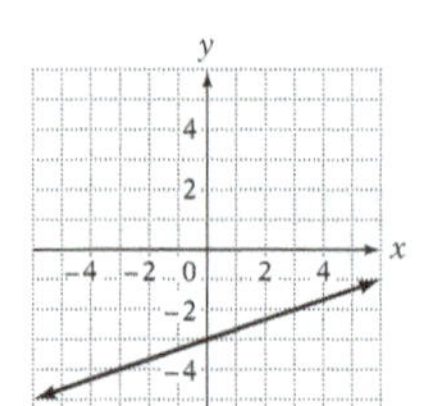

You Try It 6

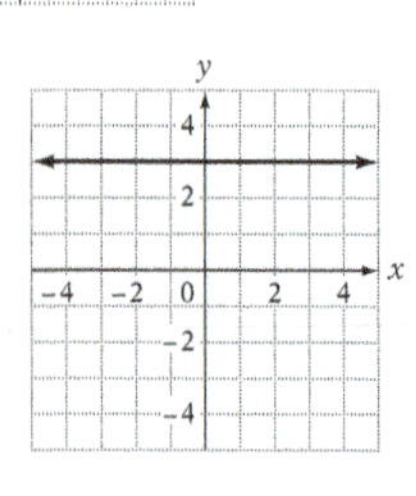

You Try It 7

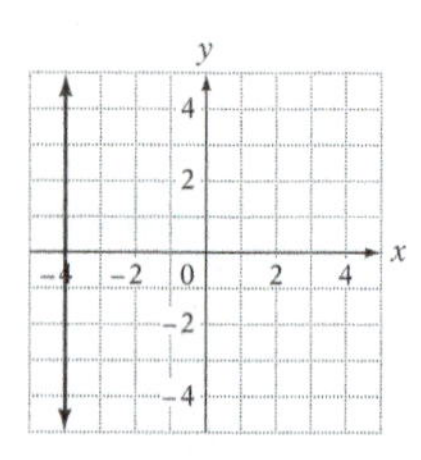

You Try It 8 The ordered pair (3, 120) means that in 3 h, the car will have traveled 120 mi.

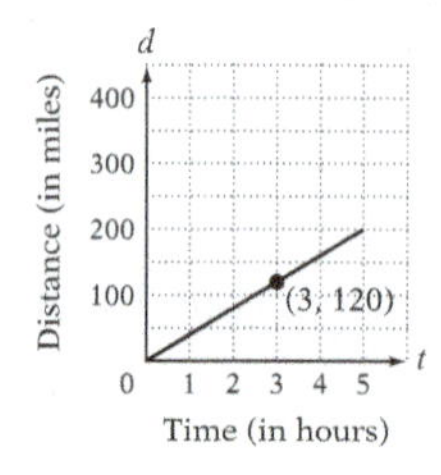

SECTION 7.3

You Try It 1

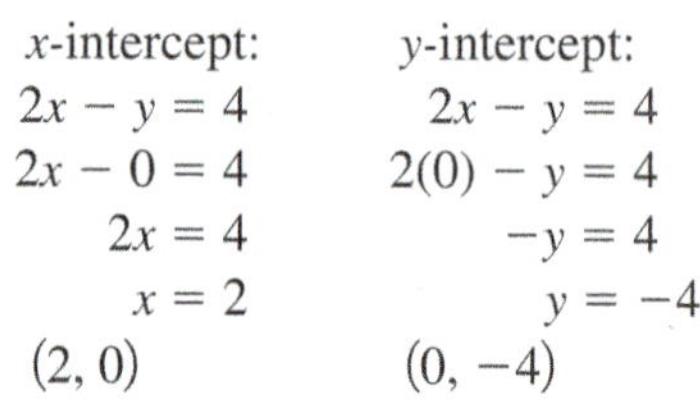

x-intercept:	y-intercept:
$2x - y = 4$	$2x - y = 4$
$2x - 0 = 4$	$2(0) - y = 4$
$2x = 4$	$-y = 4$
$x = 2$	$y = -4$
$(2, 0)$	$(0, -4)$

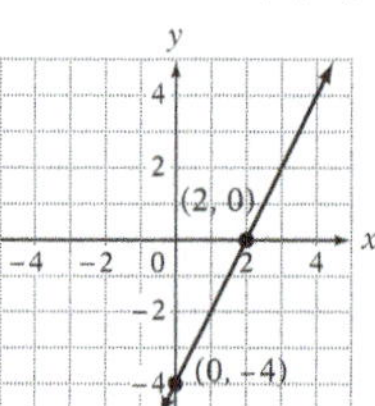

You Try It 2 Let $P_1 = (1, 4)$ and $P_2 = (-3, 8)$.

$$m = \frac{y_2 - y_1}{x_2 - x_1} = \frac{8 - 4}{-3 - 1} = \frac{4}{-4} = -1$$

The slope is -1.

You Try It 3 Let $P_1 = (-1, 2)$ and $P_2 = (4, 2)$.

$$m = \frac{y_2 - y_1}{x_2 - x_1} = \frac{2 - 2}{4 - (-1)} = \frac{0}{5} = 0$$

The slope is 0.

You Try It 4 $m = \dfrac{8650 - 6100}{1 - 4} = \dfrac{2550}{-3}$

$m = -850$

A slope of -850 means that the value of the car is decreasing at a rate of \$850 per year.

You Try It 5 y-intercept $= (0, b) = (0, -1)$

$m = -\frac{1}{4}$

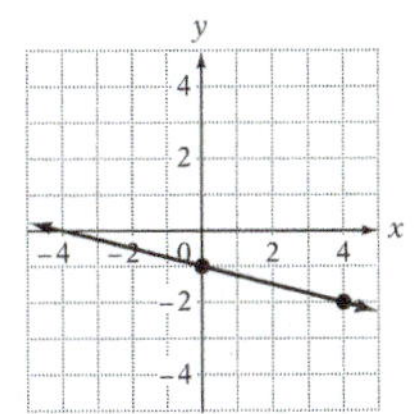

You Try It 6 Solve the equation for y.

$$x - 2y = 4$$
$$-2y = -x + 4$$
$$y = \frac{1}{2}x - 2$$

y-intercept $= (0, b) = (0, -2)$

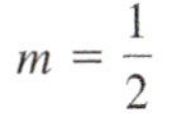

$m = \frac{1}{2}$

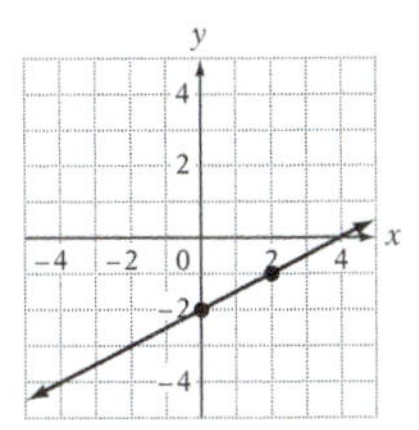

SECTION 7.4

You Try It 1 Because the slope and y-intercept are known, use the slope-intercept formula, $y = mx + b$.

$$y = mx + b$$
$$y = \frac{5}{3}x + 2 \qquad \bullet\ m = \frac{5}{3};\ b = 2$$

You Try It 2

$$y = mx + b \qquad \bullet\ \text{Slope-intercept form}$$
$$y = \frac{3}{2}x + b \qquad \bullet\ m = \frac{3}{2}$$
$$-2 = \frac{3}{2}(4) + b \qquad \bullet\ (x, y) = (4, -2)$$
$$-2 = 6 + b \qquad \bullet\ \text{Solve for } b.$$
$$-8 = b$$
$$y = \frac{3}{2}x - 8 \qquad \bullet\ m = \frac{3}{2};\ b = -8$$

The equation of the line is $y = \frac{3}{2}x - 8$.

You Try It 3 $m = \frac{3}{4}$ $\quad (x_1, y_1) = (4, -2)$

$$y - y_1 = m(x - x_1)$$
$$y - (-2) = \frac{3}{4}(x - 4)$$
$$y + 2 = \frac{3}{4}x - 3$$
$$y = \frac{3}{4}x - 5$$

The equation of the line is $y = \frac{3}{4}x - 5$.

You Try It 4 Find the slope of the line between the two points.

$P_1 = (-6, -2), P_2 = (3, 1)$

$$m = \frac{y_2 - y_1}{x_2 - x_1} = \frac{1 - (-2)}{3 - (-6)} = \frac{3}{9} = \frac{1}{3}$$

Use the point-slope formula.

$$y - y_1 = m(x - x_1)$$
$$y - (-2) = \frac{1}{3}[x - (-6)] \qquad \bullet\ y_1 = -2;\ x_1 = -6$$
$$y + 2 = \frac{1}{3}x + 2$$
$$y = \frac{1}{3}x$$

The equation of the line is $y = \frac{1}{3}x$.

Solutions To Chapter 8 "You Try It"

SECTION 8.1

You Try It 1

$2x - 5y = 8$		$-x + 3y = -5$	
$2(-1) - 5(-2)$	8	$-(-1) + 3(-2)$	-5
$-2 + 10$	8	$1 + (-6)$	-5
$8 = 8$		$-5 = -5$	

Yes, $(-1, -2)$ is a solution of the system of equations.

You Try It 2

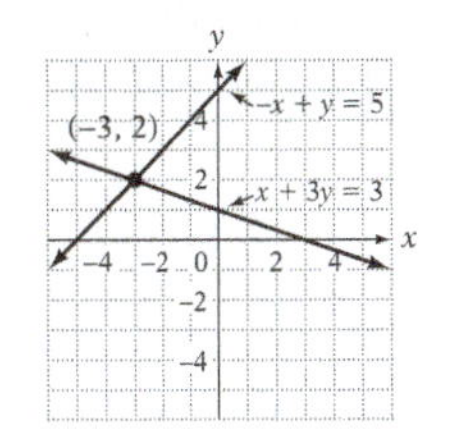

The solution is $(-3, 2)$.

You Try It 3

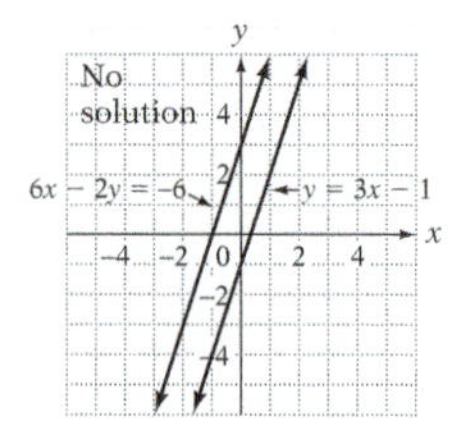

The lines are parallel. The system of equations is inconsistent and has no solution.

SECTION 8.2

You Try It 1

(1) $7x - y = 4$
(2) $3x + 2y = 9$

Solve Equation (1) for y.

$$7x - y = 4$$
$$-y = -7x + 4$$
$$y = 7x - 4$$

Substitute in Equation (2).

$$3x + 2y = 9$$
$$3x + 2(7x - 4) = 9 \quad \bullet\ y = 7x - 4$$
$$3x + 14x - 8 = 9$$
$$17x - 8 = 9$$
$$17x = 17$$
$$x = 1$$

Substitute in Equation (1).

$$7x - y = 4$$
$$7(1) - y = 4 \quad \bullet\ x = 1$$
$$7 - y = 4$$
$$-y = -3$$
$$y = 3$$

The solution is (1, 3).

You Try It 2

(1) $3x - y = 4$
(2) $y = 3x + 2$

$$3x - y = 4$$
$$3x - (3x + 2) = 4 \quad \bullet\ y = 3x + 2$$
$$3x - 3x - 2 = 4$$
$$-2 = 4$$

This is a false equation. The system of equations is inconsistent and therefore has no solution.

You Try It 3

(1) $y = -2x + 1$
(2) $6x + 3y = 3$

$$6x + 3y = 3$$
$$6x + 3(-2x + 1) = 3 \quad \bullet\ y = -2x + 1$$
$$6x - 6x + 3 = 3$$
$$3 = 3$$

The system of equations is dependent. The solutions are the ordered pairs that satisfy the equation $y = -2x + 1$.

You Try It 4

Strategy

► Amount invested at 6.5%: x
Amount invested at 4.5%: y

	Principal	Rate	Interest
Amount at 6.5%	x	0.065	$0.065x$
Amount at 4.5%	y	0.045	$0.045y$

► The sum of the two investments is \$330,000: $x + y = 330{,}000$.
The interest earned at 6.5% equals the interest earned at 4.5%: $0.065x = 0.045y$

Solution

(1) $x + y = 330{,}000$
(2) $0.065x = 0.045y$

Solve Equation (2) for y.

(3) $y = \frac{13}{9}x$

Replace y by $\frac{13}{9}x$ in Equation (1) and solve for x.

$$x + y = 330{,}000$$
$$x + \frac{13}{9}x = 330{,}000 \quad \bullet\ y = \frac{13}{9}x$$
$$\frac{22}{9}x = 330{,}000$$
$$x = 135{,}000$$

Replace x by 135,000 in Equation (3) and solve for y.

$$y = \frac{13}{9}x$$
$$= \frac{13}{9}(135{,}000) = 195{,}000 \quad \bullet\ x = 135{,}000$$

\$135,000 should be invested at 6.5%, and \$195,000 should be invested at 4.5%.

SECTION 8.3

You Try It 1

(1) $2x - 3y = 1$
(2) $-3x + 4y = 6$

Eliminate x.

$$3(2x - 3y) = 3(1) \quad \bullet\ \text{Multiply by 3.}$$
$$2(-3x + 4y) = 2(6) \quad \bullet\ \text{Multiply by 2.}$$
$$6x - 9y = 3$$
$$-6x + 8y = 12 \quad \bullet\ \text{Add the equations.}$$
$$-y = 15$$
$$y = -15$$

Replace y in Equation (1).

$$2x - 3(-15) = 1 \quad \bullet\ y = -15$$
$$2x + 45 = 1$$
$$2x = -44$$
$$x = -22$$

The solution is (−22, −15).

You Try It 2

(1) $2x - 3y = 4$
(2) $-4x + 6y = -8$

Eliminate y.

$2(2x - 3y) = 2 \cdot 4$ • Multiply by 2.
$-4x + 6y = -8$

$4x - 6y = 8$
$-4x + 6y = -8$
$0x + 0y = 0$ • Add the equations.
$0 = 0$

The system of equations is dependent. The solutions are the ordered pairs that satisfy the equation $2x - 3y = 4$.

You Try It 3

(1) $4x + 5y = 11$
(2) $3y = x + 10$

Write equation (2) in the form $Ax + By = C$.

$3y = x + 10$
$-x + 3y = 10$

Eliminate x.

$4x + 5y = 11$
$4(-x + 3y) = 4 \cdot 10$ • Multiply by 4.

$4x + 5y = 11$
$-4x + 12y = 40$ • Add the equations.
$17y = 51$
$y = 3$

Replace y in Equation (1).

$4x + 5y = 11$
$4x + 5 \cdot 3 = 11$ • $y = 3$
$4x + 15 = 11$
$4x = -4$
$x = -1$

The solution is $(-1, 3)$.

SECTION 8.4

You Try It 1

Strategy

► Rate of the current: c
Rate of the canoeist in calm water: r

	Rate	Time	Distance
With current	$r + c$	3	$3(r + c)$
Against current	$r - c$	5	$5(r - c)$

► The distance traveled with the current is 15 mi.
The distance traveled against the current is 15 mi.

Solution

$3(r + c) = 15$ $\quad \frac{1}{3} \cdot 3(r + c) = \frac{1}{3} \cdot 15$ • Multiply by $\frac{1}{3}$.

$5(r - c) = 15$ $\quad \frac{1}{5} \cdot 5(r - c) = \frac{1}{5} \cdot 15$ • Multiply by $\frac{1}{5}$.

$r + c = 5$
$r - c = 3$
$2r = 8$
$r = 4$

$r + c = 5$
$4 + c = 5$ • $r = 4$
$c = 1$

The rate of the current is 1 mph.
The rate of the canoeist in calm water is 4 mph.

You Try It 2

Strategy

► Cost of an orange tree: x
Cost of a grapefruit tree: y

First purchase:

	Amount	Unit Cost	Value
Orange trees	25	x	$25x$
Grapefruit trees	20	y	$20y$

Second purchase:

	Amount	Unit Cost	Value
Orange trees	20	x	$20x$
Grapefruit trees	30	y	$30y$

► The total cost of the first purchase was \$2900.
The total cost of the second purchase was \$3300.

Solution

$25x + 20y = 2900$ $\quad 4(25x + 20y) = 4 \cdot 2900$ • Multiply by 4.

$20x + 30y = 3300$ $\quad -5(20x + 30y) = -5 \cdot 3300$ • Multiply by -5.

$100x + 80y = 11{,}600$
$-100x - 150y = -16{,}500$
$-70y = -4900$
$y = 70$

$25x + 20y = 2900$
$25x + 20(70) = 2900$ • $y = 70$
$25x + 1400 = 2900$
$25x = 1500$
$x = 60$

The cost of an orange tree is \$60.
The cost of a grapefruit tree is \$70.

Solutions to Chapter 9 "You Try It"

SECTION 9.1

You Try It 1 $A = \{-9, -7, -5, -3, -1\}$

You Try It 2 $A = \{1, 3, 5, \ldots\}$

You Try It 3 $A \cup B = \{-2, -1, 0, 1, 2, 3, 4\}$

You Try It 4 $C \cap D = \{10, 16\}$

You Try It 5 $A \cap B = \varnothing$

You Try It 6

a. $\{x | x \leq 3\}$ is the set of real numbers less than or equal to 3. This set extends forever in the negative direction. In interval notation, this set is written $(-\infty, 3]$.

b. $\{x | -5 \leq x \leq -3\}$ is the set of real numbers between -5 and -3, including -5 and -3. In interval notation, this set is written $[-5, -3]$.

You Try It 7

a. The interval $(-3, \infty)$ is the set of real numbers greater than -3. In set-builder notation, this set is written $\{x | x > -3\}$.

b. The interval $[0, 4)$ is the set of real numbers between 0 and 4, including 0 and excluding 4. In set-builder notation, this set is written $\{x | 0 \leq x < 4\}$.

You Try It 8

a. The graph is the set of real numbers between -4 and 4, including -4 and 4. Use brackets at -4 and 4.

b. The graph is the set of real numbers greater than -3. Use a parenthesis at -3.

You Try It 9 The graph is the set of real numbers between 2 and 5, including 2 and 5. Use brackets at 2 and 5.

SECTION 9.2

You Try It 1

$$5x + 3 > 4x + 5$$
$$5x - 4x + 3 > 4x - 4x + 5 \quad \text{• Subtract } 4x.$$
$$x + 3 > 5$$
$$x + 3 - 3 > 5 - 3 \quad \text{• Subtract 3.}$$
$$x > 2$$
$$\{x | x > 2\} \quad \text{• Set-builder notation}$$
$$(2, \infty) \quad \text{• Interval notation}$$

You Try It 2

$$-3x > -9$$
$$\frac{-3x}{-3} < \frac{-9}{-3} \quad \text{• Divide by } -3.$$
$$x < 3$$
$$(-\infty, 3)$$

You Try It 3

$$-\frac{3}{4}x \geq 18$$
$$-\frac{4}{3}\left(-\frac{3}{4}x\right) \leq -\frac{4}{3}(18) \quad \text{• Multiply by } -\frac{4}{3}.$$
$$x \leq -24$$
$$\{x | x \leq -24\}$$

You Try It 4

Strategy To find the selling prices, write and solve an inequality using p to represent the possible selling prices.

Solution

$$0.70p > 942$$
$$p > 1345.71 \quad \text{• Divide by 0.70. Round to the nearest hundredth.}$$

The dealer will make a profit with any selling price greater than or equal to \$1345.71.

SECTION 9.3

You Try It 1

$$5 - 4x > 9 - 8x$$
$$5 - 4x + 8x > 9 - 8x + 8x \quad \text{• Add } 8x.$$
$$5 + 4x > 9$$
$$5 - 5 + 4x > 9 - 5 \quad \text{• Subtract 5.}$$
$$4x > 4$$
$$\frac{4x}{4} > \frac{4}{4} \quad \text{• Divide by 4.}$$
$$x > 1$$
$$(1, \infty)$$

You Try It 2

$$8 - 4(3x + 5) \leq 6(x - 8)$$
$$8 - 12x - 20 \leq 6x - 48 \quad \text{• Distributive Property}$$
$$-12 - 12x \leq 6x - 48$$
$$-12 - 12x - 6x \leq 6x - 6x - 48 \quad \text{• Subtract } 6x.$$
$$-12 - 18x \leq -48$$
$$-12 + 12 - 18x \leq -48 + 12 \quad \text{• Add 12.}$$
$$-18x \leq -36$$

$$\frac{-18x}{-18} \geq \frac{-36}{-18}$$ • Divide by −18.

$$x \geq 2$$

$$\{x|x \geq 2\}$$

You Try It 3

Strategy To find the maximum number of miles:

- Write an expression for the cost of each car, using x to represent the number of miles driven during the week.
- Write and solve an inequality.

Solution

Cost of a Company A car	is less than	cost of a Company B car

$$8(7) + 0.10x < 10(7) + 0.08x$$

$$56 + 0.10x < 70 + 0.08x$$

$$56 + 0.10x - 0.08x < 70 + 0.08x - 0.08x$$ • Subtract 0.08x.

$$56 + 0.02x < 70$$

$$56 - 56 + 0.02x < 70 - 56$$ • Subtract 56.

$$0.02x < 14$$

$$\frac{0.02x}{0.02} < \frac{14}{0.02}$$ • Divide by 0.02.

$$x < 700$$

The maximum number of miles is 699 mi.

SECTION 9.4

You Try It 1

$$x - 3y < 2$$

$$x - x - 3y < -x + 2$$ • Subtract x.

$$-3y < -x + 2$$

$$\frac{-3y}{-3} > \frac{-x + 2}{-3}$$ • Divide by −3.

$$y > \frac{1}{3}x - \frac{2}{3}$$

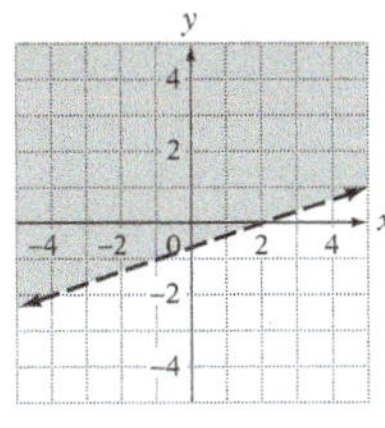

You Try It 2

$$2x - 4y \leq 8$$

$$2x - 2x - 4y \leq -2x + 8$$ • Subtract 2x.

$$-4y \leq -2x + 8$$

$$\frac{-4y}{-4} \geq \frac{-2x + 8}{-4}$$ • Divide by −4.

$$y \geq \frac{1}{2}x - 2$$

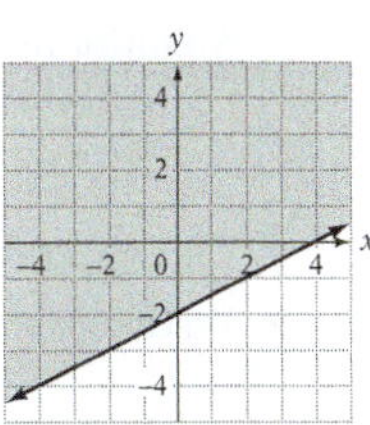

You Try It 3 $x < 3$

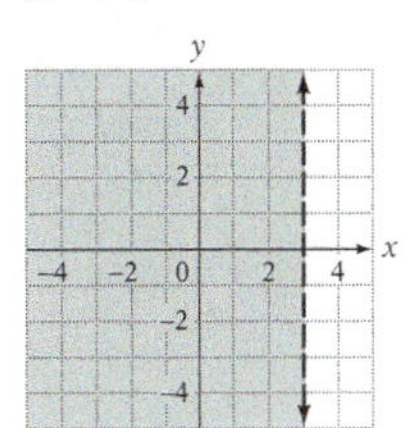

Solutions to Chapter 10 "You Try It"

SECTION 10.1

You Try It 1

$$\sqrt{216} = \sqrt{36 \cdot 6}$$ • 36 is the largest perfect square.

$$= \sqrt{36}\sqrt{6} = 6\sqrt{6}$$

You Try It 2

$$-5\sqrt{32} = -5\sqrt{16 \cdot 2}$$ • 16 is the largest perfect square.

$$= -5\sqrt{16}\sqrt{2}$$

$$= -5 \cdot 4\sqrt{2} = -20\sqrt{2}$$

You Try It 3

$$\sqrt{y^{19}} = \sqrt{y^{18} \cdot y}$$ • y^{18} is a perfect square.

$$= \sqrt{y^{18}}\sqrt{y} = y^9\sqrt{y}$$

You Try It 4

$$\sqrt{45b^7} = \sqrt{9b^6 \cdot 5b}$$ • $9b^6$ is a perfect square.

$$= \sqrt{9b^6}\sqrt{5b} = 3b^3\sqrt{5b}$$

You Try It 5

$$3a\sqrt{28a^9b^{18}} = 3a\sqrt{4a^8b^{18}(7a)}$$ • $4a^8b^{18}$ is a perfect square.

$$= 3a\sqrt{4a^8b^{18}}\sqrt{7a}$$

$$= 3a \cdot 2a^4b^9\sqrt{7a} = 6a^5b^9\sqrt{7a}$$

You Try It 6 $\sqrt{25(a + 3)^2} = 5(a + 3) = 5a + 15$

You Try It 7 $\sqrt{x^2 + 14x + 49} = \sqrt{(x + 7)^2} = x + 7$

SECTION 10.2

You Try It 1

$$9\sqrt{3} + 3\sqrt{3} - 18\sqrt{3} = (9 + 3 - 18)\sqrt{3} = -6\sqrt{3}$$

You Try It 2

$2\sqrt{50} - 5\sqrt{32}$ • Unlike radicands.
$= 2\sqrt{25\cdot 2} - 5\sqrt{16\cdot 2}$ • Simplify the radicands.
$= 2\sqrt{25}\sqrt{2} - 5\sqrt{16}\sqrt{2}$
$= 2\cdot 5\sqrt{2} - 5\cdot 4\sqrt{2}$
$= 10\sqrt{2} - 20\sqrt{2}$ • Like radicands.
$= (10 - 20)\sqrt{2}$ • Distributive Property
$= -10\sqrt{2}$

You Try It 3

$y\sqrt{28y} + 7\sqrt{63y^3}$ • Unlike radicands.
$= y\sqrt{4\cdot 7y} + 7\sqrt{9y^2\cdot 7y}$ • Simplify the radicands.
$= y\sqrt{4}\sqrt{7y} + 7\sqrt{9y^2}\sqrt{7y}$
$= y\cdot 2\sqrt{7y} + 7\cdot 3y\sqrt{7y}$
$= 2y\sqrt{7y} + 21y\sqrt{7y}$ • Like radicands.
$= (2y + 21y)\sqrt{7y}$ • Distributive Property
$= 23y\sqrt{7y}$

You Try It 4

$2\sqrt{27a^5} - 4a\sqrt{12a^3} + a^2\sqrt{75a}$
$= 2\sqrt{9a^4\cdot 3a} - 4a\sqrt{4a^2\cdot 3a} + a^2\sqrt{25\cdot 3a}$
$= 2\sqrt{9a^4}\sqrt{3a} - 4a\sqrt{4a^2}\sqrt{3a} + a^2\sqrt{25}\sqrt{3a}$
$= 2\cdot 3a^2\sqrt{3a} - 4a\cdot 2a\sqrt{3a} + a^2\cdot 5\sqrt{3a}$
$= 6a^2\sqrt{3a} - 8a^2\sqrt{3a} + 5a^2\sqrt{3a} = 3a^2\sqrt{3a}$

SECTION 10.3

You Try It 1

$\sqrt{5a}\sqrt{15a^3b^4}\sqrt{20b^5}$
$= \sqrt{1500a^4b^9} = \sqrt{100a^4b^8\cdot 15b}$
$= \sqrt{100a^4b^8}\cdot\sqrt{15b}$
$= 10a^2b^4\sqrt{15b}$

You Try It 2

$\sqrt{5x}(\sqrt{5x} - \sqrt{25y})$
$= \sqrt{25x^2} - \sqrt{125xy}$ • Distributive Property
$= \sqrt{25x^2} - \sqrt{25\cdot 5xy} = \sqrt{25x^2} - \sqrt{25}\sqrt{5xy}$
$= 5x - 5\sqrt{5xy}$

You Try It 3

$(3\sqrt{x} - \sqrt{y})(5\sqrt{x} - 2\sqrt{y})$
$= 15(\sqrt{x})^2 - 6\sqrt{xy} - 5\sqrt{xy} + 2(\sqrt{y})^2$ • FOIL
$= 15(\sqrt{x})^2 - 11\sqrt{xy} + 2(\sqrt{y})^2$
$= 15x - 11\sqrt{xy} + 2y$

You Try It 4

$(2\sqrt{x} + 7)(2\sqrt{x} - 7)$
$= 4(\sqrt{x})^2 - 7^2$ • Product of conjugates
$= 4x - 49$

You Try It 5

$$\frac{\sqrt{15x^6y^7}}{\sqrt{3x^7y^9}} = \sqrt{\frac{15x^6y^7}{3x^7y^9}} = \sqrt{\frac{5}{xy^2}} = \frac{\sqrt{5}}{\sqrt{xy^2}}$$
$$= \frac{\sqrt{5}}{y\sqrt{x}} = \frac{\sqrt{5}}{y\sqrt{x}}\cdot\frac{\sqrt{x}}{\sqrt{x}}$$ • Rationalize the denominator.
$$= \frac{\sqrt{5x}}{xy}$$

You Try It 6

$$\frac{\sqrt{3}}{\sqrt{3} - \sqrt{6}} = \frac{\sqrt{3}}{\sqrt{3} - \sqrt{6}}\cdot\frac{\sqrt{3} + \sqrt{6}}{\sqrt{3} + \sqrt{6}}$$ • Rationalize the denominator.
$$= \frac{3 + \sqrt{18}}{3 - 6} = \frac{3 + 3\sqrt{2}}{-3}$$
$$= \frac{3(1 + \sqrt{2})}{-3} = -1(1 + \sqrt{2})$$
$$= -1 - \sqrt{2}$$

You Try It 7

$$\frac{5 + \sqrt{y}}{1 - 2\sqrt{y}} = \frac{5 + \sqrt{y}}{1 - 2\sqrt{y}}\cdot\frac{1 + 2\sqrt{y}}{1 + 2\sqrt{y}}$$ • Rationalize the denominator.
$$= \frac{5 + 10\sqrt{y} + \sqrt{y} + 2(\sqrt{y})^2}{1 - 4y}$$
$$= \frac{5 + 11\sqrt{y} + 2y}{1 - 4y}$$

SECTION 10.4

You Try It 1

$\sqrt{4x} + 3 = 7$
$\sqrt{4x} = 4$ • Isolate $\sqrt{4x}$.
$(\sqrt{4x})^2 = 4^2$ • Square both sides.
$4x = 16$
$x = 4$ • Solve for x.

Check: $\sqrt{4x} + 3 = 7$

$\sqrt{4\cdot 4} + 3$	7
$\sqrt{16} + 3$	7
$4 + 3$	7

$7 = 7$

The solution is 4.

You Try It 2

$\sqrt{x} + \sqrt{x + 9} = 9$
$\sqrt{x} = 9 - \sqrt{x + 9}$ • Isolate $\sqrt{x}$.
$(\sqrt{x})^2 = (9 - \sqrt{x + 9})^2$ • Square both sides.
$x = 81 - 18\sqrt{x + 9} + (x + 9)$
$-90 = -18\sqrt{x + 9}$
$5 = \sqrt{x + 9}$ • Isolate $\sqrt{x + 9}$.
$5^2 = (\sqrt{x + 9})^2$ • Square both sides.
$25 = x + 9$
$16 = x$ • Solve for x.

Check:
$$\begin{array}{r|l} \sqrt{x} + \sqrt{x+9} = & 9 \\ \sqrt{16} + \sqrt{16+9} & 9 \\ \sqrt{16} + \sqrt{25} & 9 \\ 4 + 5 & 9 \\ 9 = & 9 \end{array}$$

The solution is 16.

You Try It 3

Strategy To find the distance, use the Pythagorean Theorem. The hypotenuse is the length of the ladder. One leg is the distance from the bottom of the ladder to the base of the building. The distance along the building from the ground to the top of the ladder is the unknown leg.

Solution
$$a = \sqrt{c^2 - b^2}$$
$$= \sqrt{(8)^2 - (3)^2} \qquad \bullet\ c = 8, b = 3$$
$$= \sqrt{64 - 9}$$
$$= \sqrt{55}$$
$$\approx 7.42$$

The distance is approximately 7.42 ft.

You Try It 4

Strategy To find the length of the pendulum, replace T in the equation with the given value and solve for L.

Solution
$$T = 2\pi\sqrt{\frac{L}{32}}$$
$$2.5 = 2(3.14)\sqrt{\frac{L}{32}} \qquad \bullet\ T = 2.5$$
$$2.5 = 6.28\sqrt{\frac{L}{32}}$$
$$\frac{2.5}{6.28} = \sqrt{\frac{L}{32}}$$
$$\left(\frac{2.5}{6.28}\right)^2 = \left(\sqrt{\frac{L}{32}}\right)^2$$
$$\frac{6.25}{39.4384} = \frac{L}{32}$$
$$(32)\left(\frac{6.25}{39.4384}\right) = (32)\left(\frac{L}{32}\right)$$
$$\frac{200}{39.4384} = L$$
$$5.07 \approx L$$

The length of the pendulum is approximately 5.07 ft.

Solutions to Chapter 11 "You Try It"

SECTION 11.1

You Try It 1

$$\frac{3y^2}{2} + y - \frac{1}{2} = 0$$
$$2\left(\frac{3y^2}{2} + y - \frac{1}{2}\right) = 2(0) \qquad \bullet\ \text{Multiply each side by 2.}$$
$$3y^2 + 2y - 1 = 0$$
$$(3y - 1)(y + 1) = 0 \qquad \bullet\ \text{Factor.}$$
$$3y - 1 = 0 \qquad y + 1 = 0 \qquad \bullet\ \text{Principle of Zero Products}$$
$$3y = 1 \qquad y = -1$$
$$y = \frac{1}{3}$$

The solutions are $\frac{1}{3}$ and -1.

You Try It 2

$$x^2 + 81 = 0$$
$$x^2 = -81 \qquad \bullet\ \text{Solve for } x^2.$$
$$\sqrt{x^2} = \sqrt{-81} \qquad \bullet\ \text{Take square roots.}$$

$\sqrt{-81}$ is not a real number.

The equation has no real number solution.

You Try It 3

$$7(z + 2)^2 = 21$$
$$(z + 2)^2 = 3 \qquad \bullet\ \text{Solve for } (z + 2)^2.$$
$$\sqrt{(z + 2)^2} = \sqrt{3} \qquad \bullet\ \text{Take square roots.}$$
$$z + 2 = \pm\sqrt{3}$$
$$z = -2 \pm \sqrt{3} \qquad \bullet\ \text{Solve for } z.$$

The solutions are $-2 + \sqrt{3}$ and $-2 - \sqrt{3}$.

SECTION 11.2

You Try It 1

$$3x^2 - 6x - 2 = 0$$
$$3x^2 - 6x = 2 \qquad \bullet\ \text{Add 2.}$$
$$\frac{1}{3}(3x^2 - 6x) = \frac{1}{3} \cdot 2 \qquad \bullet\ \text{Multiply by } \frac{1}{3}.$$
$$x^2 - 2x = \frac{2}{3} \qquad \bullet\ \text{The coefficient of } x^2 \text{ is 1.}$$

Complete the square.

$$x^2 - 2x + 1 = \frac{2}{3} + 1 \qquad \bullet\ \left[\frac{1}{2}(-2)\right]^2 = [-1]^2 = 1$$
$$(x - 1)^2 = \frac{5}{3} \qquad \bullet\ \text{Factor.}$$
$$\sqrt{(x - 1)^2} = \sqrt{\frac{5}{3}} \qquad \bullet\ \text{Take square roots.}$$
$$x - 1 = \pm\sqrt{\frac{5}{3}} \qquad \bullet\ \text{Solve for } x.$$
$$x = 1 \pm \sqrt{\frac{5}{3}}$$
$$x = 1 \pm \frac{\sqrt{15}}{3}$$
$$x = \frac{3 \pm \sqrt{15}}{3}$$

The solutions are $\frac{3+\sqrt{15}}{3}$ and $\frac{3-\sqrt{15}}{3}$.

You Try It 2

$x^2 + 6x + 12 = 0$

$x^2 + 6x = -12$ • Subtract 12.

$x^2 + 6x + 9 = -12 + 9$ • $\left(\frac{1}{2}\cdot 6\right)^2 = 3^2 = 9$

$(x+3)^2 = -3$ • Factor.

$\sqrt{(x+3)^2} = \sqrt{-3}$ • Take square roots.

$\sqrt{-3}$ is not a real number.

The quadratic equation has no real number solution.

You Try It 3

$x^2 + 8x + 8 = 0$

$x^2 + 8x = -8$ • Subtract 8.

$x^2 + 8x + 16 = -8 + 16$ • $\left(\frac{1}{2}\cdot 8\right)^2 = 4^2 = 16$

$(x+4)^2 = 8$ • Factor.

$\sqrt{(x+4)^2} = \sqrt{8}$ • Take square roots.

$x + 4 = \pm\sqrt{8}$

$x + 4 = \pm 2\sqrt{2}$

$x = -4 \pm 2\sqrt{2}$

$x = -4 + 2\sqrt{2}$ $\quad$ $x = -4 - 2\sqrt{2}$

$\approx -4 + 2(1.414)$ $\quad$ $\approx -4 - 2(1.414)$

$\approx -4 + 2.828$ $\quad$ $\approx -4 - 2.828$

≈ -1.172 $\quad$ ≈ -6.828

The solutions are approximately -1.172 and -6.828.

SECTION 11.3

You Try It 1

$3x^2 + 4x - 4 = 0$

$a = 3, b = 4, c = -4$

$$x = \frac{-(4) \pm \sqrt{(4)^2 - 4(3)(-4)}}{2\cdot 3}$$

$$= \frac{-4 \pm \sqrt{16+48}}{6}$$

$$= \frac{-4 \pm \sqrt{64}}{6} = \frac{-4 \pm 8}{6}$$

$$x = \frac{-4+8}{6} \qquad x = \frac{-4-8}{6}$$

$$= \frac{4}{6} = \frac{2}{3} \qquad = \frac{-12}{6} = -2$$

The solutions are $\frac{2}{3}$ and -2.

You Try It 2

$$\frac{x^2}{4} + \frac{x}{2} = \frac{1}{4}$$

$$4\left(\frac{x^2}{4} + \frac{x}{2}\right) = 4\left(\frac{1}{4}\right)$$ • Multiply by 4.

$x^2 + 2x = 1$ • Standard form

$x^2 + 2x - 1 = 0$

$a = 1, b = 2, c = -1$

$$x = \frac{-(2) \pm \sqrt{(2)^2 - 4(1)(-1)}}{2\cdot 1}$$

$$= \frac{-2 \pm \sqrt{4+4}}{2} = \frac{-2 \pm \sqrt{8}}{2}$$

$$= \frac{-2 \pm 2\sqrt{2}}{2} = -1 \pm \sqrt{2}$$

The solutions are $-1 + \sqrt{2}$ and $-1 - \sqrt{2}$.

SECTION 11.4

You Try It 1 $y = x^2 + 2$

x	y
-2	6
-1	3
0	2
1	3
2	6

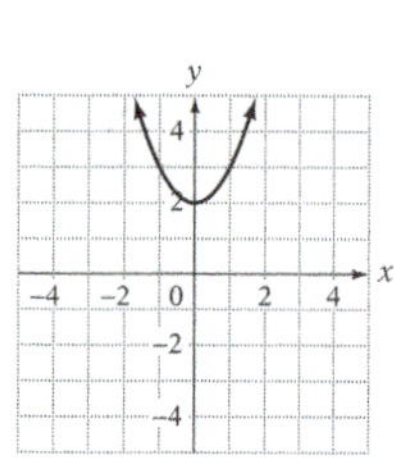

You Try It 2 To find the x-intercept, let $f(x) = 0$ and solve for x.

$f(x) = x^2 - 6x + 9$

$0 = x^2 - 6x + 9$

$0 = (x-3)(x-3)$ • Factor.

$x - 3 = 0 \quad x - 3 = 0$ • Principle of Zero Products

$x = 3 \quad x = 3$

The x-intercept is $(3, 0)$.

There is only one x-intercept. The equation has a double root.

To find the y-intercept, evaluate the function at $x = 0$.

$f(x) = x^2 - 6x + 9$

$f(0) = 0^2 - 6(0) + 9 = 9$

The y-intercept is $(0, 9)$.

SECTION 11.5

You Try It 1

Strategy

- ▶ This is a geometry problem.
- ▶ Width of the rectangle: W
  Length of the rectangle: $W + 2$
- ▶ Use the equation $A = L\cdot W$.

Solution

$A = L\cdot W$

$15 = (W+2)W$ • $A = 15, L = W + 2$

$15 = W^2 + 2W$

$0 = W^2 + 2W - 15$

$0 = (W+5)(W-3)$ • Factor.

$W + 5 = 0 \quad W - 3 = 0$ • Principle of Zero Products

$W = -5 \quad W = 3$

The solution -5 is not possible.

The width is 3 m.

Answers to Selected Exercises

Answers to Chapter 1 Selected Exercises

PREP TEST

1. 127.16 **2.** 46,514 **3.** 4517 **4.** 11,396 **5.** 508 **6.** 24 **7.** 4 **8.** $3 \cdot 7$ **9.** $\frac{2}{5}$ **10.** iv

SECTION 1.1

1a. left **b.** right **3.** absolute value **5.** $-14 < 16$ **7.** $35 > 28$ **9.** $-42 < 27$ **11.** $-17 < 0$ **13.** $-27 > -38$ **15.** iv **17.** $\{1, 2, 3\}$ **19.** $\{-5, -4, -3, -2, -1\}$ **21.** $-33, -24$ **23.** $-14, 14, 27$ **25.** $-7, -6, -5, -4, -3$ **27.** -8 **29.** 28 **31.** 14 **33.** -77 **35.** 13 **37.** 96 **39.** -53 **41.** $|-83| > |58|$ **43.** $|43| < |-52|$ **45.** $|-68| > |-42|$ **47.** $|-45| < |-61|$ **49a.** $8, 5, 2, -1, -3$ **b.** 8, 5, 2, 1, 3 **51.** True **53.** Never true **55.** True statement **57.** $\in$ **59.** $\in$

SECTION 1.2

5. -11 **7.** -5 **9.** -83 **11.** -46 **13.** 0 **15.** -5 **17.** 9 **19.** 1 **21.** -10 **23.** -18 **25.** -41 **27.** -65 **29.** -15 **31.** 22 **33.** Positive **35.** 8 **37.** -7 **39.** -9 **41.** 9 **43.** -3 **45.** 18 **47.** -9 **49.** 11 **51.** -18 **53.** 0 **55.** 2 **57.** -10 **59.** -51 **61.** -1 **63.** -21 **65.** -40 **67.** -63 **69.** Positive **71.** The difference in elevation is 7046 m. **73.** The continent with the greatest difference between the highest and lowest elevations is Asia. **75.** The difference in depth is 980 m. **77.** Yes, Mt. Everest could fit in the Tonga Trench. **79.a.** The depth of the hole below sea level is represented by -5525 m. **b.** The depth of the ocean floor below sea level is represented by -3297 m. **81.** The largest difference that can be obtained is 25. **83.** No. For example, the difference between 10 and -8 is 18, which is greater than either 10 or -8.

SECTION 1.3

1a. positive **b.** negative **3.** 60 **5.** -253 **7.** -114 **9.** -105 **11.** -216 **13.** 336 **15.** -2772 **17.** 0 **19.** 350 **21.** -352 **23.** Negative **25.** -6 **27.** 8 **29.** -7 **31.** 31 **33.** -19 **35.** 4 **37.** -17 **39.** 18 **41.** 0 **43.** -32 **45.** Undefined **47.** -1 **49.** -38 **51.** The average daily low temperature for this city is -3°F. **53.** The student's score is 74. **55.** The average annual change in the number of evening newspapers published is -25 newspapers. **59.** $-32, 64, -128$

SECTION 1.4

1. 9^5 **3.** 7^n **5.** 36 **7.** -49 **9.** 9 **11.** 81 **13.** -256 **15.** 18 **17.** -27 **19.** 216 **21.** -12 **23.** -864 **25.** -1008 **27.** 72 **29.** Negative **31.** Negative **33.** 9 **35.** 12 **37.** 1 **39.** 8 **41.** -16 **43.** 12 **45.** 13 **47.** -36 **49.** 13 **51.** 4 **53.** 15 **55.** -1 **57.** 4 **59.** ii **61.** Column A; $1{,}000{,}000 = 100^3$

CHECK YOUR PROGRESS: CHAPTER 1*

1. $\{1, 2, 3, 4, 5, 6, 7, 8\}$ [1.1A] **2.** $-7, 0$ [1.1A] **3.** 13 [1.1B] **4.** $44; -18$ [1.1B] **5.** $|31| > |-13|$ [1.1B] **6.** -24 [1.2A] **7.** 16 [1.2B] **8.** -1 [1.2A] **9.** 52 [1.2B] **10.** -32 [1.3A] **11.** 315 [1.3A] **12.** -10 [1.3B] **13.** -16 [1.3B] **14.** Undefined [1.3B] **15.** -144 [1.4A] **16.** 9 [1.4B] **17.** -31 [1.4B] **18.** 0 [1.4B] **19.** The temperature is 5°C. [1.2C] **20.** The average daily low temperature for the week is -5°C. [1.3C]

SECTION 1.5

1. 1, 2, 3, 6, 9, 18; factors **3.** 1, 13 **5.** 1, 2, 4, 7, 8, 14, 28, 56 **7.** 1, 3, 5, 9, 15, 45 **9.** 1, 29 **11.** 1, 2, 4, 13, 26, 52 **13.** 1, 2, 41, 82 **15.** 1, 3, 19, 57 **17.** 1, 2, 3, 4, 6, 8, 12, 16, 24, 48 **19.** 1, 2, 5, 10, 25, 50 **21.** 1, 7, 11, 77 **23.** 1, 2, 4, 5, 10, 20, 25, 50, 100 **25.** 1, 5, 17, 85 **27.** False **29.** $2 \cdot 7$ **31.** $2^3 \cdot 3^2$ **33.** $2^3 \cdot 3$ **35.** $2^2 \cdot 3^2$ **37.** $2 \cdot 13$ **39.** 7^2 **41.** Prime **43.** $2 \cdot 31$ **45.** Prime **47.** $2^4 \cdot 3^2$ **49.** $5^2 \cdot 7$ **51.** $2^4 \cdot 5^2$ **53.** False **55.** 24 **57.** 12 **59.** 36

**Note:* The numbers in brackets following the answers in the Check Your Progress are a reference to the objective that corresponds to that problem. For example, the reference [1.2A] stands for Section 1.2, Objective A. This notation will be used for answers to Prep Tests, Check Your Progress, Chapter Reviews, Chapter Tests, and Cumulative Reviews throughout the text.

61. 140 **63.** 36 **65.** 60 **67.** 40 **69.** 140 **71.** 36 **73.** 24 **75.** 140 **77.** 72 **79.** 140 **81.** 3 **83.** 1 **85.** 7 **87.** 14 **89.** 12 **91.** 36 **93.** 12 **95.** 2 **97.** 6 **99.** 12 **101.** 26 **103.** 18 **105.** The largest factor is 111,111,111,111 because 333,333,333,333 is not divisible by 2 and 333,333,333,333 ÷ 3 = 111,111,111,111.

SECTION 1.6

1. 3; 4; terminating **3.** equivalent; common denominator **5.** $\frac{1}{3}$ **7.** $-\frac{4}{11}$ **9.** $-\frac{2}{3}$ **11.** $\frac{3}{2}$ **13.** 0 **15.** $-\frac{3}{5}$ **17.** $-\frac{7}{5}$ **19.** −15 **21.** $\frac{1}{2}$ **23.** 0.8 **25.** $0.1\overline{6}$ **27.** $-0.\overline{3}$ **29.** $-0.\overline{2}$ **31.** $-0.58\overline{3}$ **33.** $0.91\overline{6}$ **35.** Repeating decimal **37.** $-\frac{2}{3}$ **39.** $-\frac{1}{2}$ **41.** $\frac{7}{8}$ **43.** $\frac{13}{54}$ **45.** $-\frac{5}{18}$ **47.** $-\frac{19}{60}$ **49.** $\frac{7}{24}$ **51.** $\frac{4}{3}$ **53.** $-\frac{21}{16}$ **55.** $-\frac{55}{72}$ **57.** 7.29 **59.** −3.272 **61.** 13.88 **63.** −5.769 **65.** 4.783 **67.** −5.291 **69.** $\frac{5}{16}$ **71.** $-\frac{19}{24}$ **73.** −1.17 **75.** 0 **77.** −1 **79.** $-\frac{1}{3}$ **81.** $-\frac{1}{2}$ **83.** $-\frac{5}{24}$ **85.** $\frac{7}{12}$ **87.** $-\frac{3}{26}$ **89.** $\frac{1}{12}$ **91.** $\frac{9}{8}$ **93.** $-\frac{11}{48}$ **95.** 0 **97.** $\frac{11}{24}$ **99.** −62.47 **101.** 9.12 **103.** −15.646 **105.** −7.3714 **107.** −8.477 **109.** $\frac{13}{16}$ **111.** $-\frac{14}{15}$ **113.** $-\frac{13}{48}$ **115.** Negative **117.** Positive **119.** The width is $\frac{7}{8}$ in. **121.** The five countries import 26.2 million barrels of oil per day. **123.** The largest difference is 18.5 million barrels of oil. **125.** You have consumed 91.5 mg of caffeine. **127.** Four 12-ounce sodas that together contain less caffeine than a cup of coffee are Coca-Cola, Dr. Pepper, Pepsi, and Diet Pepsi. **129.** The total strength of the lens is −2.25 diopters. **131.** Larger **133.** $\frac{17}{99} = 0.\overline{17}$; $\frac{45}{99} = 0.\overline{45}$; $\frac{73}{99} = 0.\overline{73}$; $\frac{83}{99} = 0.\overline{83}$; $\frac{33}{99} = 0.\overline{33} = 0.\overline{3}$; yes; $\frac{1}{99} = 0.\overline{01}$, yes **135.** $a = 2, b = 3, c = 6$

SECTION 1.7

1. numerators; denominators **3.** 100% **5.** $\frac{10}{21}$ **7.** $-\frac{3}{16}$ **9.** $-\frac{1}{8}$ **11.** $-\frac{4}{9}$ **13.** $\frac{9}{50}$ **15.** $\frac{9}{16}$ **17.** $\frac{5}{36}$ **19.** $\frac{3}{64}$ **21.** −7 **23.** −1.794 **25.** 0.7407 **27.** −0.408 **29.** $-\frac{3}{5}$ **31.** 1.035 **33.** Less than 1 **35.** $-\frac{2}{9}$ **37.** $\frac{1}{6}$ **39.** [illegible] **41.** $-\frac{4}{9}$ **43.** $\frac{9}{50}$ **45.** $-\frac{2}{3}$ **47.** $-\frac{15}{14}$ **49.** $-\frac{8}{27}$ **51.** 4.5 **53.** −0.35 **55.** −0.47 **57.** −0.07 **59.** −1.02 **61.** −0.25 **63.** $\frac{23}{30}$ **65.** $-\frac{1}{8}$ **67.** $-\frac{11}{18}$ **69.** 0 **71.** −2 **73.** $-\frac{4}{27}$ **75.** −4.09 **77.** −0.1238 **79.** 0 **83.** $\frac{3}{4}$, 0.75 **85.** $\frac{16}{25}$, 0.64 **87.** $\frac{7}{4}$, 1.75 **89.** $\frac{19}{100}$, 0.19 **91.** $\frac{1}{20}$, 0.05 **93.** $\frac{1}{9}$ **95.** $\frac{1}{8}$ **97.** $\frac{2}{3}$ **99.** $\frac{1}{200}$ **101.** $\frac{5}{6}$ **103.** 0.073 **105.** 0.158 **107.** 0.003 **109.** 0.099 **111.** 1.212 **113.** 15% **115.** 5% **117.** 17.5% **119.** 115% **121.** 0.8% **123.** 54% **125.** $33\frac{1}{3}\%$ **127.** $45\frac{5}{11}\%$ **129.** 87.5% **131.** $166\frac{2}{3}\%$ **133.** Greater than 100% **135.** The carpenter can cut 18 pieces from the board. **137a.** The difference is 4.3 million barrels per day. **b.** The predicted increase in oil production from 2008 to 2020 is 1.1 million barrels per day. **139.** The chef should use $1\frac{1}{8}$ c of butter. **141.** The number of servings is 16.

143. $\frac{1}{22}$ **145.**

▒	▒	▒		
█	█	█		

SECTION 1.8

1. Smaller than **3.** 6 in. **5.** 90° **7.** 28° **9.** 132° **11.** 132° **13.** 51° **15.** 77° **17.** 79° **19.** 292° **21.** 30° **23.** 15 ft 10 in. **25.** 26 m **27.** 136 cm **29.** 21.352 m **31.** 47.1 in. **33.** The cost to install the decorative border is $137.20. **35.** The cost to place the irrigation system around the flower garden is $68.58. **37.** 32 ft^2 **39.** 378 cm^2 **41.** 50.24 in^2 **43.** 16.81 m^2 **45.** 52.5 cm^2 **47.** 226.865 in^2 **49.** 138.6 gal of water should be used per day. **51.** The cost to build the design is $172. **53.** The cost to plaster the room is $990.72. **55.** No, the expression cannot be used to calculate the area of the carpet. **57.** Yes, the expression can be used to calculate the area of the carpet. **59.** Perimeter: 265.6 m; area: 4056 m^2

CHAPTER 1 REVIEW EXERCISES

1. −6 [1.2A] **2.** 0.28 [1.6A] **3.** −25 [1.4A] **4.** 10 [1.4B] **5.** 37° [1.8A] **6.** 0.062 [1.7C] **7.** −42 [1.3A] **8.** $\frac{7}{12}$ [1.6C] **9.** 34° [1.8A] **10.** −4 [1.1A] **11.** 1, 2, 4, 7, 8, 14, 28, 56 [1.5A] **12.** −1.068 [1.6C] **13.** 62.5% [1.7C]

$0.1\overline{3}$ [1.6A] **15.** -4 [1.2B] **16.** $-\frac{2}{15}$ [1.6C] **17.** 4 [1.1B] **18.** 18 cm^2 [1.8C] **19.** -20 [1.3B] **20.** $\frac{159}{200}$ [1.7C] **21.** $2 \cdot 2 \cdot 2 \cdot 5 \cdot 7$ [1.5B] **22.** 31 [1.4B] **23.** -13 [1.2A] **24.** $\frac{17}{40}$ [1.6B] **25.** $54\frac{2}{7}\%$ [1.7C] **26.** 28.26 m^2 [1.8C] **27.** -4.6224 [1.7A] **28.** -5 [1.1B] **29.** 1 [1.2B] **30.** $-\frac{8}{15}$ [1.7B] **31.** 152° [1.8A] **32.** 44 in. [1.8B] **33.** $-|6| < |-10|$ [1.1B] **34.** 1 [1.4B] **35.** The score for the exam was 98. [1.3C] **36.** 59.0% of those surveyed opposed abolishing the penny. [1.7D] **37.** The difference between the boiling point and the freezing point of mercury is 396°C. [1.2C] **38.** The sod cost $336.96. [1.8C]

CHAPTER 1 TEST

1. 17 [1.3B; Example 5] **2.** $83\frac{1}{3}\%$ [1.7C; Example 7] **3.** 62° [1.8A; Example 1] **4.** -5.3578 [1.7A; Example 3] **5.** -14 [1.2B; HOW TO 2] **6.** $\frac{3}{8}$ [1.7C; Example 6] **7.** $\frac{1}{24}$ [1.6C; HOW TO 7] **8.** 8 [1.4B; HOW TO 3] **9.** 90 [1.3A; Example 2] **10.** 84.78 in. [1.8B; You Try It 5] **11.** -108 [1.4A; Example 3] **12.** 90 cm^2 [1.8C; Example 9] **13.** $-2 > -40$ [1.1A; Example 2] **14.** $-\frac{7}{20}$ [1.6B; You Try It 4] **15.** -4 [1.1B; Example 3] **16.** $\frac{9}{20}$; 0.45 [1.7C; Example 6] **17.** -16 [1.2A; Example 2] **18.** -48 [1.3A; You Try It 3] **19.** $2 \cdot 3 \cdot 3 \cdot 5 \cdot 11$ [1.5B; Example 2] **20.** 17 [1.4B; Example 6] **21.** 4 [1.2B; HOW TO 2] **22.** $-\frac{1}{2}$ [1.7B; HOW TO 3] **23.** 47° [1.8A; Example 3] **24.** 9 [1.4B; You Try It 6] **25.** $0.\overline{7}$ [1.6A; HOW TO 3] **26a.** The 2011 annual net income for Sears Holdings would be $-\$680,000,000$. **b.** The average monthly loss for Rite Aid was $-\$25,000,000$. [1.3C; Example 8] **27.** The cost of the new fencing is $5964. [1.8B; Example 6]

Answers to Chapter 2 Selected Exercises

PREP TEST

1. 3 [1.2B] **2.** 4 [1.3B] **3.** $\frac{1}{12}$ [1.6B] **4.** $-\frac{4}{9}$ [1.7B] **5.** $\frac{3}{10}$ [1.7B] **6.** -16 [1.4A] **7.** $\frac{8}{27}$ [1.7A] **8.** 48 [1.4B] **9.** 1 [1.4B] **10.** 12 [1.4B]

SECTION 2.1

1. $2x^2, 5x, \underline{-8}$ **3.** $-a^4, \underline{6}$ **5.** $7x^2y, \underline{6xy^2}$ **7.** $1, -9$ **9.** $1, -4, -1$ **13.** 10 **15.** 32 **17.** 21 **19.** 16 **21.** -9 **23.** 41 **25.** -7 **27.** 13 **29.** -15 **31.** 41 **33.** 1 **35.** 5 **37.** 1 **39.** 57 **41.** 5 **43.** 8 **45.** -3 **47.** -2 **49.** -4 **51.** Positive **53.** Negative **55.** 41 **57.** 1 **59.** -23 **61a.** 2 **b.** 5 **c.** 6 **d.** 7; $n^x > x^n$ if $x \geq n + 1$

SECTION 2.2

1. Commutative **3.** reciprocal (or multiplicative inverse) **7.** $14x$ **9.** $5a$ **11.** $-6y$ **13.** $7 - 3b$ **15.** $5a$ **17.** $-2ab$ **19.** $5xy$ **21.** 0 **23.** $-\frac{5}{6}x$ **25.** $6.5x$ **27.** $0.45x$ **29.** $7a$ **31.** $-14x^2$ **33.** $-\frac{11}{24}x$ **35.** $17x - 3y$ **37.** $-2a - 6b$ **39.** $-3x - 8y$ **41.** $-4x^2 - 2x$ **43.** iv and v **45.** $60x$ **47.** $-10a$ **49.** $30y$ **51.** $72x$ **53.** $-28a$ **55.** $108b$ **57.** $-56x^2$ **59.** x^2 **61.** x **63.** a **65.** b **67.** x **69.** n **71.** $2x$ **73.** $-2x$ **75.** $-15a^2$ **77.** $6y$ **79.** $3y$ **81.** $-2x$ **83.** $-9y$ **85.** $8x - 6$ **87.** $-2a - 14$ **89.** $-6y + 24$ **91.** $-x - 2$ **93.** $35 - 21b$ **95.** $2 - 5y$ **97.** $15x^2 + 6x$ **99.** $2y - 18$ **101.** $-15x - 30$ **103.** $-6x^2 - 28$ **105.** $-6y^2 + 21$ **107.** $3x^2 - 3y^2$ **109.** $-4x + 12y$ **111.** $-6a^2 + 7b^2$ **113.** $4x^2 - 12x + 20$ **115.** $\frac{3}{2}x - \frac{9}{2}y + 6$ **117.** $-12a^2 - 20a + 28$ **119.** $12x^2 - 9x + 12$ **121.** $10x^2 - 20xy - 5y^2$ **123.** $-8b^2 + 6b - 9$ **125.** iii **127.** $a - 7$ **129.** $-11x + 13$ **131.** $-4y - 4$ **133.** $-2x - 16$ **135.** $14y - 45$ **137.** $a + 7b$ **139.** $6x + 28$ **141.** $5x - 75$ **143.** $4x - 4$ **145.** $2x - 9$ **147.** $1.24x + 0.36$ **149.** $-0.01x + 40$ **153a.** Yes; for example, $3 \otimes 2 = (3 \cdot 2) - (3 + 2) = 6 - 5 = 1$ and $2 \otimes 3 = (2 \cdot 3) - (2 + 3) = 6 - 5 = 1$. **b.** No; for example, $[3 \otimes 2] \otimes 4 = 1 \otimes 4 = -1$ but $3 \otimes [2 \otimes 4] = 3 \otimes 2 = 1$.

CHECK YOUR PROGRESS: CHAPTER 2

1. -12 [2.1A] **2.** 46 [2.1A] **3.** 7 [2.1A] **4.** -2 [2.1A] **5.** 6 [2.1A] **6.** -1 [2.1A] **7.** $-3y$ [2.2A] **8.** $3a + 4b$ [2.2A] **9.** $-40a$ [2.2B] **10.** z [2.2B] **11.** $36 - 24b$ [2.2C] **12.** $6x^2 - 8x + 10$ [2.2C] **13.** $-5x + 20$ [2.2D] **14.** $9a - 46$ [2.2D] **15.** $-18x + 23$ [2.2D]

SECTION 2.3

1. sum, times **3.** total, divided by **5.** $25 - x$ **7.** $8 + y$ **9.** $t + 10$ **11.** $z + 14$ **13.** $x^2 - 20$ **15.** $\frac{3}{4}n + 12$
17. $8 + \frac{n}{4}$ **19.** $3(y + 7)$ **21.** $t(t + 16)$ **23.** $\frac{1}{2}x^2 + 15$ **25.** $5n^3 + n^2$ **27.** $r - \frac{r}{3}$ **29.** $x^2 - (x + 17)$
31. $9(z + 4)$ **33.** Answers will vary. For example: The product of 5 and 1 more than the square of n, or 5 times the sum of 1 plus the square of n
35. $\frac{x}{18}$ **37.** $x + 20$ **39.** $11x - 8$ **41.** $\frac{7}{5 + x}$ **43.** $40 - \frac{x}{20}$ **45.** $x^2 + 2x$ **47.** $10(x - 50)$; $10x - 500$
49. $x - (x + 3)$; -3 **51.** $(2x - 4) + x$; $3x - 4$ **53.** $x - (3x - 8)$; $-2x + 8$ **55.** $3x + x$; $4x$ **57.** $(x + 6) + 5$; $x + 11$
59. $x - (x + 10)$; -10 **61.** $\frac{1}{6}x + \frac{4}{9}x$; $\frac{11}{18}x$ **63.** s represents the number of students enrolled in fall-term science classes.
65. Let M be the number of visitors to the Metropolitan Museum of Art; the number of visitors to the Louvre is $M + 3{,}800{,}000$.
67. Let d be the noise level, in decibels, of a car horn; the noise level of an ambulance siren is $d + 10$.
69. Let T be U2's concert ticket sales; Bruce Springsteen and the E Street Band's concert ticket sales are $T - 28{,}500{,}000$.
71. Let N be the number of bones in your body; the number of bones in your foot is $\frac{1}{4}N$.
73. Let N be the number of U.S. undergraduate students; the number of U.S. undergraduate students who attend two-year colleges is $0.46N$.
75. Let B be the attendance at major league basketball games; the attendance at major league baseball games is $B + 50{,}000{,}000$.
77. Let L be the measure of the largest angle; the measure of the smallest angle is $\frac{1}{2}L - 10$.
79. Let h be the number of hours of labor; the amount of the repair bill is $238 + 89h$.
81. Let x be the distance traveled by the slower car; the distance traveled by the faster car is $200 - x$.
83. The number of hydrogen atoms in the pound of sugar in terms of the number of oxygen atoms is $2x$.
87. Answers will vary. For example: 16 less than d; the difference between d and 16; d decreased by 16; 16 subtracted from d.
89. Answers will vary. For example: y divided by 5; the quoteint of y and 5; the ratio of y to 5.

CHAPTER 2 REVIEW EXERCISES

1. $3x^2 - 24x - 21$ [2.2C] **2.** $11x$ [2.2A] **3.** $8a - 4b$ [2.2A] **4.** $-5n$ [2.2B] **5.** 79 [2.1A]
6. $10x - 35$ [2.2C] **7.** $-42x^2$ [2.2B] **8.** $-63 - 36x$ [2.2C] **9.** $-5y$ [2.2A] **10.** -4 [2.1A]
11. $-6x - 1$ [2.2D] **12.** $-40a + 40$ [2.2D] **13.** $24y + 30$ [2.2D] **14.** $9c - 5d$ [2.2A] **15.** $20x$ [2.2B]
16. $7x + 46$ [2.2D] **17.** $-4x^2 + 6x$ [2.2A] **18.** $-90x + 25$ [2.2D] **19.** $-0.2x + 150$ [2.2D] **20.** $-\frac{1}{12}x$ [2.2A]
21. $28a^2 - 8a + 12$ [2.2C] **22.** -7 [2.1A] **23.** $36y$ [2.2B] **24.** $\frac{2}{3}(x + 10)$ [2.3A] **25.** $x - 6$ [2.3A]
26. $x + 2x$; $3x$ [2.3B] **27.** $2x - \frac{1}{2}x$; $\frac{3}{2}x$ [2.3B] **28.** $3x + 5(x - 1)$; $8x - 5$ [2.3B] **29.** Let A be the number of American League players' cards; the number of National League players' cards is $5A$. [2.3C]
30. Let T be the number of ten-dollar bills; the number of five-dollar bills is $35 - T$. [2.3C]
31. Let a be the number of calories in an apple; the number of calories in the candy bar is $2a + 8$. [2.3C]
32. Let w be the width of the Parthenon; the length of the Parthenon is $1.6w$. [2.3C]
33. Let h be the person's kneeling height; the person's standing height is $1.3h$. [2.3C]

CHAPTER 2 TEST

1. $5x$ [2.2A, HOW TO 1] **2.** $-6x^2 + 21y^2$ [2.2C, HOW TO 9] **3.** $-x + 6$ [2.2D, Example 11]
4. $-7x + 33$ [2.2D, Example 13] **5.** $-9x - 7y$ [2.2A, Example 1] **6.** 22 [2.1A, HOW TO 1]
7. $2x$ [2.2B, Example 5] **8.** $7x + 38$ [2.2D, Example 12] **9.** $-10x^2 + 15x - 30$ [2.2C, Example 9]
10. $-2x - 5y$ [2.2A, Example 1] **11.** 3 [2.1A, Example 3] **12.** $3x$ [2.2B, HOW TO 7]
13. y^2 [2.2A, Example 2] **14.** $-4x + 8$ [2.2C, You Try It 8] **15.** $-10a$ [2.2B, Example 5]
16. $2x + y$ [2.2D, Example 13] **17.** $36y$ [2.2B, You Try It 4] **18.** $15 - 35b$ [2.2C, Example 6]
19. $a^2 - b^2$ [2.3A, HOW TO 2] **20.** $10(x - 3) = 10x - 30$ [2.3B, HOW TO 3]
21. $x + 2x^2$ [2.3B, Example 4] **22.** $\frac{6}{x} - 3$ [2.3B, HOW TO 3] **23.** $b - 7b$ [2.3A, Example 2]
24. Let d be the distance from Earth to the sun; the distance from Neptune to the sun is $30d$. [2.3C,You Try It 5]
25. Let x be the length of the shorter piece; the length of the longer piece is $4x - 3$. [2.3C, Example 5]

CUMULATIVE REVIEW EXERCISES

1. -7 [1.2A] **2.** 5 [1.2B] **3.** 24 [1.3A] **4.** -5 [1.3B] **5.** 53° [1.8A] **6.** $\frac{11}{48}$ [1.6C]
7. $-\frac{1}{6}$ [1.7B] **8.** $\frac{1}{4}$ [1.7A] **9.** 75% [1.7C] **10.** -5 [1.4B] **11.** $-\frac{27}{26}$ [1.7B] **12.** 16 [2.1A]

$5x^2$ [2.2A] **14.** $-7a - 10b$ [2.2A] **15.** 153.86 cm^2 [1.8C] **16.** 96 ft [1.8B] **17.** $24 - 6x$ [2.2C]
$6y - 18$ [2.2C] **19.** $\frac{3}{8}$ [1.7C] **20.** 0.0105 [1.7C] **21.** $-8x^2 + 12y^2$ [2.2C]
22. $-9y^2 + 9y + 21$ [2.2C] **23.** $-7x + 14$ [2.2D] **24.** $5x - 43$ [2.2D] **25.** $17x - 24$ [2.2D]
26. $-3x + 21y$ [2.2D] **27.** $\frac{1}{2}b + b$ [2.3A] **28.** $\frac{10}{y - 2}$ [2.3A] **29.** $8 - \frac{x}{12}$ [2.3B]
30. $x + (x + 2)$; $2x + 2$ [2.3B] **31.** The area is 3600 ft^2. [1.8C] **32.** Let w be the speed of the wildebeest; the speed of the peregrine falcon is $4w$. [2.3C]

Answers to Chapter 3 Selected Exercises

PREP TEST

1. 0.09 [1.7C] **2.** 75% [1.7C] **3.** 63 [2.1A] **4.** $0.65R$ [2.2A] **5.** $\frac{7}{6}x$ [2.2A] **6.** $9x - 18$ [2.2C]
7. $1.66x + 1.32$ [2.2C] **8.** $5 - 2n$ [2.3B] **9.** Let s be the speed of the old card. The speed of the new card is $5s$. [2.3C]
10. The length of the shorter piece in terms of x is $5 - x$. [2.3C]

SECTION 3.1

1a. Equation **b.** Expression **c.** Expression **d.** Equation **e.** Expression **3.** i, ii, and iv are equations of the form $x + a = b$; you would subtract a from both sides. **5.** Yes **7.** No **9.** No **11.** Yes **13.** No **15.** Yes **17.** Yes **19.** No
23. 2 **25.** 15 **27.** 6 **29.** 3 **31.** 0 **33.** -7 **35.** -7 **37.** -12 **39.** -5 **41.** 15 **43.** 9 **45.** 14
47. -1 **49.** 1 **51.** $-\frac{1}{2}$ **53.** $-\frac{7}{12}$ **55.** 0.6529 **57.** 9.257 **59.** -3 **61.** 0 **63.** -2 **65.** 180 **67.** 0 **69.** 6
71. -10 **73.** 12 **75.** -12 **77.** 0 **79.** -24 **81.** $\frac{1}{3}$ **83.** 4.745 **85.** 2.06 **87.** 7 **89.** 4 **91.** 3 **93.** Positive
Negative **97.** -15 **99.** 5 **101.** 6 **103.** One possible answer is $x + 7 = 9$. **105.** $\frac{7}{11}$

SECTION 3.2

1. Amount: 30, base: 40 **3.** unknown; 30; 24 **5.** Keith had the greater average speed. **7.** 28 **9.** 0.72 **11.** 64 **13.** 24%
15. 7.2 **17.** 400 **19.** 9 **21.** 25% **23.** 200% **25.** 400 **27.** 7.7 **29.** 200 **31.** 400 **33.** 30 **35.** Less than
37. 97.9% of the participants who started the course finished the race. **39.** 82.1% of the vacation cost is charged on a credit card.
41. 12% of the accidental deaths were not attributed to motor vehicle accidents. **43.** The annual interest rate is 9%.
45. Sal will earn \$240 from the two accounts after one year. **47.** Makana earned \$63 in one year. **49.** The interest rate on the combined investment is between 6% and 9%. **51.** The percent concentration of hydrogen peroxide is 2%. **53.** Apple Dan has the greater concentration of apple juice. **55.** 12.5 g of the cream are not glycerine. **57.** The percent concentration of salt in the remaining solution is 12.5%.
59a. The distance biked by Emma is equal to the distance biked by Morgan. **b.** The time spent biking by Emma is less than the time spent biking by Morgan. **61.** The dietician's average rate of speed is 30 mph. **63.** Marcella's average rate of speed is 36 mph.
65. It would take Palmer 2.5 h to walk the same course. **67.** The two joggers will meet in 40 min. **69.** The two cyclists are 8.5 mi apart.
71. The two trains are 30 mi apart. **73.** 15° **75.** 15° **77.** No; the prices are lower than the original prices. **81a.** 18.1% of the U.S. population lives in the Northeast; 21.8% of the U.S. population lives in the Midwest; 36.8% of the U.S. population lives in the South; 23.4% of the U.S. population lives in the West. **b.** The region with the largest population is the South. The largest percent of the population lives in the South. **c.** 12.3% of the U.S. population lives in California. **d.** Approximately 520,000 residents live in Wyoming. **e.** Answers will vary.

SECTION 3.3

1a. i **b.** iii **c.** ii **d.** iv **3.** 5; 8 **5.** 3 **7.** 6 **9.** -1 **11.** -3 **13.** 2 **15.** 2 **17.** 5 **19.** -3 **21.** 6
23. 3 **25.** 1 **27.** 6 **29.** -7 **31.** 0 **33.** $\frac{3}{4}$ **35.** $\frac{4}{9}$ **37.** $\frac{1}{3}$ **39.** $-\frac{1}{2}$ **41.** $-\frac{3}{4}$ **43.** $\frac{1}{3}$ **45.** $-\frac{1}{6}$
47. 0 **49.** 0.15 **51.** $-\frac{3}{2}$ **53.** 18 **55.** 8 **57.** -16 **59.** 25 **61.** $\frac{3}{4}$ **63.** $\frac{3}{8}$ **65.** $\frac{16}{9}$ **67.** $\frac{1}{18}$ **69.** $\frac{15}{2}$
71. $-\frac{18}{5}$ **73.** 2 **75.** 3 **77.** Negative **79.** Negative **81.** $x = 7$ **83.** $y = 3$ **85.** 19 **87.** -1
89. The markup rate is 60%. **91.** The cost of the basketball is \$59. **93.** The markup rate is 44.4%. **95.** The cost of the CD is \$8.50.
True **99.** The markup rate is 54%. **101.** The discount rate is 23.2%. **103.** The regular price of the tool set was \$300.
The markdown rate is 38%. **107.** The regular price of the telescope is \$275. **109.** True **111.** The average crown spread of the baldcypress is 57 ft. **113.** There are 9 g of protein in an 8-ounce serving of the yogurt. **115.** The initial velocity is 8 ft/s.
117. The depreciated value will be \$38,000 after 2 years. **119.** The approximate length is 31.8 in. **121.** The distance the car will slide is 168 ft.

123. The regular price of a tire is \$85. **125.** The height is 14 m. **127.** The result is not a 30% discount. A 28% discount would give the same sale price.

SECTION 3.4

1. True **3.** True **5.** −2 **7.** 3 **9.** −2 **11.** −3 **13.** 2 **15.** −2 **17.** −0.2 **19.** 0 **21.** −2 **23.** −2 **25.** −2 **27.** 4 **29.** $\frac{3}{4}$ **31.** $\frac{3}{2}$ **33.** −14 **35.** 7 **37.** ii **39.** 1 **41.** 4 **43.** −1 **45.** −1 **47.** 24 **49.** 495 **51.** $\frac{1}{2}$ **53.** $-\frac{1}{3}$ **55.** $\frac{10}{3}$ **57.** $-\frac{1}{4}$ **59.** 0 **61.** The customer was driven 6 mi. **63a.** The fulcrum is 5 ft from the other person. **b.** The person who is 3 ft from the fulcrum is heavier. **c.** No, the seesaw will not balance. **65.** The fulcrum must be placed 10 ft from the child. **67.** The fulcrum must be placed 4.8 ft from the 90-pound child. **69.** The force on the lip of the can is 1770 lb. **71.** The break-even point is 260 barbecues. **73.** The break-even point is 520 recorders. **75.** The oxygen consumption is 54.8 ml/min. **77.** 4 **79.** No solution **83.** 6 **85.** Hampton's population at the beginning of the 1990s was 30,000 people.

CHECK YOUR PROGRESS: CHAPTER 3

1. Yes [3.1A] **2.** −11 [3.2B] **3.** 9 [3.1C] **4.** 72 [3.2A] **5.** 4 [3.3A] **6.** Yes [3.1A] **7.** $-\frac{1}{2}$ [3.1B] **8.** 1 [3.4B] **9.** 150 [3.2A] **10.** −1 [3.4A] **11.** No [3.1A] **12.** 100 [3.1B] **13.** $\frac{4}{5}$ [3.1C] **14.** 28 [3.3A] **15.** 25% [3.2A] **16.** $\frac{4}{3}$ [3.1C] **17.** 3 [3.4B] **18.** −7 [3.4A] **19.** 1 [3.4B] **20.** 9 [3.1C] **21.** The average daily consumption of calories today is 2199 calories. [3.2A] **22.** The trip lasts 6 h. [3.2B] **23.** The markup rate is 40%. [3.3B] **24.** The regular price is \$48. [3.3B] **25.** No, the seesaw is not balanced. [3.4C]

SECTION 3.5

1. True **3.** True **5.** Equals **7.** 1; 2; 2 **9.** $x - 15 = 7$; 22 **11.** $9 - x = 7$; 2 **13.** $5 - 2x = 1$; 2 **15.** $2x + 5 = 15$; 5 **17.** $4x - 6 = 22$; 7 **19.** $3(4x - 7) = 15$; 3 **21.** $3x = 2(20 - x)$; 8, 12 **23.** $2x - (14 - x) = 1$; 5, 9 **25.** 15, 17, 19 **27.** −1, 1, 3 **29.** 4, 6 **31.** iii **33.** The length of the Golden Gate Bridge is 1280 m. **35.** The U. S. gross national product in 1937 was \$91 billion. **37.** The lengths of the sides of the triangle are 6 ft, 6 ft, and 11 ft. **39.** The intensity of the sound of a jet engine is 140 decibels. **41.** The area of Greenland is 840,000 mi^2. **43.** The number of kilowatt-hours used is 515 kWh. **45.** The executive used the phone for 951 min. **47.** The customer pays \$.15 per text message over 300 messages. **49.** The perimeter of the larger square is 8 ft. **51.** The cyclist will complete the entire trip in $\frac{1}{3}$ additional hour. **53.** The integers are −12, −10, −8, and −6. **55.** Any three consecutive odd integers **57.** even **59.** even **61.** even **63.** even **65.** odd

SECTION 3.6

1. Acute, right, obtuse, straight **3.** No **5.** 116° **7.** 20° **9.** 20° **11.** 20° **13.** 106° **15.** 11° **17.** $m\angle a$ is 38°; $m\angle b$ is 142°. **19.** $m\angle a$ is 47°; $m\angle b$ is 133°. **21.** No **23.** 20° **25.** 47° **27.** 141° **29.** $m\angle x$ is 155°; $m\angle y$ is 70°. **31.** $m\angle a$ is 45°; $m\angle b$ is 135°. **33.** 60° **35.** 35° **37.** 102° **39.** True **41.** False **43.** True

SECTION 3.7

1. \$10.50 **3.** \$.76 **5.** 100 **7.** True **9.** False **13.** 2 lb of dog food and 3 lb of vitamin supplement should be used to make the 5-pound mixture. **15.** 8 lb of chamomile tea must be used. **17.** The cost per pound of the mixture is \$6.98. **19.** The amount of herbs costing \$1 per ounce is 20 oz. **21.** The amount of pepper cheese is 1.5 kg; the amount of Pennsylania Jack is 3.5 kg. **23.** The amount of meal costing \$.80 per pound is 300 lb. **25.** 37 lb of almonds and 63 lb of walnuts were used. **27.** The cost per pound of the breakfast cereal is \$1.40. **29.** The parks department bought 8 bundles of seedlings and 6 bundles of container-grown plants. **31.** The cost per ounce of the sunscreen is \$3. **33.** iv **35.** The resulting mixture contains $33\frac{1}{3}$% tomato juice. **37.** 80 lb of chicken feed that is 50% corn must be used. **39.** $1\frac{2}{3}$ gal of the lighter green paint must be used. **41.** The chemist should use 20 ml of the 13% solution and 30 ml of the 18% solution. **43.** The percent concentration of the resulting alloy is 50%. **45.** 10 lb of the 40% rye grass is used in the mixture. **47.** 55 kg of pure silk thread and 20 kg of 85% silk thread must be woven together. **49.** 12.5 gal of ethanol must be added. **51.** 150 oz of pure chocolate must be added. **53.** False **55.** The first plane is flying at 105 mph and the second plane is flying at 130 mph. **57.** The second skater will overtake the first skater 40 s after the second skater starts. **59.** Michael's boat will be alongside the tour boat 2 h after the tour boat leaves. **61.** The distance from the airport to the corporate offices is 120 mi. **63.** The sailboat traveled 36 mi in the first 3 h. **65.** The passenger train is traveling at 50 mph and the freight train is traveling at 30 mph. **67.** It takes 1 h for the second ship to catch up to the first ship. **69.** The rate of the faster car is 95 km/h. **71.** The second car wil not overtake the first car. **73.** The bus overtakes the car 180 mi from the starting point. **75.** The plane flew 2 h at 115 mph and 3 h at 125 mph. **77.** The mixture contains 10 lb of walnuts and 20 lb of cashews. **79.** The chemist used 3 L of pure acid and 7 L of water. **81.** 85 adults and 35 children attended the performance. **83.** The campers turned around downstream at 10:15 A.M. **85.** 3.75 gal of 20% antifreeze must be drained from the radiator and replaced by pure antifreeze. **87.** The cyclist's average speed for the trip was $13\frac{1}{3}$ mph. **89.** The round trip was 8 mi.

CHAPTER 3 REVIEW EXERCISES

1. 21 [3.1B] **2.** 10 [3.4B] **3.** 7 [3.3A] **4.** No [3.1A] **5.** 20 [3.1C] **6.** -2 [3.4B] **7.** 250% [3.2A] **8.** 4 [3.4A] **9.** -1 [3.4B] **10.** 4 [3.4A] **11.** The cost of the digital music pad is \$671.25. [3.3B] **12.** 35° [3.6A] **13.** 26° [3.6A] **14.** The force is 24 lb. [3.4C] **15.** The average speed on the winding road was 32 mph. [3.7C] **16.** The discount rate is $33\frac{1}{3}\%$. [3.3B] **17.** $m\angle x = 22°, m\angle y = 158°$ [3.6B] **18.** The amount of cranberry juice is 7 qt; the amount of apple juice is 3 qt. [3.7A] **19.** The three integers are -1, 0, and 1. [3.5A] **20.** The angles measure 75°, 60°, and 45°. [3.6B] **21.** $5n - 4 = 16; 4$ [3.5A] **22.** The height of the Eiffel Tower is 1063 ft. [3.5B] **23.** 25° [3.6A] **24.** 60° [3.6A] **25.** The jet overtakes the propeller-driven plane 600 mi from the starting point. [3.7C] **26.** The numbers are 8 and 13. [3.5A] **27.** The mixture is 14% butterfat. [3.7B]

CHAPTER 3 TEST

1. -5 [3.4A; HOW TO 1] **2.** -5 [3.1B; HOW TO 2] **3.** -3 [3.3A; Example 1] **4.** 2 [3.4B; HOW TO 2] **5.** No [3.1A; Example 1] **6.** 5 [3.3A; Example 2] **7.** 0.04 [3.2A; HOW TO 1] **8.** $-\frac{1}{3}$ [3.4B; HOW TO 2] **9.** 2 [3.4A; Example 2] **10.** -12 [3.1C; HOW TO 4] **11.** The amount of rye is 10 lb; the amount of wheat is 5 lb. [3.7A; HOW TO 1] **12.** 19° [3.6A; HOW TO 1] **13.** The discount rate is 20%. [3.3B; Example 7] **14.** 200 calculators were produced. [3.3B; Example 8] **15.** The measure of one of the equal angles is 70°. [3.6B; Example 4] **16.** The numbers are 10, 12, and 14. [3.5A; HOW TO 2] **17.** 1.25 gal of water must be added. [3.7B; HOW TO 2] **18.** $m\angle a = 138°; m\angle b = 42°$ [3.6A; HOW TO 3] **19.** $3x - 15 = 27; 14$ [3.5A; HOW TO 1] **20.** The rate of the snowmobile was 6 mph. [3.7C; HOW TO 3] **21.** The company makes 110 LCD flat-panel TVs each day. [3.5B; Example 3] **22.** The smaller number is 8; the larger number is 10. [35A; Example 1] **23.** The distance between the airports is 360 mi. [3.7C; You Try It 4] **24.** $m\angle x = 138°; m\angle y = 130°$ [3.6B; Example 3] **25.** The final temperature is 60°C. [3.4C; Example 5]

CUMULATIVE REVIEW EXERCISES

1. 6 [1.2B] **2.** -48 [1.3A] **3.** $-\frac{19}{48}$ [1.6C] **4.** -2 [1.7B] **5.** 54 [1.7A] **6.** 24 [1.4B] **7.** 6 [2.1A] **8.** $-17x$ [2.2A] **9.** $-5a - 2b$ [2.2A] **10.** $2x$ [2.2B] **11.** $36y$ [2.2B] **12.** $2x^2 + 6x - 4$ [2.2C] **13.** $-4x + 14$ [2.2D] **14.** $6x - 34$ [2.2D] **15.** Yes [3.1A] **16.** No [3.1A] **17.** 19.2 [3.2A] **18.** -25 [3.1C] **19.** -3 [3.3A] **20.** 3 [3.3A] **21.** 13 [3.4B] **22.** 2 [3.4B] **23.** -3 [3.4A] **24.** $\frac{1}{2}$ [3.4A] **25.** The final temperature is 60°C. [3.4C] **26.** $12 - 5x = -18; 6$ [3.5A] **27.** The area of the garage is 600 ft². [3.5B] **28.** 20 lb of oat flour are needed for the mixture. [3.7A] **29.** 25 g of pure gold must be added. [3.7B] **30.** The length is 12 ft; the width is 10 ft. [1.8B] **31.** 131° [3.6A] **32.** The measure of one of the equal angles is 60°. [3.6B] **33.** The length of the track is 120 m. [3.7C]

Answers to Chapter 4 Selected Exercises

PREP TEST

1. 1 [1.2B] **2.** -18 [1.3A] **3.** $\frac{2}{3}$ [1.6A] **4.** 48 [2.1A] **5.** 0 [1.6A] **6.** No [2.2A] **7.** $5x^2 - 9x - 6$ [2.2A] **8.** 0 [2.2A] **9.** $-6x + 24$ [2.2C] **10.** $-7xy + 10y$ [2.2D]

SECTION 4.1

1. Yes **3.** No **5.** No **7.** Binomial **9.** Trinomial **11.** None of these **13.** Binomial **15.** $5x^2 + 8x$ **17.** $7x^2 + xy - 4y^2$ **19.** $3a^2 - 3a + 17$ **21.** $5x^3 + 10x^2 - x - 4$ **23.** $3r^3 + 2r^2 - 11r + 7$ **25.** $-2x^2 + 3x$ **27.** $5x^2 + 7x + 20$ **29.** $x^3 + 2x^2 - 6x - 6$ **31.** $2a^3 - 3a^2 - 11a + 2$ **33.** iv **35.** $-y^2 - 13xy$ **37.** $2x^2 - 3x - 1$ **39.** $-2x^3 + x^2 + 2$ **41.** $3a^3 - 2$ **43.** $4y^3 + 2y^2 + 2y - 4$ **45.** $3y^2 - 4y - 2$ **47.** $-7x - 7$ **49.** $4x^3 + 3x^2 + 3x + 1$ **51.** $y^3 + 5y^2 - 2y - 4$ **53.** $x^2 + 9x - 11$ **55.** $2x^3 + x^2 - 5x + 6$ **57.** $x^3 - x^2 + 2x + 6$ **59.** Answers will vary. For example, $3x^2 - 4x + 7$ and $-3x^2 + 5x - 2$

SECTION 4.2

1. Product **3.** Power **5.** Power **7.** Product **9.** No **11.** No **13.** $30x^3$ **15.** $-42c^6$ **17.** $9a^7$ **19.** x^3y^4 **21.** $-10x^9y$ **23.** $12x^7y^8$ **25.** $-6x^3y^5$ **27.** x^4y^5z **29.** $a^3b^5c^4$ **31.** $-30a^5b^8$ **33.** $6a^5b$ **35.** $40y^{10}z^6$ **37.** $x^3y^3z^2$ **39.** $-24a^3b^3c^3$ **41.** $8x^7yz^6$ **43.** $30x^6y^8$ **45.** $-36a^3b^2c^3$ **47.** No **49.** Yes **51.** x^{15} **53.** x^{14}

55. x^8 **57.** y^{12} **59.** $-8x^6$ **61.** x^4y^6 **63.** $9x^4y^2$ **65.** $-243x^{15}y^{10}$ **67.** $-8x^7$ **69.** $24x^8y^7$ **71.** a^4b^6 **73.** $64x^{12}y^3$ **75.** $-18x^3y^4$ **77.** $-8a^7b^5$ **79.** $-54a^9b^3$ **81.** $12x^2$ **83.** $2x^6y^2 + 9x^4y^2$ **85.** 0 **87.** $17x^4y^8$ **89.** $-120x^{15}$

SECTION 4.3

1. Always true **3.** Sometimes true **5.** Always true **7.** Sometimes true **9.** Sometimes true **11.** $x^2 - 2x$ **13.** $-x^2 - 7x$ **15.** $3a^3 - 6a^2$ **17.** $-5x^4 + 5x^3$ **19.** $-3x^5 + 7x^3$ **21.** $12x^3 - 6x^2$ **23.** $6x^2 - 12x$ **25.** $3x^2 + 4x$ **27.** $-x^3y + xy^3$ **29.** $2x^4 - 3x^2 + 2x$ **31.** $2a^3 + 3a^2 + 2a$ **33.** $3x^6 - 3x^4 - 2x^2$ **35.** $-6y^4 - 12y^3 + 14y^2$ **37.** $-2a^3 - 6a^2 + 8a$ **39.** $6y^4 - 3y^3 + 6y^2$ **41.** $x^3y - 3x^2y^2 + xy^3$ **43.** ii and iii **45.** $x^3 - 4x^2 + 11x - 14$ **47.** $2x^3 - 9x^2 + 19x - 15$ **49.** $-2a^3 + 7a^2 - 7a + 2$ **51.** $-2a^3 - 3a^2 + 8a - 3$ **53.** $2y^3 + y^2 - 10y$ **55.** $2y^4 + 7y^3 - 4y^2 - 16y + 8$ **57.** $12y^3 + 3y^2 - 29y + 15$ **59.** $18b^4 - 33b^3 + 5b^2 + 42b - 7$ **61.** $4a^4 - 12a^3 + 13a^2 - 8a + 3$ **63.** $x^2 + 4x + 3$ **65.** $a^2 + a - 12$ **67.** $y^2 - 5y - 24$ **69.** $y^2 - 10y + 21$ **71.** $2x^2 + 15x + 7$ **73.** $3x^2 + 11x - 4$ **75.** $4x^2 - 31x + 21$ **77.** $3y^2 - 2y - 16$ **79.** $9x^2 + 54x + 77$ **81.** $21a^2 - 83a + 80$ **83.** $6a^2 - 25ab + 14b^2$ **85.** $2a^2 - 11ab - 63b^2$ **87.** $100a^2 - 100ab + 21b^2$ **89.** $15x^2 + 56xy + 48y^2$ **91.** $14x^2 - 97xy - 60y^2$ **93.** $56x^2 - 61xy + 15y^2$ **95.** $12x^2 - x - 20$ **97.** $y^2 - 36$ **99.** $16x^2 - 49$ **101.** $81x^2 - 4$ **103.** $16x^2 - 81y^2$ **105.** $y^2 - 6y + 9$ **107.** $36x^2 - 60x + 25$ **109.** $x^2 - 4xy + 4y^2$ **111.** $4a^2 - 36ab + 81b^2$ **113.** Negative **115.** Positive **117.** The area of the rectangle is $(18x^2 + 12x + 2)$ in². **119.** The area of the circle is $(\pi x^2 + 8\pi x + 16\pi)$ cm². **121.** The total area of the softball diamond and the base paths is $(90x + 2025)$ ft². **123a.** The length of the Water Cube is $(5h + 22)$ ft. **b.** The area of one exterior wall of the Water Cube is $(5h^2 + 22h)$ ft². **125.** $4ab$ **127.** $9a^4 - 24a^3 + 28a^2 - 16a + 4$ **129.** $24x^3 - 3x^2$ **131.** 1024 **133.** $12x^2 - x - 20$ **135.** $-x^3 - 1$ **137.** $-x^5 - 1$ **139.** $-x^7 - 1$

CHECK YOUR PROGRESS: CHAPTER 4

1. $4x^2 - x - 5$ [4.1A] **2.** $3y^2 + 8y - 35$ [4.3C] **3.** $20y^2 - 12y^4$ [4.3A] **4.** $-6a^5b^5$ [4.2A] **5.** $100x^2 - 9$ [4.3D] **6.** $2x^3 - 15x^2 + 23x - 30$ [4.3B] **7.** $6x^{11}y^8$ [4.2A] **8.** $81x^{24}y^{20}$ [4.2B] **9.** $2x^4 - 5x^3 - 3x^2 + 12x + 6$ [4.3B] **10.** $b^2 - 22b + 121$ [4.3D] **11.** $-32b^7$ [4.2B] **12.** $2x^3 + x^2 - 2x - 6$ [4.1B] **13.** $15x^4 - 5x^3 + 35x^2$ [4.3A] **14.** $12a^2 - 35a + 18$ [4.3C] **15.** $25 - 36y^2$ [4.3D] **16.** $9a^2 - 30ab + 25b^2$ [4.3D] **17.** The area of the rectangle is $(12x^2 - 8x)$ in². [4.3E] **18.** The area of the square is $(16x^2 + 40x + 25)$ ft². [4.3E]

SECTION 4.4

3. False **5.** True **7.** False **9.** 1; 1; 1; −2 **11.** No. 39.4 is not between 1 and 10. **13.** No. 2.4 is not an integer. **15.** y^4 **17.** a^3 **19.** p^4 **21.** $2x^3$ **23.** $2k$ **25.** m^5n^2 **27.** $\frac{3r^2}{2}$ **29.** $-\frac{2a}{3}$ **31.** $\frac{1}{y^5}$ **33.** $\frac{1}{a^6}$ **35.** $\frac{1}{3x^3}$ **37.** $\frac{2}{3x^5}$ **39.** $\frac{y^4}{x^2}$ **41.** $\frac{2}{5m^3n^8}$ **43.** $\frac{1}{p^3q}$ **45.** $\frac{1}{2y^3}$ **47.** $\frac{7xz}{8y^3}$ **49.** $\frac{p^2}{2m^3}$ **51.** $\frac{1}{25}$ **53.** 64 **55.** $\frac{1}{27}$ **57.** 2 **59.** $\frac{1}{x^2}$ **61.** a^6 **63.** $\frac{4}{x^7}$ **65.** $\frac{2}{3z^2}$ **67.** $5b^8$ **69.** $\frac{x^2}{3}$ **71.** 1 **73.** −1 **75.** $-\frac{8x^3}{y^6}$ **77.** $\frac{9}{x^2y^4}$ **79.** $\frac{2}{x^4}$ **81.** $-\frac{5}{a^8}$ **83.** $-\frac{a^5}{8b^4}$ **85.** $\frac{10y^3}{x^4}$ **87.** $\frac{1}{2x^3}$ **89.** $\frac{3}{x^3}$ **91.** $\frac{1}{2x^2y^6}$ **93.** $\frac{1}{x^6y}$ **95.** $\frac{a^4}{y^{10}}$ **97.** $-\frac{1}{6x^3}$ **99.** $-\frac{a^2b}{6c^2}$ **101.** $-\frac{7b^6}{a^2}$ **103.** $\frac{s^8t^4}{4r^{12}}$ **105.** $\frac{125p^3}{27m^{15}n^6}$ **107.** False **109.** True **111.** 8; left; 8 **113.** 3.24×10^{-9} **115.** 3×10^{-18} **117.** 3.2×10^{16} **119.** 1.22×10^{-19} **121.** 5.47×10^{8} **123.** 0.000167 **125.** 68,000,000 **127.** 0.0000305 **129.** 0.00000000102 **131.** $-n - 1$ **133.** 1.5×10^{-8} m **135.** 5.98×10^{24} **137.** 6.65×10^{-13} **139.** 2.45×10^{9} **141.** 3.9×10^{-19} **143.** 1.6×10^{10} **145.** $\frac{3}{64}$ **147.** $\frac{1}{4}, \frac{1}{2}, 1, 2, 4; 4, 2, 1, \frac{1}{2}, \frac{1}{4}$ **149.** 0.0625 **151.** 1 **153.** 0 **157a.** If every person in the world moved to Texas, every person would have 1047.6 ft² of land. **b.** If every person in the United States moved to Rhode Island, each person would have 90 ft² of land. **c. i.** 57,900 people would fit in a square mile. **ii.** 120,900 mi² of land would be required to accommodate the entire world population. **d.** If the total land area of Earth were divided equally, each person would be allocated 5.2 acres of land. **e.** The carrying capacity of Earth would be 3300 billion people.

SECTION 4.5

1. $15x^2 + 12x = 3x(5x + 4)$ **3.** True **5.** $3y$; $3y$; $6y^4$; 1 **7.** $2a - 5$ **9.** $3a + 2$ **11.** $x - 2$ **13.** $-x + 2$ **15.** $x^2 + 3x - 5$ **17.** $x^4 - 3x^2 - 1$ **19.** $xy + 2$ **21.** $-3y^3 + 5$ **23.** $3x - 2 + \frac{1}{x}$ **25.** $-3x + 7 - \frac{6}{x}$ **27.** $4a - 5 + 6b$ **29.** $9x + 6 - \frac{3}{y}$ **31.** Multipy $4x$ and $2x^2 - 3x - 1$, $4x(2x^2 - 3x - 1) = 8x^3 - 12x^2 - 4x$ **33.** $x + 2$ **35.** $2x + 1$ **37.** $x + 1 + \frac{2}{x - 1}$ **39.** $2x - 1 - \frac{2}{3x - 2}$ **41.** $b - 5 - \frac{24}{b - 3}$ **43.** $3x + 17 + \frac{64}{x - 4}$ **45.** $5y + 3 + \frac{1}{2y + 3}$ **47.** $3x - 5$ **49.** $x^2 + 2x + 3 + \frac{5}{x + 1}$ **51.** $x^2 - 3$ **53.** False **55.** $4y^2$ **57.** $x^3 - 4x^2 + 11x - 2$ **59.** $x^2 + 2x - 3$

CHAPTER 4 REVIEW EXERCISES

$8b^2 - 2b - 15$ [4.3C] **2.** $21y^2 + 4y - 1$ [4.1A] **3.** $x^4y^8z^4$ [4.2A] **4.** $\frac{2x^3}{3}$ [4.4A] **5.** $-8x^3 - 14x^2 + 18x$ [4.3A] **6.** $-\frac{1}{2a}$ [4.4A] **7.** $16u^{12}v^{16}$ [4.2B] **8.** 64 [4.2B] **9.** $2x^2 + 3x - 8$ [4.1B] **10.** $\frac{b^6}{a^4}$ [4.4A] **11.** $-108x^{18}$ [4.2B] **12.** $25y^2 - 70y + 49$ [4.3D] **13.** $100a^{15}b^{13}$ [4.2B] **14.** $4b^4 + 12b^2 - 1$ [4.5A] **15.** $-\frac{1}{16}$ [4.4A] **16.** $13y^3 - 12y^2 - 5y - 1$ [4.1B] **17.** $-x + 2 + \frac{1}{x+3}$ [4.5B] **18.** $2ax - 4ay - bx + 2by$ [4.3C] **19.** $6y^3 + 17y^2 - 2y - 21$ [4.3B] **20.** $b^2 + 5b + 2 + \frac{7}{b-7}$ [4.5B] **21.** $8a^3b^3 - 4a^2b^4 + 6ab^5$ [4.3A] **22.** $4a^2 - 25b^2$ [4.3D] **23.** $12b^5 - 4b^4 - 6b^3 - 8b^2 + 5$ [4.3B] **24.** $2x^3 + 9x^2 - 3x - 12$ [4.1A] **25.** $-4y + 8$ [4.5A] **26.** $a^2 - 49$ [4.3D] **27.** 3.756×10^{10} [4.4B] **28.** 14,600,000 [4.4B] **29.** $-54a^{13}b^5c^7$ [4.2A] **30.** $2y - 9$ [4.5B] **31.** $\frac{x^4y^6}{9}$ [4.4A] **32.** $10a^2 + 31a - 63$ [4.3C] **33.** 1.27×10^{-7} [4.4B] **34.** 0.0000000000032 [4.4B] **35.** The area is $(2w^2 - w)$ ft². [4.3E] **36.** The area is $(9x^2 - 12x + 4)$ in². [4.3E]

CHAPTER 4 TEST

1. $4x^3 - 6x^2$ [4.3A; HOW TO 1] **2.** $4x - 1 + \frac{3}{x^2}$ [4.5A; HOW TO 1] **3.** $-\frac{4}{x^6}$ [4.4A; HOW TO 12] **4.** $-6x^3y^6$ [4.2A; HOW TO 1] **5.** $x - 1 + \frac{2}{x+1}$ [4.5B; Example 3] **6.** $x^3 - 7x^2 + 17x - 15$ [4.3B; HOW TO 2] **7.** $-8a^6b^3$ [4.2B; Example 2] **8.** $\frac{9y^{10}}{x^{10}}$ [4.4A; Example 2] **9.** $a^2 + 3ab - 10b^2$ [4.3C; Example 4] **10.** $4x^4 - 2x^2 + 5$ [4.5A; HOW TO 1] **11.** $x + 7$ [4.5B; HOW TO 2] **12.** $6y^4 - 9y^3 + 18y^2$ [4.3A; HOW TO 1] **13.** $-4x^4 + 8x^3 - 3x^2 - 14x + 21$ [4.3B; You Try It 3] **14.** $16y^2 - 9$ [4.3D; Example 6] **15.** a^4b^7 [4.2A; You Try It 1] **16.** $8ab^4$ [4.4A; HOW TO 12] **17.** $4a - 7$ [4.5A; HOW TO 1] **18.** $-5a^3 + 3a^2 - 4a + 3$ [4.1B; You Try It 3] $4x^2 - 20x + 25$ [4.3D; Example 7] **20.** $2x + 3 + \frac{2}{2x-3}$ [4.5B; HOW TO 3] **21.** $-2x^3$ [4.4A; Example 2] **22.** $10x^2 - 43xy + 28y^2$ [4.3C; HOW TO 5] **23.** $3x^3 + 6x^2 - 8x + 3$ [4.1A; HOW TO 1] **24.** 3.02×10^{-9} [4.4B; You Try It 5] **25.** The area of the circle is $(\pi x^2 - 10\pi x + 25\pi)$ m². [4.3E; You Try It 8]

CUMULATIVE REVIEW EXERCISES

1. $\frac{5}{144}$ [1.6C] **2.** $\frac{5}{3}$ [1.7A] **3.** $\frac{25}{11}$ [1.7B] **4.** $-\frac{22}{9}$ [2.1A] **5.** $5x - 3xy$ [2.2A] **6.** $-9x$ [2.2B] **7.** $-18x + 12$ [2.2D] **8.** -16 [3.1C] **9.** -16 [3.4A] **10.** 15 [3.4B] **11.** 22% [3.2A] **12.** $4b^3 - 4b^2 - 8b - 4$ [4.1A] **13.** $3y^3 + 2y^2 - 10y$ [4.1B] **14.** a^9b^{15} [4.2B] **15.** $-8x^3y^6$ [4.2A] **16.** $6y^4 + 8y^3 - 16y^2$ [4.3A] **17.** $10a^3 - 39a^2 + 20a - 21$ [4.3B] **18.** $15b^2 - 31b + 14$ [4.3C] **19.** $\frac{1}{2b^2}$ [4.4A] **20.** $a - 7$ [4.5B] **21.** 0.0000609 [4.4B] **22.** $8x - 2x = 18; 3$ [3.5B] **23.** The percent concentration of orange juice in the mixture is 28%. [3.7B] **24.** The car overtakes the cyclist 25 mi from the starting point. [3.7C] **25.** The length is 15 m and the width is 6 m. [3.2A]

Answers To Chapter 5 Selected Exercises

PREP TEST

1. $2 \cdot 3 \cdot 5$ [1.5B] **2.** $-12y + 15$ [2.2C] **3.** $-a + b$ [2.2C] **4.** $-3a + 3b$ [2.2D] **5.** 0 [3.1C] **6.** $-\frac{1}{2}$ [3.3A] **7.** $x^2 - 2x - 24$ [4.3C] **8.** $6x^2 - 11x - 10$ [4.3C] **9.** x^3 [4.4A] **10.** $3x^3y$ [4.4A]

SECTION 5.1

1. 4 **3a.** x **b.** $2x - 1$ **5.** $(2x^3 - x^2) + (6x - 3)$ **7.** $5(a + 1)$ **9.** $8(2 - a^2)$ **11.** $4(2x + 3)$ **13.** $x(7x - 3)$ **15.** $a^2(3 + 5a^3)$ **17.** $2x(x^3 - 2)$ **19.** $2x^2(5x^2 - 6)$ **21.** $4a^5(2a^3 - 1)$ **23.** $xy(xy - 1)$ **25.** $3xy(xy^3 - 2)$ $3x(x^2 + 2x + 3)$ **29.** $2x^2(x^2 - 2x + 3)$ **31.** $2x(x^2 + 3x - 7)$ **33.** $y^3(2y^2 - 3y + 7)$ **35.** $xy(x^2 - 3xy + 7y^2)$ $5y(y^2 + 2y - 5)$ **39.** $3b^2(a^2 - 3a + 5)$ **41.** x^c **43.** $(b + 4)(x + 3)$ **45.** $(y - x)(a - b)$ **47.** $(x - 2)(x - y)$ **49.** $(2m - 3n)(8c - 1)$ **51.** $(x + 2)(x + 2y)$ **53.** $(p - 2)(p - 3r)$ **55.** $(a + 6)(b - 4)$ **57.** $(2z - 1)(z + y)$ **59.** $(2x - 5)(x - 3y)$ **61.** $(y - 2)(3y - a)$ **63.** $(3x - y)(y + 1)$ **65.** $(3s + t)(t - 2)$ **67.** -1 **69.** $b - 3a$

SECTION 5.2

1. -8 **3.** -2 and 6 **5.** Different **7.** $(x + 1)(x + 2)$ **9.** $(x + 1)(x - 2)$ **11.** $(a + 4)(a - 3)$ **13.** $(a - 1)(a - 2)$
15. $(a + 2)(a - 1)$ **17.** $(b - 3)(b - 3)$ **19.** $(b + 8)(b - 1)$ **21.** $(y + 11)(y - 5)$ **23.** $(y - 2)(y - 3)$
25. $(z - 5)(z - 9)$ **27.** $(z + 8)(z - 20)$ **29.** $(p + 3)(p + 9)$ **31.** $(x + 10)(x + 10)$ **33.** $(b + 4)(b - 5)$
35. $(y + 3)(y - 17)$ **37.** $(p + 3)(p - 7)$ **39.** Nonfactorable over the integers **41.** $(x - 5)(x - 15)$ **43.** $(p + 3)(p + 21)$
45. $(x + 2)(x + 19)$ **47.** Nonfactorable over the integers **49.** $(a + 4)(a - 11)$ **51.** $(a - 3)(a - 18)$ **53.** $(z + 21)(z - 7)$
55. $(c + 12)(c - 15)$ **57.** $(p + 9)(p + 15)$ **59.** $(c + 2)(c + 9)$ **61.** $(x + 15)(x - 5)$ **63.** $(x + 25)(x - 4)$
65. $(b - 4)(b - 18)$ **67.** $(a + 45)(a - 3)$ **69.** $(b - 7)(b - 18)$ **71.** $(z + 12)(z + 12)$ **73.** $(x - 4)(x - 25)$
75. $(x + 16)(x - 7)$ **77.** Positive **79.** $3(x + 2)(x + 3)$ **81.** $-(x + 6)(x - 2)$ **83.** $a(b + 8)(b - 1)$ **85.** $x(y + 3)(y + 5)$
87. $-2a(a + 1)(a + 2)$ **89.** $4y(y + 6)(y - 3)$ **91.** $2x(x^2 - x + 2)$ **93.** $6(z + 5)(z - 3)$ **95.** $3a(a + 3)(a - 6)$
97. $(x + 7y)(x - 3y)$ **99.** $(a - 5b)(a - 10b)$ **101.** $(s + 8t)(s - 6t)$ **103.** Nonfactorable over the integers
105. $z^2(z + 10)(z - 8)$ **107.** $b^2(b + 2)(b - 5)$ **109.** $3y^2(y + 3)(y + 15)$ **111.** $-x^2(x - 12)(x + 1)$ **113.** $3y(x + 3)(x - 5)$
115. $-3x(x - 3)(x - 9)$ **117.** $(x - 3y)(x - 5y)$ **119.** $(a - 6b)(a - 7b)$ **121.** $(y + z)(y + 7z)$ **123.** $3y(x + 21)(x - 1)$
125. $3x(x + 4)(x - 3)$ **127.** $2(t - 5s)(t - 7s)$ **129.** $3(a + 3b)(a - 11b)$ **131.** $5x(x + 2y)(x + 4y)$ **133a.** Yes **b.** No
135. $-2x$ **137.** $y(x + 6)(x - 9)$ **139.** $3p(p + 8)(p - 4)$ **141.** 19, 11, 9, -9, -11, -19 **143.** 15, 9, -9, -15 **145.** 6, 10, 12
147. 6, 10, 12 **149.** 4, 6

SECTION 5.3

1. $2x + 5$ **3.** $4x - 3$ **5.** 4, -5 **7.** $-2x - 6x$ **9.** $(x + 1)(2x + 1)$ **11.** $(y + 3)(2y + 1)$ **13.** $(a - 1)(2a - 1)$
15. $(b - 5)(2b - 1)$ **17.** $(x + 1)(2x - 1)$ **19.** $(x - 3)(2x + 1)$ **21.** $(t + 2)(2t - 5)$ **23.** $(p - 5)(3p - 1)$
25. $(3y - 1)(4y - 1)$ **27.** Nonfactorable over the integers **29.** $(2t - 1)(3t - 4)$ **31.** $(x + 4)(8x + 1)$
33. Nonfactorable over the integers **35.** $(3y + 1)(4y + 5)$ **37.** $(z - 14)(2z + 1)$ **39.** $(p + 8)(3p - 2)$ **41.** $2(x + 1)(2x + 1)$
43. $5(y - 1)(3y - 7)$ **45.** $x(x - 5)(2x - 1)$ **47.** $b(a - 4)(3a - 4)$ **49.** Nonfactorable over the integers
51. $-3x(x + 4)(x - 3)$ **53.** $4(4y - 1)(5y - 1)$ **55.** $z(2z + 3)(4z + 1)$ **57.** $y(2x - 5)(3x + 2)$ **59.** $5(t + 2)(2t - 5)$
61. $p(p - 5)(3p - 1)$ **63.** $2(z + 4)(13z - 3)$ **65.** $2y(y - 4)(5y - 2)$ **67.** $yz(z + 2)(4z - 3)$ **69.** $3a(2a + 3)(7a - 3)$
71. $y(3x - 5y)(3x - 5y)$ **73.** $xy(3x - 4y)(3x - 4y)$ **75.** Odd **77.** $(2x - 3)(3x - 4)$ **79.** $(b + 7)(5b - 2)$
81. $(2a - 3)(3a + 8)$ **83.** $(z + 2)(4z + 3)$ **85.** $(2p + 5)(11p - 2)$ **87.** $(y + 1)(8y + 9)$ **89.** $(3t + 1)(6t - 5)$
91. $(b + 12)(6b - 1)$ **93.** $(3x + 2)(3x + 2)$ **95.** $(2b - 3)(3b - 2)$ **97.** $(3b + 5)(11b - 7)$ **99.** $(3y - 4)(6y - 5)$
101. $(3a + 7)(5a - 3)$ **103.** $(2y - 5)(4y - 3)$ **105.** $(2z + 3)(4z - 5)$ **107.** Nonfactorable over the integers
109. $(2z - 5)(5z - 2)$ **111.** $(6z + 5)(6z + 7)$ **113.** $(x + y)(3x - 2y)$ **115.** $(a + 2b)(3a - b)$ **117.** $(y - 2z)(4y - 3z)$
119. $-(z - 7)(z + 4)$ **121.** $-(x - 1)(x + 8)$ **123.** $3(x + 5)(3x - 4)$ **125.** $4(2x - 3)(3x - 2)$ **127.** $a^2(5a + 2)(7a - 1)$
129. $5(b - 7)(3b - 2)$ **131.** $(x - 7y)(3x - 5y)$ **133.** $3(8y - 1)(9y + 1)$ **135.** One positive, one negative
137. One positive, one negative **139.** $(x - 2)(x + 3)$ **141.** $y(y + 1)$ **143.** $(3a + 2)(a + 3)$ **145.** $2y(y - 3)(4y - 1)$
147. $ab(a + 4)(a - 6)$ **149.** 7, -7, 5, -5 **151.** 7, -7, 5, -5 **153.** 11, -11, 7, -7

CHECK YOUR PROGRESS: CHAPTER 5

1. $5(4b + 1)$ [5.1A] **2.** $(b + 7)(2x - y)$ [5.1B] **3.** $(x + 10)(x + 10)$ [5.2A] **4.** $y(x + 4)(x - 6)$ [5.2B]
5. $-(x - 7)(x + 5)$ [5.2B] **6.** Nonfactorable over the integers [5.2A] **7.** $(7x + 2y)(3x - 7)$ [5.1B] **8.** $3a(2b + 3)$ [5.1A]
9. $(y - 4)(5y - 2)$ [5.3A] **10.** $(3x + 1)(4x + 9)$ [5.3B] **11.** $x(9 - 5x)$ [5.1A] **12.** $(2x + 1)(x + y)$ [5.1B]
13. $(2a + b)(4a - 3b)$ [5.3B] **14.** $(b + 4)(b + 5)$ [5.2A] **15.** $2a(a + 9)(a + 3)$ [5.2B] **16.** $(a - 5)(11a + 1)$ [5.3A]
17. $4(9y + 1)(10y - 1)$ [5.3B] **18.** $y(14y^2 + 5y + 11)$ [5.1A] **19.** $(x - 2)(x - 5)$ [5.2A]
20. Nonfactorable over the integers [5.2B] **21.** $(b + 8)(b + 5)$ [5.2A] **22.** $(2x - 5)(x - 3y)$ [5.1B]
23. $xy(x - y^2 + x^2)$ [5.1A] **24.** $(b + 4)(3b + 4)$ [5.3A] **25.** $(x + 3)(x - 14)$ [5.2A]

SECTION 5.4

1. 4; $25x^6$; $100x^4y^4$ **3.** i and iv **5.** Sometimes true **7.** Always true **9.** $3x$; 2 **11.** Answers will vary. For example:
a. $x^2 - 16$ **b.** $(x + 7)(x - 7)$ **c.** $x^2 + 10x + 25$ **d.** $(x - 3)^2$ **e.** $x^2 + 36$ **13.** $(x + 2)(x - 2)$
15. $(a + 9)(a - 9)$ **17.** $(y + 1)^2$ **19.** $(a - 1)^2$ **21.** $(2x + 1)(2x - 1)$ **23.** $(x^3 + 3)(x^3 - 3)$
25. Nonfactorable over the integers **27.** $(x + y)^2$ **29.** $(2a + 1)^2$ **31.** $(3x + 1)(3x - 1)$ **33.** $(1 + 8x)(1 - 8x)$
35. Nonfactorable over the integers **37.** $(3a + 1)^2$ **39.** $(b^2 + 4a)(b^2 - 4a)$ **41.** $(2a - 5)^2$ **43.** $(3a - 7)^2$
45. $(5z + y)(5z - y)$ **47.** $(ab + 5)(ab - 5)$ **49.** $(5x + 1)(5x - 1)$ **51.** $(2a - 3b)^2$ **53.** $(2y - 9z)^2$ **55.** (i) and (iii)
57. 9 **59.** 1 **61.** 25

SECTION 5.5

1. common **3.** $x^2 - 81$ **5.** Determine whether the polynomial is a perfect square trinomial or try to "UNFOIL" the trinomial.
9. $12(n + 2)(n - 2)$ **11.** $r(2s - 1)^2$ **13.** $(9 + t^2)(3 + t)(3 - t)$ **15.** $(x + 2)(x + 8)$ **17.** $4c^2(3c - 2)^2$
19. $2(4s^2 + 1)(2s + 1)(2s - 1)$ **21.** $(3 + 4a)^2$ **23.** $4x(x + 5)$ **25.** $(2x + 3 + 2y)(2x + 3 - 2y)$ **27.** $2(x + 3)(x - 3)$
29. $y(y - 5)^2$ **31.** $a^2(a - 3)(a - 8)$ **33.** $6(y - 2)(y - 6)$ **35.** Nonfactorable over the integers **37.** $3b(a + 9)(a - 2)$
39. $b(b^2 - 8b - 7)$ **41.** $3(y + 7)(y - 7)$ **43.** $3(2a - 3)^2$ **45.** $a^2(b + 11)(b - 8)$ **47.** $4(2x - y)(2x - 3y)$
49. $-2(x + 6)(x - 6)$ **51.** $b^2(a + 3)^2$ **53.** $xy(x - 2y)(2x - 3y)$ **55.** $2a(3a + 2)^2$ **57.** $3(25 + 9y^2)$ **59.** $3x(2x - 5)(4x - 1)$
61. $2a(a - 2b)^2$ **63.** $b^2(a - 3)^2$ **65.** $-x^2(2x - 3)(x + 7)$ **67.** $b^2(b + a)(b - a)$ **69.** $2x(4y - 3)^2$ **71.** $-y^2(x - 3)(x + 5)$

73. $3(x + 3y)(x - 3y)$ **75.** $y(y + 3)(y - 3)$ **77.** $x^2y^2(5x + 4y)(3x - 5y)$ **79.** $2(x - 1)(a + b)$ **81.** $(x - 2)(x + 1)(x - 1)$ $(x + 2)(x - 2)(a + b)$ **85.** $(x - 5)(2 + x)(2 - x)$ **87.** $(4x - 3 + y)(4x - 3 - y)$ **89.** $(x - 2 + y)(x - 2 - y)$
91. 19 **93.** $(\text{middle term})^2 - 1 = (\text{first term}) \cdot (\text{third term})$
Let the numbers be $n - 1$, n, and $n + 1$. Then $n^2 - 1 = (n + 1)(n - 1)$.

SECTION 5.6

1a. Yes **b.** No **c.** Yes **3a.** Yes **b.** Yes **c.** No **d.** Yes **e.** No **f.** Yes **5.** $-3, -2$ **7.** $7, 3$ **9.** $0, 5$ **11.** $0, 9$ **13.** $0, -\frac{3}{2}$ **15.** $0, \frac{2}{3}$ **17.** $-2, 5$ **19.** $9, -9$ **21.** $\frac{7}{2}, -\frac{7}{2}$ **23.** $\frac{1}{3}, -\frac{1}{3}$ **25.** $-4, -2$ **27.** $2, -7$ **29.** $-\frac{1}{2}, 5$ **31.** $-\frac{1}{3}, -\frac{1}{2}$ **33.** $0, 3$ **35.** $0, 7$ **37.** $-1, -4$ **39.** $2, 3$ **41.** $\frac{1}{2}, -4$ **43.** $\frac{1}{3}, 4$ **45.** $3, 9$ **47.** $9, -2$ **49.** $-1, -2$ **51.** $5, -9$ **53.** $4, -7$ **55.** $-2, -3$ **57.** $-8, 9$ **59.** $1, 4$ **61.** $-5, 2$ **63.** Less than **65.** The number is 6. **67.** The numbers are 2 and 4. **69.** ii **71.** The numbers are 4 and 5. **73.** The numbers are 15 and 16. **75.** The base of the triangle is 18 ft. The height is 6 ft. **77.** The length of the rectangle is 18 ft. The width is 8 ft. **79.** The length of a side of the original square is 4 m. **81.** The radius of the original circle is 3.81 in. **83.** The dimensions are 4 in. by 7 in. **85.** The width of the lane is 16 ft. **87.** The object will hit the ground in 4 s. **89.** There are 15 consecutive natural numbers beginning with 1 that will give a sum of 120. **91.** There are 10 teams in the league. **93.** The golf ball will return to the ground in 3 s. **95.** $\frac{3}{2}, -4$ **97.** $-1, -9$ **99.** $0, 7$ **101.** $18, 1$ **103.** 2 or -128 **107.** The length of the piece of cardboard is 20 in. The width is 10 in.

CHAPTER 5 REVIEW EXERCISES

1. $(b - 3)(b - 10)$ [5.2A] **2.** $(x - 3)(4x + 5)$ [5.1B] **3.** Nonfactorable over the integers [5.3A] **4.** $5x(x^2 + 2x + 7)$ [5.1A] **5.** $7y^3(2y^6 - 7y^3 + 1)$ [5.1A] **6.** $(y - 4)(y + 9)$ [5.2A] **7.** $(2x - 7)(3x - 4)$ [5.3A] **8.** $3ab(4a + b)$ [5.1A] **9.** $(a^3 + 10)(a^3 - 10)$ [5.4A] **10.** $n^2(n + 1)(n - 3)$ [5.2B] **11.** $(6y - 1)(2y + 3)$ [5.3A] **12.** $2b(3b - 4)(2b - 7)$ [5.5A] **13.** $(3y^2 + 5z)(3y^2 - 5z)$ [5.4A] **14.** $(c + 6)(c + 2)$ [5.2A] **15.** $(6a - 5)(3a + 2)$ [5.3B] **16.** $\frac{1}{4}, -7$ [5.6A] **17.** $4x(x - 6)(x + 1)$ [5.2B] **18.** $3(a + 2)(a - 7)$ [5.2B] **19.** $(2a + 5)(a - 12)$ [5.3B] $-3, 7$ [5.6A] **21.** $(3a - 5b)(7x + 2y)$ [5.1B] **22.** $(ab + 1)(ab - 1)$ [5.4A] **23.** $(2x + 5)(5x + 2y)$ [5.1B] $5(x + 2)(x - 3)$ [5.2B] **25.** $3(x + 6)^2$ [5.5A] **26.** $(3x - 2)(x - 5)$ [5.3B] **27.** The length is 100 yd. The width is 60 yd. [5.6B] **28.** The distance is 20 ft. [5.6B] **29.** The width of the frame is 1.5 in. or $1\frac{1}{2}$ in. [5.6B] **30.** The two integers are 4 and 5. [5.6B]

CHAPTER 5 TEST

1. $(b + 6)(a - 3)$ [5.1B; Example 6] **2.** $2y^2(y + 1)(y - 8)$ [5.2B; Example 3] **3.** $4(x + 4)(2x - 3)$ [5.3B; Example 4] **4.** $(2x + 1)(3x + 8)$ [5.3A; HOW TO 2] **5.** $(a - 3)(a - 16)$ [5.2A; Example 1] **6.** $2x(3x^2 - 4x + 5)$ [5.1A; HOW TO 2] **7.** $(x + 5)(x - 3)$ [5.2A; Example 2] **8.** $\frac{1}{2}, -\frac{1}{2}$ [5.6A; Example 2] **9.** $5(x^2 - 9x - 3)$ [5.1A; HOW TO 2] **10.** $(p + 6)^2$ [5.4A; Example 3] **11.** $3, 5$ [5.6A; Example 3] **12.** $3(x + 2y)^2$ [5.5A; Example 1] **13.** $(b + 4)(b - 4)$ [5.4A; You Try It 1] **14.** $3y^2(2x + 1)(x + 1)$ [5.3B; Example 4] **15.** $(p + 2)(p + 3)$ [5.2A; You Try It 1] **16.** $(x - 2)(a + b)$ [5.1B; Example 4] **17.** $(p + 1)(x - 1)$ [5.1B; Example 4] **18.** $3(a + 5)(a - 5)$ [5.5A; Example 1] **19.** Nonfactorable over the integers [5.3B; HOW TO 6] **20.** $(x + 3)(x - 12)$ [5.2A; HOW TO 2] **21.** $(2a - 3b)^2$ [5.4A; HOW TO 3] **22.** $(2x + 7y)(2x - 7y)$ [5.4A; Example 1] **23.** $\frac{3}{2}, -7$ [5.6A; HOW TO 1] **24.** The two numbers are 3 and 7. [5.6B; Example 4] **25.** The length is 15 cm. The width is 6 cm. [5.6B; You Try It 5]

CUMULATIVE REVIEW EXERCISES

1. 7 [1.2B] **2.** 4 [1.4B] **3.** -7 [2.1A] **4.** $15x^2$ [2.2B] **5.** 12 [2.2D] **6.** $\frac{2}{3}$ [3.1C] **7.** $\frac{7}{4}$ [3.4A] **8.** 3 [3.4B] **9.** 45 [3.2A] **10.** $9a^6b^4$ [4.2B] **11.** $x^3 - 3x^2 - 6x + 8$ [4.3B] **12.** $4x + 8 + \frac{21}{2x - 3}$ [4.5B] **13.** $\frac{y^6}{x^8}$ [4.4A] **14.** $(a - b)(3 - x)$ [5.1B] **15.** $5xy^2(3 - 4y^2)$ [5.1A] **16.** $(x - 7y)(x + 2y)$ [5.2A] **17.** $(p - 10)(p + 1)$ [5.2A] **18.** $3a(2a + 5)(3a + 2)$ [5.5A] **19.** $(6a - 7b)(6a + 7b)$ [5.4A] **20.** $(2x + 7y)^2$ [5.4A] $(3x - 2)(3x + 7)$ [5.3A] **22.** $2(3x - 4y)^2$ [5.5A] **23.** $(x - 3)(3y - 2)$ [5.1B] **24.** $\frac{2}{3}, -7$ [5.6A] **25.** The shorter piece is 4 ft long. The longer piece is 6 ft long. [3.5B] **26.** The discount rate is 40%. [3.3B] **27.** The measure of $\angle a$ is 72°. The measure of $\angle b$ is 108°. [3.6A] **28.** The distance to the resort is 168 mi. [3.7C] **29.** The integers are 10, 12, and 14. [3.5A] **30.** The length of the base of the triangle is 12 in. [5.6B]

Answers to Chapter 6 Selected Exercises

PREP TEST

1. 36 [1.5C] **2.** $\frac{3x}{y^3}$ [4.4A] **3.** $-\frac{5}{36}$ [1.6C] **4.** $-\frac{10}{11}$ [1.7B] **5.** No [1.7B] **6.** $\frac{19}{8}$ [3.3A] **7.** 130° [3.6B] **8.** $(x-6)(x+2)$ [5.2A] **9.** $(2x-3)(x+1)$ [5.3A] **10.** 9:40 A.M. [3.7C]

SECTION 6.1

5. $\frac{3}{4x}$ **7.** $\frac{1}{x+3}$ **9.** -1 **11.** $\frac{2}{3y}$ **13.** $-\frac{3}{4x}$ **15.** $\frac{a}{b}$ **17.** $-\frac{2}{x}$ **19.** $\frac{y-2}{y-3}$ **21.** $\frac{x+5}{x+4}$ **23.** $\frac{x+4}{x-3}$ **25.** $-\frac{x+2}{x+5}$ **27.** $\frac{2(x+2)}{x+3}$ **29.** $\frac{2x-1}{2x+3}$ **31.** $-\frac{x+7}{x+6}$ **33.** $\frac{2}{3xy}$ **35.** $\frac{8xy^2ab}{3}$ **37.** $\frac{2}{9}$ **39.** $\frac{y^2}{x}$ **41.** $\frac{y(x+4)}{x(x+1)}$ **43.** $\frac{x^3(x-7)}{y^2(x-4)}$ **45.** $-\frac{y}{x}$ **47.** $\frac{x+3}{x+1}$ **49.** $\frac{x-5}{x+3}$ **51.** $-\frac{x+3}{x+5}$ **53.** $-\frac{x+3}{x-12}$ **55.** $\frac{x+2}{x+4}$ **57.** 1 **59.** 1 **61.** $\frac{7a^3y^2}{40bx}$ **63.** $\frac{4}{3}$ **65.** $\frac{3a}{2}$ **67.** $\frac{x^2(x+4)}{y^2(x+2)}$ **69.** $\frac{x(x-2)}{y(x-6)}$ **71.** $-\frac{3by}{ax}$ **73.** $\frac{(x+6)(x-3)}{(x+7)(x-6)}$ **75.** 1 **77.** $-\frac{x+8}{x-4}$ **79.** $\frac{2n+1}{2n-3}$ **81.** Yes **83.** No **85.** 5, -1 **87.** $\frac{4}{25}$ **89.** $\frac{x+4}{x-3}$ and $\frac{2x-1}{3x+1}$ or $\frac{x+4}{3x+1}$ and $\frac{2x-1}{x-3}$

SECTION 6.2

1. True **3.** False **5.** $24x^3y^2$ **7.** $6x^2y(x+4)$ **9.** $36x(x+2)^2$ **11.** $6(x+1)^2$ **13.** $(x-1)(x+2)(x+3)$ **15.** $(2x+3)^2(x-5)$ **17.** $(x-1)(x-2)$ **19.** $(x-3)(x+2)(x+4)$ **21.** $(x+4)(x+1)(x-7)$ **23.** $(x-6)(x+6)(x+4)$ **25.** $(2x-1)(x-3)(x+1)$ **27.** $(x+2)(x-3)$ **29.** $\frac{4x}{x^2}, \frac{3}{x^2}$ **31.** $\frac{4x}{12y^2}, \frac{3yz}{12y^2}$ **33.** $\frac{xy}{x^2(x-3)}, \frac{6x-18}{x^2(x-3)}$ **35.** $\frac{9x}{x(x-1)^2}, \frac{6x-6}{x(x-1)^2}$ **37.** $\frac{3x}{x(x-3)}, -\frac{5}{x(x-3)}$ **39.** $\frac{x^2-6x+8}{(x+3)(x-4)}, \frac{x^2+3x}{(x+3)(x-4)}$ **41.** $\frac{3}{(x+2)(x-1)}, \frac{x^2-x}{(x+2)(x-1)}$ **43.** $\frac{x^2-3x}{(x+3)(x-3)(x-2)}, \frac{2x^2-4x}{(x+3)(x-3)(x-2)}$ **45.** $\frac{300}{10^4}; \frac{5}{10^4}$ **47.** $\frac{b^2}{b}; \frac{5}{b}$

SECTION 6.3

1. False **3.** False **5.** $\frac{11}{y^2}$ **7.** $-\frac{7}{x+4}$ **9.** $\frac{8x}{2x+3}$ **11.** $\frac{5x+7}{x-3}$ **13.** $\frac{2x-5}{x+9}$ **15.** $\frac{-3x-4}{2x+7}$ **17.** $\frac{1}{x+5}$ **19.** $\frac{1}{x-6}$ **21.** $\frac{3}{2y-1}$ **23.** $\frac{1}{x-5}$ **25.** i and iv **27.** $\frac{4y+5x}{xy}$ **29.** $\frac{19}{2x}$ **31.** $\frac{5}{12x}$ **33.** $\frac{19x-12}{6x^2}$ **35.** $\frac{52y-35x}{20xy}$ **37.** $\frac{13x+2}{15x}$ **39.** $\frac{7}{24}$ **41.** $\frac{x+90}{45x}$ **43.** $\frac{x^2+2x+2}{2x^2}$ **45.** $\frac{2x^2+3x-10}{4x^2}$ **47.** $\frac{-x^2-4x+4}{x+4}$ **49.** $\frac{4x+7}{x+1}$ **51.** $\frac{4x^2+9x+9}{24x^2}$ **53.** $\frac{3x-1-2xy-3y}{xy^2}$ **55.** $\frac{20x^2+28x-12xy+9y}{24x^2y^2}$ **57.** $\frac{9x^2-3x-2xy-10y}{18xy^2}$ **59.** $\frac{7x-23}{(x-3)(x-4)}$ **61.** $\frac{-y-33}{(y+6)(y-3)}$ **63.** $\frac{3x^2+20x-8}{(x-4)(x+6)}$ **65.** $\frac{3(4x^2+5x-5)}{(x+5)(2x+3)}$ **67.** $\frac{-4x+5}{x-6}$ **69.** $\frac{2(y+2)}{(y-4)(y+4)}$ **71.** $-\frac{4x}{(x+1)^2}$ **73.** $\frac{2x-1}{(1+x)(1-x)}$ **75.** $\frac{14}{(x-5)^2}$ **77.** $\frac{-2(x+7)}{(x+6)(x-7)}$ **79.** $\frac{x-4}{x-6}$ **81.** $\frac{2x+1}{x-1}$ **83.** $\frac{-3(x^2+8x+25)}{(x-3)(x+7)}$ **85.** $\frac{5}{a}+\frac{4}{b}$ **87.** $\frac{3}{y^2}+\frac{4}{xy}$ **89a.** $\frac{44{,}400}{x}$ dollars **b.** $\frac{222{,}000}{x(x+5)}$ dollars **c.** You will save $296 in one year.

SECTION 6.4

1. $\frac{2}{2}$ **3.** $\frac{(x-1)(x+4)}{(x-1)(x+4)}$ **5.** True **7.** $\frac{x}{x-3}$ **9.** $\frac{2}{3}$ **11.** $\frac{y+3}{y-4}$ **13.** $\frac{2(2x+13)}{5x+36}$ **15.** $\frac{x+2}{x+3}$ **17.** $\frac{x-6}{x+5}$ **19.** $\frac{-x+2}{x+1}$ **21.** $x-1$ **23.** $\frac{1}{2x-1}$ **25.** $\frac{x-3}{x+5}$ **27.** $\frac{x-7}{x-8}$ **29.** $\frac{2y-1}{2y+1}$ **31.** $\frac{x-2}{2x-5}$ **33.** $\frac{-x-1}{4x-3}$ **35.** $\frac{x+1}{2(5x-2)}$ **37.** True **39.** $\frac{8}{5}$ **41.** $-\frac{1}{y}$ **43.** y^2-x^2 **45.** The total resistance in the circuit is $\frac{6}{5}$ ohms.

CHECK YOUR PROGRESS: CHAPTER 6

$\frac{x+2}{x+5}$ [6.1A] **2.** $\frac{5}{3}$ [6.1B] **3.** $\frac{b^4x^2y}{a^2}$ [6.1C] **4.** $\frac{a^2(a+4)}{b^5(a+2)}$ [6.1C] **5.** $30x^4y^2$ [6.2A] **6.** $8x^2(x+2)$ [6.2A]
7. $\frac{3x}{x^2(x+2)}, \frac{4x+8}{x^2(x+2)}$ [6.2B] **8.** $-\frac{2a}{3a-1}$ [6.3A] **9.** $\frac{a+3}{a+5}$ [6.3B] **10.** $\frac{19x+6}{8x-15}$ [6.4A]

SECTION 6.5

1. Multiplication Property of Equations **3.** We can clear denominators in an *equation*, as in part (a), but not in an *expression*, as in part (b).
5. $-1, 2$ **7.** $0, 9$ **9.** 1 **11.** 3 **13.** 2 **15.** 2 **17.** $\frac{2}{3}$ **19.** 4 **21.** -3 **23.** $\frac{3}{4}$ **25.** 7 **27.** -7
29. -1 **31.** -1 **33.** No solution **35.** $2, -6$ **37.** $-\frac{2}{3}, 5$ **39.** $-1, 6$ **41.** 0 **43.** $0, -\frac{2}{3}$
45. The intensity of the illumination is 4 lm. **47.** A 320-candela-light source is needed. **49.** The light source must be placed 2 m from the desk surface.

SECTION 6.6

1. A ratio is the quotient of two quantities that have the same unit. A rate is the quotient of two quantities that have different units.
3a. Rate, $\frac{25 \text{ ft}}{2 \text{ s}}$ **b.** Ratio, $\frac{4}{3}$ **c.** Rate, $\frac{10 \text{ mi}}{1 \text{ h}}$ **d.** Ratio, $\frac{1}{6}$ **5a.** YZ **b.** $\angle R$ **7.** 9 **9.** 12 **11.** 7 **13.** 6 **15.** 1
17. -6 **19.** 4 **21.** $-\frac{2}{3}$ **23.** 20,000 people voted in favor of the amendment. **25.** 45 million Americans do not have health insurance.
27. 140 air vents are required for the office building. **29.** The length of the sea scorpion's claw was 1.23 ft. **31.** There are approximately 800 fish in the lake. **33.** 180 panels are needed to provide 600 watts of power. **35.** Yes, the shipment will be accepted. **37.** The height of the person is 67.5 in. **39.** There are 750 mi between the two cities. **41.** The engine burns 127,500 lb of fuel in 45 s. **43.** 22.5 gal of yellow paint are needed. **45.** 10 additional acres must be planted. **47.** AC is 6.7 cm. **49.** The height is 2.9 m.
51. The perimeter is 22.5 ft. **53.** The area is 48 m^2. **55.** BC measures 6.25 cm. **57.** DA measures 6 in. **59.** OP measures 13 cm.

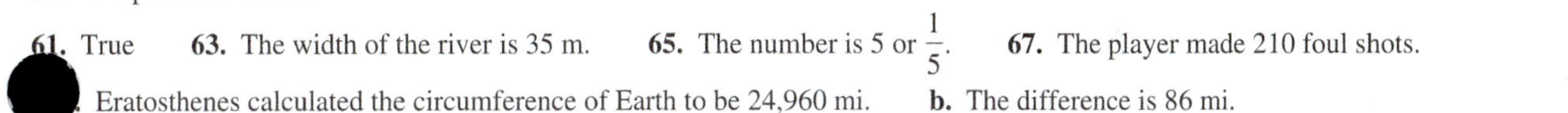

61. True **63.** The width of the river is 35 m. **65.** The number is 5 or $\frac{1}{5}$. **67.** The player made 210 foul shots.
Eratosthenes calculated the circumference of Earth to be 24,960 mi. **b.** The difference is 86 mi.

SECTION 6.7

1. True **3.** R **5.** $t = \frac{d}{r}$ **7.** $T = \frac{PV}{nR}$ **9.** $l = \frac{P-2w}{2}$ **11.** $b_1 = \frac{2A - hb_2}{h}$ **13.** $h = \frac{3V}{A}$ **15.** $S = C - Rt$
17. $P = \frac{A}{1+rt}$ **19.** $w = \frac{A}{S+1}$ **21.** $y = -3x + 10$ **23.** $y = 4x - 3$ **25.** $y = -\frac{3}{2}x + 3$ **27.** $y = \frac{2}{5}x - 2$
29. $y = -\frac{2}{7}x + 2$ **31.** $y = -\frac{1}{3}x + 2$ **33.** $x = -3y + 6$ **35.** $x = \frac{1}{3}y + 1$ **37.** $x = -\frac{5}{2}y + 5$ **39.** $x = 2y - 1$
41a. Yes **b.** Yes **43.** $R_2 = \frac{RR_1}{R_1 - R}$

SECTION 6.8

3. $\frac{1}{x}$ **5.** Jen has the greater rate of work. **7a.** Chris's rate of work is $\frac{1}{x}$ of the job per hour. **b.** Chris can lay $\frac{3}{x}$ of the floor in 3 h.
9. The faster printer printed $\frac{h}{5}$ of the brochures. **11a.** The speed of the boat traveling with the current is 12 mph. **b.** The speed of the boat traveling against the current is 4 mph. **13.** Row 1: $\frac{1}{10}, t, \frac{t}{10}$; Row 2: $\frac{1}{12}, t, \frac{t}{12}$ **15.** It will take 2 h to fill the fountain with both sprinklers operating. **17.** With both skiploaders working together, it would take 3 h to transfer the earth. **19.** It would take both computers, working together, 30 h to solve the problem. **21.** With both air conditioners working, it would take 24 min to cool the room 5°F. **23.** It would take the second welder, working alone, 15 h to complete the task. **25.** It would take the second pipeline, working alone, 90 min to fill the tank.
27. It would take 3 h to harvest the field using only the older reaper. **29.** It will take the second technician 3 h to complete the wiring.
31. It would take the small unit, working alone, $14\frac{2}{3}$ h to heat the pool. **33.** It will take the apprentice, working alone, 3 h to complete the repairs. **35.** t is less than k. **37a.** Row 1: 1440, $380 - r$, $\frac{1440}{380 - r}$; Row 2: 1600, $380 + r$, $\frac{1600}{380 + r}$ **b.** $\frac{1440}{380 - r}; \frac{1600}{380 + r}$
The camper hiked at 4 mph. **41.** The rate of the jet is 360 mph. **43.** The rate of the boat for the first 15 mi was 7.5 mph.
The technician traveled at 20 mph through the congested traffic. **47.** The family can travel 21.6 mi down the river and still return the boat in 3 h.
49. The rate of the river's current is 5 mph. **51.** The rate of the freight train is 30 mph, and the rate of the express train is 50 mph.

53. The rate of the current is 2 mph. **55.** The rate of the jet stream is 50 mph. **57.** The rate of the current is 5 mph. **59.** It would take $1\frac{1}{19}$ h to fill the tank with all three pipes operating. **61.** The amount of time spent traveling by canoe was 2 h. **63.** The bus usually travels 60 mph.

CHAPTER 6 REVIEW EXERCISES

1. $\frac{b^3y}{10ax}$ [6.1C] **2.** $\frac{7x+22}{60x}$ [6.3B] **3.** $\frac{2xy}{5}$ [6.1B] **4.** $\frac{2xy}{3(x+y)}$ [6.1C] **5.** $\frac{x-2}{3x-10}$ [6.4A] **6.** $-\frac{x+6}{x+3}$ [6.1A] **7.** $\frac{2x^4}{3y^7}$ [6.1A] **8.** 62 [6.6A] **9.** $\frac{(3y-2)^2}{(y-1)(y-2)}$ [6.1C] **10.** $x = \frac{5}{3a-1}$ [6.7A] **11.** 8 [6.5A] **12.** $\frac{x^2+3y}{xy}$ [6.3B] **13.** $y = -\frac{5}{4}x + 5$ [6.7A] **14.** $\frac{by^3}{6ax^2}$ [6.1B] **15.** $\frac{x}{x-7}$ [6.4A] **16.** $\frac{3x^2-x}{(2x+3)(6x-1)(3x-1)}, \frac{24x^3-4x^2}{(2x+3)(6x-1)(3x-1)}$ [6.2B] **17.** $a = \frac{T-2bc}{2b+2c}$ [6.7A] **18.** 2 [6.5A] **19.** $\frac{2x+1}{3x-2}$ [6.4A] **20.** $\frac{x^2+5}{(x-5)(x-2)}$ [6.3B] **21.** $c = \frac{100m}{i}$ [6.7A] **22.** No solution [6.5A] **23.** $\frac{1}{x^2}$ [6.1C] **24.** $\frac{2y-3}{5y-7}$ [6.3B] **25.** $\frac{1}{x+3}$ [6.3A] **26.** $(5x-3)(2x-1)(4x-1)$ [6.2A] **27.** $y = -\frac{4}{9}x + 2$ [6.7A] **28.** $\frac{2x+1}{x+2}$ [6.1B] **29.** 5 [6.5A] **30.** $\frac{3x-1}{x-5}$ [6.3B] **31.** 10 [6.6A] **32.** 12 [6.6A] **33.** The length of QO is 15 cm. [6.6B] **34.** The area is $\frac{256}{3}$ in^2. [6.6B] **35.** It would take 6 h to fill the pool. [6.8A] **36.** The rate of the car is 45 mph. [6.8B] **37.** The rate of the wind is 20 mph. [6.8B] **38.** The pitcher's ERA is 1.35. [6.6A]

CHAPTER 6 TEST

1. $\frac{x^2-4x+5}{(x-2)(x+3)}$ [6.3B; Example 6] **2.** -1 [6.6A; You Try It 1B] **3.** $\frac{(x-5)(2x-1)}{(x+3)(2x+5)}$ [6.1B; Example 5] **4.** $\frac{2x^3}{3y^3}$ [6.1A; Example 1] **5.** $t = \frac{d-s}{r}$ [6.7A; Example 3] **6.** 2 [6.5A; Example 2] **7.** $-\frac{x+5}{x+1}$ [6.1A; Example 3] **8.** $3(2x-1)(x+1)$ [6.2A; HOW TO 1] **9.** $\frac{5}{(2x-1)(3x+1)}$ [6.3B; Example 6] **10.** $\frac{x+5}{x+4}$ [6.1C; Example 7] **11.** $\frac{x-3}{x-2}$ [6.4A; Example 2] **12.** $\frac{3x+6}{x(x-2)(x+2)}, \frac{x^2}{x(x-2)(x+2)}$ [6.2B; Example 4] **13.** $\frac{2}{x+5}$ [6.3A; Example 1] **14.** $y = \frac{3}{8}x - 2$ [6.7A; Example 1] **15.** No solution [6.5A; HOW TO 2] **16.** $\frac{x+1}{x^3(x-2)}$ [6.1B; Example 4] **17.** CE is 12.8 ft. [6.6B; Example 3] **18.** 6 lb of salt are needed. [6.6A; Example 2] **19.** It would take 4 h to fill the pool. [6.8A; HOW TO 1] **20.** The rate of the wind is 20 mph. [6.8B; HOW TO 2] **21.** 54 sprinklers are needed for a 3600-square-foot lawn. [6.6A; You Try It 2]

CUMULATIVE REVIEW EXERCISES

1. $\frac{31}{30}$ [1.7A] **2.** 21 [2.1A] **3.** $5x - 2y$ [2.2A] **4.** $-8x + 26$ [2.2D] **5.** $-\frac{9}{2}$ [3.3A] **6.** -12 [3.4B] **7.** 10 [3.2A] **8.** a^3b^7 [4.2A] **9.** $a^2 + ab - 12b^2$ [4.3C] **10.** $3b^3 - b + 2$ [4.5A] **11.** $x^2 + 2x + 4$ [4.5B] **12.** $(4x+1)(3x-1)$ [5.3A] **13.** $(y-6)(y-1)$ [5.2A] **14.** $a(2a-3)(a+5)$ [5.3A] **15.** $4(b+5)(b-5)$ [5.5A] **16.** $-3, \frac{5}{2}$ [5.6A] **17.** $\frac{2x^3}{3y^5}$ [6.1A] **18.** $-\frac{x-2}{x+5}$ [6.1A] **19.** 1 [6.1C] **20.** $\frac{3}{(2x-1)(x+1)}$ [6.3B] **21.** $\frac{x+3}{x+5}$ [6.4A] **22.** 4 [6.5A] **23.** 3 [6.6A] **24.** $t = \frac{f-v}{a}$ [6.7A] **25.** $5x - 13 = -8; x = 1$ [3.5A] **26.** The 120-gram alloy is 70% silver. [3.7B] **27.** The base is 10 in. The height is 6 in. [5.6B] **28.** The cost of a $5000 policy is $80. [6.6A] **29.** It would take both pipes 6 min to fill the tank. [6.8A] **30.** The rate of the current is 2 mph. [6.8B]

Answers to Chapter 7 Selected Exercises

PREP TEST

1. 3 [1.4B] **2.** -1 [2.1A] **3.** $-3x + 12$ [2.2C] **4.** -2 [3.3A] **5.** $x = 5$ [3.3A] **6.** $y = -2$ [3.3A] **7.** $-4x + 5$ [4.5A] **8.** 4 [6.6A] **9.** $y = \frac{3}{5}x - 3$ [6.7A] **10.** $y = -\frac{1}{2}x - 5$ [6.7A]

SECTION 7.1

1. Quadrant II **3.** y-axis **5.** Answers will vary. For example, $(-3, 2)$ and $(5, 2)$ **7.** right; down
9. $(6, -5)$ **11.** x; y **13.** ordered pairs; domain; range **15.**

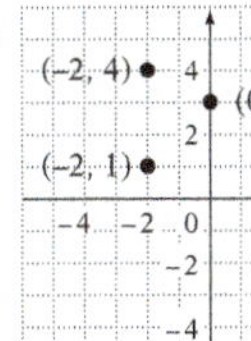

17.

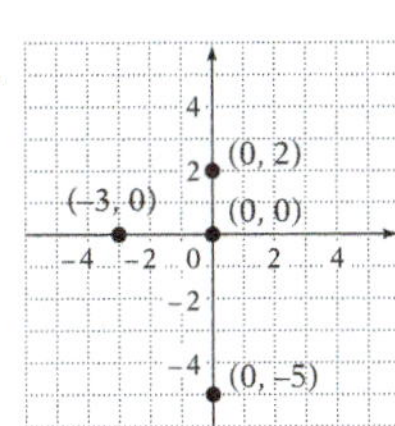

19.

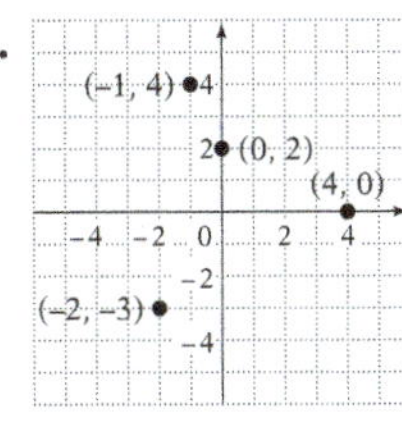

21. $A(2, 3)$, $B(4, 0)$, $C(-4, 1)$, $D(-2, -2)$

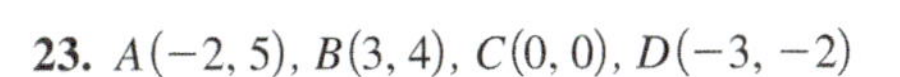

23. $A(-2, 5)$, $B(3, 4)$, $C(0, 0)$, $D(-3, -2)$ **25a.** $2, -4$ **b.** $1, -3$ **27a.** I **b.** II **c.** IV **d.** III **29.** Yes **31.** No
33. No **35.** Negative **37.**

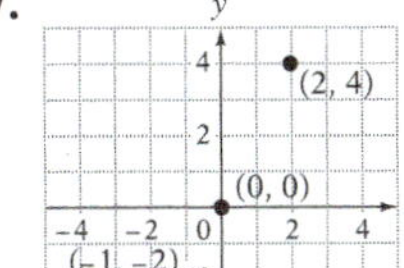

39.

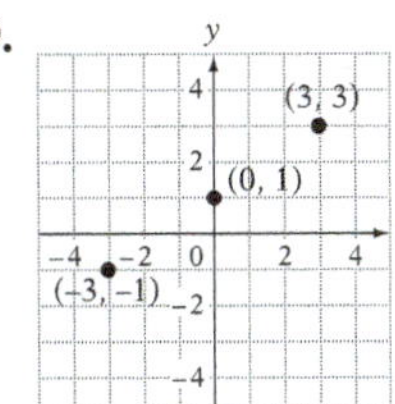

41.

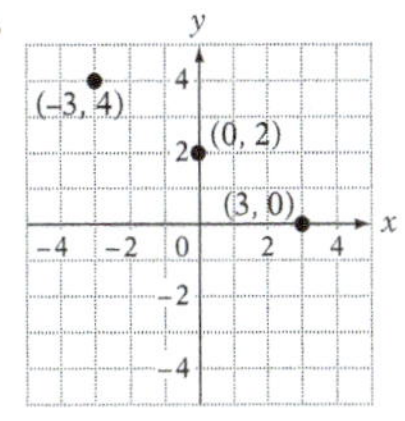

43. No **45.** $\{(35, 7.50), (45, 7.58), (38, 7.63), (24, 7.78), (47, 7.80), (51, 7.86), (35, 7.89), (48, 7.92)\}$ No, the relation is not a function. **47.** $\{(1600, 18), (2000, 20), (2200, 24), (2500, 25), (2800, 31)\}$ Yes, the relation is a function. **49.** D: $\{0, 2, 4, 6\}$; R: $\{0\}$; yes
51. D: $\{2\}$; R: $\{2, 4, 6, 8\}$; no **53.** Yes **55.** Yes **57.** 11 **59.** 0 **61.** 6 **63.** $-\frac{4}{3}$ **65.** 11 **67.** $\frac{6}{7}$ **69.** Either
71. Positive **73.** 4 units **75.** 2 units **77.** 5 units

SECTION 7.2

1. i and ii **3.** b and d are graphs of straight lines. **5.** Multiples of 3, such as $-3, 0, 3$, and 6
7. **9.** **11.**

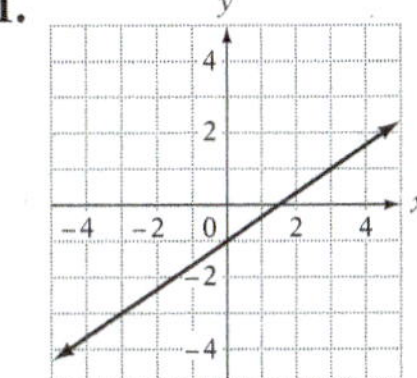

13.

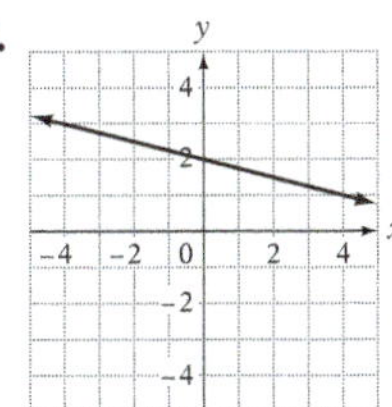

15.

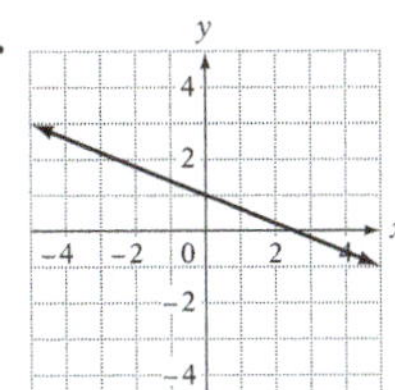

17.

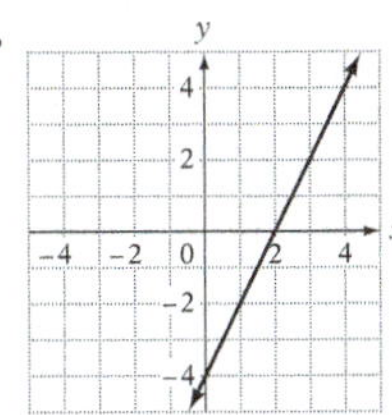

19.

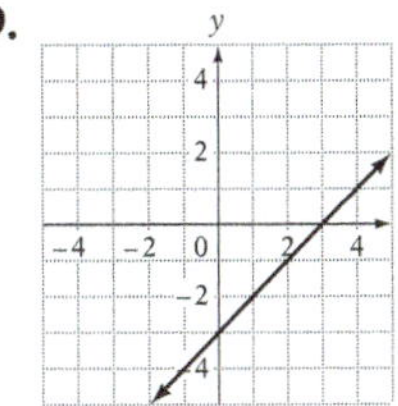

21.

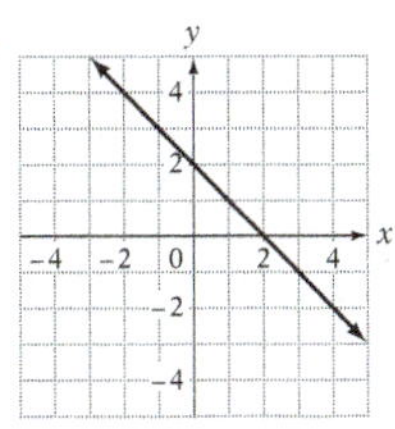

23.

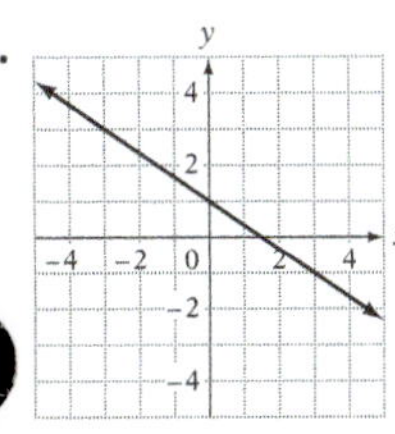

25. 0 **27.** $y = -2x + 5$ **29.** $y = 5x - 7$ **31.** $y = -\frac{2}{3}x + 3$ **33.** $y = \frac{5}{2}x - 2$
35. $y = \frac{6}{5}x - 2$ **37.** $y = \frac{1}{4}x - 3$

39. 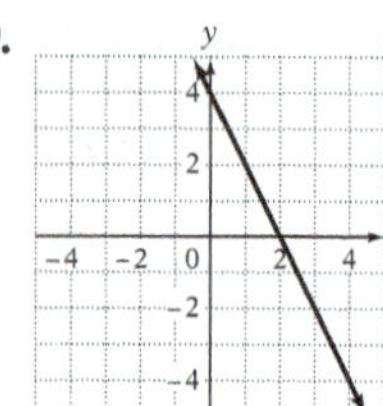

41. 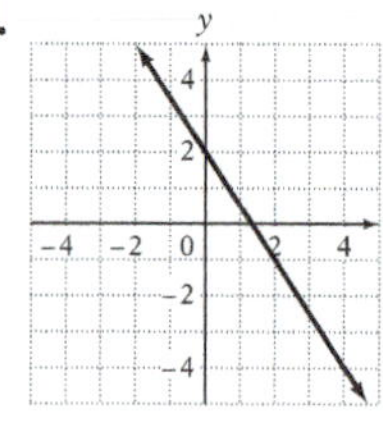

43. 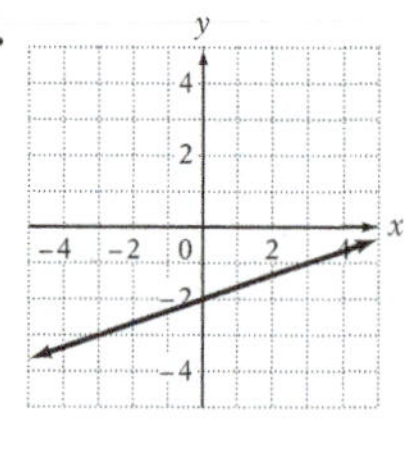

45. 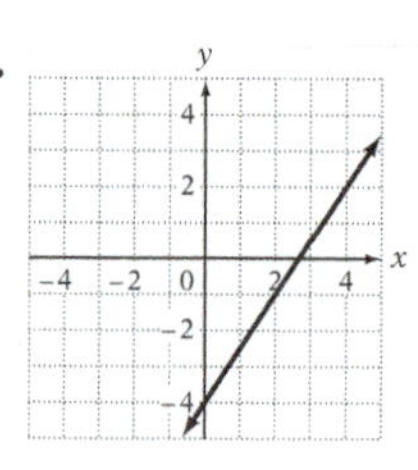

47. 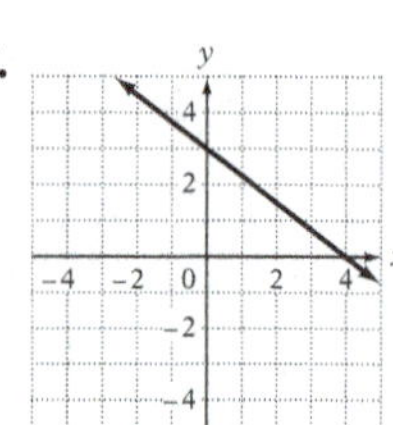

49. 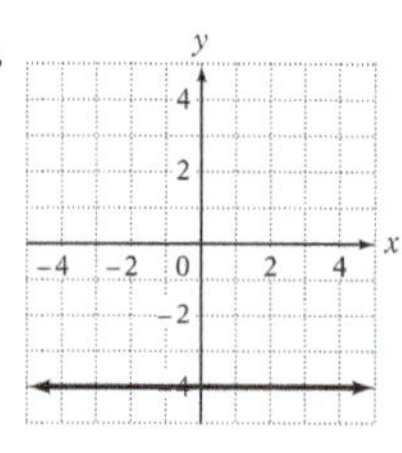

51. 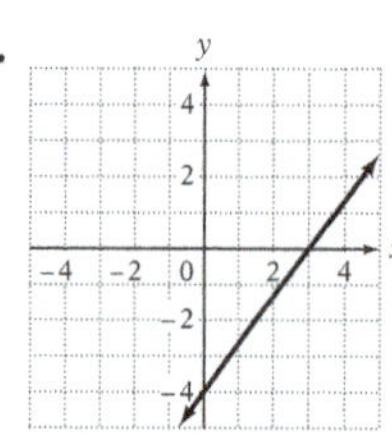

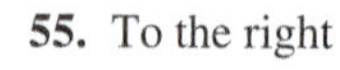
53. A **55.** To the right

57. A custom sign 15 ft^2 in area costs \$182.50.

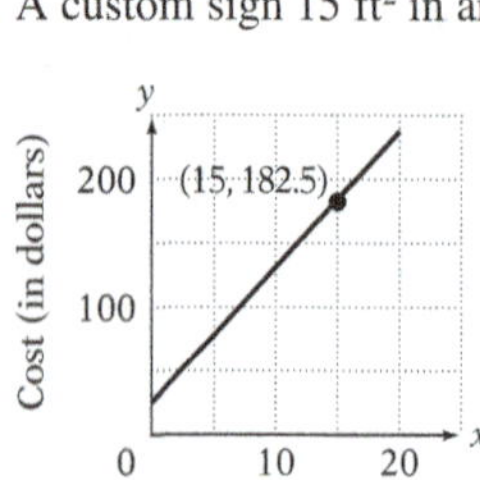

59. A dog 6 years old is equivalent in age to a human 40 years old.

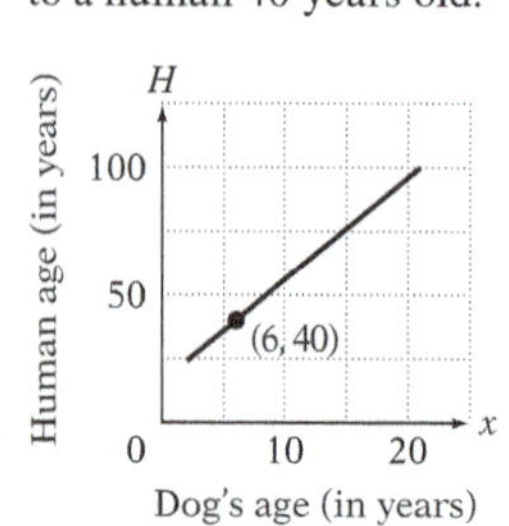

61. Answers will vary. For example, $y = 2x$

CHECK YOUR PROGRESS: CHAPTER 7

1. [7.1A]

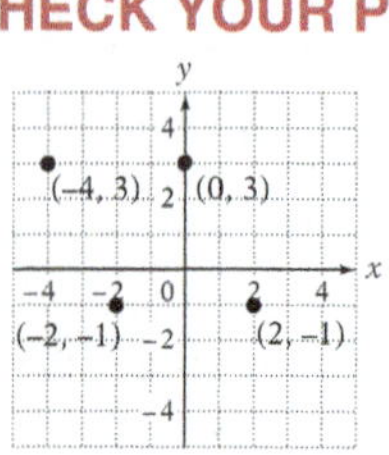

2. [7.2A]

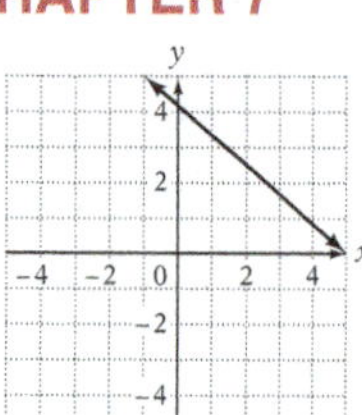

3. [7.2B]

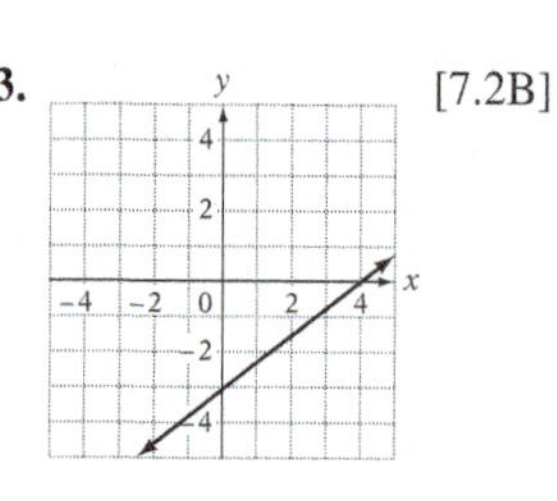

4. $(-1, 5), (0, 2), (1, -1), (2, -4)$ [7.1B] **5.** The graph is a vertical line passing through $(-5, 0)$. [7.2B] **6.** D: $\{-3, -2, -1\}$; R: $\{-2, -1, 0\}$; yes [7.1C] **7.** 0 [7.1D] **8.** Yes [7.1B] **9.** Yes [7.1C]

SECTION 7.3

1. m **3a.** positive **b.** negative **c.** zero **d.** undefined **5.** x-coordinate **7.** 2; -4; 3; 1 **9.** Vertical **11.** $\frac{6}{5}$ **13.** $(3, 0), (0, -3)$ **15.** $(2, 0), (0, -6)$ **17.** $(10, 0), (0, -2)$ **19.** $(-4, 0), (0, 12)$ **21.** $(0, 0), (0, 0)$ **23.** $(6, 0), (0, 3)$

25. 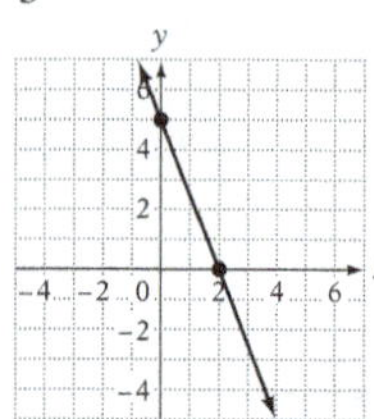

27. 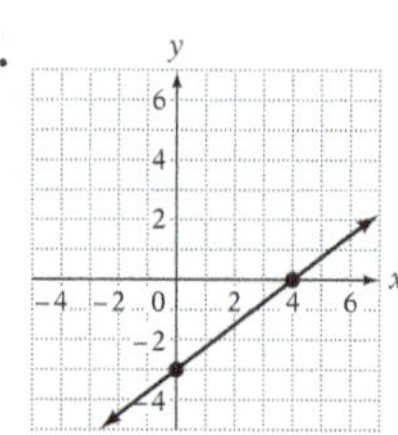

29. 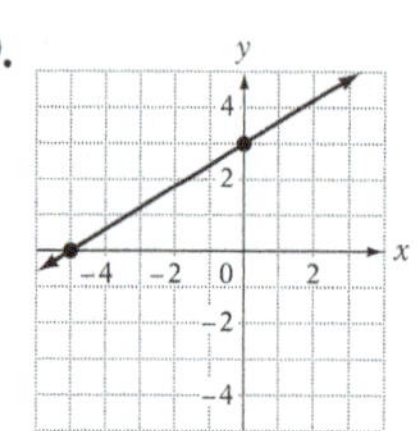

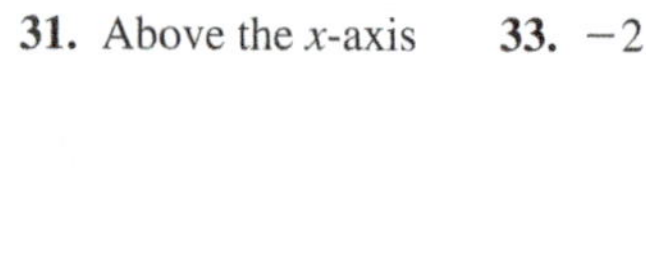
31. Above the x-axis **33.** -2

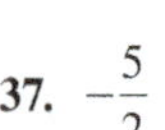
35. $\frac{1}{3}$ **37.** $-\frac{5}{2}$ **39.** Undefined **41.** Zero **43.** $-\frac{1}{3}$ **47.** $b = d, a \neq c$ **49.** No **51.** No

53. Parallel **55.** Perpendicular **57.** Neither **59.** Perpendicular **61.** $m = -\frac{19}{30}$. The water in the lock decreases by $0.6\overline{3}$ million gallons each minute. **63.** $m = 70$. Walking burns 70 calories per mile. **65.** $m = 2.25$. The percent of people using seat belts has increased by 2.25% per year. **67.** $m = -\frac{3}{8}$, $(0, 5)$ **69.** $m = \frac{2}{3}$, $(0, -2)$ **71.** $m = -\frac{2}{5}$, $(0, 2)$ **73.** $m = \frac{1}{4}$, $(0, 0)$

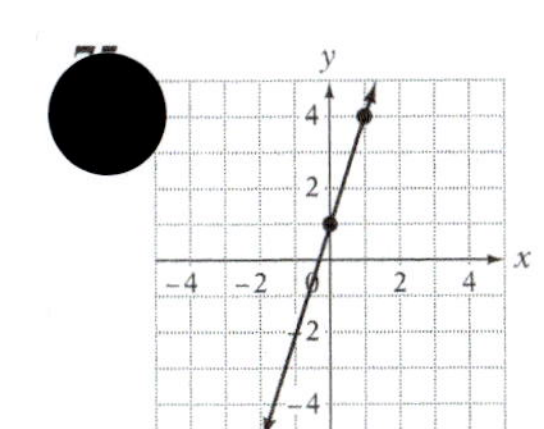

77. **79.**

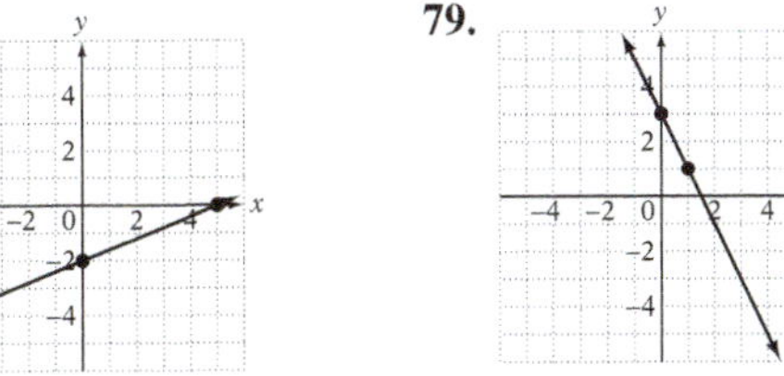

81.

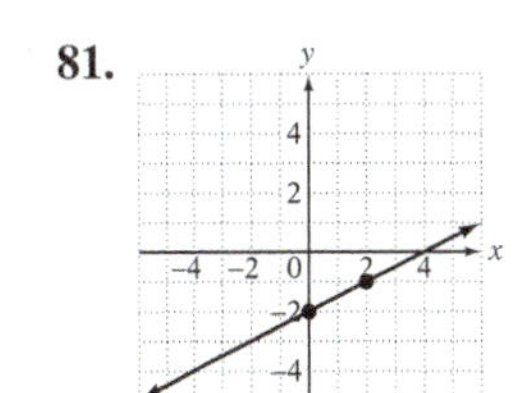

83.

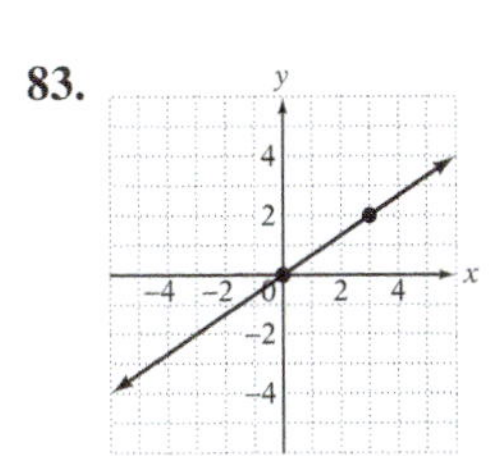

85.

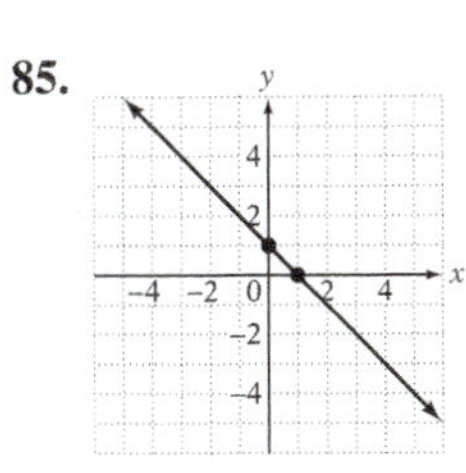

87.

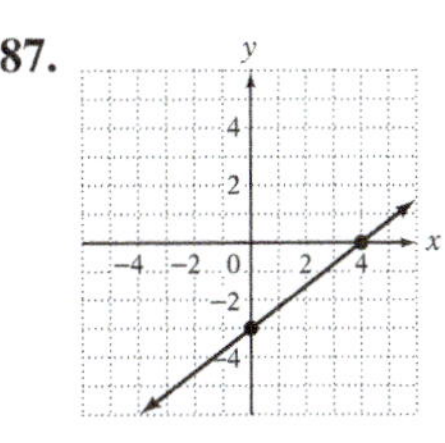

89.

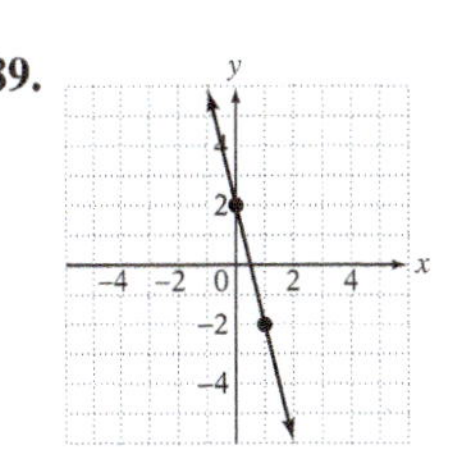

91. Above; upward to the right **93.** Decreases the slope **95.** Decreases the y-coordinate of the y-intercept
97. No; for example, $x = 2$ **99.** Line a slants upward to the right. Line b slants downward to the right.
101. Line a has a y-intercept of $(0, 5)$. Line b has a y-intercept of $(0, -5)$. **103.** Line a is a horizontal line. Line b is a vertical line.

105.

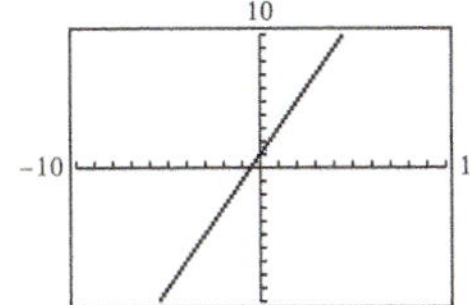

107.

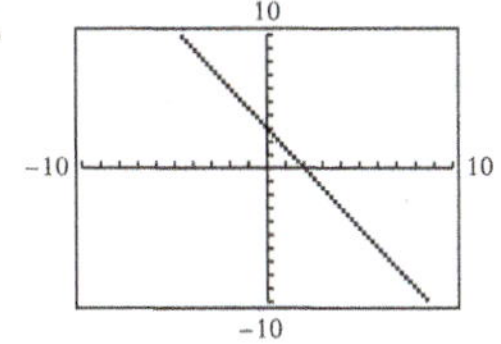

SECTION 7.4

 7 **3.** 0; 2 **5.** 3; 1; $3x + 1$ **7.** $y = 2x + 2$ **9.** $y = -3x - 1$ **11.** $y = \frac{1}{3}x$ **13.** $y = \frac{3}{4}x - 5$ **15.** $y = -\frac{3}{5}x$
17. $y = \frac{1}{4}x + \frac{5}{2}$ **19.** $y = -\frac{2}{3}x - 7$ **21.** $y = 2x - 3$ **23.** $y = -2x - 3$ **25.** $y = \frac{2}{3}x$ **27.** $y = \frac{1}{2}x + 2$ **29.** $y = -\frac{3}{4}x - 2$
31. $y = \frac{3}{4}x + \frac{5}{2}$ **33.** $y = -\frac{4}{3}x - 9$ **35.** $y = mx + b$ **37.** $y = 3x + 4$ **39.** $y = -x - 4$ **41.** $y = -\frac{6}{5}x + 5$
43. $y = -\frac{2}{5}x - 7$ **45.** $y = 5$ **47.** $x = 5$ **49.** $y = \frac{4}{5}x + 8$ **51.** $y = -\frac{1}{2}x - 2$ **53.** $y = -\frac{4}{3}x - 3$
55. $y = 3x - 3$ **57.** $y = 3x$ **59.** $x = 3$ **61.** 2 **63.** Yes; $y = \frac{1}{2}x - 3$ **65.** Yes; $y = -\frac{1}{3}x$ **67.** 1 **69.** -8
71. $(3, 0)$; $(0, 2)$; $-\frac{2}{3}$; $y = -\frac{2}{3}x + 2$ **73.** $(-1, 0)$; $(0, -2)$; -2; $y = -2x - 2$

CHAPTER 7 REVIEW EXERCISES

1a.

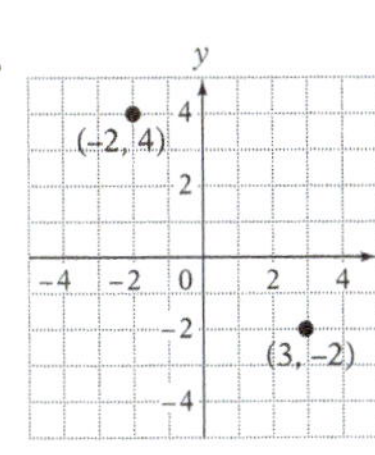

2.

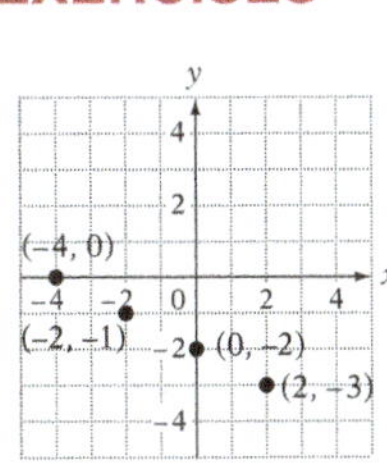

[7.1B]

3. $y = -\frac{8}{3}x + \frac{1}{3}$ [7.4C] **4.** $y = -\frac{5}{2}x + 16$ [7.4A]

b. -2
c. -4 [7.1A]

5.

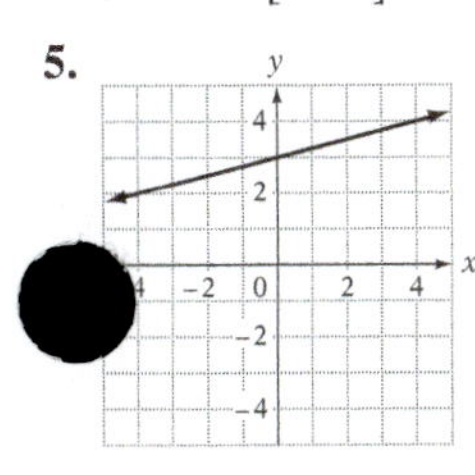

[7.2A]

6.

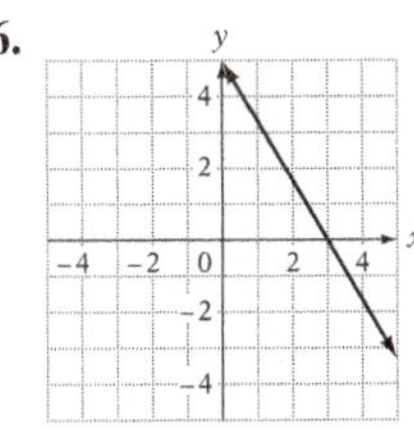

[7.2B]

7. Neither [7.3B] **8.** -1 [7.1D]

9. Yes [7.1C] **10.** $\frac{7}{11}$ [7.3B] **11.** $(8, 0), (0, -12)$ [7.3A] **12.** 0 [7.3B]

13.

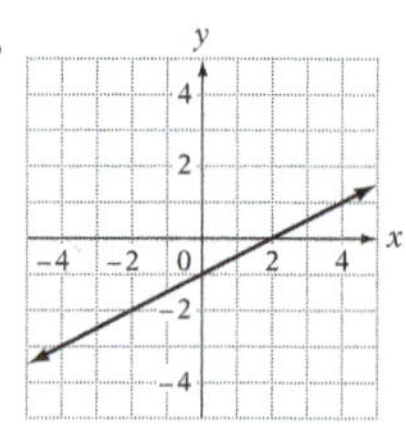

[7.3C]

14.

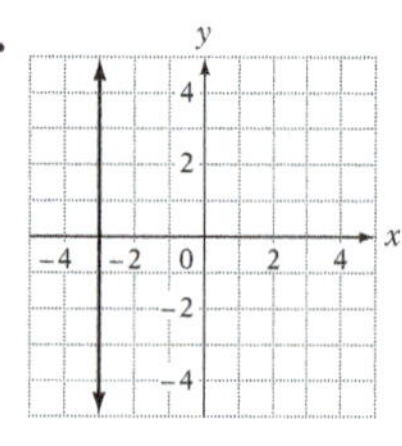

[7.2B]

15.

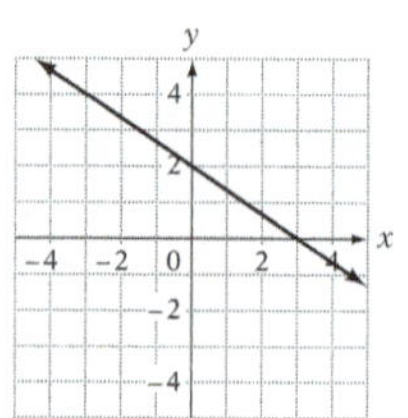

[7.3C]

16.

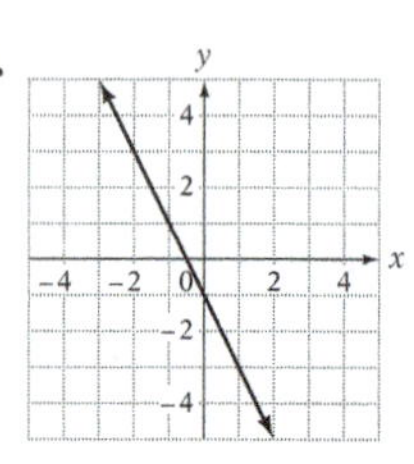

[7.2A]

17.

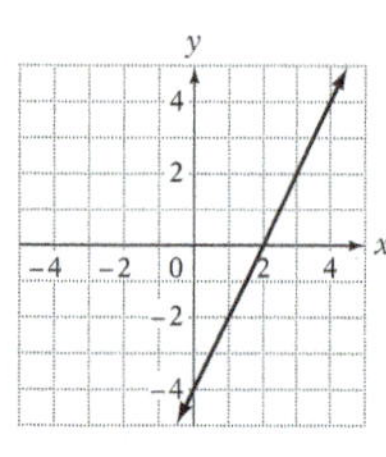

[7.3C]

18.

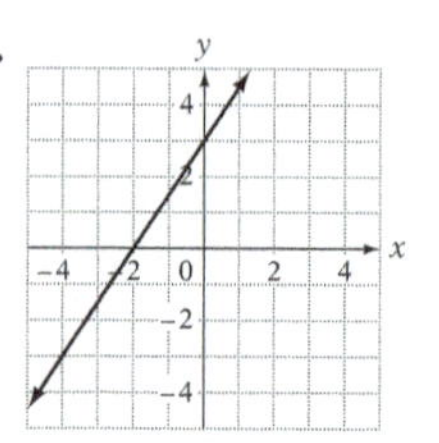

[7.2B]

19. $\{(55, 95), (57, 101), (53, 94), (57, 98), (60, 100), (61, 105), (58, 97), (54, 95)\}$; no [7.1C]

20. The cost of 50 min of access time for one month is \$97.50.

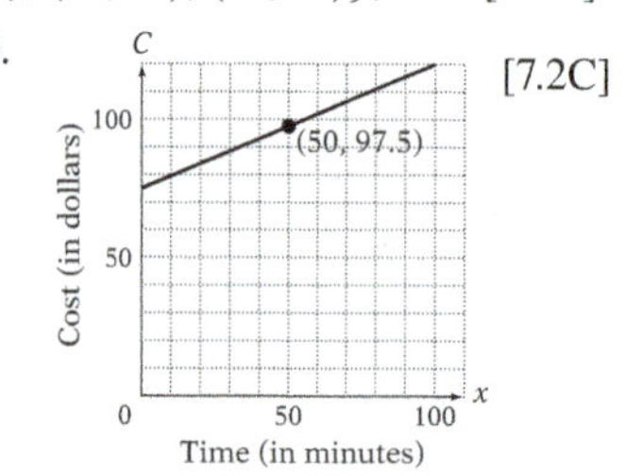

[7.2C]

CHAPTER 7 TEST

1. $(3, -3)$ [7.1B; HOW TO 2]

2.

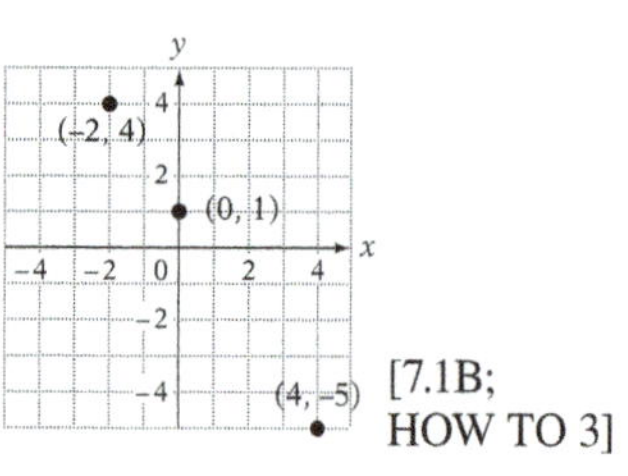

[7.1B; HOW TO 3]

3. Yes [7.1C; Example 6] **4.** 6 [7.1D; HOW TO 4]

5. 3 [7.1D; HOW TO 4] **6.** $\{(3.5, 25), (4.0, 30), (5.2, 45), (5.0, 38), (4.0, 42), (6.3, 12), (5.4, 34)\}$; no [7.1C; Example 5]

7.

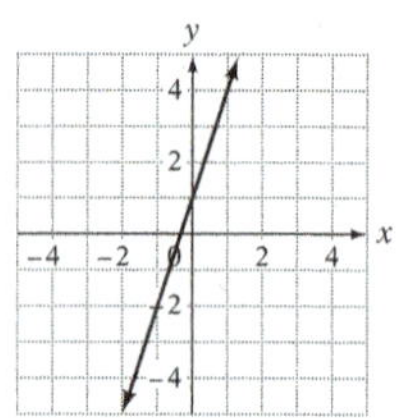

[7.2A; Example 1]

8. [7.2A; Example 3]

9.

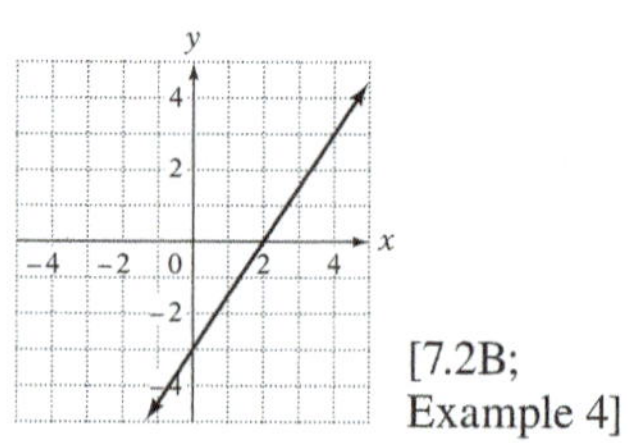

[7.2B; Example 4]

10.

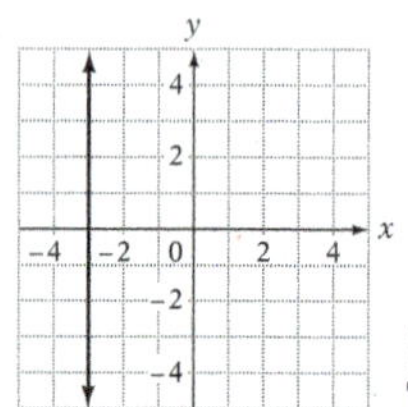
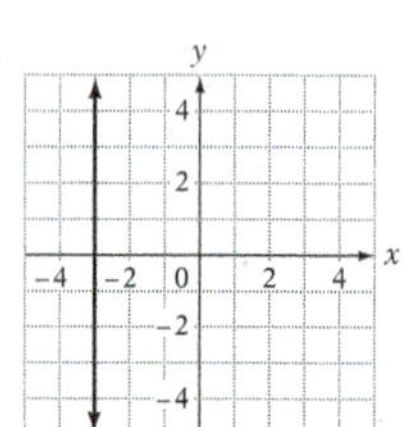

[7.2B; You Try It 7]

11. [7.3C; Example 5]

12.

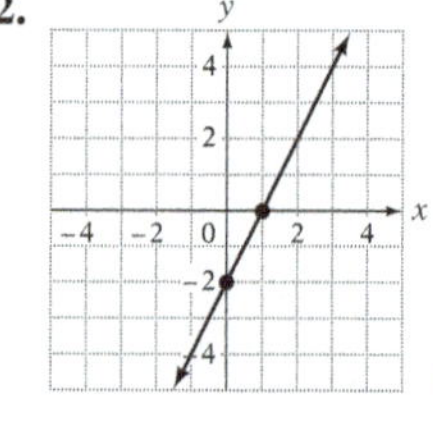
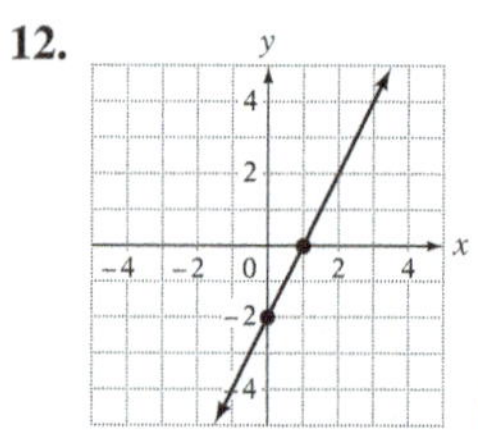

[7.3C; Example 5]

After 1 s, the ball is traveling 96 ft/s. [7.2C; Example 8] **14.** (2, 0), (0, −3) [7.3A; Example 1]

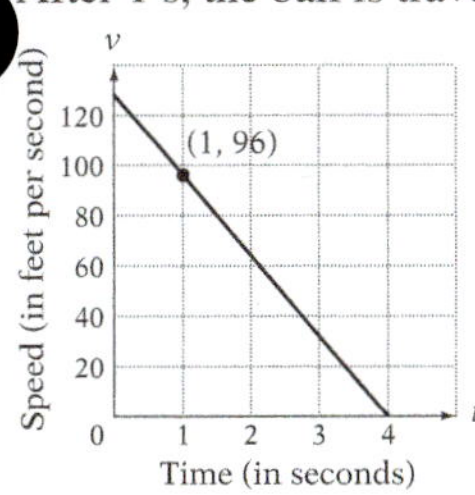

15. (−2, 0), (0, 1) [7.3A; Example 1] **16.** 2 [7.3B; Example 2] **17.** Parallel [7.3B; Example 2] **18.** Undefined [7.3B; Example 3] **19.** $-\frac{2}{3}$ [7.3B; HOW TO 2] **20.** $y = 3x - 1$ [7.4A; Example 1] **21.** $y = \frac{2}{3}x + 3$ [7.4B; You Try It 3]
22. $y = -\frac{5}{8}x - \frac{7}{8}$ [7.4C; HOW TO 3] **23.** $y = -\frac{2}{7}x - \frac{4}{7}$ [7.4C; Example 4]

CUMULATIVE REVIEW EXERCISES

1. −12 [1.4B] **2.** $-\frac{5}{8}$ [2.1A] **3.** $f(-2) = -\frac{2}{3}$ [7.1D] **4.** $\frac{3}{2}$ [3.3A] **5.** $\frac{19}{18}$ [3.4B] **6.** $\frac{1}{15}$ [1.7C]
7. $-32x^8y^7$ [4.2B] **8.** $-3x^2$ [4.4A] **9.** $x + 3$ [4.5B] **10.** $5(x + 2)(x + 1)$ [5.2B]
11. $(a + 2)(x + y)$ [5.1B] **12.** 4 and −2 [5.6A] **13.** $\frac{x^3(x + 3)}{y(x + 2)}$ [6.1B] **14.** $\frac{3}{x + 8}$ [6.3A] **15.** 2 [6.5A]
16. $y = \frac{4}{5}x - 3$ [6.7A] **17.** (−2, −5) [7.1B] **18.** Zero [7.3B] **19.** $y = \frac{1}{2}x - 2$ [7.4A]
20. $y = -3x + 2$ [7.4A] **21.** $y = 2x + 2$ [7.4B] **22.** $y = \frac{2}{3}x - 3$ [7.4B] **23.** The sale price is \$62.30. [3.3B]
24. The angles measure 46°, 43°, and 91°. [3.6B] **25.** The value of the home is \$1,100,000. [6.6A]

It would take $3\frac{3}{4}$ h for both, working together, to wire the garage. [6.8A]

27.

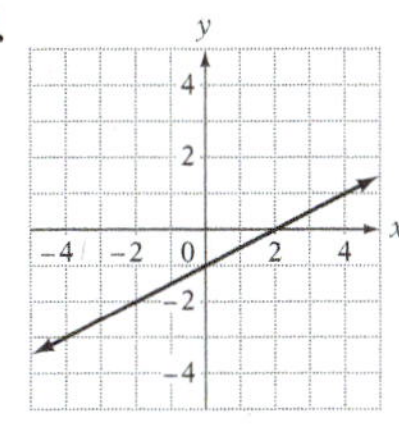

[7.2A]

28.

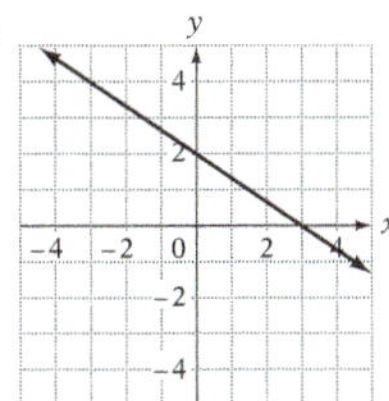

[7.3C]

Answers to Chapter 8 Selected Exercises

PREP TEST

1. $y = \frac{3}{4}x - 6$ [6.7A] **2.** 1000 [3.4B] **3.** $33y$ [2.2D] **4.** $10x - 10$ [2.2D] **5.** Yes [7.1B]
6. (4, 0), (0, −3) [7.3A] **7.** Yes [7.3B] **8.**

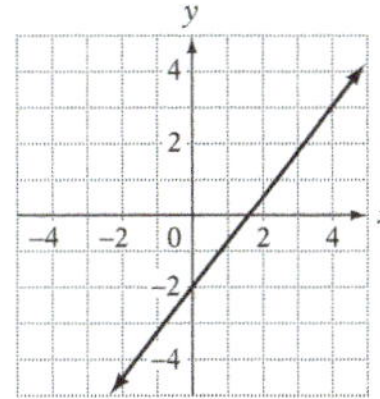

[7.3C]

9. 5 ml of 55% acetic acid are needed. [3.7B] **10.** The hikers will be side-by-side 1.5 h after the second hiker starts. [3.7C]

CTION 8.1

Always true **3.** Never true **5.** Yes **7.** No **9.** Yes **11.** Yes **13.** iii **15.** i **17.** (2, −1)
19. The ordered-pair solutions of $y = -\frac{3}{2}x + 1$ **21.** No solution

23. 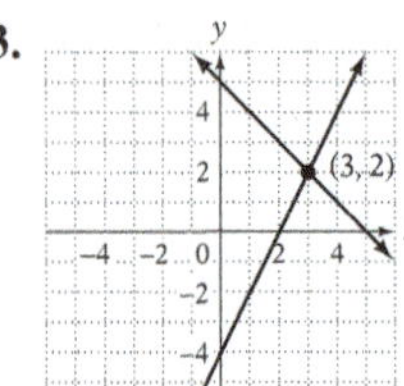

25. 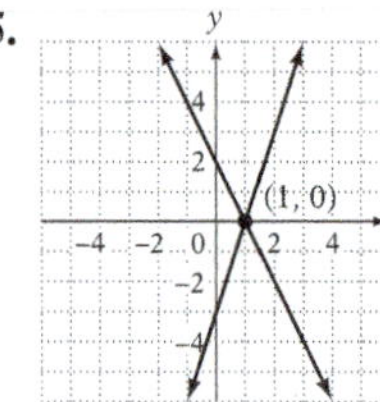

27. 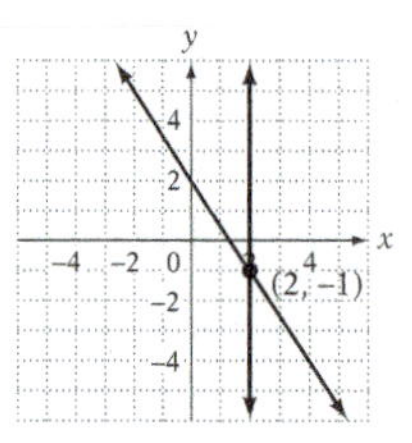

29. 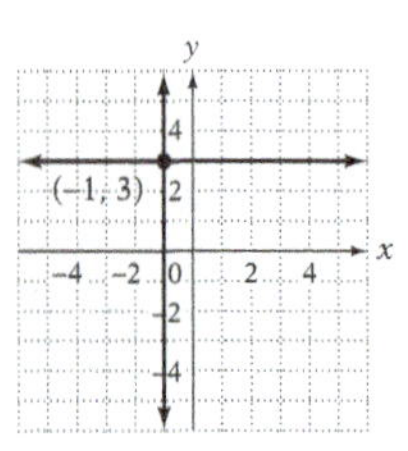

31. 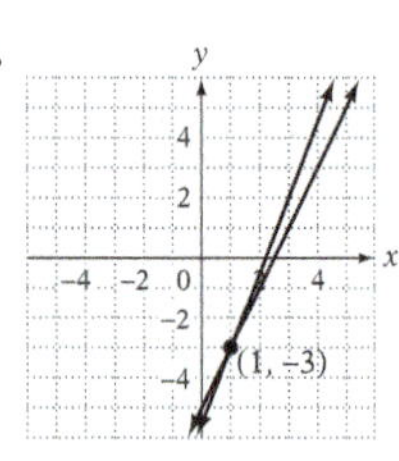

33. 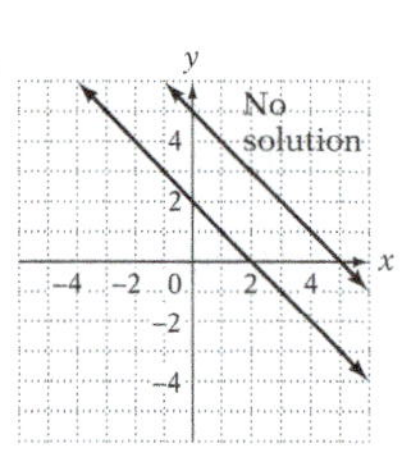

35. 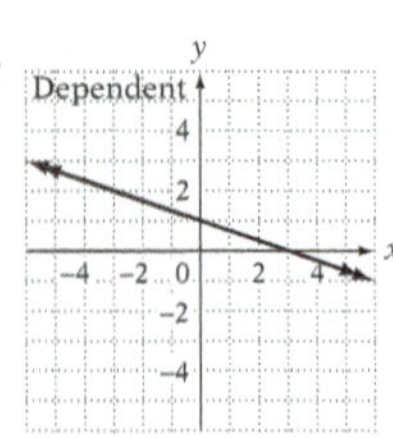

The ordered-pair solutions of $y = -\frac{1}{3}x + 1$ 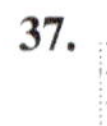

37. 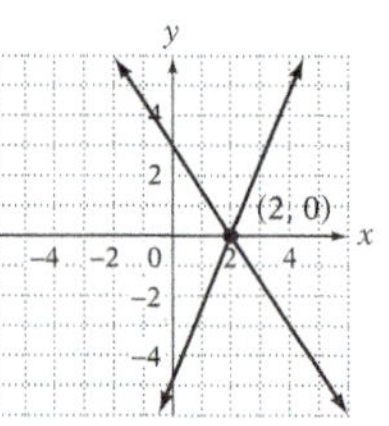

39. 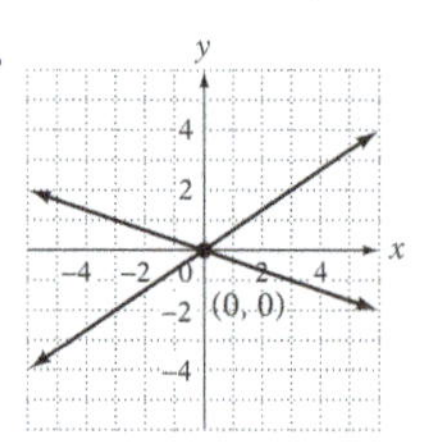

41. 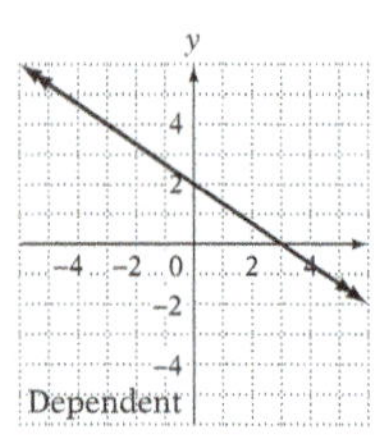

The ordered-pair solutions of $4x + 6y = 12$ **43.** Independent **45.** $x = 3$, $y = x - 1$

47. $y = 2x - 2$, $y = \frac{2}{3}x + \frac{2}{3}$ **49.** Answers will vary. For example: **a.** $y = x + 8$, $y = -x + 2$ **b.** $y = 2x - 3$, $y = 2x + 4$ **c.** $y = 3x - 5$, $3x - y = 5$

SECTION 8.2

3. True **5.** False **7.** (2, 1) **9.** (4, 1) **11.** (−1, 1) **13.** No solution **15.** No solution **17.** $\left(-\frac{3}{4}, -\frac{3}{4}\right)$ **19.** (1, 1) **21.** (2, 0) **23.** (1, −2) **25.** (0, 0) **27.** Dependent. The solutions satisfy the equation $2x - y = 2$. **29.** (−4, −2) **31.** (10, 31) **33.** (3, −10) **35.** (−22, −5) **37.** Dependent **39.** x = amount invested at 8%, y = amount invested at 6.5%; $x + y = 10{,}000$ represents the fact that the sum of the two investments is \$10,000; $0.08x + 0.065y = 710$ represents the fact that the total interest earned by the two investments is \$710. **41.** The amounts invested should be \$1900 at 5% and \$1600 at 7.5%. **43.** The amounts invested were \$3600 at 6% and \$2400 at 9%. **45.** The amounts invested should be \$4400 at 8% and \$1600 at 11%. **47.** The amount invested at 6.5% was \$21,000. **49.** The amounts invested were \$12,000 at 8% and \$8000 at 7%. **51.** The amount invested in the trust deed was \$3750. **53.** (1, 5) **55.** (−5, 2) **57.** (2, 100) **59.** The amounts invested were \$12,000 at 9%, \$21,000 at 8%, and \$27,000 at 9.5%. **61.** 2 **63.** 2 **65.** The value of the CD in 5 years is \$3589.07.

CHECK YOUR PROGRESS: CHAPTER 8

1. 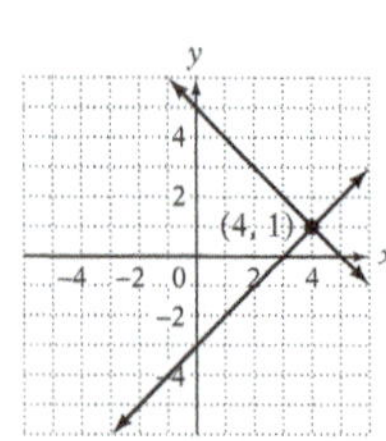

(4, 1) [8.1A] **2.** The ordered pair solutions of $y = -\frac{4}{3}x + 4$. [8.1A]

3. 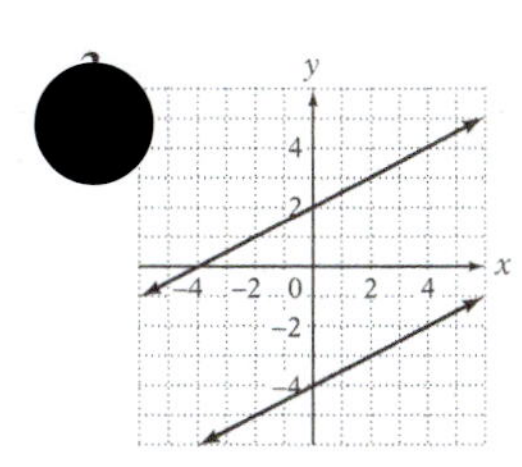
No solution [8.1A] **4.** Yes [8.1A] **5.** $(-2, 4)$ [8.2A] **6.** The ordered-pair solutions of $y = \frac{1}{3}x + 4$ [8.2A]

7. The amounts invested were \$18,000 at 6.5% and \$12,000 at 8.5%. [8.2B]

SECTION 8.3

1a. 3 **b.** -4 **3.** $(5, -1)$ **5.** $(1, 3)$ **7.** $(1, 1)$ **9.** $(3, -2)$ **11.** Dependent. The solutions satisfy the equation $2x - y = 1$. **13.** $(3, 1)$ **15.** Dependent. The solutions satisfy the equation $2x - 3y = 1$. **17.** $\left(\frac{2}{3}, \frac{1}{2}\right)$ **19.** $(2, 0)$ **21.** $(0, 0)$ **23.** $(5, -2)$ **25.** $\left(\frac{32}{19}, -\frac{9}{19}\right)$ **27.** $\left(\frac{7}{4}, -\frac{5}{16}\right)$ **29.** $(1, -1)$ **31.** No solution **33.** $(3, 1)$ **35.** $(-1, 2)$ **37.** $(1, 1)$ **39.** Dependent **41.** Independent **43.** $A = 3$; $B = -1$

SECTION 8.4

1. True **3.** False **5.** $100x + 50y$ **7.** m is greater than n. **9.** The rowing rate in calm water was 14 km/h. The rate of the current was 6 km/h. **11.** The rate of the whale in calm water was 35 mph. The rate of the current was 5 mph. **13.** The rate of the Learjet was 525 mph. The rate of the wind was 35 mph. **15.** The rate of the helicopter in calm air was 225 mph. The rate of the wind was 45 mph. **17.** The rate of the boat in calm water was 7 mph. The rate of the current was 3 mph. **19.** Less than **21.** x = cost of an adult ticket, y = cost of a child ticket; $4x + 2y = 320$ represents the fact that you spent \$320 on four adult tickets and two child tickets; $2x + 3y = 240$ represents the fact that your neighbor spent \$240 on two adult tickets and three child tickets. **23.** The cost per pound of the wheat flour was \$.65. The cost per pound of the rye flour was \$.70. **25.** The delicatessen charges \$6.25 for a turkey sandwich and \$1.90 for an order of fries. **27.** The pastry chef used 15 oz of the 20% solution and 35 oz of the 40% solution. **29.** Both formulas give the same ideal body weight at 72 in. **31.** The original postage value of the Lincoln stamp was \$.90. The original postage value of the Jefferson stamp was \$.10. The original postage value of the Henry Clay stamp was \$.12. **33.** The measures of the two angles are 18° and 72°. **35.** The time is approximately 65.5 min. **37.** $(2.875, 1.1875)$ **39.** $(-19, -7)$

CHAPTER 8 REVIEW EXERCISES

1. Yes [8.1A] **2.** No [8.1A] **3.** (1, −3) [8.1A] **4.** Dependent [8.1A] The solutions are the ordered pairs that satisfy the equation $y = 2x - 4$.

5. 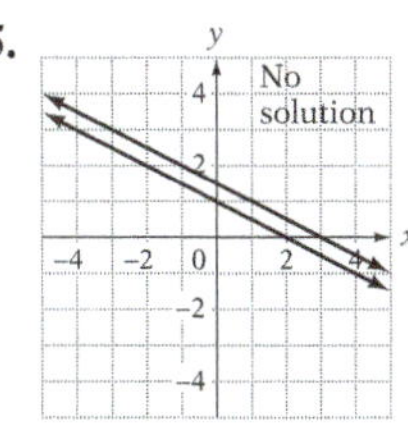

[8.1A] **6.** $(-1, 1)$ [8.2A] **7.** $(1, 6)$ [8.2A] **8.** $(-3, 1)$ [8.3A] **9.** $\left(-\frac{5}{6}, \frac{1}{2}\right)$ [8.3A]

10. No solution [8.2A] **11.** $(1, 6)$ [8.2A] **12.** $(1, -5)$ [8.3A] **13.** No solution [8.3A] **14.** Dependent. The solutions satisfy the equation $y = -\frac{4}{3}x + 4$. [8.2A] **15.** $(-1, -3)$ [8.2A] **16.** Dependent. The solutions satisfy the equation $3x + y = -2$. [8.3A] **17.** $\left(\frac{2}{3}, -\frac{1}{6}\right)$ [8.3A] **18.** The rate of the sculling team in calm water was 9 mph. The rate of the current was 3 mph. [8.4A] **19.** The investor bought 1300 \$6 shares, and 200 \$25 shares. [8.4B] **20.** The rate of the flight crew in calm air was 125 km/h. The rate of the wind was 15 km/h. [8.4A] **21.** The rate of the plane in calm air was 105 mph. The rate of the wind was 15 mph. [8.4A] **22.** The service charge per hour for regular service is \$1.00. The service charge per hour for premium service is \$2.50. [8.4B] **23.** The amounts invested are \$7000 at 7% and \$5000 at 8.5%. [8.2B] **24.** There were originally 350 bushels of lentils and 200 bushels of corn in the silo. [8.4B] **25.** The amounts invested were \$165,000 at 5.4% and \$135,000 at 6.6%. [8.2B]

CHAPTER 8 TEST

1. Yes [8.1A; Example 1] **2.** Yes [8.1A; Example 1] **3.**

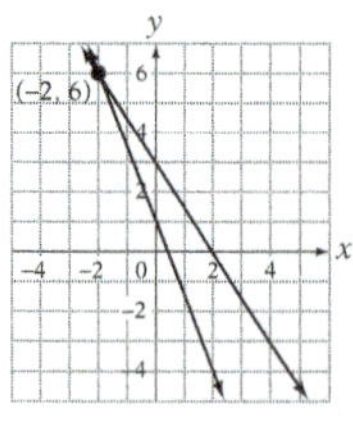

[8.1A, Example 2] **4.** (3, 1) [8.2A; HOW TO 1]

5. $(1, -1)$ [8.2A; HOW TO 1] **6.** $(2, -1)$ [8.2A; Example 1] **7.** $\left(\frac{22}{7}, -\frac{5}{7}\right)$ [8.2A; You Try It 1]

8. No solution [8.2A; Example 2] **9.** $(2, 1)$ [8.3A; Example 1] **10.** $\left(\frac{1}{2}, -1\right)$ [8.3A; Example 1]

11. Dependent. The solutions satisfy the equation $x + 2y = 8$. [8.3A; Example 2] **12.** $(2, -1)$ [8.3A; Example 3]

13. $(1, -2)$ [8.3A; You Try It 3] **14.** The rate of the plane in calm air is 100 mph. The rate of the wind is 20 mph. [8.4A; Example 1]

15. The price of a reserved-seat ticket was \$10. The price of a general-admission ticket was \$6. [8.4B; Example 2]

16. The amounts invested were \$15,200 at 6.4% and \$12,800 at 7.6%. [8.2B; You Try It 4]

CUMULATIVE REVIEW EXERCISES

1. $\frac{3}{2}$ [2.1A] **2.** $-\frac{3}{2}$ [3.1C] **3.** 7 [7.1D] **4.** $-6a^3 + 13a^2 - 9a + 2$ [4.3B] **5.** $-2x^5y^2$ [4.4A]

6. $2b - 1 + \frac{1}{2b - 3}$ [4.5B] **7.** $-\frac{4y}{x^3}$ [4.4A] **8.** $4y^2(xy - 4)(xy + 4)$ [5.5A] **9.** $4, -1$ [5.6A]

10. $x - 2$ [6.1C] **11.** $\frac{x^2 + 2}{(x + 2)(x - 1)}$ [6.3B] **12.** $\frac{x - 3}{x + 1}$ [6.4A] **13.** $-\frac{1}{5}$ [6.5A] **14.** $r = \frac{A - P}{Pt}$ [6.7A]

15. x-intercept: $(6, 0)$; y-intercept: $(0, -4)$ [7.3A] **16.** $-\frac{7}{5}$ [7.3B] **17.** $y = -\frac{3}{2}x$ [7.4A] **18.** Yes [8.1A]

19. $(-6, 1)$ [8.2A] **20.** $(4, -3)$ [8.3A] **21.**

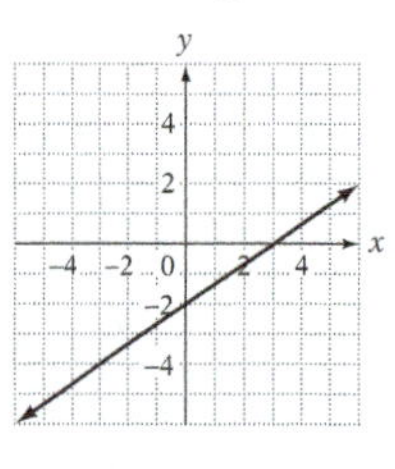

[7.2B] **22.**

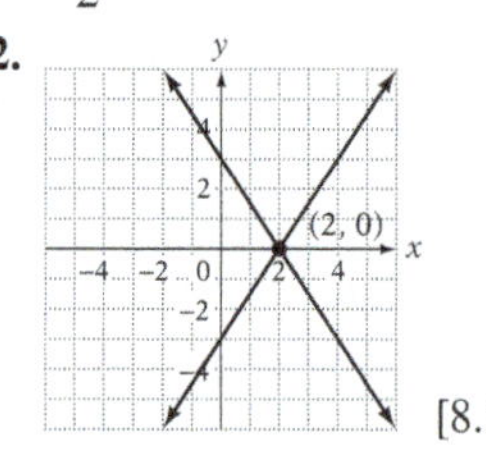

[8.1A]

23. The amounts invested should be \$3750 at 9.6% and \$5000 at 7.2%. [8.2B]

24. The rate of the freight train is 48 mph. The rate of the passenger train is 56 mph. [3.7C]

25. The length of a side of the original square is 8 in. [5.6B] **26.** The rate of the wind is 30 mph. [8.4A]

27. The rate of the motorboat in calm water is 14 mph. [8.4A] **28.** The percent concentration of sugar in the mixture is 35.3%. [3.7A]

Answers to Chapter 9 Selected Exercises

PREP TEST

1. $-45 < -27$ [1.1A] **2.** $-7x + 15$ [2.2D] **3.** The same number can be added to each side of an equation without changing the solution of the equation. [3.1B] **4.** Each side of an equation can be multiplied by the same nonzero number without changing the solution of the equation. [3.1C] **5.** There is 0.45 lb of fat in 3 lb of this grade of hamburger. [3.2A]

6. 2 [3.4B] **7.** [7.2A]

SECTION 9.1

oster; set-builder; interval **3.** $A = \{16, 17, 18, 19, 20, 21\}$ **5.** $A = \{9, 11, 13, 15, 17\}$ **7.** $A \cup B = \{3, 4, 5, 6\}$
9. $A \cup B = \{-10, -9, -8, 8, 9, 10\}$ **11.** $A \cup B = \{1, 3, 7, 9, 11, 13\}$ **13.** $A \cap B = \{4, 5\}$ **15.** $A \cap B = \varnothing$
17. $A \cap B = \{c, d, e\}$ **19.** $\{x|x > -5, x \in \text{negative integers}\}$ **21.** $\{x|x > 30, x \in \text{integers}\}$ **23.** $\{x|x > 8\}$
25. $(1, 2)$ **27.** $(3, \infty)$ **29.** $[-4, 5)$ **31.** $(-\infty, 2]$ **33.** $[-3, 1]$ **35.** $\{x|-5 < x < -3\}$ **37.** $\{x|x \leq -2\}$
39. $\{x|-3 \leq x \leq -2\}$ **41.** $\{x|x \leq 6\}$ **43.**  -5 -4 -3 -2 -1 0 1 2 3 4 5 **45.** 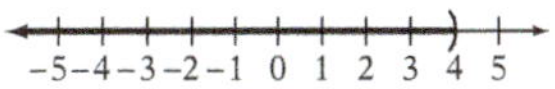 -5 -4 -3 -2 -1 0 1 2 3 4 5
47. 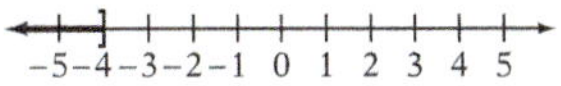 -5 -4 -3 -2 -1 0 1 2 3 4 5 **49.** 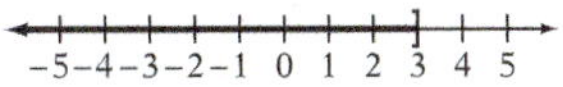 -5 -4 -3 -2 -1 0 1 2 3 4 5 **51.** 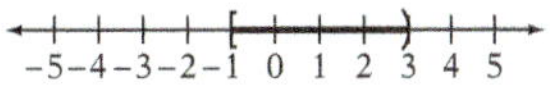 -5 -4 -3 -2 -1 0 1 2 3 4 5 **53.** 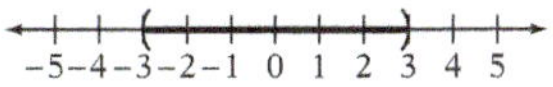 -5 -4 -3 -2 -1 0 1 2 3 4 5
55. 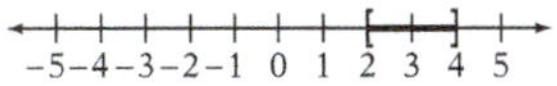 -5 -4 -3 -2 -1 0 1 2 3 4 5 **57.** 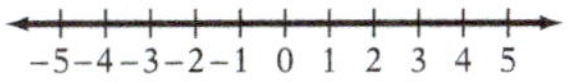 -5 -4 -3 -2 -1 0 1 2 3 4 5 **59.** None **61.** $m \geq 250$ **63.** True
65. Answers will vary. For example, $A = \{1, 2, 3, 4\}$ and $B = \{1, 2, 3, 4\}$

SECTION 9.2

1a. No **b.** No **c.** Yes **d.** No **e.** No **f.** Yes **3.** i, ii, iii **5.** does not include; >
7. $\{x|x < 2\}$ -5 -4 -3 -2 -1 0 1 2 3 4 5 **9.** $\{x|x > 3\}$ -5 -4 -3 -2 -1 0 1 2 3 4 5
11. $\{n|n \geq 3\}$ -5 -4 -3 -2 -1 0 1 2 3 4 5 **13.** $\{x|x \leq -4\}$ -5 -4 -3 -2 -1 0 1 2 3 4 5 **15.** $[-9, \infty)$
17. $(-\infty, 12)$ **19.** $[5, \infty)$ **21.** $(-\infty, -11)$ **23.** $(-\infty, 10]$ **25.** $[-6, \infty)$ **27.** $\{x|x > 2\}$ **29.** $\left\{d\middle|d < -\frac{1}{6}\right\}$
31. $\left\{x\middle|x \geq -\frac{31}{24}\right\}$ **33.** $\left\{x\middle|x < \frac{5}{8}\right\}$ **35.** $\left\{x\middle|x < \frac{5}{4}\right\}$ **37.** $\{x|x < 5.6\}$ **39.** Negative **41.** Negative and positive
43. $\{x|x < 4\}$ -5 -4 -3 -2 -1 0 1 2 3 4 5 **45.** $\{y|y \geq 3\}$ -5 -4 -3 -2 -1 0 1 2 3 4 5
47. $\{x|x \leq 1\}$ -5 -4 -3 -2 -1 0 1 2 3 4 5 **49.** $\{x|x < -1\}$ -5 -4 -3 -2 -1 0 1 2 3 4 5
51. $\{b|b < -4\}$ -5 -4 -3 -2 -1 0 1 2 3 4 5 **53.** $(-\infty, 0]$ **55.** $\left(\frac{2}{7}, \infty\right)$ **57.** $(-\infty, -3]$ **59.** $(-2, \infty)$ **61.** $(-\infty, 18)$
$[16, \infty)$ **65.** $\{b|b \leq 33\}$ **67.** $\{x|x > 0\}$ **69.** $\left\{x\middle|x \leq -\frac{12}{7}\right\}$ **71.** $\left\{x\middle|x > \frac{2}{3}\right\}$ **73.** $\{x|x \leq 4.2\}$ **75.** $\{m|m > -8\}$
77. ii **79.** iii **81.** The couple's monthly household income is $5395 or more.
83. The patient must reduce his cholesterol level by 75 or more units. **85.** The student must receive a grade of 78 or higher.
87. The height of the tallest wind turbine you can install is 45 ft. **89.** $x \leq 4$ includes the element 4; $x < 4$ does not. **91.** $x \leq -2$
93. 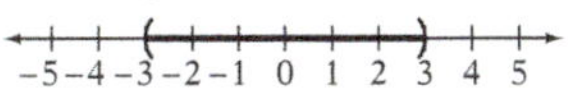 -5 -4 -3 -2 -1 0 1 2 3 4 5 **95.** 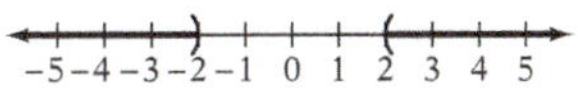 -5 -4 -3 -2 -1 0 1 2 3 4 5

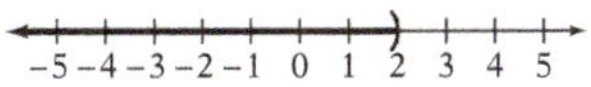

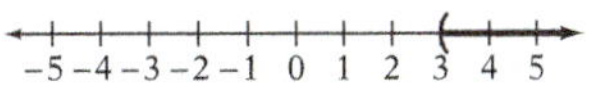

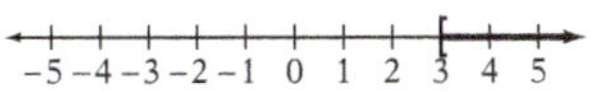

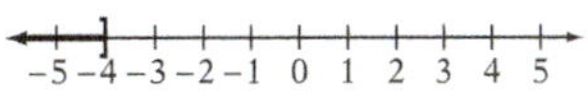

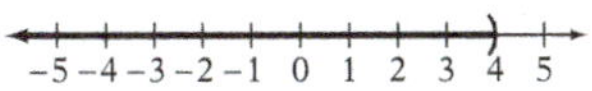

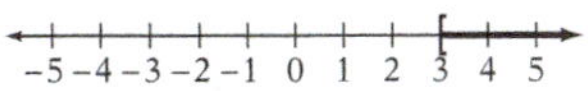

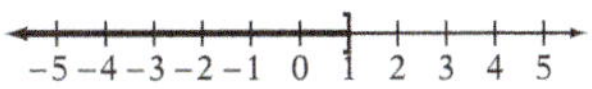

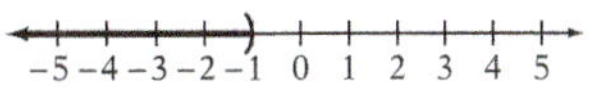

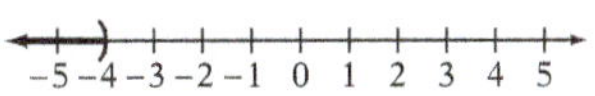

CHECK YOUR PROGRESS: CHAPTER 9

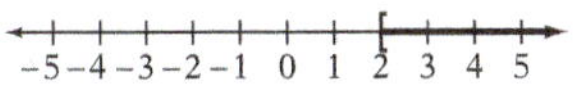

1. $\{-11, -10\}$ [9.1A] **2.** $A \cup B = \{4, 8, 16, 20, 24\}$ [9.1A] **3.** $A \cap B = \{20, 40\}$ [9.1A] **4.** $A \cap B = \varnothing$ [9.1A]
5. $[-1, 3]$ [9.1B] **6.** $(8, \infty)$ [9.1B] **7.** $\{x|x \geq -9\}$ [9.1B] **8.** $\{x|-4 < x \leq 7\}$ [9.1B]
9. 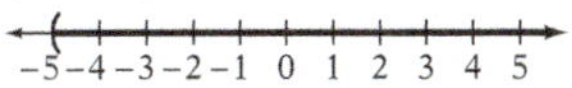 -5 -4 -3 -2 -1 0 1 2 3 4 5 [9.1B] **10.** 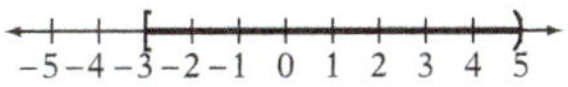 -5 -4 -3 -2 -1 0 1 2 3 4 5 [9.1B]
11. $\{x|x \geq 2\}$ -5 -4 -3 -2 -1 0 1 2 3 4 5 [9.2A] **12.** $(-3, \infty)$ -5 -4 -3 -2 -1 0 1 2 3 4 5 [9.2A]
13. $\{x|x \leq -5\}$ [9.2A] **14.** $(-\infty, 4)$ [9.2B]
15. The student must get a 62 or higher on the last test to receive an A in the course. [9.2C]

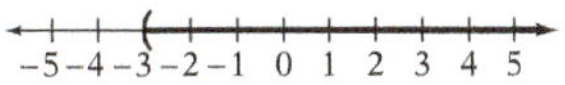

SECTION 9.3

1. False **3.** True **5.** $(-\infty, 4)$ **7.** $(-\infty, -4)$ **9.** $[1, \infty)$ **11.** $(-\infty, 5)$ 13. $(-\infty, 0)$ 15. $\{x|x < 20\}$ **17.** $\left\{y\middle|y \leq \frac{5}{2}\right\}$
19. $\left\{x\middle|x < \frac{25}{11}\right\}$ **21.** $\left\{n\middle|n \leq \frac{11}{18}\right\}$ **23.** $\{x|x \geq 6\}$ **25.** iii and iv **27.** In one month, the agent expects to make sales totaling $20,000 or less. **29.** The company must own 8 or more individual computers for the site license to be the more economical choice.
31. The amount of artificial flavors that can be added is 8 oz or less. **33.** 3 **35.** Between 8 in. and 28 in.

SECTION 9.4

1. Yes **3.** No

5.

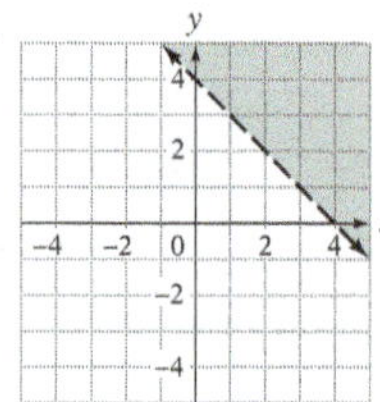

7.

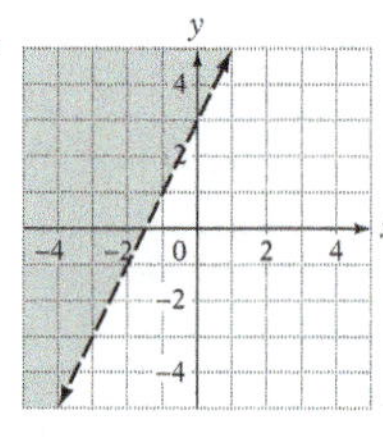

9.

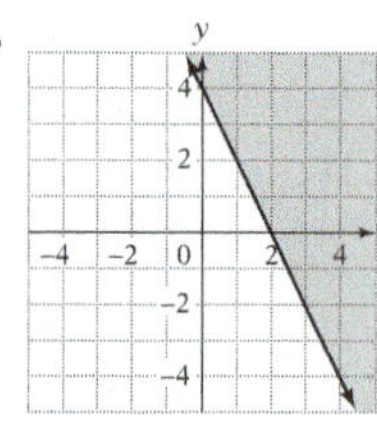

11.

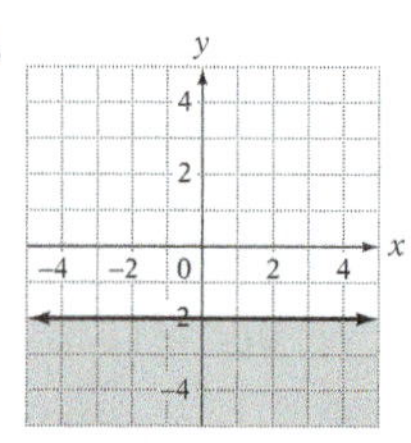

13.

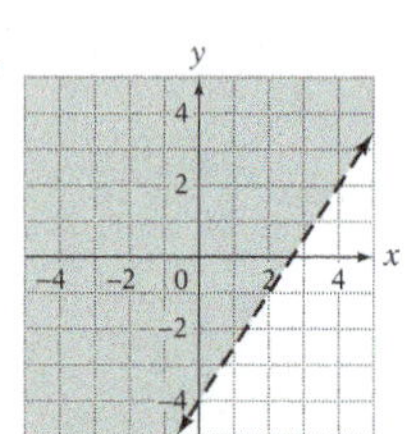

15.

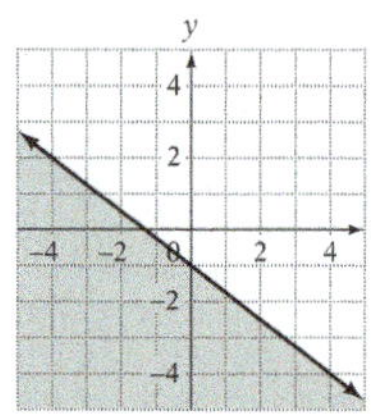

17.

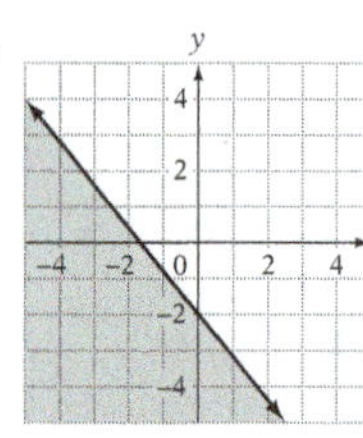

19.

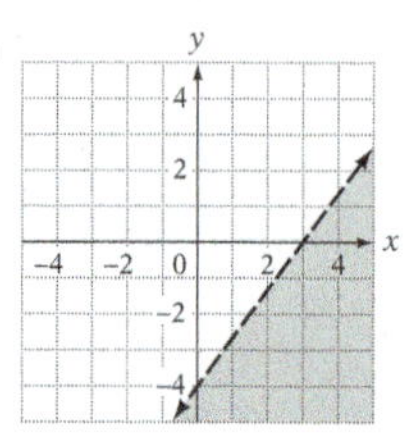

21.

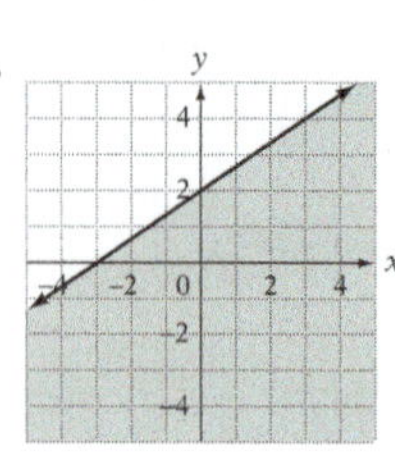

23. Negative **25.** $y > 2$ **27.** $y \le -\frac{2}{3}x + 2$

CHAPTER 9 REVIEW EXERCISES

1. $\{x|x > 18\}$ [9.2A] **2.** $A \cap B = \varnothing$ [9.1A] **3.** $\{x|x > -8, x \in \text{odd integers}\}$ [9.1B]
4. $A \cup B = \{2, 4, 6, 8, 10\}$ [9.1A] **5.** $A = \{1, 3, 5, 7\}$ [9.1A] **6.** $[4, \infty)$ [9.3A]
7. −5 −4 −3 −2 −1 0 1 2 3 4 5 [9.1B] **8.** $\{x|x \ge -4\}$ [9.3A] **9.**

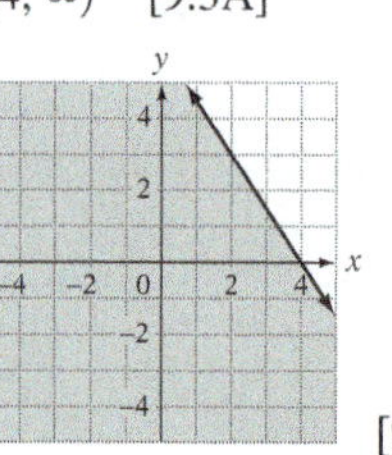

[9.4A]

10.

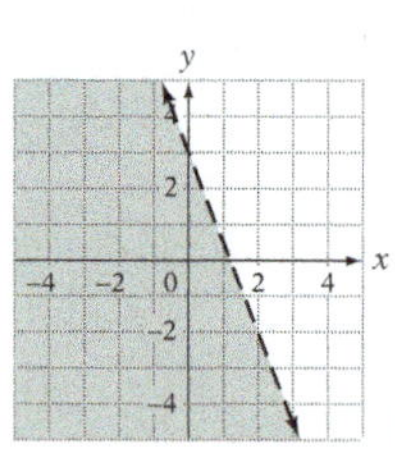

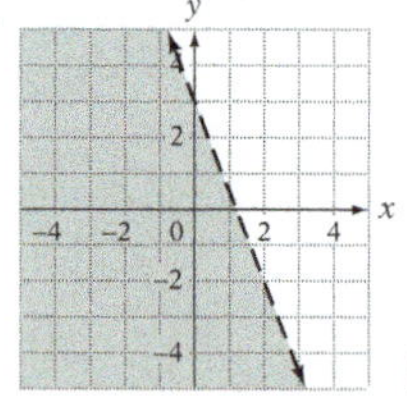

[9.4A]

11. $(-4, \infty)$ [9.1B] **12.** $(2, \infty)$

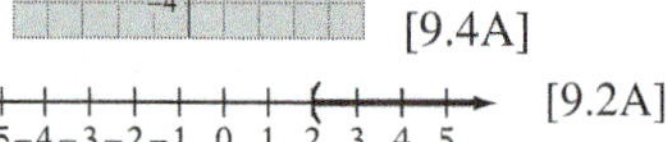

[9.2A]

13. $A \cap B = \{1, 5, 9\}$ [9.1A] **14.** −5 −4 −3 −2 −1 0 1 2 3 4 5 [9.1B] **15.** −5 −4 −3 −2 −1 0 1 2 3 4 5 [9.1B]

16. $\{x|x \ge -3\}$ [9.2B] **17.** $(-18, \infty)$ [9.3A] **18.** $\left\{x\middle|x < \frac{1}{2}\right\}$ [9.3A] **19.** $\left\{x\middle|x < -\frac{8}{9}\right\}$ [9.2B]

20. $[4, \infty)$ [9.3A] **21.**

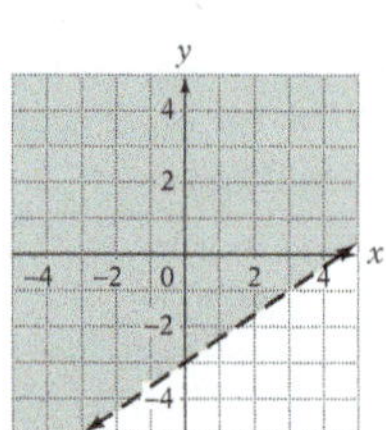

[9.4A]

22. For florist B to be more economical, there must be 3 or more residents in the nursing home. [9.3B]

23. The minimum length is 24 ft. [9.3B] **24.** The smallest integer that satisfies the inequality is 32. [9.2C]
25. 72 is the lowest score that the student can receive and still attain a minimum of 480 points. [9.2C]

CHAPTER 9 TEST

1. 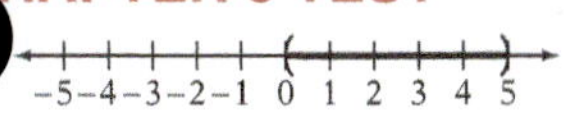 [number line] [9.1B; Example 9] **2.** $\{x|x < 50, x \in \text{positive integers}\}$ [9.1B; HOW TO 3]

3. $A = \{4, 6, 8\}$ [9.1A; Example 1] **4.** $(-\infty, -3]$ [9.3A; Example 1] **5.** $\left\{x \middle| x > \frac{1}{8}\right\}$ [9.2A; HOW TO 1]

6. 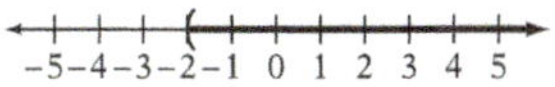 [number line] [9.1B; You Try It 8b] **7.** $(-\infty, -1)$ [9.3A; You Try It 1]

8. $\{x|x > -23\}$ [9.1B; HOW TO 4] **9.**

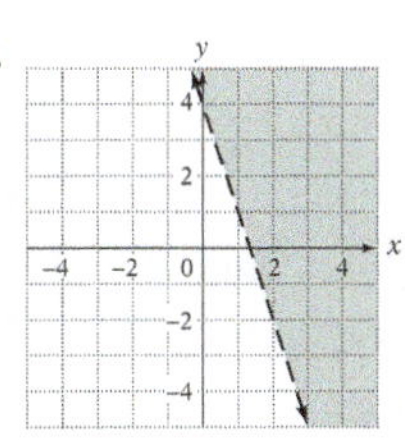

[9.4A; Example 1]

10.

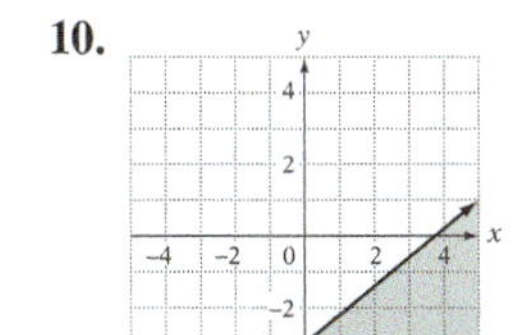

[9.4A; You Try It 2] **11.** $A \cap B = \{12\}$ [9.1A; Example 4]

12. $\{x|x < -3\}$ [number line] [9.2A; HOW TO 1] **13.** $\left\{x \middle| x \geq -\frac{40}{3}\right\}$ [9.2B; HOW TO 3]

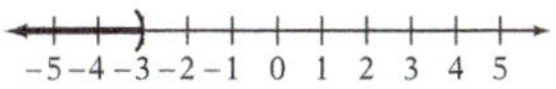

14. $\left(-\infty, -\frac{22}{7}\right)$ [9.3A; Example 2] **15.** $[3, \infty)$ [number line] [9.2B; Example 2]

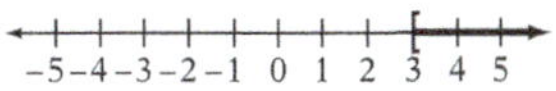

16. $\{x|x \geq -4\}$ [9.3A; Example 2] **17.** The child must grow 5 in. or more. [9.2C; Example 4] **18.** The maximum width 1 ft. [9.3B; Example 3] **19.** The diameter must be between 0.0389 in. and 0.0395 in. [9.2C; You Try It 4] **20.** The total value of the ck processed by the broker was \$200,000 or less. [9.3B; Example 3]

CUMULATIVE REVIEW EXERCISES

1. $40a - 28$ [2.2D] **2.** $\frac{1}{8}$ [3.3A] **3.** 4 [3.4B] **4.** $-12a^7b^4$ [4.2B] **5.** $-\frac{1}{b^4}$ [4.4A]

6. $4x - 2 - \frac{4}{4x - 1}$ [4.5B] **7.** 0 [7.1D] **8.** $3a^2(3x - 1)(3x + 1)$ [5.5A] **9.** $\frac{1}{x + 2}$ [6.1C]

10. $\frac{18a}{(2a - 3)(a + 3)}$ [6.3B] **11.** $-\frac{5}{9}$ [6.5A] **12.** $C = S + Rt$ [6.7A] **13.** $-\frac{7}{3}$ [7.3B]

14. $y = -\frac{3}{2}x - \frac{3}{2}$ [7.4A] **15.** (4, 1) [8.2A] **16.** (1, −4) [8.3A] **17.** $A \cup B = \{-10, -2, 0, 1, 2\}$ [9.1A]

18. $\{x|x < 48\}$ [9.1B] **19.** $(-\infty, 4)$ [9.1B] **20.** [number line] [9.2B]

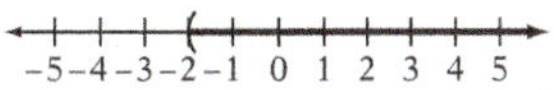

21. $x < -15$ [9.2B] **22.** $x > 2$ [9.3A] **23.** 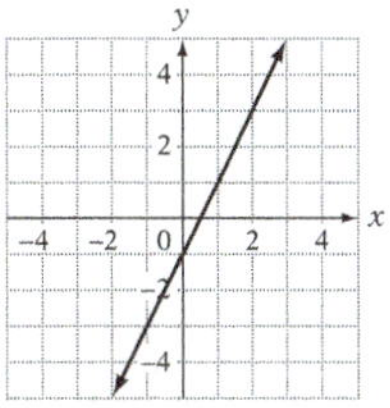 [graph] [7.2A] **24.**

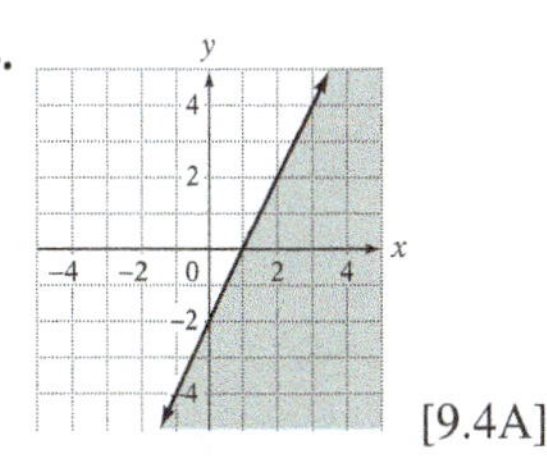

[9.4A]

25. $\{x|x \leq -26, x \in \text{integers}\}$ [9.2C] **26.** The maximum number of miles is 359 mi. [9.3B]
27. There are an estimated 5000 fish in the lake. [6.6A] **28.** The angle measures are 65°, 35°, and 80°. [3.6B]

Answers to Chapter 10 Selected Exercises

PREP TEST

1. -14 [1.1B] **2.** $-2x^2y - 4xy^2$ [2.2A] **3.** 14 [3.1C] **4.** $\frac{7}{5}$ [3.4A] **5.** x^6 [4.2A] **6.** $x^2 + 2xy + y^2$ [4.3D] **7.** $4x^2 - 12x + 9$ [4.3D] **8.** $4 - 9v^2$ [4.3D] **9.** $a^2 - 25$ [4.3D] **10.** $\frac{x^2y^2}{9}$ [4.4A]

SECTION 10.1

1. radical sign; radicand **5.** 4 **7.** 7 **9.** $4\sqrt{2}$ **11.** $2\sqrt{2}$ **13.** $-18\sqrt{2}$ **15.** $10\sqrt{10}$ **17.** $\sqrt{15}$ **19.** $\sqrt{29}$ **21.** $-54\sqrt{2}$ **23.** $3\sqrt{5}$ **25.** 0 **27.** $48\sqrt{2}$ **29.** -11 and -10 **31.** 2 and 3 **33.** 15.492 **35.** 16.971 **37.** 18.708 **39.** x^7 **41.** $y^7\sqrt{y}$ **43.** a^{10} **45.** x^2y^2 **47.** $2x^2$ **49.** $2x\sqrt{6}$ **51.** $2x^2\sqrt{15x}$ **53.** $7a^2b^4$ **55.** $3x^2y^3\sqrt{2xy}$ **57.** $2x^5y^3\sqrt{10xy}$ **59.** $4a^4b^5\sqrt{5a}$ **61.** $-8ab\sqrt{b}$ **63.** x^3y **65.** $-8a^2b^3\sqrt{5b}$ **67.** $6x^2y^3\sqrt{3y}$ **69.** $4x^3y\sqrt{2y}$ **71.** $5a + 20$ **73.** $2x^2 + 8x + 8$ **75.** $x + 2$ **77.** $y + 1$ **79.** Rational **81.** Irrational **83a.** The average number of credit cards for a first-year student is 2.3. **b.** The average number of credit cards for a sophomore is 3.3. **c.** The average number of credit cards for a junior is 4.0. **d.** The average number of credit cards for a senior is 4.6. **85a.** The speed of the car was $12\sqrt{15}$ mph. **b.** 46 mph

SECTION 10.2

1. 2, 20, and 50 **3.** Yes **5.** Yes **7.** $3\sqrt{2}$ **9.** $-\sqrt{7}$ **11.** $-11\sqrt{11}$ **13.** $10\sqrt{x}$ **15.** $-2\sqrt{y}$ **17.** $-11\sqrt{3b}$ **19.** $2x\sqrt{2}$ **21.** $-3a\sqrt{3a}$ **23.** $-5\sqrt{xy}$ **25.** $8\sqrt{5}$ **27.** $8\sqrt{2}$ **29.** $15\sqrt{2} - 10\sqrt{3}$ **31.** $\sqrt{x}$ **33.** $-12x\sqrt{3}$ **35.** $2xy\sqrt{x} - 3xy\sqrt{y}$ **37.** $-9x\sqrt{3x}$ **39.** $-13y^2\sqrt{2y}$ **41.** $4a^2b^2\sqrt{ab}$ **43.** $7\sqrt{2}$ **45.** $6\sqrt{x}$ **47.** $-3\sqrt{y}$ **49.** $-45\sqrt{2}$ **51.** $13\sqrt{3} - 12\sqrt{5}$ **53.** $32\sqrt{3} - 3\sqrt{11}$ **55.** $6\sqrt{x}$ **57.** $-34\sqrt{3x}$ **59.** $10a\sqrt{3b} + 10a\sqrt{5b}$ **61.** $-2xy\sqrt{3}$ **63.** iv **65.** $2ab\sqrt{6ab}$ **67.** The perimeter is $8\sqrt{2}$ cm.

SECTION 10.3

1. $3 - \sqrt{5}$ **3.** $\sqrt{2a} + 8$ **5.** $25 - y$ **7.** $\frac{\sqrt{x}}{\sqrt{x}}$ **11.** 5 **13.** 6 **15.** x **17.** x^3y^2 **19.** $3ab^6\sqrt{2a}$ **21.** $12a^4b\sqrt{b}$ **23.** $10abc$ **25.** $2 - \sqrt{6}$ **27.** $x - \sqrt{xy}$ **29.** $5\sqrt{2} - \sqrt{5x}$ **31.** $3a - 3\sqrt{ab}$ **33.** $x - 6\sqrt{x} + 9$ **35.** $-2 + 2\sqrt{5}$ **37.** $16 + 10\sqrt{2}$ **39.** $6x + 10\sqrt{x} - 4$ **41.** $15x - 22y\sqrt{x} + 8y^2$ **43.** 4 **45.** $9x - 16$ **47.** Less than **49.** 4 **51.** 7 **53.** 3 **55.** $x\sqrt{5}$ **57.** $\frac{a^2}{7}$ **59.** $\frac{y\sqrt{3}}{3}$ **61.** $\sqrt{2y}$ **63.** $-\frac{\sqrt{2} + 3}{7}$ **65.** $\frac{15 - 3\sqrt{5}}{20}$ **67.** $-\frac{7\sqrt{2} + 49}{47}$ **69.** $\sqrt{15} + 2\sqrt{5}$ **71.** $\frac{x\sqrt{y} + y\sqrt{x}}{x - y}$ **73.** $3 + \sqrt{6}$ **75.** $-\frac{20 + 7\sqrt{3}}{23}$ **77.** $\frac{6 + 5\sqrt{x} + x}{4 - x}$ **79.** Equal to **81.** The area is 59 m². **83.** $\frac{5}{8}$ **85.** $\frac{5}{4}$

CHECK YOUR PROGRESS CHAPTER 10

1. $10\sqrt{3}$ [10.1A] **2.** $30\sqrt{5}$ [10.1A] **3.** $8x^5$ [10.1B] **4.** $3x^2y^2\sqrt{2x}$ [10.1B] **5.** $-3\sqrt{5}$ [10.2A] **6.** $-14a\sqrt{ab}$ [10.2A] **7.** $8a^2b^5$ [10.3A] **8.** $4 - 2\sqrt{10}$ [10.3A] **9.** $3a - 7\sqrt{a} - 6$ [10.3A] **10.** $2y - 25$ [10.3A] **11.** 5 [10.3B] **12.** $\frac{\sqrt{3x}}{3}$ [10.3B] **13.** $\frac{49 + 7\sqrt{2}}{47}$ [10.3B] **14.** $\frac{17 + 8\sqrt{2}}{7}$ [10.3B]

SECTION 10.4

1. No **3.** Yes **5.** Sometimes true **7.** Always true **9.** 90°; legs **11.** 25 **13.** 144 **15.** 5 **17.** 16 **19.** 8 **21.** No solution **23.** 6 **25.** 24 **27.** $-\frac{2}{5}$ **29.** $\frac{4}{3}$ **31.** -1 **33.** 15 **35.** 5 **37.** 1 **39.** 1 **41.** 1 **43.** 2 **45.** No solution **47.** iii **49.** The number is 11. **51.** The length of the hypotenuse is 10.30 cm. **53.** The length of the other leg of the triangle is 9.75 ft. **55.** The length of the diagonal is 12.1 mi. **57.** The depth of the water is 12.5 ft. **59.** The pitcher's mound is more than halfway between home plate and second base. **61.** Yes, she will be able to call a friend on the dock. **63.** Yes, the ladder will be long enough to reach the gutters. **65.** The length of the pendulum is 1.83 ft. **67.** The bridge is 64 ft high. **69.** 5 **71.** 8 **73a.** The perimeter of the triangle is $12\sqrt{2}$ cm. **b.** The area of the triangle is 12 cm². **77.** *AB* is 6.4 units.

CHAPTER 10 REVIEW EXERCISES

1. 3 [10.3A] **2.** $9a^2\sqrt{2ab}$ [10.1B] **3.** 12 [10.1A] **4.** $3a\sqrt{2} + 2a\sqrt{3}$ [10.3A] **5.** $2\sqrt{6}$ [10.3B] **6.** $-8\sqrt{2}$ [10.2A] **7.** 2 [10.3A] **8.** 1 [10.4A] **9.** $-x\sqrt{3} - x\sqrt{5}$ [10.3B] **10.** $-6\sqrt{30}$ [10.1A]

20 [10.4A] **12.** $20\sqrt{3}$ [10.1A] **13.** $7x^2y^4$ [10.3B] **14.** No solution [10.4A] **15.** $18a\sqrt{5b} + 5a\sqrt{b}$ [10.2A] **16.** $20\sqrt{10}$ [10.1A] **17.** $7x^2y\sqrt{15xy}$ [10.2A] **18.** $8y + 10\sqrt{5y} - 15$ [10.3A] **19.** $26\sqrt{3x}$ [10.2A] **20.** No solution [10.4A] **21.** $\dfrac{8\sqrt{x} + 24}{x - 9}$ [10.3B] **22.** $36x^8y^5\sqrt{3xy}$ [10.1B] **23.** $2y^4\sqrt{6}$ [10.1B] **24.** -1 [10.4A] **25.** $-6x^3y^2\sqrt{2y}$ [10.2A] **26.** $\dfrac{16\sqrt{a}}{a}$ [10.3B] **27.** The distance across the pond is approximately 43 ft. [10.4B] **28.** The explorer weighs 144 lb on the surface of Earth. [10.4B] **29.** The depth of the water is 100 ft. [10.4B] **30.** The radius of the sharpest corner is 25 ft. [10.4B]

CHAPTER 10 TEST

1. $11x^4y$ [10.1B; Example 5] **2.** $6x^2y\sqrt{y}$ [10.3A; Example 1] **3.** $-5\sqrt{2}$ [10.2A; Example 2] **4.** $3\sqrt{5}$ [10.1A; HOW TO 1] **5.** 9 [10.3B; HOW TO 7] **6.** 25 [10.4A; Example 1] **7.** $4a^2b^5\sqrt{2ab}$ [10.1B; Example 5] **8.** $7ab\sqrt{a}$ [10.3B; HOW TO 7] **9.** $\sqrt{3} + 1$ [10.3B; HOW TO 9] **10.** $4x^2y^2\sqrt{5y}$ [10.3A; HOW TO 1] **11.** 9 [10.4A; You Try It 2] **12.** $21\sqrt{2y} - 12\sqrt{2x}$ [10.2A; Example 4] **13.** $6x^3y\sqrt{2x}$ [10.1B; Example 5] **14.** $y + 2\sqrt{y} - 15$ [10.3A; HOW TO 3] **15.** $-2xy\sqrt{3xy} - 3xy\sqrt{xy}$ [10.2A; Example 4] **16.** $\dfrac{17 - 8\sqrt{5}}{31}$ [10.3B; Example 7] **17.** $a - \sqrt{ab}$ [10.3A; Example 2] **18.** $5\sqrt{3}$ [10.1A; HOW TO 1] **19.** The length of the pendulum is 7.30 ft. [10.4B; You Try It 4] **20.** The rope should be secured about 7 ft from the base of the pole. [10.4B; Example 3]

CUMULATIVE REVIEW EXERCISES

1. $-\dfrac{1}{12}$ [1.7A] **2.** $2x + 18$ [2.2D] **3.** $\dfrac{1}{13}$ [3.4B] **4.** $6x^5y^5$ [4.2A] **5.** $-2b^2 + 1 - \dfrac{1}{3b^2}$ [4.5A] **6.** 1 [7.1D] **7.** $2a(a - 5)(a - 3)$ [5.2B] **8.** $\dfrac{1}{4(x + 1)}$ [6.1B] **9.** $\dfrac{x + 3}{x - 3}$ [6.3B] **10.** $\dfrac{5}{3}$ [6.5A] **11.** $y = \dfrac{1}{2}x - 2$ [7.4A] **12.** (1, 1) [8.2A] **13.** (3, −2) [8.3A] **14.** $x \le -\dfrac{9}{2}$ [9.3A] **15.** $6\sqrt{3}$ [10.1A] **16.** $-4\sqrt{2}$ [10.2A] **17.** $4ab\sqrt{2ab} - 5ab\sqrt{ab}$ [10.2A] **18.** $14a^5b^2\sqrt{2a}$ [10.3A] **19.** $3\sqrt{2} - x\sqrt{3}$ [10.3A] **20.** 8 [10.3B] **21.** $-6 - 3\sqrt{5}$ [10.3B] **22.** 6 [10.4A] **23.** The cost of the book is \$49.50. [3.3B] **24.** 56 oz of water must be added. [3.7B] **25.** The numbers are 8 and 13. [5.6B] **26.** It would take the small pipe, working alone, 48 h. [6.8A]

27. [8.1A]

28.

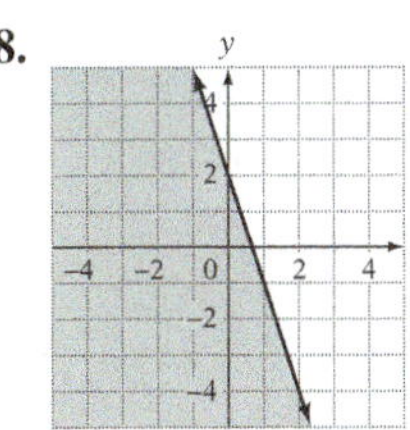

[9.4A]

29. The smaller integer is 40. [10.4B]
30. The height of the building is 400 ft. [10.4B]

Answers to Chapter 11 Selected Exercises

PREP TEST

1. 41 [2.1A] **2.** $-\dfrac{1}{5}$ [3.3A] **3.** $(x + 4)(x - 3)$ [5.2A] **4.** $(2x - 3)^2$ [5.4A] **5.** Yes [5.4A] **6.** 3 [6.5A]

7.

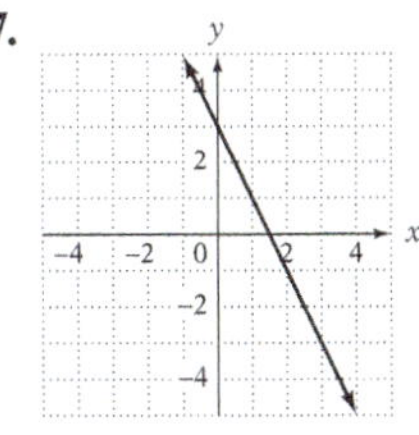

[7.2A]

8. $2\sqrt{7}$ [10.1A] **9.** $|a|$ [10.1B] **10.** The length of the hiking trail is 3.6 mi. [3.7C]

SECTION 11.1

1. $3x + 4, x - 7$ **3.** $x^2 - 3x - 8 = 0$ **5.** $x^2 - 4x - 5 = 0$ **7.** $-\frac{5}{2}, \frac{1}{3}$ **9.** $-5, 3$ **11.** $1, 3$ **13.** $-2, -1$ **15.** 3

17. $-\frac{2}{3}, 0$ **19.** $-2, 5$ **21.** $\frac{2}{3}, 1$ **23.** $-3, \frac{1}{3}$ **25.** $\frac{2}{3}$ **27.** $-\frac{1}{2}, \frac{3}{2}$ **29.** $\frac{1}{2}$ **31.** $-3, 3$ **33.** $-\frac{1}{2}, \frac{1}{2}$ **35.** $-3, 5$

37. $1, 5$ **39.** iii **41.** ± 7 **43.** ± 8 **45.** $\pm\frac{8}{3}$ **47.** $\pm\frac{5}{2}$ **49.** $\pm\frac{8}{5}$ **51.** No real number solution **53.** $\pm 4\sqrt{3}$

55. $-9, 5$ **57.** $-2, 8$ **59.** $-\frac{15}{2}, \frac{3}{2}$ **61.** $\frac{10}{9}, \frac{26}{9}$ **63.** $-5 \pm 5\sqrt{2}$ **65.** $\frac{1}{2} \pm \sqrt{6}$ **67.** One **69.** Two **71.** $11, 35$

73. The annual interest rate was 9%.

SECTION 11.2

1. perfect-square trinomial **3.** $x^2 - 6x + 9, (x - 3)^2$ **5.** $x^2 - 5x + \frac{25}{4}, \left(x - \frac{5}{2}\right)^2$ **7.** $-3, 1$ **9.** $-2, 8$ **11.** 2

13. No real number solution **15.** $-4, -1$ **17.** $-8, 1$ **19.** $-2 \pm \sqrt{3}$ **21.** $-3 \pm \sqrt{14}$ **23.** $1 \pm \sqrt{2}$ **25.** $\frac{-3 \pm \sqrt{13}}{2}$

27. $1, 2$ **29.** $\frac{-1 \pm \sqrt{13}}{2}$ **31.** $-5 \pm 4\sqrt{2}$ **33.** $\frac{3 \pm \sqrt{29}}{2}$ **35.** $\frac{1 \pm \sqrt{17}}{2}$ **37.** No real number solution **39.** $\frac{1}{2}, 1$

41. $-3, \frac{1}{2}$ **43.** $\frac{7 \pm \sqrt{41}}{4}$ **45.** $\frac{-1 \pm \sqrt{73}}{12}$ **47.** $-\frac{1}{2}, \frac{4}{3}$ **49.** There is one negative and one positive solution.

51. $-5.372, 0.372$ **53.** $-3.212, 1.712$ **55.** $-4 \pm \sqrt{30}$ **57.** $4 \pm \sqrt{3}$ **61.** The ball will hit the ground in 4.81 s.

SECTION 11.3

1. $\frac{1 + \sqrt{13}}{2}$ and $\frac{1 - \sqrt{13}}{2}$ **5.** $-1, 5$ **7.** $-1, 3$ **9.** $-\frac{1}{2}, 1$ **11.** No real number solution **13.** $-\frac{5}{2}, \frac{3}{2}$

15. No real number solution **17.** $1 \pm \sqrt{6}$ **19.** $-3 \pm \sqrt{10}$ **21.** $2 \pm \sqrt{13}$ **23.** $\frac{-1 \pm \sqrt{2}}{3}$ **25.** $-\frac{1}{2}$

27. No real number solution **29.** $\frac{-4 \pm \sqrt{5}}{2}$ **31.** $\frac{1 \pm 2\sqrt{3}}{2}$ **33.** $\frac{-5 \pm \sqrt{2}}{3}$ **35.** True **37.** $-3.690, 5.690$

39. $-1.690, 7.690$ **41.** $-1.089, 4.589$ **43.** $-2.118, 0.118$ **45.** $-0.905, 1.105$ **47.** $2\sqrt{23}$ **49.** $3 \pm \sqrt{13}$

53. Yes **55.** Yes

CHECK YOUR PROGRESS: CHAPTER 11

1. $-11, 9$ [11.1A] **2.** $-\frac{3}{2}, \frac{4}{3}$ [11.1A] **3.** $-6, 4$ [11.1B] **4.** $1 \pm \sqrt{6}$ [11.2A] **5.** $1 \pm \sqrt{7}$ [11.3A]

6. $-\frac{4}{3}, \frac{7}{2}$ [11.1A] **7.** $4 \pm 2\sqrt{5}$ [11.1B] **8.** $-3 \pm \sqrt{5}$ [11.2A] **9.** $\frac{3 \pm 2\sqrt{6}}{2}$ [11.3A] **10.** $\pm 2\sqrt{3}$ [11.1B]

11. $-3, \frac{4}{5}$ [11.1A] **12.** $\frac{2 \pm \sqrt{6}}{2}$ [11.2A] **13.** $3 \pm \sqrt{2}$ [11.3A] **14.** No real number solution [11.1B]

15. $0.151, -1.651$ [11.3A]

SECTION 11.4

1. Parabola **3.** Let $y = 0$ and solve for x. **5.** Down **7.** Up **9.** 4 **11.** -5 **13.** -42

15. **17.**

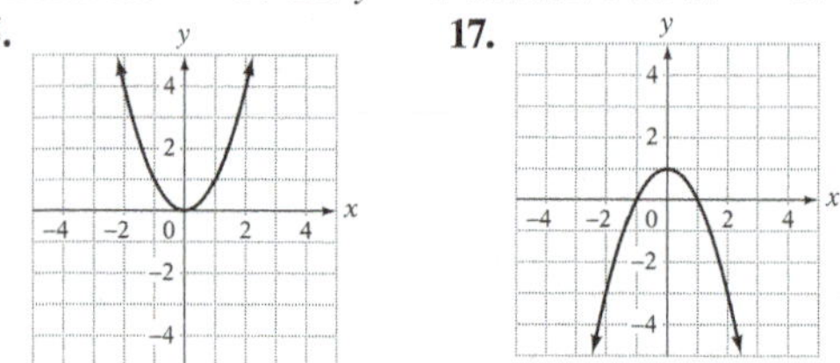

19. 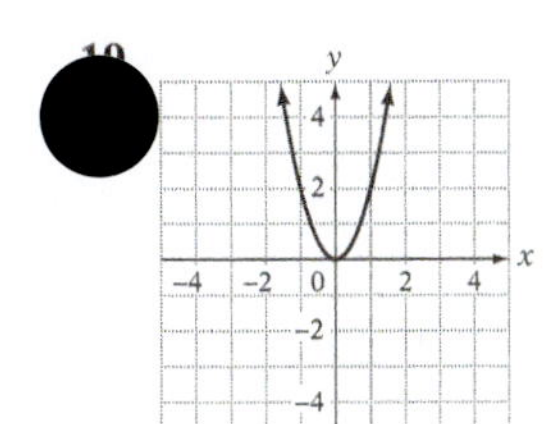

21. 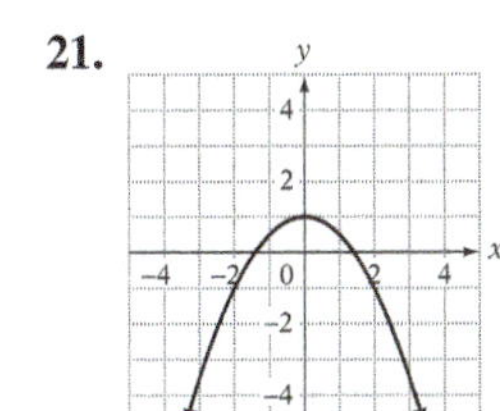

23. 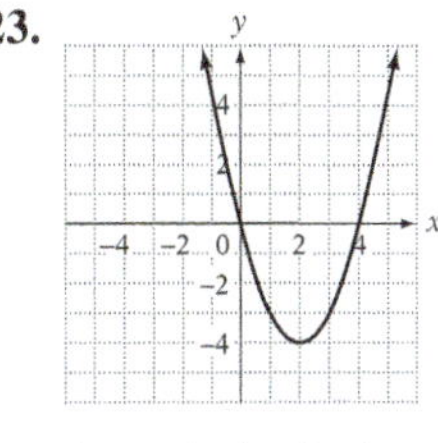

25. 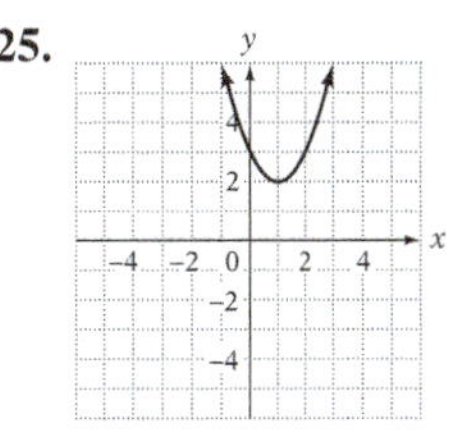

27. 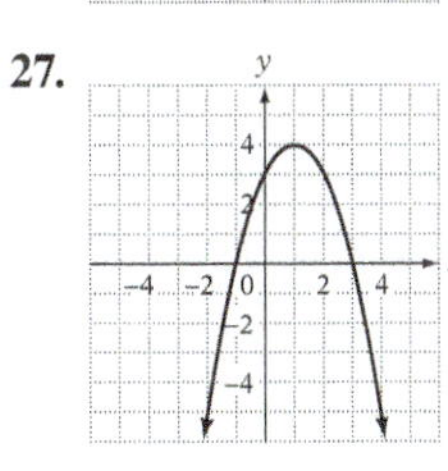

29. 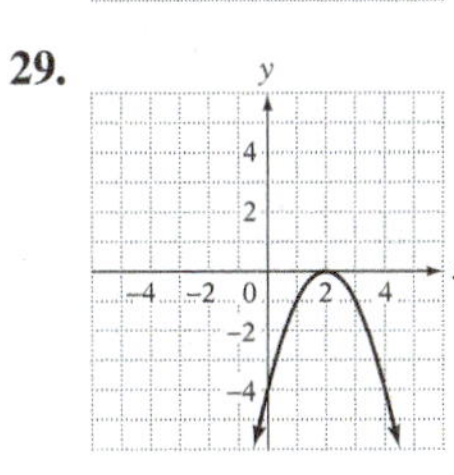

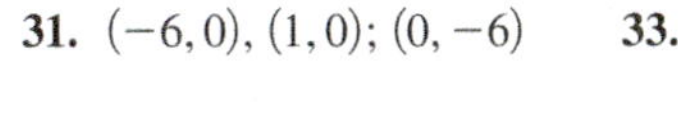

31. $(-6, 0), (1, 0); (0, -6)$ **33.** $(-6, 0); (0, 36)$

35. $(-2 - \sqrt{6}, 0), (-2 + \sqrt{6}, 0); (0, -2)$ **37.** No x-intercepts; $(0, 1)$ **39.** $\left(\frac{3}{2}, 0\right), (5, 0); (0, 15)$

41. $\left(\frac{-3 - \sqrt{33}}{6}, 0\right), \left(\frac{-3 + \sqrt{33}}{6}, 0\right); (0, 2)$ **43.** Negative **45.** Linear **47.** Neither **49.** Quadratic

51a. $(-2, 0), (2, 0)$ **b.** $(0, -4)$ **c.** It is positive. **d.** 0 **e.** -3 **53.** Answers will vary. For example, the graph of $y = -x^2 + 6x - 8$. **55.** -2 **57.** $-1, 5$ **59.** 0.5936307095, −0.3158529318 **61.** −1.766291404, 1.059184622

SECTION 11.5

1. $2W + 3$ **3.** $r - 30$ **5.** The height of the triangle is 10 m. The length of the base is 4 m. **7.** The length is 6 ft. The width is 4 ft. **9.** Working alone, the first drain would take 24 min to empty the tank. Working alone, the second drain would take 8 min. **11.** The length is 100 ft. The width is 50 ft. **13.** It would take the first engine 12 h and the second engine 6 h to power the ferryboat across the channel. **15.** The rate of the plane in calm air was 100 mph. **17.** The cyclist's rate during the first 150 mi was 50 mph. **19.** The arrow will be 32 ft above the ground at 1 s and at 2 s. **21.** The weed will cover an area of 10 m² after 25 days. **23.** There will be [illegible] million people aged 65 or older in the year 2017. **25.** The ball has been in the air for 1.58 s. **27.** The hang time is 5.5 s. **29.** False **31.** The lengths of the legs are 2 cm and 3 cm. **33.** The radius of the cone is 7.98 cm. **35.** The dimensions of the cardboard are 20 in. by 20 in. **37a.** $12 = 2L + 2W$ **b.** $A = LW$ **c.** $L = 6 - W; A = (6 - W)W; A = -W^2 + 6W$ **d.** Length: 3 ft; width: 3 ft

CHAPTER 11 REVIEW EXERCISES

1. $-\frac{7}{2}, \frac{4}{3}$ [11.1A] **2.** $\pm\frac{5}{7}$ [11.1B] **3.** $-6, 4$ [11.2A] **4.** $-6, 1$ [11.3A] **5.** $-4, \frac{3}{2}$ [11.2A]

6. $2, \frac{5}{12}$ [11.1A] **7.** $-2 \pm 2\sqrt{6}$ [11.1B] **8.** $1, \frac{3}{2}$ [11.3A] **9.** $-\frac{1}{2}, -\frac{1}{3}$ [11.1A] **10.** No real number solution [11.1B]

11. $2 \pm \sqrt{3}$ [11.2A] **12.** $\frac{3 \pm \sqrt{29}}{2}$ [11.3A] **13.** No real number solution [11.2A] **14.** $-10, -7$ [11.1A]

15. $-1, 2$ [11.1B] **16.** $\frac{-4 \pm \sqrt{23}}{2}$ [11.2A] **17.** No real number solution [11.3A] **18.** $-2, -\frac{1}{2}$ [11.3A]

19. 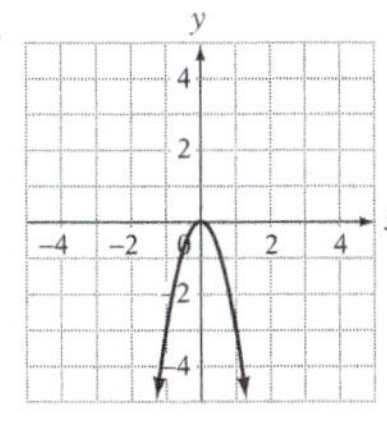  [11.4A]

20. 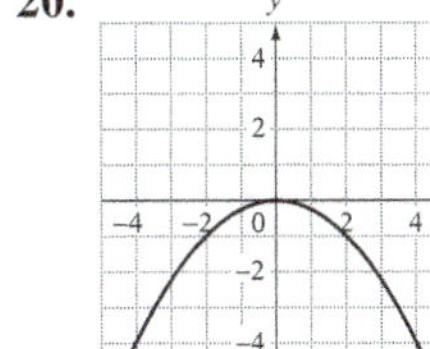 [11.4A]

21. 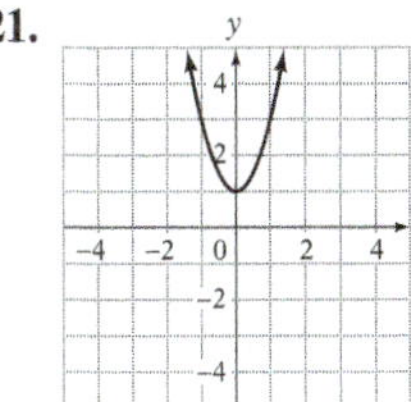  [11.4A]

22. [11.4A]

23. 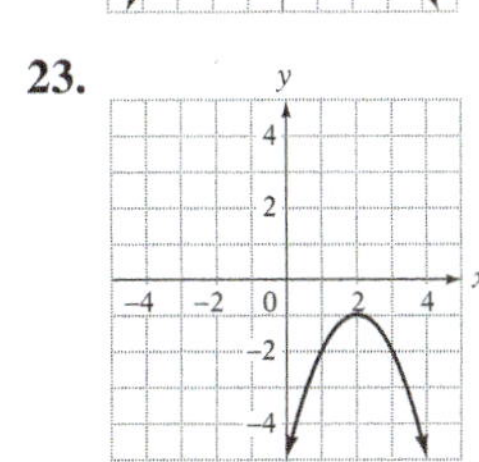 [11.4A]

24. x-intercepts: $(-3, 0), (5, 0)$; y-intercepts: $(0, -15)$ [11.4A] **25.** The rate of the hawk in calm air is 75 mph. [11.5A]

CHAPTER 11 TEST

1. $-1, 6$ [11.1A; HOW TO 1] **2.** $-4, \frac{5}{3}$ [11.1A; HOW TO 1] **3.** $-\frac{1}{2}, 0$ [11.1A; HOW TO 1] **4.** $\pm\frac{3}{2}$ [11.1B; HOW TO 5] **5.** $0, 10$ [11.1B; HOW TO 6] **6.** $-4 \pm 2\sqrt{5}$ [11.1B; HOW TO 6] **7.** $-2 \pm 2\sqrt{5}$ [11.2A; HOW TO 3] **8.** $\frac{-3 \pm \sqrt{41}}{2}$ [11.2A; HOW TO 3] **9.** $\frac{3 \pm \sqrt{7}}{2}$ [11.2A; Example 1] **10.** $\frac{-4 \pm \sqrt{22}}{2}$ [11.2A; Example 1] **11.** $-2 \pm \sqrt{2}$ [11.3A; HOW TO 1] **12.** $\frac{3 \pm \sqrt{33}}{2}$ [11.3A; HOW TO 1] **13.** $-\frac{1}{2}, 3$ [11.3A; You Try It 1] **14.** $\frac{1 \pm \sqrt{13}}{6}$ [11.3A; HOW TO 1] **15.** $-1.651, 0.151$ [11.3A; Example 1] **16.** $-1.387, 0.721$ [11.3A; You Try It 1]

17. [11.4A; HOW TO 2] **18.** x-intercepts: $(-4, 0)$, $(3, 0)$; y-intercept: $(0, -12)$ [11.4A; Example 2]

19. The length is 8 ft. The width is 5 ft. [11.5A; You Try It 1] **20.** The rate of the boat in calm water is 11 mph. [11.5A; HOW TO 1]

CUMULATIVE REVIEW EXERCISES

1. $-28x + 27$ [2.2D] **2.** $\frac{3}{2}$ [3.1C] **3.** 3 [3.4B] **4.** $-12a^8b^4$ [4.2B] **5.** $x + 2 - \frac{4}{x - 2}$ [4.5B] **6.** $x(3x - 4)(x + 2)$ [5.3A/5.3B] **7.** $\frac{9x^2(x - 2)^2}{(2x - 3)^2}$ [6.1C] **8.** $\frac{x + 2}{2(x + 1)}$ [6.3B] **9.** $\frac{x - 4}{2x + 5}$ [6.4A] **10.** x-intercept: $(3, 0)$; y-intercept: $(0, -4)$ [7.3A] **11.** $y = -\frac{4}{3}x - 2$ [7.4A/7.4B] **12.** $(2, 1)$ [8.2A] **13.** $(2, -2)$ [8.3A] **14.** $x > \frac{1}{9}$ [9.3A] **15.** $a - 2$ [10.3A] **16.** $6ab\sqrt{a}$ [10.3B] **17.** $\frac{-6 + 5\sqrt{3}}{13}$ [10.3B] **18.** 5 [10.4A] **19.** $\frac{5}{2}, \frac{1}{3}$ [11.1A] **20.** $5 \pm 3\sqrt{2}$ [11.1B] **21.** $\frac{-7 \pm \sqrt{13}}{6}$ [11.2A] **22.** $-\frac{1}{2}, 2$ [11.3A] **23.** The cost of the mixture is $2.90 per pound. [3.7A] **24.** 250 additional shares are required. [6.6A] **25.** The rate of the plane in still air is 200 mph. The rate of the wind is 40 mph. [8.4A] **26.** The score on the last test must be 77 or more points. [9.2C] **27.** The middle odd integer can be -5 or 5. [11.5A] **28.** The rate for the last 8 mi is 4 mph. [11.5A]

29.

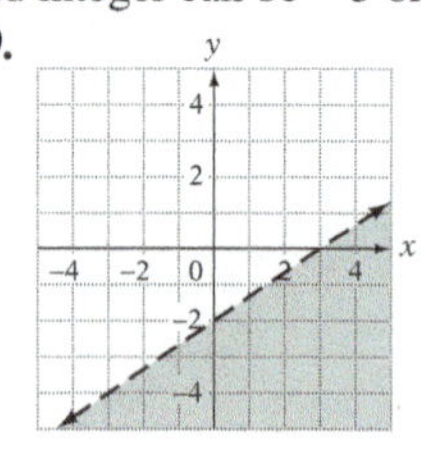

[9.4A]

30.

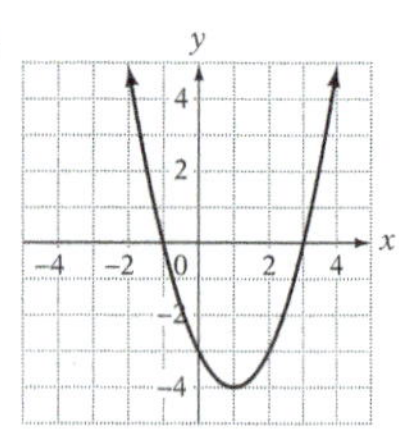

[11.4A]

FINAL EXAM

1. -3 [1.1B] **2.** -6 [1.2B] **3.** -256 [1.4A] **4.** -11 [1.4B] **5.** $-\frac{15}{2}$ [2.1A] **6.** $9x + 6y$ [2.2A] **7.** $6z$ [2.2B] **8.** $16x - 52$ [2.2D] **9.** -50 [3.1C] **10.** -3 [3.4B] **11.** 12.5% [1.7C] **12.** 15.2 [3.2A] **13.** $-3x^2 - 3x + 8$ [4.1B] **14.** $81x^4y^{12}$ [4.2B] **15.** $6x^3 + 7x^2 - 7x - 6$ [4.3B] **16.** $-\frac{x^4y}{2}$ [4.4A] **17.** $\frac{3x}{y} - 4x^2 - \frac{5}{x}$ [4.5A] **18.** $5x - 12 + \frac{23}{x + 2}$ [4.5B] **19.** $\frac{4y^6}{x^6}$ [4.4A] **20.** $\frac{3}{4}$ [7.1D] **21.** $(x - 6)(x + 1)$ [5.2A] **22.** $(3x + 2)(2x - 3)$ [5.3A/5.3B] **23.** $4x(2x - 1)(x - 3)$ [5.5A] **24.** $(5x - 4)(5x + 4)$ [5.4A] **25.** $2(a + 3)(4 - x)$ [5.1B] **26.** $3y(5 - 2x)(5 + 2x)$ [5.5A] **27.** $\frac{1}{2}, 3$ [5.6A] **28.** $\frac{2(x + 1)}{x - 1}$ [6.1B] **29.** $\frac{-3x^2 + x - 25}{(2x - 5)(x + 3)}$ [6.3B] **30.** $\frac{x^2 - 2x}{x - 1}$ [6.4A] **31.** 2 [6.5A] **32.** $a = b$ [6.7A]

$\frac{2}{3}$ [7.3B] **34.** $y = -\frac{2}{3}x - 2$ [7.4A/7.4B] **35.** $(6, 17)$ [8.2A] **36.** $(2, -1)$ [8.3A] **37.** $x \leq -3$ [9.2B]

38. $y \geq \frac{5}{2}$ [9.3A] **39.** $7x^3$ [10.1B] **40.** $38\sqrt{3a}$ [10.2A] **41.** $\sqrt{15} + 2\sqrt{3}$ [10.3B] **42.** 2 [10.4A]

43. $-1, \frac{4}{3}$ [11.1A] **44.** $\frac{1 \pm \sqrt{5}}{4}$ [11.3A] **45.** $2x + 3(x - 2)$; $5x - 6$ [2.3B] **46.** The original value is $6000. [3.2A]

47. The markup rate is 65%. [3.3B] **48.** $6000 must be invested at 11%. [8.2B] **49.** The cost of the mixture is $4 per pound. [3.7A]

50. The percent concentration of acid in the mixture is 36%. [3.7B] **51.** The distance traveled in the first hour was 215 km. [3.7C]

52. The angles measure 50°, 60°, and 70°. [3.6B] **53.** The middle integer can be −4 or 4. [11.5A]

54. Working together, it would take them 36 min or 0.6 h. [6.8A] **55.** The width is 5 m. The length is 10 m. [5.6B]

56. 16 oz of dye are required. [6.6A] **57.** The rate of the boat in calm water is 15 mph. The rate of the current is 5 mph. [8.4A]

58. The rate of the wind is 25 mph. [11.5A] **59.** −5 −4 −3 −2 −1 0 1 2 3 4 5 [9.1B]

60.

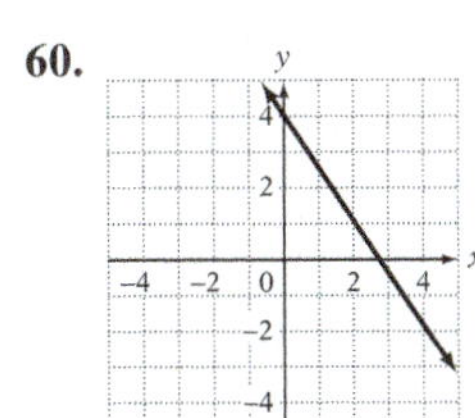

[7.2A]

61.

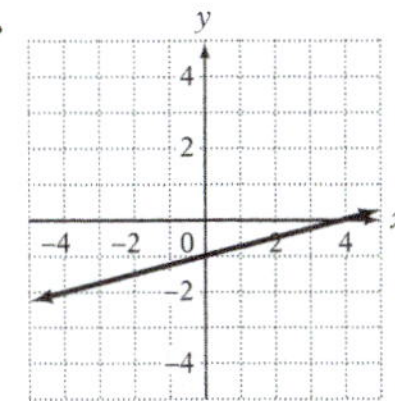

[7.2B]

62.

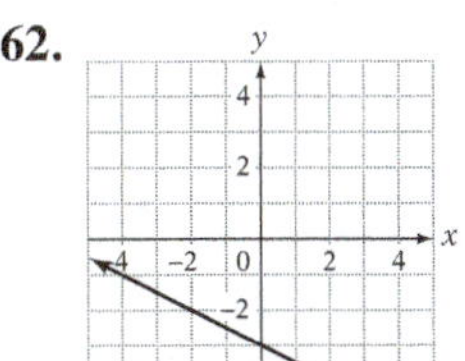

[7.3C]

63.

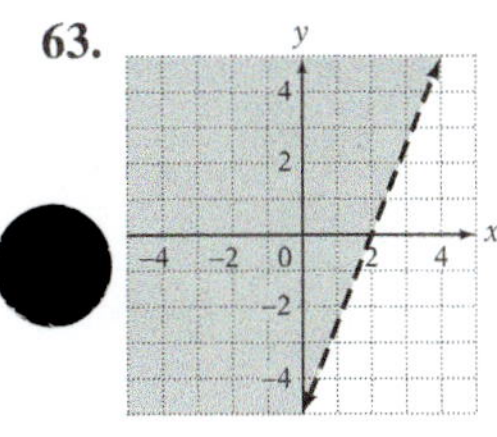

[9.4A]

64.

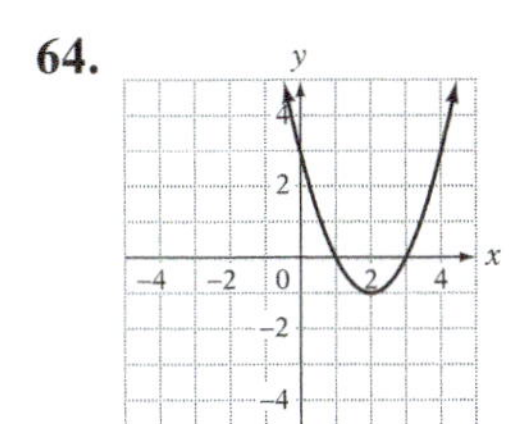

[11.4A]

Glossary

abscissa The first number in an ordered pair. It measures a horizontal distance and is also called the first coordinate. [7.1]

absolute value of a number The distance of the number from zero on the number line. [1.1]

acute angle An angle whose measure is between 0° and 90°. [3.6]

addend In addition, a number being added. [1.2]

addition The process of finding the total of two numbers. [1.2]

addition method An algebraic method of finding an exact solution of a system of linear equations. [8.3]

additive inverses Numbers that are the same distance from zero on the number line, but on opposite sides; also called opposites. [1.1/2.2]

adjacent angles Two angles that share a common side. [3.6]

alternate exterior angles Two nonadjacent angles that are on opposite sides of the transversal and outside the parallel lines. [3.6]

alternate interior angles Two nonadjacent angles that are on opposite sides of the transversal and between the parallel lines. [3.6]

analytic geometry Geometry in which a coordinate system is used to study the relationships between variables. [7.1]

angle Figure formed when two rays start from the same point. [1.8]

axes The two number lines that form a rectangular coordinate system; also called coordinate axes. [7.1]

base In exponential notation, the factor that is multiplied the number of times shown by the exponent. [1.4]

basic percent equation Percent times base equals amount. [3.2]

binomial A polynomial of two terms. [4.1]

binomial factor A factor that has two terms. [5.1]

center of a circle The point from which all points on the circle are equidistant. [1.8]

circle Plane figure in which all points are the same distance from its center. [1.8]

circumference The perimeter of a circle. [1.8]

clearing denominators Removing denominators from an equation that contains fractions by multiplying each side of the equation by the LCM of the denominators. [3.3]

coefficient The number part of a variable term. [2.1]

combining like terms Using the Distributive Property to add the coefficients of like variable terms; adding like terms of a variable expression. [2.2]

complementary angles Two angles whose sum is 90°. [1.8]

completing the square Adding to a binomial the constant term that makes it a perfect-square trinomial. [11.2]

complex fraction A fraction whose numerator or denominator contains one or more fractions. [6.4]

composite number A natural number greater than 1 that is not a prime number. [1.5]

conjugates Binomial expressions that differ only in the sign of a term. The expressions $a + b$ and $a - b$ are conjugates. [10.3]

consecutive even integers Even integers that follow one another in order. [3.5]

consecutive integers Integers that follow one another in order. [3.5]

consecutive odd integers Odd integers that follow one another in order. [3.5]

constant term A term that includes no variable part; also called a constant. [2.1]

coordinate axes The two number lines that form a rectangular coordinate system; also simply called axes. [7.1]

coordinates of a point The numbers in an ordered pair that is associated with a point. [7.1]

corresponding angles Two angles that are on the same side of the transversal and are both acute angles or are both obtuse angles. [3.6]

cost The price that a business pays for a product. [3.3]

decimal notation Notation in which a number consists of a whole-number part, a decimal point, and a decimal part. [1.6]

degree A unit used to measure angles. [1.8]

degree of a polynomial in one variable The largest exponent that appears on the variable. [4.1]

dependent system A system of equations that has an infinite number of solutions. [8.1]

dependent variable In a function, the variable whose value depends on the value of another variable known as the independent variable. [7.1]

descending order The terms of a polynomial in one variable arranged so that the exponents on the variable decrease from left to right. The polynomial $9x^5 - 2x^4 + 7x^3 + x^2 - 8x + 1$ is in descending order. [4.1]

diameter Line segment across a circle that passes through the circle's center. [1.8]

difference of two squares A polynomial of the form $a^2 - b^2$. [5.4]

discount The amount by which a retailer reduces the regular price of a product for a promotional sale. [3.3]

discount rate The percent of the regular price that the discount represents. [3.3]

domain The set of first coordinates of the ordered pairs in a relation. [7.1]

double root The two equal roots of a quadratic equation, which occurs when the discriminant $b^2 - 4ac$ equals zero. [11.1]

element of a set One of the objects in a set. [1.1/9.1]

empty set The set that contains no elements; also called the null set. [9.1]

equation A statement of the equality of two mathematical expressions. [3.1]

equilateral triangle A triangle in which all three sides are of equal length. [1.8]

equivalent equations Equations that have the same solution. [3.1]

evaluating a function Replacing x in $f(x)$ with some value and then simplifying the numerical expression that results. [7.1]

evaluating a variable expression Replacing each variable by its value and then simplifying the resulting numerical expression. [2.1]

even integer An integer that is divisible by 2. [3.5]

exponent In exponential notation, the elevated number that indicates how many times the base occurs in the multiplication. [1.4]

exponential form The expression 2^5 is in exponential form. Compare *factored form.* [1.4]

exterior angle of a triangle Angle adjacent to an interior angle of a triangle. [3.6]

factor a polynomial To write the polynomial as a product of other polynomials. [5.1]

factor a trinomial of the form $x^2 + bx + c$ To express the trinomial as the product of two binomials. [5.2]

factor by grouping Process of grouping and factoring terms in a polynomial in such a way that a common binomial factor is found. [5.1]

factor completely Refers to writing a polynomial as a product of factors that are nonfactorable over the integers. [5.2]

factor of a number In multiplication, a number being multiplied. [1.5]

factored form The expression $2 \cdot 2 \cdot 2 \cdot 2 \cdot 2$ is in factored form. Compare *exponential form.* [1.4]

first coordinate The first number in an ordered pair. It measures a horizontal distance and is also called the abscissa. [7.1]

first-degree equation in two variables An equation of the form $y = mx + b$, where m is the coefficient and b is a constant; also called a linear equation in two variables or a linear function. [7.2]

FOIL A method of finding the product of two binomials; the letters stand for First, Outer, Inner, and Last. [4.3]

formula A literal equation that states rules about measurements. [6.7]

function A relation in which no two ordered pairs that have the same first coordinate have different second coordinates. [7.1]

function notation A function designated by $f(x)$, which is the value of the function at x. [7.1]

graph a point in the plane To place a dot at the location given by the ordered pair; also called plotting a point in the plane. [7.1]

graph of a relation The graph of the ordered pairs that belong to the relation. [7.1]

graph of an equation in two variables A graph of the ordered-pair solutions of the equation. [7.2]

graph of an integer A heavy dot directly above that number on the number line. [1.1]

graph of an ordered pair The dot drawn at the coordinates of the point in the plane. [7.1]

graph of $x = a$ A vertical line passing through the point $(a, 0)$. [7.2]

graph of $y = b$ A horizontal line passing through the point $(0, b)$. [7.2]

greater than A number a is greater than another number b, written $a > b$, if a is to the right of b on the number line. [1.1]

greater than or equal to The symbol $\geq$ means "is greater than or equal to." [1.1]

greatest common factor (GCF) The greatest common factor of two or more integers is the greatest integer that is a factor of all the integers. [1.5]

greatest common factor (GCF) of two or more monomials The product of the GCF of the coefficients and the common variable factors. [5.1]

half-plane The solution set of an inequality in two variables. [9.4]

hypotenuse In a right triangle, the side opposite the 90° angle. [10.4]

inconsistent system A system of equations that has no solution. [8.1]

independent system A system of equations that has one solution. [8.1]

independent variable In a function, the variable that varies independently and whose value determines the value of the dependent variable. [7.1]

inequality An expression that contains the symbol $>$, $<$, $\geq$ (is greater than or equal to), or $\leq$ (is less than or equal to). [1.1]

integers The numbers ..., $-3, -2, -1, 0, 1, 2, 3$, ... [1.1]

interior angle of a triangle An angle within the region enclosed by a triangle. [3.6]

intersecting lines Lines that cross at a point in a plane. [1.8]

intersection of sets A and B The set that contains the elements that are common to both A and B. [9.1]

irrational number The decimal representation of an irrational number never repeats or terminates and can only be approximated. [1.6/10.1]

isosceles triangle A triangle that has two equal angles and two equal sides. [1.8]

least common denominator The smallest number that is a multiple of each denominator in question. [1.6]

least common multiple (LCM) The LCM of two or more numbers is the smallest number that contains the prime factorization of each number. [1.5]

least common multiple (LCM) of two or more polynomials The polynomial of least degree that contains all the factors of each polynomial. [6.2]

legs The sides opposite the acute angles in a right triangle. [10.4]

less than A number a is less than another number b, written $a < b$, if a is to the left of b on the number line. [1.1]

less than or equal to The symbol $\leq$ means "is less than or equal to." [1.1]

like terms Terms of a variable expression that have the same variable part. [2.2]

line Having no width, it extends indefinitely in two directions in a plane. [1.8]

line segment Part of a line; a line segment has two endpoints. [1.8]

linear equation in two variables An equation of the form $y = mx + b$, where m and b are constants; also called a linear function or a first-degree equation in two variables. [7.2]

linear function An equation of the form $y = mx + b$, where m and b are constants; also called a linear equation in two variables or a first-degree equation in two variables. [7.2]

literal equation An equation that contains more than one variable. [6.7]

markdown The amount by which a retailer reduces the regular price of a product for a promotional sale. [3.3]

markup The difference between selling price and cost. [3.3]

markup rate The percent of retailer's cost that the markup represents. [3.3]

monomial A number, a variable, or a product of numbers and variables; a polynomial of one term. [4.1]

multiplicative inverse The reciprocal of a number. [2.2]

natural numbers The numbers 1, 2, 3, ... [1.1]

negative integers The numbers ..., $-4, -3, -2, -1$. [1.1]

negative slope A property of a line that slants downward to the right. [7.3]

nonfactorable over the integers A polynomial that does not factor using only integers. [5.2]

null set The set that contains no elements; also called the empty set. [9.1]

numerical coefficient The number part of a variable term. When the numerical coefficient is 1 or -1, the 1 is usually not written. [2.1]

obtuse angle An angle whose measure is between 90° and 180°. [3.6]

odd integer An integer that is not divisible by 2. [3.5]

opposite of a polynomial The polynomial created when the sign of each term of the original polynomial is changed. [4.1]

opposites Numbers that are the same distance from zero on the number line, but on opposite sides; also called additive inverses. [1.1]

ordered pair Pair of numbers of the form (a, b) that can be used to identify a point in the plane determined by the axes of a rectangular coordinate system. [7.1]

Order of Operations Agreement A set of rules that tell us in what order to perform the operations that occur in a numerical expression. [1.4]

ordinate The second number in an ordered pair. It measures a vertical distance and is also called the second coordinate. [7.1]

origin The point of intersection of the two coordinate axes that form a rectangular coordinate system. [7.1]

parabola The graph of a quadratic equation in two variables. [11.4]

parallel lines Lines that never meet; the distance between them is always the same. Parallel lines have the same slope. [1.8/7.3]

parallelogram Four-sided plane figure with opposite sides parallel. [1.8]

percent Parts of 100. [1.7]

perfect square The square of an integer. [10.1]

perfect-square trinomial A trinomial that is the product of a binomial and itself. [5.4/11.2]

perimeter The distance around a plane geometric figure. [1.8]

perpendicular lines Intersecting lines that form right angles. [1.8/7.3]

plane Flat surface that extends indefinitely. [1.8/7.1]

plane figure Figure that lies entirely in a plane. [1.8]

plot a point in the plane To place a dot at the location given by the ordered pair; to graph a point in the plane. [7.1]

point-slope formula If (x_1, y_1) is a point on a line with slope m, then $y - y_1 = m(x - x_1)$. [7.4]

polynomial A variable expression in which the terms are monomials. [4.1]

positive integers The integers, 1, 2, 3, 4, ... [1.1]

positive slope A property of a line that slants upward to the right. [7.3]

prime factorization Expressing a number as a product of its prime factors. [1.5]

prime number Number whose only factors are 1 and the number. [1.5]

prime polynomial A polynomial that is nonfactorable over the integers. [5.2]

principal square root The positive square root of a number. [10.1]

product In multiplication, the result of multiplying two numbers. [1.3]

proportion An equation that states the equality of two ratios or rates. [6.6]

Pythagorean Theorem The square of the hypotenuse of a right triangle is equal to the sum of the squares of the two legs. [10.4]

quadrant One of the four regions into which the two axes of a rectangular coordinate system divide the plane. [7.1]

quadratic equation An equation of the form $ax^2 + bx + c = 0$, where a, b, and c are constants and a is not equal to zero; also called a second-degree equation. [5.6/11.1]

quadratic equation in two variables An equation of the form $y = ax^2 + bx + c$, where a is not equal to zero. [11.4]

quadratic function A quadratic function is given by $f(x) = ax^2 + bx + c$, where a is not equal to zero. [11.4]

radical equation An equation that contains a variable expression in a radicand. [10.4]

radical sign The symbol $\sqrt{}$, which is used to indicate the positive, or principal, square root of a number. [10.1]

radicand In a radical expression, the expression under the radical sign. [10.1]

radius Line segment from the center of a circle to a point on the circle. [1.8]

range The set of second coordinates of the ordered pairs in a relation. [7.1]

rate The quotient of two quantities that have different units. [6.6]

rate of work That part of a task that is completed in one unit of time. [6.8]

ratio The quotient of two quantities that have the same unit. [6.6]

rational expression A fraction in which the numerator and denominator is a polynomial. [6.1]

rational number A number that can be written in the form a/b where a and b are integers and b is not equal to zero. [1.6]

rationalizing the denominator The procedure used to remove a radical from the denominator of a fraction. [10.3]

ray Line that starts at a point and extends indefinitely in one direction. [1.8]

real numbers The rational numbers and the irrational numbers. [1.6]

reciprocal of a fraction Fraction that results when the numerator and denominator of a fraction are interchanged. [1.7]

reciprocal of a rational expression A rational expression in which the numerator and denominator have been interchanged. [6.1]

rectangle Parallelogram that has four right angles. [1.8]

rectangular coordinate system System formed by two number lines, one horizontal and one vertical, that intersect at the zero point of each line. [7.1]

relation Any set of ordered pairs. [7.1]

repeating decimal Decimal that is formed when the division of the numerator of its fractional counterpart by the denominator results in a decimal part wherein a block of digits repeats infinitely. [1.6]

right angle An angle whose measure is 90°. [1.8]

right triangle A triangle that contains a 90° angle. [10.4]

roster method Method of writing a set by enclosing a list of the elements in braces. [1.1/9.1]

scientific notation Notation in which each number is expressed as the product of two factors, one a number between 1 and 10 and the other a power of 10. [4.4]

second coordinate The second number in an ordered pair. It measures a vertical distance and is also called the ordinate. [7.1]

second-degree equation An equation of the form $ax^2 + bx + c = 0$, where a, b, and c are constants and a is not equal to zero; also called a quadratic equation. [11.1]

selling price The price for which a business sells a product to a customer. [3.3]

set A collection of objects. [1.1/9.1]

set-builder notation A method of designating a set that makes use of a variable and a certain property that only elements of that set possess. [9.1]

similar objects Similar objects have the same shape but not necessarily the same size. [6.6]

simplest form of a fraction A fraction in which the numerator and denominator have no common factors other than 1. [1.6]

simplest form of a rational expression A rational expression is in simplest form when the numerator and denominator have no common factors. [6.1]

slope The measure of the slant of a line. The symbol for slope is m. [7.3]

slope-intercept form The slope-intercept form of an equation of a straight line is $y = mx + b$. [7.3]

solid An object that exists in space. [1.8]

solution of a system of equations in two variables An ordered pair that is a solution of each equation of the system. [8.1]

solution of an equation A number that, when substituted for the variable, results in a true equation. [3.1]

solution of an equation in two variables An ordered pair whose coordinates make the equation a true statement. [7.1]

solution set of an inequality A set of numbers, each element of which, when substituted for the variable, results in a true inequality. [9.2]

solving an equation Finding a solution of the equation. [3.1]

square Rectangle with four equal sides. [1.8]

square of a binomial A polynomial that can be expressed in the form $(a + b)^2$. [11.2]

square root A square root of a positive number x is a number a for which $a^2 = x$. [10.1]

standard form A quadratic equation is in standard form when the polynomial is in descending order and equal to zero. $ax^2 + bx + c = 0$ is in standard form. [5.6/11.1]

standard form of a linear equation in two variables An equation of the form $Ax + By = C$, where A and B are coefficients and C is a constant. [7.2]

straight angle An angle whose measure is 180°. [1.8]

substitution method An algebraic method of finding an exact solution of a system of equations. [8.2]

sum In addition, the total of two or more numbers. [1.2]

supplementary angles Two angles whose sum is 180°. [1.8]

system of equations Equations that are considered together. [8.1]

terminating decimal Decimal that is formed when the division of the numerator of its fractional counterpart by the denominator results in a remainder of zero. [1.6]

terms of a variable expression The addends of the expression. [2.1]

transversal A line intersecting two other lines at two different points. [3.6]

triangle A three-sided closed figure. [1.8]

trinomial A polynomial of three terms. [4.1]

undefined slope A property of a vertical line. [7.3]

uniform motion The motion of a moving object whose speed and direction do not change. [3.2/6.8]

union of sets A and B The set that contains all the elements of A and all the elements of B. [9.1]

value of a function at x The result of evaluating a variable expression, represented by the symbol $f(x)$. [7.1]

value of a variable The number assigned to the variable. [2.1]

variable A letter of the alphabet used to stand for a number that is unknown or that can change. [1.1]

variable expression An expression that contains one or more variables. [2.1]

variable part In a variable term, the variable or variables and their exponents. [2.1]

variable term A term composed of a numerical coefficient and a variable part. [2.1]

vertex Point at which the rays that form an angle meet. [1.8]

vertical angles Two angles that are on opposite sides of the intersect[illegible] two lines. [3.6]

x-coordinate The abscissa in an xy-coordinate system. [7.1]

x-intercept The point at which a graph crosses the x-axis. [7.3]

xy-coordinate system A rectangular coordinate system in which the horizontal axis is labeled x and the vertical axis is labeled y. [7.1]

y-coordinate The ordinate in an xy-coordinate system. [7.1]

y-intercept The point at which a graph crosses the y-axis. [7.3]

zero of a function A value of x for which $f(x) = 0$. [11.4]

zero slope A property of a horizontal line. [7.3]

Index

SUPPLEMENTAL MATERIAL

- **A** Factoring a binomial
- **B** Factoring four-term polynomials

A Factoring a Binomial

We discuss here two other types of binomials that can be factored.

Sum of Two Cubes

Consider the following products:

$$(a + b)(a^2 - ab + b^2) = a^3 + b^3$$
$$(x + 2y)(x^2 - 2xy + 4y^2) = x^3 + 8y^3$$
$$(2 + 3a)(4 - 6a + 9a^2) = 8 + 27a^3$$
$$(3x^2 + 4y^2)(9x^4 - 12x^2y^2 + 16y^4) = 27x^6 + 64y^6$$

The product is the sum of two perfect cube terms.

The first factor is the sum of the respective cube roots of the two cube terms.

$$a^3 + 27b^3 = (a + 3b)(\quad)$$

cube root

cube root

The second factor consists of three terms and can be arrived at easily from the first factor.

The terms of the second factor are

the square of the first term in the first factor,
the negative of the product of the two terms in the first factor, and
the square of the second term in the first factor.

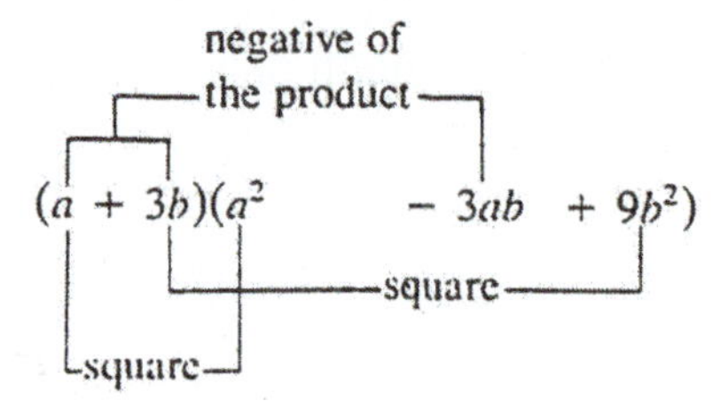

EXAMPLES

1. $8x^3 + 1 = (2x + 1)(4x^2 - 2x + 1)$

2. $64 + b^3 = (4 + b)(16 - 4b + b^2)$

3. $(a + b)^3 + c^3 = [(a + b) + c][(a + b)^2 - c(a + b) + c^2]$

4. $54a^3 + 16b^3 = 2(27a^3 + 8b^3)$
   $= 2(3a + 2b)(9a^2 - 6ab + 4b^2)$

5. $x^6 + y^6 = (x^2 + y^2)(x^4 - x^2y^2 + y^4)$

Difference of Two Cubes

Consider the following products:

$$(a - b)(a^2 + ab + b^2) = a^3 - b^3$$
$$(2a - b)(4a^2 + 2ab + b^2) = 8a^3 - b^3$$
$$(5a - 3)(25a^2 + 15a + 9) = 125a^3 - 27$$

The product is the difference of two perfect cube terms.

The first factor is the difference of the respective cube roots of the two cube terms.

The second factor consists of three terms and can be arrived at easily from the first factor.

The terms of the second factor are

the square of the first term in the first factor,
the negative of the product of the two terms in the first factor, and
the square of the second term in the first factor.

EXAMPLES

1. $a^3 - 64 = (a - 4)(a^2 + 4a + 16)$
2. $27x^3 - 1 = (3x - 1)(9x^2 + 3x + 1)$
3. $16x^3 - 250y^3 = 2(8x^3 - 125y^3)$
   $= 2(2x - 5y)(4x^2 + 10xy + 25y^2)$
4. $(a - b)^3 - (c - d)^3$
   $= [(a - b) - (c - d)][(a - b)^2 + (a - b)(c - d) + (c - d)^2]$

Note When the polynomial can be factored as the difference of either two squares or two cubes, it should be factored as the difference of two squares. •

EXAMPLE

$$x^6 - y^6 = (x^3 + y^3)(x^3 - y^3)$$
$$= (x + y)(x^2 - xy + y^2)(x - y)(x^2 + xy + y^2)$$

EXERCISE A

Factor completely:

1. $x^3 + 1$
2. $x^3 + 8$
3. $x^3 + 27$
4. $x^3 + 64$
5. $x^3 + 216$
6. $x^3 - 1$
7. $x^3 - 8y^3$
8. $27 - x^3$
9. $x^3 - 125$
10. $64x^3 - y^3$
11. $8x^3 - 27y^3$
12. $x^4 + 8x$
13. $x^3y + y^4$
14. $4x^3 + 32y^3$
15. $54x^4 + 2xy^3$
16. $16 - 2x^3$

17. $x^4y^2 - xy^5$

18. $250x^3 - 2$

19. $7x^3 - 56y^3$

20. $4x^3 - 32$

21. $x^6 + y^3$

22. $16x^3 + 54y^3$

23. $40x^5 + 5x^2$

24. $81x^3 + 24y^3$

25. $2x^6 + 16y^3$

26. $3x^3y^6 + 81$

27. $54x^4 - 2x$

28. $54x^3 - 16$

29. $x^6 - x^3$

30. $x^6 - 8y^6$

31. $x^6 - 27y^6$

32. $x^6 - 1$

33. $64 - x^6$

34. $x^6 + 1$

35. $64x^6 + 1$

36. $x^8 + x^2y^6$

37. $x^3 + (y + 2)^3$

38. $x^3 + (y - 3)^3$

39. $8x^3 - (2y + 1)^3$

40. $x^3 - (y - 2)^3$

41. $(x + 2)^3 + y^3$

42. $(x - 1)^3 + 8y^3$

43. $(x + 3)^3 - 27y^3$

44. $(x - 2)^3 - 8y^3$

45. $(a + b)^3 + (c - d)^3$

46. $(x + y)^3 - (a - b)^3$

B Factoring Four-Term Polynomials

The methods of factoring polynomials with more than three terms are called **factoring by grouping**. There are two types of four-term polynomials that can be factored. In tne first type the terms are grouped three terms in one group and the fourth term as the other group. In the second type the terms are grouped in pairs.

Grouping as Three and One

The polynomial $(x + y)^2 - z^2$ can be factored as the difference of two squares.

When $(x + y)^2 - z^2$ is expanded, we get

$$(x + y)^2 - z^2 = x^2 + 2xy + y^2 - z^2$$

Note that, disregarding the signs, three of the four terms, x^2, y^2, z^2, are square terms. The fourth term, $2xy$, equals $2\sqrt{x^2}\sqrt{y^2}$. This fourth term and the related two square terms form one group that, when factored, results in a square quantity:

$$x^2 + 2xy + y^2 = (x + y)^2$$

EXAMPLE Factor $x^2 - y^2 + 4z^2 - 4xz$.

SOLUTION There are three square terms x^2, y^2, and $4z^2$.

The fourth term is $4xz = 2\sqrt{x^2}\sqrt{4z^2}$.

The two square terms related to $4xz$ are x^2 and $4z^2$.

Hence x^2, $4xz$, and $4z^2$ form one group.

$$\begin{aligned} x^2 - y^2 + 4z^2 - 4xz &= (x^2 - 4xz + 4z^2) - y^2 \\ &= (x - 2z)^2 - y^2 \\ &= [(x - 2z) + y][(x - 2z) - y] \\ &= (x - 2z + y)(x - 2z - y) \end{aligned}$$

EXAMPLE Factor $9x^2 - y^2 - 25z^2 + 10yz$.

SOLUTION

$$\begin{aligned} 9x^2 - y^2 - 25z^2 + 10yz &= 9x^2 - (y^2 - 10yz + 25z^2) \\ &= 9x^2 - (y - 5z)^2 \\ &= [3x + (y - 5z)][3x - (y - 5z)] \\ &= (3x + y - 5z)(3x - y + 5z) \end{aligned}$$

EXAMPLE Factor $x^2 - y^2 - 9 - 6y$.

SOLUTION

$$\begin{aligned} x^2 - y^2 - 9 - 6y &= x^2 - (y^2 + 6y + 9) \\ &= x^2 - (y + 3)^2 \\ &= [x + (y + 3)][x - (y + 3)] \\ &= (x + y + 3)(x - y - 3) \end{aligned}$$

Grouping in Pairs

When the four terms cannot be grouped as three and one, group them in pairs.

The following examples illustrate the principle behind grouping in pairs.

EXAMPLE Factor $x^3 + x^2 + 2x + 2$.

SOLUTION

Group the first two terms in one group and the last two terms in a second group.

$$\begin{aligned} x^3 + x^2 + 2x + 2 &= (x^3 + x^2) + (2x + 2) \\ &= x^2(x + 1) + 2(x + 1) \end{aligned}$$

Now we have a common factor $(x + 1)$.

$$x^3 + x^2 + 2x + 2 = (x + 1)(x^2 + 2)$$

EXAMPLE Factor $ax + ay + bx + by$.

SOLUTION

$$\begin{aligned} ax + ay + bx + by &= (ax + ay) + (bx + by) \\ &= a(x + y) + b(x + y) \\ &= (x + y)(a + b) \end{aligned}$$

Note A different grouping is possible in some problems, but remember the final factors will be the same, except for their order.

$$\begin{aligned} ax + ay + bx + by &= (ax + bx) + (ay + by) \\ &= x(a + b) + y(a + b) \\ &= (a + b)(x + y) \end{aligned}$$

EXAMPLE Factor $12ax - 20bx - 9ay + 15by$.

SOLUTION

$$12ax - 20bx - 9ay + 15by = (12ax - 20bx) - (9ay - 15by)$$

When you enclose $-9ay + 15by$ in parentheses preceded by a minus sign, you get $-(9ay - 15by)$.

$$\begin{aligned} 12ax - 20bx - 9ay + 15by &= 4x(3a - 5b) - 3y(3a - 5b) \\ &= (3a - 5b)(4x - 3y) \end{aligned}$$

Note If there is no common factor, group the terms differently. •

EXAMPLE Factor $x^3 + x^2 - 2x - 8$.

SOLUTION

Grouping the first two terms in one group and the last two terms in a second group does not yield a common factor.

$$\begin{aligned} x^3 + x^2 - 2x - 8 &= (x^3 + x^2) - (2x + 8) \\ &= x^2(x + 1) - 2(x + 4) \end{aligned}$$

Since there is no common factor, we try another grouping.

$$\begin{aligned} x^3 + x^2 - 2x - 8 &= (x^3 - 8) + (x^2 - 2x) \\ &= (x - 2)(x^2 + 2x + 4) + x(x - 2) \\ &= (x - 2)[(x^2 + 2x + 4) + x] \\ &= (x - 2)(x^2 + 2x + 4 + x) \\ &= (x - 2)(x^2 + 3x + 4) \end{aligned}$$

Note When there are two cubes in the polynomial, try grouping them together. •

EXAMPLE Factor $27x^3 - 9x^2 + y^2 + y^3$.

SOLUTION

$$\begin{aligned} 27x^3 - 9x^2 + y^2 + y^3 &= (27x^3 + y^3) - (9x^2 - y^2) \\ &= (3x + y)(9x^2 - 3xy + y^2) - (3x + y)(3x - y) \\ &= (3x + y)[(9x^2 - 3xy + y^2) - (3x - y)] \\ &= (3x + y)(9x^2 - 3xy + y^2 - 3x + y) \end{aligned}$$

EXAMPLE Factor $8x^3 + 2x - y^3 - y$.

SOLUTION

$$\begin{aligned} 8x^3 + 2x - y^3 - y &= (8x^3 - y^3) + (2x - y) \\ &= (2x - y)(4x^2 + 2xy + y^2) + (2x - y) \\ &= (2x - y)[(4x^2 + 2xy + y^2) + 1] \\ &= (2x - y)(4x^2 + 2xy + y^2 + 1) \end{aligned}$$

Note When factoring out a common factor, the second factor is the result of dividing every term of the polynomial by the common factor. •

EXERCISE B

Factor completely:

1. $x^2 + 2xy + y^2 - z^2$
2. $x^2 - 2xy + y^2 - z^2$
3. $4x^2 - 4xy + y^2 - 4z^2$
4. $x^2 + 4xy + 4y^2 - 16z^2$
5. $x^2 - y^2 + 4x + 4$
6. $y^2 - 4x^2 + 2y + 1$
7. $y^2 - 9x^2 + 6y + 9$
8. $x^2 - 4 + 4y^2 - 4xy$
9. $4x^2 + 4xy - 25 + y^2$
10. $9x^2 + y^2 - 6xy - 36$
11. $4x^2 + 4y^2 + 8xy - 25$
12. $9x^2 - 4 + 9y^2 - 18xy$
13. $2x^2 + 2y^2 - 18 - 4xy$
14. $4x^2 - 1 + 24xy + 36y^2$
15. $x^3 - 16x + 2x^2y + xy^2$
16. $4x^2y - 9y - 4xy^2 + y^3$
17. $x^2 - y^2 - z^2 - 2yz$
18. $4x^2 - 4z^2 - y^2 - 4yz$
19. $9x^2 - 9 - y^2 - 6y$
20. $x^2 - 4y^2 - 16y - 16$
21. $25x^2 - 9y^2 - 9 - 18y$
22. $1 - x^2 - y^2 - 2xy$
23. $4 - 4xy - x^2 - 4y^2$
24. $16 - y^2 - 4x^2 - 4xy$
25. $9 - 4x^2 - 8xy - 4y^2$
26. $49 - 81x^2 - 54xy - 9y^2$
27. $2x^2 - 2y^2 - 16y - 32$
28. $3x^4 - 12y^2 - 3z^2 - 12yz$
29. $x^3 - x - xy^2 - 2xy$
30. $16 - 4x^4 - 4y^2 - 8x^2y$
31. $y^2 - 4z^2 - x^2 + 4xz$
32. $4x^2 - y^2 - z^4 + 2yz^2$
33. $9x^4 - 9y^2 - 4 + 12y$
34. $4x^2 - 9y^2 - 81 + 54y$
35. $16x^2 - y^4 - 16 + 8y^2$
36. $36y^2 - x^4 - 1 + 2x^2$
37. $1 - x^4 - 4y^2 + 4x^2y$
38. $4 - 4x^2 - y^4 + 4xy^2$
39. $9 - 4y^2 - 36x^2 + 24xy$
40. $1 - 16x^2 - 16y^2 + 32xy$
41. $25 - x^2 + 6xy - 9y^2$
42. $4 - 25x^2 - 25y^2 + 50xy$
43. $6xz + 3y^2 - 3x^2 - 3z^2$
44. $8 + 36xy - 18x^2 - 18y^2$
45. $4 + 64xy - 16x^2 - 64y^2$
46. $30xy - 45x^2 + 45 - 5y^2$
47. $2x^2y + 4x - x^3 - xy^2$
48. $36x^2 - x^2y^2 - x^4 + 2x^3y$
49. $3x^2 - xy - 6x + 2y$
50. $x^2 + y + x + xy$
51. $x^2 - 3y - 3x + xy$
52. $2x^2 + 5x - 2xy^2 - 5y^2$
53. $6xy - 3yz - 14x + 7z$
54. $8xy + 3z - 8xz - 3y$
55. $27x^2 + 12x - 18xy - 8y$
56. $2ax + 3by + 2bx + 3ay$
57. $14ax + 7by - 14ay - 7bx$
58. $6a^2x^2 + 3a^2y + 6b^2x^2 + 3b^2y$
59. $12x^3 - 4x^2y - 4y^3 + 12xy^2$
60. $40ax - 45bx + 24ay - 27by$
61. $x^3 - x - y^3 + y$
62. $8x^3 + 27y^3 + 2x + 3y$
63. $x^3 + 5y - 125y^3 - x$
64. $3x + 27x^3 - 2y - 8y^3$
65. $64x^3 - 4x + y^3 - y$
66. $x^3 - 4x + y^3 - 4y$
67. $8x^3 - 6x + y^3 - 3y$
68. $x^3 + 6y - 6x - y^3$
69. $x^3 - 8y^3 - 6y + 3x$
70. $x^3 + x^2 - 8y^3 - 4y^2$
71. $8x^3 - 4x^2 - 27y^3 + 9y^2$
72. $y^3 + y^2 + 216x^3 - 36x^2$
73. $x^2 - 25y^2 + 125y^3 + x^3$
74. $16y^2 + x^3 - x^2 - 64y^3$
75. $x^3 + 3x^2 - 9x - 27$
76. $x^3 + 8 - 2x^2 - 4x$
77. $4x^3 + 2 - x - 8x^2$
78. $18x^3 - 16 - 32x + 9x^2$
79. $x^4 + x^3 + x + 1$
80. $x^4 - 16 + 2x^3 - 8x$
81. $x^4 - 54 - 2x^3 + 27x$
82. $8x^4 + 24x^3 + x + 3$

APPENDIX EXERCISE A, page 434

1. $(x + 1)(x^2 - x + 1)$
3. $(x + 3)(x^2 - 3x + 9)$
5. $(x + 6)(x^2 - 6x + 36)$
7. $(x - 2y)(x^2 + 2xy + 4y^2)$
9. $(x - 5)(x^2 + 5x + 25)$
11. $(2x - 3y)(4x^2 + 6xy + 9y^2)$
13. $y(x + y)(x^2 - xy + y^2)$
15. $2x(3x + y)(9x^2 - 3xy + y^2)$
17. $xy^2(x - y)(x^2 + xy + y^2)$
19. $7(x - 2y)(x^2 + 2xy + 4y^2)$
21. $(x^2 + y)(x^4 - x^2y + y^2)$
23. $5x^2(2x + 1)(4x^2 - 2x + 1)$
25. $2(x^2 + 2y)(x^4 - 2x^2y + 4y^2)$
27. $2x(3x - 1)(9x^2 + 3x + 1)$
29. $x^3(x - 1)(x^2 + x + 1)$
31. $(x^2 - 3y^2)(x^4 + 3x^2y^2 + 9y^4)$
33. $(2 + x)(4 - 2x + x^2)(2 - x)(4 + 2x + x^2)$
35. $(4x^2 + 1)(16x^4 - 4x^2 + 1)$
37. $[x + (y + 2)][x^2 - x(y + 2) + (y + 2)^2]$
39. $[2x - (2y + 1)][4x^2 + 2x(2y + 1) + (2y + 1)^2]$
41. $[(x + 2) + y][(x + 2)^2 - y(x + 2) + y^2]$
43. $[(x + 3) - 3y][(x + 3)^2 + 3y(x + 3) + 9y^2]$
45. $[(a + b) + (c - d)][(a + b)^2 - (a + b)(c - d) + (c - d)^2]$

APPENDIX EXERCISE B, page 438

1. $(x + y + z)(x + y - z)$
3. $(2x - y + 2z)(2x - y - 2z)$
5. $(x + 2 + y)(x + 2 - y)$
7. $(y + 3 + 3x)(y + 3 - 3x)$
9. $(2x + y + 5)(2x + y - 5)$
11. $(2x + 2y + 5)(2x + 2y - 5)$
13. $2(x - y + 3)(x - y - 3)$
15. $x(x + y + 4)(x + y - 4)$
17. $(x + y + z)(x - y - z)$
19. $(3x + y + 3)(3x - y - 3)$
21. $(5x + 3y + 3)(5x - 3y - 3)$
23. $(2 + x + 2y)(2 - x - 2y)$
25. $(3 + 2x + 2y)(3 - 2x - 2y)$
27. $2(x + y + 4)(x - y - 4)$
29. $x(x + y + 1)(x - y - 1)$
31. $(y + x - 2z)(y - x + 2z)$
33. $(3x^2 + 3y - 2)(3x^2 - 3y + 2)$
35. $(4x + y^2 - 4)(4x - y^2 + 4)$
37. $(1 + x^2 - 2y)(1 - x^2 + 2y)$
39. $(3 + 6x - 2y)(3 - 6x + 2y)$
41. $(5 + x - 3y)(5 - x + 3y)$
43. $3(y + x - z)(y - x + z)$
45. $4(1 + 2x - 4y)(1 - 2x + 4y)$
47. $x(2 + x - y)(2 - x + y)$
49. $(3x - y)(x - 2)$
51. $(x - 3)(x + y)$
53. $(2x - z)(3y - 7)$
55. $(9x + 4)(3x - 2y)$
57. $7(2a - b)(x - y)$
59. $4(3x - y)(x^2 + y^2)$
61. $(x - y)(x^2 + xy + y^2 - 1)$
63. $(x - 5y)(x^2 + 5xy + 25y^2 - 1)$
65. $(4x + y)(16x^2 - 4xy + y^2 - 1)$
67. $(2x + y)(4x^2 - 2xy + y^2 - 3)$
69. $(x - 2y)(x^2 + 2xy + 4y^2 + 3)$
71. $(2x - 3y)(4x^2 + 6xy + 9y^2 - 2x - 3y)$
73. $(x + 5y)(x - 5y + x^2 - 5xy + 25y^2)$

75. $(x - 3)(x + 3)^2$

77. $(x - 2)(2x + 1)(2x - 1)$

79. $(x + 1)^2(x^2 - x + 1)$

81. $(x - 2)(x + 3)(x^2 - 3x + 9)$

APPENDIX EXERCISE C, page 439

1. 5

3. $\sqrt{5}$

5. $\sqrt{21}$

7. $3\sqrt{2}$

9. $\sqrt{5}$

11. $\sqrt{2}$

13. $3\sqrt{2}$

TI-30X IIS

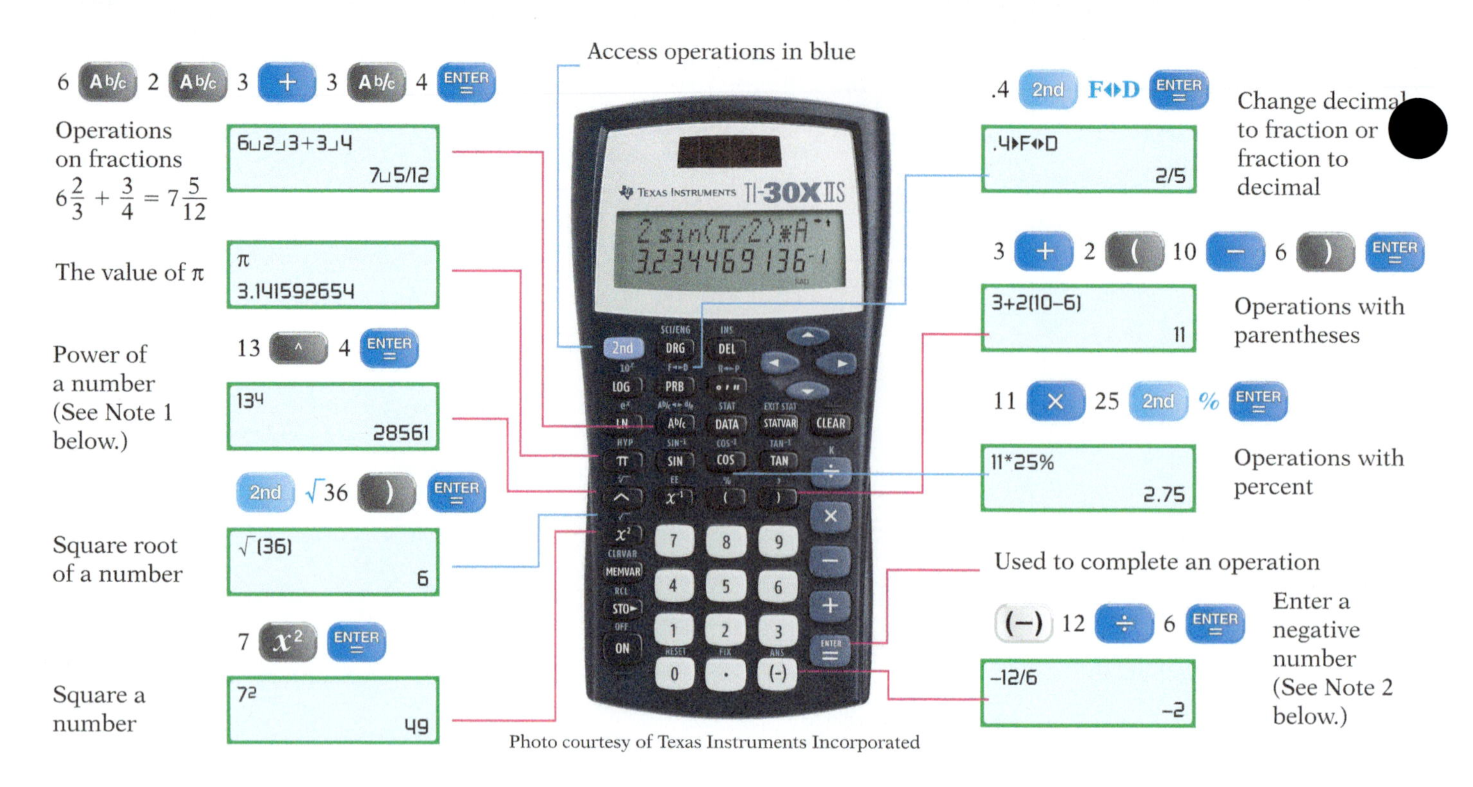

fx-300MS

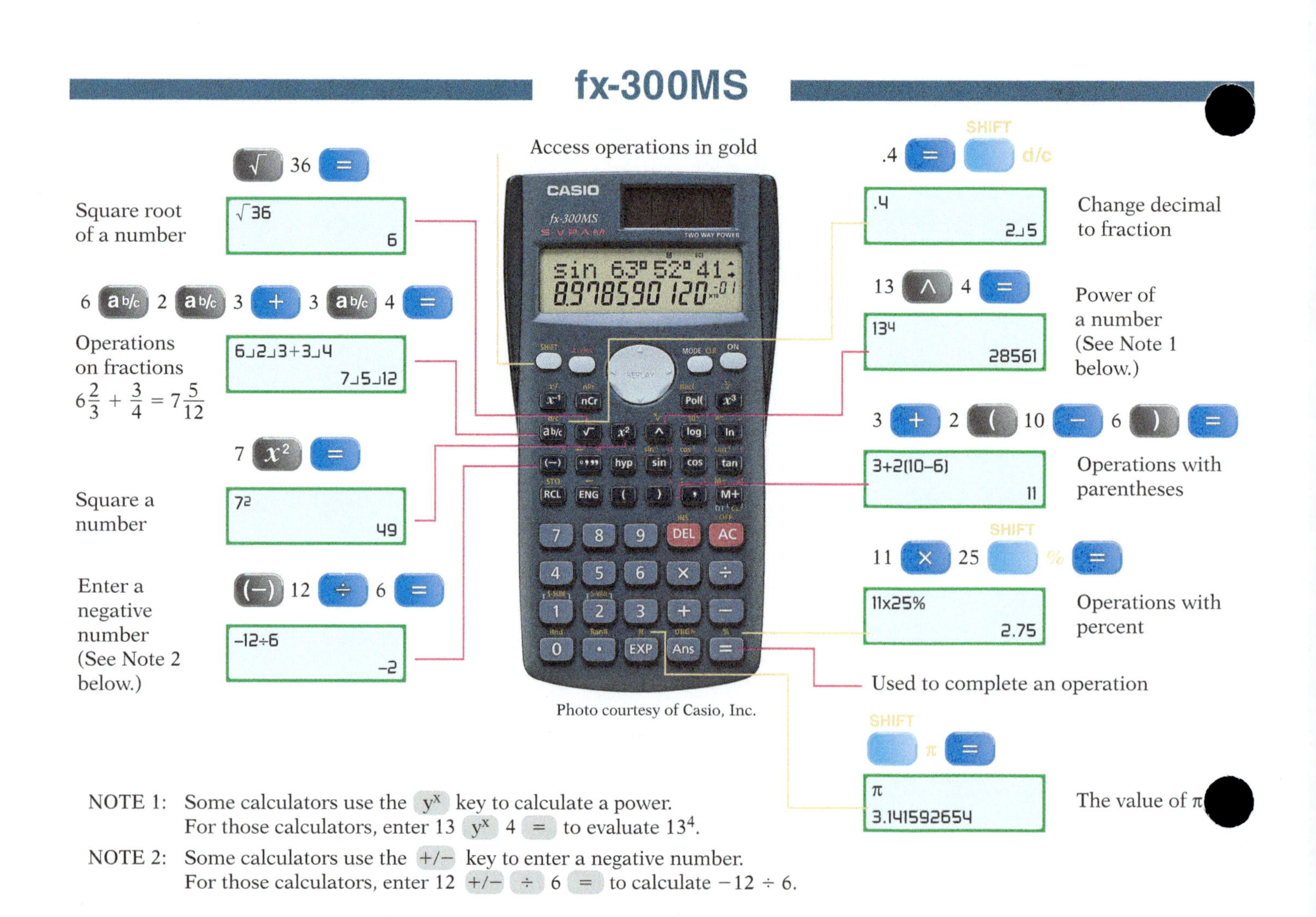

NOTE 1: Some calculators use the y^x key to calculate a power. For those calculators, enter 13 y^x 4 = to evaluate 13^4.

NOTE 2: Some calculators use the +/− key to enter a negative number. For those calculators, enter 12 +/− ÷ 6 = to calculate $-12 \div 6$.